# The Birds of
# NORFOLK

Moss Taylor       Michael Seago

Peter Allard       Don Dorling

**PICA PRESS**

**SUSSEX**

Editor: Nigel Redman
Copy editor: Roger Ruston
Designer: Julie Reynolds

Production and design by Fluke Art, Bexhill on Sea, East Sussex
Printed by Giunti Industrie Grafiche, Italy

Publication of this book
has been aided by financial assistance from

Norfolk & Norwich Naturalists' Society
and
Chris Knights

# CONTENTS

*This book is dedicated to the memory of*

Richard Richardson
(1922-1977)

Field Ornithologist, Bird Artist,
Warden of Cley Bird Observatory (1949-1963)

*A friend and inspiration to all four authors*

Tragically, Michael Seago died just a few weeks before this book was published.
His contribution to the project was enormous and, although the work had
been completed at the time of his death, we are deeply saddened
that he did not live to see the finished product.
We hope that it will serve as a fitting tribute to Michael, without whose extensive
knowledge of Norfolk birds this book would not have been possible.

*M.T., P.A., D.D.*

# ACKNOWLEDGEMENTS

A county avifauna the size of *The Birds of Norfolk* would never have been possible without the help of a large number of contributors. First and foremost, we would like to acknowledge the enormous debt of gratitude that is owed to all the observers who have submitted the records upon which the Systematic List is based.

Amongst the very many people who have more directly contributed to the writing of this book, we would like to express our sincere thanks to the following:

Lord Buxton for his generously-worded Foreword, and to Martin George and Andy Stoddart who wrote two of the introductory chapters. Sue Adams, Graham Appleton, Phil Atkinson, Andrew Bloomfield, Nicholas Branson, Stephen Browne, John Buxton, Nick Carter, Jacquie Clark, Nigel Clark, Peter Dolton, Keith Dye, Julianne Evans, Paul Fisher, Steve Gantlett, Jennifer Gill, Simon Gillings, Barrie Harding, Phil Heath, Ian Henderson, Jan Keddie, John Kemp, Rowena Langstone, Durwyn Liley, Stewart Linsell, Phil Lockwood, Lys Muirhead, Andy Musgrove, Tony Prater, Mark Smart, Bill Sutherland, Mike Toms, Steve Votier, Steve Wakeman and John Williamson contributed species accounts for the Systematic List. Also Dawn Balmer, John Brown, James Cadbury, Chris Durdin, John Goldsmith, Mick Fiszer, Ron Hoblyn, Tony Irwin, Bill Landells, James McCallum, Richard Millington, Carl Mitchell, Joe Reed and Tony Vine willingly helped in the preparation or checking of certain species accounts. The Earl of Leicester and Chris Knights allowed access to the game books for their respective estates.

John Bruhn, Margaret and Peter Clarke, Allan Hale, Alison Kew, Chris Mead, John Middleton, Martin Preston, David Sadler, and the staff of the British Trust for Ornithology (BTO) Ringing Unit, in particular Jacquie Clark and Mike Toms, helped with the introductory chapter on A History of Bird Ringing in Norfolk and/or the ringing and recovery summaries at the end of the species accounts.

Ringing data were provided by the BTO Ringing Scheme, which is supported by the BTO, the Joint Nature Conservation Committee (on behalf of the Countryside Council for Wales, The Department of the Environment (Northern Ireland), English Nature, Scottish Natural Heritage), The Heritage Service – National Parks and Wildlife (Ireland) and the ringers themselves. The Breeding Bird Survey (BBS) data were supplied by the National Organiser, Richard Bashford. The BBS is organised by the BTO, and jointly funded by the BTO, the Joint Nature Conservation Committee and the Royal Society for the Protection of Birds.

David Parkin, the immediate past chairman, and Tony Marr, the current chairman, of the British Ornithologists' Union's Records Committee provided invaluable advice on species currently on the British List, as well as those in Categories D and E. Giles Dunmore checked records of rarities included in the Systematic List and provided information as to which of the 1998 rarities reported in Norfolk had been accepted by the British Birds Records Committee.

A book such as this is enormously enhanced by the inclusion of high quality photographs and illustrations. We are especially grateful to Norman Arlott for his highly evocative dust jacket and to the other illustrators and photographers who provided material. These included Julian Bhalerao, Andrew Bloomfield, Bryan Bland, Nik Borrow, John Buxton, Robin Chittenden, Carl Donner, Mary Dorling, Geoff and Pat Douglas, Eastern County Newspapers, Graham Easy, Robert Gillmor, Barry Jarvis, Reg Jones, Chris Knights, Iain Leach, Tim Loseby, Richard Millington, Norfolk Museums Service, Norfolk Wildlife Trust, Dave Nye, Mike Page, Rod Powley, Joe Reed, Richard Richardson, Alan Tate, Rob Wilson, Gary Wright and John Wright. The weather maps in the introductory chapter on Migration in Norfolk are reproduced with the kind permission of The Meteorological Office at Bracknell.

For help received when writing the Conservation chapter, Martin George would particularly like to thank the following: Graham Elliott, Ian Robertson and Peter Bradley of the RSPB, Reg Land, Harry Bowell and Mary Dorling of the NWT, Merlin Waterson of the NT, Clive Doarks, Keith McNaught, George Hinton, Maurice Massey and Malcolm Rush of EN, Chris Preston of the RSNC, Graham King of the Norfolk CC, Rob Driscoll of the Castle Museum, Monica O'Donnell of the Farming and Rural Conservation Agency, the staff of the Norfolk Record Office and Richard Hobbs. He is especially grateful to Chris Durdin of the RSPB for answering numerous questions, and to Peter Lambley for kindly reading through the entire chapter.

We are all aware of the sacrifices made by our wives during the preparation of this book, but would particularly like to thank Mary Dorling who undertook much of the typing and helped with the compilation of the extensive Bibliography.

Finally, we are grateful to Pica Press for the confidence they have shown in our ability to produce a text worthy of the high standards for which they are justly renowned. In particular, our thanks to their editor Nigel Redman, who has guided us with great expertise.

All royalties from the sale of this book will be donated to wildlife conservation projects within Norfolk.

*Moss Taylor, Michael Seago, Peter Allard & Don Dorling*

# FOREWORD

*by*

## Lord Buxton KCVO, MC

Norfolk is the most luxurious bird county in the United Kingdom. Its wonderful diversity of habitat attracts and shelters a wide range of species, and its coastline facing the North Sea means that a vast number of migrants using the coasts of Scandinavia, Europe and the North Atlantic are liable to alight in Norfolk at some stage on their way north or south. As a result thousands of human observers flock to the county as well.

It is not surprising, therefore, that Norfolk's bird literature has been prolific, but there have always been three peaks in the output, summarising all that was known at the time about Norfolk birds. The peaks were first, Henry Stevenson (1866) supported by Thomas Southwell (1890); secondly, Bernard Riviere (1930); and then after the war a superbly useful handbook by Michael Seago (1967). Now, almost incredibly, at just the right interval, Michael Seago has managed to achieve a double and scaled a fourth peak for the rapidly expanding ornithological world. He will now become a legend in Norfolk natural history, along with his highly competent team of co-authors, Moss Taylor, Peter Allard and Don Dorling.

In their turn the authors have recruited over thirty contributors with specialist experience, in order to bring the story of Norfolk birds right up to date. This new book is no mere handbook, and all the rich prose and detailed information of the original 'peaks' have been combined with the systematic list and recognition signals of previous handbooks. It is wonderful reading. There is something in this magical volume for everyone, and when I started reading the typescript myself, on the Bittern, or Pinkfoot, or whatever, I could hardly put it down.

Norfolk birdlife is a substantial component of Norfolk life, in that it provides the impulse for the conservation of much of its unspoilt and picturesque scenery. This fine work, *The Birds of Norfolk*, will act as an important public re-enforcement for the conservation of our increasingly threatened landscape.

Aubrey Buxton
Stiffkey, Norfolk

# GEOGRAPHICAL INTRODUCTION

*by*

## Don Dorling

It would seem appropriate to follow precedent set in previous regional avifaunas by including in these introductory chapters a brief resumé of the geographical variations found in Norfolk. This should help the reader who is not fully conversant with Norfolk's geography to put into context the wide mix of habitats found here and the resulting wide variety of birds which has helped the county to earn the reputation as one of the best areas in the British Isles for birds and birdwatching.

In size, it is the third largest English county with a maximum length from east to west of approximately 105km and a width of some 65km from the north coast to the Waveney and Little Ouse Valleys. There is a coastline of over 130km stretching from beyond King's Lynn in the west to just south of Yarmouth in the east. This, together with the Fenland rivers to the south-west and the Rivers Little Ouse and Waveney which make the southern boundary, creates a virtual island.

The underlying rock is predominantly chalk which slopes downwards from west to east. It is exposed in the west on Hunstanton cliffs, Ringstead Downs and again, briefly, further east on the seabed at low tide between Sheringham and Cromer. Over much of the county the chalk has been covered by a series of glacial deposits left after the glaciers had receded at the end of various ice ages, the last of which was at its peak some 18,000 years ago. The resulting soils vary from the heavy boulder clays over much of central Norfolk to the lighter sands and gravels which have given rise, for example, to the Breckland heaths and other areas of heathland, now much fragmented, north of Norwich and in the west of the county.

Henry Stevenson, when writing in 1866 a similar introduction to the first volume of the three-part *The Birds of Norfolk*, divided the county into six geographical areas, namely 'Broad', 'Cliff', 'Meal', 'Breck', 'Fen' and the 'Enclosed' regions. Whilst we might combine the Cliff and Meal under a heading of the 'Coast', these subdivisions of the county are still relevant today when considering the variations of habitat and their avian inhabitants, although much of the detail under each will have changed greatly since Stevenson's day. English Nature's recently introduced Natural Areas approach to dividing the country follows a very similar breakdown of Norfolk with Broadland, Breckland, the Fens, North Norfolk and the East Anglian Plain. Only the last two differ substantially from the ideas of Stevenson although the boundaries of each may differ from his interpretation. The North Norfolk Natural Area covers much of the coastal belt eastwards from Hunstanton but penetrates further inland and follows the sandy heathland areas in both east and west, south to Norwich and King's Lynn respectively, leaving the heavier clay soils in the East Anglian Plain area which extends into Suffolk. The following summaries basically follow the 'districts' of Stevenson.

## THE BROADS

Broadland as a whole consists of that eastern triangle of Norfolk from Yarmouth almost to Norwich, north to beyond Stalham and also including a small area of north-eastern Suffolk inland of Lowestoft. It extends beyond the sinuous formal boundaries of the area looked after by The Broads Authority. When Stevenson wrote his review of the region, it was thought that the Broads area was the relict of a large silted estuary. These beliefs were amended when Dr Joyce Lambert and others published the results of their research in the early 1950s which demonstrated conclusively that the numerous areas of open water and many of the adjacent fens arose as a result of peat digging in the Middle Ages (Lambert 1953).

At the end of the last ice age, some 8,000 years ago, the rivers of eastern Norfolk were faster running than their present counterparts, with steeper-sided valleys. They drained via a large open estuary into the recently flooded North Sea. As the sea levels rose, the rivers came increasingly under tidal influence, resulting in slower rates of flow and the creation of conditions suitable for the growth of peat. Following the development of a shingle ridge over the mouth of the River Yare about 5,000 years ago, and a subsequent series of breaches coupled with higher sea levels, conditions in the river valleys allowed the growth of peat, alternating at times by tidally-influenced deposits of mud. It was these peat beds that were exploited for fuel in medieval times and which subsequently became flooded to create the open areas of water and adjacent fens: the famous Norfolk Broads.

The deeper workings have remained open water but many of the shallower pits, some of which were worked until the early years of the 20th century, have been subject to the natural progression of reedbeds drying out to form wet woodland, known locally as 'carr'. The main concentration of reedbeds surround the open waters and along some river edges but many of the rivers are bordered by wet, alder-dominated carr.

The third major habitat type of the area is the grazing marsh. This is found on the flood plains of the rivers but principally on the Halvergate Marshes which abut on to the fourth major habitat, Breydon Water, a large area of tidal mudflats just inland from Great Yarmouth. It is included here as a part of Broadland but by nature of its tidal character it overlaps with the coastal district.

There have been considerable changes in the quality of the open water, reedbed and carr habitats in Broadland over the last 50 years. These have been brought about largely by the pollution of the waterways caused by a variety of factors including inadequate sewage treatment before water is released to the river systems, thus creating a build-up of phosphates. This, when mixed with the high level of nutrients, mainly nitrogen, in the run-off from agricultural land and the vastly increased use of powered river craft, have all added to the deterioration of water quality. These changes have resulted in an almost complete elimination of aquatic vegetation and a serious regression of many reedbeds with the consequent loss of the associated vertebrate and invertebrate fauna.

Fortunately, there are signs of hope in that the problems have been recognised. Remedial measures are slowly being put in hand by The Broads Authority, other conservation bodies and Anglian Water, as and when the considerable sums of money required become available. Evidence of what can be achieved is demonstrated in Cockshoot Broad and Dyke which, after being isolated from the river system by the construction of a bund at the mouth of the dyke, were mud-pumped to clear out the pollution stored in the mud. The water soon cleared and aquatic plants have grown and, in summer, there are many dragon-flies and other water-based insects on the wing. At the time of writing the much larger Barton Broad is also undergoing a similar treatment regime. There are also hopeful signs from elsewhere – for example, water quality has improved substantially on Hickling Broad allowing the growth of aquatic vegetation which is once again becoming a problem for boats.

The birds most closely associated with the extensive reedbeds of Broadland are Bearded Tits, Bitterns, Marsh Harriers and Water Rails. As will be seen in detail later under the species accounts, these birds have experienced mixed fortunes in recent years. The Bearded Tit has always been very dependent on the mildness or severity of our winters, particularly the duration of snow cover. Despite a series of relatively mild seasons in recent years, the population appears to be in decline. The Bittern has undergone a serious decline in numbers in its Broadland haunts. Having become extinct in the mid-19th century, it had re-turned as a breeder to the Hickling area by 1911. The population steadily built up to a maximum of 55 boomers in 1954 but has since declined dramatically in the Broads with only one successful pair and an additional boomer in 1998. The Marsh Harrier story has a happier outcome. In the 1970s the British population was almost extinct with none breeding in the Broadland reedbeds. During the last few years a change in fortune has resulted in the rapid growth of the local population with 23 known nests in 1998.

The large areas of grazing marsh have also undergone considerable change in the post-war years. This can be seen to great effect in the very large area of the Halvergate Levels, that ancient grazing marsh immedi-ately north and west of Breydon Water. The substantial improvement in drainage methods, largely resulting from the extensive use of electrically-powered pumps, has lowered the water levels in the marsh dykes and consequently the level of the water-table over the greater part of this habitat. This has had a significant impact on the previously typical breeding birds of these marshes, such as Redshanks, Snipe, Lapwings, Yellow Wagtails, etc. Encouraged by the Common Agricultural Policy, some owners have put areas of the marsh under the plough for cereal production, thus further reducing their value as suitable habitat for breeding waders and other grassland birds. Fortunately, the Royal Society for the Protection of Birds has acquired a substantial block of these marshes at Berney where conditions more suitable for the avian residents and visitors are being created. Also, much of the area has been designated as an Environmentally Sensitive Area with the result that grants are available to encourage grazing in a more traditional manner. The grazing marshes bordering the River Yare upstream towards Norwich have become a most important wintering area for wildfowl including thousands of Wigeon together with England's only regular wintering flock of Taiga Bean Geese. A substantial part of this important habitat, much of which is owned or leased by the RSPB, was declared a National Nature Reserve in October 1997.

The tidal estuary of Breydon Water has long been an important feeding area for large numbers of wildfowl and waders. For very many years it was a favoured haunt of wildfowlers and other gunners seeking rare birds for their collections or for sale for the pot. Some protection was given as far back as 1888 when the estuary became one of Britain's first protected areas and a close-season 'Watcher' appointed.

Shooting is now controlled on the estuary and it is a significant wintering refuge for substantial numbers of wildfowl and waders. Recent counts have shown that up to 40,000 Lapwings, 7,000 Golden Plovers, 1,000 Black-tailed Godwits, with large herds of Curlews and various ducks numbered in many hundreds (often including up to 6,000 Wigeon), are resting or feeding on the extensive mudflats at low tide. Records of rarities continue to arise from here, now thanks to the ultra-sharp eyes of the local band of birdwatchers rather than the accurate aim of the gunners. The estuary was declared a Special Protected Area and a Ramsar Site in April 1996 due to the internationally important numbers of birds regularly present.

## THE COAST

Linking Stevenson's 'Meal' and 'Cliff' districts into one section dealing with the whole of Norfolk's extensive coastline will allow the reader to journey from west to east taking the differing habitat types in sequence.

The extreme western end of the county's coastline at Terrington is where the fen meets the Wash, giving rise to a low area of land reclaimed for agriculture and protected from the sea by man-made banks, some of very ancient origin. In places there are stretches of saltmarsh before the open water is reached. The River Great Ouse, which passes through this landscape as it enters the Wash, is tidal for a considerable distance inland creating a useful feeding area for wading birds along its muddy edges.

At low tide the extensive mudflats of the Wash itself are a most important feeding area for spectacular numbers of waders and wildfowl particularly during the winter months, and as a stopover for thousands of birds moving to and from their breeding and wintering quarters in autumn and spring. Its international significance has been recognised by the number of conservation designations which apply to the site: an SSSI, a Special Protection Area, a Ramsar Site and a candidate for notification as a Special Area of Conservation. High tides force the huge numbers of birds feeding there on to favoured roosting areas, and an important location used for this purpose is the RSPB's Reserve at Snettisham: a series of flooded pits separated from the sea by the shingle beach which has replaced the saltmarshes of further south.

The seaside resort of Hunstanton brings about a dramatic change of scenery with the sudden rise of Norfolk's only hard cliffs. Stretching for about 800m north of the town, are the easily recognised red and white chalk cliffs resting on a layer of brown carstone, an iron-rich sandstone of the Lower Cretaceous period. Rising to about 20m, these chalk cliffs of Upper Cretaceous age provide a reasonably secure nesting site for Fulmars which have bred there since 1964. Formerly, Swifts and House Martins also found conditions in the cracks and crevices suitable for nesting. In winter, numbers of grebes and sea-ducks can be seen offshore. The cliffs soon dip down to beach level and another habitat; flat sandy beaches backed by sand dunes stretching initially northwards and then eastwards as far as Thornham Harbour. Located in this first stretch of dunes on the extreme north-west corner of the county are the neighbouring Holme Dunes Reserve of the Norfolk Wildlife Trust and the smaller reserve of the Norfolk Ornithologists' Association which includes an observatory – both well-known sites for the regular occurrence of spring and autumn migrants.

A large area of saltmarsh begins at Thornham with sections stretching eastwards as far as the Cley West Bank and creating an internationally important natural resource of over 2,100ha in extent. There are many large and small creeks and estuaries within the saltmarsh including the harbours at Thornham itself, Brancaster, Overy Staithe, Wells, Morston and Blakeney, the last being tidal as far as Cley Mill. These areas support large numbers of birds throughout the year with Shelducks, Redshanks and, in the winter, Brent Geese being typical examples. These marshes are all liable to regular flooding on the highest spring tides so do not act as satisfactory nesting areas. Notwithstanding the hazards, many gulls attempt to nest annually. Although the saltmarshes are divided into two main sections by the dunes at Holkham and Wells, there is a new saltmarsh developing quite rapidly on the flat muddy area of beach at Holkham and Wells between the main dunes and a series of smaller outer dunes. This stretch of coast includes the RSPB Reserve at Titchwell and the Holkham National Nature Reserve. The latter comprises the extensive dunes mentioned below plus the fresh marshes which wintering geese find so attractive.

Much of the main saltmarsh and the majority of the harbours are protected from the direct impact of the sea by the extensive dunes and shingle ridges which form Scolt Head Island and Blakeney Point. Both are nature reserves in the care of the National Trust, each with large breeding colonies of terns at their western ends.

These extensive areas of sand dunes, particularly those at Holme, Scolt Head, Holkham, Wells and Blakeney Point are the Meals (or Meols) referred to by Stevenson. Generally a fragile habitat, they are subject to attack from both the sea and strong winds. The dunes at Holkham were planted with Corsican pines during the 19th century to give stability. This large conifer wood is a great attraction to migrants arriving from across the North Sea and a favoured venue for birdwatchers in late summer and autumn when, from time to time, large 'falls' of Scandinavian migrants occur, filling the woods with warblers, chats and thrushes.

There are further areas of saltmarsh east of Holkham and Wells which end with the fresh marshes of Blakeney, Cley and Salthouse. Both Blakeney and Cley Marshes were reclaimed from the saltings in the middle of the 17th century when Dutch engineers created embankments to exclude the sea. These have been protected from direct attacks from the sea by the 10km of shingle bank which runs from Weybourne in the east to Blakeney Point. This shingle ridge has gradually been moving land-wards at the average rate of a metre a year for at least the last 350 years. Around 1850 it had closed the Salthouse channel which had run between the shingle and the marshes and by 1920 had swamped the north bank of Cley Marsh thus removing the indirect protection it previously provided. The vegetated sections of this shingle are attractive in winter to many seed-eating birds such as finches and Snow Buntings.

The North Sea is subject to periodic surges, or 'rages' as they were known by our Victorian forebears, when certain conditions of wind and tide coincide. These frequently result in substantial movements of the shingle and the flooding, by sea water, of the fresh marshes. At Cley, for example, the marsh has been subject to such flooding about seven times a century since its original enclosure. The 1953 surge, which caused considerable loss of life along the east coast and also in The Netherlands, was estimated to have rolled the shingle bank land-wards by about 50m and left over 3m of salt water on Cley marsh. Since then, the shingle has been subject to regular reprofiling by large machinery to give adequate protection to the marshes and, more particularly, the village of Salthouse. The last major breach of the shingle which resulted in considerable flooding occurred on 19th–20th February 1996 when Cley Marsh was under some one and a half metres of water. At the time of writing, new strategies for protecting this coast are under consideration and the probable solution will be the construction of an earth bank between the coast road and the shingle bank. The latter will then be allowed to develop its natural profile to provide once again an outer line of defence.

Eastwards from the end of the shingle bank at Weybourne, Norfolk's second range of cliffs commence, this time made up glacial deposits of sands and clays. They extend for about 23km south-eastwards dropping down to sea level again at Bacton, having reached their maximum height of 60m at Trimingham. These soft cliffs are subject to serious erosion in places, consequently they do not provide ideal conditions for cliff nesters although Fulmars have colonised some of these cliffs since the early 1950s. At Dead Man's Wood, on the top of the cliffs between Weybourne and Sheringham, a ringing station has been established and many records of rarities have been obtained since the early 1970s.

Southwards from Bacton we return to areas of sandy beaches and dunes which include the Winterton Dunes National Nature Reserve, an area of great ornithological interest at times of easterly winds during the migration seasons. South of Winterton are low cliffs extending to Caister which as recently as 1995 have been colonised by Fulmars. The North Denes at Yarmouth is towards the southern end of this stretch of sandy shore and in the summer months is home to Britain's largest colony of Little Terns. In a wardened and fenced section of this extensive and busy holiday beach, about 200 pairs of Little Terns have nested in recent years with varying degrees of success.

The town of Yarmouth itself is built on a spit which over many centuries has diverted the mouth of the River Yare southwards. On the land-ward side of this spit and the town is the large tidal estuary of Breydon Water referred to in the Broadland section but which, as mentioned above, is a coastal habitat by nature. The River Yare crossing Breydon and flowing out to sea at the harbour's mouth was originally the county boundary but now Norfolk takes in Gorleston and a few more kilometres of coast to Hopton-on-Sea, an area of sandy beaches backed by low cliffs.

## THE BRECKS

The Brecks, or Breckland as the area was named by W. G. Clarke in the latter part of the 19th century, is an area of some 94,000ha of light, nutrient-poor sandy soils overlaying the chalk, centred on the town of Thetford. There have been varying descriptions of its boundaries over the years but in general terms, it stretches from Swaffham in the north, almost to Attleborough in the east; the western edge abuts on to the Fens and in the south it extends across the Suffolk county boundary as far as Mildenhall, Cavenham and Culford.

At one time much of the land was open sandy heath, parts of which in times of need were 'broken' (hence the term Brecks) for use as arable land. As circumstances changed these were allowed to revert back to heath, sheep-walks and rabbit warrens. In the days when the area was a vast open plain and hand-sown rye the likely crop of any farming activity, it was the home of the last droves of Great Bustards which finally became extinct as a native species in 1838. From time to time, these open heaths have been subjected to sand-storms, and on one occasion they were of such severity that the border village of Santon Downham and the nearby River Little Ouse were overwhelmed.

Arguably, Breckland has undergone greater change since the time of Stevenson than any other of the county's regions. Indeed the change had begun before he wrote his first volume, in which he expressed the opinion that the demise of the Great Bustard was principally due to changes in agricultural practice, such as the planting of shelter belts of Scots pine and the introduction of the seed-drill, rather than from the activities of the collectors. These changes have accelerated greatly in the 20th century. First, the Forestry Commission, created after the First World War with the remit to produce home-grown timber, commenced an extensive planting programme in Breckland in 1922 near Swaffham. Today the total area of the Thetford Forest, some of which is in Suffolk, is over 20,000ha. Secondly, advances in agricultural practices, including the extensive use of fertilisers and the introduction of sophisticated irrigation apparatus, have allowed vast areas of poor land to be farmed profitably. The net result of these parallel developments has been a substantial reduction in the area of open heath. At the beginning of the 20th century there were 29,000ha of heathland and dry grassland, but nearly a hundred years later this has been reduced to only 7,000ha.

The vast areas of Scots and Corsican pines, larches and other introduced conifers making up Thetford Forest, which have changed the landscape beyond recognition, have also had a major impact on the bird life of the region. Whilst the plantations have become colonised by tits, Goldcrests, various finches, including Redpolls and Crossbills, and other woodland edge species, they have led to the abandonment of the Brecks by Ringed Plovers, Whinchats and a great reduction in numbers of the Stone Curlew, or Norfolk Plover. In the 1930s there were 1,500 pairs of this speciality of the region but by 1991 the population had declined to 100 pairs. The trend of reduction or extinction of the local species, which has continued and accelerated, had, as mentioned above, already started by the middle of the 19th century (Stevenson). The last known breeding by Red-backed Shrikes in the county took place on the Norfolk side of the river near Santon Downham in 1988 with a solitary male returning to the same area for the next two years.

A further major impact on the remaining areas of traditional heathland was the sudden demise of the huge population of rabbits following the outbreak of myxomatosis in 1953. Since their introduction in the Middle Ages, the grazing by rabbits had been a major factor in the nature of much of the ground flora of the open heaths, providing the short sward and patches of disturbed ground which Stone Curlews and other ground-nesting species seemed to find so essential for nesting and feeding. In Stevenson's day even the White-tailed Eagle made annual winter visits to the teeming rabbit warrens near Thetford. The absence of the intense grazing pressure after 1953 led to a much taller growth which many ground nesters found unacceptable, and the lack of rabbit holes for nesting hit the Wheatear population.

There are still some areas which remind us of the traditional Breck scenery, such as the Norfolk Wildlife Trust's Reserves at East Wretham and Weeting. At the latter site, there is a substantial population of rabbits and consequently Stone Curlews and Wood Larks continue to thrive. The largest surviving area of traditional Breck scenery is in the military Stanford Training Area. The population of five villages was evacuated in 1942 to create the 7,000ha 'Battle Area', now known as the Stanford Training Area or STANTA. Over half a century later the military are still in occupation with much of the land being extensively grazed by sheep and where many specialist Breckland species continue to prosper despite much noisy activity by the armed forces.

Recently the decline in numbers of certain Breckland specialities has been halted or reversed. Thanks to active monitoring by the RSPB and the co-operation of local farmers, Stone Curlews are increasingly successful at breeding on some areas of farmland. In the forest, trees have been reaching maturity and large blocks of pines are being harvested, resulting in many clear-felled and replanted sites which have provided a succession of areas of suitable habitat for Nightjars and Wood Larks.

Consideration of the Brecks would not be complete without mention of the meres; those enigmatic areas of water where the levels can fluctuate so dramatically. The best-known and most readily accessible of these are Langmere and Ringmere on the East Wretham Reserve, and Fowlmere with the nearby Devil's Punchbowl, which are situated some 3km further to the west along the ancient Weeting Drove Road. None of these bodies of water is stream fed but each one depends on the level of the water-table in the underlying chalk for its supply. At times of high water level they are home to Moorhens, Coots, Little Grebes and various ducks, with Lapwings and other passing waders feeding around their margins. The level of water in Ringmere has been known to flood the nearby main road to such a depth that horses were knee-deep when passing through. Similarly, Fowlmere has at times in the past contained up to five and a half metres of water extending to an area of 12ha, the sudden rise in levels there resulting in a number of Moorhens' nests being found within old Blackbirds' nests in the hedges (Clarke 1937). In 1988 the bird hide at Langmere became flooded and unusable for a time because of the high water level in the mere. In these conditions diving ducks and other wildfowl are regularly seen.

More recently Langmere, Ringmere and Fowlmere have been completely dry resulting in a considerable growth of vegetation on their beds, with the last named being grazed by sheep during the summer of 1998. However, by early 1999 water again appeared following a period of higher than average rainfall. Although there is evidence that recent substantial increases in water extraction from bore-holes in the chalk has lowered the water-table, thus affecting the meres, the phenomenon of them being completely dry is not a new feature. W. G. Clarke, again in his *Breckland Wilds* (1937), reported that during a dry spell in 1859–62, Fowlmere was planted with oats, wheat and vetches.

There are other important areas of water in the district: meres in Wretham Park, at Tottington and West Tofts together with the two large lakes, Stanford Water and Thompson Water. These last two are stream fed and with stable water levels have more permanent populations of waterfowl. In winter they have been visited by Whooper and Bewick's Swans and an occasional Bittern has been reported. The main river flowing through Breckland is the Little Ouse which for much of its length forms the county boundary with Suffolk. The Rivers Nar and Wissey also drain the northern section of the district.

## THE FENS

Whilst the last region has probably changed the most since Stevenson knew it, the Fens would almost certainly be instantly recognisable to him. His description of the district is still applicable today: 'Hardly a hedge is seen, but the surface is intersected every few hundred yards by deep ditches, cut at right angles to each other and communicating with wider ditches, which are locally known as "lodes" and , running into the still larger water-courses, assist the more thorough drainage of the land.' The area is still largely devoid of trees and hedges, apart from those near dwellings, and is intensively farmed throughout.

Fenland stretches from King's Lynn to the south, west into Cambridgeshire and Lincolnshire. The area is made up of both silt and peat deposits which have been drained over many centuries for agricultural use. The Norfolk section of this large region has the salt marshes of the Wash on its northern boundary and includes areas of both silt and peat deposits. The silt-lands bordering the River Great Ouse, usually known as Marshland, have been used profitably since medieval times as witnessed by the great churches such as those at the Wiggenhalls.

Further south, much traditional peat fen habitat was drained over a long period culminating in the work of Cornelius Vermuyden who was commissioned by the fourth Earl of Bedford in the 17th century. The two Bedford Rivers, which run north-east from Erith to Denver, were created to relieve the River Great Ouse in taking flood water from the Midlands to the sea. These parallel rivers with their flood plain in between, have formed a most important ornithological site; the famous Ouse Washes, the northern section of which is in Norfolk. Much of the area of grazing marsh enclosed by the two man-made rivers is now in the ownership of conservation bodies. It is the breeding ground of Black-tailed Godwits, and the Welney Reserve of the Wildfowl and Wetlands Trust is renowned for its wintering herds of Whooper and

Bewick's Swans and hundreds of – mainly drake – Pochards together with lesser numbers of many other species of wildfowl.

No summary of the ornithological interest of the Fens could be complete without mentioning Wisbech Sewage Farm which was built straddling the county boundary with Cambridgeshire by the River Nene in 1874. Situated merely ten kilometres inland from the Wash, its flooded filter-beds became a mecca for birdwatchers and a haven for a wide variety of waders and other water-loving birds. See the entry for John Moyes in the personalities chapter for details of the avian highlights at this famous site.

Small areas of the fenland basin have in fairly recent times been planted with poplars for the match and pallet trade. One such site just on the Suffolk side of the border became suitable for the Golden Oriole to colonise, and subsequently these birds extended their limited range into similar habitat nearby in the Norfolk Fens.

## THE ENCLOSED OR FARMLAND DISTRICTS

The remaining areas of the county Stevenson grouped under the heading 'The Enclosed District' which covered all the agricultural regions stretching from the borders of the Brecks and Fens in the west to the Broads in the east and the coastal belt in the north to the southern river valleys. Agriculture is still the principal activity in this part of the county and one which has changed much since Stevenson knew it, although he had already witnessed changes brought about by the intensification of agricultural practices. It is a district of differing soils and character with areas of sands and gravels, good loams and heavy clays. In the north-west there are large fields on the 'Good Sands' with straight roads and hedgerows whilst in the south, on the boulder clay, there are, or were, smaller irregular fields. These equate to the 'Planned' and 'Ancient' countryside types described by Oliver Rackham (1986a). Whilst a good deal of the field and hedge-row pattern extant in the middle of the 20th century owed its existence to the various Enclosure Acts of the 17th and 18th centuries – which resulted in the demise of the open field system of agriculture and the loss of much common land – there were, in places, extensive field systems in existence long before the Parliamentary enclosures. For example, some of the field patterns spreading northwards from the Waveney Valley are thought to pre-date the Roman occupation as they are dissected by a Roman Road (the present-day A140), much as a modern motorway cuts through existing landscape features (Williamson 1993).

The large fields of the north-west corner have in recent years become the winter home of vast numbers of Pink-footed Geese which find the debris left on sugar-beet fields after the crop has been harvested much to their liking. At times, dusk can bring the spectacular sight of very large skeins of these geese flighting to roost at Snettisham, Scolt Head or near Wells.

The second half of the 20th century has witnessed a great deal of change to the rural landscape of Norfolk. The need to accommodate larger and larger machinery has resulted in the need for bigger fields with consequent loss of their hedges, field margins and ditches. Between 1946 and 1970 an estimated 22,000km of hedgerow were removed in the county. A survey covering the large south Norfolk parish of Kenninghall disclosed that in 50 years 80% of hedges and field boundaries in the parish had been removed (McMullen 1997). To retain a good variety of species and a high density of birds in farmland, there needs to be at least 60m in length of hedge per hectare, which represents an average field size of around 7ha (Lack 1992) – a situation not widely achieved under modern arable practice in the county. Larger fields may be attractive to certain ground nesting species but the total variety and numbers have been shown to reduce once the density of hedgerows falls below this optimum.

Other advances in agricultural practice, such as the 'improvement' and draining of ancient grassland, autumn cereal sowing resulting in a considerable reduction in stubbles, the absence of stack-yards and the extensive use of pesticides and herbicides have all combined to cause a considerable reduction in the populations of the once familiar farmland and wet meadow birds. The species which have suffered most under these changed circumstances include the Lapwing, Snipe, Skylark, Tree Sparrow, Yellowhammer, Corn Bunting and various finches, details of which will appear under the species accounts in the Systematic List.

Despite the pressures put upon farmers to improve efficiency and intensify their operations, there are some glimmers of hope. Some enlightened landowners divide their largest fields with 'beetle-banks' and leave unsprayed margins around the field headlands. These activities are beneficial to many species of birds and other wildlife in addition to the gamebirds on these farms. Whilst in no way replacing the autumn stubbles, areas of set-aside have provided some vital overwintering feeding areas for our beleaguered farmland birds. It is to be hoped that when the Common Agricultural Policy is eventually up-dated more emphasis can be directed towards sympathetic husbandry rather than for mere production.

The county's few remaining ancient woods also occur in this 'district'. At the time of Domesday in 1086, woodland in Norfolk was concentrated in a crescent stretching from Bungay through Attleborough and East Dereham towards Cromer (Rackham 1986b). Today it is found mainly, but not exclusively, on the boulder clay plateau and includes Ashwellthorpe, Brooke, Foxley, Hedenham, Hockering, Thursford and Wayland. Each woodland has its particular undisturbed mix of soil types which create the diversity of both trees and ground flora. They are home to many woodland birds including woodpeckers, tits, finches, and the summer-visiting warblers. Although these woods had long been managed as a resource for wood and timber, over recent decades many have become neglected. Fortunately, a number of these historic sites, such as those belonging to the Norfolk Wildlife Trust, are having the traditional management practice of coppice with standards reintroduced. The result is a much enhanced variety of cover making the woods more attractive to a wider selection of plants, insects and birds. Significant stands of mature woodland also occur elsewhere including Felbrigg and Swanton Novers in the north of the county. Both of these have been at times the chosen sites of nesting Honey Buzzards.

Many mature trees also exist in the large areas of parkland associated with the stately homes which are located particularly in the northern half of the county, such as the halls at Sandringham, Houghton, Raynham, Holkham, Sennowe, Felbrigg, Blickling and Mannington. These parks are home to wood-peckers and other tree-loving species including tits, Nuthatches, Treecreepers and occasionally, such as in Holkham Park, the elusive Hawfinch. Where the park contains a lake, the variety of birds is widened considerably, not only by the introduced geese but also a variety of other waterfowl such as grebes, diving ducks, Moorhens and, usually in large numbers, Coots. Where permitted, Cormorants will visit to fish or roost and Ospreys will seek a meal as they pass through en route to or from their northern nesting grounds.

The ever expanding urban area of greater Norwich falls within this 'district'. It will have grown sub-stantially from the city known to Stevenson but still provides a mixture of habitats both semi-natural and man-made which have been adopted by a wide variety of birds. The widespread habit of feeding birds in gardens, particularly in winter, has helped to maintain a large and varied urban and suburban avian popu-lation. Although suburban gardens with their man-made hazards are no real substitute for their natural habitats, they do provide some food and cover for a number of species (Cannon 1998). Gone are the rookeries in the vicinity of Surrey Street, mentioned by Stevenson, but Carrion Crows still appear there, one of them proving to be a great nuisance to a colleague of the writer as it persistently did battle with its own reflection in the window of his tower-block office! When these modern buildings were being con-structed, Black Redstarts used them as nesting sites.

Blackbirds still sing and nest in the City centre, Starlings and gulls join the Feral Pigeons seeking easy pickings around the provision market and Pied Wagtails can be heard as they explore the many flat roofs. This last species has adopted city-centre trees for winter roosting notwithstanding the human activities just below or, indeed, the Christmas lights decorating the trees themselves. House Martins and Swallows are now confined to the outer suburbs but Norwich can still boast a good population of Swifts, thanks in part to the foresight of the City Fathers in providing nest boxes for Swifts when re-roofing large numbers of the council-owned housing, an activity which usually results in the properties being no longer suitable for this species.

The Rivers Wensum and Yare which dissect and skirt the City, respectively, bring another habitat to the urban scene. In addition to the inevitable Moorhens, Mallards and Mute Swans, improved water quality has encouraged the Kingfisher and Great Crested Grebe to frequent the city centre, occasionally to be joined briefly by a wintering diver or, during summer, a passing Common Tern. The University Broad, a flooded gravel working in the valley of the Yare, provides sanctuary for Great Crested Grebes, various species of duck including Tufted Duck, Pochard and in several recent winters, Goosander.

Leaving the city and travelling up-stream along these two major rivers, we enter other important habitats, albeit much modified by man. There are a number of water-mills along the Yare, in particular, providing short stretches of faster moving water which a few pairs of Grey Wagtails find acceptable. Occa-sionally, a wintering Dipper will also spend some time at such a locality. Few riverside water meadows remain and the excited calling of the Redshank or the drumming of the Snipe are unlikely to be heard here during the summer. Many of these low-lying areas have been excavated for gravel and sand leaving large areas of open water which were soon adopted by a wide variety of bird life. At times, these gravel workings have been used by Little Ringed Plovers even whilst the site is being worked. As soon as the open sandy areas become overgrown, they are no longer suitable for these visitors but finches and summer-visiting warblers move in as scrub develops around the perimeters of the pits. Common Terns are also summer visitors to many such locations.

Although much of the county was subject to the consequences of the Enclosure Acts there still remain a number of commons and some of these retain an ornithological interest. Many have lost their traditional usage of grazing and have become covered in scrub rather than areas of (usually wet) grassland. Common lands on the lighter soils are sometimes host to Nightjars, with Nightingales occasionally using dense stands of scrub.

## THE FUTURE

Throughout much of this volume we regularly refer to events as recorded by Stevenson who was writing in the second half of the 19th century. We have tried to record the ornithological scene in Norfolk at the end of the 20th century. What changes can we expect to occur in the county over the next hundred years?

Much has been written of late on the subject of global warming. That it is happening there can be little doubt; the debate has been over the impact of man's activities in accelerating this process. There are two major ways in which this slow change in our climate will probably affect Norfolk and its ornithology. First, a steady rise in sea level is the inevitable result of a warmer world and this will have a significant impact on a county with a long and vulnerable coastline. Large areas of the saltmarshes and sand dunes along the north coast must be particularly at risk from erosion. The important tern colonies at Scolt Head and Blakeney Point, which are now occasionally flooded by high tides, could be major casualties of a higher sea level. Similarly, the fresh marshes such as those at Holme, Holkham, and between Blakeney and Salthouse, will be difficult to defend once the dunes are severely damaged, putting at risk the freshwater reserves at Titchwell, Holkham and Cley. Whilst they could remain of interest as saline pools, their importance as breeding grounds for waders, such as Redshanks and Avocets, could be jeopardised.

An increased tidal range in the eastern rivers could have serious consequences on the Broads brought about by the increase in salinity in their complex and delicate ecosystems. Furthermore, this whole area is dependent on the protection from major incursions of salt water by the dune systems along the east coast. A substantial increase in sea level must make a repeat of the 1938 floods in this area more likely in the long term unless major protection measures are put in place at the most vulnerable sites.

However, a warming of the climate will probably result in the continuing colonisation of the county by southern species. The Cetti's Warbler could expand its toehold before being joined by the Penduline Tit and the Common Rosefinch. Perhaps the Dartford Warbler will spread northwards from its Suffolk out-post, to be joined by other southern species making the short hop across the Channel. These newcomers will help to replace other species which will retreat northwards in the face of global warming. A more stormy autumn and winter in the Atlantic could also result in an increase in stragglers from the New World appearing here to cause delight amongst twenty-first-century twitchers.

Apart from climatic change there are political developments which could have a significant influence on an agricultural region such as Norfolk. A major reform in the Common Agricultural Policy could bring about substantial changes in the way farming is carried out both here and in an expanded Common Market in eastern Europe. It is to be hoped that the emphasis of future financial support will be aimed at the production of food in such a way that is sympathetic to the environment, thus granting a reprieve to our threatened farmland birds. The spread of the present support system into eastern Europe's agriculture would be catastrophic for many species and this would be felt here by a reduction in numbers and variety of our avian winter visitors from the east, a trend which is showing signs of already having begun.

A greater awareness of, and interest in, our rich heritage of wildlife in general, and birds in particular, may well result in an extension and enforcement of laws throughout all of Europe to give migrant birds greater security from shooting in southern Europe. Such wishes might be too late for the Turtle Dove; we can but hope!

# ORNITHOLOGY IN NORFOLK:
# HISTORY AND PERSONALITIES

*by*

## Michael Seago

Norfolk can claim a well-documented ornithological history extending back to the early years of the 19th century. During this period there have been remarkable changes not only in bird numbers and distribution, but also great changes in social history and the arrival of modern farming. Early ornithologists were often owners of large estates and bird records were confirmed by forming collections of mounted birds contained in glass cases. Today's observers have the great advantages of excellent reference works and sophisticated optical aids.

On the once extensive denes at Yarmouth many migrants were netted by the bird-catchers with the aid of decoys; Arthur Patterson described them 'placing their traps and hiding behind tufts of marram before pulling nets upon the wretched Linnets, Twites and Snow Buntings lured to their doom and all destined as cage birds or for the table'. Inland of the town, Breydon estuary provided a fleet of punt-gunners with an abundance of wildfowl and waders. All would be offered for sale on the market game stalls, 'rarer examples being placed in a more conspicuous position upon a fruit tray'. Such displays resulted in the discovery of rarities which were rapidly acquired by local taxidermists.

The following pages include short biographies of a selection of observers who have contributed so much to the history of ornithology in Norfolk.

One of the earliest known Norfolk naturalists was **Sir Thomas Browne** who lived in Norwich for 46 years. His letters and his *Notes on Certain Birds Found in Norfolk* reveal the Hoopoe as a 'gallant marked bird which I have often seen and it is not hard to shoot them'; Avocets were 'summer marsh birds' and Spoonbills 'formerly built in the hernery at Claxton and Reedham'.

Duck decoys were introduced into Norfolk from The Netherlands. Writing in 1663 Sir Thomas Browne commented on their abundance 'especially between Norwich and the sea making this place very much to abound in wildfowl'. Decoys established at Acle, Hemsby and Waxham are thought to be the oldest in the country. For over 200 years Norfolk was a land of decoys, and details are known of 30 sites. These were located at Acle, Besthorpe, Cawston, Dersingham, Didlington, Feltwell, Gunton, Hemsby, Hempstead, Hillington, Hilgay, Hockwold, Holkham, Langham, Mautby, Merton, Methwold, Micklemere, Narford, Northwold, Ranworth, South Acre, Sutton, Stow Bardolph, Waxham, Westwick, Winterton, Wolterton, Woodbastwick and Wormegay.

However, by 1890 when Thomas Southwell was completing the final volume of the *Birds of Norfolk* the total number of active decoys had declined to five in the county. Wetland drainage was a major contributory factor, shooting became increasingly popular and wildfowl taken in Dutch decoys undersold local birds in the London markets.

Abandoned decoys rapidly became derelict and forlorn. The pipes silted-up, alders advanced and wrecked the hoops. Tattered netting waved among the branches and there was an air of decay. Where once hundreds, even thousands of ducks came to rest each day in a fancied but really perilous security, the pool waters drained away to be replaced by tangles of matted vegetation. Many a decoy pool developed into alder and willow carr. One site (Besthorpe) is covered by the Attleborough by-pass. Nowadays, decoy sites are remembered merely as names on a map: Decoy Carr, Decoy Covert, Decoy Farm, Decoy Fen, Decoy House, Decoy Marsh, Decoy Road and Decoy Wood.

How did a decoy operate? Once ducks had been encouraged to rest in the shelter of the pool (usually between one and three acres in extent) they needed to enter one of the curved pipes leading away from the pool. Most decoys had three to six pipes, occasionally eight and even ten. Each of these fatal retreats was covered in a tunnel of netting stretched on hoops and flanked with overlapping reed screens cunningly arranged so that the decoyman was invisible to the ducks on the pool, but could at the critical moment, appear behind the birds in the pipe preventing their retreat. There was then no alternative but to fly further up the ever-narrowing pipe and round its bend.

The most surprising method of enticing ducks further into the pipe was by using a small dog. As the dog advanced from screen to screen – ever obedient to the motions of the decoyman – the ducks, fascinated, readily followed. Then the wily 'coyman' would show himself and panic them into entering the detachable tunnel net. Mallard, Teal and Wigeon formed the main catch at local decoys. At Ranworth where the decoy contained ten pipes the variety extended to Pintail, Tufted Duck, Garganey, Goosander, Woodcock and Pheasant.

The Gadwall had long been known as a winter visitor, but establishment as a breeder in Breckland was the result of releasing a pinioned pair at Narford lake by the Revd John Fountaine. Increasing numbers of their descendants have continued to breed, doubtless attracting migrant Gadwall to stay and nest. The original pair had been taken at Dersingham decoy by George Skelton. Two generations of the Skelton family were famed for their skills in building and working decoys. Many of Norfolk's examples were known to have been constructed or redesigned by the Skeltons. The father died in his 80th year and is buried in Winterton churchyard.

Surviving records reveal how deadly the decoys could be. Winterton decoy once took 1,100 Teal in a single week. One of the last active decoys was at Micklemere where the largest seasonal catch was 1,807 birds in 1896–97. High totals were also recorded in 1900–01 with 1,354, 1906–07 with 1,259 and 1913–14 with 1,283 birds. This decoy became inactive in the early 1920s. More recently, during the 1925–26 winter 3,302 Mallards, 11 Wigeon and 37 Teal were taken at Fritton (Ashby End). During 1968 two pipes at Dersingham decoy were restored for ringing purposes. This decoy, constructed by George Skelton the younger, was in active use from 1818 until 1870 (Southwell 1879).

Secretive by nature, the decoyman's occupation was pursued in solitude. Not surprisingly few decoy books have survived, but details of Hempstead decoy for 1831–32 are lodged in Norfolk Record Office (Baker 1985). Such volumes provide a fascinating insight into a way of life which has passed into history.

Among early clergyman naturalists was **Richard Lubbock** whose book, *The Fauna of Norfolk* (1845), was revised by Thomas Southwell in 1879. Lubbock described a countryside little altered for generations. His curacies were carefully selected to enable him to continue ornithological observations in the Fens, the Wash and the Broads. The Gurney family, the great Quaker bankers and philanthropists, moving out to country houses and estates from their Norwich mansions almost all became – along with their close family and business connections, the Barclays, Birkbecks and Buxtons – field sportsmen and naturalists. For decades **John Henry Gurney senior** and his son **John Henry Gurney** wrote books and published annual ornithological reports for Norfolk which appeared in the *Zoologist* and the *Transactions of the Norfolk & Norwich Naturalists' Society*.

**Henry Stevenson**

Henry Stevenson's three-volume *Birds of Norfolk* is a most impressive work. It includes summaries of the information contained in earlier books together with detailed accounts of all species then included in the county list.

Stevenson was born in Norwich in 1833. His father's residence in Surrey Street was directly opposite the trees in Samuel Bignold's garden and coachyard. He was educated at King's College School in London. He then entered the family business in Norwich, occupying offices in the present-day Guildhall Hill. He became stationer, publisher, printer and proprietor of the Norfolk Chronicle and the Norfolk Mail. Although serving as Sheriff of Norwich he never took an active part in municipal affairs.

When just 22 he was elected honorary secretary to the Norfolk & Norwich Museum, a post which he held until the time of his death. Nine years later he was doubly honoured, becoming a member of the British Ornithologists' Union and a Fellow of the Linnean Society. At the opening meeting of the newly formed Norfolk & Norwich Naturalists' Society, Stevenson was nominated a vice-president, soon filling the office of president. Like almost all Victorian naturalists, Henry Stevenson was also a keen sportsman. It was the Broadland scene in high summer which provided the inspiration for his most attractive writing.

His greatest pleasures were derived from his aviary, his collection of locally mounted birds, his library and his widespread circle of correspondents. The first volume of his magnum opus was published in 1866, the second not until four years later. Almost a third of the final volume was compiled by Stevenson, his writing breaking off in mid-sentence when drafting the Gadwall essay. The third volume was completed in 1890 by Thomas Southwell.

Henry Stevenson's account of the ornithology of Victorian Norwich makes fascinating reading. In those times the 'city in an orchard' attracted 'spotted flycatchers and redstarts which returned year after year to the same nests on the vine stem or in the ivy-covered wall'. Stevenson recalled a Dipper obtained near the lower Close ferry and Black Terns collected as they towered over Foundry Bridge. Vagrant Little Auks and Little Grebes were regularly recovered in the streets and once in Rose Lane a stranded Storm Petrel. Nightingales were heard along 'every road leading out of the city and Stone Curlews nested on the high grounds at Thorpe'.

Finally, leaving the house at 10 Unthank Road, Norwich, which he had so long occupied, this great Victorian died less than a year later in August 1888. The greater part of his mounted bird collection was sold. Arthur Patterson recorded details of the auction when the precious cases of Broad-billed and Pectoral Sandpipers, Golden Orioles and Rose-coloured Starling, Sabine's Gull and Roller, Squacco Heron and Black Terns came under the hammer. Some specimens survive in the Castle Museum, Norwich to this day including the Squacco Heron from Surlingham. Most expensive was the case containing a pair of Bee-eaters obtained by a passing wherryman at Coldham Hall along the River Yare. This historic case, still in excellent condition, has recently come to light – housed in the National Trust's Sheringham Hall.

**Thomas Southwell** (1831–1909) is almost forgotten today although he completed the greater part of the third volume of Henry Stevenson's classic *Birds of Norfolk* using the author's letters and manuscripts combined with his own detailed knowledge of the county's wildlife. The world of banking provided Southwell with a career. He entered the service of Gurney's Bank (later to become Barclays) in King's Lynn before moving to Fakenham and finally to the impressive Barclays Head Office in Norwich. Southwell achieved 50 years' service in banking. His duties enabled frequent branch visits which provided opportunities to explore the world of natural history.

Southwell took an active part in the affairs of the Norfolk & Norwich Naturalists' Society acting as secretary for many years, was twice honoured, being elected as president, and was a long-standing member of the journal committee. He published well over a hundred papers in the Naturalists' Society's periodicals. His field was wide including research into Dutch and English duck decoys and stranded leviathans along the Norfolk coast. Other major contributions were his revised edition of Lubbock's *Fauna of Norfolk* published in 1879 and the *Natural History of Norfolk* by Sir Thomas Browne which he republished in 1902.

The activities of Holkham shooting parties attracted Southwell's attention. He recorded that during a 14-year period over 14,000 hares, 2,000 Woodcock and 1,600 Snipe were taken on the great estate. Further papers followed including one on St Helen's swanpit close to Norwich Cathedral, where young Mute Swans were fattened for Corporation banquets. He supported local bird protection societies formed at Yarmouth, Blakeney and Wells; compiled educational booklets for the Society for the Protection of Birds (nowadays the RSPB), an official Guide to Norwich Museum and a catalogue of birds in the former Connop collection, at Rollesby Hall. Thomas Southwell died on 5th September 1909 at 10 The Crescent in Norwich, his home for many years.

Well known in his day as 'Gunn of Norwich', **Thomas Edward Gunn** (1844–1923) kept a taxidermist's shop at 86 St Giles Street. In its heyday several staff were employed and the establishment became the largest and best known of its kind in East Anglia.

Thomas Gunn was the son of Robert Gunn, a carriage builder of King Street, Norwich. After schooldays he assisted his father in coach-painting and as an heraldic artist. Later he became an assistant master at Norwich School of Art and then entered the taxidermy business. During those times collecting was considered a worthy pursuit for gentlemen, including the clergy. The observation of birds wild and free was but the whim of a very few eccentrics. It was desirable to shoot each strange bird to prove it was genuine. As a result the art of taxidermy thrived in every town and each taxidermist created his own style. Cases by the top professionals are readily recognisable by their case labels. Surviving sales catalogues, press reports of sales, as well as labels, make it possible to trace the fortunes of important specimens over the years. Thomas Gunn was considered the master craftsman and he was awarded 30 prizes including gold, silver and bronze medals and silver cups. On one memorable occasion his display at a London exhibition extended to 135 cases, including three cases all of otters.

Gunn had three sons and four daughters. He was described as an odd looking bearded man complete with a Norfolk jacket and deer-stalker hat. The irreverent knew him as Robinson Crusoe. Few realised the knowledge and skill concealed by the old naturalist's homely exterior. He was a Fellow of the Linnean Society, a founder member of the Norfolk & Norwich Naturalists' Society and was one of those fortunate people whose livelihood was also his hobby. Gunn was a friend of Edward Booth and set up many of the collector's birds including the Osprey which Booth had obtained at Breydon. Booth's vast collection, now faded but still intact, remains on display in Brighton. Once when collecting at Blakeney Point, Gunn secured a Great Snipe and a Bluethroat with right and left shots in the sandhills. During his later years his delight was to show visitors the rarities he had obtained himself including Aquatic Warblers shot at Cley.

**Thomas Gunn**

During almost three decades Thomas Gunn did a great deal of work for Fergus Menteith Ogilvie, one of the last naturalist collectors. His vast assembly of British birds, extending to 235 habitat cases, is regarded as one of the period's finest surviving major collections. It is on display in Ipswich Museum. By keeping the cases in shaded conditions the Ogilvie collection remains in excellent condition. All the birds were mounted and cased by Gunn. Most specimens were obtained towards the end of the last century on Ogilvie's 6,500 acre Suffolk estate at Sizewell which included Minsmere Level – now one of the finest RSPB reserves.

Thomas Gunn died on 13th July 1923 at his home, St Catherine's Cottage in Ber Street, Norwich. Just one of his diaries: *Notes on the Natural History of Norfolk* is in the Library at the Castle Museum, Norwich (number 26). Almost all the bird information is in the form of undated photographs of mounted specimens and extracts from *The Naturalist* and *The Zoologist*. A highlight is a delicate watercolour of two Pallas's Sandgrouse.

The finest collection of mounted birds in the county is housed in the Castle Museum, Norwich and includes collections formed by Robert Rising, Bernard Riviere and E. C. Arnold. Among the well-documented historic specimens are Little Shearwater, Black-capped Petrel, Steller's Eider, Bufflehead, Gyr Falcon, Caspian Plover, Sharp-tailed Sandpiper, Great Spotted Cuckoo, Savi's Warbler and Yellow-breasted Bunting.

At King's Lynn Museum, among the most interesting specimens are the county's earliest Sooty Shearwater, a Sharp-tailed Sandpiper and one of the first British examples of Pallas's Sandgrouse. The Ancient House Museum in Thetford still displays an ancient Raven taken at Hargham, together with an 1817 Norfolk Great Bustard and examples of taxidermy by T. E. Gunn, Cole and Roberts, all of Norwich, and Lowne of Yarmouth.

Clifford Borrer's collection, still in excellent condition, may be found in the Museum of the Department of Zoology at Cambridge University. It consists of some 450 specimens representing 210 species, the majority obtained in Norfolk. The latest additions include Rose-coloured Starling taken at Cley in 1945 and Pectoral Sandpiper at Salthouse in 1948. The Holkham Hall collection extends to 220 species on display in the old servants hall. Nearly all the specimens were taken locally including Britain's second-ever Yellow-breasted Bunting.

At Yarmouth, the Tolhouse collection established in 1892 was almost entirely destroyed during an air-raid on 8th April 1941. Over 300 species once occupied the floor-to-ceiling glass cases including seven Spoonbills, five Bitterns, Glossy Ibis, Pectoral Sandpipers and White-winged Black Tern. Amongst the few survivors, an ancient Leach's Storm Petrel is believed to be the earliest Norfolk record, being found on Yarmouth beach in 1829.

The Connop collection originally housed at Rollesby Hall when catalogued by Thomas Southwell in 1897, consisted of 434 cases and shades containing 336 species. A copy of the catalogue signed by Southwell is held in the Natural History Department in the Castle Museum, Norwich. Many of the historic specimens had been previously owned by a succession of local naturalists. For example, a White Stork shot at Oby in 1865 passed through the collections of Overend, Stevenson, Spelman and finally Connop. Ernest Connop died in 1911 and the complete collection was sold in May 1912 to W. R. Lysaght of Chepstow. The sale catalogue indicated that a number of the choicest specimens including the 1896 Cley Pallas's Warbler, an 1840 South Walsham Savi's Warbler and the 1896 Yarmouth Great Spotted Cuckoo, were acquired by the Birmingham Museum and Art Gallery. Although formerly displayed in the original cases at Birmingham, the specimens became casualties of the mania for reducing storage space. Once removed it became difficult if not impossible to distinguish the work of individuals as the labels were often incomplete.

The Booth collection in Brighton remains intact although many specimens have faded. It features 229 species and occupies 308 cases including many rarities obtained in Norfolk. Among the most prized are five White-winged Black Terns obtained at Hickling and contained in case number 251. According to Booth's catalogue the unfortunate birds had 'formed part of a flock of seven hovering within a few feet of the punt, little realising their lives were to be cut short'.

**Harry Smith's** collection was little known. A marshman, he lived at Three-mile House along the River Bure at West Caister and died in 1972. Although he was unable to read or write he taught himself the art of taxidermy and made his own cases. The collection included Cattle Egret, Glossy Ibis, Green-winged Teal, Red-crested Pochard and Little Bustard – all obtained on the local marshes. As was to be expected, few were documented and their present whereabouts are unknown.

Two National Trust stately homes in the county contain collections of mounted birds. By far the more important is at Sheringham Hall and is in excellent condition. Special arrangements are necessary to view the impressive display of 190 cases and shades which formerly belonged to Henry Morris Upcher. The majority of the birds were set up by Thomas Gunn, but among older examples is a pair of Bee-eaters shot by a wherryman at Coldham Hall on the River Yare in 1854 and mounted by John Sayer (Thomas Gunn had been apprenticed to Sayer and when the latter died in 1866 Gunn took over the business in St Giles Street, Norwich). For many years the Bee-eaters formed part of Stevenson's collection until it was auctioned in September 1887. Also highly valuable is a magnificent case, undoubtedly by Gunn, of 12 Ruffs each in full nuptial array and two previously undiscovered rarities: a Baillon's Crake shot at Ranworth by Lubbock about 1840, which was acquired by Stevenson in 1879, and a Tengmalm's Owl obtained at Rainthorpe Park, near Norwich, in July 1903.

At nearby Felbrigg Hall the collection containing 52 cases covers some 160 species. Thomas Wyndham Cremer, who died in 1894, had spent his life adding to his assortment of local birds. Among the cases prepared by Thomas Gunn is one containing ten Waxwings. Apart from two Pallas's Sandgrouse, and in the absence of an original catalogue, the most intriguing birds at Felbrigg are the Honey Buzzards. Were they local breeders?

*Notes on the Birds of Cley, Norfolk*, published in 1925, contains extracts from the diaries of **Nash Pashley** (1843–1925) over a period of almost 40 years. Most fascinating are his 'Recollections'. Like Arthur Patterson at Yarmouth, he vividly chronicles and brings to life the activities of the old-time wildfowlers and punt-gunners.

Pashley was born in Holt and showed an interest in natural history from an early age. When aged 18 he moved to Norwich where he became among other callings an inspector at the Waterworks. Seven years later an opportunity occurred to return to north Norfolk and he became landlord of the Fisherman's Arms at Cley. This occupation allowed him ample opportunity to practice the art of taxidermy as a hobby, but it was not until he was over 40 that he decided to set up as a professional taxidermist.

He was influenced in his decision by two keen collectors: Drs F. D. and G. E. Power who were the first to offer him regular employment. This encouragement enabled him to open the little shop (now a private residence) in Cley village, where he remained for the remainder of his days. Pashley's fame as a taxidermist soon spread. Lord Lilford arranged a bird-stuffing competition through the columns of *The Field*. More than a hundred entries were received and Pashley was awarded one of the five prizes for a Turnstone mounted in flight; the historic specimen remains in a farmhouse near Welney. This success was subsequently mentioned on Pashley's attractive case labels. His shop became a focal point for collectors and ornithologists. Throughout birding history Cley has been renowned as a mecca of British ornithology. For a great many years no pilgrimage there was considered complete without including a visit to Mr Pashley. Bernard Riviere paints the scene:

> H. N. Pashley was a perfect host, perfectly at ease in any company with a gentle old-world courtesy peculiarly his own, he knew the magic which could make time fly and the hours

passed all too quickly whilst one listened to his tales of bird life on this bleak north Norfolk coast. Outside when at last one left was the call of migrating birds passing overhead and the memory of that small enchanted room with all its associations will live long in one's pleasantest dreams.

During Pashley's long reign high prices were paid for rarities. On one occasion his son-in-law, Ted Ramm (his portrait appears in Billy Bishop's *Cley Marsh and its Birds*), was out collecting along Cley sea-wall when he chanced upon a mystery warbler. It was promptly obtained and the veteran taxidermist correctly identified it as a Pallas's Warbler; the first British record. It was purchased for £40 by E. M. Connop.

Much has changed since the final entries in Pashley's diaries. The Black-tailed Godwit, no specimen of which found its way into his shop until the taxidermist was in his seventies, now visits Cley Marsh in large flights. Sandwich Terns, rare passers-by a century ago, today breed in abundance on Blakeney Point. Of the Carrion Crow, he wrote 'I have never yet seen this bird in the flesh nor known it to have been ever seen or taken in the neighbourhood'. The Pallas's Sandgrouse is but a distant memory, yet Pashley received 33 specimens from Morston during a great irruption.

When Pashley died it was the close of a way of life. The heyday of the collectors had ended. Wild bird protection legislation meant the cessation of indiscriminate shooting of exotics. Taxidermy declined and bird-watching became fashionable.

Throughout the collecting era taxidermists resident in Yarmouth enjoyed exceptional opportunities for receiving rare specimens. The denes were regularly patrolled while Broadland keepers and marshmen were constantly on the lookout. But it was Breydon which became renowned for providing 'good' birds. As a result it attracted wildfowlers and provided a living for generations of Breydoners until enforced protection laws put them out of business.

Arthur Patterson's books vividly portray these characters. With the passing years his detailed accounts describing a vanished scene become ever more valuable. However, it is not easy to discover details of the day-to-day work of even the best-known Yarmouth taxidermists. As a race they remained highly reticent. Even when cases of mounted birds have survived, apart from an attached faded trade label or a highly distinctive style, almost nothing may be known about the man himself.

Fortunately, the work of **Walter Lowne** (1854–1915) has been described following the discovery of his almost unique ledger (Morris 1988), providing a detailed insight into the work and income of a small-town taxidermist over a period of a quarter-century. A record book listing the more notable specimens passing through Lowne's hands has also come to light. Both items had been originally rescued by Arthur Patterson during the First World War. Although he knew Lowne, having lived in an adjoining house for some years, he never learned anything of his youth.

After serving his apprenticeship in Martham, Lowne moved to Yarmouth taking up work as a carpenter. He never moved away. In his early twenties Lowne decided to take up taxidermy (initially in his spare time) and Patterson gave him a book on the subject. He worked from a garden shed until taking over a game-dealer's shop at 40 Fullers Hill. Patterson noted that 'Walter and I went in for stuffing together. He sat at it all night, frequently after a day's work as a carpenter. I foolishly went courting. We each excelled in our own way. He made a living of stuffing. I got an excellent wife.' In fact, Lowne also married and his wife, two years his junior, outlived him by 29 years.

Countless rarities passed through Lowne's hands including: Sabine's Gull, White-tailed Eagle, Roller, Pallas's Sandgrouse, Little Bustard and Allen's Gallinule. The final entry in his diary was dated 28th October 1913 recording a Glossy Ibis obtained on Acle Marshes. Lowne was evidently in poor health for many years. Not a single photograph or any other documents relating to Walter Lowne have been traced. In addition to his work, he was a keen angler and secretary of a local club for many years. His association with anglers was good for business: he mounted almost 600 freshwater fish in 26 years. He was also an accomplished aviculturist, winning prizes for cage birds and ornamental fowl at national shows.

My introduction to Breydon and its birds was through the pages of a shelf full of books written by **Arthur Henry Patterson** (1857–1935), the self-taught Yarmouth naturalist. Visits to the estuary followed, rambling along the flintstone-edged north wall peering into wildfowlers' little houseboats permanently anchored on the saltings. Close to Lockgate Farm (no longer standing) Patterson had secured his houseboat observatory, 'The Moorhen'. I could picture him seated in the sternsheets, sweeping the flats with his telescope and then pushing off in his punt towards newly arrived Spoonbills or Avocets. He vividly described 'the laden wherries tacking and quanting against the breeze . . . the grandest sunsets . . . stars reflected in the cool depths and the moon flinging her radiance on rippling waters'.

I became intrigued with Patterson's writings. A visit to Yarmouth's Tolhouse Museum revealed galleries of mounted birds in glass cases all obtained on or near Breydon by local fowlers and gentlemen gunners. Arthur Patterson was largely responsible for assembling the collection, which extended to over 300 species. Sadly, war-time bombing resulted in its almost total destruction.

**Arthur Patterson**

*Wildfowlers and Poachers*, one of Patterson's last books, vividly describes the hardy race of Breydon punt-gunners who made a precarious living shooting wildfowl on the estuary. As a supplement to their earnings from gamedealers they were constantly on the lookout for rarities. The author's wordcraft and style perfected, he was able to paint a magical verbal picture of his first acquaintance with the Breydoners. As he approached the Bowling Green pub which stood within sight of Breydon at the entrance to the River Bure, 'the creaking of the tavern sign-board added to the witchery of the gathering shadows . . . voicing eerily . . . a welcome. There were stuffed birds on shelves behind the counter . . . and lounging smokers on worn settles, some arguing guns . . . others silent and meditative, yet alert to pick up advantageous gossip . . . the faces of the men, lined and hardened by storm and sun, were full of character . . .'

Arthur Patterson, son of a shoemaker, was brought up in one of the old Yarmouth Rows in a sunless cottage that he said 'should have been a rabbit hutch'. He was the youngest of eight children and the only one to survive beyond the of age 21. He was in turn a pupil teacher, pedlar, showman, zookeeper, warehouseman and finally a school attendance officer – chasing truants round the stacks of timber and the herring barrels on the Yarmouth Quays. He had fallen under the spell of Breydon and was making himself an authority on its wildlife. His greatest memorial is 26 books. He also contributed hundreds of articles to local newspapers under the name of John Knowlittle and sketched delightfully. He seldom wrote a letter without covering the envelope in drawings. Patterson's *Nature in Eastern Norfolk* (1905) has great appeal. It lists all the birds recorded within a ten-mile radius of Yarmouth, providing full details of occurrences together with an autobiographical sketch. There is also a 90-page essay describing, in fascinating detail, the local scene when 'the furze grew luxuriantly from Caister Hills to the workhouse walls . . . and where hundreds of tombstones are crumbling in the strong air bird-catchers placed their traps. There was not a single brick disfiguring the virgin hills north of Regent Road . . .'

For some 60 years Arthur Patterson enjoyed Breydon in all its moods until early in July 1935 when he walked there for the last time. He died on 27th October and is buried in Gorleston Cemetery. Among the wreaths was a spray of wild flowers gathered from his beloved Breydon by young Ted Ellis.

**Emma Louise Turner** (1866–1940) was a pioneer of bird photography. Her two best-known works are still sought by collectors of local bird volumes. *Broadland Birds*, published in 1924, is a valuable record full of accurate observations. It was followed four years later by *Bird Watching on Scolt Head*.

Much of her photographic work, for which she was awarded the gold medal of the Royal Photographic Society, was carried out in Norfolk. She spent weeks at a time living aboard the houseboat 'Water Rail' on Hickling Broad. The mooring point at the entrance to Heigham Corner is still known as Miss Turner's Island. Here she possessed a thatched wooden hut which she occupied for more than 20 years. The vandalised remains lingered until the mid-1970s and the once neat lawn has long been abandoned. In addition to the houseboat, Emma Turner's fleet included a canoe 'Gzekiel', a rowing boat 'Merrythought' and a sailing dinghy 'Bittern'. Cheerfully tolerating conditions which would have daunted most ladies in those days and working with primitive cameras, she achieved results which at the time were unsurpassed.

One of Miss Turner's great successes was photographing the first young Bitterns known to have been hatched in Norfolk, after having been exterminated as a breeder some 40 years previously. She thought nothing of photographing a nesting Reeve at Hickling, concealed beneath marsh litter, despite 'slowly sinking into the swamp'. During the lengthy sessions Snipe and Redshank constantly settled on her; on one occasion, 'four Redshank and a Snipe running over me together' (Turner's *Broadland Birds*). In 1923 Emma Turner undertook the duties of Watcher for the National Trust on Scolt Head Island. She had been approached by the indefatigable Sydney Long who had remarked: 'I cannot find a watcher for Scolt Head'. In a fit of recklessness, Emma replied: 'Why not have me?' She lived on the Island for 18 months in the Watcher's hut and collected the material for her book. Emma also made prolonged stays during the spring and autumn migration.

Emma Turner was one of the first women to be elected a Fellow of the Linnean Society and was also one of the first honorary lady members of the British Ornithologists' Union. Her articles published in *British Birds* covering courtship and breeding behaviour of Ruffs, Avocets, Bitterns, Water Rails, Black Terns and Stonechats have stood the test of time. Unknown to many, references to these accounts feature in *Birds of the Western Palearctic* published years later.

Bernard Riviere provided an obituary emphasising Emma's indomitable pluck: 'Even the loss of sight, which in the last two years of her life cut her off from all she cared for, left her courage undimmed.'

**Sydney Long**

An appreciation of the work of **Dr Sydney Long** (1870–1939) features in the Conservation chapter. He began his association with wildlife in Norfolk as secretary of the Norfolk & Norwich Naturalists' Society, a post he held for 24 years. He became physician to the Norfolk & Norwich and Jenny Lind Hospitals for 40 years, taking a prominent part in the administration of both institutions. Sydney Long had little use for indoor entertainments. From his home in a tall Georgian terrace in Surrey Street, Norwich, he travelled throughout Norfolk at all seasons and always in an open car. His annual holiday was spent on his beloved Scolt Head where he invariably slept under the stars. A wall plaque marks his Norwich house today.

**Edward Charles Saunders** (1872–1956) taught himself taxidermy with the aid of a book and maintained a diary of the birds passing through his workshop. He was persuaded by Bernard Riviere to add personal recollections. These were never published, but copies are available. In his introduction, Saunders described the great attraction of visiting Lowne's shop as a boy. No doubt he was influenced by Lowne initially, but he soon evolved his own style.

Saunders began mounting his first specimens when aged 15, commencing business at 10 Church Plain, Yarmouth, two years later. His very first completed case so impressed Arthur Patterson that he was reluctant to believe Saunders himself had set it up. Another of his earliest displays, three Dotterel and a Turnstone, still survives in the Turnstone public house at Hopton. About the same period he acquired fame by mounting Norfolk's first specimen of the Great Spotted Cuckoo. It had been taken on Yarmouth North Denes and remains on display in the City of Birmingham Museum.

Eleven years later, Saunders made headlines when he purchased no less than eight Red-crested Pochards shot on Breydon. A remarkable large flight of 13 had arrived on the estuary during a heatwave. During the First World War, when a Cattle Egret (only the second occurrence for Britain) was collected on Breydon marshes, it was Edward Saunders who set it up. One of his final exhibits, created after a half-century of taxidermy, was a Bluethroat in perfect plumage which had struck a girder in a Yarmouth bus depot in 1939. The case was discovered in a Yarmouth antique shop a few years ago and was quickly purchased by a private collector of the master craftsman's work.

Edward Saunders was the last professional Yarmouth taxidermist, and died on 7th January 1956.

An introduction to the paintings of **Frank Southgate** was provided in Arthur Patterson's *Notes of an East Coast Naturalist* and *Nature in Eastern Norfolk*. These local classics vividly described wildlife in south-east Norfolk. Both appeared during the opening years of the 20th century and each contained a dozen Southgate colour plates.

This was a prolific period for the artist. No fewer than 50 of his watercolours featured in William

Dutt's *The Norfolk Broads*, published in 1903. Many depict scenes long since vanished. Three years later, Dutt's *Wild Life in East Anglia* again featured Southgate's illustrations. The late Sir Peter Scott described him as 'the first bird painter in this country to introduce a freedom of technique, even an impressionist technique, to the painting of birds'. He spent the golden Edwardian years painting and wildfowling. The latter was his pleasure and the former his profession. The influence the wildfowler exerted on the artist is very apparent from even a glance at his work. This was mostly in watercolour, but he also had considerable ability in oils. Southgate derived much of his inspiration from the marshes, creeks, shimmering sands and pine belts of the Wells to Holkham coastline. Nowhere is this influence better expressed than in his final work *Wildfowl and Waders*, not published until 12 years after his death.

Born on 1st August 1872 Frank Southgate grew up in Hunstanton where his father was a stationer and postmaster. Little is known of his early years, although he studied in Cambridge and at the Slade School of Art in London. He became a professional artist around 1900. A member of the Royal Society of British Artists, Frank Southgate exhibited regularly at the Society's gallery in Pall Mall between 1904 and 1912. He also exhibited at the Royal Academy.

When war broke out in 1914 Southgate joined the Sportsmen's Battalion of the Royal Fusiliers, although he was over 40 years of age. Despite his familiarity with the often harsh conditions of wildfowling, the rigours of military life proved too much. He died, not of bullet wounds, but of heart failure in 1916 after running two miles to a front-line position. Frank Southgate's life was tragically short, yet he produced a wealth of exciting and beautiful pictures.

The Norfolk Naturalists' Trust Golden Jubilee celebrations in 1976 provided a special opportunity to exhibit wildlife paintings and 23 of Frank Southgate's paintings were featured. In 1986 Norfolk Museums Service mounted a major exhibition in Yarmouth. This became a unique occasion to view 50 of the artist's watercolours. Among the treasures were the originals of Breydon wader and wildfowl paintings from Patterson's volumes.

**Bernard Beryl Riviere** (1880–1953), whose *A History of the Birds of Norfolk* was published in 1930, combined a career in medicine with notable services to the study of ornithology in his adopted county. The son of an artist, Briton Riviere RA, he graduated from St Andrew's University from where he passed to St Bartholomew's Hospital, London. Coming to Norfolk in about 1908 he joined a practice in St Giles, Norwich, also serving the Jenny Lind Hospital (as did Dr Sydney Long) as honorary surgeon. After a breakdown in health he lived for a time in Switzerland and South Africa, eventually retiring from practice in 1926. In some circles he was best known as an authority on gun-dogs, publishing a book on training retrievers and enjoying many successes in field trials.

Bernard Riviere was a member of the Norfolk & Norwich Naturalists' Society for 45 years. His magnum

**Bernard Riviere (left) with Harry Witherby and Jim Vincent (right).**

opus on the county's birds spanned the period from the collecting age to the formative years of the county trust. Less well known was his detailed twelve-year study covering the autumn movements of the army of Herring and Great Black-backed Gulls on the Norfolk coast. At that time the East Anglian herring fishing industry was still in its prime. Almost 1,000 drifters fished from Yarmouth alone. Riviere stayed 'at every habitable spot upon the coast between Yarmouth and Hunstanton at some period of the autumn, beside making trips aboard a drifter'. It was between the North Sea herring grounds where the drifters fished and three main coastal resting places that the gull movements took place.

Moving to Woodbastwick in 1932 Riviere's residence overlooked a small broad where Kingfishers nested each spring in a bank formed by the upturned roots of a fallen birch. A summary of his observations featured in *British Birds*. His detailed notes covering Kingfisher courtship and breeding season habits have stood the test of time. Quotations from his diaries feature in *Birds of the Western Palearctic*, published years after his death.

Detailed county bird reports were somewhat rare in the 1920s and 1930s. However, for well over a decade during this period Bernard Riviere enjoyed the luxury of 'The Ornithological Report for Norfolk', complete with weather maps, appearing annually in *British Birds*. In the later years of his life he devoted much time to the development and administration of the Norfolk Naturalists Trust. He held the key role of honorary treasurer until the time of his death on 27th December 1953 at his home, Salhouse Lodge.

A series of coincidences has connected Surrey Street, Norwich with the history of Norfolk ornithology. Earliest among the naturalists linked with the busy thoroughfare was Henry Stevenson who was brought up to the cawing of Rooks in the trees in an old walled garden. Dr Long, the founder of the Norfolk Naturalists Trust, also resided in the street. Bernard Riviere, as medical director of the Norwich Union Insurance Group for 24 years, was a regular visitor to Surrey Street. The connection has continued; two of the authors of this book (D.D. and M.S.) spent almost their entire working lives with Norwich Union in this same street.

**Anthony Buxton** (1882–1970) was born in Essex, the youngest son of Edward North Buxton who gave Hatfield Forest to the nation. He was educated at Harrow and took the Natural Science Tripos at Trinity College, Cambridge. When studying at Cambridge he was Master of the Trinity Foot Beagles whom, half a century afterwards, he used to invite to Horsey for an annual day's sport after marsh hares. He served throughout the First World War with the Essex Yeomanry and the 10th Royal Hussars and was awarded the DSO.

Afterwards, hoping to serve the cause of world peace, he became a member of the League of Nations Secretariat in Geneva where he founded a pack of beagles with George Crees (who later became the devoted keeper and warden on the Horsey estate) as kennelman. Anthony Buxton served the League for 12 years. He purchased Horsey Hall and estate from Lady Lucas in 1930, living there for the remainder of his long life. As a landowner his enlightened attitude demonstrated how a large estate could be managed for nature conservation as

**Anthony Buxton**

well as for sporting purposes. Another outstanding example was Lord Desborough at nearby Hickling.

Eight years later, disaster struck at Horsey. On the night of 12th February 1938, a north-west gale, coinciding with a full moon, caused a tidal surge breaching the sand dunes with an almost half-a-mile wide gap. Sea water poured inland over-topping the flood walls beside Somerton Dyke, Martham Broad and Horsey Mere. An area totalling 7,500 acres was flooded – in some places to a depth of over seven feet. Anthony Buxton became very active in the recovery of the district, and fully documented the effects of the flood in the annual *Transactions of the Norfolk & Norwich Naturalists' Society*. His diary sets the scene: 'For three months until the breach was sealed we lived a strange existence on an island at the mercy of the North Sea, the water rising and falling according to tide and to the force and direction of the wind.'

During the Second World War, Anthony Buxton worked for the Red Cross and served as High Sheriff of Norfolk in 1945–46. One of his books, *Fisherman Naturalist*, contains delightful chapters on the special Broadland birds. All birds of prey appealed, but Montagu's was his favourite harrier and indeed one of his favourite birds. More than once during those early years at Horsey three pairs of Montagu's nested on the estate.

In his declining years, although his long tramps across the marshes were over and he could no longer leap the dykes, Anthony Buxton could still enjoy the sheltered Horsey Hall gardens. Here, early migrants appeared in spring including such colourful travellers as Hoopoes and Golden Orioles.

**Hickling marsh-mowing gang: extreme right, Jim Vincent and on his right, Ted Piggin.**

At nearby Hickling, you will find no bird observation hide named in memory of **Jim Vincent** (1884–1944), yet for many years he was one of the best-known naturalists in Norfolk. Living all his life at Hickling – apart from when he served as groundcrew at Yarmouth with the Royal Flying Corps during the First World War – he had unique opportunities to record Broadland wildlife.

He was the first son of Robert Vincent, a professional wildfowler and eel-catcher. Jim followed in his father's footsteps. In those days shooting and fishing were free on Hickling, Heigham Sounds and Horsey Mere. When aged 16 he was recommended to a visiting Cambridge undergraduate: the Hon Edwin Montagu, an enthusiastic bird and egg collector. It was the beginning of a relationship that transformed the young Vincent's life. At the time he was working with a steam threshing tackle outfit travelling from farm to farm and was on the point of training for the Methodist Ministry.

When Vincent was in his mid-20s Edwin Montagu again made his acquaintance. On this occasion he was in company with Lord Lucas. These two gentlemen had become early conservationists and the following year they were joined by Sir Edward Grey. Fate had provided Vincent with wealthy and influential mentors. They enjoyed shooting, but confined their quarry to ducks, coot and the then plentiful Snipe. Together they rented Whiteslea Lodge Estate at Hickling and financed its maintenance as a sporting estate-cum-bird sanctuary. Vincent was employed as keeper, occupying a rent-free cottage near Hickling Church. In those early years Jim Vincent usually travelled by punt from the Pleasure Boat Inn to Whiteslea Lodge. The only approach by land was by a rough cart track until this was replaced by a cinder-ash road. All guests to the Lodge were met at the inn and ferried across the Broad. The three partners regularly visited Hickling, especially in winter and again in spring.

In 1912 Lord Lucas acquired Horsey Hall. About this time, Montagu's Harriers were attempting to re-colonise the upper Thurne reedbeds. Vincent discovered the first nest and arranged for a hide to be positioned nearby, complete with full-time watchers from the estate workforce. Just two years after the return of Montagu's Harriers, Vincent found a newly hatched Bittern at Sutton Broad which was photographed by Emma Turner. No Bitterns had been known to nest in Broadland during the previous quarter-century. As a result of such events Edwin Montagu persuaded Vincent to maintain a diary. The set of these diaries is held in the Norfolk Wildlife Trust's offices in Norwich. The opening year – 1911 – was published as a book illustrated with watercolours by George Lodge, one of the best-known bird painters of the period and a frequent guest at Whiteslea. Montagu and his friends encouraged Vincent to attract more and more birds to Hickling by a highly successful policy of cutting, grazing and flooding. Rush Hills was created from a reedbed over many years. How well Vincent succeeded is demonstrated in the splendid Roland Green frieze in Whiteslea Lodge featuring all the birds recorded at Hickling. During the two decades before the Second World War Vincent attracted to Hickling the finest ornithologists, bird artists and bird photographers the country had known.

**Roland Green** was born in Kent the son of a taxidermist who, as a keen naturalist and wildfowler, was accompanied by his son whenever he roamed the Kentish marshes. The young Roland learned in the taxidermist's shop how to skin, stuff and set up birds, rapidly acquiring a knowledge of anatomy and plumage. He showed a gift for drawing and painting birds while still a schoolboy, studying afterwards at Rochester School of Art and at the Regent Street Polytechnic. Then he found work in London at the Natural History Museum. He often said he became a professional painter as he could settle to nothing else.

In the First World War, Roland Green joined the London Rifle Brigade, later transferring to the Royal Engineers. He employed his draughtsmanship in providing maps for the Royal Flying Corps. After the conflict, he found a generous patron in Lord Desborough who then owned the Hickling estate and used the thatched Whiteslea Lodge as his shooting lodge. Desborough commissioned Roland Green to paint the now famous frieze which – running round the walls of the Lodge – shows each species of bird recorded on Hickling Broad and in the surrounding reedbeds, marshes and wader pools. The artist's world became centred on Hickling. At first he lived in a houseboat suitably named 'Avis', anchored at the foot of a derelict drainage mill which was used as a studio and lookout.

As he became established and the demand for his work increased, Roland was able to build a bungalow and studio on a swampy promontory on the Broad's edge. It was idyllic, thatched with reed, shaded by ancient willows and sur-

Roland Green

rounded on three sides by water. This was where Roland Green, who remained a bachelor, worked for the rest of his life.

For many years Roland Green had successful exhibitions in London where he would be surrounded by 60 or more of his pictures. He also exhibited in Norwich and completed a good deal of work as a book and magazine illustrator. Roland Green was one of the artists providing illustrations for Whistler's *Popular Handbook of Indian Birds*. His series of cigarette cards *Game Birds and Wildfowl* have been greatly sought-after.

During the Second World War Roland gave many talks, accompanied by lightning sketches, to the armed forces stationed in Norfolk. At one period, London agents were selling more of his water-colours to American visitors than to English collectors. He was a regular visitor to Breydon, especially during early autumn. He enjoyed staying a few days aboard Robin Harrison's houseboat moored along the north wall of the estuary. Some of his finest paintings resulted from these visits. He died on 18th December 1972 aged 82.

I first met **John Cyril Harrison** at his Hainford studio, greatly admiring the impressive collection of bird sketches and landscapes, ranging from Scottish mountain tops to the African veldt. The greatest surprise were the paintings of African game. At the time I did not know that Jack Harrison was a frequent visitor to southern Africa. He always travelled there aboard a Union Castle mail liner.

Jack Harrison was born in Wiltshire in 1898. He lived in British Columbia for four years from 1912 where his family ran a fruit farm. He began collecting birds' skins and – like Roland Green – studied taxidermy. After the First World War, Harrison decided to become a bird artist. He studied at the Slade

School of Art and a few years later moved to Norfolk where he worked for the remainder of his life. For well over half a century he captured the atmosphere of Norfolk, recording in detail its game birds, wild-fowl and birds of prey.

Jack Harrison

He travelled extensively, regularly enjoying visits to Scotland. As a result he illustrated Seton Gordon's *Days with the Golden Eagle*. He also painted in Norway and Iceland. He began painting Christmas cards for the newly formed Norfolk Naturalists Trust in 1930 and the first subject was a Breckland scene featuring a fiery male Crossbill. This arrange-ment continued over several decades. Early commissions included wildfowl plates in Witherby's five-volume *Hand-book of British Birds* and the frontispiece to Riviere's *History of the Birds of Norfolk*. Fine examples of Harrison's work appeared in *Bird Portraits* and in *Pheasants of the World* by Jean Delacour. Harrison was a principal illustrator for *Ea-gles, Hawks and Falcons of the World*. More recently he was commissioned for the artwork illustrating *The Birds of Prey of the British Islands*. This publication, which rapidly became a collector's piece, was limited to 275 signed and numbered copies. As a final tribute, 25 Harrison watercolours were selected for reproduction in another limited edition volume, *Game Birds of the British Isles*. The large-scale plates in this luxurious book reveal great mastery in depicting birds on the wing.

The Norfolk Naturalists Trust celebrated its Golden Jubilee in 1976. Among the special events was an exhibition of wildlife paintings in the Castle Museum, Norwich, at which the work of 16 artists was fea-tured, including two dozen Harrisons. The impressive longevity of many wildlife artists was rivalled by Jack Harrison. He had just completed the watercolours for his springtime London exhibition before enter-ing St Michael's Hospital in Aylsham. He died on 13th May 1985.

Christopher Cadbury

A full acknowledgement of the contribution of **Christopher Cadbury** (1909–1995) to wildlife in Norfolk appears in the Conservation chapter. One of the most en-dearing things about Christopher was his reluctance to see his generosity publicised. As a result, few appreciated just how much he had done to further the cause of nature con-servation. The list of reserves in this country he purchased makes astonishing reading. His acquisitions abroad were equally remarkable, ranging from Aride in the Seychelles to a set of nine islands in the Falklands.

Among visiting personalities was **T. A. Coward**, author of the once indispensable *Birds of the British Isles and their eggs* which remained almost continuously in print for nearly half a century. He stayed on Scolt Head to study the spring migration in 1924.

The decade following publication of Riviere's *History of the Birds of Norfolk* (1930) covered the formative years of the Norfolk Wildlife Trust. The annual Ornithological Report for Norfolk had continued to appear in *British Birds* until 1928 but subsequently it featured in the Trust's *Wild Bird Protection in Norfolk*. In the 1930s **Robin Harrison**, following in Patterson's footsteps, an-chored his houseboat 'Lapwing' on a small rond edging the north shore of Breydon. For many years from this unusual observatory he recorded the birds of the estuary, contributing a weekly feature in the *Eastern Evening News* until 1985.

It was an exciting time at Hickling too, where the leading bird photographers arrived each spring to photograph nesting harriers, Bitterns, Bearded Tits, Water Rails and Short-eared Owls. **Walter Higham** (1900–1965) showed his then unique film of Montagu's Harriers nesting at Hickling to the Norfolk &

Norwich Naturalists' Society in 1930. Another success was taking the first pictures of nesting Marsh Harriers in Britain – again at Hickling. Eric Hosking described Higham as in a class on his own. His *Birds in Colour* (1946) was the first bird book in this country illustrated entirely with colour photographs. Higham photographed in many parts of the country, but the Broads fascinated him most and he returned season after season. After the War, his Broadland Birds colour film attracted a capacity audience in Yarmouth Town Hall – a triumph for the local naturalists society organisers.

**Nat Tracy** featured regularly in the bird reports during the 1920s and 1930s. His sanctuary woodland at South Wootton attracted breeding Wood Warblers and Redstarts. His articles concerning Great Spotted Woodpeckers published in *British Birds* were freely quoted many years later in *Birds of the Western Palearctic*. One of the highlights of 1949 was the establishment of Cley Bird Observatory. An empty military observation tower and derelict gun emplacements immediately behind the beach became the headquarters. Richard Richardson became warden, ably supported by Peggy Meiklejohn, Peter Clarke, Paul Kirby and Peter Jackson. Despite sea-flooding and gales the observatory functioned until 1963.

**Richard Alan Richardson** (1922–1977) was one of the county's finest field ornithologists. He was also a highly skilled bird artist. Born at Blackheath in south London, he served with the Royal Norfolk Regiment in south-east Asia, spending a year in Singapore following the Japanese capitulation in 1945. Richard 'fell in love with the island and the time spent there long remained one of the most pleasant of memories'. Whilst there, he even designed an exquisite Christmas card entitled 'Greetings from Singapore'.

Richard moved to Cley in 1949 and it became his home for the remainder of his life. He was most fortunate to find lodgings almost immediately with Mrs Davison. He stayed with her, even when she moved house, until his final illness. He became in effect an adopted son and she miraculously outlived him. Richard was well satisfied to spend his time living simply in a small cottage happily producing the drawings and watercolours from which he gained an international reputation. All the artwork was produced at a small kitchen table using a standard paintbox. His major publications were the illustrations completed for Richard Fitter's *Pocket Guide to British Birds* followed two years later by a companion volume *Pocket Guide to Nests and Eggs*. In the earlier work it was quite a *tour de force* for the artist to illustrate all British birds one after another. The volume is regarded as the first of the modern high-quality field guides. In the second he created some of the best illustrations of birds' nests.

**Richard Richardson**

Richard completed comparatively little book illustration after this, confining himself largely to private work and drawings for the societies in which he was interested. When *British Birds* celebrated its first half-century in 1957, he was commissioned to produce a splendid watercolour of Collared Doves. At the time these birds were still newly arrived in this country. The same volume also included the artist's illustrated paper fully describing this addition to the British bird list. Richard's evocative vignettes graced the pages of the *Norfolk Bird Report* for almost two decades. For three years in succession, the fortunes of the Cley Black-tailed Godwits appeared in the same publication. Copiously illustrated, this excellent series of display drawings formed the basis of the godwit figures appearing in the monumental *Birds of the Western Palearctic*. His masterly writing revealed in his surviving diaries includes a description of a Cley male godwit in song flight: 'The wings moved alternately . . . one half-flexed, the other fully spread . . . and the fanned tail swerved first to one side and then to the other, the body rocking drunkenly as the bird limped about the sky . . . ' Enchanting baby godwits were vividly described 'tramping about with comically adult self-importance pecking flies from the grass blades, their light weight and enormous toes enabling them to negotiate the most impossible barriers of rank vegetation by the simple expedient of walking over the top'.

Richard's final work were the wader drawings published in *The Atlas of Breeding Birds in Britain and*

*Ireland*. Waders were among his favourites, but he was equally skilled portraying the migrant flycatchers, chats and warblers which are such an attractive feature of the north Norfolk coast. He was an entirely self-taught artist, able to work in the most cramped surroundings. He seldom took a notebook or pencil with him in the field, but when an unusual bird appeared he would study it closely with those penetrating blue eyes that missed nothing. Within an hour or so of returning home he would have produced a painting that omitted no detail of plumage or attitude, and was also an excellent picture.

Richard was also deeply devoted to Fair Isle. The island almost became his second home and he made one or two visits each year. In fact 'Norfolk Week' became an established event in the observatory's calendar. His last stay was his 23rd visit. Shetland and its music became one of Richard's loves. He was a keen reader and collector of Shetland books.

Richard contributed greatly to organised ornithology and conservation including the founding of Cley Bird Observatory and its ringing station. He became President of Holme Bird Observatory and was an honorary life member of the Norfolk & Norwich Naturalists' Society. His untimely death was a severe blow to Norfolk ornithology. His memory is perpetuated at Cley by a plaque in the Norfolk Wildlife Trust's Visitor Centre overlooking the marsh, and also by an annual award to a promising young artist organised by *British Birds*. Almost all his diaries have disappeared, but fortunately the Cley Observatory photograph album survives.

Paying tribute, the renowned Norfolk naturalist Ted Ellis so aptly expressed the feelings of us all: 'Richard has left a permanent memorial in his contribution to Norfolk ornithology by his influence on those who had the good fortune to come under his spell.'

**David Lack** (1910–1973), who attended Gresham's School in Holt, was a prolific writer. *The Life of the Robin* and *Swifts in a Tower* were both fascinating and highly readable. Earlier he had written *The Birds of Cambridgeshire*. During the Second World War David Lack was involved in top secret work on radar. At first the mysterious radar echoes were inexplicable and referred to as 'angels'. It was some time before it was accepted that they were really migrating birds. Subsequently much of Lack's work on migration across the southern North Sea was conducted from Norfolk. The supporting field work was provided by Richard Richardson.

During the summers before the Second World War **Reginald Gaze** (1895–1974) became known to many visitors as a seasonal warden at Blakeney Point. At that time 2,200 pairs of Common Terns nested there, but only a score of Oystercatchers. The war years saw the Point 'out of bounds', having been taken over by the Admiralty. However, Ted Eales assumed wardenship in 1946 and for almost 20 years Reggie Gaze was his assistant. A slight figure, he welcomed each boatload of visitors, but woe betide any schoolboy intent on concealing terns' eggs in his lunch-box. Reggie wrote and illustrated with his own photographs several books. Best remembered is *Bird Sanctuary*, a large-format volume full of studies of Blakeney Point's nesting birds. He was also a regular lecturer. Among his historic illustrations were portraits of the first Kittiwakes to nest on the Point in the midst of 800 pairs of Sandwich Terns. Ted Ellis wrote in Reggie Gaze's obituary that 'his happy hunting grounds were chiefly in Costessey Park, then an unspoilt paradise full of Nightingales each summer . . . In appearance, manner and speech Reggie was himself remarkably bird-like in a modest and gentle kind of way.'

**William Francis Bishop** (1913–1986), or 'Billy Bishop' as he was invariably known, was born in Blakeney, one of a large family. His father William was a fisherman and a lifeboatman. During Billy's lifetime the world changed dramatically. As a lad an autumn highlight was the arrival of the collectors – the gentlemen gunners. Anything that moved was shot in the hope that it would prove to be a rarity. Billy's father was factotum to one of these collectors – Frank Izod Richards, a London solicitor – and was employed during September at the then princely rate of ten shillings (or 50p) a day. Richards hired the old fishing smack *Britannia*, anchored off Blakeney Point. It was this solicitor who gave Billy his first lessons in wader identification. Still a lad, he transported beer and cartridges to the *Britannia* for two shillings weekly.

The last of the gentleman gunners was Clifford Borrer who lived in the Old Manor House in Cley. The final addition to his collection was a Pectoral Sandpiper. It was a fearless individual feeding on the very flood-marsh belonging to the collector. It did not stand a chance. Billy Bishop succeeded his grandfather as Cley Marsh warden in 1937. He was appointed by Sydney Long who had founded the Norfolk Naturalists Trust in 1926. He was paid two guineas a week less three shillings for the rent of the newly built Watcher's Cottage. Billy considered he had the ideal job compared with farmworkers' wages.

After wartime service in the Royal Navy, including escorting convoys to northern Russia, Billy returned to his beloved marsh where he spent the remainder of his life. For many years, Cley East Bank overlooking Arnold's Marsh attracted the crowds. Unfortunately, Arnold's was shrinking and often too deeply flooded for waders. Billy resolved to create alternative pools on the main reserve. At first only limited progress was possible because of the difficulty of access and heavy rain. However, the potential was obvious. Discussing the project with Justin Carter, Billy agreed to a proposed fund to finance new pools or scrapes. A local plant hire firm soon became enthusiastic. Single-handed, Billy obtained sufficient funds for the excavation of pools and the construction of observation hides. Water level control was improved. At last, ever increasing numbers of birdwatchers were able to enjoy close-up views of a galaxy of shore birds. Daukes hide in particular became renowned for its viewing highlights.

**Billy Bishop**

Billy retired at the end of 1978 and, at the following Annual General Meeting of the Trust in May, a telegram from the Duke of Edinburgh was read out and presentations were made on behalf of his many well-wishers. Sadly, Billy Bishop did not enjoy good health in retirement. However, he retained great enthusiasm for Cley Marsh, at times reminiscing about the days when 20 pairs of Garganey arrived each spring and 14 pairs of Red-backed Shrikes nested within 2km of the Reserve. Perhaps his greatest achievement was attracting a successful breeding colony of Avocets to the marsh.

**Aubrey Buxton** was a junior member of the Norfolk Naturalists Trust in 1928, at the age of 10. During the Second World War, whilst in Burma, he compiled the first list ever published of the birds of Arakan. For over 50 years since the end of the war he has campaigned for wildlife conservation. He was one of the founders of the Council for Nature and the World Wildlife Fund. He has served on the Nature Conservancy Council, the Countryside Commission and the Royal Commission on Pollution. Perhaps Aubrey Buxton's most significant contribution to public understanding and support for natural history was through his television series *Survival* which commenced in 1960 and became renowned worldwide. The brilliant team of wildlife photographers produced over 700 episodes from all round the globe and even the earliest films are still repeated today. At his home on the north Norfolk coast he has created a fine mix of agriculture and wildlife conservation where stubble remains to provide a winter attraction for Pink-footed Geese and finches, and water meadows are lightly grazed to encourage nesting Lapwings. The new Stiffkey Fen, created in 1996, already contains a thriving breeding colony of Avocets and has attracted a variety of unusual visitors including Pectoral Sandpiper and a party of four Temminck's Stints.

The year 1952 saw the publication of *Three Studies in Bird Character: Bitterns, Herons and Water Rails* by **Lord William Percy**. Little-known today, it is a fascinating volume full of original observations made when the author was living at Catfield Hall.

Post-war ornithology soon began to attract numbers of young people, many contributing a wealth of observations. Naturally the bulk of the Norfolk Naturalists Trust's publication dealt with events at its reserves. This situation coincided with the appointment of **Jim Taylor-Page** as secretary of the Norfolk & Norwich Naturalists' Society. Ever enthusiastic to develop the Society, Jim set up a series of groups which resulted in the birth of the *Norfolk Bird Report* covering the events of 1953. The new Report was warmly welcomed by the Norfolk Naturalists Trust which became joint publisher until 1982. The early issues were illustrated with Richard Richardson's delightful vignettes (a great innovation at the time) and **Dick Bagnall-Oakeley's** equally new 'away from the nest' photographs. Dick, the Hemsby parson's son, studied at Cambridge and then returned to his old school, Gresham's, to teach geography for 30 years. He pioneered colour cine-photography, especially seeking the unusual migrants appearing in north Norfolk. The Blakeney Red-rumped Swallow and the Cley Little Egret (county firsts) were two of his early successes. Each Christmas, Dick's latest films shown in the always crowded Music Room at the Assembly House in Norwich were eagerly anticipated by the Naturalists' Society's members. He was also a regular contributor to BBC TV

East Anglia. Dick died suddenly at the wheel of his car whilst in Scotland on a lecture tour for the Scottish Ornithologists' Club.

At the time of the appearance of the first issue of the *Norfolk Bird Report* (in May 1954), the Cambridge Bird Club covered in full the complete Fenland and Wash area including parts of west Norfolk. An artificial eastern boundary ran from Hunstanton southwards through Sandringham and Stoke Ferry to the Suffolk border near Lakenheath. Fortunately, there was free exchange of records for the overlapping areas. The 'season' for studying autumn migration then usually ended at the end of September. However, the discovery of a Pallas's Warbler at Holme by a field excursion of Cambridge Bird Club members on 17th November 1957 rapidly extended the birding year. But it was not until a decade later in 1967 that the tiny plantation on Blakeney Point (long regarded as *the* spot for rare migrants) began to lose much of its appeal. Holkham Meals, until then the haunt of pioneers, had been discovered! Holkham National Nature Reserve was declared the same year.

Over a period of three decades the name **John Moyes** became synonymous with the ornithological riches to be found at Wisbech Sewage Farm. Senior birdwatchers will recall that the old-style sewage works provided a rewarding magnet for flocks of migrant waders – especially in early autumn. But what was the strange attraction of these seemingly uninviting places for both birds and birdwatchers? Typically, the sewage farms of yesteryear contained a series of lagoons used on a rotational basis. Such man-made wetlands ranged from soft mud to flooded grassland and attracted a great variety of birds.

Many old sewage farms became famed for their waders, none more so than Wisbech, close to the River Nene. Surprisingly, part of this farm (situated on Walpole Island) was in Norfolk, only 10km inland with the river acting as a guideline for birds heading overland from the Wash. Construction of Wisbech Sewage Farm began in 1874, but little is known of its early ornithological history. Infrequent visits were made by Cambridge Bird Club members from the mid-1940s onwards. It was not until 1955 that the true value of the farm was realised following almost daily autumn counts made by John Moyes (who was often in company with Tony Vine). Fortunately, this increased observation coincided with a remarkable return migration that autumn. The lagoons attracted a flock of 40 Spotted Redshanks and 100 Curlew Sandpipers. The wader list finally increased to 27 species with the concurrent visits of both Pectoral and White-rumped Sandpipers.

Towards the end of the 1950s flooding of the tanks was regulated on a more casual regime. The farm manager became sympathetic to the requirements of birds and birdwatchers. Additional shallow floods were made available to feeding waders during peak migration periods with spectacular results. The numbers of more common species and some of the scarcer migrants visiting the farm increased dramatically. This trend was maintained throughout the 1960s, which became the best period ornithologically in the history of the farm. It had long been realised that the state of the tides in the Wash greatly influenced both numbers and variety of birds at the site. A large commuter population of small waders became established in most years with birds flighting in to feed at the farm in the mornings and out again in the late evenings. In the years when plant growth became rank the lagoons were less attractive to shorebirds such as Dunlins, Curlew Sandpipers and Little Stints – but more favoured by Wood and Green Sandpipers with always the chance of a Spotted Crake.

By mid-August each year migration through the farm was well underway, with the second week often producing the greatest variety. As many as 31 Green, 37 Wood and 80 Common Sandpipers would be on show. Ruff totals could be as high as 200 or even 250, but numbers of the larger waders was mainly governed by the Wash tides. High-tide roosting groups of 50 or even 60 Spotted Redshanks could be expected. Flights of 20 to 30 Greenshanks regularly headed inland following the Nene. Whimbrel numbers showed a similar pattern. On occasions, 24 wader species were observed in the pools. Under suitable conditions early September produced peak numbers of Dunlins, Curlew Sandpipers and Little Stints, the combined flock often totalling 2,000 birds. Groups of 130 Little Stints and 400 Curlew Sandpipers were attained.

Weed-grown tanks were much favoured by Common Snipe with peak numbers of 800 on record. Unique numbers of Jack Snipe appeared one autumn attaining a maximum of 50 birds. By contrast, the rare Great Snipe would only stay for a few days. Temminck's Stints and Red-necked Phalaropes were regular, but Grey Phalaropes remained rare with just two observations during 30 years. Dotterel appeared among the Golden Plover flocks and a Black-winged Stilt once stayed a few days.

Most birdwatchers came to the farm anticipating the sight of Nearctic waders. The least rare of these transatlantic wanderers was the Pectoral Sandpiper with a 30-year total of nearly 50 birds. Next in the order of frequency was the White-rumped Sandpiper. Since its first recorded visit in 1955, it was noted a further five times. A total of five Wilson's Phalaropes appeared; also Spotted Sandpiper, Semipalmated Sandpiper and Long-billed Dowitcher. A star arrival in the history of Wisbech Sewage Farm was the Stilt Sandpiper trapped and ringed in 1963. It was only the second record for Europe. Another was discovered there just two years later.

Towards the close of 1985 work began draining the remaining water and levelling the banks. It was ironic that the resulting exposure of mud brought about a dramatic wader build-up. Pectoral and Buff-breasted Sandpipers featured among the final highlights.

Apart from the wealth of waders, other surprises included two Blue-winged Teal which remained for a month and a total of 50 Great and 100 Arctic Skuas which swept over the farm on 14th September 1980 and continued heading inland. Overgrown lagoons attracted many wintering seed-eaters: up to 20,000 Greenfinches, 3,000 Bramblings and 2,000 Tree Sparrows. Today, nothing but the name remains. The sewage farm acres have merged with those of the surrounding fens.

During the 1960s the Alexander brothers were regular visitors to north Norfolk. I had first met **Horace Alexander** aboard a troopship when he became my mentor during the long but exciting voyage to India. 'HG' (as he was called in distinction from his also famous birdwatching brother 'WB') wrote of his uniquely long career in *Seventy Years of Birdwatching*. He was a lifelong Quaker and spent many years in India following in the footsteps of British servicemen and civilians who had founded Indian ornithology early in the 19th century. 'HG' attained the remarkable age of 100 before he died in Pennsylvania in 1989. His brother produced the pocket guide *Birds of the Ocean*. This volume transformed the art of seawatching.

Following the untimely death of Richard Richardson, the East Bank at Cley lost its centre of attraction and provider of the latest news. Birdwatching was becoming ever more popular, especially among Richard's former devotees. A news centre soon became established in Nancy's café in the High Street at Cley. Over a period of 17 years **Nancy Gull** became internationally famous for her catering and for her telephone and log-book service. Few, however, appreciated that the free use of Nancy's private telephone had developed from her generous consent that a few birders she knew could leave occasional messages. The constant ringing of the telephone at all hours eventually became unbearable. An independent message system to handle the growing demand for up-to-date news was needed. Roy Robinson introduced the first answerphone service, based at Walsey Hills. For technical reasons, however, this was not a success.

After this experiment, a team comprising Lee Evans, Steve Gantlett and Richard and Hazel Millington successfully developed the Bird Information Service in 1987. The BIS offers, on a subscription basis, a monthly magazine *(Birding World)* and a 24-hour answerphone hotline known as Birdline. Now in its twelfth year of publication, *Birding World* has developed into an up-to-date and successful magazine. The Bird Information Service liaises closely with landowners, the RSPB and reserve wardens. When detailed directions (often with map references) for the latest sightings are involved this can often lead to excellent fund-raising opportunities. All observations reaching BIS are passed to the appropriate county recorders. Rare breeding birds are not normally featured, nor are rarities appearing at sensitive locations with limited access.

Birdline tends to specialise in national rarities and it became a natural development for a series of regional centres to be formed. All joined forces under the BIS umbrella to become the regional Birdlines. Robin Chittenden and Dave Holman became the East Anglian team and remain so to this day.

**Steve Gantlett**, a qualified optician, 'retired' in 1982 to become a full-time ornithologist. He has edited *Birding World* since its inception. His life-list extends to well over 500 species seen in Britain. He has written *The Birds of Cley* and *The Birds of Scilly* and was a co-author of *Rare Birds in Britain and Ireland*. **Richard Millington**, the voice of Birdline, has been assistant editor of *Birding World* since its launch. A fine artist and illustrator of bird books (over 20 titles), Richard was author and illustrator of *A Twitcher's Diary*. His artwork appears regularly in magazines. **Simon Harrap** joined the *Birding World* editorial board in 1991. In addition to many contributions to a selection of magazines and journals and was co-author of *Bird Watching in Britain: A Site by Site Guide* and author of *Tits, Nuthatches and Treecreepers*.

**Robin Chittenden** established the *Rare Bird Photographic Library* in 1988, superseded by *Harlequin Pictures* in 1995, to market his own photographs. Robin is a photographic research consultant for *British Birds* and *Birding World*. He has travelled widely for bird photography and his work features regularly in leading magazines. **Dave Holman** has been a freelance tour leader for ornithological tour companies since 1981. He has travelled extensively, including visits to Antarctica, Argentina, Chile, Ethiopia and Russia.

Dave was a member of the British Birds Rarities Committee for ten years and of the county Records Committee from its formation in 1976 for ten years, and again from 1991 to 1996.

A further development in the dissemination of news of rarities was the advent of the pager. *Rare Bird Alert* pagers, founded by **Dick Filby** in Norwich, pioneered this technology for rare bird news and many birders now carry pagers, providing them with constant up-to-date news. Dick also leads birding tours for WildWings in his spare time and has visited Antarctica on many occasions.

**Bryan Bland** has been fascinated by natural history, and in particular birds, for as long as he can remember, but it was not until 1974 that he decided to resign his directorships to pioneer a new style of residential birdwatching course in Norfolk. His original methods combined with his ability to caricature the diagnostic points of any species quickly, led him to be regarded as one of the leading teachers in practical ornithology. These courses are alternated with birding trips abroad which Bryan leads as a director of Sunbird. His 'Birds-and-Music' and 'Birds-and-History' combinations (reflecting other interests outside ornithology) have become very popular. Bryan has watched birds in over 50 countries including North, Central and South America; North and East Africa; Asia and throughout Europe. He is also much in demand as a lecturer and after-dinner speaker. He has therefore been responsible, over the last quarter-century, for directly and personally enthusing thousands of today's birdwatchers, together with many more through broadcasts on radio and TV. Bryan's interest in identification is evinced by the fact that he has served on the records committees of both Norfolk and Scilly and has over the last 30 years discovered numerous rarities. To date he has seen 380 species in Norfolk, 334 of them in the Cley square and his window list has passed the 200 mark. But above all Bryan retains an interest in and love of the common birds. He is also well known as an illustrator, his first published drawing appearing when he was two years old. More recently there have been numerous illustrations for several other books and magazines. Britain's first breeding Parrot Crossbills used trimmings from Bryan's beard when nesting at Wells in 1984!

**Norman Sills'** interest in birds began at the age of 11. After leaving school in 1963 he enquired about employment in conservation. At that time situations were scarce and the main employer, The Nature Conservancy (now English Nature) demanded a degree. Wanting to be outdoors for part of his working life, Norman became a trainee quantity surveyor in Coventry.

He helped to form and run a conservation group on a marsh and sand-quarry complex alongside the River Avon in Warwickshire. Seven years later with professional studies completed, he was set for a career in surveying. But then a record sleeve of Sibelius' music depicting a magnificent view over the tundra of northern Finland resulted in a change of course. Combined with the desire to see Snow Buntings, Shorelarks and Lapland Buntings on their breeding grounds, Norman and three friends made a seven-week camping trip to northern Scandinavia during the summer of 1970. The expedition meant resigning from the surveyors work in Coventry. However, an advertisement in the RSPB magazine resulted in Norman becoming warden of Cowpen Marsh Reserve in Teesside. The following year, he spent two weeks leave in north Norfolk which included views of Montagu's Harriers, at a locality he had never heard of – Titchwell. He promptly wrote to the RSPB Reserves Manager (John Crudass) suggesting the marshland at Titchwell could be developed into a worthwhile reserve. Not surprisingly, Norman was amazed and pleased when the Reserves Manager replied by return of post to say that the Society had just bought it!

He successfully applied for the Titchwell warden's job and on 29th March 1973 moved there to begin what subsequently became a success story. In 1983 he produced a 116 page report entitled *Titchwell Marsh, the First Ten Years*. Norman added 'that at one time in the mid-1970s I thought we would never see the back of diggers'. Much remedial work was needed following the tidal surges of 3rd January 1976 and 11th January 1978. A succession of events followed, including the first Bittern booming in 1979, the Marsh Harriers first nest-building in 1980, the first Avocets nesting in 1984, a Wilson's Phalarope, winter flocks of Golden Plovers, the first Penduline Tit, Spoonbills and a Ross's Gull. Above all, Norman recalls the interest and excitement of the thousands of visitors who annually visit Titchwell Marsh to watch birds and to enjoy the wildness of the area.

Early in 1997, after 24 years at Titchwell, Norman moved to Lakenheath Fen, a new RSPB reserve in Suffolk: 'There was no fen there before we started work but old carrot fields are gradually being converted to pools, channels and reedbeds as part of the Society's aim in creating new reedbeds inland. Hopefully, in a few years, Reed Warblers, Bearded Tits, Marsh Harriers and Bitterns will occupy Lakenheath Fen and will find it an idyllic place.'

Another stalwart of the north Norfolk ornithological scene is **Andrew Bloomfield**, who was born on the Holkham Estate and has studied the birds of the area for much of his life. In 1993 Andrew shared the results of his observations when he published the *Birds of The Holkham Area*.

**Norman Arlott** spent his childhood and early years in Reading. Like many youngsters, he sometimes searched for birds' nests and eggs before he joined the British Trust for Ornithology. Of all his school activities art was the most appealing, but Norman agreed with his parents that education should be practical. A successful five-year apprenticeship in mechanical engineering followed. His career seemed set and he accepted his first job, but at the same time and without any formal art training, Norman began painting birds. Bird illustration rapidly took over his life. His work (he was *British Birds* Bird Illustrator of the Year in both 1980 and 1981) has appeared in over 90 wildlife books commencing with *Minsmere – Portrait of a Bird Reserve*. The list also includes the multi-volume *Handbook of the Birds of the World*, the nine-volume *Birds of the Western Palearctic, Birds of Southern Africa, Complete Guide to British Wildlife, A Field Guide to the Birds of East Africa* and *Birds of Britain and Europe*.

Norman – a member of the Society of Wildlife Artists – has exhibited widely in Britain and also in North America. Less well known are Norman's stamp commissions, mostly received through the Crown Agents. He has designed over 40 issues, commencing with a set for Jamaica in 1982. The list of commissions has since included Ascension Island, Bermuda, British Virgin Islands, Fiji, Liberia, Pitcairn Island, Seychelles, Solomon Islands and Trinidad and Tobago. He lives in a small village in the Norfolk Fens.

Attracted by the county's wealth of birds, **John Kemp** came to Norfolk in 1974. His first employment was as a dairy herdsman in Castle Acre. Ten years later he became the Welney Reserve stockman. Early every morning from May to November, John begins the twice-daily cattle round at the Wildfowl and Wetlands Trust Reserve, criss-crossing 400ha of wash grassland by motor cycle. Each head of stock is counted to check that none has strayed. By peak season there will be 900 cattle – many with calves. The greatest danger is of cattle falling into a ditch during the night. The livestock at Welney belong to local farmers, many of whom have been grazing the washes for years.

In winter Welney Wash is transformed, and at times following heavy rain, the reserve becomes an inland sea. At this season and in early spring, John is in attendance at the main observatory. Among the thousands of birds on view few, if any, will escape his ever vigilant eye. His Welney catalogue extends to the discovery of Night Heron, Cattle Egrets, Great White Egrets, American Wigeon, Blue-winged Teal, Canvasback, Sociable Plover, Great Snipe, Long-billed Dowitcher, Lesser Yellowlegs, Spotted Sandpiper and Whiskered Terns.

Elsewhere in the county John's list of Norfolk first records includes the Two-barred Greenish Warbler. He was also one of the first observers to identify the Holkham Yellow-browed Bunting. Other highlights feature the first Surf Scoter in modern times as well as White-winged Black Terns, Red-throated Pipit, and Pallas's, Radde's and Dusky Warblers.

**Dr John Lines**, after working in Bermuda as a junior psychiatrist (and identifying the first Little Stint for the island), came to Norfolk in 1976. He soon found the 'honeypot' sites along the north Norfolk coast 'rather overcrowded'. John is also an ardent conservationist always prepared to tackle authority. He has devoted most of his spare time at Middleton, Pentney and Tottenhill Gravel Pits, Pentney Heath and King's Lynn beet factory. Regular observations, management plans and surveys at these County Wildlife Sites may well guarantee their future. John is still best known for his discovery of a White-winged Lark at Lynn Beet Factory. The sighting has become even more valuable with the passage of time, having been elevated from the fifth to the second fully accepted British record.

**Robert Gillmor**, born on 6th July 1936 in Reading, was 16 when his first illustrations were published in *British Birds*. He illustrated his first book in 1958. Since then his work has appeared in over 100 books, numerous magazines and countless Christmas cards. He has also designed jackets for the *New Naturalist* series since 1985.

In the early 1960s, with Eric Ennion and others, Robert founded the Society of Wildlife Artists and, after serving as its secretary and chairman for many years, he was elected president in 1984. He began a freelance career as a wildlife artist and illustrator in 1965, painting in watercolour but also producing many pen and ink illustrations and distinctive linocut designs.

Between 1966 and 1994 Robert was art editor of the nine-volume *Birds of the Western Palearctic*. This great task completed, he became deeply involved in the subsequent two-volume concise edition, containing a high proportion of new colour plates.

After spending extensive periods each May at Titchwell Marsh, Robert has succumbed to the delights of living in north Norfolk – at Cley and within a stone's throw of the former cottage home of Richard Richardson.

**Moss Taylor** moved to Norfolk in 1969 and worked as a general medical practitioner at Sheringham from 1972 until 1995, when he took early retirement. He served as BTO Regional Representive for Norfolk from 1978 to 1991, and again from 1995, during which time he served on BTO Council, holding the posts of both Honorary Secretary and Treasurer. He has also been a member of the Councils of the Norfolk Wildlife Trust and the Norfolk & Norwich Naturalists' Society. His main interest has been the study of migration along the north Norfolk coast, aided by ringing, with which he has been involved for almost 40 years. For many years he was a member of the editorial team of the *Norfolk Bird Report*, including responsibility for the ringing section. His first book, *The Birds of Sheringham*, was published in 1987 and the following year he was awarded the BTO Jubilee Medal for services to the Trust.

**Don Dorling** is retired having spent his working life with the Norwich Union Insurance Group in Norwich. He has been interested in natural history, particularly ornithology, since schooldays and has been actively involved with the Norfolk & Norwich Naturalists' Society in a range of capacities for over 35 years, including his appointment as a vice-president. Don joined the Norfolk Wildlife Trust in 1965 and has acted as a volunteer at the Cley, Hickling and Ranworth Reserves. He has completed six years as a member of the Trust Council and has recently been appointed its Chairman. For decades he has been deeply involved in behind-the-scenes production of the *Norfolk Bird Report* as a county recorder and, particularly, as the compiler of the annual card index of the year's sightings.

No pen picture of the guardians of Breydon would be complete without an appreciation of **Peter Allard.** He has recorded the birds of this estuary and the adjoining marshland for forty years, following his first birding trips to Runham and Mautby Marshes assisting an aunt in delivering mail to the isolated cottages and farms. When aged just 14 he found Norfolk's first Red-breasted Goose amongst White-fronted Geese on Halvergate Marshes. Through the years, a catalogue of rarities has featured in the *Norfolk Bird Reports* under the soon to be famed PRA initials; often the records were the first for the county. The highly impressive list includes two Purple Herons, Black Stork, four American Wigeons, two Green-winged Teals, Blue-winged Teal, five Red-footed Falcons, a unique total of 51 Kentish Plovers, American Golden Plover, Pacific Golden Plover, Greater Sand Plover, Collared Pratincole, six White-rumped Sandpipers, a remarkable 19 Broad-billed Sandpipers, four Pectoral Sandpipers, two Greater Yellowlegs, four Terek Sandpipers, Wilson's Phalarope, two Caspian Terns, White-winged Black Tern, Gull-billed Tern, Short-toed Lark, Tawny Pipit, four Red-throated Pipits, Red-flanked Bluetail, Isabelline Wheatear, Pied Wheatear, two Great Reed Warblers, Greenish Warbler, Arctic Warbler, Pallas's Warbler, Dusky Warbler, Western Bonelli's Warbler, Lesser Grey Shrike, Nutcrackers, Cirl Bunting and Rustic Bunting. During a single summer at Yarmouth, Peter located 17 breeding pairs of Black Redstarts which reared a total of 50 or more young. He became a warden guarding the Winterton Little Tern colony from 1967 for three years, a voluntary warden at Breydon from 1969, a county bird recorder from 1977 to 1994 and a founder member and first secretary of Yarmouth Bird Club in 1989. Terns have always had a special appeal and the construction of Common Tern nesting platforms on Breydon was one of Peter's most successful ventures.

Peter's *Birds of Great Yarmouth*, published by the Norfolk & Norwich Naturalists' Society in 1990, covers, in a pleasantly discursive style reminiscent of Arthur Patterson, a wealth of facts and figures.

Breydon (declared a Local Nature Reserve in 1968) casts a spell on its watchers and Peter is no exception. Due almost entirely to his regular counts of waders and wildfowl, it has become a Site of Special Scientific Interest, a Special Protection Area under the EU Birds Directive and also a Wetland of International Importance under the Ramsar Convention. In addition to these varied activities, Peter has helped with the preparation of the annual *Norfolk Bird Report* since 1964 as a county recorder and county archivist.

The joint tasks of being editor and also responsible for assembling the systematic list of the *Norfolk Bird Report* finally became too great a burden for one person. The responsibility for the compilation of the systematic list was taken over by **Michael Rooney** on behalf of the Norfolk Bird Club, who with an extended team prepared the systematic list covering the events of 1994. This arrangement has enabled a much more detailed presentation of records, particularly those of the once common species, and the Report has been brought into line with those of other counties. As a result of this and other changes in style and content, the 1994 *Norfolk Bird Report* was successful in the *British Birds* Best Annual Bird Report competition, sharing first place with those of Avon and Essex. **Giles Dunmore** and **Neil Lawton** became county recorders and editors of the systematic list for the 1995 Report, and the amicable arrangements with the Norfolk Bird Club have continued.

M. S.

No chapter dealing with the ornithological personalities of Norfolk would be complete without a glowing reference to the work of one of the joint authors of this volume – **Michael Seago**. His dedication to the study of the county's birds over nearly 60 years puts him in the same class as the great Henry Stevenson, John Henry Gurney Jr and Bernard Riviere, who between them recorded the avian events in Norfolk for more than a hundred years.

Michael began his interest in birdwatching in the early 1940s with visits to Breydon and other similar estuary and marshland areas, where he developed his particular interest in waders. Amongst those who gave encouragement during those early years were H. G. Alexander (whom he met on board a troopship en route to India during his military service), Bernard Riviere, and Ted Ellis.

Until 1953 the county did not have an annual bird report although over the years much had been published in regular reports in *British Birds,* the *Transactions of the Norfolk & Norwich Naturalists' Society* and the annual reports of the Wild Birds' Protection Committee in which Michael first had an item in the issue covering the year 1944. With the encouragement of Bernard Riviere, Dick Bagnall-Oakeley and Richard Richardson, amongst others, Michael undertook to remedy this situation and the first issue covering the events of 1953 appeared in 1954. For the next 29 years this annual report was published jointly by the (then) Norfolk Naturalists Trust and the Norfolk & Norwich Naturalists' Society; from the 1982 report onwards the Society assumed sole responsibility with the support of, originally, the Norfolk Ornithologists' Association and latterly the Norfolk Bird Club. The latest report – that for 1997 – appeared in autumn 1998 with Michael still acting as senior editor. It was the 45th issue under his control. We believe this to be a unique record in British ornithological recording. His meticulous attention for detail has maintained the highest of standards throughout, resulting in the *Norfolk Bird Report's* wide popularity and well deserved reputation for accuracy.

**Michael Seago**

During this long period many important innovations were introduced to make each issue attractive, as well as an accurate record of events; for example line drawings to break up the text were an early feature, soon to be followed by photographs, initially in black and white, but since 1986 in full colour. These features, with the much enhanced Systematic List of recent years, have received national recognition by being awarded a joint first (1994 Report) and a second place (1997 Report) in the 'Best Annual Bird Report Awards' organised by *British Birds.*

Also active in the field, Michael is credited with recording the county's first Little Ringed Plover when he found two on Breydon in June 1943, and 13 years later he was involved in the discovery of a new breeding bird for Britain when Collared Doves first bred in north Norfolk.

In addition to his editing, he has written regularly in the local press for nearly half a century and produced two editions of his book *Birds of Norfolk,* the first appearing in 1967. He has also taken an active part in local natural history organisations, serving at various times as Honorary Secretary to the Great Yarmouth Naturalists' Society, Council member and vice-president of the Norfolk Wildlife Trust and Council member, vice-president and President of the Norfolk & Norwich Naturalists' Society. For many years he was the RSPB's representative for the county. He has also devoted much time and effort on conservation matters including giving advice on reserve management and encouraging the protection of rare breeding birds. In recognition of this long and dedicated service, Michael was presented with the Sydney Long Memorial Medal at the Annual General Meeting of the Norfolk Wildlife Trust in 1993.

D. D., P. A., M. T.

# BIRD MIGRATION IN NORFOLK

*by*

## Andy Stoddart

## INTRODUCTION

For countries in the world's temperate mid-latitudes, there are marked seasonal variations in climate. Day-to-day weather systems are also highly mobile, bringing rapid changes in air masses and therefore temperature and wind speed and direction.

These forces both initiate and influence great seasonal movements of birds. Though their scale is vast, they are often only fully visible at the edges of land masses. In this context, Norfolk's location on a prominent bulge of the British coast extending out towards the Continent and into the southern North Sea places it in an enviable position for the recording and study of migratory birds.

Indeed it is these seasonal movements which have the most profound and visible effect on the local avifauna. Day-to-day birdwatching in the county, particularly at the coast, is largely dominated by the phenomenon of migration, and an account of bird movements in the county is in effect an account of a birdwatching year.

As a result, this chapter takes a month by month view of the ebb and flow of the county's bird movements, describing those events which might be seen as typical, whilst also highlighting significant events and occurrences from Norfolk's long history of bird recording. Inevitably, a discussion of the effects of weather plays a prominent part in the picture.

## JANUARY

This month might be thought of as the least likely of the year to feature bird migration, with wintering populations at their most stable. Even at this time of year, however, weather fluctuations can provoke widespread dispersals of birds, both into the county from the Continent, and also out of the county to the south and west. With rising pressure and tumbling temperatures in Russia and north-west Europe, Norfolk becomes either a refuge or a stopping-off point for thousands of fleeing birds.

Certain groups are particularly prone to this type of weather displacement. At the onset of a cold spell, typical immigrants will be divers, grebes and wildfowl, Lapwings, Woodcock, Golden Plover, gulls, thrushes and Skylarks. The sudden arrivals of those species normally present in tiny numbers, such as Smew and Tundra Bean Geese, are normally the most visible manifestations, but the numbers of commoner species on the move can also be truly dramatic.

Amongst the coldest Januarys were those of 1947, 1963 and 1987. The year 1963 saw particularly high numbers of Smew in the county with 14 on the Bure and 16 at Breydon, whereas the cold spell of 1987 pushed numbers of Bewick's Swans at Welney to over 6,000 and Smew and Goosanders became widespread. Nine of the former were at Denver Sluice, with over 100 of the latter in the area at the same time.

Falling temperatures and winds from an easterly quarter at this time of year can also add extra impetus to irruptive movements of certain passerine groups. If food-related dispersals of species such as Waxwing and Mealy Redpoll are already occurring in Europe, weather can play a key role in extending these movements into Norfolk. This was demonstrated most clearly in January 1996, when the widespread arrival of Mealy Redpolls in the previous late autumn received an extra impetus, sending many three-figure flocks of these finches into local birch and alder woods and weedy fields, amongst them unprecedented numbers of Arctic Redpolls. January 1996 also witnessed the start of Norfolk's largest ever Waxwing invasion, whilst massive numbers of thrushes, notably Fieldfares, roamed the county and invaded urban parks and gardens.

In other years, January can be much more benign, with the increasing daylight in the last days of the month sometimes prompting the early emigration of the Yare Valley Taiga Bean Geese.

Amongst January's most notable events, however, must be the Cory's Shearwater found dead on Salthouse beach on 29th January 1966 and 100 Glaucous Gulls seen off Cley on 22nd January 1922.

# FEBRUARY

This month often continues the theme set by January, with cold-weather movements and continued irruptions prominent in some years. The Waxwing avalanche of 1996 reached its peak in February, with small incoming parties roaming through the coastal villages, whilst numbers in Norwich built up to at least 300, and probably more, as the flocks swirled around the city.

The cold weather of January 1963 also continued into February, pushing the Smew count at Rockland Broad to over 40. This spell of weather was also doubtless responsible for the arrival of the Great Bustard found dead beneath wires at South Creake in late March of that year.

February 1979 again saw particularly severe weather and prompted significant arrivals of Red-necked and Slavonian Grebes, Smew, Goosanders and Red-breasted Mergansers. Over 70 of the first-named were judged to be in the county at the time. At the height of this cold spell a Great Bustard was at East Somerton and Winterton.

February 1987 remained particularly severe and prompted further arrivals of birds from the near-Continent. Chief amongst these were two Great Bustards at New Buckenham on 7th–10th February, part of a small invasion into north-west Europe at that time, whilst Smew were again prominent with up to 14 present at Hickling.

At the coast, sudden mild conditions in the second half of February can, however, witness the first tentative movements of Meadow Pipits, Pied Wagtails and Linnets, whilst Stonechats can put in an odd appearance, although north Norfolk witnessed an astonishing arrival of at least 75 on 27th February 1994, with 23 at Cley alone.

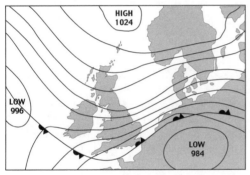

Figure 1. 14th February 1979. Cold-weather movements in a bitter easterly airstream flowing from Russia and the Baltic.

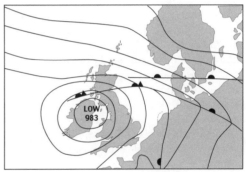

Figure 2. 27th February 1994. A strong Stonechat influx in mild conditions and southerly winds on the eastern flank of a low-pressure area.

On occasions, February can witness the stunningly early arrivals of summer visitors. Amongst the more spectacular examples were a Kentish Plover at Yarmouth on 1st February 1836, a Ring Ouzel near Acle on 2nd February 1927 and a Common Tern at Wroxham on 3rd February 1967.

At sea, large offshore movements of seabirds can take place in strong winds, sometimes inducing 'wrecks' such as that of auks in February 1983. Rough weather in the north-east Atlantic on 5th prompted a large-scale beaching of over 5,000 dead auks, displaced from waters further north.

# MARCH

March sees further progress, albeit slow, towards spring. Numbers of wintering wildfowl decline significantly, and anywhere in the county Bewick's Swans can appear unexpectedly in the skies, heading strongly east from their Fenland winter haunts. March has also provided increasing evidence of through-passage of wildfowl in the form of sudden occurrences of Green-winged Teal and American Wigeon, doubtless moving north from winter quarters elsewhere. Movements of gulls, particularly Common and Lesser Black-backed Gulls, are also of particular interest at this time of year although this may be more obvious to watchers at single sites where the daily turnover of birds can be high.

As wildfowl melt away from lakes and marshes, their place is taken by incoming waders. The coastal scrapes and lagoons are reclaimed by Avocets and Ringed Plovers, whilst colourful flocks of Black-tailed

Godwits become very obvious. March also sees the first arrivals of rarer breeders such as Garganey and Little Ringed Plover.

The departures of wintering thrushes, Robins and Goldcrests, however, can be very unobtrusive, although the movement of the thrushes is given away as they call overhead at night. Other wintering passerines may gather and start to wander in preparation for departure. Norfolk's largest ever flock of Arctic Redpolls occurred at this time, with 20 frequenting Norwich's Mousehold Heath in mid-March 1990. Passage of incoming passerines becomes more concerted, with coastal movements of Meadow Pipits, White and Pied Wagtails and Linnets also joined by the very first hirundines at the end of the month. The pivotal moment for many is the first Wheatear, an event always witnessed before the month's end, and Black Redstarts and Ring Ouzels are regular at coastal locations too, as can be Firecrests in some years. Rather more unusual were the Cuckoo at Horsey on 21st March 1903 and the Red-backed Shrike at Weybourne on 30th March 1957.

A fall of Saharan dust occurred in early March 1977. These rare events are caused by strong surface winds whipping up Saharan sand to great altitudes. This is then carried northwards before descending to earth, usually with rain. Such warm conditions in 1977 also prompted a number of remarkably early summer migrants including Wheatears and Chiffchaffs on 6th, a House Martin on 8th, a Yellow Wagtail on 13th and a Tawny Pipit on 19th.

Norfolk's geography makes the county a particularly good place to look for bird of prey movements in early spring. On occasions, numbers of Common Buzzards have occurred, for example eight over Breydon in an hour on 28th March 1969 and thirteen west at Walsey Hills, Salthouse on 31st March 1996, whilst 18th March 1988 witnessed a large arrival of continental Red Kites throughout the county in a period of mild weather.

## APRIL

April sees the first full flowering of spring, although sustained spells of cold weather can put progress 'on hold' for frustratingly long periods. It is at this time of year that Norfolk's north-easterly aspect can be particularly obvious, with arrivals of incoming migrants lagging far behind those taking place in the south and south-west. Periods of cold northerly or north-easterly winds at this time of year can, however, 'stall' numbers of Ring Ouzels in coastal fields. For example, 27 were at Winterton on 30th April 1974 and 35 were in north Norfolk on 16th April 1988, 20 of these being at Holme. Great Grey Shrikes can also make their typically sudden, dramatic appearances around this time, most notably in 1971, when 14 were recorded in the county.

More species join the visible passage taking place at the coast with White and Yellow Wagtails particularly prominent. Very large passages take place in some years, Cley, for example, hosting 400 of the latter on 24th April 1986. Birds of the Blue-headed continental race *flava* are invariably involved in these movements. Hooded Crows are now scarce visitors indeed but early spring provides the best chance to encounter one amongst small-scale movements of Carrion Crows, Rooks and Jackdaws, though 40 were seen together in a single tree at Winterton on 7th April 1974. Amongst the most remarkable migrations of recent years must be the passage of Common Buzzards westwards along the north coast on 20th April 1995, when no fewer than 32 (including a flock of 21) passed Sheringham. The Swift at Cley on 3rd April 1949 was, however, even more exceptional.

During the month, most summer visitors will make their first appearances, amongst the most obvious arrivals being the breeding Common, Arctic, Little and Sandwich Terns and noisy flocks of Whimbrels in coastal fields.

The first small passerine night migrants now appear in coastal bushes at the same time as others reclaim their inland breeding areas. Willow Warblers and Chiffchaffs are most obvious, sharing cover with the last of the departing thrushes, Robins and Goldcrests. Easterly conditions can prompt small 'falls' of migrants, for example 30 Robins arrived at Holme on 27th April 1965, amongst them a Swedish-ringed bird. A Robin ringed there on 29th was trapped within the week at the mouth of the Elbe in Germany.

This last week of the month traditionally sees a 'step-change' in migrant activity, with both numbers and species diversity expanding dramatically, particularly in pulses of warm air. For example, 70 Wheatears were present at Holme and on Blakeney Point with large numbers elsewhere around the coast between 24th and 28th April 1992. Scarcer species such as Serin, Wryneck, Hoopoe and Tawny Pipit are often encountered in the county at this time, and true rarities may also make their first appearances, perhaps the most exciting recent example being the male Rock Thrush at Horsey on 30th April 1989 during a strong influx of migrants.

April is not noted as a time to look out to sea, though twelve Arctic and four Great Skuas were seen off Cley on 20th April 1980.

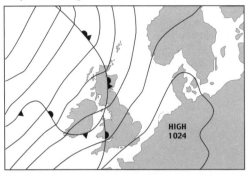

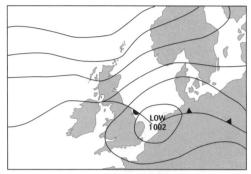

Figure 3. 30th April 1989. Excellent conditions for a large arrival of spring migrants in the mild south-westerly conditions on the western flank of a high-pressure area.

Figure 4. 14th May 1985. A strong Bluethroat arrival in easterly conditions on the northern edge of a low-pressure area.

## MAY

Spring can now be said truly to have arrived, with the greatest variety of species passing through the county and the best chances of the spring to encounter scarce and rare species. Large influxes of commoner species can readily be associated with incursions of warm air, but, in the dash for breeding grounds, the arrival of many birds shows little obvious correlation with specific weather conditions.

However, from mid-month onwards easterly winds from areas of low pressure to the south or high pressure over northern Europe can produce arrivals of passerine migrants bound for eastern Europe and Scandinavia. Amongst the most eagerly-awaited are Bluethroats of the Red-spotted Scandinavian form *svecica* which, in recent years, have become a feature of mid-May – a complete reversal of their former status as an early September migrant. The largest arrivals of this species took place in 1985, when 54 were seen, including 14 along Blakeney Point and eleven at Holme on 14th, and 1987, with a minimum of 26, eleven of which were at Blakeney Point.

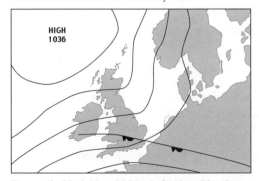

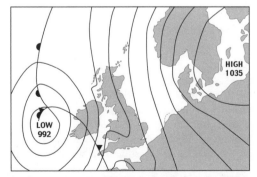

Figure 5. 23rd May 1987. A further Bluethroat influx, this time in easterly winds on the south-eastern flank of a high-pressure area.

Figure 6. 14th May 1992. A sudden influx of Red-footed Falcons in hot, long-range south-easterly winds.

At the same time, and often in the same conditions, regularly recorded drift migrants include Pied Fly-catcher and Wryneck, whilst rarer, but still regular, visitors include Icterine Warbler, Red-backed Shrike, Grey-headed Wagtail and Red-throated Pipit, these latter two surprisingly often in each other's company. One of the more stunning May events of recent years occurred on 14th May 1992, when a sudden and long-range blast of hot air from south-east Europe filled the skies of Norfolk with Red-footed Falcons, around a dozen of these delightful birds being seen on that day alone, along with five Red-throated Pipits and high numbers of Grey-headed Wagtails.

Equally unexpected were the nine Rough-legged Buzzards which passed over Holme on 13th May 1979, after a particularly good winter for the species, though even this had been eclipsed by the twelve at Winterton on 1st May 1975.

The sporadic arrivals of Black Terns in the county can also be dramatic. These too are associated with south-easterly winds, usually early in the month. Major influxes occurred in 1970, when 1,000 passed through Cley on 5th and 6th, and 1990, when over 1,000 passed along the north coast on 2nd.

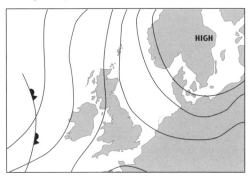

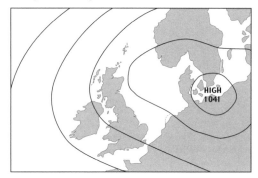

Figure 7. 5th May 1970. A Black Tern influx in south-easterly winds.

Figure 8. 2nd May 1990. A further Black Tern influx in similar south-easterly conditions.

An overview of May migration must also make mention of the rarities which have occurred at this time of year. The annual parade usually involves overshooting Mediterranean species such as herons, Subalpine Warbler, Woodchat Shrike, Short-toed Lark, Alpine Swift and Red-rumped Swallow, but almost anything is technically possible. Chief amongst the truly astonishing rarities must rank the pair of Slender-billed Gulls at Cley in May 1987 and the Pacific Swift which graced Cley for several hours on 30th May 1993. Many such rarities can turn up in the closing days of the month, at a time when movements of common migrants have largely ceased. Indeed the days after, say, 25th May can seem strangely quiet, but this has proved time and time again to be a time of year to maintain full concentration!

Wader passage reaches its peak in May, with estuaries full of breeding-plumaged Arctic-bound Dunlins and Ringed Plovers and scrapes also hosting the occasional Wood and Curlew Sandpipers, Little and Temminck's Stints or even a Broad-billed Sandpiper amongst commoner cousins.

Late May can see major movements of hirundines. However, the days of large passages of Turtle Doves are over, the 1,300 at Snettisham on 24th May 1985 being something of a recent exception.

## JUNE

June can appear a particularly quiet month for migration, although movement can still be detected in the first week or so, particularly of Swallows and also, historically, of Turtle Doves. In addition, some county 'firsts' have appeared early in the month, for example, in north Norfolk at Cley, a Spotted Sandpiper appeared on 7th–8th June 1956 and in 1966 the county's second record of a Sooty Tern occurred between Scolt Head and Blakeney Point on 14th–19th. Breydon has been particularly favoured in June with a Terek Sandpiper on 1st in 1975, an American Golden Plover on the 8th a year later, with the county's first Franklin's Gull there on 30th June 1991.

Small passerine migrants are now extremely scarce, though this can be a good period to look out for the spring's very latest drift migrants. Any small migrants encountered this late in the season may well be rare, with Marsh and Icterine Warblers and Common Rosefinch being particularly prone to June occurrences, as was Britain's only Rock Sparrow, at Cley on 14th June 1981.

There is no 'clean break' between the spring and autumn migration, and from mid-month onwards female Spotted Redshanks return and it is not unusual to see them in Norfolk from the second week. Ruffs and Green Sandpipers arrive at the end of the month, occasionally a little earlier. Curlew totals increase from the last week and the first Lapwing flocks are forming on the marshes from both immigrant and locally bred birds. However, the party of 16 Wood Sandpipers at Salthouse on 28th June 1997 was more remarkable.

At sea, the first stirrings of autumn can be visible, with Manx Shearwaters possible offshore, particularly in windy conditions.

## JULY

Migration in July is dominated by waders, and in most years this month can produce the greatest variety, as the local Ringed Plovers, Oystercatchers and Redshanks are joined by incomers from Scandinavia and points further east. Coastal pools and estuaries fill up, firstly with moulting adult Dunlins, Spotted Redshanks, Greenshanks, Common, Green and Wood Sandpipers, Grey and Golden Plovers, Whimbrels, Knots and Bar-tailed Godwits, followed later in the month by the first pristine juveniles.

July has proved to be a good period for scarcer waders too, most notably a Pacific Golden Plover at Holme and Thornham in 1989 and a Red-necked Stint at Cley in 1992, both neatly illustrating the distances which many of our commoner Arctic-breeding waders have also travelled.

The first Arctic Skuas appear at this time, though their numbers vary from year to year, and at the month's end the first migrant passerines become visible, in the form of scattered juvenile Wheatears and Willow Warblers. A Pallid Swift over Burnham Overy fresh marshes on 25th July 1993 was another first record for Norfolk.

## AUGUST

Migration quickens significantly in August. The wader passage which has built up in July continues strongly and remains obvious for the whole month. The richest rare wader prize has also occurred at this time in the form of England's only Little Whimbrel, at Blakeney, Cley and Salthouse from 24th August to 2nd September 1985.

August, however, sees the first concerted passerine migration of the autumn. Coastal arrivals can take place after the second week of the month, and as August progresses, the chances increase of birds from Scandinavia and central Europe, typically Willow and Garden Warblers, Wheatears, Whinchats and Pied Flycatchers, but also Wrynecks, Red-backed Shrikes and Barred and Icterine Warblers.

Occasionally, spectacular 'fall' conditions occur. These events require very specific timings and conjunctions of weather systems. A typical scenario involves an overnight exodus of birds from Scandinavia in favourable migration conditions (clear skies or light cloud, light winds from between north-north-west and east-north-east and falling temperatures). These conditions arise within high-pressure areas which also generate an airflow from between north-east and south-east over the southern North Sea. This airflow can in turn be strengthened by areas of low pressure and associated fronts, rain and poor visibility encroaching from the south, thus drifting birds to the west of their preferred route, out over open water and grounding them at the first landfall. No two 'falls' are the same, but the largest arrivals will invariably involve a variation on the above scenario, typically with a low-pressure area centred over or just off the Dutch coast. The triggers for these arrivals are, however, complex, and smaller 'falls' of birds can also take place in other, less 'classic', conditions. For example, high pressure in the southern North Sea can prompt small arrivals, as can the north-westerly winds found to the rear of depressions leaving Britain towards the Continent. North-westerly winds, for example, have often been linked with occurrences of Barred Warblers. Much will depend on the track taken by the eastbound depressions. In years when they track to the north of the county, Norfolk will receive periods of unremitting westerly winds, with hardly a small bird to be seen, whereas if the low-pressure centres pass over Norfolk or to the south, the results can be dramatically different.

Such was the case on 25th August 1987, when a low-pressure area and its associated low cloud and rain moved up from the south and reached north Norfolk in the early morning, grounding thousands of birds. On that day 80 Garden Warblers were on Blakeney Point and 80 Pied Flycatchers were in Holkham Meals, with over 70 Wrynecks recorded in the county, 25 of which were on East Hills, Wells alone. This 'fall' was also notable for Greenish Warblers, always something of a late August speciality in north Norfolk, but on this memorable occasion at least seven were found.

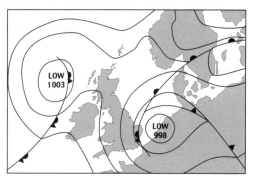

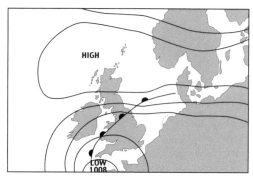

Figure 9. 25th August 1987. Classic conditions for a large 'fall' of migrants in autumn in the north-easterly winds to the rear of a low-pressure area in the southern North Sea.

Figure 10. 2nd September 1956. Good conditions for producing autumn migrants, with high pressure to the north and low pressure to the south, producing a long-range easterly airflow.

## SEPTEMBER

This is really the autumn's pivotal month, with the scale and nature of migration shaped almost entirely by the prevailing weather. Days shorten rapidly, and whilst the early part of the month can be balmy, the end of the month can have an entirely different feel.

Passerine migration can be at its most exciting during this month, with its 'mid-autumn' position leading to great species diversity and the prospect both of large 'falls' of birds and of unexpected vagrants. September 'falls' have always been erratic, those of 1956, 1958 and 1963 being notable, involving Scandinavian and eastern European birds such as Wrynecks, Barred Warblers, Red-breasted Flycatchers, Red-backed Shrikes, Bluethroats, Icterine Warblers and Ortolans amongst larger numbers of Willow and Garden Warblers, Redstarts, Pied Flycatchers, Wheatears and Whinchats.

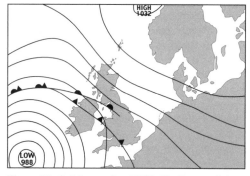

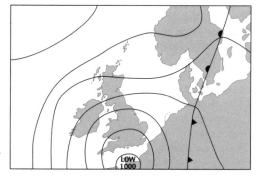

Figure 11. 3rd September 1958. Similar conditions to those in Fig. 10, but this time with a south-easterly orientation to the airflow.

Figure 12. 1st September 1963. A further instance of an influx of birds in the easterly winds to the north of an area of low pressure.

All these 'falls' were, however, truly overshadowed by the events of 3rd September 1965, when an avalanche of Redstarts and other migrants cascaded into East Anglia. The main focus of the 'fall' was in east Suffolk, but massive numbers of birds also reached Norfolk, with 17 Wrynecks at Holme, 25–30 Wrynecks and a dozen Bluethroats between Salthouse and Blakeney Point, over 1,000 Redstarts and 500 Pied Flycatchers being estimated at Winterton and in Yarmouth Cemeteries another 1,000 Redstarts, 600 Pied Flycatchers, 200 Wheatears, 120 Whinchats and 150 Garden Warblers.

A recent example of a late September 'fall' occurred on 29th September 1991, when rather slack north-easterly conditions near the centre of a low-pressure area yielded 50 Redstarts, 35 Blackcaps, five Siberian Stonechats, Red-throated Pipit, Wryneck and Icterine Warbler on Blakeney Point.

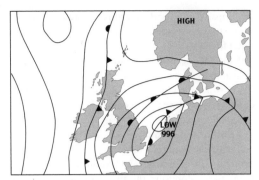

Figure 13. 3rd September 1965. Classic conditions, producing Norfolk's largest ever 'fall' of migrants. Note the similarity to Figure 9.

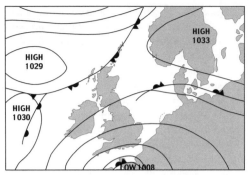

Figure 14. 18th September 1995. A large 'fall' of Redstarts in typical easterly conditions.

More recently, 18th September 1995 witnessed another very large arrival of birds, again predominantly Redstarts. Spot-counts at sites round the county revealed hundreds at each and the Norfolk total must have run into many thousands.

After the second week of the month, the 'migration window' starts to open further to the east and arrivals of European migrants can coincide with those of passerines, almost exclusively of birds in their first autumn, originating from Siberia. These are birds from the taiga zone whose true wintering ranges lie largely to the south-east, in China and south-east Asia, and which have therefore travelled in almost exactly the 'wrong' direction. This phe-

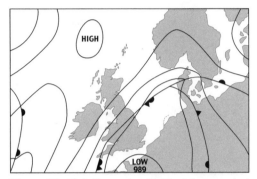

Figure 15. 29th September 1991. A large arrival of migrants in slack north-easterly conditions.

nomenon has become more obvious in Norfolk in recent years, though the observations of Gatke on Heligoland at the end of the 19th century confirm that these arrivals have occurred for longer than we may have recognised in this country.

The 'classic' Siberian species to appear after mid-month are Richard's Pipit and Yellow-browed Warbler. Arrivals of these two species can take place in clear anticyclonic weather and show characteristics of concerted, almost irruptive, behaviour rather than of accidental vagrancy. Yellow-browed Warbler was something of a Norfolk rarity until 1967, when nine appeared in the county. After that year, occurrences increased, with a new record of 18 set in 1975. From 1984, however, numbers surged dramatically, with over 40 in that year and perhaps as many as 70 in 1988.

Many theories have been advanced for this phenomenon, including the concept of 'reversed migration', where birds 'mistakenly' travel west instead of east. Equally, we may be witnessing more 'deliberate' attempts by populations of these species to establish more westerly wintering and breeding ranges, perhaps regaining territory occupied prior to the last Ice Age. Post-fledging dispersal from Siberian breeding ranges may, however, be taking place to all points of the compass, but the odds are severely stacked against those individuals heading north or south, where their unobserved flights will in any case soon be cut short by mountains, deserts or Arctic ice. Those travelling west which successfully break through to western Europe before winter 'closes the door' not only stand at least a slim chance of survival, but pass through areas such as Norfolk where birdwatchers may see them.

Other factors doubtless come into play as well. For example, the southern fringes of Siberia have long been noted for anomalies in the Earth's magnetic field, which may be responsible for some navigational interference, and recent severe environmental degradation in that area from forest clearance, acid rain and widespread forest fires may also be influencing the dispersal patterns of young birds, as has now been demonstrated elsewhere in the case of tits. German studies have shown that pollution-related structural changes in forests induce large-scale dispersals of Coal and Crested Tits and that such micro-evolutionary

51

change can be detected during spans of only a few generations. Whatever the reasons for the occurrences of these Siberian species, it is clear that European weather systems in mid-autumn merely influence the final stages of a process driven by much more fundamental forces.

Other Siberian species, such as Little Bunting and Siberian Stonechat, may also follow the same track in September, whilst increasing observer coverage is starting to reveal prizes which were formerly the almost exclusive preserve of the Northern Isles. These have so far included Lanceolated Warbler, Yellow-breasted Bunting and Siberian Thrush; others will doubtless follow in years to come.

Whilst early and mid-September passerine movements are dominated by chats, warblers and flycatchers bound for sub-Saharan Africa, the species profile changes markedly after mid-month. Goldcrests, Robins, *abietinus* Chiffchaffs and Blackcaps start to appear, along with the autumn's first thrushes. Initially these are continental Song Thrushes, but they are soon joined by the first Redwings, whilst Snow and Lapland Buntings traditionally make their first appearances at this time, alongside the first arrivals of Meadow Pipits, Skylarks and Chaffinches. Many of these will pass through to wintering grounds in south-west Europe and North Africa, but a great number will also winter in Britain.

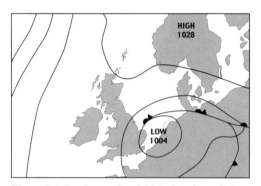

**Figure 16. 1st September 1994. Good conditions for passerine migrants, as shown here, can also be good for seabirds, in this case Long-tailed Skuas in the northerly winds to the rear of a low-pressure area in the southern North Sea.**

September is not just about passerines, however. It can also produce the most exciting events at sea. Again, each year is very different, but strong on-shore winds will produce passages of Gannets, Kittiwakes, Manx and Sooty Shearwaters and Great and Arctic Skuas along with small numbers of the more sought-after species such as Leach's Petrel, Mediterranean Shearwater, Sabine's Gull and Long-tailed Skua. This last species used to be rare in Norfolk, but increasing observer skill has shown it to be regular, sometimes even in significant numbers. This, however, varies wildly from year to year, depending on breeding success and the extent to which weather systems in the north-east Atlantic move birds into the North Sea. When such factors coincide, the results can be dramatic, most obviously so on 1st September 1994 when an unprecedented 126 Long-tailed Skuas passed Sheringham.

Movements of the commoner species can also be dramatic: 150 Sooty Shearwaters passed Cley on 3rd September 1986 and 250 Arctic Skuas were seen there on 5th September 1983. Skua movements are of particular interest in the west of the county, where numbers of birds have, over the years, been seen heading inland from the Wash. For example, 100 Arctic Skuas moved inland at the Nene mouth and passed over the former Wisbech Sewage Farm on 14th September 1980.

If August sees the peak of wader variety, September can see great influxes of some high Arctic-breeding species. In some years Little Stints and Curlew Sandpipers are few and far between, but in others the combination of high numbers of juveniles and particular weather circumstances can lead to near-invasions. Early September 1985 saw a depression linger over Scandinavia and the Baltic, the result being extremely high numbers of Curlew Sandpipers, over 1,300 being estimated across the county. Little Stints demonstrate similar pronounced arrivals, with over 100 having been seen at Cley in several Septembers, though there is little correlation between the arrivals of the two species. As the Wash and other estuarine areas attract wintering waders, coastal scrapes and pools come to be dominated progressively by returning wildfowl, notably Wigeon.

American waders can also feature at this time of year, recent examples including Baird's and Buff-breasted Sandpipers, but their arrivals are difficult to predict and link to particular weather systems, as Norfolk is unlikely to have been their first landfall. Indeed, the ranges of some species such as Pectoral Sandpiper and Long-billed Dowitcher extend so far west into Siberia, that an American origin cannot necessarily be assumed for these birds.

# OCTOBER

Of all months October is arguably the most dominated by the phenomenon of migration. The onset of winter becomes suddenly obvious, temperatures plunge over northern Europe and Russia, the days continue to shorten rapidly and the weather systems over western Europe become progressively more hazardous to migrant birds. In most years the lazy days and balmy nights of August seem far behind. A real sense of urgency dictates movements as birds are seized by the imperative need to reach suitable wintering areas as quickly as possible.

Small-bird migration swells noticeably as arrivals intending to winter in this country start to appear in force. This involves both nocturnal migrants, notably Redwings, Fieldfares, Blackbirds, Robins and Goldcrests, and diurnal migrants, chiefly Starlings, Skylarks and Chaffinches, though with significant numbers of Bramblings in some years. Much of the nocturnal arrival takes place unseen, evidenced only by a chorus of calls overhead. The coast is normally overflown at height, leaving little trace of the true scale of the movements. Nevertheless, adverse or 'fall' conditions can lead to impressive coastal arrivals. Such was the case in October 1990. On 18th, visibility was so poor that, throughout the county, thousands of thrushes cascaded vertically into coastal woods and hedges and even on to cliff-tops and shingle ridges as they suddenly discerned land beneath them. In Holkham Meals 24 Ring Ouzels were counted and other typical October migrants arriving included Long-eared Owls, Great Grey Shrikes, Woodcock, Black Redstarts, Blackcaps and Chiffchaffs, including both *abietinus* and the much rarer *tristis*.

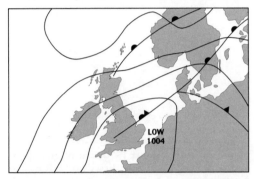

Figure 17. 18th October 1990. A large 'fall' in poor visibility associated with slack north-easterly winds and the northward passage of an occluded front. Note the similarities to Figure 14.

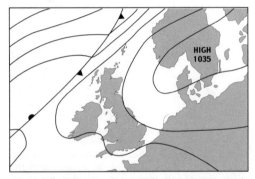

Figure 18. 16th October 1988. Arrivals in easterly conditions from a high-pressure area over southern Scandinavia.

Large arrivals of thrushes and associated migrants also occurred on 16th October 1988, though under rather different circumstances.

A remarkable event, the famous 'Robin rush', occurred in 'fall' conditions on 1st October 1952 and, at Cley alone, 2,000–3,000 were present, many in an exhausted state.

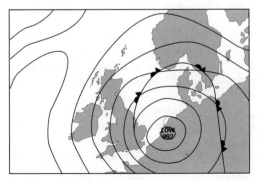

Figure 19. 1st October 1952. A massive arrival of Robins in typical 'fall' conditions. Note the similarity to Figures 9 & 13.

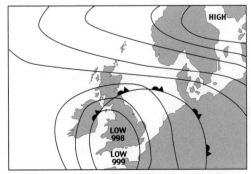

Figure 20. 12th October 1988. The largest ever arrival of Yellow-browed Warblers, typically in south-easterly winds.

Three years later, another sizeable fall of Robins took place, with 500 estimated on Blakeney Point on 23rd October 1955.

By the end of the month summer migrants are all but gone, typically only the odd Swallow and House Martin remaining. However, a Spotted Flycatcher was on Blakeney Point on 27th October 1991, a day more notable for an arrival of Long-eared Owls.

In recent years, October has become increasingly associated with further arrivals of small passerines from Siberia, continuing the phenomenon highlighted above for September. Arrivals of both Yellow-browed Warblers and Richard's Pipits can continue well into October, but peak numbers are concentrated into the first half of the month. The largest single count of Yellow-browed Warblers was one of at least 18 birds at Wells on 12th October 1988. On that day, the Dell's birch stands must have more closely resembled the outskirts of Irkutsk in Russia than a Norfolk wood!

As numbers of Yellow-browed Warblers decline during the month their place has come to be taken by their even more charismatic cousin, Pallas's Warbler. With a breeding range centred on southern Siberia, a distance of some 3,000 miles, this was a major British rarity before the 1970s but now it too occurs in irruption-like waves. The defining moment for this amazing change in occurrence was 15th October 1982, when Holkham Meals alone played host to at least ten of these tiny sprites.

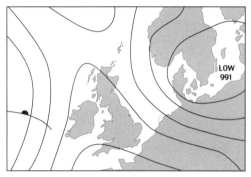 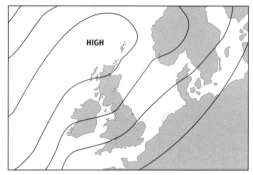

Figure 21. 15th October 1982. A large influx of Pallas's Warblers. An example of an arrival in the north-westerly winds to the rear of a departing low-pressure area.

Figure 22. 10th October 1975. The beginnings of a sustained easterly airflow directly from Russia to Norfolk.

Since then they have continued to come in force, peak years being 1994 with twelve and 1996 with a new record of 28. They are now very much an eagerly-awaited part of the October scene. This trend has been echoed, though to a much lesser degree, by other species whose breeding range also lies beyond the Urals, notably Radde's and Dusky Warblers, both of which are now almost routine in easterly conditions. Olive-backed Pipits, though less predictable, are also making a strong bid to become a regular rarity, with 14 county records since the first in 1975. Central Asia can also send small birds to our shores. October is the best time to search for such desirable birds as Desert and Pied Wheatears, Hume's Warbler and Isabelline Shrike.

More than any other year, 1975 opened eyes to the eastern possibilities of October. That year saw a sustained high pressure over Scandinavia and northern Russia and a long-range easterly airflow, along which came birds which were, at the time, truly astonishing – the county's first Olive-backed Pipit, the first multiple arrival of Pallas's Warblers, Black-throated Thrush, Isabelline Shrike and, best of all, Britain's first Yellow-browed Bunting, all in Holkham Meals between 10th and 22nd.

Since then, the county has continued to demonstrate its ability to host the rarest eastern birds, with Yarmouth claiming a Red-flanked Bluetail in 1995, and Wells hosting a Two-barred Greenish Warbler in 1996, hot on the heels of a Blyth's Pipit at Weybourne.

Norfolk is also well-placed to witness diurnal movements at this time of year, as great hordes of Lapwings, Starlings, Chaffinches and Skylarks, and sometimes thrushes too, enter the county from Russia and Scandinavia via Denmark, Germany and the Low Countries. These movements represent a westward extension of the great migrations documented for well over a century at sites such as Helgoland and Rossitten. In north Norfolk these movements can be witnessed from daybreak as flocks pass westwards, often into a westerly breeze. East of Sheringham, however, a stream of birds becomes progressively more obvious to the south-east and then the south as one nears the Suffolk border. In the last century, the north-west corner of the county was noted to be particularly rewarding for documenting these movements as birds turned either south along the shore of the Wash or struck out towards Lincolnshire. This phenomenon occurs today. In October 1996, for example, 120,000 Starlings passed through this area on 11th, nearly 6,000 Chaffinches on 24th and 60,000 Redwings on 29th, with 30,000 Fieldfares on the following day.

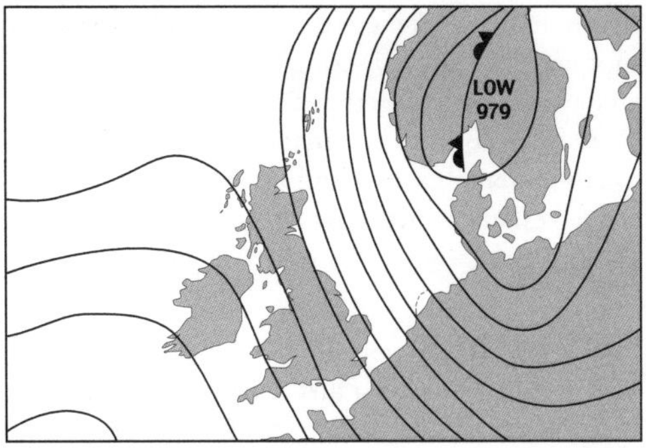

In the past these passages used to be notable for the numbers of Hooded Crows, but the only

**Figure 23. 29th October 1996. A day of particularly strong diurnal passage of Redwings in north-westerly winds behind a low-pressure area.**

significant count since the 1960s involved 100 through Snettisham in October 1972.

The month is often characterised by the erratic appearances of certain irruptive species which may be almost entirely absent for a number of years before suddenly appearing in force. These irruptions are driven by food shortages, and Norfolk's geography makes it either a first port of call or a final destination for many such species fleeing the Continent. 'Classic' species in this category include Mealy Redpoll, Waxwing, Rough-legged Buzzard and Jay; arrivals of any of these often first becoming evident during this month. In some years, tits and Great Spotted Woodpeckers can also be involved.

October 1983 will long be remembered for its Jays, with perhaps over 1,500 passing through the county, the highest single counts being 134 west at Cley on 13th and 138 south at Snettisham on 19th. Most of these merely passed through and enormous numbers later gathered in south-west England. Influxes of Rough-legged Buzzards occurred in 1966, 1973, 1974, 1978, 1985 and 1994, and in each of these years birds lingered in the county throughout the winter. An exceptional total of nine was present together at Cley on 26th October 1973. The widespread arrivals of Mealy and Arctic Redpolls which took place in the winters of 1990–91, and more fully in 1995–96, were both presaged by small coastal arrivals in October.

Waxwings are always exciting, and though invasions may sometimes not occur until late in the winter, they are often underway in October. In 1965 there was a particularly strong early influx, with Beeston, Wiveton and Roydon Common each hosting flocks of 300 at the end of the month.

Tit movements occurred on an unusual scale in October 1957. Coastal areas witnessed large arrivals and westerly movements of Blue Tits, with the most spectacular numbers occurring in west Norfolk. On 13th October an amazing 600 moved south at Hunstanton in an hour and a half, while 300 per hour were passing Snettisham, with others occupying the fields and ditches behind the sea-walls. Others were noted from drifters off Yarmouth and aboard the Smith's Knoll and Haisboro' light-vessels. The year 1996 saw an influx of continental Coal Tits, 42 of which were noted passing through Hunstanton during October. Despite its unfavourable position for receiving American landbirds, Norfolk has not missed out entirely on this phenomenon, thanks to Britain's (so far) only Red-breasted Nuthatch, discovered in Holkham Meals in October 1989. The route by which it contrived to reach Norfolk will never be clear, but its appearance is nonetheless astonishing.

Activity also remains obvious at sea, with major arrivals of wildfowl taking place during the month. Spectacular coastal passages occur of Dark-bellied Brent Geese from Arctic Siberia, along with a wide variety of other wildfowl (notably Common Scoter), grebes and divers, whilst strong onshore winds can still produce strong sea movements, particularly of auks, Kittiwakes and Fulmars. In years of high breeding success, Pomarine Skuas can also be obvious, with large numbers of juveniles sometimes close inshore. The years 1970, 1985 and 1997 witnessed such events, with over 100 in a day being seen off the north coast in each of those years.

Little Auks have also become a feature of October, though not necessarily associated with strong onshore winds. Incursions of cold northerly air can precipitate inshore processions of these tiny high Arctic seabirds, whirring past in the breakers or tagging onto passing groups of waders and Starlings. These birds are often in a weakened state, frequently being found just inland in coastal pools or ditches. Their appearance may be caused by conditions to the north, where their ability to feed is hampered by rough weather. Unlike the larger auks they are not deep divers and in sustained rough conditions, when their prey dives to greater depths, they are unable to reach it.

In extreme gale conditions even inland areas can witness seabirds, as evidenced by the two juvenile Sabine's Gulls which took up residence at Dickleburgh after the infamous 'hurricane' of early October 1987.

## NOVEMBER

This month witnesses a further descent into winter, though the first half sees a continuation of the events of October. Visible passage continues and thrush immigration can be particularly heavy. Some 30,000 Skylarks passed over Cley, for example, on 1st November 1959, while the 173 Hooded Crows at Wells on 9th November 1955 are sadly a taste of days gone by. The 5th November 1961 witnessed an enormous arrival of Blackbirds. At that time, drifter crews fishing in the Smith's Knoll area reported hundreds of Blackbirds around their vessels at night, whilst 1,000 per hour were arriving at Scolt Head, 3,000 were at Holme and large numbers were reported well inland. Woodcock can be prominent in late autumn arrivals, often coinciding with these large Blackbird movements.

Pallas's Warblers can also be as much a feature of November as they are of October. In the record 1996 influx already referred to, 21 arrived in a concerted wave between 11th and 15th November. Dusky Warbler and Desert Wheatear are the other two Asian rarities which show a high incidence of November occurrences. Of the 30 county records of the former to the end of 1996, half have been in this month. The only other warblers present at this time will be sparse numbers of Chiffchaffs and Blackcaps, many of which will be intent on overwintering in the county or elsewhere in Britain. The very last Swallows and House Martins will now be seen, but they are worth examining closely for, this late in the season, there is a high chance of a Red-rumped Swallow.

A further remarkable Saharan dust-fall took place in early November 1994, producing a Nightingale on Blakeney Point and reports of Swifts at eight coastal localities.

Any irruptions which commenced in October may now gather even greater force. The Mealy Redpoll invasion of 1995 swelled during November, producing large flocks throughout the county, initially at the coast, but subsequently at inland wintering sites, for example 90 at Holt Lowes and 50 at Heigham Sound. Similarly, the 1965 Waxwing invasion continued apace, with further arrivals of small parties augmenting the large flocks already present.

At sea, arrivals of wildfowl can still be heavy, whilst Pomarine Skuas can be readily visible offshore in some years and Little Auk extravaganzas are as likely in November as they are in the preceding month.

Although November produces far fewer surprises than the peak period of autumn migration, final mention should not be made of the month without recalling the bizarre inland occurrence of an American Black-and-white Warbler in Trowse, Norwich in 1996.

## DECEMBER

December is generally regarded as the year's quietest month, the shortness of the days and the increasing preoccupation of birdwatchers with Christmas also ensuring that little migration gets recorded. Nevertheless, keeping an ear open to the skies can still reveal significant nocturnal thrush activity. Both Redwings and Fieldfares are notable for their erratic wintering habits, showing great annual variations in the timing and strength of their arrivals and little site fidelity, either during a winter or from one year to the next. In some years they can be few and far between, whilst in other years they can seemingly be everywhere. December 1995 saw very large numbers of Fieldfares entering the county, alongside the Waxwing and Redpoll arrivals of that year. Counts included 7,000 at Flitcham and, by Christmas, many had penetrated into urban areas, roaming parks and gardens for berries.

Rarities at this time of year are few, though a Pacific Golden Plover spent four days at Cley and Blakeney in December 1991, and the swarms of Dark-bellied Brent Geese may harbour a Pale-bellied Brent, a Black Brant or, exceptionally, a Red-breasted Goose. The discovery of the county's first Black-and-white Warbler at How Hill 3rd December 1985 certainly added excitement to the winter that year.

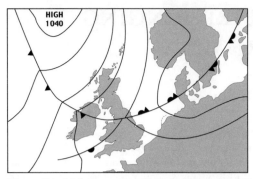

**Figure 24. 26th December 1962. An incursion of long-range polar air precipitating cold-weather movements into the county.**

Early cold weather can prompt the types of movement described earlier in this chapter. This occurred most notably in 1962, when plunging temperatures at Christmas were the forerunner of one of the most prolonged periods of severe weather ever witnessed in the county. Severe frosts and biting winds set in which were to continue for ten weeks. Large numbers of wildfowl reached Norfolk under these conditions, particularly 'sawbills' and other diving duck. That December also saw large numbers of Redwings, Fieldfares and Blackbirds entering urban areas and Redwings even foraged beneath the stalls in Norwich fruit market.

Even Christmas Day has produced its ornithological surprises, with a Siberian Thrush in the Yarmouth Cemeteries in 1977, and at Walcott in 1991 a Laughing Gull added to the festivities. By contrast, a late Garganey was at Ranworth in mid-December 1930, whilst the prize for 'most unseasonal bird' must be taken by the Corncrake seen at Cley on the last day of December 1962!

# A HISTORY OF BIRD RINGING
# IN NORFOLK

*by*
## Moss Taylor

Exactly one hundred years before the publication of this book, in 1899, the Danish ornithologist H. C. Mortensen ringed 164 Starlings with rings bearing both a number and an address. Thus bird ringing, as we know it today, was born. During the following decade, other private and national ringing schemes began, although it was not until 1909 that the first official British ringing scheme was founded. Initially, two independent sets of rings were produced – one by Harry Witherby in connection with the journal *British Birds* and the other by A. Landsborough Thomson through Aberdeen University. However, the latter came to an end during the First World War, while control of Harry Witherby's scheme was transferred to the BTO in 1937 (Mead 1974).

The earliest record of a recovery in Norfolk of a marked bird from abroad was in 1908 – a Hooded Crow shot at Yarmouth on 8th November carried a note around its neck, written in Danish, that it had been caught and marked on a ship off the coast of Denmark on 23rd October. The first Norfolk recovery of a foreign-ringed bird was of a Black-headed Gull marked as a nestling at Rossitten, Germany on 4th July 1912 found at Terrington in October. More, from other German breeding colonies, were to follow over the next couple of winters. In the east of the county a Sandwich Tern found dead at Yarmouth in 1917 had been ringed five years earlier as a chick in The Netherlands, while a Snipe carrying ring number E978 shot at South Walsham in 1913 had been ringed as a chick on 2nd May 1912 at Sandy, Bedfordshire – one of the first recoveries in Norfolk of a bird marked under the British national ringing scheme. One of the earliest passerine recoveries concerned a Redwing ringed on Helgoland, Germany on 14th April 1924 and found in Norwich on 3rd February 1927 by Dr Sydney Long, founder of the Norfolk Naturalists Trust.

In those early days the vast majority of birds were ringed as nestlings and the colonies of terns and Black-headed Gulls on the north Norfolk coast attracted the attention of the county's first ringers. Large numbers of Sandwich Tern chicks were ringed at Scolt Head, Blakeney Point and Salthouse from 1925 to the outbreak of the Second World War in 1939, and over 70 were recovered in West Africa, providing the first proof of the species' winter quarters; others were reported from Iberia during their journey south in autumn. Of three ringed at Blakeney Point on 30th June 1928, two were recovered in Angola the following January and another in the Ivory Coast three years later. The first foreign recovery of a Norfolk-ringed Black-headed Gull was a chick ringed at Scolt Head in 1925 and found in Portugal three years later. Ringing the larger raptor nestlings also appealed to these early ringers and a Montagu's Harrier marked in the nest at Waxham in 1927 was reported the following May in Northamptonshire, while a Short-eared Owl nestling ringed in the Broads on 13th July 1928 had flown north to be found at Roughton in late August. The annual report of the Wild Birds' Protection Committee of the Norfolk & Norwich Naturalists' Society and later the Norfolk Naturalists Trust, known as *Wild Bird Protection in Norfolk* and the forerunner of the annual *Norfolk Bird Report*, first mentioned ringing in 1930 under the entry for Red-backed Shrike: 'As usual, a pair nested on the Cley marsh, and the five young were ringed on June 27th'.

The first site in Norfolk at which birds were trapped and ringed on a regular basis appears to have been the Little Eye at Salthouse, where Ronald Garnett of Kelling established Norfolk's first coastal ringing station, which was in operation between 1933 and 1937. Using just simple traps he was able to ring over 450 birds of 31 species, including four Pied Flycatchers, Grasshopper Warbler, Black Redstart and four Bluethroats. His efforts were further rewarded with the recovery of a Starling in Denmark and a Meadow Pipit in Portugal. Writing in the *Norfolk Bird Report 1957*, Richard Richardson described Ronald Garnett as 'a pioneer in this branch of ornithology'. The same ringer was also responsible for one of the first foreign recoveries of a Cuckoo – a nestling ringed at Kelling in June 1931 and found in France three months later.

Following the end of hostilities in 1945, several years were to pass before ringing recommenced in the county. As before nestlings, and in particular young terns, were the main targets of the few ringers operating in Norfolk. At the forefront was the local Yarmouth naturalist Robin Harrison who started to ring

Lapwing and Redshank chicks on the Breydon Marshes from 1951, and who between 1952 and 1965 organised the ringing of 3,500 Sandwich and Common Terns chicks at the breeding colony on Scroby Sands, which lay 5km east of Yarmouth. Unfortunately, the size of this sandbank was considerably diminished by storms during the winter of 1965–66 and it was consequently submerged long before each high tide. As a result the terns did not breed again there for several years and ringing on Scroby ceased.

The end of the Second World War also heralded the arrival in Norfolk of one of the county's most influential birdwatchers of the 20th century, Richard Richardson, in whose memory this book is dedicated. Initially living at Aylsham, he moved to Cley in 1949 where he lived until his untimely death in 1977. The following account of Richard's involvement in the Cley Bird Observatory and the establishment of Holme Bird Observatory are largely based on notes provided by Peter and Margaret Clarke to whom I am most grateful.

Cley Bird Observatory was established by Richard Richardson in autumn 1949, with sponsorship from the Norfolk Naturalists' Trust. Under his direction the Heligoland-type traps were erected along the south wall of a line of wartime gun emplacements on the beach at Cley. Ringing records and a small reference library were kept on the top floor of the adjacent Coastguard's lookout. During this first year 402 birds of 45 species were ringed, including the first Purple Sandpiper to be ringed in the British Isles. The following year saw the BTO officially recognise Cley as the ninth British bird observatory and amongst the birds ringed in that year were 143 Snow Buntings. Forty years were to pass before similar numbers were trapped again in Norfolk in a single year! In 1951 another full-sized Heligoland trap was built in the blackthorn thicket at Walsey Hills, about half a mile inland, at the edge of the great marshlands between Cley and Salthouse. At this time the majority of birds were caught in traps or clap nets, or else were ringed as nestlings. The observatory 'area', however, appears to have included most of Norfolk, with Black Redstarts ringed in the nest at Yarmouth included in the annual ringing total!

One day in October 1951 will long remain in Peter Clarke's memory:

> Richard alerted me to a tremendous 'fall' of Robins at Cley. There were Robins everywhere along the coast, hopping in their dozens amongst the old gun emplacements. Kick any small clump of cover and half a dozen Robins would spill out. We were ringing them as fast as we could remove them from the catching boxes of the Heligoland traps. Over one hundred Robins were ringed in half a day (it would have been more, but our ring stocks ran out!).

A 'fall' of Robins in October 1998 was equally impressive and is described at the end of the chapter.

Unfortunately, disaster struck in 1953 when the great east coast gale and terrible sea-surge on 31st January demolished the gun emplacements and undermined the lookout tower. The Heligoland traps were buried under eight feet of shingle, while the trap in Walsey Hills was choked with marsh debris and floating baulks of timber delivered by the surge. Richard must have been heartbroken, after all his hard work in establishing the observatory, and his report in the first *Norfolk Bird Report* in 1953 reads:

> The elements combined to make 1953 a disastrous year for the observatory at Cley. The spectacle on the morning of 1st February, after the site had been pounded for hours by mountainous seas, was devastating to say the least. The solid office building remained apparently undamaged and escaped flooding, but the coastal gun-emplacements which sheltered the traps were reduced to great slabs of masonry scattered over the adjacent arable field. The beach had advanced thirty yards inland and all the bushes round the observatory were buried under five feet of shingle. There was no sign of the three 'Heligoland' traps, although a couple of catching boxes and other fragments were picked up in Cley village a mile away.

Undeterred, Richard and his band of assistants soon had the trap in Walsey Hills back in working order, and it now became the centre of activity. The following year the National Trust gave permission for two small Heligoland-type traps and a ringing/accommodation hut to be erected at The Hood on Blakeney Point, which at the time, was without equal in mainland Britain for migratory bird 'falls'. Ringing operations were also carried out at a vast communal roost in rhododendrons on Salthouse Heath where over

600 Blackbirds and finches were netted by torchlight one winter. Richard's account of progress at the observatory in the *Norfolk Bird Report 1954* also includes the following:

> The Warden of Cley marsh, W. F. Bishop, caught several species in his duck-trap, including a pair of scaup. His son Bernard also caught over fifty greenfinches in a small trap in the garden of Watchers Cottage, and all these were ringed. A few of the voluntary helpers at the observatory with experience of ringing, also carried out work in their own localities and Peter Clarke ringed forty-five nightingales and thirty-six red-backed shrikes, a remarkable achievement.

The year 1956, however, was the turning point for ringers in Britain, with the introduction from Japan of the mist-net. This method of catching birds totally revolutionised ringing and had an enormous impact on ringers' ability to catch passerines, especially at sites such as Cley, where many migrants passed through in spring and autumn. It was also the year in which Collared Doves were ringed for the first time in Britain – two nestlings ringed by Andrew Church at Overstrand. Yet again, disaster struck the observatory in 1957, when a severe gale in November lifted the observatory building at The Hood and reduced it to matchwood and the traps were destroyed. As a result the ringing site there was eventually abandoned. Mist-nets really came into their own on Blakeney Point during the great 'fall' of drift migrants in early September 1958 and Peter Clarke can well remember the Rustic Bunting that dropped out of the sky and into a mist-net that had been erected in the 'plantation'. Almost forty years were to pass before the next one was ringed in the county. The following year saw a record 2,846 birds of 102 species ringed by the observatory, due both to the effectiveness of mist-nets and the presence of Barry Spence as assistant warden for fifteen weeks. He was later to become the long-serving warden of Spurn Bird Observatory. It was Barry who, on a return visit to Cley in October 1961, trapped the county's first Radde's Warbler on Blakeney Point, which at the time was only the second British record. It was taken back to Cley and as it could not be identified with certainty it was kept overnight in Richard Richardson's outdoor aviary until confirmation of its identity could be made by Ken Williamson the following day, who travelled overnight from Scotland! (Richardson *et al.* 1962). It remains the only one to have been ringed in the county.

Sadly, the observatory closed at the end of 1963 with the retirement, as Honorary Warden, of Richard Richardson. During the 14 years of its existence 17,544 birds of 154 species had been ringed and, in addition to the Radde's Warbler, the observatory had added three other species to the county list – Semipalmated Sandpiper, Melodious Warbler (still the only two county records) and Subalpine Warbler (the first three records for the county). Richard and the observatory were also responsible for publishing in 1962 the *Checklist of the Birds of Cley*. The assistance and encouragement given by Richard to all visiting birdwatchers, particularly younger people, cannot be overemphasised. Apart from 3,000 birds ringed at Blakeney Point by Michael Cant in 1966–69 and 4,000 birds at Walsey Hills by Jack Reynolds under the auspices of the Norfolk Ornithologists' Association in 1970–72, the Cley area has not seen any regular ringing since the closure of the observatory.

The demise, however, of one bird observatory in the county coincided with the establishment of another, at Holme in September 1962. This was a ringing site previously used by members of the Cambridge Bird Club in the late 1950s. Amongst the most enthusiastic of the CBC members to ring at Holme was Clive Minton. At times a decrepit caravan near the Firs was used as overnight accommodation and the nets were up at dawn. One day, in spring, a Bluethroat appeared in the net and a delighted Clive ignored the other birds to take out the best one, exclaiming 'It's a male Bluethroat – and red-spotted'. The other ringers at the net realised he was telling the truth, but unfortunately the bird got out of the bag, flew down the net for all to see and was not seen again!

Founded in 1962 by Richard's great friend and long-time assistant, Peter Clarke, Holme Bird Observatory was to take over where Cley left off. During the 1960s and 1970s the observatory's main task was the daily recording of migration and the ringing of birds in the observatory area – an average of 1,350 birds was ringed annually. However, by the 1980s, after Holme had left the BTO's Bird Observatory network, Peter Clarke, the Director and Warden, had changed the emphasis to the servicing of the many visitors to the area. Amongst Peter's many ringing memories was a day in October 1963 when during a good 'fall' of warblers and Goldcrests, helpers were bringing in bagged birds from the traps for him to ring. Imagine his surprise and thrill when, on removing a small bird from one of the bags, it dawned on him that he was holding a Pallas's Warbler, only the third Norfolk record. One week earlier he had ringed a Yellow-browed Warbler, only the second county record in 45 years.

Elsewhere in the county, other ringers in the 1950s and 1960s were concentrating their efforts on wildfowl. A duck decoy at How Hill was run by Michael and Christopher Boardman between 1951 and 1963, while Rob Berry ringed wildfowl at Dersingham Decoy from 1963 to 1969 before moving on to become warden at the Snettisham Gravel Pits Reserve, which was later taken over by the RSPB. The numbers ringed at Dersingham were particularly impressive, peaking in 1967 with 977 Mallard, 479 Teal and two Garganey, one of which was recovered in Turkey.

Waders were also not neglected in these early days and ringing visits to Wisbech Sewage Farm by members of the Cambridge Bird Club were a regular feature of the mid- to late 1950s. Many of the ringers from those early times are still actively involved in ornithology today – Clive Minton, Chris Mead, David Ballance, Tony Vine, Robin Cox and John Bruhn, to name but a few. Of the many stories that are told two merit repeating. First, the discovery of only the second record of White-rumped Sandpiper for the county, trapped unknowingly with four Dunlins in November 1955 at Wisbech Sewage Farm, and secondly, the night that the cottage on the river bank used by the ringers was raided by the police. Amongst the 8–10 ringers present asleep on the floor, prior to a pre-dawn start, were Clive Minton, Chris Mead and John Bruhn who were rudely awoken in the middle of the night by the rapidly-approaching sound of a police bell clanging away. The police, who were searching for the Great Train Robbers, had been given a tip-off that some suspicious-looking characters were sleeping at the cottage. Names and addresses of all those present were taken and as John Bruhn says 'there were a few raised eyebrows, as we were a mixed-looking company in sleeping bags on the floor'! Chris Mead's abiding memory of that night is Richard Wilson, who had arrived late and was sleeping in his car, breaking away from police custody and running towards the cottage shouting 'Tell them I'm with you Clive!' We had earlier been asked whether the person in the car was anything to do with us which we had all denied! As a direct result of wader ringing at Wisbech Sewage Farm the first seeds began to germinate which were to lead to the eventual formation of the Wash Wader Ringing Group. Allison Kew takes up the story:

> In 1959 relatively little was known about the waders using the Wash, at that time only 100 Knot and 12 Grey Plover had ever been ringed in Britain. Certainly ideas such as turnover, site fidelity, migration patterns, timing of movement, moult strategies and survival rates – knowledge of which we take for granted now – was a faint gleam in a few scientists' eyes. The problem was how to catch these wild and spectacular birds within the vast and untamed expanse of the Wash. On 18th August 1959 a group of ringers brought together by Clive Minton's boundless enthusiasm made the first-ever catch of waders using a rocket net on a field at Terrington and thus inaugurated the Wash Wader Ringing Group (WWRG). This was the start of a programme of monitoring waders on the Wash which has continued to the present day and has seen the ringing of more than 235,000 wading birds on the Wash.
>
> Catching know-how developed rapidly leading to the introduction of the cannon-net in a form which has changed relatively little in the past 30 years and, in 1967, the first catching (of Oystercatchers) on a beach. Terms such as jiggler, dropper, twinkle, grotting and chocolate block were introduced into ringing terminology and are still going strong. On a more serious note the early years of catching were critical for the Wash. Crucial findings about the extremely high levels of turnover led to dramatic reassessments of the number of waders using the Wash. Site fidelity of some species during winter, but also during the spring and autumn migration periods was soon noted. This improved knowledge was to prove an important factor in the recognition of the Wash as one of the most important estuaries for wading birds.
>
> Throughout its history WWRG has recognised that the Wash is only part of the wader story. As a result cannon-netting technology first developed on the Wash has been spread throughout the world – without the efforts of the many hundreds of ringers (both amateur and professional) active on other sites we would know very much less about waders using the Wash. The development of large-scale wader ringing along the Western Palearctic flyway has frequently involved sharing of expertise acquired on the Wash. In more recent times interest has spread even wider, and 1998 alone has seen Group members assisting in far-

away places such as Australia, Argentina, Brazil and the USA as well as estuaries across the British Isles.

Today the WWRG still has many features of the Group first formed in 1959. Its membership of 150 people ranges from the professional ornithologist and conservationist to the pure amateur, all of whom have one thing in common – a deep passion for waders using the Wash. Also continued is the tradition of welcoming anyone who wants to participate in the Group's activities.

Long-term monitoring based on regular catching for nearly 40 years remains central to the Group's work. Issues such as the recent large-scale declines in Oystercatchers and the major Redshank mortality of 1991 are more clearly understood through the presence of ringed birds – 10% of the most common species have rings. Work is now generally more focused towards catching samples of the 11 study species at a range of sites throughout the year.

No one knows precisely what the future will bring to the Wash and its waders, but WWRG will continue to provide a better understanding of the waders using the Wash so that decisions relating to the estuary can be taken in the light of factual information.

One of the most memorable catches made by the WWRG was at Gore Point, Holme on 15th October 1989. The ringing team rose at 03:00hrs to set nets on the outer spit and to enable them to be back in the camouflaged hide two hours before the dawn high tide. It was a bright moonlit night and in the first light, silhouetted against the full moon, great swirling flocks of Knots began to arrive. As the tide rose, pushing the birds ever closer, and as it became fully light, it was apparent this was an exceptionally large flock of Knots. By high tide there was a carpet of birds, nearly all Knots, stretching from the outer end of the spit to within a few metres of the hide. Counts indicated that 90,000 Knots were present and it later transpired that they completely covered an area 170m by 10m. This represented about a quarter of the Canadian/Greenland population from which they would have originated! After the net had been fired it initially appeared that only a few hundred had been caught but the birds were so tightly packed that it soon became apparent that a large catch had been made. In fact, once the birds had been processed and released it was found that the catch consisted of 1,478 Knots and just two Oystercatchers. The resulting data and subsequent recoveries added substantially to the understanding of the importance to the Wash for Knot (Ireland 1990).

However, not all attempts at catching waders were so successful as Chris Mead recalls:

> Before radios could be used, as dusk fell, it was necessary to use a complicated system of signalling involving the lights from the Land Rover which was deployed to gently move the birds under the net. It got darker and darker, and everyone thought that it was time to pack up. Still the Land Rover remained on the field and there was no way for the people at the firing point to communicate with it. Then the signal came to fire the right hand net – really spectacular in the darkness and very worrying for the Land Rover's occupants as it almost caught them. They had decided to give up and were simply switching on the side-lights! On another occasion an air/sea rescue helicopter had been deployed to search for a drifting dinghy. Seeing, from above, birdwatchers apparently looking out to sea it landed in the cannon-net catching area! All potentially live wires were unplugged and we prayed that the induced currents from the Whirlwind would not do anything to the net. We had a pleasant conversation with the crew and the helicopter took off – by then the tide had turned and we caught nothing.

During the 1960s Sand Martins were the subject of a most successful nationwide, co-ordinated ringing effort. One of the leading Sand Martin ringers in Norfolk was John Bruhn who provides an account of that time in the history of ringing in the county:

> The species was common, and encouraging results from ringing at west Norfolk colonies soon led to systematic coverage of large sections of the county, to include locating and counting breeding sites and roosts year on year.
>
> Colonies were found right across the county, even on the outskirts of Norwich. Freshly excavated sand banks were plentiful when birds returned in April, and they were readily occupied. Typical colonies would hold from 200 to more than 500 pairs, although a notable

one at Sparham numbered in excess of 1,500 pairs in the mid-1960s. Some sites were more unusual: in 1966 a few pairs used blocked drainage holes under the Lowestoft road at Trowse, for example.

Retrapping at colonies showed that adult birds sometimes visited closely-neighbouring sites during the day, less so towards nightfall, but adults' fidelity to breeding sites appeared to be maintained from year to year. Juveniles were clearly inclined to wander, and quick long-distance movements of recently-fledged young between Norfolk colonies and sites in Oxfordshire, Cheshire, Shropshire and Yorkshire made the degree of site fidelity difficult to judge, although many returned in later years near to their original ringing site.

Autumn recaptures suggested a southerly movement on a narrow front to Kent or Sussex roosts, then to the French Biscay coast, although there were unusual early autumn recoveries in Belgium and the Rhone Valley. Autumn ringing outside the county at a very large roost at March, Cambridgeshire presented a parallel picture, birds caught there having previously been ringed at colonies from Yorkshire and Lancashire north as far as the Moray Firth, and provided subsequent recoveries in Sussex and western France.

Recaptures on spring migration were fewer, but such as there were indicated movement north on a broader front, stretching from Guipuzcoa in northern Spain to Algeria and Tunisia in the east, with the occasional bird overshooting to Belgium or The Netherlands before turning back to Norfolk.

Locating an African wintering area was to follow in 1969. A Caistor St Edmunds' bird was among a number of British Sand Martins handled by French ringers in Senegal early that April, and a July control at Sparham had previously been ringed in Senegal. Catches there in February 1971 contained four more from Norfolk, effectively confirming that at least some of our breeding population were wintering in that part of West Africa. Ringing in Norfolk has continued, producing recoveries in Spain and Morocco to add detail to the picture while movements between Norfolk and a mid-Wales roost demonstrate the extent to which juvenile birds disperse after fledging.

Another target of the Cambridge Bird Club were the Grey Heron nestlings at two sites at Denver and Islington in west Norfolk. At the latter site the trees were enormous – ashes up to 25m high – and many held from five to six nests each. Chris Mead's job was to haul the lighter members of the team up into the trees! The team included Tony Vine who had been studying the species since the 1940s, while in east and central Norfolk the irrepressible John Bruhn co-ordinated the effort. Once again, he kindly provided the following account:

Between 1965 and 1978 regular visits to a number of heronries in the Bure and Yare Valleys and elsewhere in the Broads resulted in 1,072 pulli being ringed, the years 1969 and 1970 providing nearly 400 of these. Nests in the Broadland carrs were usually built in alders, sometimes a mere 15 feet above ground, though more usually 25–30 feet up.

Taller ivy-covered pines at Wickhampton were also favoured, one holding four nests in 1970, and occasional nests were found in oak and silver birch. Though any new nest seemed perilously fragile, its careful construction ensured its survival for the season, as did the repairs made to older nests that appeared quite unstable by virtue of their size.

Typically by early May only a few pulli would be large enough to ring, and the earliest visit each year was more usefully spent re-mapping the heronry after the winter gales, recording clutch size and planning the date for a follow-up visit. It was suggested at the time that young in other parts of the country were more advanced and were of a ringable size by mid-April.

Normal clutch size was 3–4. We found three clutches of five eggs, but there was no evidence that more than three chicks fledged from any of them. Statistics collected over these years point to a fledging rate of between 1.8 and 2.7 young per occupied nest depending on the season.

Regurgitation provided evidence of food brought to the young – mostly eels and a wide variety of freshwater fish including sticklebacks, also frogs and young Mallard. Goldfish were taken in the Wroxham and Ranworth areas, while moles and water voles were found in nests at Wickhampton.

First-year recoveries indicated a random dispersal to the north, west and south often no further than the boundaries of East Anglia, but many individuals moved further, to Yorkshire, the Lakes, Worcestershire and Dorset, with others found in The Netherlands and northern France. Movements to Cheshire by 2nd August and Sussex by 30th were particularly quick. But pride of place must go to one ringed near Ranworth on 25th May 1968 and found dead just north of Gibraltar on 24th September the same year.

The fate met by most of the birds recovered will remain a mystery. A few were shot at trout farms, perhaps legally, others hit wires or swallowed a fish hook or a sponge. The remainder were 'found dead', though we strongly suspect that too many of these were intentionally killed.

Inevitably the highest casualty rate was among first-year birds. Thereafter chances of survival improved, and there is ample evidence to suggest that birds tended to return to their natal area on reaching breeding maturity. Of three birds that survived 14 or more years, two were found dead during the breeding season, in April and June, within a few miles of the heronry where they were originally ringed.

The 1970s saw an upsurge in interest in ringing at migration sites around the Norfolk coast. Mary Unsworth, a retired teacher from Essex, spent her spring and autumn holidays netting in the small garden of a holiday cottage directly behind the sand dunes at Happisburgh. In just a few weeks each year she caught many hundreds of migrants passing through the garden – especially hirundines and goldfinches in spring, and warblers and Goldcrests in autumn. She was particularly excited by the two Pallas's Warblers she caught in successive Octobers. The vast majority of the birds she ringed were on active migration and many produced rapid recoveries as they continued on their journey around the east coast of England. Nearby at the Bacton Gas Terminal, Ray Gribble found that the powerful lights at the site attracted many migrants to a long line of bushes on the periphery, although the bushes were unfortunately grubbed up just as their potential as a ringing site was being fully realised. Further south, the garden of Shangri-La, a holiday chalet at Waxham, became the ringing site for David Frost (who was to die tragically young while ringing seabirds as assistant warden of Fair Isle Bird Observatory) and Ted Williams, who netted Norfolk's first Sardinian Warbler there in April 1973. The site has continued to be used in recent years by John Houghton. Also in east Norfolk, John Goldsmith was ringing at Winterton North Dunes.

Meanwhile in north Norfolk, Jack Reynolds ringed on the NOA Reserve at Dodman's Farm, Titchwell from 1973 to 1981. During this period over 15,000 birds were ringed, including no less than 369 Long-tailed Tits in 1974 and an Arctic Warbler in 1975 on the extraordinary date of 5th July. Also in 1972 the writer started ringing at Dead Man's Wood, Sheringham. From the outset he was assisted by David Sadler, who as a pupil at Gresham's School had been lowered on a rope over the cliffs at Weybourne by Dick Bagnall-Oakeley, to cut out the first Fulmar ledges in 1947. For David, therefore, it was a return to his old stamping ground and he remains the only one of the original group still to ring at this site 27 years later! During this time over 37,000 birds of 121 species have been ringed at Dead Man's Wood, which although not an 'official' member of the BTO Bird Observatory Network, is now known as Sheringham Bird Observatory. Ringed birds found or controlled in the area have included a Tree Pipit from Italy, Reed Warbler from Estonia and Goldcrest from Russia. For over 20 years standardised scientific procedures have been used to collect data on both ringing and visible migration and Sheringham Bird Observatory is now one of the most important sites in East Anglia for the study of coastal migration. There can be few birdwatchers in the county who have not visited the site to see the latest rarity to have been discovered either on the cliff-top fields or in the wood itself. A total of 21 species of warblers has been ringed there, including Lanceolated and Paddyfield Warblers, both additions to the county list, as was an Alpine Accentor in 1978. Apart from David Sadler, the other stalwart who has helped to put Sheringham on the ornithological map is Kevin Shepherd. Few people in the county can have found as many different species in Norfolk as Kevin has, and the vast majority in the Sheringham area.

The early 1970s was also the period when large numbers of cardueline finches were being ringed in the county – both at Dead Man's Wood in spring and also in gravel pits at Boughton, Mintlyn and Leziate, near King's Lynn, where Fred Britton ringed many hundreds of Redpolls, Chaffinches and Bramblings.

Nestlings were not being neglected, particularly in the south-west of the county where Paul Holness and Ron Hoblyn were concentrating on ringing the pulli of many of the Breckland specialities, a project which has continued to this day. Much of our current knowledge of the movements of Stone Curlews and Wood-larks comes from the tireless efforts of these two ringers in locating the nesting sites of these species. The mid-1970s also saw much effort put into the ringing of the moulting Canada Geese at Holkham Park Lake. On 11th July 1976, no less than 900 were rounded-up, but many had to be released unmarked as only 500 rings were available! Financial pressure prevented the project continuing for more than a couple of years – at the time each ring cost just over 5p. Nowadays, it would cost over £300 to ring 500 Canada Geese!

Meanwhile, in east Norfolk, Peter Allard had started to ring the Common Tern chicks on the breeding platforms at Breydon. Since 1978, he has ringed over 2,000 pulli at the colony which currently occupies six platforms and is the most successful breeding site for the species in Norfolk. Recoveries of these terns in winter have mirrored those from tern ringing at the north coast colonies over 50 years ago. Also in east Norfolk, mention should be made of the sterling efforts of Arthur Bowles and his small team who have been responsible for ringing almost 1,500 Little Tern chicks at the colony on Yarmouth north beach; a total which includes 486 ringed in 1998 alone.

Another species ringed in large numbers in the 1930s, the Black-headed Gull, attracted the attention of Ray Marsh in the 1980s, who ringed over 300 pulli at the Cantley Beet Factory colony in 1986. Recoveries of these nestlings confirmed that Norfolk-bred Black-headed Gulls moved south and west in autumn, whereas the trapping and ringing of adult gulls in the county, especially by John Bruhn and his team in gardens and at rubbish tips around Norwich, demonstrated that those in the county in winter were visitors from mainland Europe. Perhaps surprisingly, comparatively little ringing has been carried out in Broadland in recent years, apart from the efforts of Ray Gribble and his team at Hardley Flood in the 1980s. At this site large numbers of *Acrocephalus* warblers and swallows were ringed at a reedbed roost and amongst the species trapped was a Hobby, which was to be recovered the following year in The Netherlands. In the south of the county, along the Waveney Valley, Wally Thrower has been ringing for many years at Garboldisham and South Lopham Fen, where most of the Cetti's Warblers to have been ringed in the county have been caught.

An annual event in the calendar of Norfolk ringers is the evening meeting at the Phoenix Hotel at East Dereham on the first Thursday of March. Started in 1982, it has been held every year since and anyone interested in ringing in the county is warmly welcomed. Although it has become an enjoyable social occasion, it has also spawned several single-species ringing studies in the county, including those covering Greenfinches and Siskins. Particular interest in the latter species was stimulated by Ted Crosby who had been ringing in his woodland 'garden' at Banningham since 1971 but had only managed to ring 12 Siskins up to 1988. Then he started to hang out peanuts and netted over 500 between 1989 and 1993. As a result many other ringers in the county were encouraged to attract the species to their gardens and the ringing data were collected in a standardised form. Over 6,500 Siskins were ringed in Norfolk in 1994 and 1995, and a summary of the results of this joint study can be found at the end of the Siskin species account in the Systematic List.

Also as a direct result of these annual meetings, Kevin Elsby produced, edited and largely wrote, the *Norfolk Ringers Newsletter*. It ran for 16 issues from May 1993 to January 1997 and was a useful contribution to the county ornithological literature. Hopefully it will be resurrected at some time in the future. The other publication in which the results of ringing in Norfolk are available to a wider audience is the recovery section of the *Norfolk Bird Report*. Since this part of the county report was first introduced by Richard Richardson in 1954, there have been only four authors – Richard Richardson (1954–61), John Bruhn (1962–78), Moss Taylor (1979–88) and Allan Hale (1989– ). Annual ringing reports have also been produced by Sheringham Bird Observatory (initially as Dead Man's Wood reports) and the North West Norfolk Ringing Group, as well as reports based on ringing at Weybourne Camp, South Lopham Fen and Garboldisham.

Although the writer had been ringing at Weybourne Camp intermittently since 1975, the arrival of Martin Preston in the village in 1991 heralded the establishment of Weybourne's first regular ringing site. The garden of Denmark House, where Martin lives, must be every ringer's dream, although to be fair he has had to put an enormous amount of time and effort, not to mention money, into developing the site. Lying immediately behind the shingle bank, Martin has created an oasis for migrants by the planting of many trees and shrubs, and the creation of several freshwater pools. Between 1991 and 1998 he has ringed over 15,500 birds of 95 species including 11 Little Stints, three Wrynecks, four Waxwings, single Great Reed and Sardinian Warblers, four Yellow-browed Warblers, Great Grey Shrike and two Little Buntings; and all these just in his garden! He has, however, failed to add Storm Petrel to his list, despite several mid-summer attempts by teams of ringers to attract them on to the beach at Weybourne by means of a tape-lure – although one petrel did escape from the net one night before it could be reached!

The arrival of the BTO in Thetford in the 1980s spawned the formation of the Wissey Ringing Group. One project undertaken by this group includes extensive nest box experiments on the estate at Hilborough, to find out whether any particular designs of box are preferred by the birds. Almost 400 boxes are now sited on the estate but so far none has attracted the local Tree Sparrows. Chris Mead, who founded the Wissey Ringing Group, began to feed and ring the birds in his Hilborough garden in 1990. Initially no Greenfinches remained over the winter, but this species is now present throughout the year, with 200–300 adults caught each summer and many more in the winter. By feeding in several parts of his garden very large numbers are attracted. On one spring day alone, during cold weather, over 600 Greenfinches were caught. Over 100 individuals of five other species have also been caught in a single day in his garden – Blue and Great Tits, Siskin, Chaffinch and Brambling.

Wildfowl ringing may not have been so popular in recent years, but Robert Baker took up the challenge at Pensthorpe and for several winters, from the late 1980s, trapped some very impressive numbers of many species of wild duck, attracted by the pinioned birds in the wildfowl collection there. In fact the site became the most important one in the British Isles for the ringing of Wigeon. The North West Norfolk Ringing Group under the chairmanship of John Middleton has steadily grown since its formation in 1990 and has been responsible for the ringing of about 30,000 birds. One of its strengths is the encouragement it gives to its members to undertake specific ringing projects. Over the years these have included work on the population structure and racial origin of wintering Snow Buntings, the incidence and timing of spring passage of the Greenland Wheatear, a colour ringing and dye-marking programme of wintering Twite and an investigation into the breeding biology of the Ringed Plover by colour ringing and trapping at the nest. More recently the group was involved in the re-establishment of a ringing programme at Holme, although this has been taken over by a separate ringing group based at the observatory.

This account of the history of ringing in Norfolk would be incomplete without a mention of the remarkable 'fall' of Scandinavian migrants in October 1998, which particularly involved Robins and to a lesser extent Goldcrests. During the first week of October over 3,000 birds (of which half were Robins) were ringed at just three north Norfolk coastal ringing sites – Sheringham Bird Observatory, Martin Preston's garden at Weybourne and Weybourne Camp – all within a 3km radius! The 'fall' affected the entire Norfolk coastline and the number of Robins involved must have been unprecedented, even exceeding that in October 1951. Some indication of the origin of the birds involved in the 'fall' was provided by a Norwegian-ringed Robin and two ringed Dunnocks, one each from Norway and Sweden – only two other foreign-ringed Dunnocks have ever been found in Norfolk.

In line with BTO policy, future ringing in Norfolk is bound to become more oriented towards conservation-based projects and with record numbers of trained ringers now living in the county (43 with 'A' permits and 37 with 'C' permits, who between them ringed over 42,000 birds in 1998), Norfolk is well placed to continue making a most valuable contribution to this important branch of ornithology.

# NATURE CONSERVATION IN NORFOLK

*by*

## Martin George

## THE ROLE OF THE LOCAL PROTECTION SOCIETIES

The first conservation body in Norfolk, and perhaps in Britain, was the Breydon Wild Birds Protection Society. Formed in March 1888 following a public meeting in Yarmouth, this employed Samuel 'Ducker' Chambers, and from 1900 onwards, George Jary, as watchers on Breydon Water during the close season. For the first year or so another individual, R. J. Buddery, was asked by the Society to ensure that the game dealers in Yarmouth did not trade in protected species. The first President of the Society was H. E. Buxton, but following his death in 1905, his place was taken by his son, A. R. Buxton.

On the basis of evidence provided by its watchers, the Society instituted several prosecutions; for instance, Albert Beckett, landlord of the Lord Nelson, was fined 40 shillings for shooting two spoonbills in June 1888 (Allard 1988). But the presence of a watcher quickly led to an improvement in the local wildfowlers' understanding of the legislation, and no prosecutions had to be mounted in 1889 (Clarke 1921). Similarly, it was reported in 1904 that 'not a gun was fired on Breydon during the close season, notwithstanding the visits of many rare birds'.

A bird protection society was set up in the Wells area in 1890 on the initiative of Charles Hammond, a local landowner and keen naturalist. He and his friends contributed sufficient funds to employ Tom Cringle as watcher during the close season, much of his time being spent guarding Stiffkey Binks where, as now, there was an important Little Tern colony. The task of wardening the site was assumed by one of the keepers employed by its owner, the Holkham Estate, in 1910.

A third county protection society was established for the Blakeney-Cley area in 1901 at the instigation of Quentin Gurney of Northrepps Hall, who remained its honorary secretary and treasurer until 1921, and a fourth at Wolferton in 1904. The latter was formed on the initiative of Colonel George Cresswell to safeguard a ternery which at that time was located on a shingle bank beside the Wash. H.M. King Edward VII, and later H.M. King George V agreed to act as patrons of this Society in view of the fact that the Sandringham Estate leased the sporting rights over the area. One, or sometimes two, of the Estate's keepers were employed as watchers during the close season.

The reports produced by the seasonal watchers employed by these protection societies are briefly summarised in the 'Miscellaneous notes and observations' sections of the Transactions of the Norfolk & Norwich Naturalists' Society published between 1902 and 1920, and it is clear that they fulfilled a very valuable role. But although all four had indirect links with the latter Society – their founders all being members of it – each was self-financing and autonomous. This, together with their strictly local remit, was always going to make it difficult for them to raise the funds they required, and by 1921 the Wolferton society was the only one of the four to have a credit balance (Long 1921). In addition to the increasingly difficult financial situation, members of the Norfolk & Norwich Naturalists' Society (NNNS) had become increasingly aware that that there was a need for a central fund, to be drawn upon when a warden was required unexpectedly at a hitherto unprotected site. In view of this, the Society decided in 1921 to set up a unified Wild Birds Protection Committee to take over responsibility for safeguarding birds throughout the county. The job of administering this Committee, and raising the funds it required, was assumed by the Norfolk Naturalists Trust (NNT) in 1933 (Long 1934).

The new Committee was initially chaired by J. H. Gurney, the author of nearly 600 papers, articles and books on natural history, many of which were about the birdlife of Norfolk (Anon. 1923). On Gurney's death in 1922 the chairmanship was assumed by Russell Colman (1923 to 1945) and Sir Henry Upcher (1946 to 1952). Lists of those who contributed towards the cost of the Committee's work were included in its annual reports, and these show that subscriptions and donations from the 110 members totalled only £158 11s. 11d. in 1922 (c. £5,000 at 1998 prices), but rose to a maximum of £425 in 1936 (c. £16,650 at 1998 prices). The funds available tailed off during the Second World War, but increased to £411 10s. 1d. from 456 members in 1952, the increased number of contributors being undoubtedly related to the fact that from 1933 onward those paying more than ten shillings automatically became members of the NNT.

Most of the monies available to the Committee were used to pay the wages of its seasonal watchers at Breydon Water, namely George Jary up to 1927 (Allard 1990), and then William Betts (1928), Walter Bulldeath (1929–1939) and Robin Harrison (1946–1952). In addition, under an agreement negotiated with the National Trust, the Committee not only paid the lion's share of the cost of employing Charles Chestney, the first full-time warden on Scolt Head Island, but until 1939, contributed to the wages of the Trust's warden on Blakeney Point. In 1926 the Committee reluctantly decided not to continue wardening the Wolferton ternery as the site was being grossly disturbed by its exploitation as a source of sand and gravel for concrete making. This would have provided naturalists of the day with a foretaste of the fate to befall many other scientifically important sites in the county during the ensuing 50 years.

Although the regulations relating to bird protection seem to have been enforced reasonably well at Breydon Water from the turn of the century onwards, this was far from being the case elsewhere in the county, the complexity of the legislation making it very difficult to prosecute offenders successfully. Despite this, Albert Wyatt, a farm bailiff, was, in March 1926, found guilty of taking 27 eggs from some Crossbill nests near Thetford, and was fined £6 19s. 0d. (c. £235 at 1998 prices). The individual he was stealing the eggs for (Edgar Chance, the author of *The Cuckoo's Secret*, was fined £13 10s. 0d. (c. £450 at 1998 prices) for aiding and abetting Wyatt (Long 1926). Another successful prosecution was brought in September 1936 when two persons were fined £1 each for shooting Sandwich Terns at Salthouse. But even on the wardened sites it proved difficult to enforce the regulations, and the Minutes of the County Council's Wild Birds Protection Committee show that in July 1933 Sydney Long drew its attention to the indiscriminate shooting of protected species taking place on Blakeney Point, and asking – to no avail – for police action.

The Committee's reports, the principal sections of which were reproduced annually in the Transactions between 1922 and 1952, form a major source of data about the birdlife of the county during this period. Much of the information in the earlier reports was contributed by those concerned with Breydon Water and Blakeney Point, and the new nature reserves being established in the county, e.g. Scolt Head Island, Cley, Hickling and Horsey. However, records of birds seen elsewhere in the county were often included, and these observations gradually evolved into 'Classified Notes', arranged on a species by species basis, and occupying an increasing amount of space in each report.

In 1952 the NNT decided to disband the Committee on the grounds that its activities were so nearly related to those of the Trust that it was no longer necessary to maintain it as a separate entity. As part of this reorganisation, it assumed responsibility for paying the wages of the seasonal warden at Breydon, Robin Harrison, until his retirement in 1968. In addition, following discussions between the Trust and the NNNS, it was agreed that they would in future share the cost of producing annual 'Bird Reports', each of which would be allocated a place in the series of *Transactions* produced by the Society. The first of these reports was published in 1953 under the editorship of Michael Seago, who has continued to act in this capacity up to the present time.

# THE COAST BETWEEN WEYBOURNE AND HUNSTANTON

## Blakeney Point, Scolt Head Island and Cley Marsh

Those interested in natural history had long been aware of the special features of the north Norfolk coast, and in particular its birdlife, whose richness and variety are recognised in records dating from the early 19th century right up to the present day. In the circumstances, it is hardly surprising that a local protection society for the Blakeney-Cley area was formed to ensure that the close season was observed there. Both Common and Little Terns, together with other shore-nesting birds such as Ringed Plover and Oyster-catcher, had long bred on Blakeney Point, but their breeding success had always been poor as their eggs were regularly taken by local people for culinary purposes. Thanks to the efforts of Robert Pinchen, a local wildfowler from Cley who was taken on by the Protection Committee as a watcher during the spring and summer months, this practice largely ceased, and there was a rapid build-up in the number of birds breeding on the Point. For example, the number of Common Tern and Little Tern nests (which had been 140 and 60 respectively in 1901) trebled or quadrupled; in addition, one or sometimes two pairs of Oyster-catchers bred from 1906 onwards (Cozens-Hardy & Oliver 1914).

The Blakeney-Cley area has also long been renowned for the passage migrants likely to be seen there. Stevenson notes that rarities such as Black-winged Stilt ('killed at Blakeney in 1851'), Avocet and Marsh Harrier were regularly 'procured' or 'taken' in what he terms the 'Meals District' (i.e. the coast between Salthouse and Hunstanton). Powers (1885), who spent a fortnight in the Cley-Blakeney area in September 1884, records seeing no fewer than 80–100 Bluethroats, together with a number of other rarities including Melodious Warbler, Barred Warbler, Black-headed Bunting and Wryneck, while a few years later, the first Pallas's Warbler to be recorded in Britain was shot at Cley (Dresser 1897). In an annotated bird list, Rowan (1918) identified 210 species as having been recorded from Blakeney Point up to 1917 (of which 15 had bred on the site), and by 1980, these totals had increased to 263 and 33 respectively (White 1981).

Blakeney Point was, and indeed still is, of very considerable botanical as well as ornithological interest, and the presence of plants as rare as Matted Sea Lavender and Sea Heath, both of which were first recorded in Britain from the 'coast of Norfolk' in 1746 (Petch & Swann 1968), would have formed a major attraction to botanists. So too would the group of four Oyster Plants which was discovered by Pinchen in 1905 (Burrell 1906), since between then and 1931, when the last plant succumbed, Blakeney was the southernmost location for this species in Europe.

Academics as well as naturalists had long known about the Blakeney-Cley area, not just because of the richness of its bird and plant life, but as a result of the occurrence there of sand dunes and vegetated shingle formations in close juxtaposition with intertidal mudflats, salt and freshwater marshes and reedbeds. One of the first to take advantage of the obvious educational potential of the area was F. W. Oliver FRS, Professor of Botany at University College, London (UCL) who started to take his students on ecological field trips to Blakeney Point in the early years of the present century. In 1910, anxious to put these visits on a firmer footing, he persuaded the owner of the site, Lord Calthorpe, to grant the University a licence to pursue these studies, and make use of the Old Lifeboat Station as a work base. Lord Calthorpe died the following year, and the greater part of his Norfolk estate was purchased by a Mr A. Crundall. However, following negotiations with Professor Oliver, he agreed to sell off the Point separately, the principal donor of the funds required being the Hon. Charles Rothschild, who at that time was actively engaged in setting up the Society for the Promotion of Nature Reserves.

Professor Oliver was a member of the Executive Committee of the National Trust (which had been formally established in 1885), and on his recommendation the Trust agreed in the Autumn of 1912 to accept the site as a gift. The Point, together with some saltmarshes east of Blakeney Quay purchased anonymously a few months later, was the Trust's forty-ninth acquisition and the first nature reserve in Norfolk to be safeguarded by freehold purchase. The site was subsequently declared inalienable under the terms of the National Trust Act, 1907.

The Trust established an executive committee to manage the newly acquired reserve, and reports of this for the years 1913, 1914, 1915 and 1916 were published in the Transactions of the NNNS (Cozens-Hardy & Oliver 1914, 1915 and 1918). One of the Committee's first decisions was that Pinchen should continue as a watcher during the close season. It also granted UCL permission to continue using the site for field-based studies, and to build with the help of funds obtained from a public appeal a laboratory a short distance east of the University's existing base in the Old Lifeboat Station. Although this was primarily intended for use by personnel from UCL, academics from other universities, including Cambridge, also made use of its facilities, the net result being that numerous important papers about the ecology, birdlife and coastal physiography of the Point were published from 1914 onwards, e.g. Oliver & Salisbury (1913), Watson (1921) and Coward (1923). Further information on these topics is included in the Research Station's reports for various years between 1913 and 1929 (Oliver, 1914, 1915, 1918 , 1923, and 1926 ), and in a booklet edited for the National Trust by Allison & Morley in 1989.

One of the more important policy decisions taken by the Committee was that the leaseholders of the seven bungalows which had been built on the Point when it was owned by Lord Calthorpe, together with three houseboats moored nearby, would not be allowed to pass them on to a third party. The object of this was to ensure that in the fullness of time the Trust would be able to demolish or remove these buildings, several of which were rather unsightly. Similarly, although students working on the reserve were allowed to live under canvas in the early days, this was frowned on by the Trust, and from the 1950s onwards they have slept in the building originally built as a laboratory, now renamed 'the bunk house'.

In 1922 the Trust purchased the Watch House from the Royal National Lifeboat Institution, and the following year converted part of it into residential accommodation for Pinchen (who had been made a full-time warden in 1921), and the remainder into a tea-room for the increasing numbers of visitors who by this time were being ferried across to the Point from Morston and Blakeney Quay. Pinchen retired in 1930, and was replaced by W. Eales, whose son, Ted, took over from him in 1939. Ted (whose memoirs, published in 1986, contain much interesting information about the reserve) retired in 1980, his place being taken by the present warden, Jo Reed, the following year.

Most of the members of the Blakeney Point Executive Committee had strong Norfolk connections, and Dr Sydney Long, who had become a member of it in about 1916 was no exception. He had been elected a member of the NNNS in 1899, had served as its President a mere eight years later, and had become its Honorary Secretary in 1912. Dr Long was born and brought up in Wells, and would have had a detailed knowledge of the north Norfolk coast, including Scolt Head Island. Professor Oliver, too, was familiar with the Island, and may well have taken some of his students to visit it before or just after the First World War. Although the ownership of the Island had been subject to a long-standing dispute in the early years of the century, this was resolved in Lord Orford's favour in 1921, and during the course of a site visit the following year, Professor Oliver and Dr Long decided that the Island was so unspoilt, and of such outstanding ecological and physiographical interest, that it was essential that it be safeguarded for posterity. Oliver, in particular, felt that the botanical and physiographical features of Blakeney and Scolt were complementary, and subsequently wrote that 'the two together are far more than twice as valuable as either considered separately' (Long 1923). In the circumstances, the two men had no hesitation in agreeing that the site should be purchased and handed over to the National Trust.

With the Trust's agreement, Lord Leicester, who had acquired the Island from Lord Orford in 1922, was approached, and agreed to sell all but its extreme eastern end for £500 (c. £15,750 at 1998 prices) on the understanding that the site would be safeguarded in perpetuity. With the help of Russell Colman (another past president of the NNNS) a public appeal was launched, a target figure of £600 being set to cover both the purchase price and the cost of providing accommodation on the Island for a watcher or visiting research workers. In the event, over £700 was raised within three weeks, and the deeds of the Island were formally handed over to Viscount Ullswater, Vice-Chairman of the National Trust, on 11th June 1923. The eastern end of the Island, part of which was used as a scout camp up to the Second World War, was purchased by the Norfolk Naturalists Trust for a nominal sum in 1945.

As in the case of Blakeney Point, the Trust placed the management of the new reserve in the hands of a local committee, and this met for the first time in August 1923. It decided to invite Edward Boardman (the architect and then owner of How Hill) to design the hut which still forms such a distinctive feature of the Island, and this was built by Alfred Cushion of Norwich the following year. The Committee also agreed that Miss Emma Turner should act as a seasonal watcher for the years 1924 and 1925. She was an experienced ornithologist (it was she who, with Jim Vincent, 'rediscovered' Bitterns near Sutton Broad in 1911), and it was on her recommendation that it was decided that it would be essential to employ a full-time warden on the site. Charles Chestney was appointed to this post in October 1925, and when he was forced to resign through ill health in 1950 he was succeeded by his son Robert ('Bobby') who served for no less than 36 years. Until 1979 the Chestneys were expected to live in Dial House, a property beside the harbour at Brancaster Staithe which had been purchased by the Norfolk Naturalists Trust in 1929 as living accommodation for the warden. That Charles Chestney worked on a reserve owned by one organisation (the National Trust) lived in a house owned by another (the NNT) and had his wages largely paid between 1929 and 1933 by a third – the NNNS's Wild Birds Protection Committee – can be attributed to the negotiating skills of Sydney Long, who was closely associated with all three bodies. Colin Campbell took over from Bob Chestney as warden in 1986, but retired in 1994; Michael Rooney assumed responsibility for the management of the Island in 1996.

The new reserve, like Blakeney Point, had much educational potential, and this has been heavily exploited over the years, mainly by staff and students from Cambridge University. By good fortune, some outbuildings, plus a storage barn (now used as an interpretive centre) were included in the Dial House purchase, and in the early 1930s these were adapted for use as a simple dormitory, plus laboratory, to supplement the accommodation available in the hut on the Island. Numerous papers about the bird, plant and animal life of the reserve, and its ecology and physiography, have resulted from these field trips, much of the information available having been summarised by Steers (1960), and in a more abbreviated form by Allison & Morley (1989). In addition, Bob Chestney has written an anecdotal account of his life, with special reference to the birdlife of the Island (Chestney, 1993).

In 1926 a third site on the coast – Cley Marsh – was safeguarded as a reserve following the death of Mr A. W. Cozens-Hardy of Cley Hall, the owner of this 165ha block of grazing marsh, and his executors' decision to put the site up for auction in March that year. Much of the site had started to revert to a reedbed, following a sea flood in 1921, and reports by various observers, including Robert Pinchen, had revealed, not only how varied the birdlife of the marsh was, but that several new species, including Ruff, had started to breed on it following the flood. Clearly, it had great potential as a reserve if it could be managed sympathetically and wardened on a year-round basis. Cley Marsh adjoins the Blakeney Point reserve and would have formed a logical extension to the latter. However, the National Trust, the membership of which was only 973 in 1925 (Waterson 1995), indicated during the course of discussions that it could not afford to purchase the site. In view of this, Sydney Long decided, after consulting several potential donors, that he would attend the auction in a personal capacity. In the event, his bid of £5,160 (c. £173,600 at 1998 prices) secured both the marsh, and a building plot beside the coast road. At the time, the identity of the principal donor was not disclosed, but it later became known that Mr J. W. Castle had contributed £4,000. Sidney Long (1932) subsequently commented that Cley Marsh could not have been purchased without this 'munificent gift', and that 'the formation of the Norfolk Naturalists Trust would (also) have been indefinitely postponed'.

Having purchased the site, Sydney Long set about establishing an organisation constitutionally able to own and manage it, and others like it. His first step was to present his ideas to a group of friends at a lunch party held at the George Hotel, Cley, a week after the auction. Fowler (1976) provides us with an extract from his speech:

> When one considers the changes in the face of the county that are being made or contemplated by Forestry Commissioners, Drainage Boards, speculative builders and the like, one is anxious to preserve for future generations areas of marsh, heath, woods and undrained fenland (of which there still remain a few acres in the county) with their natural wealth of flora and fauna. At the present time, most of Broadland is in the hands of owners who can be relied upon not to interfere with the natural beauties of the district, but who can say what will happen in a hundred or even ten years time?

Sydney Long's prophetic views were well received in the county, and the Norfolk Naturalists Trust was formally incorporated in November 1926, Russell Colman being made the first President, and Long himself taking on the job of Honorary Secretary. The original intention was that the membership of the new organisation would be limited to one hundred, but this idea was quickly abandoned, and Long would undoubtedly be amazed and delighted to learn that the Trust today has some 17,500 members.

Professor Oliver would have been well aware of the reasons why the NNT had been established by his friend and colleague, Sydney Long, and during the course of a speech at the British Association's conference at Leeds in 1927, he expressed the hope that naturalists in other counties would follow suit. Here, he said, 'we have the germ which may lead to far-reaching results' (Oliver 1927). Given that there are now 47 county wildlife trusts, how right he was! And what foresight the two men had shown!

## The steps taken to safeguard other sites on the north coast

Ted Eales and Billy Bishop served in the Royal Navy during the War, and Bob Chestney was called up for service in the Army in 1944, and consequently the management of the Blakeney, Cley and Scolt reserves was put 'on hold' during this time. However, a number of discussions took place during the 1940s about the measures which would need to be taken to safeguard wildlife when hostilities ended. Chief among these was the convening by the Society for the Promotion of Nature Reserves (SPNR) in 1941 of a conference on 'Nature preservation in post-war Reconstruction'. Copies of the conclusions reached at this were sent to the Government, which responded by suggesting that a committee be formed to advise it on matters relating to nature reserves. This was done in the guise of the 'Nature Reserve Investigation Committee' (NRIC), which was asked by the SPNR, *inter alia*, to 'report on the types and approximate areas of reserves and sanctuaries which should be provided and the localities where they should be situated'. To assist the Committee in its task, regional sub-committees were formed, the one for Norfolk being chaired by Anthony Buxton. It included in its membership such well-known naturalists as R. B. Riviere, E. A. Ellis, J. E. Sainty and E. L. Swann.

During the ensuing months, the NRIC compared the lists submitted by its regional sub-committees with those produced previously These included a submission by the SPNR to the Board of Agriculture in 1915, and lists of proposed nature reserves compiled during the 1940s by the Royal Entomological Society, the British Ecological Society and the RSPB. There was general agreement that the north Norfolk coast was of major ecological interest, and that the existing reserves should be extended. The Norfolk Sub-committee of the NRIC, for example, suggested that the foreshore between Scolt Head and Holme should be protected, and that the Cley reserve be enlarged to include the Salthouse Marshes (Buxton 1943). However, these recommendations were not endorsed by the NRIC, which merely pointed out that both Blakeney Point and Scolt Head Island had been acquired for conservation purposes by the National Trust, and that they should be managed in the same way as the 47 sites in England and Wales which it recommended should be established as national nature reserves (SPNR 1945).

The NRIC's recommendations were broadly accepted by the Wild Life Conservation Special Committee set up by the Government in 1947 (Ministry of Town & Country Planning 1947a). However, although the members of this agreed that only Blakeney Point and Scolt Head Island need be established as national nature reserves, they took the view that the whole of the north Norfolk coast should be classed as a 'Scientific Area', covering some 44 square miles.

One of the Wild Life Conservation Special Committee's principal recommendations was that a 'Biological Service', staffed by scientists with appropriate qualifications should be set up within the Government machine. This would, *inter alia*, carry out survey and research, manage the sites which the Committee had nominated as proposed national nature reserves, and provide advice to Government, local authorities and others on the conservation of wildlife.

This recommendation was accepted by the Government, and wildlife conservation in the country generally, and in Norfolk in particular, was greatly strengthened by the formation in March 1949 of the Nature Conservancy, a Corporation incorporated by Royal Charter. A few months later, the new organisation's statutory duties were set out in the National Parks & Access to the Countryside Act, 1949. One of the Conservancy's first tasks was to review the list of 73 sites which the Wild Life Special Committee had recommended should be established as national nature reserves. This contained three other sites in Norfolk besides Blakeney Point and Scolt Head Island, namely Winterton Dunes, Barton Broad and Hickling Broad, and Horsey Mere. Despite the strictly limited resources available to it in the early 1950s, the Conservancy leased Scolt Head from its owners, the National Trust and the NNT, and the Island was formally declared a national nature reserve in March 1954.

The proposal by the Wild Life Conservation Special Committee that 35 'Scientific Areas' should be designated in England and Wales had caused some unease in Government circles, and the 1949 Act therefore made no reference to it. However, as a compromise, Section 23 of the Act made it obligatory for the Conservancy to notify local authorities of sites which it considered to be of special scientific interest (SSSIs), and in 1954 it issued the first list of sites in Norfolk to be scheduled in this way. This comprised 48 sites, of which seven, namely Blakeney Point (classified as a proposed national nature reserve), Cley and Salthouse Marshes, Holkham Lake, Hunstanton Cliffs, Morston Cliff, Thornham West Island (a misnomer for Holme Dunes) and Wells Dunes and Marshes, were on or very near the north coast.

The inclusion of Cley Marsh on this list reflects the success with which the NNT had set about managing the site after acquiring it. Robert Bishop, the first 'watcher' had retired in 1937, and been replaced by his grandson, Billy Bishop, who during his 41 years as warden put into effect a wide range of measures designed to enhance the birdlife of the reserve. These included adjusting the grazing regime on the marshes, creating various scrapes and pools for waders and wildfowl, harvesting the reeds in a way best suited to the needs of species such as Bittern and Bearded Tit, and controlling rats, stoats and other predators. Hides were also provided, and although these were not nearly so sophisticated as those now in place, they proved immensely popular with birdwatchers. The ornithological value of the site was further enhanced in 1962, when the NNT leased from the National Trust the brackish lagoon located beside the East Bank known, because of its previous ownership, as Arnold's Marsh. This brought the size of the reserve up to its present total of 180ha.

In 1964 the NNT decided not to continue leasing the shooting rights over the site, this despite the significant loss of revenue which would result. Two years later, Cley Marsh, together with Arnold's Marsh, was made subject to a Sanctuary Order, thus ensuring that anyone who went on to the site without permission could be prosecuted. These decisions led to a large increase in the number of wildfowl and waders frequenting the site during the winter months.

Billy Bishop's son Bernard became Assistant Warden in 1972, and when Billy retired in 1978, he became the full-time warden. Since then, he has, like his father before him, initiated a series of measures aimed at developing the reserve's potential still further. Billy's book about the reserve (Bishop 1983), updated by Bernard in 1996, contains a description of these management works. It also includes an annotated bird list, as well as a fascinating account of the activities of the wildfowlers who frequented the site in pre-War days.

In 1962 a bird observatory was established at Holme next the Sea on the initiative of Peter Clarke. Although only about 2ha in extent, the bushes and scrub pines surrounding the lake known as Broad Water were frequented by many birds, particularly those on passage migration, and by the early 1990s some 300 different species had been recorded. The Observatory proved very popular with birdwatchers as well as ringers, and in 1970 the Norfolk Ornithologists' Association was formed to take over the management of the site. Since then, a number of other areas on and near the coast have been acquired by the Association, including the Walsey Hills Information Centre and Migration Watch Point, and Redwell Marsh, Holme, purchased in 1973 and 1985 respectively.

In 1965 the Norfolk Naturalists Trust established its Holme Dunes reserve on land adjoining the Observatory. This initially included some 162ha of dunes and marshes, together with the house known as 'The Firs'. The latter provides accommodation for the site warden, and also a small flat for self-catering visitors. The reserve has, like the adjoining Observatory, proved very popular with visitors, and has been enlarged by the Trust on several occasions over the past 30 years or so. Using powers conferred upon it by Section 35 (1) c of the Wildlife and Countryside Act, 1981, English Nature declared the site a national nature reserve in 1994. By then, its hectarage was 187, but the area managed by the Trust has subsequently increased to 255ha. Of this, 127ha is owned, 75ha leased, and 53ha subject to a management agreement.

Thanks to the generosity of the Fifth Earl of Leicester, and with the agreement of his tenants, the Nature Conservancy was able to announce in 1967 that it had negotiated a management agreement over a substantial hectarage of saltmarsh, dune (much of it pine-covered) and drained marsh owned by the Holkham Estate. This area, together with much of the foreshore between Scolt Head Island and Blakeney Point which the Conservancy leased from the Crown Estates Commissioners, covered 3,955ha, making it then the second, and even now the third, largest national nature reserve in England. Charles Johnson was appointed as warden soon after the formal declaration of the reserve in July, 1967, and he at once tackled the two most urgent problems facing the Conservancy – the heavy recreational pressure to which the dune system west of Wells was subject, particularly during the summer months, and secondly, the tendency for Corsican Pine seedlings to invade the foredunes.

Holkham was known to be of very considerable ornithological importance, even before it was established as a reserve, but the management regime initiated by the Conservancy has led to it becoming one of the best sites in the county for birds, 319 species having been recorded from it by 1993 (Bloomfield 1993). Two of these, namely Yellow-browed Bunting and Red-breasted Nuthatch, were additions to the British List, and seven others represent new records for the county.

The Conservancy's successor from 1973 onwards, the Nature Conservancy Council (NCC), received special plaudits from birdwatchers during the 1980s in respect of the drained marshland area. This was far too dry during the preceding 20 years to support many birds, and indeed it was only included in the reserve at the insistence of Max Nicholson, the Conservancy's Director-General between 1952 and 1966, who believed, rightly as it turned out, that the flocks of grey geese which frequented these marshes during the 1920s and 1930s, but which had deserted it during the War, would one day return. In the event, small numbers of Pinkfeet and Whitefronts started to visit the area in the early 1980s, and in 1986 the then Senior Warden, David Henshilwood, started to install a system of dams and sluices capable of raising the water table in parts of the marshland between Lady Anne's Drive and the Overy sea-wall (Harold 1994). Similar control structures were installed in the Burnham Norton marshes, following the Holkham Estate's agreement in 1988 that this area should be included within the reserve. During the course of these negotiations, it was decided that no useful purpose would be served by retaining within the latter the landward block of arable marshes between Wells and Lady Anne's Drive, since it would have been both difficult and costly to raise their water table to the level attainable elsewhere. The net result of these changes was that the total hectarage of the reserve declined by about 30ha.

The seasonal flooding which took pace as a result of Henshilwood's endeavours, together with other changes in the way the marshes were managed, notably a decision to curtail the grazing season to the period between 20th May and 15th October, brought about a dramatic increase in the numbers of both breeding and wintering birds. For instance, although only five drumming Snipe were recorded in 1986, their numbers had increased to 26 in 1993; comparable figures for pairs of Redshank were 8 and 56. Similarly, the numbers of Pinkfeet on the marshes peaked at 825 in 1983/4, but attained a maximum of 6,600 in 1992/3 (Harold 1994). Another initiative for which Henshilwood was responsible was the creation in 1986 of a new 'scrape' near Meols House. This has subsequently been substantially extended in size, and, like the marshland to the west, is overlooked by a hide for visiting birdwatchers. Henshilwood was posted to another part of the country in 1990, but his successor, Ron Harold, has continued actively to pursue the management objectives set out in his 1993 paper, thus still further enhancing the birdlife of the reserve.

Meanwhile, a survey carried out in 1963 by the National Trust had demonstrated that about a third of the coastline of England, Wales and Northern Ireland – a distance of some 900 miles – remained of sufficient natural beauty to warrant being safeguarded, and in May 1965 the 'Enterprise Neptune' campaign was formally launched to raise funds to enable the Trust to acquire as many of these unspoilt sections of coast as possible (Waterson 1994). Three sites in north Norfolk were acquired with the help of 'Enterprise Neptune' funds, the first being the 626ha Brancaster Manor Estate. This was purchased in 1967, and comprises Brancaster Beach, together with the saltings and intertidal sand and mudflats lying to the south and south-west of Scolt Head Island. Richard Lowe was appointed as warden of the site in 1982, and took up residence in Dial House, following its purchase and renovation by the Trust.

The other two sites safeguarded by the Trust with the help of 'Enterprise Neptune' funds were Morston Saltmarshes (225ha) and Stiffkey Saltmarshes (197ha), purchased in 1973 and 1976 respectively. The intertidal creeks which traverse these saltings form part of the foreshore areas previously leased by the Nature Conservancy for inclusion in the Holkham NNR, and the National Trust's acquisition of the marshes themselves meant, in effect, that the largest and most species-rich block of saltmarsh in Eastern England was being cared for by conservation organisations.

The ever-increasing popularity of the Cley reserve encouraged the NNT to expand its holdings on this part of the coast eastwards, and in 1971 it concluded a management agreement over some 81 ha of the Salthouse Marshes. As part of the deal, it sold to the National Trust Great and Little Eye (4ha) and The Eye, Salthouse (8.5ha) which it had purchased in 1937 and 1955 respectively. The new reserve was subsequently extended, and the Trust (which renamed itself the Norfolk Wildlife Trust (NWT) in 1994 following a referendum) now owns some 57 ha, and leases a further 26 ha, in the Salthouse Marshes area.

The RSPB had long been anxious to acquire a reserve on the north Norfolk coast, and in 1972 it decided, after taking advice from coastal defence experts, to purchase a 166ha block of marsh at Titchwell. A former saltmarsh, this had been embanked and drained in the 1780s. However, the banks were breached by the 1953 surge, and during the ensuing decades the land started to revert to its former condition as a consequence of tidal flooding. Norman Sills was appointed as warden, and he masterminded the creation of the embanked fresh and brackish water reedbeds and lagoons which form such a conspicuous and well-loved feature of the site. Further improvements were brought about in 1993, when the RSPB leased from the Crown Estates Commissioners the foreshore adjoining the reserve, thus including within it what is generally regarded as one of the best beaches for waders in the county. The dunes and some of the saltmarshes to the west of the reserve were leased the same year, and in 1994 an access agreement was negotiated over the remaining saltings betwen Tichwell and Thornham. These acquisitions brought the hectarage of the reserve up to its present total of 379. In 1996 Norman Sills was transferred from Titchwell to the RSPB's new Fenland reserve at Lakenheath, his place being taken by the present warden, Peter Bradley.

Because of the number and variety of habitats represented on the reserve, it has a very rich and varied avifauna (Sills 1983). Equally important, the latter is readily observable from the excellent hides which the Society has constructed overlooking the lagoons. A survey carried out in 1998 indicated that the reserve was visited by some 128,000 persons, making it by a considerable margin the most popular site for birdwatching in Britain (Bradley pers. comm.).

Unfortunately, the relatively rapid rate at which this section of the north Norfolk coast is retreating means that the reserve will not indefinitely remain in its present condition. Indeed, some of the sand dunes fronting it, together with part of the walkway leading to the beach, were washed away during winter storms in 1996–97. The RSPB was advised of this long-term threat when it was considering whether or not to purchase the site, but decided, nonetheless, to proceed. In retrospect, this was an excellent decision given the reserve's outstanding ornithological interest and consequent popularity with birdwatchers. Moreover, the Society's determination to continue managing the site as a reserve for as long as physically practicable is reflected in its recent decision to improve the facilities for visitors and extend the adjoining car park.

During the 1960s the deficiencies in the list of proposed national nature reserves contained in the 1947 Report of the Wild Life Special Committee became increasingly apparent, and the Conservancy therefore embarked on a major survey, aimed at identifying all those sites which are of national ecological interest. This Domesday-like project was finally published in 1977 as a two-volume 'Nature Conservation Review'; it contains a detailed rationale for site selection, as well as descriptions of the 735 sites in Great Britain considered to be of Grade 1 or 2 national importance (Ratcliffe 1977). Of these sites 33 are located partly or wholly in Norfolk, and local conservationists were gratified, but hardly surprised, to find that those responsible for compiling the Coastal Section of the Review had had no hesitation in categorising virtually the entire coast between Holme and Salthouse as being of Grade 1 importance.

The county list of SSSIs was revised every few years by the Nature Conservancy (and from 1973 onwards, its successor the NCC), the opportunity being taken to add new sites and amend the boundaries of existing ones. The result was that, by 1981, 14 sites on or very near the north Norfolk coast were included on the schedule as SSSIs, together with the two national nature reserves, Scolt Head Island and Holkham.

During the 1980s the NCC decided to abandon the system employed in the Nature Conservation Review of applying gradings to individual sites. It did this on the grounds that if this process was taken to its logical conclusion, it would mean categorising all SSSIs according to whether they were adjudged to be of regional or merely local significance. Such an arrangement could be misinterpreted by outside interests as implying that some sites were considered by the NCC as being more deserving of protection than others. Instead, the NCC made it known that all SSSIs had been selected in accordance with agreed and well-publicised criteria (NCC 1989), and that each should be regarded as an integral part of a carefully chosen, unified series, every component of which needed to be safeguarded in the national interest.

Section 28 of the Wildlife and Countryside Act 1981 made it necessary for the Nature Conservancy Council and its successor, English Nature (one of the three country councils established in 1991 under the provisions of the Environmental Protection Act 1990) to carry out a comprehensive revision of its lists of SSSIs. In particular, it became obligatory to notify, not only local authorities, the Ministry of Agriculture, the Forestry Commission and other statutory bodies of sites deemed to be of SSSI quality, but to inform the owners and occupiers of such sites why the land was of special interest – the citation – and any operations likely to damage these features. This was an onerous and time-consuming task, involving as it did identifying and corresponding with approximately eight hundred individuals who own or occupy scheduled land in the country. In the circumstances, the revised list of SSSIs in Norfolk was not issued until 1986.

During the course of the revision, it was decided that 8 of the 14 existing SSSIs on the north coast, plus the Scolt and Holkham National Nature Reserves (which the 1981 Act required should be formally notified as SSSIs) should be amalgamated to form a single large site, covering about 7,887ha, to be known as the North Norfolk Coast SSSI. Five of the remaining SSSIs on the 1981 schedule were small geological sites which would be renotified as separate entities, whilst the fourteenth, Holkham Lake, would be descheduled on the grounds that its scientific interest was not sufficient to justify its retention as an SSSI.

Apart from the Wells caravan site and harbour channel, and some arable marshland between the town and Lady Anne's Drive, virtually the entire coastline between Holme and Salthouse is included within the north Norfolk coast SSSI, a distance of some 25 miles. Equally importantly, most parts of the SSSI are included within one or another of the nature reserves described above. As if this near-unique level of protection were not sufficient, no fewer than five international designations have been applied to, or sought for, the north Norfolk coast. Scolt Head Island, Holkham, Blakeney Point and the Cley/Salthouse Marshes together form a Biosphere Reserve, designated in 1977, while the SSSI is coterminous with a Ramsar site and Special Protection Area. Parts of the SSSI are also included within two Candidate Special Areas of Conservation, one terrestrial and the other marine. Last, but not least, the Government announced in April 1999 that following extensive consultations, the north Norfolk coast, together with the Wash, had been short-listed as one of 25 candidates for World Heritage Status.

Those familiar with north Norfolk, and in particular its coast, will be aware that it has a special character of its own, a point recognised in landscape terms in 1967 when it was designated as an 'Area of Outstanding Natural Beauty' by the National Parks Commission. The wildlife of the whole area, too, is of above-average interest, and in the 1960s this was recognized, albeit informally, when the Conservancy advised local planning authorities and various other organisations that it regarded north Norfolk, and also Breckland and Broadland, as 'Nature Conservation Zones'.

Although this concept was useful at the time as a way of drawing attention to the high value placed on these areas by conservationists, and also making the point that the wildlife of the 'Wider Countryside' was just as deserving of protection as that in individual nature reserves and SSSIs, staff resource and other constraints made it impossible to develop it to the extent originally intended. The same general idea was, however, revived by English Nature in the early 1990s, each of the three areas which had originally been termed Nature Conservation Zones being enlarged and renamed 'Natural Areas', the stated object being 'to unite statutory, voluntary and others' effort for nature conservation, to involve more people and maximise benefits for the natural heritage' (English Nature 1994). Put in another and perhaps more comprehensible way, 'The Natural Areas approach gives us a way of determining priorities for nature conservation areas with ecological and landscape integrity, and to set objectives which reflect these priorities' (Langslow 1997). English Nature regards the 'profiles' which have been written for each of the 120 Natural Areas which it has recognised in England as one of its contributions to Britain's Biodiversity Action Plan, being compiled following the Rio Earth Summit.

The profile for the North Norfolk Natural Area has been compiled by Lambley (1997), This contains a description of its nature conservation interest, including lists of the more uncommon plants, birds and animals which occur within it, a review of the impacts and trends affecting the Area, and the objectives which need to be achieved if its biodiversity is to be enhanced.

## BRECKLAND

Breckland is an area of light sandy soils and low rainfall, roughly bounded to the north by Swaffham, to the south by Kentford and Risby, to the east by Watton and East Harling, and to the west by the edge of the Fenland Basin. Various boundaries have been proposed for the region over the years, but that chosen by the Ministry of Agriculture, Fisheries and Food in 1986 for the Breckland Environmentally Sensitive Area is probably the most convenient. Clarke (1894), who was first to apply the name 'Breckland' to the region, based it on a 17th-century definition of a 'breck' as 'a piece of land which having lain uncultivated is ploughed again one year' (Lambley 1994).

The feature for which the region is perhaps most famous is the presence of meres in which the water levels are subject to erratic fluctuations. There are eleven such meres, all of which are in Norfolk. Each is in communication with the chalk aquifer underlying the region, but there is usually a time lag between a prolonged wet spell and the appearance of water in a mere. In addition, it is not unknown for some meres to be water-filled, while their near-neighbours are dry, and vice versa (Clarke 1903 and 1937). The meres are also renowned for remaining dry for several years at a stretch, and then suddenly, and quite unexpectedly, filling with water, and staying thus, even during prolonged dry spells.

The meres vary greatly in size and shape, and all are scenically very attractive when water-filled. Being located in an otherwise barren landscape, they tend to attract numerous birds, Gadwall being a species particularly characteristic of them. The two best-known meres are Ringmere and Langmere which are situated on East Wretham Heath, quite close to the A1075 Thetford–Watton road. However, Fowlmere, with a water surface of about 7ha when full, is somewhat larger.

In his account of the land-use history of the region, Schober (1937) points out that until medieval times it would have consisted largely of open, sandy heathland grazed by numerous sheep and rabbits. The dry sandy soils would have been subject to serious wind erosion, and dust and sand storms would have been frequent. Rabbits formed a very important 'crop' during this period, and by 1700 there was an almost continuous series of warrens from Mildenhall north to Brandon, and east to Thetford (Duffey 1976). At least two thirds of the region was still heath or 'waste land' at the end of the 18th century and there were very few trees, apart from those in the parks of the major landowners. Birds characteristic of the region at this time would have included Great Bustard, Stone Curlew, Wheatear, Ringed Plover and Red-backed Shrike.

Major land use changes took place following the passing of the General Enclosure Act of 1801, and many of the Scots Pine windbreaks, which form such a characteristic feature of the Breckland landscape would have been planted by the 1820s. The first Forestry Commission plantations were established near Wangford in 1922, and by 1935 some 14,170ha, mainly of open heathland, had been purchased (usually for about £3 per acre) and afforested (Long 1936). The planting of conifers continued thereafter, albeit at a reduced pace, and by 1951 some 12,760ha had been planted. The combined hectarage of Thetford Chase and the Swaffham and Kings Forests is currently about 20,800 (Haggett 1994).

Heathland was lost as a result of changes in agricultural management practice, as well as afforestation. Following pioneer work on the Earl of Iveagh's estate during the 1930s, it was found possible to bring large areas of relatively infertile soil into permanent arable production by introducing into the rotation such crops as mustard and lucerne. After the Second World War, the same effect was achieved with the help of chemical fertilisers.

These changes in agricultural management fragmented the areas of heathland not already planted up with conifers. In addition, the increasingly widespread use of herbicides had a devastating effect on the status of the rare arable weeds (e.g. the annual speedwells *Veronica praecox, V. verna* and *V. triphyllos*) for which the region is botanically famed.

Members of the NNT, and in particular Sydney Long, were greatly concerned by the progressive loss of heathland taking place in the region, and when the Forestry Commission purchased the c. 2,430ha Culford Estate in 1935, Long tried hard to persuade it to sell to the Trust a 485ha block of heathland for establishment as a nature reserve. Sadly, this approach was rejected, and virtually the entire Estate was planted up with conifers to form what is now the King's Forest.

The same year, the Trust became aware that the Forestry Commission was hoping to buy another large expanse of heathland in the region, namely Lakenheath Warren. This site is a common, and its management could therefore only be altered if all the commoners agreed. In the circumstances, the Trust purchased two cottages in Lakenheath village to which commoner's rights were attached, thus putting itself in a position where it could prevent the site being afforested. Although this move was successful, the north-western side of the Warren was requisitioned in 1942, and is now occupied by RAF Lakenheath. The building of this base resulted in the destruction of the largest remaining system of inland dunes in the region; this was estimated to occupy some 280ha in 1835 (Duffey 1976).

It is clear that Sydney Long continued to hope to acquire a Breckland reserve for the Trust, as there is a reference in the Council Minutes for 10 November 1937 to the discussions which had taken place with Sir John Dewrance, the then owner of East Wretham Heath (146.5ha). Sadly, however, Long died in January, 1939 without having seen these negotiations brought to a successful conclusion. Nevertheless, the site was later purchased from the Dewrance Estate by a consortium of members and local landowners, because the Council Minutes for 30 December 1940 record that East Wretham Heath had been sold to the Trust by 'Lord Fisher and others' for the nominal sum of £100.

Sydney Long's concern to ensure that the Trust which he had set up would continue to prosper is illustrated by the fact that he left it a bequest of £5,000 (c. £170,000 at 1998 prices) to be paid on the death of his widow. In addition, his will contained a clause offering the Trust an option on his house in Norwich (31 Surrey Street) for use as an office, an offer which in the event was not taken up. At his request, his ashes were scattered on his beloved Scolt Head Island. However, given his anxiety that the Trust should acquire a reserve in Breckland, it was decided that a monument to his memory should be erected on East Wretham Heath, overlooking Langmere.

By a strange quirk of fate, Sydney Long's passing coincided with the arrival in Norfolk of another major figure in the world of natural history and conservation, namely Christopher Cadbury. He was born in 1908, and after reading history at King's College, Cambridge, he started working as a salesman for the family firm. He was based in Norfolk during the early 1930s, and the business trips which he made in his

Riley 9 frequently took him through Breckland. As a keen birdwatcher, he was delighted to see the Stone Curlews, Ringed Plovers and other species characteristic of the region, but at the same time, horrified, like Sydney Long, by the rate at which heathlands were disappearing. Determined to do something about the problem, he persuaded Mr R. F. C. Parrott of Fengate Farm to sell him the main part of Weeting Heath in 1942, and donated this area to the NNT the same year. The compartment nearest the river was bought by Cadbury from Mr Parrott three years later, and when he also donated this area to the Trust, it brought the hectarage of the reserve up to its present total of 137.

At the behest of the War Agricultural Executive Committee, the conversion of heathland to arable continued during the early 1940s, one of the sites affected being the southern part of the new reserve at Weeting. However, the losses were partially offset by the creation in 1942 of the Stanford Practical Training Area, now usually known as STANTA. This involved the requisition by the War Department of c. 6,700ha, and the eviction of some 750 residents. Parts of the site were under the plough at the time, and these were allowed to revert to grass heath, later to be sheep-grazed. Today, about two thirds of the total amount of heathland and dry grassland left in Breckland is located in STANTA. This, plus the fact that the site contains several meres, a tributary of the R. Wissey and a wide variety of other habitats, makes it of the utmost importance for birds and other forms of wildlife, a fact recognised in 1971 when 4,748ha, or about two thirds of the area, was scheduled as an SSSI. Fortunately, the army is fully aware of this interest, and although the needs of battle training always have to take precedence, the management of the site is subject to a very satisfactory ongoing dialogue between conservationists and the military authorities.

There was a surge of heathland reclamation after the War, the c. 9,300ha Elveden Estate (which had been bought by the First Earl of Iveagh from Lord Albermarle in 1894) being particularly active. Its staff put some 445ha under the plough between 1948 and 1950, but curiously it was during this period that Christopher Cadbury persuaded the Second Earl to sell Thetford Heath (101ha) to the NNT for £1,125. This was duly reported to the Trust Council in November, 1949, with a note to the effect that the site had been paid for by Cadbury.

The report of the Wild Life Conservation Special Committee had only listed two potential national nature reserves in Breckland, both of which were in what was then West Suffolk (now Suffolk), rather than in Norfolk. In the circumstances, it is not altogether surprising that the first SSSI schedule for the latter county included only five Breckland sites – Barnhamcross Common, Foulden Common, Thompson Water, East Wretham Heath and Weeting Heath (which was listed as a proposed national nature reserve). The two latter sites, plus Grime's Graves, had been included on the list of sites which the Norfolk Sub-committee of the Nature Reserves Investigations Committee considered should be safeguarded in what it termed the Breckland 'Scheduled Area', but in the event, Grime's Graves was not formally notified as an SSSI until 1991. The NNT's Thetford Heath reserve, which is located just south of the county boundary, together with Lakenheath Warren, Foxhole Heath and a number of other ecologically important sites, was included on the first SSSI schedule for West Suffolk, produced, like the one for Norfolk, in 1954.

Nature reserve agreements over both Weeting and Thetford Heaths were negotiated by the Nature Conservancy during 1957, the object being to ensure that the latter could pay the Trust three quarters of the cost of mutually agreed management works. The two sites were formally declared national nature reserves in June the following year.

The southern part of Weeting Heath, which had been put under the plough in 1942, was allowed to revert immediately afterwards, and by the early 1950s almost the entire reserve was clothed with the type of terrain particularly favoured by Stone Curlews and Wheatears, namely bare stony heathland, heavily grazed by rabbits. However, the arrival of myxomatosis and the consequent collapse of the rabbit population allowed the grassy vegetation to increase in height, rendering the site far less attractive to these birds. In an attempt to prevent Stone Curlews deserting the site altogether, a number of small plots were put under the plough and rotavated. But these were not particularly successful, and in 1959, Christopher Cadbury paid for a 16ha rabbit-proof enclosure to be constructed just south of the Weeting-Hockwold road. The rabbit population within this thrived, and in most years since the early 1960s, up to three pairs of Stone Curlews have bred here. The enclosure was also frequented by numerous breeding Wheatears during the 1950s and 1960s, but for reasons not fully understood, the numbers of this species then started to decline, and none has bred on the site since 1992. Fortunately, this loss has been offset by the fact that several pairs of Wood Larks now breed on the reserve (Nicholls pers. comm.).

The first of two hides overlooking the enclosure was installed by the NNT in 1972, and seasonal wardens have been employed on the reserve each year since 1974. Only two or three hundred persons visited the hides for the first year or so, but numbers increased rapidly as it became known that they enabled birdwatchers to have what are arguably some of the best views of breeding Stone Curlews and Woodlarks obtainable in Britain. A small Interpretive Centre is due to be opened beside the enclosure in the Spring of 1999.

The nature reserve agreements over the Weeting and Thetford reserves were re-negotiated in the mid-1990s, with the result that responsibility for their management is now vested solely in the NWT, rather than jointly with English Nature; the latter does, however, continue to assist financially through its Reserve Enhancement Scheme. Other Trust reserves in Breckland include Hockham Fen (c. 8ha) – a valley mire in the centre of the Cranberry Rough SSSI, which it purchased in 1962, a short section of disused railway track at Narborough (c. 8ha of chalk grassland bought in 1985) and Thompson Common (c. 133ha purchased in 1981 and subsequently extended). The latter site contains what are probably the best examples of pingos in Britain. These are small, water-filled depressions, each of which was formed under tundra-like conditions when groundwater collected and froze, so creating beneath the soil surface a dome-like structure. As the climate warmed up, the ice melted, leaving a crater in the centre with a sandy rampart around the rim.

The revisions of the county SSSI schedule carried out during the 1960s and 1970s led to further areas being notified and by 1981 13 sites in the Norfolk part of Breckland, with a total hectarage of 6,021, had been afforded this status. In carrying out this review, Conservancy staff would have been mindful of the conclusions reached in 'The Nature Conservation Review ' (referred to in the description of the north Norfolk coast). This had identified no fewer than eleven 'nationally elite' sites in Breckland, eight of which are located wholly or partly in Norfolk.

The need to review the list of SSSIs and re-schedule them under Section 28 of the 1981 Act resulted in further sites being notified and boundary amendments being made to virtually all the existing ones. Brief descriptions of the 23 sites in the Norfolk part of Breckland currently notified as biological SSSIs are given in Appendix 1; together they cover an area of c. 6,242ha. A further 32 SSSIs, with a hectarage of 2,363, are located in the Suffolk part of the Brecks. Thus, some 8% of the region is currently notified as being of special scientific interest, almost half of which is located in the Stanford Training Area (Rothera 1998). Breckland has not been afforded the plethora of international designations applied to the north Norfolk coast, but it has been put forward by the UK Government as a Candidate Special Area of Conservation.

Shortly after the passing of the 1981 Act, the owner of Brettenham Heath (236ha) informed the Nature Conservancy Council that he was minded to put up to 18,000 free-range pigs on the site. This would have completely destroyed its ecological interest, and the NCC therefore negotiated a lease over the site; it was declared a national nature reserve in 1983. Much of the site was bracken-dominated at the time it was taken over by the NCC, but thanks to a vigorous programme of bracken-crushing and spraying, and the introduction of a sheep grazing regime, grass heath now predominates. The birdlife of the site, too, is more varied now than it was in the early 1980s, Woodlarks and other species having colonised it.

Major benefits accrued to the wildlife of the region following its designation in 1988 as an Environmentally Sensitive Area. One of the 'tiers' in this is aimed at the owners of heathland, who are eligible for annual payments of £140 per hectare provided they adhere to the relevant prescriptions. These include a ban on ploughing, cultivating or spray-irrigating the land, or applying lime, insecticides, fungicides, organic or inorganic fertilisers to it. To qualify for the subsidy, applicants must hard-graze the land with sheep or cattle, a proviso written into the regulations specifically to meet the needs of Stone Curlews, which, when nesting on heathland, prefer to nest on bare stony ground located within a tightly grazed sward. The owners of 3,248ha are currently receiving payments under this tier, but it should be noted that part of the area concerned will be located in Suffolk, rather than Norfolk.

The owners of a further 251ha are currently registered for the Heathland Reversion tier of the scheme, for which grants of £350 per hectare are payable, while other tiers include River Valley Grassland (£130 per ha), Uncropped Wildlife Strips (£370 per ha), Conservation Headlands (£110 per ha) and Winter Stubbles (£100 per ha). The latter tier was added to the scheme recently in the hope that it will prove beneficial to Tree Sparrows, Woodlarks and finches.

Thanks largely to the ESA, many Breckland heaths are now in much better shape from the Stone

Curlew's point-of-view than they were in the 1980s. However, a significant number of pairs continue to breed on set-aside and arable land, and the RSPB has therefore made special efforts over the past few years to inform the farmers of the fields where the birds are nesting so that they can avoid unwittingly damaging them. This initiative has proved very successful; indeed, the principal objective set in English Nature's Species Recovery Programme for the Stone Curlew, namely that steps be taken to increase the total breeding population of these birds from about 145 pairs in 1995 to 200 pairs by the year 2000, was exceeded by 15 pairs in 1998 (RSPB 1998b).

# BROADLAND

## The role of the voluntary bodies

Broadland has long been renowned for the richness of its bird, animal and plant life, and innumerable papers, books and reports have been written about the region over the past 150 years or so. Breydon Water was, as pointed out earlier in this chapter, the first site in the region to be wardened, but it became apparent during the early years of the present century that many more reserves would need to be established if the wildlife of the region was to receive the level of protection it deserved.

No one was more aware of this than Sydney Long, and in 1928 he was instrumental in persuading the NNT to purchase for £140 (c. £4,860 at 1998 prices) a 10.5ha area of reed and sedge beds near Martham known as Starch Grass. The site was then, and indeed still is, frequented by three of Broadland's avian 'specials', namely Marsh Harrier, Bittern and Bearded Tit. Alderfen Broad and its adjoining fens (21ha) was acquired by the Trust two years later, primarily because of the site's varied plant life, and the fact that it was isolated by a sluice from the main river system, and not therefore accessible to holiday craft. Land values were low in the late 1920s, and the Trust's successful bid – £2,200 (c. £79,420 at 1998 prices) – prompted the auctioneer to exclaim 'I wish all the land in Norfolk was water!'

The 1943 report of the Norfolk Sub-committee of the Nature Reserves Investigation Committee recommended that the valley of the Bure below Wroxham, together with its broads and waterways, and the Ant and Thurne and the Yare valley below Norwich, also with its associated broads, should all be 'scheduled areas'. The Sub-committee also decided that the most suitable area for a Broadland nature reserve was the Hickling-Horsey district, to include some 2,430ha between the northern end of the Brayden Marshes and the Thurne, and encompassing the Starch Grass reserve. The Committee considered that eight other sites should be established as reserves in the region. These were Calthorpe Broad, Decoy and Cockshoot Broads and the Woodbastwick Fens, Ranworth Broad and the fens to the north, Upton Great and Little Broads and the 'Doles', Sutton Broad, Barton Broad, Wheatfen and the adjoining fens, and Buckenham Broad and the fens nearby.

After comparing these proposals with those submitted by the Royal Entomological Society, the British Ecological Society and the RSPB, the NRIC decided that two sites in Broadland, namely the Hickling-Horsey-Winterton area, and Barton Broad should be given an 'A' rating to indicate that they were of such outstanding importance as to merit being established as national nature reserves. The Committee also decided that the northern part of Broadland should form one of the 25 'Conservation Areas' which it had identified as being of particular natural history interest in England. In addition, several sites in the Bure, Ant, Thurne and Yare valleys, including Cockshoot, Decoy, Ranworth, Upton, Alderfen, Sutton, Calthorpe, Surlingham and Rockland Broads were singled out as being of 'special importance' (SPNR 1945).

These recommendations were broadly accepted by the Wild Life Conservation Special Committee in its 1947 report. However, Winterton Dunes was separated from the proposed Hickling-Horsey reserve, Barton Broad was singled out as being of special importance, and the region as a whole was termed a 'Scientific Area', rather than a 'Conservation Area'.

The fact that the Hickling-Horsey area is mentioned by all those invited to nominate sites of particular natural history interest is a reflection of the way this part of the region had been managed since the early years of the century. The Whiteslea Estate at Hickling had, as was mentioned earlier, been purchased by Lord Lucas in 1909, and had from then onwards been managed by a syndicate as a sporting estate-cum-bird sanctuary, special efforts being made to safeguard the Bitterns, Montagu's Harriers, Marsh Harriers and Bearded Tits which frequented the site. One of the members of the syndicate was the Hon. Edwin Montagu, and it was he who employed Jim Vincent, the legendary head keeper of the Estate. Lord Lucas was killed on active service in France in 1917, and the Estate was taken over by the Hon. Ivor Grenfell. On his death in 1923, following a road accident, his father, Lord Desborough, assumed responsibility, not only for managing the Estate in the same way as the syndicate had done, but for extending it as and when the opportunity arose. As a result, by the mid-1940s he owned the southern half of the Broad and the adjoining fens and marshes, together totalling some 256ha, and leased from Col. John Mills a further 208ha, comprising the northern part of the Broad, plus various adjoining parcels of land.

In 1944, following a tip-off from Jim Vincent, Christopher Cadbury opened negotiations with Lord Desborough for the purchase of the Estate. His offer of £5,000 (c. £133,320 at 1998 prices) was accepted, but unfortunately Lord Desborough died before the sale could be completed, and the Estate passed to his daughter, Lady Gage. Because of the need to pay death duties, she was obliged to raise the price (Linsell 1990), but with Cadbury's agreement, and with the help of a major donation from him, and grants from the Pilgrim Trust, the RSPB and the SPNR, the Estate was purchased by the NNT in 1945 for £8,972 (c. £227,000 at 1998 prices).

In the meantime the Horsey area was being managed along the same lines as the Whiteslea Estate, at first by Lord Lucas, and from 1917 onwards by his widow. However, following her remarriage she sold the Horsey Estate to the late Anthony Buxton in 1930 who donated it to the National Trust in 1948 on a lease-back arrangement. Since then, the Mere and the adjoining fens and marshes have been managed as a private reserve, at first by Mr Buxton, and since 1970 by his son, John.

Other reserves established in the region just after the Second World War include Barton Broad, which was purchased by the NNT in 1946, and Bargate Island, opposite Brundall in the Yare valley, which was given to it in 1948. The following year, Ranworth and Cockshoot Broads were donated to the Trust by the late Col. H. J. Cator, whilst Surlingham Broad was purchased in 1952 for £1,112 (c. £17,640 at 1998 prices). Like Hickling, all these reserves include substantial areas of unreclaimed fen as well as open water.

The Trust remained a fairly small organisation throughout the 1950s, and this restricted its ability to establish further reserves. However, thanks to the growing interest in conservation, its membership and financial resources increased rapidly from the mid-1960s onwards, and this enabled it to acquire additional sites in Broadland. These include Smallburgh Fen (leased in 1972), Upton Fen (purchased in 1979), and part of Ranworth Fen (leased in 1984). In the early 1980s, the Trust extended its Barton Broad reserve eastwards by leasing parts of Catfield Fen, and also leased some 4ha at Burgh Common. In 1996 it extended its portfolio of Broadland reserves still further by purchasing for just under £56,000 the Ebb and Flow Marshes, a 43ha block of carr, reed and sedge-fen on the north side of the River Bure, a short distance downstream of Horning. The sites which the Trust currently manage in Broadland have a total hectarage of over 1,000ha, representing almost half of its total holdings in the county.

Most of these sites, like other reserves in Broadland, require active management, and between the early 1950s and the mid-1990s the Trust benefited repeatedly from Christopher Cadbury's willingness, not only to provide the funds needed to purchase sites, but to make contributions towards the cost of managing them. This was especially true at Hickling, where much of the equipment needed in connection with the management of the site, the 'scrapes' (one of which is named after him) and the hides overlooking them, were paid for by Christopher, usually anonymously. A further example of his generosity occurred in 1968, when he purchased from John Norman, the then owner of the Somerton Hall Estate, Martham North and South Broads and the reed and sedge beds surrounding them. He did so in the knowledge that this 60ha site had long been one of the chief strongholds in the county for Marsh Harrier, Bearded Tit and Bittern, and in the belief, now generally shared, that if the latter is to survive as a breeding species anywhere in Broadland, it will be in the Somerton area. Having bought the site, Christopher promptly donated virtually all of it to the SPNR, of which he was President between 1962 and 1988. (In 1976, the SPNR was renamed the Society for the Promotion of Nature Conservation, and this became the Royal Society for Nature Conservation in 1981. The RSNC currently acts as the umbrella body for the 47 County Wildlife Trusts.) The NNT leased the site three years later, and it today forms one of the best sites for birds in the region. On Christopher's death in 1995, the 8ha area which he had retained passed to his step-son, Tim Peet, who continues to manage it as a private nature reserve.

The RSPB acquired a direct managerial interest in Broadland in 1975, when it leased Strumpshaw Broad and the adjoining fens and marshes, together covering 127ha, from the Trustees of the Holmes Estate. It subsequently purchased a further 53ha of fen, and leased two other areas, the net result being that the Strumpshaw reserve now covers some 196ha. The Society started to acquire land on the south side of the Yare valley in the late 1970s, and it leased Surlingham Broad from the NWT in 1995; it currently owns some 121ha, and leases a further 132ha in the Surlingham-Rockland area. Parts of the RSPB-controlled land lie adjacent to the Ted Ellis reserve, a c. 50ha mixture of fen, alder carr and open water managed by a Trust; this was set up following the death in 1986 of the renowned Norfolk naturalist.

Although some of the reserves acquired by the NNT from the 1940s onwards included grazing marshland, as well as fen and open water, conservationists tended to concentrate their attention on the latter two habitats as it was thought that these supported a greater wealth of plant and animal life. However, surveys commissioned by the NCC from the early 1970s onwards showed that grass marshland not only has its own intrinsic interest, but that the dyke system associated with it provides a refuge for most of the aquatic plants and animals formerly found in the rivers and broads, but now largely eliminated as a consequence of nutrient enrichment (George 1992). In addition, it is now realised that Broadland's fens, open waters and grass marshes are ecologically interdependent. Marsh Harriers, for instance, breed in the former, but range widely over the adjoining countryside, obtaining much of their food from the Drained Marshland Area.

In view of this, a substantial hectarage of grass marshland has been acquired by conservation organisations since the 1980s. The RSPB, for instance, started to acquire land in the vicinity of Berney Arms in 1985, and currently owns some 365ha in this area. It also extended its holdings in the Yare valley in 1993 by acquiring 350ha of marshland in the Buckenham-Cantley area, just down-valley from the Strumpshaw Fen reserve. In the meantime, the National Trust had succeeded in purchasing, with the help of grants from the National Heritage Memorial Fund, the NCC and the Broads Authority, the area known as Heigham Holmes. This consists of some 186ha of marshland, located in close proximity to the Hickling, Horsey and Martham reserves.

## The Broads Environmentally Sensitive Area

Valuable as these initiatives were, conservationists were dismayed during the early 1980s by the steps being taken by growing numbers of farmers to put their marshland under the plough. A full description of the furore which resulted, and in particular the saga over the Halvergate marshes, is included in George (1992). Suffice here to say that following the success of a pioneer scheme, known as the Broads Grazing Marshes Conservation Scheme, launched in 1995, the Broads Environmentally Sensitive Area (ESA) was set up two years later. In essence, this provides a tiered structure enabling farmers to be financially compensated for maintaining their land under grass, rather putting it under the plough, and to receive additional payments in the event that they are prepared to carry out other environmentally desirable works.

The prescriptions for Tier 1 (for which payments of £135/ha are currently available) place restrictions on mowing, reseeding, stocking densities, and the use of herbicides and other agrochemicals. No more than 125kg of nitrogen, or 30 tonnes of organic manure, may be applied to the marsh per hectare per year. Tier 2 imposes additional restrictions on the way the land can be managed. In particular, no more than 44kg of nitrogen can be applied per hectare per year, and the use of organic manure is banned. In the interests of breeding birds, mechanical operations such as hay cutting are not permitted until after 16th July, and grazing is only allowed between 1st April and 30th December. Another key prescription, as far as birds are concerned, is that dyke water levels must not be allowed to drop more than 45cm below the marsh surface between 1st April and 30th December, the object being to ensure that the substrate remains sufficiently soft for birds such as Redshank and Snipe to probe for food. Those prepared to adhere to these prescriptions are currently eligible for annual payments of £225 per ha.

The prescriptions for Tier 3 impose further restrictions. The dyke water level must be maintained at the marsh surface between January and May, the object being to ensure that temporary pools form on the latter after heavy rain, thus making the land more attractive to both waders and wildfowl. Grazing is not permitted until mid-May, and then only at low stocking densities, and no fertilisers or organic manure may be applied to the land. £310 per hectare is at present payable under this Tier, and those qualifying for payments under both the latter and Tier 2 are eligible for grants towards the cost of providing the control structures needed to maintain dyke water levels at the prescribed standard.

Other Tiers in the ESA include one targeted at arable marsh owners wishing to put their land back under permanent grass. A Fen Tier was introduced in 1997 for those prepared to manage their land in accordance with the provisions of a Fenland Management Plan.

When the ESA was first designated, it covered some 30,000ha, comprising Broadland, and the flood plains of the rivers Bure and Waveney as far upstream as Aylsham and Eye (Suffolk) respectively. However, the boundary of the designated area was extended in 1992 (mainly by including the River Wensum to its sources near East Rudham and South Raynham) and in 1997 it was increased by a further 7,000ha to its present total of about 43,000ha, this time by including the floodplain of the Yare, as well as the upper tributaries of all the rivers in the east of the county.

The 'take-up' of the Scheme by farmers has been high, some 9,245ha and 6,821ha out of a possible c. 20,000ha being currently subject to payments under Tiers 1 and 2 respectively. In addition, c. 390 ha of arable marshland has been put back under permanent grass. The cost of the Scheme has been correspondingly great, the total payments made to farmers under its provisions amounting to £3.27m in 1997. But although it has, by preventing a continuance of the arable conversion so rife in the 1970s, been very beneficial from the landscape point-of-view, the Scheme's effects on birdlife, particularly waders are less clear cut. This is apparent from a survey of four of the breeding species particularly characteristic of the Drained Marshland Area, namely Snipe, Redshank, Lapwing and Oystercatcher, which was carried out by David Weaver in 1995, the object being to provide information for a review of the ESA due to be made the following year (Weaver 1997).

Weaver also compared the information he had collected with that obtained in 1982 by Murfitt & Weaver (1983), and in 1988 for the RSPB by O'Brien & Buckingham (1989). He concluded that the introduction of Tier 3 had, as had been expected, increased the numbers of breeding Snipe, Redshank and Lapwing, but that because of the limited take-up by farmers of this option, its potential was not being fully realised. Indeed, although the total number of Redshanks breeding in the area had remained fairly constant between 1988 and 1995 (following a significant increase between 1982 and 1988), and the numbers of Oystercatchers had apparently risen, the decline in the numbers of Snipes and Lapwings observed between 1882 and 1988 had continued, thus confirming the downward trend in the status of these species nationally.

The area covered by the ESA is frequented by numerous waterfowl during the winter months, and the populations of these were surveyed from mid-November 1996, to the end of February 1997 by Babbs, Cook & Durdin (1997). The following six species were found to the present in internationally important numbers: Bewick's Swan, Pink-footed Goose, Wigeon, Gadwall, Shoveler and Lapwing, while an additional seven species – Mute Swan, Whooper Swan, Bean Goose, White-fronted Goose, Tufted Duck, Coot and Golden Plover – were recorded in nationally important numbers. Sites under Tier 3 management were, as for breeding waders, particularly attractive to wintering waterfowl, peak counts for Wigeon being obtained from the Buckenham and Berney Marshes (6,844 and 4,735 respectively). Heigham Holmes had 2,400 Pink-footed Geese, by far the largest number found in the region.

## The Nature Conservancy's role in Broadland

One of the Nature Conservancy's first tasks was, as elsewhere, to review the list of sites which the Wild Life Conservation Special Committee had suggested should be established as national nature reserves. Two sites in Broadland had been nominated, namely Barton Broad and the Hickling-Horsey area, but Dr Joyce Lambert had carried out a great deal of research on the ecology of the fens and the origin of the broads since the Committee had compiled its report, and in the circumstances her views were sought on the merits of the two sites recommended relative to other parts of the region. In the light of her comments, the Conservancy decided that some of the fens and broads in the middle Bure valley, subsequently (but somewhat illogically) known as the Bure Marshes, should be substituted for Barton Broad. This decision was taken in the belief then current (but now disproved) that there was a wider range of fen communities here than in the Ant valley, and because the five broads selected for inclusion in the proposed reserve (Ranworth, Cockshoot, Decoy and Hoveton Great Broads plus Hudson's Bay) were not subject to disturbance by boat traffic, as was Barton Broad. Dr Lambert also argued that since Ranworth Broad occupied a deeper basin than the latter, reedswamp communities would grow over it more slowly, and it would therefore be less expensive to maintain as open water. Neither she, nor anyone else could have known at the time that marginal reedswamp communities would disappear almost completely from all six sites during the ensuing 15 years!

Although Barton Broad and its adjoining fens was dropped from the list of sites which the Conservancy felt should be established as national nature reserves, two sites were added. The first of these was the

Surlingham-Wheatfen-Rockland area, whose natural history interest had been extensively studied by Ted Ellis, while the second was Calthorpe Broad, which had been given to the Conservancy in 1953 by Mrs S. G. Gurney, widow of the well-known Norfolk naturalist, Robert Gurney.

Soon after these decisions were made, the Conservancy initiated discussions with the NNT and Major J. M. Mills (who had inherited responsibility for his father's estate in 1947) concerning the possibility of establishing Hickling Broad and its adjoining fens and marshes as a national nature reserve. The negotiations were fairly protracted, but were brought to a successful conclusion in 1957, with the coming into force of nature reserve agreements covering 487ha; the site was formally declared in June 1958. Additional areas acquired by the Trust subsequently were made subject to supplementary agreements with the Conservancy in 1974 and 1975. Under the agreements, the Trust remains responsible for the day-to-day management and staffing of the reserve, and for the first 30 years or so, overall policy was determined by a management committee made up of representatives of the Conservancy and the Trust, and chaired by Christopher Cadbury. At the Trust's insistence, this was subsequently replaced by an advisory committee, and this in turn was disbanded in 1995, a few months before Cadbury's death.

Originally, the Conservancy provided the Trust with a substantial annual grant towards the overall cost of running the reserve, but this arrangement was later modified, and English Nature now contributes towards the cost of specified management tasks. It was agreed at the outset that no shooting would be permitted over the south-west corner of the reserve. However, a shooting syndicate continued to operate over the remainder of the site until 1965, when the Trust decided that it could afford to forego the not-inconsiderable revenue which it derived from this source. The coot shoots, which had taken place over the site for as long as anyone could remember, and which are described by Gurney (1901), ceased in 1963. A detailed account of the history, management and birdlife of the Hickling reserve – which has long been regarded as the 'jewel in the NNT's crown' – is contained in Linsell (1990).

While the discussions over the Hickling reserve were in train, the Conservancy negotiated nature reserve agreements with the NNT over Ranworth and Cockshoot Broads and their adjoining fens, and with Mr John Cator over Decoy Broad and the Woodbastwick Fens; the two areas, together covering 297ha, were declared as the Bure Marshes NNR in June 1958. Three months later the Hoveton Great Broad – Hudson's Bay area (115ha) was added to the reserve under an agreement negotiated with Mr T. R. C. Blofeld.

In the early 1960s the Conservancy embarked on a major programme of management works on the Woodbastwick Fens, the overall objective being to recreate the mosaic of vegetation types which would have existed up to the 1920s as a consequence of their exploitation as a source of reed, saw-sedge, sheaf, litter, fen hay and alder poles (George 1992). Great importance was also attached to renovating the network of dykes on the site, since these were known to be capable of supporting a very rich aquatic fauna and flora; in addition, they made it possible to transport fen produce and equipment from one part of the reserve to another by boat, a difficult task otherwise because of the soft, waterlogged terrain. Many of the techniques now in widespread use in the region were pioneered here during this period. Examples include the mechanical clearance of fens heavily invaded by scrub and woodland, and the suction dredging of semi-derelict waterways. Another innovative feature of the Conservancy's work in the 1960s was the laying out beside Hoveton Great Broad of the first nature trail to be established in Broadland. This is still in use each summer, having been visited and enjoyed by countless thousands of persons since it was first opened in 1967.

Reference has been made earlier to the growing concern felt by conservationists during the 1970s and early 1980s about the ploughing up of grass marshland in the region, and in face of this threat, the Nature Conservancy Council purchased a 73ha block of this terrain near Ludham. This was formally declared a national nature reserve in 1987, and is generally regarded as one of the best remaining examples of this habitat in the region; the dykes, in particular, contain an exceptionally rich and varied aquatic fauna and flora.

In addition to its role in relation to the establishment of national nature reserves, the Conservancy, and its successor the Nature Conservancy Council, was obliged, as was pointed out in the section about the north Norfolk coast, to schedule areas which it considered to be of special scientific interest. Broadland sites included on the first such county schedule (dated 1954) comprised the two areas (Barton Broad and Hickling & Horsey) which were then regarded as proposed national nature reserves, plus seven biological and four geological sites. By 1959, the list included the two declared and two proposed national reserves (Calthorpe Broad and the Surlingham and Rockland area), together with twelve biological and four geological sites, while by 1971, the schedule listed the two national nature reserves, four geological and sixteen biological sites (two of which had appeared on the previous schedules as proposed national nature reserves), plus Breydon Water (453ha), which had been established as the first local authority nature reserve in the county in 1967. By 1981, the number of biological SSSIs in the region had risen to 24, with a total hectarage of 3,116 instead of 1,741.

The comprehensive revision of the county lists of SSSIs made necessary by the passing of the Wildlife and Countryside Act 1981 led to the notification of a further six sites in Broadland, the net result being that no fewer than 30 biological sites in the region are currently afforded this status, all but two of these being in Norfolk. The total hectarage of these 28 sites is c. 6,863, a figure which includes the three existing national nature reserves, namely the Bure Marshes (451ha), Hickling Broad (487ha) and Ludham Marshes (73ha). Using powers conferred upon it by Section 35 of the 1981 Act, English Nature established four further national nature reserves in the region during the 1990s. These are Martham Broad, declared in 1994 (59ha), the Ant Broads and Marshes (1994 – 154ha), Calthorpe Broad (1996 – 44ha) and the Mid-Yare National Nature Reserve (1997 – 779ha), the latter comprising the majority of the RSPB's holdings in the Strumpshaw, Surlingham, Rockland, Buckenham and Cantley areas.

In addition to safeguarding sites as NNRs and SSSIs, the NCC initiated during the 1970s a major investigation of the causes of the damaging ecological changes which by that time were occuring in the region (George 1992). The data obtained as a result of these studies, together with follow-up research at the University of East Anglia, and by the National Rivers Authority (now the Environment Agency) and the Broads Authority, have been used to develop the programme of restoration work now in progress in the region; this is briefly described in the following section.

## The Broads Authority

The first organisation to canvas the idea of establishing a series of national parks in Great Britain was the Council for the Protection of Rural England (CPRE) which submitted a memorandum on the subject to the then Prime Minister, Ramsay Macdonald, in 1929. The idea was examined by the Addison Committee, set up as a result of this approach (Addison 1931), and further discussions (summarised by Sheail 1976) took place before, during and immediately following the War, the Norfolk Broads being one of twelve areas recommended for designation by the Hobhouse Committee in 1947 (Ministry of Town & Country Planning 1947b). However, although ten of the sites suggested had been established as national parks by 1955, Broadland was not afforded this status. George (1992) identifies two reasons for this lack of action: the strong commercial pressures to which the region was already subject, and the very high cost of restoring the broads to their former condition. Arguments for and against designation continued throughout the 1950s, and the national park proposal was officially abandoned by the Government in 1961 on the recommendation of the then National Park Commission (NPC).

Subsequent events are fully described by George (1992), and it will suffice here to say that increasing concern was expressed by environmentalists during the 1970s about the multiplicity of organisations having statutory responsibilities in the region, and their inability to work together harmoniously. In 1976, the Countryside Commission (which had inherited the responsibilities of the NPC in 1968) re-opened the debate by issuing the first of a series of Consultation Papers about the future of the region. This revealed that some organisations were strongly in favour of national park designation, while others were resolutely against. A turning point was reached in January 1978, when the Norfolk County Council (in many ways the key organisation concerned) decided that it was opposed to the national park idea – an attitude labelled 'despicable' by several local conservation bodies. Stung by the criticism levelled at it, the County Council agreed to participate in discussions about the region which had shortly before been initiated by the Norfolk Branch of the Association of District Councils, and these ultimately led to the formation, under the terms of the Local Government Act 1972, of a new administrative body which became known as the 'Broads Authority'.

The new organisation quickly embarked on a programme of works of direct benefit to the region's well-being, and in particular its bird, plant and animal life. For instance, the Authority gave grants to bodies such as the NNT and the RSPB to assist them with the management of their reserves. In addition, it set up various work groups, the net result being that literally thousands of man-days were spent carrying out practical tasks on sites in need of management. It also commissioned a number of research projects aimed at improving our understanding of the ecology of the region, and embarked upon a programme of works aimed at restoring selected broads to the condition prior to the 1950s. The Authority's acquisition in 1983 of the 148ha How Hill Estate received widespread plaudits, since the Ant valley fens have long been managed by traditional techniques, and are of exceptional ornithological as well as botanical and entomological importance.

Unfortunately, through no fault of its own, the Authority suffered from a number of defects, most notably the fact that responsibility for navigation, arguably one of the most important activities practised in the region, remained vested in a separate organisation, the Great Yarmouth Port & Haven Commission. The relationship between the two bodies was not an easy one, and in 1983 the Countryside Commission issued a further Consultation Paper about the future of the region. This revealed that there was strong support locally for a special, 'one-off' statutory authority to be formed to take over, not only the functions of the existing Broads Authority, but responsibility for navigation on the rivers and broads. Such a body could only be set up by Act of Parliament, and after a prolonged saga (described in detail by George 1992) involving an abortive attempt to obtain the necessary powers by a Private Bill, the drafting by the Government of the necessary 'hybrid' Bill, and arguments in Parliament and Select Committee about the 'balance' to be struck in this between the sometimes competing interests of navigation and conservation, the Norfolk & Suffolk Broads Act came into force in April 1989.

From the outset, the 'new' Broads Authority adopted, and when possible, extended many of the policies pursued by its predecessor. For instance, with the help of funds provided by the Environment Agency and the EEC's LIFE-Environment programme, it expanded its research and experimental management programme to include, *inter alia* , Alderfen, Belaugh, Hoveton Little, Hoveton Great and Ormesby Broads. The results obtained were subsequently written up in the form of a series of four technical reports (usefully summarised by Madgwick 1996) linking science with the practical techniques (now generally referred to as 'biomanipulation') which can be used to restore nutrient-enriched lakes (Broads Authority 1996).

In 1995 the Authority embarked on its most ambitious project to date – the restoration of Barton Broad. The objectives of the scheme, which became known as Clear Water 2000 and which is being funded with the help of a £1.15m grant from the Millennium Commission, are described in the Authority's Annual Report for 1996–97. But in essence, the intention is not only to increase the depth of the site, and improve the quality of the water therein, but to restore the ornithologically important reedswamp communities which formerly fringed the Broad.

The Authority is currently engaged in a number of other projects of direct benefit to the bird and plant life of the region. One of the most notable of these is being carried out in conjunction with the RSPB and English Nature, and with financial assistance from the EEC's LIFE partnership, and has involved the construction of a prototype wetland harvester capable of mechanising many of the management operations formerly carried out on fens by hand. The new machine was used successfully on a number of fens in the region in 1998, and during the next year or so it is hoped to find ways of transporting the cut material off the site quickly and efficiently, and develop markets for the dried produce. These could include animal feed or bedding, bio-fuel or domestic fuel briquettes. Another commendable initiative is to use livestock, including Konik ponies imported from Poland, to graze fens on an extensive basis, the object being to control the growth of vegetation, particularly woody species, but at the same time avoid damaging the site by poaching (Tolhurst 1997).

It is impossible in a summary account such as this to do more than touch on some of the activities currently being pursued by the Authority, and those wishing to learn more about what it is doing to safeguard the region's wildlife should refer to its Plan for the region, published in 1997, its annual reports and its Research Register. Another useful source of data about the region is the 'Broads Natural Area Profile' compiled in 1996 by Heather Holve and jointly edited by Jane Madgwick of the Broads Authority and Clive Doarks of English Nature.

# THE CONSERVATION OF SITES IN OTHER PARTS OF NORFOLK

Despite being one of the most intensively farmed counties in Britain, the nature conservation interest of those parts of Norfolk away from Breckland, Broadland and the north coast is surprisingly high. This was recognised by the Norfolk Sub-committee of the NRIC, which identified in its report a number of heaths, commons, fens, and woodlands as being of outstanding natural history interest, and which it therefore recommended should be established as nature reserves (Buxton 1943). Inevitably, a few of these sites have been drained (e.g. Caldecote Fen) or damaged by heavy public pressure (e.g. Mousehold Heath) or lack of management (Dersingham Common). However, the majority have survived, and many of them have been established as nature reserves by the NWT (e.g. Buxton Heath, Holt Lowes, Roydon Common and Ringstead Downs). These, together with most of the remaining sites listed by the Sub-committee, are now SSSIs, examples being Kelling Heath, Bryant's Heath, Swannington Upgate Common, Booton Common, Flordon Common, Dereham Rush Meadows, Felbrigg Great Wood and Winterton Dunes.

Members of the Sub-committee would perhaps have been rather disappointed to find that only one of these sites, namely Winterton Dunes, is mentioned in the report of its parent body, the NRIC (SPNR 1945) as being deserving of national nature reserve status. However, the NRIC's idea that Winterton should be linked with Horsey Mere and Hickling Broad as a single reserve was rejected by the Wildlife Conservation Special Committee, which listed the site as separate entity in its report (Ministry of Town & Country Planning 1947a). In the event, Winterton Dunes was declared a national nature reserve in 1956 under an agreement negotiated by the Nature Conservancy with its then owner, the late Captain Watt.

Fifteen sites in the county away from the north coast, Breckland and Broadland were identified in the Nature Conservation Review as being of prime nature conservation interest. These comprise five of the sites already mentioned (Buxton Heath, Felbrigg Woods, Holt Lowes, Roydon Common and Winterton Dunes) plus Foxley Wood, the Ouse Washes, Redgrave and South Lopham Fen, Sandringham Warren (including Dersingham Bog), Scarning Fen, Sexton Wood, Swanton Novers Woods, Thompson Common, the Wash and Wayland Wood. Most of these sites are now being managed as reserves, either by the NWT, or, in the case of Swanton Novers Woods, the Lincolnshire part of the Wash, and Dersingham Bog, by English Nature. Redgrave and South Lopham Fen, and Roydon Common, were designated as national nature reserves under S.35 of the 1981 Act in 1993 and 1994 respectively.

Few of these reserves were established primarily because of their birdlife, the main exceptions being the RSPB's Snettisham reserve, and the Wildfowl and Wetland Trust's Welney Wildfowl Refuge on the Ouse Washes. However, many of the other sites listed in Appendix 2 provide opportunities for birdwatching, and some of them are frequented by rare and interesting species. For instance, Honey Buzzards breed in at least one of the ancient woodlands which have been safeguarded.

# NATURE CONSERVATION IN NORFOLK BETWEEN 1949 AND 1999 – AN APPRAISAL

Profound changes have occurred in our countryside, and, equally importantly, our attitude towards it, over the past 50 years, and if they were alive today Sydney Long and his friends would find it difficult to reconcile the situation as they knew it just prior to the Second World War, with that with which we are familiar. In particular, they would be appalled, not so much by the loss of some of the sites which they regarded as potential nature reserves, (although a few of these have indeed been damaged or destroyed), as by the general attrition of wildlife habitats in the wider countryside. They would have also been dismayed to discover that once-abundant birds such as Song Thrush, Skylark, House Sparrow and Starling had become much less common than they were in the past, and to note the oft-repeated claims by the British Trust for Ornithology, RSPB and others that this is attributable to changes in farm management practice. The losses of both habitats and birdlife have certainly been particularly noticeable in Norfolk, where the drive to improve agricultural productivity has been long-continued, and often ruthless.

Fortunately, the growing pressures on the Norfolk countryside have been matched by large increases in the numbers of persons engaged in one way or another in safeguarding it. It is doubtful whether there were more than ten such individuals in the county in the early 1950s (i.e. Miss Gay, the then secretary of the NNT, Eric Duffey, who was appointed as the NC's Regional Officer for East Anglia in 1954, and the field staff employed on the Scolt Head Island, Blakeney Point, Cley Marshes and Hickling Broad reserves), whereas today there are probably nearly 80 – the NWT alone employs some 35 full-time staff, plus various short-term and seasonal assistants.

The growth in the financial strength and membership of bodies such as the NWT and the RSPB is a reflection in the change in the attitude towards preserving the countryside which has occurred over the past 30 years or so. 'Conservation' and 'the environment' would have been novel, and for many persons, unfamiliar, words in the immediate post-War period, but today they are in near-universal usage. More importantly, the majority of people are now generally supportive of the steps being taken to safeguard wildlife, and although concepts such as 'sustainability', 'biodiversity' and the 'precautionary principle' are still relatively unfamiliar, they will probably soon become part of everyday speech.

It is quite difficult, in retrospect, to decide which of the various initiatives taken by conservationists in the 1960s and 1970s to focus attention on the need to safeguard wildlife and the environment had the most effect. The first hides for use by visiting birdwatchers were provided on the Hickling Broad reserve in 1959, and at Cley a year or so later. However, the numbers of persons making use of them in the early 1960s remained pitifully low by today's standards; for instance, in 1960 the then Head Keeper of Hickling, Ted Piggin, reported with some pride that 40 to 50 persons had used the Rush Hills and Swim Coots hides that year.

National Nature Week, organised in May 1963 by the Council for Nature and commemorated by a special set of stamps, was marked in Norwich by the laying out of two nature trails on Mousehold Heath – a 'first' for Norfolk. The techniques used were simple in the extreme – stencilled hand-outs and numbered posts liberally smeared with grease to deter vandals. But both trails were heavily used by school parties, and some of those who walked round them would have learnt from the experience. So, too, would those who saw the film 'The Living Pattern', produced for the NC in 1963 about the need to safeguard wildlife, which was widely shown locally. In the meantime, the word 'environment' was featuring prominently in the discussions taking place during and after the Duke of Edinburgh's Study Conference on 'The Countryside in 1970', held in November 1963, and attended by representatives of numerous local organisations.

Rachel Carson's book, *Silent Spring*, published in 1963, focused widespread attention on the disastrous mortalities suffered by birds and other forms of wildlife as a result of the use of persistent, organochlorine-based pesticides. However, it must have come as a shock to many bird lovers in Norfolk to learn, as a result of research carried out from 1962 onwards by Dr Norman Moore and his colleagues at the Conservancy's Monks Wood Experimental Station, that the near-total failure of Sparrowhawks (certainly) and Marsh Harriers (probably) to breed successfully in the county was attributable to the same factor.

The publication in 1965 of the Conservancy's *Report on Broadland*, with its dire warning that 'Time is not on the side of Broadland. To do nothing is to abandon the region to erosion, conflict and decay' served to focus attention on many of the problems currently being tackled by the Broads Authority and the Environment Agency. Other noteworthy events during this period include the opening of the Hoveton Great Broad Nature Trail in 1968, the Hickling Water Trail in 1970, and the Ranworth Conservation Centre in 1976. All three venues proved very popular with visitors, the latter having being visited by over 140,000 persons by 1986.

Meanwhile, both the quality and the number of films shown on television about birds and other forms of wildlife were rapidly increasing, Anglia TV's Survival Series, and the work of David Attenborough in particular, both regularly attracting millions of viewers. Although the conservation 'message' in these films was often implicit, rather than explicit, viewers would not have found it too difficult to decipher. Even easier to appreciate was the 'message' in David Weaver's hard-hitting film for Anglia TV – *No Lullaby for Broadland*. This was networked to 13 other companies, and when screened at peak viewing time on 29 November 1979, was, to the dismay of the boat-hire industry, seen by some 9 million people.

One of the encouraging symptoms of the growing acceptance of the principle of conservation, is what many would regard as a U-turn in the policies of bodies such as the Ministry of Agriculture and Fisheries, and the Forestry Commission. In the 1950s and 1960s, these organisations were, at best, unsympathetic towards nature conservation interests, whereas today they are very supportive; indeed, some of their activities have been expressly designed to benefit birds, plants and animals. Examples include the Breckland and Broadland ESAs (previously mentioned) and the Countryside Stewardship Scheme. This was launched by the Countryside Commission in 1991, but was subsequently taken over by the Ministry five years later, with the overall aim 'of making conservation part of farming and land management practice'. To this end, grants are awarded to those carrying out projects designed, *inter alia*, 'to sustain the beauty and diversity of the landscape, to extend and improve wildlife habitats, to restore neglected land or features, and create new habitats and landscapes' (MAFF 1997). The habitats afforded priority for grant assistance in Norfolk include river valleys, lowland heaths, chalk grassland, coastal grazing marshes and old meadows. Some three hundred schemes have so far been grant-aided in the county, at a total cost expected to amount to c. £11.4 million by 2008.

The increasing number of persons working for conservation organisations, and the improving financial status of the latter, is reflected in the growing number of reserves established over the past 50 years or so. As will be seen from Appendix 2, there were still only about 15 largish sites safeguarded in the county in 1960, but by 1980 there were 44, and today there are nearly twice this number. Grants towards the cost of purchasing land were available from the NCC from 1980 onwards, and several of the ornithologically important reserves listed in Appendix 2 were acquired with help from this quarter. Examples include Salthouse Marshes (£4,000 in 1980), How Hill (£22,500 in 1983), Heigham Holmes (£75,000 in 1986), Blakeney Freshes (£40,000 in 1987 and £20,000 in 1988), and the Buckenham and Cantley Marshes (£20,000 in 1992). All told, some £466,190 has so far been made available by the NCC and English Nature towards the cost of purchasing reserves in the county.

The NCC helped to fund the management of reserves, and provide interpretive facilities on them, from 1974 onwards. Examples include the provision of hides and an information room at Snettisham (£685 in 1974), the Ranworth Interpretive Centre (£2,500 in 1975), the Bean Goose hide at Buckenham (£200 in 1976), cleaning out dykes at Cley (£250 in 1984), strengthening the sea defences at Titchwell (£10,179 in 1986) and employing an RSPB seasonal warden for Stone Curlew protection in Breckland (£3,034 in 1986). When English Nature took over the NCC's responsibilities in 1991, it decided to reorganise its grant-giving functions by introducing, *inter alia*, a Reserves Enhancement Scheme. The aims of this are to improve the management of reserves which are SSSIs, encourage the involvement of volunteers, increase the accessibility of selected reserves to members of the public, and enhance the latter's appreciation of the natural heritage. Five-year management grants are given for defined habitat types, and 50% funding is available for capital projects, special consideration being given to reserves where the prospects of income generation are low. Fifteen of the the NWT's reserves, including Alderfen Broad, Hickling Broad, Hockham Fen, Ringstead Downs, Thetford Heath and Weeting Heath were accepted into the Scheme in 1994. Financial help with the cost of reserves which are not SSSIs has been forthcoming from the Countryside Stewardship Scheme.

The NWT has been remarkably successful over the past few years in attracting funds for reserve management from other quarters. The two outstanding examples of this are, first, a grant of £373,500 from the Heritage Lottery Fund (HLF) for a three-year programme of work, costed at nearly £0.5 million, and aimed at up-grading the management of the marshes and fens to the south of Hickling Broad, and improving the visitor facilities on this reserve. The second major grant was obtained as a result of a successful application to the HLF by the RSNC on behalf of the Wildlife Trusts. The £2,293,400 allocated to the NWT will enable it to carry out a five-year programme of work on 26 of its reserves, starting in 1999, and costing £3,057,462 (Joyce 1998).

The Trust is also beginning to benefit financially as a result of becoming an approved 'Environment Body', since this makes it eligible to receive funding from the Landfill Tax Credit Scheme; in 1987 it received £85,500 from the landfill operator 'Antiwaste' in respect of this scheme. The Trust's finances also continue to benefit from grants made available to it by bodies such as the Environment Agency, the European Commission and local authorities, and from the payments it receives from the Ministry of Agriculture in respect of Trust-owned land within the Broadland and Breckland ESAs.

During the 1960s and 1970s, the scientific staff of the Conservancy spent much of their time identifying sites which merited designation as SSSIs. Where, as in the case of woodlands, a formation was particularly well represented in the county, surveys had to be mounted to decide which were the best examples. The fact that the number of SSSIs in the county more than doubled between 1954 and 1981 is indicative of the emphasis placed on such studies. Since then, additional information has been assembled about the county's fauna and flora, and more particularly about its geology and physiography, and this has resulted in further sites being scheduled.

A major change in the NCC's working practices took place following the passing of the 1981 Act. This made it obligatory, not only to assess and re-notify all the existing SSSIs in the county, but to provide their owners and occupiers with far more information about them than was deemed necessary in the 1950s. In the past, staff of the NC seldom had the time to contact such individuals and explain the reasons why their property had been scheduled, and how the Conservancy would like to see it managed. Today, in contrast, they receive not only a formal list of potentially damaging operations (PDOs), but a quarterly newsletter – 'Site Lines' – providing general information and management advice.

English Nature hopes to arrange for all its biological SSSIs, including those in Norfolk, to be subject to a sustainable form of management by 2000. To this end, it offers tailor-made advice and support to the owners and occupiers of such sites, backed when necessary by financial inducements in the form of short-term management grants. These are designed to bring positive benefits for nature conservation, and are increasingly being negotiated under its Wildlife Enhancement Scheme. Such agreements are gradually replacing the compensation (i.e. 'proven-loss') arrangements negotiable under the provisions of the 1981 Act. In addition to offering financial inducements, English Nature intends that each biological SSSI should be subject to a Site Management Statement, agreed with its owners and occupiers, and providing guidance on how the particular features of interest of the site can best be safeguarded. So far about 240 such statements have been agreed in respect of the biological SSSIs in the county, out of a target figure of about 500 (McNaught pers. comm.).

From the early 1960s onwards conservationists became increasingly aware of the need to safeguard wildlife in the wider countryside, as well as in nature reserves and SSSIs. The problem for many years was a basic lack of knowledge about this 'resource', and an inability to make available the funds needed to overcome this. However, in 1983, a comprehensive survey of the county's wildlife was mounted by the NNT in conjunction with the NCC, and this led to the identification of some 1,200 'C' sites of above-average natural history interest. Details of these were sent to local planning authorities, the object being to ensure that their existence could be taken into account when development applications were being considered. Similar arrangements were made with the National Rivers Authority and other bodies having statutory responsibilities in the county.

All the sites were resurveyed by the NWT in 1995, and the database updated, thus improving its ability to deal with the numerous enquiries it receives each year in respect of what are now known as 'County Wildlife Sites' (CWS). The key to safeguarding the latter does, of course, lie in ensuring that their owners are aware of their particular features of interest, and to this end the Trust has recently produced a Handbook, describing, *inter alia*, the ways in which the habitats represented on CWS can best be managed (Schneidau 1998). In some cases, the owners of CWS are not in a position to manage them themselves, and will agree to the Trust doing so, often with the help of grants from the Countryside Stewardship Scheme or English Nature. Heathlands, one of the most threatened habitats in Norfolk have been specially targeted, and the Trust is now managing seven of the eleven best examples in the county. This is proving very beneficial to their birdlife, and Nightjars and Woodlarks have returned to at least one of the sites concerned.

The problems and challenges faced by conservationists have changed in many other ways over the past 50 years or so, the phenomenon of coastal retreat providing a good example. The dilemma faced by the RSPB concerning the future of the Titchwell Marsh reserve has already been mentioned, but this is far from being the only site affected. The shingle bank which protects the Cley-Salthouse area from sea flooding is now extremely weak, and staff of the English Nature and the NWT have been heavily involved in discussions regarding the Environment Agency's proposal to build a flood wall to the rear of it. Talks are also taking place concerning the longer-term future of sites such as Cley and Titchwell. Where and how can substitute freshwater and brackish marshes be provided as the relative sea level rises as a result of global warming? Is 'set-back' a realistic option, here and elsewhere? Similar problems are being encountered in Broadland. The tidal flood banks protecting the Drained Marshland Area are in a parlous state as a result of long-continued neglect, and some £75 million is to be spent on strengthening them and restoring them to their previous height over the next ten years or so. But a scheme of this magnitude has major implications for nature conservation interests, and staff of English Nature have consequently been obliged to attend numerous meetings about it during the past few years.

Another example of the way in which the work of conservationists has changed over the years is attributable to the international designations now applied to the north Norfolk coast, Breckland and Broadland. These are already involving staff of English Nature, the RSPB and the NWT in a large number of additional consultations, an example being the controversy which developed in 1998 following the recolonisation of Hickling Broad by a dense mass of waterweeds, including several Red Data Book species. As a result of strong representations from boating interests, the Broads Authority asked English Nature and the NWT (as managers of this reserve) to agree to a limited weed-cutting programme to be carried out in 1999. However, mindful of the international as well as the national designations applied to the site, both organisations felt obliged to object to this, on the grounds that it would jeopardise, not only the ecology of the reserve, but the status of the numerous waterfowl (including c. 2,500 Coot and several hundreds of Mute Swans, Pochards and Tufted Ducks) which were feeding on the waterweeds. At the time of writing, this conflict of interest has not been resolved.

English Nature has launched a number of new initiatives since it was formed in 1991, one of these being a 'Species Recovery Programme'. The aim of this is 'to increase the population of species that are threatened with extinction, with the ultimate goal of achieving the survival of self-sustaining populations in the wild.' The Bittern, a Norfolk 'special', and the one currently under the greatest threat as a breeding species both here and elsewhere in the country, was added to the 'Species Recovery Programme' in 1994. The objects of this move were (a) to arrest the Bittern's decline, maintain at least 20 booming males over the present range, and place the population on an upward trend by 2000, and (b) enhance the management of existing reedbeds and link, extend, or create new reedbeds both within and away from the present core Bittern areas. Partners with English Nature in the project include the Norfolk and Lincolnshire Wildlife Trusts, Pioneer Aggregates and the Environment Agency.

The hopes of achieving these objectives received a major boost in 1996 when the RSPB and a consortium of other conservation agencies was awarded a European Union LIFE nature grant in respect of the species. This will involve spending some £2.8 million by the year 2000, half of which will come from the European Union, and half from the managers of the 13 reserves in England and Wales where projects aimed at creating suitable habitat for breeding Bitterns are in progress. Six of these sites, namely Cley Marsh, East Ruston Common, Hickling Broad, Holme Dunes, Strumpshaw Fen and Titchwell Marsh are in Norfolk, and will therefore benefit from the EU grant.

Conservation organisations such as the NCC, NWT and RSPB have long considered it desirable to compile management plans for their reserves. These describe each site's particular features of interest, the reasons why it has been safeguarded, and how it should be managed. Progress with preparing such plans was slow at first, but the pace quickened during the 1970s, and by the mid-1980s management plans for most of the reserves in the county had been compiled. Unfortunately, from about that time onwards, staff in all three organisations became increasingly burdened with the bureaucratic procedures associated with the preparation of other types of plans and reports. Examples are legion, and range from the need for field staff to carry out a 'Risk Assessment' before any out-of-the-ordinary tasks can be carried out on a reserve, to the quarterly reports, corporate plans and strategies now deemed necessary if an organisation is to be efficiently managed.

The situation worsened for conservationists following the 1992 Rio Earth Summit Conference since they are now expected to produce 'Biodiversity Action Plans' for both habitats and species, at local as well as national level. Useful as these may be as a sort of 'aide memoire' for highly endangered species such as Bitterns, one cannot help wondering where it will all end. Will the individuals concerned be expected to produce such plans for every single rare bird, mammal, invertebrate and plant? And if they do, who will have time even to read these documents, let alone implement them?

One gains the impression that planning and reporting is now all too often regarded as an end in itself, rather than as a means to an end. In this respect, conservation organisations are probably no better or worse off, than, say, the Environment Agency, schools and the National Health Service, all of whom are subject to a new-fangled management 'ethos', and a plethora of stultifying bureaucratic procedures. The fact that conservationists are embroiled in such procedures is a retrograde development, and represents the 'down side' of what is, overall, an exhilarating improvement in the state of conservation in the county over the past 50 years.

# SYSTEMATIC LIST OF
# THE BIRDS OF NORFOLK

## INTRODUCTION

The production of an up-to-date avifauna of such a bird-rich county as Norfolk is only possible with a large team of contributors. The following species texts were written by 39 authors, many of whom are authorities on or have a special interest in the species involved. Varying degrees of editorial changes were made to the texts submitted in order to achieve a measure of uniformity throughout the book, while at the same time endeavouring to maintain the author's individual style. The authors responsible for each species are credited at the end of each account.

Every species text commences with a brief summary of the species' current status in Norfolk. The terms and numerical ranges used are identical to those appearing in the *Birds of Sussex* (James 1996):

|                | Breeding Pairs        | Winter/Passage        |
|----------------|-----------------------|-----------------------|
| Very rare      | 1–10 records in total | 1–10 records in total |
| Rare           | less than annual      | less than annual      |
| Very scarce    | 1–10 per year         | 1–20 per year         |
| Scarce         | 11–100                | 21–200                |
| Fairly common  | 101–1,000             | 201–2,000             |
| Common         | 1,001–5,000           | 2,001–10,000          |
| Very common    | 5,001–30,000          | 10,001–60,000         |
| Abundant       | 30,000+               | 60,000+               |

Breeding can be assumed for all residents and summer visitors, except those species categorised as being rare, in which case if breeding occurs it is stated. The total number of county records is included in the status line for all species classified as very rare.

The introductory paragraph includes details of the world, Western Palearctic and/or European distribution depending on the species. This information has been taken from either *The Handbook of the Birds of the Western Palearctic* or *The EBCC Atlas of European Breeding Birds*, both of which are listed under the Standard References included later. The status of the species in the British Isles then follows. This information enables the reader to place in context the bird's distribution and status within Norfolk. The summary of historical records extends back to at least the 19th century and is largely based on the excellent county avifaunas of Stevenson (1866–90) and Riviere (1930). Although Volume 3 of Stevenson's *The Birds of Norfolk* was completed by Thomas Southwell and published in 1890, after Stevenson's death, all three volumes have been included as a Standard Reference under the name of Stevenson. More recent records have been extracted from the *Birds of Norfolk* (Seago 1967 and 1977), as well as the *Norfolk Bird Reports* which have covered the years since 1953. The breeding status of many species has been based on *The Norfolk Bird Atlas* (Kelly 1986), updated where appropriate from data gathered under the 1994–97 BTO/ JNCC/RSPB Breeding Bird Survey in Norfolk. In addition, information on both breeding and wintering populations has been obtained from single species surveys organised by the BTO, RSPB, English Nature, Norfolk Bird Club and privately, for species such as Grey Heron, Mute Swan, Lapwing, Nightingale and Rook. Also data from annual surveys such as the National Wildfowl Counts and the Wetland Bird Survey have been included. Surprisingly little data are available on visible migration and the annual reports based on records made in the Sheringham area since 1976 have provided a rich source of material. Finally, an analysis of the results of ringing in the county concludes the species accounts.

Records of rare and scarce species have only been included if they have been formally accepted by the BOURC and/or BBRC, where appropriate, or the County Records Committee. The only exceptions are records on which decisions are pending (mainly from 1998) but which the County Recorders believe will be accepted by the relevant recording committee in the light of the details submitted. Where this applies it has been indicated after the record.

Readers will notice the absence of any distribution maps. The inclusion of these would have made the present volume excessively large and the necessary data collection would have postponed publication by about five years. It was therefore decided to undertake fieldwork for an up-to-date atlas of the distribution of birds within Norfolk from December 1999 to run for a minimum of three years. The distribution of both breeding and wintering birds will be mapped and the results will be published as a companion volume to this book.

## NOMENCLATURE AND SEQUENCE

The scientific names and the sequence used follow the first edition of the British Ornithologists' Union's *The British List* published in 1998. However, the English names that are most familiar have been retained and, where different, those used in *The British List* are given in parentheses. The only exception is to give full specific status to Yellow-legged Gull *Larus cachinnans*. All species that have occurred in Norfolk and which are included in Categories A to C of *The British List*, including those that have recently been deleted from the county list after review, are included in the Systematic List. Other species which have been recorded in a wild state in Norfolk are included in a section after the Systematic List. As at the end of 1998, the county list stands at 409 species (excluding albatross sp. and Fea's/Zino's Petrel).

## AREA AND PERIOD COVERED

Following local government reorganisation in 1974, a small part of the district of Lothingland in east Suffolk was transferred to Norfolk. The county gained the remaining parts of the southern shore of Breydon that were in Suffolk and the county boundary was extended to the south of Hopton, to embrace the parishes of Bradwell, Burgh Castle, Belton, Fritton and Hopton, as well as parts of Corton and Herringfleet. The new boundary extended down the centre of two sites of ornithological interest, Lound Waterworks and Fritton Lake, to include the extensive Waveney Forest and the remnants of Belton Common. The result of this change in 1974 was to benefit Norfolk, although Suffolk still continues to recognise this area under the Watsonian vice-county system. Two species, White-throated Sparrow and Allen's Gallinule are therefore now included in the Norfolk list.

In order to make the book up to date, an attempt has been made to include as many 1998 records as possible, with the caveat concerning records of rare and scarce species mentioned above. However, it is known that not all records were available at the time of publication and not all the ringing recoveries reported during 1998 were available for inclusion in the analyses.

## STANDARD REFERENCES AND ABBREVIATIONS USED

Certain standard references are used frequently in the species texts and are abbreviated as below. To avoid repetition in each introductory paragraph, the reference for each species' distribution outside the British Isles is not given (see above).

| | |
|---|---|
| **BWP** | Cramp, S. (ed.) 1977–94. *The Handbook of the Birds of Europe, The Middle East and North Africa: The Birds of the Western Palearctic.* Vols. 1–9. Oxford University Press, Oxford. |
| **European Atlas** | Hagemeijer, E. J. M. and Blair, M. J. (eds.) 1997. *The EBCC Atlas of European Birds: Their Distribution and Abundance.* T. & A. D. Poyser, London. |
| **Historical Atlas** | Holloway, S. 1996. *The Historical Atlas of Breeding Birds in Britain and Ireland 1875–1900.* T. & A. D. Poyser, London. |
| **New Atlas** | Gibbons, D. W., Reid, J. B. and Chapman, R. A. 1993. *The New Atlas of Breeding Birds in Britain and Ireland 1988–1991.* T. & A. D. Poyser, London. |
| **Norfolk Atlas** | Kelly, G. 1986. *The Norfolk Bird Atlas.* Norfolk & Norwich Naturalists Society. |
| **Riviere** | Riviere, B. B. 1930. *A History of the Birds of Norfolk.* H. F. & G. Witherby, London. |
| **68–72 BTO Atlas** | Sharrock, J. T. R. 1976. *The Atlas of Breeding Birds in Britain and Ireland.* T. & A. D. Poyser, Berkhamsted. |
| **Stevenson** | Stevenson, H. 1866–90. *The Birds of Norfolk.* Vols. 1–3. John Van Voorst and Gurney & Jackson, London. |

**Winter Atlas**      Lack, P. 1986. *The Atlas of Wintering Birds in Britain and Ireland.* T. & A. D. Poyser, Calton.

## Other Abbreviations Used in the Text

| | |
|---|---|
| BBRC | British Birds Rarities Committee |
| BBS | Breeding Bird Survey (BTO/JNCC/RSPB) |
| BOURC | British Ornithologists' Union Records Committee |
| BTO | British Trust for Ornithology |
| CBC | Common Bird Census (BTO) |
| ESA | Environmentally Sensitive Area |
| JNCC | Joint Nature Conservation Committee |
| NBC | Norfolk Bird Club |
| NCC | Nature Conservancy Council (now English Nature) |
| NNR | National Nature Reserve |
| NNT | Norfolk Naturalists Trust (now Norfolk Wildlife Trust) |
| NOA | Norfolk Ornithologists' Association |
| NWT | Norfolk Wildlife Trust |
| RSPB | Royal Society for the Protection of Birds |
| RSPCA | Royal Society for the Prevention of Cruelty to Animals |
| SNH | Scottish Natural Heritage |
| 10km square | 10km x 10km square of the British National Grid |
| tetrad | 2km x 2km square of the British National Grid |
| UEA | University of East Anglia |
| WeBS | Wetland Bird Survey |
| WWRG | Wash Wader Ringing Group |

**Spotted Redshanks by Richard Richardson**. A fine example of Richard's work – a bird he could readily attract by imitating its call.

**Welney Wash** (*Chris Knights*). The Welney Washes are famous for their wintering swans.

**Whooper and Bewick's Swans** (*Chris Knights*). Internationally important numbers of both Whooper and Bewick's Swans winter at Welney.

**Canvasback** (*Iain Leach*). This North American Canvasback was added to the county list in 1997.

**Pectoral Sandpiper** (*Iain Leach*). As many as four Pectoral Sandpipers have passed through Welney flashes during a single autumn.

**Holkham NNR** (*Mike Page*). A most important site for migrant, wintering and breeding birds.

**White-fronted Geese** (*Chris Knights*). Flocks of this species regularly winter at Holkham and also in east Norfolk.

**Stiffkey Fen** (*Andrew Bloomfield*). This recently created series of pools between the coast road and the saltmarsh is proving attractive to many waders including nesting Avocets.

**Avocets** (*Chris Knights*). Since they returned to breed in the county at Cley in 1977, this attractive species has extended its range to include much of the north coast, and also Broadland floods and Welney.

**Ringmere** (*Mary Dorling*). This Breckland mere is often a favoured nesting haunt of Little Grebes.

**Langmere** (*Mary Dorling*). The depth of water in the Breckland meres fluctuates regularly and depends on the water table in the underlying chalk which can be affected by local water extraction.

**Common Crossbills** (*Andrew Bloomfield*). A small population of Common Crossbills is usually present in the Brecks; numbers are augmented in irruption years.

**Nightjar** (*Chris Knights*). Breckland is the stronghold for Norfolk's Nightjar population.

**A Hornbeam grove at East Wretham** (*Chris Knights*). Hornbeams are particularly favoured by Hawfinches.

**Hawfinch at nest** (*Chris Knights*). In Norfolk the elusive Hawfinch has become restricted to Breckland as a breeding species.

**Hunstanton Cliffs** (*Chris Knights*). These colourful red and white cliffs are one of the few breeding sites for Fulmars in East Anglia.

**Fulmars** (*Don Dorling*). The hard cliffs at Hunstanton provide stable ledges for nesting Fulmars.

**Cley Marsh** (*Chris Knights*). Long famous for its migrant birds, Cley Marsh became the first reserve of the Norfolk Wildlife Trust in 1926.

**Spoonbills** (*Chris Knights*). Titchwell, Cley and Berney are favoured locations for visiting Spoonbills.

**Frog Hill, Breckland** (*Chris Knights*). A typical Breckland scene in the Stanford Training Area.

**Stone Curlews** (*Chris Knights*). Many pairs of Stone Curlews use large ploughed fields as breeding sites.

**Wood Lark** (*Rod Powley*). A recent success story is the increasing population of Wood Larks which are spreading back to the open heathland from their favoured forestry plantations.

**Little Owl** (*Iain Leach*). Although still widespread in Broadland, few remain in its Fenland and Breckland former strongholds.

**Titchwell and the north coast** (*Mike Page*). Titchwell has proved to be the RSPB's most visited reserve.

**Black-winged Stilt** (*Barry Jarvis*). This stilt, 'resident' since 1993, has been a favourite attraction at Titchwell.

**Mediterranean Gull** (*Joe Reed*). Having first bred successfully in the county in 1993, two pairs fledged four young at Blakeney Point in 1996.

**Sandwich Terns** (*Reg Jones*). Scolt Head Island and Blakeney Point are the regular breeding sites, with over 3,000 pairs present.

**Pink-footed Geese** (*Andrew Bloomfield*). Pinkfeet winter in north Norfolk in very large numbers and are increasing again in the east of the county.

**Dark-bellied Brent Geese** (*Chris Knights*). These geese winter in Norfolk in internationally important numbers.

**Common Crane** (*John Buxton*). History was made when the Common Crane returned as a breeder to Broadland. This is the 1997 brood.

**Great Crested Grebe** (*Chris Knights*). Great Crested Grebes now breed on suitable waters throughout the county, including occasional broods on the River Wensum in the centre of Norwich.

**Bittern** (*Reg Jones*). Hopefully, current habitat work will bring this Broadland speciality back from the brink of local extinction.

**Bearded Tit** (*Rod Powley*).　　　　　　　　　　**Marsh Harrier** (*John Buxton*).
Two typical species of the Broadland and coastal reedbeds. The years of large-scale autumn influxes from the Netherlands will be long remembered. Marsh Harriers have also colonised cereal fields adjoining the Wash.

**Golden Orioles** (*Chris Knights*). A small breeding population is present in Fenland poplar plantations.

**Penduline Tit** (*Alan Tate*). A rare visitor to the reedbeds.

**Beach Road, Cley** (*Mary Dorling*). Cley marsh underwent one of its periodic saltwater floodings in February 1996.

**Arnold's Marsh, Cley** (*Mary Dorling*). A favoured feeding location for waders and ducks.

**Thompson Water** (*Chris Knights*). One of Breckland's permanent areas of open water.

**River Yare and Buckenham Marsh** (*Mike Page*). A favoured area for wintering wildfowl, including England's only regular flock of Bean Geese.

**Hoopoe** (*Barry Jarvis*). An annual passage migrant in small numbers. It has overwintered.

**Red-footed Falcon** (*Dave Nye*). An unprecedented influx of these scarce vagrants appeared in 1992 following a vast anticyclone centred over Scandinavia and surges of warm air from the south-east.

**Rose-coloured Starling** (*Julian Bhalero*). A vagrant which usually occurs in spring.

**Rock Thrush** (*Robin Chittenden*). This rare vagrant appeared in north Norfolk in May 1995.

**A Breckland Road** (*Chris Knights*). Once a typical Breckland scene, habitats like this are now largely confined to military training areas.

**Curlew** (*Rod Powley*). A relatively recent colonist of the Breckland heaths.

**Rockland Broad** (*Robin Chittenden*). This Yare Valley broad is a favourite of migrating marsh terns and Ospreys.

**Grey Heron** (*Reg Jones*). A survey in 1998 produced a total of 313 nests in the county, the highest total since 1971.

**Waxwings** (*Chris Knights*). Periodic irruptions occasionally result in large flocks wintering in the county.

**Red-breasted Goose** (*Chris Knights*). A rare vagrant to Norfolk – usually found with Dark-bellied Brent or Pink-footed Geese.

**Desert Wheatear** (*Barry Jarvis*). A rare late autumn vagrant.

**Oriental Pratincole** (*R. G. Wilson*). This bird, which occurred in May 1993, is the only county record of this great rarity.

**Holme** (*Mike Page*). This north-west corner of the county attracts many common and rare migrants.

**Foxley Wood** (*Mary Dorling*). One of a number of ancient woodlands which are important sites for both resident and migrant breeders.

**Red-flanked Bluetail** (*Robin Chittenden*). Added to the county list in October 1994 when this bird appeared in Yarmouth Cemeteries.

**Desert Warbler** (*R. G. Wilson*). The only record for the county was this bird at Blakeney Point in 1993.

**Kingfisher** (*Rod Powley*). A declining resident whose numbers are affected by severe winters.

**Shore Lark** (*Iain Leach*). A remarkable autumn influx totalling several hundred birds appeared in 1998.

**Goldfinch** (*Rod Powley*). A common breeder through-out the county.

**Barn Owl and brood** (*Rod Powley*). North Norfolk is the stronghold of this uncommon species.

**Strumpshaw Fen** (*Mike Page*). This RSPB reserve has Cetti's Warblers and Marsh Harriers amongst its breeding species.

**North Norfolk saltmarsh** (*Chris Knights*). There are 2,000 hectares of this important habitat along the north coast.

**Little Egret** (*Dave Nye*). An increasing visitor which has occasionally overwintered.

**Long-billed Dowitcher** (*Robin Chittenden*). A rare vagrant form North America.

**Slavonian Grebe** (*Dave Nye*). Autumn concentrations have become a regular feature in Holkham Bay.

**Black-necked Grebe** (*Iain Leach*). This bird overwintered at Holkham Lake, assuming summer plumage before departure.

## Red-throated Diver | off CLEY 8·10·1986.      *Gavia stellata*

**A fairly common winter visitor and passage migrant; rare in mid-summer and very scarce inland.**

During the breeding season, the Red-throated Diver is the most northerly and most densely distributed of the divers in the Western Palearctic. In the British Isles it breeds in north and west Scotland and on offshore island groups, in particular Shetland and Orkney (New Atlas). In winter a sizeable part of the Western Palearctic population is present in British and Irish coastal waters, especially along the east coasts of England and Scotland (Winter Atlas).

Stevenson called the Red-throated Diver, the 'sprat loon' and stated that it was less frequently found on freshwater than either the Black-throated or even the Great Northern Diver. He quoted two instances where large numbers were recorded offshore – in late October 1872 'some hundreds' attracted by the shoals of herring were observed from the herring fleet outside Cross Sands, off Yarmouth and on 1st October 1880 an almost constant stream flew east for almost four hours, a quarter of a mile offshore at Cley. He also pointed out that fossil remains had been identified in the post-glacial deposit known as 'Mundesley River Bed' and the species is thus one of the first to have been recorded in Norfolk!

It remains the most numerous species of diver to be recorded off the Norfolk coast and although it has been seen in every month of the year, it is rare in June and July. A few are normally noted from mid to late August, which may represent birds from the Shetland population, but it is not until October that small numbers are regularly seen off the coast of north Norfolk, by which time there is probably a direct movement from Scandinavia (Winter Atlas). During the last 20 years, increasing numbers of Red-throated Divers have been seen off the coast of Norfolk with maximum counts generally between mid-December and early March. Up to 50 or more may be present offshore at favoured localities. In north-west Norfolk the maximum count has been 373 west and 86 east at Holme on 12th January 1997. Elsewhere in north Norfolk the highest counts have often involved birds flying east, in ones or twos, but occasionally in loose parties of up to 20–30, during the first few hours after dawn. This 'passage' has been noted at several sites between Cley and Paston, day-counts of 200–300 being not unusual. The maximum counts have been 339 east at Paston on 10th January 1982, 711 north at Walcott on January 4th 1992, 820 east at Sheringham on 29th January 1992, 455 east at Mundesley on January 16th 1994, 750 east at Sheringham on 2nd December 1995 and 359 east at Trimingham on 19th January 1997. More confusing were 250 east and 270 west at Sheringham on 30th December 1993. Further south, the maximum count in the Yarmouth area has been 126 south on 9th February 1983, with 168 off Horsey on 28th February 1998.

These movements are always difficult to interpret, but are thought to be daily feeding excursions, although the large morning movements are rarely followed by return ones later in the day. They do not occur during times of strong onshore winds but are often associated with periods of colder weather. It may be that there is a general southerly movement into the southern North Sea as the winter progresses and that under certain weather conditions large numbers of Red-throated Divers, which are wintering far offshore, move into inshore waters to feed. Large gatherings at Overstrand between January and March 1996, peaking at 350 on 15th February, may have been the destination for up to 370 flying east at Sheringham on several dates in early February 1996. Sites regularly holding at least 50 birds are of national importance for this species and so the waters off the north Norfolk coast are of considerable conservation value.

Spring passage is not easy to recognise, but 130 flying north at Winterton on 16th March 1980 and 500 west at Cromer on 16th March 1995, may possibly have represented a return movement. Most birds have left by the end of April, with a few stragglers in mid to late May. Records of Red-throated Divers are rare in June or July, but have included one in full breeding plumage at Hickling Broad on 22nd–23rd July 1953, one with a length of fishing wire entangled around its legs at Burnham Overy Harbour from 31st May to July 1984 (Bloomfield 1993) and records of one (or several) between Blakeney Point and Yarmouth between 1st June and 12th July 1986. During the 1990s one or two have been noted most years in mid-summer mainly off the north Norfolk coast but this may be a direct result of increased observer coverage.

Each year a few Red-throated Divers are found on inland waters, the majority between December and March. During the last 40 years, over 50 inland sites have hosted Red-throated Divers, of which almost half have been in Broadland. Most places have only recorded the species on one or two occasions, but over 15 have been noted at both Hickling and Horsey Broads, while Breydon was particularly favoured in the early part of the 20th century. Other inland habitats visited have included gravel pits, park lakes and rivers. Only single birds are usually involved, but occasionally two, and there were three at Tottenhill Gravel Pit on 9th February 1982 and four at Hickling Broad on 29th August 1985. Prolonged stays have been recorded at Martham Broad from 18th April to 25th May 1987 and at Thetford Gravel Pit from 4th April to 4th May 1988.

*Moss Taylor*

## Black-throated Diver                                          *Gavia arctica*

**A scarce winter visitor and passage migrant; very scarce inland.**

The Black-throated Diver has a northern Holarctic breeding distribution. Unlike the Red-throated Diver it prefers boreal habitats and fairly large, deep lakes. In the British Isles it is a breeding summer visitor to the larger lochs in the more remote parts of north and west Scotland and the Outer Hebrides (New Atlas). The majority winter in sheltered coastal waters.

Both Stevenson and Riviere stated that it was commonest between January and March, being more frequent on inland rather than tidal waters. Of the 24 specimens described by Stevenson, 18 had been obtained inland. During the 1950s, far fewer were recorded in Norfolk than is the case today, in particular there has been an increase in the number of records since the late 1970s. For example, the average number of records submitted annually in the early 1950s was six, whereas there were 112 in 1983, more than 150 in 1984 and 92 in 1989. Even allowing for duplication there has clearly been a remarkable increase in some years. This is, at least in part, due to increased observer coverage, better optical equipment and most importantly a better understanding of the identification features of Black-throated Diver.

Autumn passage starts in late August or early September with a few being recorded along the north Norfolk coast. The earliest was one at Titchwell on 18th August 1984. Peak numbers generally occur in October or November, Holkham Bay being a favoured locality in recent years with maximum counts of ten on 22nd October 1989, five on 4th November 1982 and five from 21st October to 30th November 1990; also ten at Titchwell on 6th November 1997 and nine at Scolt Head three days later. The autumn of 1989 was noteworthy for the number of records of Black-throated Diver and in addition to those given above for Holkham, up to seven graced the inshore waters between Sheringham and Blakeney Point (often off Salthouse) and the species was present daily off Cley from 6th October to 29th November. During October and November 1995, over 20 were scattered along the coast between Hunstanton and Caister.

In mid-winter, the majority of coastal records continue to come from north Norfolk, particularly between Hunstanton and Cromer, and most refer to single birds, however, 16 were present off Hunstanton on 3rd January 1982, six at Scolt Head on 5th January 1997 and six east at Trimingham on 19th January 1997. In most years very few are seen off east Norfolk. The main wintering grounds of the Western Palearctic breeding population lie in the Baltic area and down the west coast of Europe, and Britain therefore supports only a small proportion of the population (Winter Atlas). Those wintering in Norfolk are probably of Scandinavian origin.

Spring passage is usually evident from early March, but as at other times only small numbers are involved and most records refer to single birds. However, at Snettisham Gravel Pits there were four on 20th March 1955 and up to five from 19th February to 20th May 1956, while an exceptional assembly of 36 were counted off Winterton on 17th March 1979. The last bird of the spring is generally noted in mid-May, but occasional birds are seen later and there are four June records – one at Blakeney Point on 1st June 1986 and two at Cley the following day, one between Blakeney Point and Cley on 7th–10th June 1994 and one at Sheringham on 24th June 1995.

As in Stevenson's day, a few Black-throated Divers continue to be located on inland waters in most years, generally in January and February, but on occasions during the time of spring passage. 1979 was exceptional with 19 inland records between January and April. Usually the birds remain for only a few days but longer-staying individuals have been recorded – at Hardley Flood from 21st March to 19th April 1958, Haddiscoe Cut from 15th January to 15th February 1961, Rollesby/Ormesby/Filby Broads from 27th December 1991 to 17th February 1992 and on the River Wensum in the centre of Norwich from 31st December 1996 to 19th January 1997. The only multiple records were of two on the lower River Bure on 21st January 1956 and two on Filby/Rollesby Broads on 14th–16th February 1993, while the latest to be recorded on an inland water was at Rockland Broad on 15th May 1979. As Black-throated Divers need a long take-off before becoming airborne, unlike Red-throated Divers, they tend to be found on the larger areas of inland water.

*Moss Taylor*

# Great Northern Diver *Gavia immer*

**A very scarce winter visitor and spring passage migrant; very rare in mid-summer and rare inland.**

In the Western Palearctic the Great Northern Diver, which is predominantly a Nearctic breeding species, breeds regularly only in Iceland, although one pair nested in Scotland in 1970. The species winters around the coast of Britain and Ireland, the largest concentrations being off the west coast of Ireland, western Scotland and Orkney and Shetland (Winter Atlas). In the absence of any ringing recoveries, the origin of those wintering off the British Isles is uncertain, but they are probably from both Iceland and Greenland, and may even include some from mainland Canada.

Both Stevenson and Riviere described it as an irregular winter visitor and the most rarely recorded diver off the coast. Occasionally found on the Broads and inland lakes, it had never been seen in adult breeding plumage off Norfolk. Stevenson stated that it was sometimes known as the 'herring loon' in contrast to the 'sprat loon' or Red-throated Diver.

Today it remains the scarcest of the three annually recorded divers, less than 20 individuals usually being seen during the course of a year. Most Great Northern Divers leave their breeding grounds, singly or in pairs, in September and October, with only a minority (probably immatures or failed breeders) reaching their wintering areas off Scotland in mid-August (BWP). In Norfolk, the first birds generally pass offshore during the second half of September, although in some years it is earlier. The earliest autumn record was of one off Horsey on 4th August 1988.

Small numbers of Great Northern Divers are recorded annually during the winter months along the tidal waters of north Norfolk, peaking between November and January. On the inshore waters of east Norfolk they are decidedly rare. Normally occurring only singly, or occasionally in twos, up to seven were close inshore at Cley during the last week of December 1963, five at Cromer on 5th January 1978 and seven off Scolt Head on 7th December 1998. Unusual numbers were recorded in 1989 when up to three were present daily between Cromer and Blakeney Point from 1st November to the end of the year, with a maximum of six off Sheringham on 9th November, and four in Holkham Bay on 4th–19th November. Monthly totals of 21 in November and 31 in December 1995 were probably unprecedented in Norfolk and included four flying east at Weybourne on 2nd December. The following April, up to five were present at Holme, a month in which few Great Northern Divers are normally reported.

In recent years, a small spring passage has been noted in May with the last normally recorded during the last ten days of the month. However, in five of the years between 1973 and 1989, singles were recorded in the first four days of June and there have been three additional records for that month – one flying east at Sheringham on 10th June 1994, one offshore at Sheringham on 23rd June 1995 and one flying east at Weybourne on 28th June 1995. An exceptional record involved at least four in breeding plumage between Burnham Overy and Holme in late May 1991.

Since 1953, there have been 11 records from inland sites, the majority in Broadland, but including singles at Taverham Gravel Pit on 30th January 1954, Downham Market on 24th February 1979, Pentney Gravel Pits on 23rd–26th December 1979 and Denver Sluice on 11th–22nd January 1995. Most have only stayed for a single day but one was at the Flegg Broads on 5th–15th February 1976 and the longest-staying was at Lynford Gravel Pit from 25th December 1997 to 31st January 1998, on which date it was seen to fly off.

*Moss Taylor*

# White-billed Diver (Yellow-billed Diver) *Gavia adamsii*

**A very rare vagrant; five records.**

The White-billed Diver breeds within a relatively narrow band about 600 miles wide, lying mainly north of the Arctic Circle extending from Varanger Fjord in northern Norway, eastwards to the Siberian tundra, Alaska and north-west Canada. In winter, pack ice forces the species southwards with substantial numbers spending the period off the Norwegian coast. It seems most likely that virtually all the British records relate to birds wandering south from this wintering population, although there is recent evidence of summering in Shetland and spring migration along the western side of the British Isles.

The first Norfolk record was of an adult in non-breeding plumage with other divers found by C.J. and

J. A. Hazell off Halfway House, Blakeney Point on 29th September 1985 and observed surprisingly by over 150 observers (Hazell 1987). The second record was of one found 'long dead' on the edge of the Blakeney Point ternery in July 1986. On close examination, it was considered by the state of the moult, to have died in February, possibly following oiling. The remains were deposited at the Castle Museum, Norwich.

An immature was seen at Cley coastguards for ten minutes only on 4th October 1986 with the same or possibly another on 17th October which soon drifted westwards and was later seen off Blakeney Point. An adult was found dead on Winterton beach on 11th April 1996. A second-winter bird was seen close inshore at Cley and Salthouse on 7th–8th October 1996, at times in close company with a Black-throated Diver. It was last seen flying west towards Blakeney Point.

*Peter Allard*

## Pied-billed Grebe                                        *Podilymbus podiceps*

**A very rare vagrant; one record.**

The Pied-billed Grebe breeds widely in North, Central and South America, with the Canadian population moving south in autumn to winter in the USA. An unlikely vagrant, it was first recorded in the British Isles in 1963. One which frequented Welney Washes on 9th–12th November 1968 was found by Graham Easy and Colin Kirkland and constituted only the third British record.

*Peter Allard*

## Little Grebe      Loddon. R.Chet. (5) 2·12·1992.      *Tachybaptus ruficollis*

**A fairly common resident, and scarce passage migrant and winter visitor.**

The Little Grebe is widespread and common in the central region of the Western Palearctic south of the Baltic, eastwards into Russia and south to Spain, Italy and north-western North Africa.

Stevenson stated that this, our smallest grebe, was widespread throughout the county; mainly appearing on the smaller waters rather than the larger Broads. It was present all through the year with the coastal dykes being particularly favoured in bad weather during the winter months. The situation had changed little by the time Riviere summarised the Dabchick's status in 1930. He was able to demonstrate evidence of its migratory powers by recording occurrences, usually fatal, in autumn and spring on the offshore light-vessels and at coastal lighthouses. More recent evidence of this behaviour was one on the Smith's Knoll light-vessel on 20th October 1968 and again in November 1986 when one was found exhausted on a gas platform 55 miles north-east of Yarmouth and flown ashore by helicopter (Allard 1990).

Breeding continues to be widespread throughout the county on suitable smaller waters. The Norfolk Atlas survey found Little Grebes in 122 tetrads with confirmed breeding in 69. In north Norfolk the breeding population in the Holkham area spread out from a few pairs on Holkham Lake into the grazing marshes in 1982, where 20 pairs were present by 1989, increasing to 42 pairs by 1993 when there were also ten pairs on the lake. The total for the Holkham Fresh Marshes in 1996 was 31 pairs and a further five on the lake. A colony of up to 15 pairs became established in the dykes adjoining Breydon in the mid-1970s but the number of pairs subsequently decreased to between eight and ten (Allard 1990). In 1998, the total for the Breydon and Berney Reserve area was 20 pairs.

The Breckland Meres in the south-west of the county were long-established breeding locations and in 1980 Little Grebes were recorded at Fowlmere, Ring Mere, West Tofts Mere, Stanford Water, West Mere, Tottington Mere, Brandon, Santon Downham, Gooderstone and Cockley Cley. There were 13 pairs on Langmere in 1982. Following the drop in the local water table many of the meres now have very low water levels or are completely dry, and have become unsuitable for grebes and other diving fowl. In the east the large open waters of the main Broads have never been favoured breeding localities but single pairs bred on Ormesby Broad in 1976 and at Hickling in 1996. However, they are used as assembly areas with 14 on Hickling Broad in January and 17 in October 1996 while 23 had gathered on Heigham Sounds by December that year. These counts were exceeded on 18th January 1998 when 29 were present on Hickling Broad.

Other high winter counts have included 47 on Well's Boating Lake in January 1953 and 50 in Blakeney Harbour in November 1967. In January 1986 the WeBS count included 84 in north Norfolk and 62 in the Wash. A count along the intertidal habitat between Holme and Weybourne in November 1997 located 70 birds including ten in Burnham Overy Harbour. A few are occasionally seen offshore in winter with exceptional numbers being recorded along the north coast in November 1986. Snettisham Pits is a favoured winter locality with 162 in January 1971 and a recent maximum of 139 in December 1995.

*Don Dorling*

## Great Crested Grebe HARDLEY FLOODS. 19-4-1992. *Podiceps cristatus*

**A fairly common resident, and scarce passage migrant and winter visitor.**

The Western Palearctic distribution of the Great Crested Grebe stretches from Britain and Ireland south-westwards to Portugal, Spain and France and eastwards into Russia, between the latitudes 45°N and 60°N with extensions southwards to Italy, Greece, Turkey and a few colonies in North Africa. The species shows a clear preference for breeding in lowland Britain and Ireland (New Atlas). In line with the rest of Europe the fortunes of the Great Crested Grebe in Norfolk have swung from common at the beginning of the 19th century to near extinction in the 1850s and 1860s and back again to common and widespread today.

The species was known to Sir Thomas Browne as a summer visitor to the 'broad waters' who considered the grebe or loon 'an handsome and specious fowle' and it was still described as common on Filby, Surlingham and other broads by Hunt in his *List of Norfolk Birds*. However, its fortunes rapidly declined as a result of extensive collecting of eggs and the demands of the millinery trade for the feathers from adult birds. By the middle of the 19th century extinction as a Norfolk bird was being forecast. Fortunately a few pairs survived on private broads; part of a national population estimated to be only 42 pairs. Following the introduction of various bird protection Acts from 1869 onwards, the population in the county greatly improved.

By the time Riviere published his book he was able to describe the Great Crested Grebe as abundant throughout the whole of the Broads, with smaller populations on other suitable waters elsewhere in the county. These included Holkham Lake from 1922 and the large Breckland meres, commencing with Fowlmere in 1926. The extensive extraction of sand and gravel in the river valleys, from the time of the Second World War, created numerous additional suitable sites as the abandoned pits become flooded and the population has continued to grow.

The first full county census of breeding Great Crested Grebes was carried out in 1931, the next was 21 years later in 1954. Five other full counts have been attempted, the last in 1998 (Seago 1999). A summary of these surveys is given in Table 1.

**Table 1: Total number of adult Great Crested Grebes in Norfolk during seven breeding seasons.**

|  | 1931 | 1954 | 1961 | 1965 | 1973 | 1975 | 1998 |
|---|---|---|---|---|---|---|---|
| Broadland | 260 | 254 | 387 | 284 | 261 | 358 | 422 |
| Lakes & Gravel Pits etc. | 76 | 51 | 44 | 37 | 110 | 111 | 138 |
| Breckland | 68 | 39 | 48 | 34 | 23 | 20 | 34 |
| Fenland | - | - | 3 | - | 75 | 66 | 121 |
| **Total** | 404 | 344 | 482 | 355 | 469 | 555 | 715 |

As can be seen, during the 42 years between 1931 and 1973 the Broadland population remained relatively stable with the exception of a peak in 1961 resulting from particularly high counts on some of the larger Broads. For example, in 1961 there were at least 42 on Barton Broad, 40 on Ormesby and 69 on Rollesby compared with their (1931) and 1975 totals of (eight) 33, (12) 18 and (20) 13 respectively. The increase in Broadland by 1975 was largely due to an apparent expansion of range into the Rivers Yare, Bure and Ant where 100 individuals were counted. This trend has continued and the 1998 surveyors discovered 179 adults on these rivers.

On the actual Broads, in most cases, numbers have not recovered to their peak levels of 1961. On Barton Broad, for example, there were between 42 and 60 in 1961 with only 18 present during the 1998 breeding season count, although there had been 32 there in the previous October. The greatest decline has occurred on the Flegg Broads with the 1961 total for Filby, Rollesby, Lady and Ormesby of 125 adults being reduced to only eight in 1998. However, the Hickling/Heigham Sounds complex has reversed the trend with the 1961 total of 22 adults increasing to 20 pairs in 1997 with 39 birds being counted in 1998.

These increased population figures probably result from the vastly improved water quality and subsequent aquatic plant growth in Hickling Broad, witnessed from 1997 onwards.

Similarly, the increase in Fenland numbers has resulted from the colonisation of the main rivers and drains including the Relief Channel and the Cut-off Channel. These waterways contained 104 individuals during the 1998 counts. The substantial growth in the Lakes and Gravel Pits category reflects the expansion of the extraction of sand and gravel in the upper river valleys during the post-war years; 65 birds in the 1975 census were found on flooded gravel pits with over 80 in this habitat in 1998. The drop in the Breckland breeding population is partly a result of the lowering of the water table in the area and the subsequent drying out of many of the meres although the desertion of East Wretham Park and Stanford Water has added to the decline.

The fieldwork for the Norfolk Atlas recorded Great Crested Grebes in 149 tetrads with confirmed breeding in 81. The fluctuations in the population at any one site can be demonstrated by the changes recorded at Holkham Lake, a traditional breeding area. There were six pairs there early in the 20th century, a reduction to irregular breeding in the early 1980s, recovering to three pairs by 1993 but only one pair again in 1996 with three birds present at the time of the 1998 count. Five pairs breeding on the River Wensum in Norwich in 1996 was also of interest.

There have been a number of reports of successful early/late breeding, for example, in 1975 at Narborough Gravel Pits, a bird was sitting on eggs by 11th March and three young were seen riding on their parents' backs on 8th April. However, these dates were surpassed in the mid-1990s with two pairs incubating at Broom Heath on 17th February 1993, and young being seen at Horning on 27th February. At the latter site, a pair had young on 1st December 1994 and a nest with eggs was seen three days later. By 12th February 1995 a fully grown young bird was noted and there was a new clutch of eggs in a nest the same day. While in November 1997 a pair nested at Barton Turf and two juveniles were present in January 1998.

In 1968, up to 18 were noted in summer on Breydon establishing a pattern that has continued with 56 there in July 1976, 86 in August 1987 and 108 on 11th August 1990. Another interesting summer record was that of 103 on the sea off Snettisham in June 1981. The birds generally leave their breeding waters in the autumn for the coastal estuaries and inshore waters with, for example, 100 between Snettisham and Holme in November 1958, 250 in the same area in December 1961 and 181 between Snettisham and Brancaster in 1994. Occasionally large parties remain in Broadland, a notable gathering being 45 at Filby during the winter of 1979–80. However, the majority of Norfolk's breeding grebes must move elsewhere for the winter months and the large concentrations on Graffham Water in Cambridgeshire, Abberton Reservoir in Essex and the London reservoirs may provide some of the answers.

Coastal movements are recorded annually with maximum day-counts of 49 west at Blakeney Point on 26th October 1986, 25 west at Cley on 8th October 1988, 33 east at Holme on 14th October 1993, 35 west at Sheringham on 31st December 1994 and 22 east at Holme on 20th October 1997.

Only four Great Crested Grebes have been ringed in Norfolk but a bird of the year ringed at Pensthorpe in September 1988, was recovered at Calais, France four months later; the first of only two foreign recoveries of a British-ringed bird of this species.

*Don Dorling*

## Red-necked Grebe                               *Podiceps grisegena*

**A scarce passage migrant and winter visitor; very rare in mid-summer.**

The Red-necked Grebe has a Holarctic breeding distribution with the Western Palearctic population concentrated in Russia, Poland, Finland and Denmark. It prefers smaller, shallower areas of inland water on which to breed, compared with the Great Crested Grebe (68–72 BTO Atlas). Since attempted breeding was first confirmed in both England and Scotland in 1988, a few pairs have summered in the British Isles but to date breeding has not been successful. In Britain the species is best known as a winter visitor, mainly along the east and south coasts from the Firth of Forth to Poole Harbour (Winter Atlas).

Stevenson recorded it as a regular winter visitor, occurring in small numbers on the Broads and inland waters between November and mid-March. He also described the first recorded major influx of Red-necked Grebes in February 1865, following severe weather, when at least 35 obtained at Yarmouth, Salthouse and Blakeney were brought into Norwich alone, where many were acquired by local taxidermists. The next influx was noted in February 1922, during which the Cley taxidermist, Pashley '... had in 7 or 8 and might have bought double that number...' (Pashley 1925). The species remained very scarce in Norfolk until January–February 1937, when the third recorded influx occurred, again related to severe weather in the Baltic. During this period, all five species of British grebes were present at Holkham Lake at the same time, including 13 Red-necked Grebes, with up to 19 on the flooded Salthouse levels.

Apart from these major influxes, Red-necked Grebes remained very scarce in the county until the late 1970s, with annual totals rarely reaching double figures. However, since then it has become a far more numerous autumn passage migrant and winter visitor. A similar increase has been noted in both Hampshire (Clark & Eyre 1993) and Sussex (James 1996).

Red-necked Grebes have been recorded in Norfolk in every month of the year but are very rare in July. Since 1980, the first birds of the autumn have generally been noted offshore during August, often in the first half of the month. The earliest have been at Cley on 19th July 1987 and at Holme on 20th July 1986, although one was seen at Brancaster on 8th June and 6th July 1983. Autumn passage peaks in October and continues until late November, with many records relating to birds flying west along the north Norfolk coast. During this period, notable counts have included ten west at Blakeney Point on 26th October 1986, 15 west at Cley on 8th October 1988, 13 west at Sheringham on 4th October 1992 and 11 at Scolt Head on 6th November 1997.

Fewer birds are generally recorded in mid-winter, although late 1995 was an exception. Following a good autumn passage, increasing numbers lingered into the New Year, as illustrated by the monthly totals for the county – August 9, September 12, October 30, November 45, December 53 and January 31. Notable concentrations at coastal sites included nine at Holkham Bay on 5th November and 15 at Holme on 10th December, where up to seven remained until mid-January 1996. On average, about 150 Red-necked Grebes overwinter in Britain (Stone *et al.* 1997) and it would appear that a high proportion of these pass through Norfolk waters.

In recent years, the only mid-winter influx occurred in February 1979 and as on previous occasions it was associated with a prolonged period of strong easterly winds and freezing temperatures. Many birds were displaced from the western Baltic and the Continental North Sea coast, including Red-necked Grebes. During this time, at least 70 were located in Norfolk, of which 50 were present at over 25 inland localities. The maximum coastal count was ten between Hunstanton and Holme, while inland four were present at Lound Waterworks and also on the lower Bure at Yarmouth.

The majority of birds have left the county by mid-March, although the occasional straggler remains into April. Although there is no obvious spring passage, birds, often in breeding plumage, occasionally are reported offshore in May and even into June. Amongst the more interesting observations have been two summer-plumaged birds displaying off Hunstanton on 15th April 1984, two in breeding plumage flying west at Sheringham on 29th May 1976 and one at Snettisham from 28th June to 4th July 1997. The first mid-summer record was of one at Yarmouth in June 1852 (Ticehurst 1932).

While most Red-necked Grebes are recorded offshore between the Wash and Paston, a few are found almost annually on inland waters. Since 1950, over 150 have been located inland, with over half in Broadland. Although all of the Broads have hosted the species at some time or other, the most favoured localities have been Hickling, Horsey, Breydon and Rockland. Many inland waters in the west of the county have held Red-necked Grebes, the most popular being the Great Ouse and Pentney Gravel Pits. Elsewhere in the county, the species has been recorded on the lakes near the Halls at Blickling, Gunton, Kelling and Holkham.

The two longest-staying individuals were both at Rockland Broad – one from 23rd January to 6th March 1966 and the other from 22nd January to 7th April 1987, although this bird also spent time along the River Yare. There have been three mid-summer records from inland waters – at Rollesby Broad from 23rd May to 4th July 1968, at Surlingham Broad on 5th July 1970 and at Pentney Gravel Pits on 4th June 1987.

*Moss Taylor*

## Slavonian Grebe                                              *Podiceps auritus*

**A scarce passage migrant and winter visitor.**

The Slavonian Grebe has an almost circumpolar breeding distribution, extending to more northerly latitudes than the other grebes. In the Western Palearctic it breeds in Iceland, Fennoscandia and Russia. It winters on inshore waters and large lakes. In the British Isles, it is a scarce colonial breeder on shallow, freshwater lochs in the Scottish Highlands, (68–72 BTO Atlas).

Both Stevenson and Riviere found it to be a regular passage migrant and winter visitor with maximum numbers in January and February, particularly during periods of severe weather. Such was the case in February 1897 when exceptional numbers were present and again in January–February 1922, at the same time as an influx of Red-necked Grebes.

The first Slavonian Grebes of the autumn are generally recorded towards the end of September, although singles were at Holme on 9th August 1995, at Titchwell intermittently from 9th to 30th August 1998, at Holme/Thornham from 10th August to 2nd September 1983, at Sea Palling on 14th August and at Holme on 15th August 1996. One was found freshly dead, in winter plumage and in wing moult, on Holkham beach in July 1994. Autumn passage peaks in October and November, with small numbers passing offshore along the north Norfolk coast. However, an unprecedented 33 were counted flying west off Blakeney Point on 26th October 1986 during a seven hour seawatch and ten flew west at Cley on 5th December 1954. Many of these passage birds feed in Holkham Bay, where numbers often build up in late autumn and early winter. High counts have included 21 on 8th December 1984, 20 on 5th–12th November 1989, 19 on 7th November 1990 and 18 (including ten in a single party) on 4th November 1982.

The Wash has always been favoured by Slavonian Grebes, both during late autumn and mid-winter. During the 1950s, peak counts at Snettisham Gravel Pits (before acquisition by the RSPB) included nine on 27th October 1957 and seven on 18th November 1956, while off Hunstanton a maximum of 20 on 1st March 1959 may have involved birds on spring passage. The highest count in the 1960s concerned 16 at Holme on 8th December 1963. During the severe cold weather of early 1979, there was a noticeable influx of Slavonian Grebes (along with Red-necked Grebes) and about 40 individuals were located in Norfolk.

During the 1990s, the birds in Holkham Bay have tended to move west to winter on the inshore waters between Hunstanton and Titchwell, with 20 during February 1991 and an impressive 36 at Holme and 37 at Titchwell on 10th December 1995. Small numbers are recorded in March and April, presumably birds on spring passage, including a maximum of nine off Titchwell on 15th March 1983 and 12 small eared grebes, almost certainly Slavonian Grebes, and mainly paired, off Scolt Head three days later. Birds making prolonged stays, often attaining summer plumage, have included singles at Snettisham from 16th February to 6th April 1991 and on Blakeney Freshes from 9th March to 2nd May 1993. Occasional birds remain into May, including singles at Cley on 20th May 1955 and Titchwell on 18th May 1980. The latest, however, was one off Scolt Head on 13th June 1982.

Slavonian Grebes are scarce along the east Norfolk coast and only a few are recorded annually on inland waters. However, during the period January–March in both 1979 and 1996, at least 20 were found inland each year, as usual the majority on the Broads, including 4–5 at Hickling during March 1979 and up to three at Horsey Mere in March 1996. A single bird appeared on the River Wensum close to Foundry Bridge in the centre of Norwich on 26th–28th February 1991. In 1995, a pair was displaying and calling at Colney on 22nd–30th April and a late bird in breeding plumage was at Hickling on 14th May 1981.

*Moss Taylor*

## Black-necked Grebe HARDLEY FLOODS. 5·11·2000.        *Podiceps nigricollis*

**A very scarce passage migrant and winter visitor.**

The Black-necked Grebe breeds widely in the eastern half of the middle latitudes of the Western Palearctic, but has only a scattered distribution in the western part of its range. In autumn it moves south to winter on lakes, reservoirs and coastal waters. In the British Isles breeding was first proved in Wales in 1904 although it may well have bred in East Anglia during the 19th century (Stevenson). In recent years, it has remained a scarce breeding bird in Scotland and in England, where the stronghold is in the east Midlands (New Atlas).

The first British example of a Black-necked Grebe was one caught alive by a spaniel near Yarmouth in autumn 1817 (Shepherd & Whitear 1827). The majority of records included by Stevenson were of birds obtained during the spring, although fewer were found after 1862. By the time of Riviere, the species had become more frequent in winter, although a fascinating account of possible breeding in 1931 appears in *British Birds* (Riviere 1932). On 27th August, W. B. Alexander and Miss M. Barclay had seen a pair of Black-necked Grebes accompanied by what appeared to be a fully-grown young one on one of the west Norfolk meres. Three days later, Riviere also saw one of the adults diving and feeding two young grebes, as large as itself. However, the light was bad and the appearance of the young birds did not tally with the description of juvenile Black-necked Grebe. He therefore wondered if the pair of adult Black-necked Grebes had 'adopted' some juvenile Little Grebes. W. B. Alexander felt sure that the young were not Dabchicks and Miss Barclay had noted the upturned tilt of the bill, characteristic of Black-necked Grebe. Riviere, however, remained cautious and felt that the verdict must remain 'unproven'.

Black-necked Grebes
(Nik Borrow)

Since 1953, Black-necked Grebes have been recorded annually in Norfolk in varying numbers but rarely have more than about 15 individuals been found in a single year. The date of the first autumn record has varied from July to late October, with the earliest at Wells Quay on 8th July 1998 (and possibly earlier), at Hardley Flood on 23rd July 1994 and at Tottenhill Gravel Pit on 14th August 1971. Between 1954 and the mid-1960s, the inshore waters of the Wash held the only concentration of Black-necked Grebes in Norfolk with maximum counts off Hunstanton of 15 on 6th March 1960 and 10–15 from late November to mid-December 1961. A count between Heacham and Hunstanton on 17th December 1961 achieved an unprecedented total of 35, a county record which still stands. Numbers in the Wash have decreased since those days and the largest numbers to be recorded in the 1980s were up to ten in Blakeney Pit from late November 1986 to early January 1987.

In recent years, the species has become less frequently found during the winter, with the majority of sightings being of single birds in autumn and in spring, when they are usually in breeding plumage. Records away from the coast are not unusual and many of those found in spring are on inland waters, such as the Broads or the gravel pits in west Norfolk. Since 1987, Pentney Gravel Pits have become a favoured locality for spring passage Black-necked Grebes, with one or two appearing almost annually in mid to late May. While up to seven different individuals were recorded at Welney during April 1998, and six at Cantley Beet Factory between 4th and 18th September 1998. A long-staying bird was at Holme grazing marshes from 28th April to 19th May 1996, with another at Holkham Lake from 10th January to 11th April 1998. The latest spring records for the county were three at Thornham Point on 9th June 1989 and one at Rockland Broad on 4th–6th June 1991.

*Moss Taylor*

# Albatross sp.                                          *Diomedea* sp.

**A very rare vagrant; four records.**

Albatrosses breed in the southern hemisphere and disperse northwards towards the tropics outside the breeding season. None of the four sightings off Norfolk was specifically identified, but presumably related to the Black-browed Albatross *D. melanophris*, which is a vagrant from the southern oceans to the waters around the British Isles.

The first record was of one seen by M. King and C. O'Neil flying east at Cley on 19th October 1977.

The next was one moving east at Happisburgh on 9th November 1986. An adult albatross, almost certainly Black-browed, flew east at Cley on 11th October 1987. Remarkably, this was followed a week later by an immature albatross off Cromer and Sheringham on 18th October, later being seen again off Salthouse for about ten minutes before disappearing west. This last individual was seen by at least eight observers.

*Peter Allard*

| **Fulmar (Northern Fulmar)** | HUNSTANTON. 8-9-1985. | *Fulmarus glacialis* |

**A fairly common but localised breeder and common passage migrant; very scarce inland.**

Although the Fulmar was a widespread breeding species around the coast of the North Atlantic, the sole British breeding colony until the late 19th century was on St Kilda. In 1878 Fulmars first bred on Foula in Shetland since when most of the suitable cliffs of the British Isles have been colonised (68–72 BTO Atlas).

Both Stevenson and Riviere described the Fulmar as a not uncommon visitor to the offshore herring grounds during autumn and winter. Inshore records related mainly to storm-driven birds, many of which were exhausted or found as tideline corpses.

Potential breeding sites are often prospected for several years prior to colonisation as has been the case in Norfolk. In 1940 Fulmars were first noted prospecting the boulder-clay cliffs at Weybourne. But it was not until 1947, encouraged by artificial ledges cut out by the well-known Norfolk ornithologist Dick Bagnall-Oakeley and his pupils at Gresham's School, that successful breeding was first proved, when five pairs were present.

By 1956 the cliffs between Weybourne and Cromer held 40–50 pairs, although only about 20 nests were reported. This illustrates the difficulty in estimating the breeding population – many non-breeding pairs are present during the summer months and many of the ledges and holes in the cliff are not easily accessible for the presence of an egg or nestling to be confirmed. Numbers steadily increased over the next 20 years and in 1974 a total of 64 young was counted along the Weybourne to Cromer cliffs. Apart from some annual fluctuations, the number of successful breeding pairs remained stable until 1990, in which year 57 young were counted along a similar stretch of coastline. However, in that year, 80–100 breeding pairs were estimated to be present between Weybourne and Sheringham alone, although only 40 young were counted on ledges in early August. Rat predation was thought to be a major cause of failure, with at least 25% of the young he population has steadily increased and a count on 7th June 1994 found an unprecedented total of 431 adults sitting on the cliffs and an additional 30 swimming offshore. The breeding adults clearly favoured the vegetated parts of the cliff and from the 124 breeding pairs, 107 nestlings fledged (Schmitt 1994). The number of breeding pairs peaked at about 200 in 1995, with 120 in 1996 and 186 in 1997. However, the number of young has fallen with only 43 successfully fledged in 1997.

In east Norfolk a few Fulmars have also nested on the cliffs at Happisburgh intermittently since 1978, with five young fledged in 1990. Further south, at least one pair was prospecting the cliffs at Hopton in 1950 and mating took place, but human disturbance from the nearby holiday camps drove the birds away. Hopton and Gorleston cliffs are still regularly visited by Fulmars during the summer months, but successful breeding has yet to be proved. One was even recorded circling and attempting to land on Gorleston Church tower in September 1962! At Scratby two pairs laid eggs in 1995 and by 1997 up to 16 birds were present in spring with five presumed to be incubating in May but, as elsewhere, failed due to human activities. However, four birds were sitting on ledges in May 1998, from one of which a nestling was successfully reared.

Operation Seafarer revealed a county total of 146 breeding pairs in 1969 and a similar census in 1982 produced 247 occupied breeding sites. Unfortunately the number has subsequently fallen with a county total of 175 pairs in 1990 and fewer than 150 in 1994. It is to be hoped that this trend will be reversed.

Fulmars frequent their breeding ledges during the winter months, the only British seabird to do so (Winter Atlas). A single egg is laid and the majority of young have left their ledges by early September. Breeding colonies and inshore waters are deserted in mid-September and the adults begin to return in late October or early November, presumably after moulting at sea. Occasional birds, however, do reappear during this period of absence in stormy or foggy weather, suggesting that some may not have wandered far since leaving the colonies.

Large movements of Fulmars are invariably associated with a north or north-easterly gale, the birds

# ERRATA

**1. The fourth paragraph of the systematic entry for Fulmar on page 106 should read as follows:**

By 1956 the cliffs between Weybourne and Cromer held 40–50 pairs, although only about 20 nests were reported. This illustrates the difficulty in estimating the breeding population – many non-breeding pairs are present during the summer months and many of the ledges and holes in the cliff are not easily accessible for the presence of an egg or nestling to be confirmed. Numbers steadily increased over the next 20 years and in 1974 a total of 64 young was counted along the Weybourne to Cromer cliffs. Apart from some annual fluctuations, the number of successful breeding pairs remained stable until 1990, in which year 57 young were counted along a similar stretch of coastline. However, in that year, 80-100 breeding pairs were estimated to be present between Weybourne and Sheringham alone, although only 40 young were counted on ledges in early August. Rat predation was thought to be a major cause of failure, with at least 25% of the young being taken. Since then the numbers of breeding pairs along this section of coastline has continued to fall and only three or four were fledged in each of the years 1994-96. This more recent decline is believed to be due to predation by foxes and possibly rats, as well as continuing loss of breeding sites due to erosion of the sandy cliffs. Fulmars had also been prospecting in west Norfolk since the early 1950s but did not breed on the chalk and carrstone cliffs of Hunstanton until 1965. Since then the population has steadily increased and a count on 7th June 1994 found an unprecedented total of 431 adults sitting on the cliffs and an additional 30 swimming offshore. The breeding adults clearly favoured the vegetated parts of the cliff and from the 124 breeding pairs, 107 nestlings fledged (Schmitt 1994). The number of breeding pairs peaked at about 200 in 1995, with 120 in 1996 and 186 in 1997. However, the number of young has fallen with only 43 successfully fledged in 1997.

*ADD AFTER "YOUNG" AND BEFORE "POPULATION"*

**2. The aerial photographs of Holme and Titchwell are transposed.**

moving in an easterly direction. Significant spring movements are unusual and 1,600 east at Sheringham on 19th March 1980 was exceptional. However, the heaviest 'wreck' occurred in February and March 1962 when 200 corpses were washed up on the Norfolk beaches and one observer reported 'dead Fulmars every few yards' between Gorleston and Hopton on 28th February. This 'wreck' affected not only the North Sea coasts of eastern England, but also Sweden, Denmark and The Netherlands. A large proportion of the dead Fulmars were 'blue phase' birds and the cause of the 'wreck' was thought to be particularly severe weather on the Newfoundland Banks, where birds from Greenland and arctic Canada gather in winter. As a result they were unable to feed, became weak and were driven east and then south by intense depressions into the North Sea.

The largest mid-summer movement was noted on 26th June 1997 with the highest count of 1,000 east at Sheringham. In autumn the vast majority of the large movements of Fulmars have been recorded off the north coast in September, mainly in mid-month. Peak counts have been 2,200 at Sheringham and 'thousands' at Cley on 14th September 1975, 2,500 at Hunstanton on 16th September 1986, 1,800 at Sheringham on 9th September 1989, 2,000 at Sheringham on 1st September 1994 and 1,800 west at Holme, 3,050 at Cley and 2,100 west at Sheringham on 13th September 1996. All these movements, however, were overshadowed by an amazing passage all along the north Norfolk coast in an easterly gale and driving rain on 14th September 1993. Counts included 7,600 east at Sheringham and 4,364 east in six hours at Paston. The only notable movements later in the year have been 1,200 at Paston on 19th November 1991 and 800 east at Sheringham on 22nd December 1996.

In recent years occasional Fulmars have been recorded annually inland, the majority in May and June. While most have been within 15km of the coast, birds have been seen between Norwich and East Dereham, over East Wretham and Weeting in the Brecks, and over Welney and Ten Mile Bank in the west of the county.

The so-called 'blue phase' Fulmar, the darker colour morph which forms the great majority of the population in the High Arctic, is normally a very scarce visitor to inshore waters (but see above). A few are normally recorded during the heavy passages, such as those described above, including six east on 14th September 1993. More often though, 'blue phase' birds are noted during the late autumn or winter with maximum counts all at Sheringham of nine east on 3rd January 1986 and 10th December 1990, 14 east on 12th November 1996, 59 east on 4th January 1997 and 16 east the following day. Of particular interest was one which remained at the Sheringham colony from March to June 1993 and returned intermittently in 1994 and 1995.

There are three records of single albino Fulmars, two during the heavy movements along the north coast on both 14th September 1975 and 1993, and off Cley on 8th September 1996. In addition an unusually pale bird bred successfully at Sheringham between 1988 and 1990, although its young were of a normal colour.

Over 600 Fulmars have been ringed at the Norfolk colonies, the majority as nestlings, of which 22 have been recovered away from the site of ringing. In addition, 37 Fulmars ringed outside the county have been found in Norfolk. Of these, 32 were ringed at Scottish colonies (Shetland, Orkney, the Scottish mainland and Isle of May), and singles at the Farne Islands, Northumberland and in Ireland, Iceland, Norway and the North Sea, of which 70% were ringed as nestlings. These included two trapped as breeding birds at Sheringham and Hunstanton, 10 and 13 years respectively, after ringing. This indicates that recruitment from colonies further north is continuing. In common with many species of seabird, Fulmars take several years to reach sexual maturity and are usually 6–12 years old before first attempting to breed. Only one Norfolk-ringed nestling has been found as a definite breeding adult at its natal colony – a 12-year-old bird at Sheringham, although two others were found dead on the beach in July, not far from their natal ledges, seven and eight years respectively, after hatching (Taylor 1985).

Breeding adults normally show site fidelity, although two ringed at Sheringham were found in July off the south-west coast of Norway and on a Belgian beach, possibly suggesting a change in breeding area. Young birds disperse widely in their first few years, as shown by recoveries of Sheringham-ringed nestlings in The Netherlands (3), Germany and Denmark, and in Britain to Durham and to the west coast of Scotland at Ardrossan in Ayrshire. Fulmars are long-lived birds and a nestling ringed on Auskerry in Orkney on 6th August 1963 was found dead at Sheringham on 12th June 1988, in its 25th year. The current longevity record for a British-ringed Fulmar is nearly 41 years!

*Moss Taylor*

## Fea's or Zino's Petrel                                    *Pterodroma feae/madeira*

**A very rare vagrant; one record.**

The Fea's and Zino's Petrels were formerly lumped with Soft-plumaged Petrel *P. mollis* of the southern oceans. The world population of Fea's Petrel, about 1,200 pairs, breeds on the island of Bugio in the Desertas off Madeira and in the mountains of the Cape Verde Islands. The very much rarer Zino's Petrel only breeds in the high mountains of Madeira, with a known population of only 20 pairs in 1996. Fea's Petrel formerly occurred as a vagrant off the eastern coast of the USA, but has been recorded annually off North Carolina in small numbers since the early 1990s. Elsewhere it is a vagrant off Canada and western Europe and a very rare vagrant to the British Isles with just 23 accepted records up to the end of 1997. Zino's Petrel has never been conclusively identified away from its breeding site on Madeira.

A Fea's or Zino's Petrel, the first accepted record for the county, flew east along the north Norfolk coast on 26th June 1997. It was seen passing the Blakeney Point seawatching hide at 13:40 hrs by Stefan McElwee and subsequently offshore at Cley, Sheringham and, finally, Mundesley at 15:37 hrs (McElwee 1997, 1998). Owing to the difficulties in separating these species in the field, particularly in the case of a lone bird, this individual was accepted only as a Fea's/Zino's Petrel by the BBRC, although it was considered almost certainly to have been a Fea's Petrel.

*Peter Allard*

## Black-capped Petrel (Capped Petrel)                       *Pterodroma hasitata*

**A very rare vagrant; one record in 1850.**

The only known breeding site of the distinctive Black-capped Petrel is in the forested slopes and cliffsides of Hispaniola (mainly Haiti) in the Caribbean Sea. It was formerly much more widespread in the West Indies, and it may still breed in Cuba and other Caribbean Islands. Outside the breeding season it disperses both north and south.

The first of only two British records was one found on a heath at Southacre, near Swaffham after severe gales in March or April 1850. It was first observed flapping from one furze bush to another by a boy who eventually caught the bird. Although exhausted, it violently bit his hand and he immediately killed it. The bird, a female, formed the chief attraction of the Newcombe collection at Feltwell Hall. It is presently housed at the Castle Museum, Norwich.

The only other British record was one found long-dead as a tideline corpse at Barnston, East Yorkshire on 16th December 1984.

*Peter Allard*

## Cory's Shearwater                                          *Calonectris diomedea*

**A very scarce autumn migrant, rare in spring and mid-summer; one winter record.**

Cory's Shearwater breeds along rocky coasts and islands of the Mediterranean and Atlantic Ocean. It disperses across the Atlantic with many reaching North America but most winter off the coasts of Namibia and South Africa. This shearwater is an annual visitor to the North Sea and English Channel. Greatly increased interest in seawatching has revealed periodic late summer movements in the south-western approaches dependent on winds, rain and mist. On such occasions large feeding flocks appear inshore.

The first county record was of one found dead at Salthouse on 29th January 1966. It is now in the Castle Museum, Norwich and was assigned to the North Atlantic race *C. d. borealis*. The county total currently stands at 76, of which one has been in January, four in May, 11 in June, three in July, 20 in August, 20 in September and 14 in October, with a peak in the last week of August and first of September. The latest dates have been 12th October 1997 at Cley, 13th October 1993 at Sheringham and 25th October 1998 at Cley (subject to acceptance by the County Records Committee). Multiple sightings of twos and threes have taken place on nine occasions. Since 1992 this shearwater has appeared annually off the Norfolk coast with 8–10 in 1993, 1996 and 1997.

A high proportion of Cory's Shearwater sightings along the Norfolk coast are made between Cley and Sheringham. Others have been observed off Snettisham, Hunstanton, Holme, Thornham Point, Titchwell,

Blakeney Point, West Runton (subject to acceptance by the County Records Committee), Overstrand, Mundesley, Walcott, Sea Palling, Horsey, Winterton and Yarmouth. One picked up alive on Yarmouth beach on 23rd July 1977 proved to be a second example of the North Atlantic race *borealis*. This bird was kept alive for several days but died on 28th.

On 26th September 1993 a large albino shearwater flew east at Sheringham. It was seen by many observers and from its size, proportions and flight was considered to be either a Cory's or Great Shearwater (Votier & Shepherd 1994). By a remarkable coincidence a large albino shearwater again flew east at Sheringham on 19th September 1995 – on this occasion the bird was considered most likely to have been a Sooty Shearwater.

*Michael Seago*

## Great Shearwater            *Puffinus gravis*

**A rare autumn vagrant; two winter records.**

The Great Shearwater breeds in the South Atlantic principally in the Tristan da Cunha group and on Gough Island to the south. The breeding colonies are abandoned in April or May the birds moving towards the coast of Brazil and reaching the Atlantic coast of North America in May and early June. It is an annual visitor to British and Irish waters but in varying numbers and because of the relatively late arrival, between August and October, most are presumed to be non-breeders.

Riviere included the first county record, one picked up on Caister beach on 22nd December 1892. It was on display for many years in the Connop Collection at Rollesby Hall and later at Wroxham, but its present whereabouts are unknown. Another appeared off Cley on 14th August 1896 and probably the same bird was seen there again on 25th August. A further shore-line casualty, recovered at Gorleston on 7th January 1929, is in the Castle Museum, Norwich. Since then, an additional 11 Great Shearwaters have been recorded, most following strong northerly winds, taking the county total to 14:

1892:   One picked up dead on Caister beach on 22nd December
1896:   Cley on 14th August and probably the same bird on 25th August
1929:   One picked up dead at Gorleston 7th January
1939:   One picked up at Cley on 29th October following a north-easterly gale
1960:   Cley on 20th September
1972:   Two off Weybourne on 18th August
          Cley on 22nd September
          Cley on 27th October
1973:   Cley/Sheringham on 30th September
          Happisburgh on 6th October
1974:   Winterton on 18th August
1979:   Paston/Bacton on 16th October
1997:   Cley on 9th September

*Michael Seago*

## Sooty Shearwater            *Puffinus griseus*

**A scarce autumn passage migrant; very rare in winter and spring.**

The Sooty Shearwater, a transequatorial migrant, breeds on islands off South America, Australia and New Zealand. The nearest breeding colonies to the British Isles are in the Falkland Islands and it is the most distant regular passage migrant to the waters off the coast of Norfolk.

The first record for the county concerned one caught alive by a boy on a fishing vessel, while it slept on the water at the mouth of the River Ouse on 25th July 1851 (Stevenson). The bird survived for five days before being set up by a Mr Foster of Wisbech and it was then deposited in King's Lynn Museum, where it remains to this day. The next was one seen flying north off Yarmouth by Richard Richardson on 31st August 1947, while he was on a pleasure trip in the 'Yarmouth Roads' (Allard 1990). The third record was most unusual, in that it involved a bird flying south-south-east inland at South Wootton on 23rd August

1953, and the fourth was off Salthouse on 14th September 1956. Since the next two at Cley in 1959, the species has been recorded annually off the Norfolk coast, but in greatly varying numbers. In some years as few as three have been recorded, in others as many as a hundred or more, with a record total of 182 in 1995.

Although occasional birds have been seen as early as 9th July (assuming that one at Scolt Head on 27th June 1997 was a late spring migrant) the main autumn passage occurs between late August and early October, with a clear peak in mid-September. Maximum day-counts do not usually exceed 20, although as early as 1960, when there had been only 11 previous county records, 30–40 flew west at Cley on 20th September. Similar counts in north Norfolk have included 30 at Weybourne on 15th September 1968, 30 at Cley on 27th August 1977, 13th September 1988 and 9th September 1997, and 50 at Sheringham on 4th October 1992 and 5th October 1996. Typically, autumn movements occur during northerly gales with birds moving north along the east coast and west along the north coast, although 55 flew east at Sheringham on 13th September 1998. In east Norfolk the largest numbers have been noted at Winterton/ Horsey with 43 on 17th September 1977, 57 on 26th August 1978 and 45 on 17th September 1994.

Three years, in particular, will be long-remembered for the unprecedented numbers of Sooty Shearwaters. In 1986 a very impressive seabird movement took place during gale-force northerly winds on 3rd September. The counts for Sooty Shearwaters included 150 at Blakeney Point, 125 at Cley and 29 at Paston. In 1996 the species was recorded almost daily from 28th August to 13th September with maximum day-counts of 65 at Holme, 123 at Cley, 125 at Sheringham and 67 at Sea Palling. In 1997 it was recorded in every month from May to November, the highest counts being on 2nd October with 80 at Cley and 115 at Sheringham.

Occasional birds have been recorded in November, the latest on 29th November 1969 at Weybourne and on 30th November 1997 at Sheringham and Overstrand. There have been three mid-winter records – singles at Salthouse on 23rd December 1986, off both Hunstanton and Blakeney Point on 30th December 1989 and at Cley on 14th January 1987. Eight birds have been recorded in spring – at Paston on 29th March 1987, Sheringham on 11th April 1998, Winterton on 20th April 1991, Sheringham three on 6th May 1997, Holme on 22nd May 1984 and Scolt Head on 27th June 1997.

*Moss Taylor*

Manx Shearwaters
(*Norman Arlott*)

## Manx Shearwater                                        *Puffinus puffinus*

**A fairly common passage migrant; very rare in winter and rare inland.**

The majority of the European population of the Manx Shearwater breeds in western Britain, especially on the islands of Rhum, Skokholm and Skomer. Important colonies also are found in Ireland, the Faeroes and Iceland. With the exception of Rhum, all of the colonies which hold more than a few pairs are on rat-free islands or on cliffs inaccessible to rats. After breeding, the adults desert the colonies and begin to move south in July, followed by the juveniles in September, to winter in the waters off eastern South America.

Stevenson described the Manx Shearwater as a rare bird off the Norfolk coast, although every autumn it was noted far out to sea, accompanying the fishing boats. He also commented that considering its great rarity, it was surprising that seven had been 'captured' so far inland, in addition to another five found at Breydon. It was still only an 'occasional autumn visitor' in Riviere's time, with all Norfolk records between mid-August and mid-October, except for one shot at Breydon on 18th December 1877.

By the mid-1950s a few were being recorded during the spring in most years, with occasional mid-summer records, and the species has subsequently been recorded in all months of the year. The first birds of the spring are generally noted offshore in early May, although occasionally earlier. There have been nine March records, involving a total of 19 birds, all singles except for six at Winterton on 16th March 1978, four at Waxham on 25th March 1990 and three at Holme on 12th March 1993, the earliest spring date. Occasional birds are seen in April with a maximum of five at Cley on 24th April 1981. Numbers in spring are usually small, rarely exceeding 20 birds in a day, but an exceptional passage was noted on 27th May 1996 with 45 west at Terrington, 50 north at Hunstanton and 550 east at Holme, including 81 in a single group. Birds are recorded most years in mid-summer with maximum counts of 250 east at Cley in 20 minutes in strong north-west winds on 28th June 1984, and 150 at Hunstanton and 180 at Sheringham on 5th July 1990, while on 26th June 1997 these totals were exceeded at several sites along the north coast with 347 east and 47 west at Scolt Head, 200 east at Cley, 253 east at Sheringham, 243 east at Overstrand and 134 east at Mundesley.

Adults begin to desert the colonies in July and by mid-month some impressive counts have been made off Norfolk. The highest July totals have been 650 north-east in four hours at Hunstanton on 15th July 1970 and 600 at Hunstanton and Holme on 15th July 1988. By late August the juveniles are beginning to leave the colonies and between then and mid-September peak counts are normally recorded. The largest-ever movement noted off Norfolk occurred in strong northerlies on 27th August 1989, with birds moving east around the coast and the counts included 640 at Hunstanton, 1,200 at Cley, 880 at Sheringham and 265 at Paston. Other large autumn movements have involved 326 at Hunstanton (including 83 in one group) on 5th August 1985, 300 at Holme on 14th September 1988, 350 recorded at several sites between Cley and Cromer on 25th August 1989 and 300 at the Ouse Mouth on 9th September 1989.

Often the highest numbers have been recorded in the Wash, but there is clear evidence from the counts at sites between Hunstanton and Sheringham that birds in autumn are often flying all along the north Norfolk coast from west to east. Far smaller numbers have been recorded at Paston and even fewer further south at Winterton, indicating that the shearwaters are continuing to fly east on reaching the north-east 'corner' of Norfolk, before heading south, out of sight of land, through the southern North Sea and into the English Channel. This is demonstrated by the highest-ever count at Winterton of only 23 on 31st August 1980.

·Normally only a few Manx Shearwaters are recorded into October with the last sightings generally being between mid-October and mid-November. However, 1997 was exceptional with 80 at Titchwell and Sheringham on 2nd October, 40 west at Scolt Head and 60 east at Sheringham on 12th October, and 51 west at Scolt Head and 35 at Sheringham on the following day. There have been six December records, all involving single birds, apart from two east at Sheringham on 10th December 1990. The only other mid-winter records have been singles at Sheringham on 31st January 1986 and 16th February 1992, two at Cley on 17th February 1978 and one found dead on Snettisham beach on 28th February 1954.

Including seven birds at Breydon, there have been 21 inland records of Manx Shearwater, ten of which have been since 1953. Except for one at Breydon in December 1877, all have been in autumn. Three were found between 3rd and 8th September 1988 at Wolferton Common, Beechamwell and Breydon, the latter bird swimming with Wigeon, while another swimming on the main lagoon at Welney on 27th–28th July 1996 was found dead on 1st August.

Four ringed Manx Shearwaters have been recovered in Norfolk, all ringed as nestlings and all found dead in September–October, the month after ringing – two from Welsh island colonies, Skokholm in 1967 and Skomer in 1983, and singles from Rhum, Invernesshire in 1978 and Copeland, County Down in 1997.

*Moss Taylor*

# Mediterranean Shearwater      *Puffinus yelkouan*

**A very scarce autumn passage migrant; very rare in mid-summer.**

The Mediterranean Shearwater breeds on islands and isolated headlands around the Mediterranean. After breeding, the species becomes more widely dispersed, with many if not all of the birds of the western race *P. y. mauretanicus* passing through the Straits of Gibraltar to emerge into the Atlantic. Some of these then move north off the coasts of western Europe to Britain, especially along the English Channel. The taxonomy of the *Puffinus* shearwaters is complex and the Mediterranean Shearwater was officially split from the Manx Shearwater by the BOURC in 1991. The two races of Mediterranean Shearwater are now sometimes considered to be separate species: Levantine Shearwater *P. yelkouan* and Balearic Shearwater *P. mauretanicus*.

The first to be recorded in Norfolk were two shot by George Long at Blakeney on 22nd September 1891. The next to be recorded was one seen by Peter Clarke off Blakeney Point on 7th August 1955, after which sightings became more regular, if not annual, and generally involved single birds. The species has been noted annually since 1988, with at least ten individuals each year between 1992 and 1998. A total of about 160 has been recorded off Norfolk.

The earliest have been four at Cley on 6th June 1992 and one at Sheringham on 10th June 1995. The remainder have been recorded between late June and late November with a distinct peak from mid-August to mid-September. Although the species has been seen from all the regular seawatching points, the majority of sightings have been made along the north coast. The highest day-counts have been 11 at Holme on 31st August 1975 and a party of six east off Cley and Weybourne on 9th July 1995. Heavy rain and strong northerly winds on 1st September 1994 resulted in sightings of one to two at six localities between Hunstanton and Mundesley. One was regularly seen fishing close inshore between Blakeney Point and Weybourne from 1st to 8th September 1990. Only a few have been recorded after mid-October, including singles at Cley, Weybourne and Sheringham on 10th–12th November 1996, at Cley on 22nd November 1989 and the latest at Happisburgh on 26th November 1996. The highest east-coast count has been three at Horsey on 17th September 1994.

All the accepted records are birds of the western Mediterranean race *mauretanicus*, although there have been several sightings of shearwaters apparently showing the characteristics of the nominate eastern Mediterranean race *P. y. yelkouan*, which has yet to be accepted as having occurred in British waters.

*Moss Taylor*

## Little Shearwater                                    *Puffinus assimilis*

**A very rare vagrant; three records.**

The Little Shearwater is an oceanic species that breeds on islands in the Atlantic, Pacific and Indian Oceans. Outside the breeding season it disperses far out to sea, although the North Atlantic population *P. a. baroli* rarely wanders far from its breeding grounds on Madeira, the Canary Islands and the Azores.

The three birds that have been found dead in the county all relate to the North Atlantic population. One found at Earsham by a gamekeeper on the 10th April 1858 proved to be a male and constituted the first British record. Another, a female, was picked up at Blakeney Point on the 11th May 1929 with the third also found there on 1st May 1960. The first two specimens are retained at the Castle Museum, Norwich, whilst the third is in the British Museum collection at Tring. Despite increased seawatching around the coastline of Norfolk none of the claimed sight records has as yet been accepted by the BBRC.

*Peter Allard*

## Storm Petrel (European Storm-petrel)            *Hydrobates pelagicus*

**A rare autumn passage migrant; very rare in winter.**

The Storm Petrel breeds on rocky ground and offshore islands and stacks in the north-east Atlantic from southern Iceland and western Norway southward to the Mediterranean. The nearest breeding colonies include many of the Western Isles in Scotland, also Orkney and Shetland. During the autumn it disperses to sea with many wintering off south-west Africa, Namibia and South Africa.

Stevenson referred to periodic 'wrecks' during severe weather. In November 1824, for example, 200–300 Storm Petrels were shot at Yarmouth following gales. At the same locality on 27th October 1834 a total of 25 exhausted birds was taken while swimming offshore and seven, still alive, reached a local taxidermist. On another occasion many became casualties 'flying against the floating light off Yarmouth beach'. In the autumn of 1855 'many were knocked down with sticks in Lynn Harbour, where they flew . . . as thick as sand martins'. Prolonged storms during October 1869 resulted in many casualties. Thomas Gunn described them being swept inland 'following the course of the Yare as far as Norwich scarcely able to keep on the wing. Several were readily knocked down with sticks near Foundry Bridge in the city.'

E. T. Booth is quoted by Stevenson when describing a prolonged seven-day easterly gale during November 1872. Storm Petrels were flitting bat-like between the piers at Yarmouth Harbour entrance. Some made their way up-river to the fish wharves. Buffeted by storms day after day many petrels became completely exhausted and were swept on to Breydon muds. North of the harbour Booth described dozens fluttering over the yawning troughs like marionettes. Periodically during squalls the weakest birds were swept across the roadway. Starvation hastened their end. Eventually the wind did drop and Booth steamed aboard the tug Reliance through Yarmouth Roads on waters as smooth as glass. His reward during one of the earliest 'pelagics' was immense numbers of Storm Petrels extending from Winterton to Lowestoft each asleep on the water resembling a fluffy sooty ball. Two days later all had disappeared. On a later occasion following a north-west gale two Storm Petrels were taken at Harford Bridges on the outskirts of Norwich on 1st November 1880. Riviere remarked that the numbers of gale victims of this smallest of European seabirds were much lower than was once the case. This decline has continued. During the second half of the 20th century there have been just three inland occurrences – at Norwich following severe south-westerly gales in south-west England on 8th December 1959, at Blickling on 22nd October 1970 and at Downham Market on 30th November 1991. Also of interest was one flying up the River Bure at Yarmouth on 12th November 1952 and another on the sea-front boating lake there on 14th November 1959.

The cumulative monthly totals of all records for the period 1953–97 include one at Wells Quay on 21st June 1997.

**Table 2. Monthly totals of Storm Petrels recorded in Norfolk 1953–97.**

| Jan | Mar | Apr | Jun | Jul | Aug | Sep | Oct | Nov | Dec |
|-----|-----|-----|-----|-----|-----|-----|-----|-----|-----|
| 2 | 1 | 2 | 2 | 4 | 2 | 11 | 48 | 20 | 4 |

Since the late 1980s observers manning the shelters at Sheringham seafront in storm conditions have produced the majority of observations. A severe south-west gale on 29th October 1989 resulted in records at Holkham Bay, Blakeney Point, Cley (two), West Runton and Cromer (four), while on 25th November 1990 there were four at Sheringham and one in Holkham Bay. Apart from these, all occurrences have been of ones and twos. All autumn records have involved birds between Holkham and Sheringham except for singles at Mundesley on 27th September 1993, Waxham on 14th November 1997 and Eccles on 12th October 1998. There is a single winter record at Blakeney Point on 25th January 1987 and spring sightings of one at Cley on 2nd March 1990 and two at Sheringham on 14th April 1994.

One found long-dead on the beach at Waxham on 27th July 1992 had been ringed as an adult at Gossabrough, Yell, Shetland on 21st August 1986.

*Michael Seago*

## Leach's Petrel (Leach's Storm-petrel)    *Oceanodroma leucorhoa*

**A scarce autumn passage migrant; rare in spring.**

In the Western Palearctic colonies of Leach's Petrels in the North Atlantic breed from Iceland, the Faeroes, northern Scotland and north-east Norway, occupying offshore islands on high ground and on slopes. The birds move south to winter in the tropics off West Africa.

The first county example was found on Yarmouth beach on 5th December 1823 and is still in the Tolhouse Museum, Yarmouth. Stevenson and Riviere recorded between 40 and 50 including storm-driven birds recovered well inland at East Bradenham, Gooderstone and Downham Market where one was found in the talons of a Sparrowhawk shot at Ryston Hall.

Leach's Petrels
(*Norman Arlott*)

An unprecedented county total of 75 struggling eastwards off Sheringham on 9th September 1989 in a north-east gale formed the highlight of an extended passage from 25th August to 10th October when observations were made along the coast from Ouse Mouth to Yarmouth. There have been only two other comparable movements – one involving 52 Leach's Petrels passing east off Sheringham on 15th September 1994 and the other of 41 west at Holme and 25 west at Cley on 9th September 1997. The majority of records have related to birds passing along the north coast, usually during periods of strong northerly winds; the species is less often recorded in east Norfolk where the largest counts have been eight at Horsey on 25th September 1983 and five at Winterton on 11th October 1988.

**Table 3. Monthly totals of Leach's Petrels recorded in Norfolk 1953–97.**

| Apr | May | Jun | Aug | Sep | Oct | Nov |
|-----|-----|-----|-----|-----|-----|-----|
| 13 | 1 | 2 | 19 | 532 | 183 | 38 |

Since Riviere, stranded examples have included one at Berney Marshes on 7th November 1943, a 'telegraphed' casualty beside the Acle New Road on 13th November 1949, one which spent all day at Breydon often flying with waders on 21st September 1963 and another inland at Narborough on 6th December 1983.

*Michael Seago*

## Gannet (Northern Gannet) HUNSTANTON. 8-9-1985. *Morus bassanus*

**A common passage migrant; rare inland.**

The Gannet spends most of its time at sea, only coming ashore during the breeding season. It breeds mainly in colonies on isolated stacks and small, uninhabited offshore islands in the North Atlantic. On the eastern seaboard, the breeding range extends from Norway and Iceland, through Britain and Ireland, south to northern France. The European colonies are concentrated in north-western Britain, where 70% of the population breeds. As a result of reduced human persecution and possibly climatic amelioration, Gannet numbers have increased annually by about 3% during the 20th century. In 1900, a total of 13 European gannetries existed; this had increased to 36 by 1988.

Both Stevenson and Riviere described the Gannet as mainly being seen offshore in small numbers during the autumn, with even fewer in spring. During the 18th and 19th centuries it would have been well-known to the trawlermen, by whom it was called the 'herring gant'. The steady increase in the numbers of breeding Gannets, particularly since the late 1930s, is clearly shown by the increasing abundance of birds passing through the inshore waters of Norfolk in autumn. During the 1950s and 1960s, the maximum day-count never exceeded 400, whereas in the 1970s it was 800, rising to over 2,000 during the 1980s and 1990s. This cannot entirely be explained by the dramatic increase in the interest in seawatching during the last 20 years. Although Gannets are seen off the Norfolk coast throughout the year, there is a clear peak in autumn and a smaller peak in spring, with comparatively few records in mid-winter or mid-summer.

After fledging, young Gannets move south in August and September to their wintering quarters as far south as the waters off West Africa; whereas the breeding adults are partial migrants, some remaining near the colonies during the winter months and others dispersing south to the Bay of Biscay and the Mediterranean. Autumn passage off the Norfolk coast begins in late July, peaking in September and October. Maximum numbers are recorded off the north Norfolk coast during onshore gales, with the birds almost invariably moving east. A day-count of 1,000 passing Sheringham on 5th October 1984 was noteworthy, as being the first occasion that a four-figure count had been made off Norfolk. Since 1988 similarly impressive totals have been recorded almost annually. The birds are clearly following the north Norfolk coastline as shown by counts of 1,500 at Holme and 2,000 at Blakeney Point on 27th August 1989, with a further 1,500 past Blakeney Point on 9th September 1989. Again on 7th October 1990, 1,150 moved east off Holme and 1,600 at Sheringham, while on 4th October 1992 a total of 1,600 at Sheringham was eclipsed by a record count of 2,320 off Paston. The most recent large count was of 1,650 at Sheringham on 20th October 1995. The only significant movement involving Gannets flying west in autumn was 1,200 at Holme on 13th September 1996, although a total of 400 also flew east. In east Norfolk, where far smaller numbers of Gannets have been recorded, the highest counts were all in 1997 with 900 at Horsey on 20th September, 500 at Scratby on 12th October, and 700 at Sea Palling and 327 south at Yarmouth on 22nd October.

The small number of Gannets that are seen between December and March are almost invariably in full adult plumage and are thus at least five years old. However, counts of 300 flying east at Sheringham during northerly gales on 14th February 1994 and 22nd January 1996, indicate that there are larger numbers in the southern North Sea during winter than are normally recorded off the Norfolk coast. Return spring passage is variable, again numbers being dependant on onshore gales and the direction of movement is not always as expected. The highest counts each month have been 550 east at Sheringham on 19th March 1980, 600 north at Snettisham on 28th April 1990 and 440 east at Sheringham on 6th May 1997. Only small numbers are usually noted in June, but 1997 was an exception with 380 east and 140 west at Scolt Head and 641 east at Mundesley on 26th, 330 east and 100 west at Scolt Head on 27th and 250 east at Sheringham on 28th, all during strong onshore winds. Storm-driven Gannets have been recorded inland in Norfolk since at least the 18th century (Browne 1835–36), while others, such as one near Fakenham on 10th October 1870, arrived in calm conditions (Stevenson). Up to the mid-19th century, Gannets visited Breydon to fish, but since 1879, there have only been two records at this locality, on 1st October 1960 and 26th October 1991. Since 1950 there have been over 20 inland records of Gannets, up to 40km from the sea. Usually only single birds are involved, but three were seen over Wolferton and Flitcham, on both occasions during or after thick fog. An exceptional storm with heavy rain on 25th–26th April 1981 resulted in many storm-driven Arctic Terns being recorded at both coastal and inland localities in Norfolk; associated with this were 30 Gannets at the Ouse Mouth, which were still diving for fish in the vicinity of Lynn ferry on 27th April. Photographs of this unique event feature in the *Norfolk Bird Report 1981*. On this same date, two Gannets flew north over Stoke Ferry and another north-east at Frettenham, presumably making their way back to the coast. Unfortunately, it is not uncommon to see Gannets flying along trailing coloured nylon string or fishing line from their bills, as was the case with one flying inland over East Tuddenham. A sick or injured adult Gannet, which was present on the small island on Kelling Water Meadows on 4th–5th June 1997, caused considerable alarm to the nesting Avocets. Unfortunately, two pairs deserted as a direct result of its presence. The Gannet was subsequently found dead on 6th June.

There have been 28 recoveries of Gannets ringed as nestlings at Scottish colonies and one from Wales. The earliest was as long ago as 1941 and the most recent was found on Scolt Head in 1993, 23 years after being ringed, but still two years short of the longevity record for a British-ringed Gannet. Three nestlings ringed in Norwegian colonies, two at Skarvklakken and one at Gjesvaerstappen have been found in Norfolk between September and December. Both these localities are well inside the Arctic Circle and are two of the most northerly colonies in the Western Palearctic. Another nestling ringed at Sulnasker, Iceland in 1978 was found freshly dead at Holme on 27th December 1985, one of only seven Icelandic-ringed Gannets to have been recovered in the British Isles.

*Moss Taylor*

## Cormorant (Great Cormorant)    *Phalacrocorax carbo*

TITCHWELL.
8-9-1985.

**A fairly common winter visitor and passage migrant; formerly bred.**

The Cormorant has an extensive world range including Asia, Australasia, Africa and parts of eastern North America. Two races breed in Europe, the nominate *P. c. carbo* which nests on sea cliffs around the coasts of Iceland, Norway, France and the British Isles, and *P. c. sinensis* which is largely a tree-nesting bird in the rest of Europe. Since 1981, growing numbers of tree-nesters have started to colonise inland locations in the Midlands and southern England and there are now 1,200 pairs of inland tree-nesting Cormorants which are considered to be *sinensis* (Millington 1998b).

The Cormorant has had a rather chequered history in Norfolk. Once a regular breeder, it ceased to nest in the early 1800s. A few attempts since have not, unfortunately, led to the hoped-for recolonisation. Since the turn of the 20th century it has increased as both a winter visitor and a passage migrant, with good numbers now regularly oversummering. Formerly thought of as just a bird of the Broads and coast, feeding at sea, in saltmarsh creeks, harbour mouths and freshwater lagoons, it has since expanded to inland lakes, rivers and gravel pits.

Early recorders of Norfolk birdlife all mentioned the county as being home to breeding Cormorants. Writing in 1544, Turner commented that they regularly nested in tall riverside trees, usually amongst herons. Sir Thomas Browne (1835–36) recorded Cormorants nest building at Reedham in the 17th century, whilst Lubbock (1879) spoke of them breeding in the Fritton/Herringfleet area on the Suffolk border. He found 50 or 60 nests in 1825, but by 1827, however, none was seen. No more breeding attempts in the county were recorded until 1914 when a pair reared four young in a disused Grey Heron's nest at Melton Constable Park. Their portraits appear in Emma Turner's *Broadland Birds*. In the Fens at Feltwell another pair bred (again in an old Grey Heron's nest) in 1916, but upon their return the following year were shot. After a long absence as a county breeder, west Norfolk once more hosted nesting Cormorants in 1988. Two pairs bred unsuccessfully at Narford, but by 1989 three pairs reared three young with another pair at Black Dyke near Feltwell. With 14 pairs nesting at Narford in 1990, hopes were high for the species' return as a regular Norfolk breeder. Such thoughts, however, were short-lived as in 1991 they were 'discouraged' from returning and no further breeding attempts were made until two nests were found in 1998. The trout lakes and angling clubs of the Nar Valley were obviously too close for comfort! Persecution of Cormorants in Norfolk has never been as pronounced as in Scotland or the Midlands during the 1990s, although it is interesting to note that whenever Cormorants (or Shags) appeared on Hickling Broad in its pre-nature-reserve days they were soon shot. Since the premature departure of the growing Narford colony the only other evidence of attempted breeding in Norfolk is of nests being constructed at both How Hill and Snettisham in 1992. With ever-increasing numbers of Cormorants now breeding in the Midlands and the south, perhaps we can remain optimistic at the thought of the Cormorant once more becoming a permanent county breeder.

Whilst the Cormorant has been lost as a breeding bird, the numbers seen during the winter months and on passage have increased dramatically during the 20th century. In 1890 Stevenson described the Cormorant as 'an occasional visitor to our coast, less frequently still inland' and 'essentially a spring and autumn visitor, never numerous but by no means rare'. Riviere added that Cormorants were noted every month with a few summering on Breydon. Up until the 1940s its status remained much the same. Increasing numbers began to winter and appear on passage with east Norfolk (Breydon in particular) proving the favoured spot. With the offshore sandbank of Scroby not far away, a regular safe roosting ground was assured. Peak numbers were reached in December 1963 when 220 were present there. When Scroby Sands became unsuitable due to erosion from storms and high tides, it was soon abandoned (in 1966). Breydon's and east Norfolk's growing Cormorant numbers then moved to the safety of waterside alders at Ranworth Broad as an overnight roost. Up to 100 had already been noted there in March 1964, but with Scroby abandoned numbers soon reached 200 by the end of 1966. Meanwhile in the north and west of Norfolk, Cormorants still remained relatively scarce. Small numbers wintered and were seen on passage, 80 at Snettisham on a single day in September 1961 was thought to be highly exceptional. In 1968 the maximum day-count from the Wash was only ten!

By the 1970s, however, growing numbers led to the formation of more roost-sites. Fritton Lake had been a traditional roost as far back as 1775 when 'thousands' were said to arrive each night (Payn 1962), but it was not until 1973 that Cormorants once more began to appear there (by 1998 an estimated 300 were using the roost at times). In the Fens, overhead power cables at Welney were first used in December 1976, whilst on the north coast the wooded islands of Holkham Lake became another important roost-site. By 1976–77, peak winter counts included 22 at Fritton, 300 at Ranworth, 84 at Holkham Lake and 41 at Welney. Daytime assemblies in this period peaked at 115 at Filby Broad in December 1975 (when water level was low) and 158 at Breydon in October 1976. With ever more Cormorants wintering, new roost-sites formed through the 1980s and 1990s and included Eau Brink, Narford Lake and Snettisham in the west, Bayfield in the north, Colney/Bawburgh Gravel Pits, Hempton, Mill Street and Sennowe Park in the Wensum Valley, Marlingford and Strumpshaw (in 1985 only) in the Yare Valley and Seamere in central Norfolk. The Holkham Lake roost was abandoned in 1997 following disturbance from a local fishing syndicate who considered them 'undesirable', the presence of the roost being blamed for a reduction in fish stocks. However, an intensive study over four years by McCallum (1998a) had found that usually only 1–3 Cormorants fished at the lake at any one time, and never more than six, irrespective of the size of the night-time roost, which peaked at 400 in 1995. The trees previously used by the roosting Cormorants on the North Island were subsequently felled (McCallum 1998b). Some of the birds then took to roosting on Holkham Fresh Marshes where again disturbance led to desertion, after which they resettled at Bayfield Lake, although 200–300 were once again roosting at Holkham Fresh Marshes in July–August 1998. As well as overnight roosts, daytime collections became a regular feature through the 1980s at places such as Snettisham, Gore Point, Thornham Point, Titchwell, Scolt Head, Overy Harbour, Wells Harbour, Blakeney

Point and Cley. The only roost sites which have been counted regularly since 1980 are Welney and Ranworth Broad.

**Table 4. Annual peak counts of Cormorants roosting at Welney and Ranworth Broad 1980–97.**

|  | 80 | 81 | 82 | 83 | 84 | 85 | 86 | 87 | 88 | 89 | 90 | 91 | 92 | 93 | 94 | 95 | 96 | 97 |
|---|---|---|---|---|---|---|---|---|---|---|---|---|---|---|---|---|---|---|
| **Welney** | 74 | 86 | 70 | 65 | 80 | 120 | 133 | 135 | 147 | 165 | 192 | 165 | 233 | 248 | 269 | 174 | 254 | 197 |
| **Ranworth** | – | 300 | 350 | 350 | 400 | 298 | 300 | 330 | 368 | 320 | 325 | 329 | 319 | 267 | 270 | 462 | 278 | 405 |

Elsewhere, notable roost counts have included a maximum of 50 at Narford in 1984, 82 at Eau Brink in 1985, 154 at Snettisham in 1994 and 222 at Fritton in 1996. A national survey carried out early in 1997 showed that Norfolk held the most inland roosts, at a total of 11 sites (Hughes & Sellers 1998). One roost site that deserves a mention is the spire of Norwich Cathedral. During a spell of heavy rain up to five were seen alighting there at dusk on 10th September 1950. Another had also been seen there on 7th–8th September 1926. At 97m in height Norwich Cathedral's spire is the county's tallest structure. In addition one was shot on Necton Church tower in March 1883. Daytime peak counts have included 198 at Breydon in August 1995 and 210 at Titchwell in August 1993.

Peak numbers at most of the roost-sites are usually attained during the mid-winter period. However, since the late 1980s largest numbers began to arrive at some of the sites (particularly Holkham) in the late summer and early autumn months. With a number of colour-ringed individuals from the nesting colony at Abberton Reservoir in Essex detected amongst the Holkham birds, a clear pattern began to emerge. Post-breeding dispersal from Abberton usually begins at the end of June, with juveniles appearing throughout southern England thereafter. By August some will have reached France, The Netherlands, Germany and Spain, where they then spend the winter (G. Ekins *in litt.*). This evidence gleaned from the ringing programme clearly fits in with the highs and lows of Holkham's roost counts. As well as increasing numbers of Abberton birds being identified (both wintering and on passage), ringed birds from Anglesey, Dyfed, Shetland, the Farnes, France and The Netherlands have also been found in the county. The complex routes and long distances undertaken by Cormorants is well illustrated by the movements of a radio-tagged bird. Roosting usually at Little Paxton in Cambridgeshire, it stayed for 38 days within 15km of that site. On three occasions, however, it made journeys of up to 82km, one of which went via the Wash to the Holkham roost, before finally heading 30km out to sea to feed (Wynde & Hume 1997).

Birds of the race *sinensis* have been noted annually in small numbers at most of the main sites for a number of years. However, careful study of the Cormorants at Cley has revealed that the vast majority in at least summer and autumn are of the race *sinensis* (Millington 1998b). Nowadays groups of up to 50 may be seen 'loafing' on the North Scrape at Cley at this time of year, and of 100 or more that were seen during August 1998, only one or two were identified as *carbo*. A similar situation exists at Titchwell and possibly at other sites throughout the county. Due to the complexities and previously incomplete understanding of the identification features of this race, peak counts of *sinensis* in earlier years had included six at Pentney Gravel Pits on 15th February 1994, eight at Welney on 12th March 1994 and 22 at Ranworth on 18th February 1996.

Over 80 Cormorants ringed as nestlings have been reported in Norfolk, including birds from colonies in Scotland (16), Wales (30) and northern England, mainly the Farne Islands (22), while birds of the race *sinensis* have originated from Abberton Reservoir, Essex and from Nottinghamshire, The Netherlands and Denmark. The reporting of colour-ringed birds has allowed the often wide-ranging movements of individual birds to be recorded. A nestling ringed at Abberton with orange ring number A1 in April 1994 was seen intermittently at Strumpshaw between October 1994 and May 1995, at Breydon in July–August 1995 and at Strumpshaw from October 1995 to August 1996, before returning to Abberton where it was noted in March 1997 and April 1998, and most recently again at Strumpshaw in May 1998. Of 128 Cormorants at Breydon on 24th July 1998, a total of 14 had been colour-ringed at Abberton Reservoir. A nestling ringed at Oostvaardersplassen, The Netherlands on 5th June 1989 was seen at Welney in January 1990 and was back at Oostvaardersplassen in May and again in March 1991. Another colour-ringed *sinensis* ringed at Abberton was in Norfolk in the autumn, in France for the winter and back to Essex in the summer, and it made this same journey in two successive years (Millington 1998b). The nominate race *carbo* will also travel widely and rapidly – a nestling ringed on Puffin Island, Anglesey on 11th July 1983 was found at Ormesby Broad only 17 days later, having travelled a distance of 387km.

*Andrew Bloomfield*

# Shag (European Shag)

*Phalacrocorax aristotelis*

**A scarce winter visitor and autumn passage migrant; very rare in mid-summer and very scarce inland.**

The Shag is typically a bird of rocky coastlines and is almost exclusively restricted to the north-east Atlantic, the North Sea and the Mediterranean. It is found from Iceland east to Norway and the Kola Peninsula, around parts of the French and Iberian coastline to north-west Africa, on most of the Mediterranean islands and along the Aegean coast to the Black Sea in the east. In the British Isles it breeds around most of the coastline of Ireland, Wales and Scotland, including the Northern and Western Isles. Smaller numbers are also found in the south-west and on the east coast of England as far south as Flamborough Head in Humberside.

In Norfolk the Shag has always been regarded as a scarce visitor, usually in the winter months (particularly during gales), but also occasionally in the summer. Passage birds appear from September to November and again in March and April. As expected, the majority of sightings are coastal, although inland records of 'wrecked' or sick birds, following storms are not infrequent. Stevenson described the Shag as a very rare winter visitor, whilst Riviere noted it as being ' rather uncommon, usually in the autumn and winter'. In particular he included a reference to the unusually high numbers which followed severe gales between 30th December 1921 and 5th January 1922, following which up to three immatures remained inland on the River Wensum at Norwich until 26th May. Patterson writing in 1905 associated Shags with the arrival of large herring shoals offshore from Yarmouth and considered them to be increasing. Recent years have seen an increase in the number of Shags recorded in Norfolk, perhaps due to greater observer awareness. The Shag still remains somewhat scarce, although it probably winters more regularly at favoured sites such as Hunstanton, Brancaster, Wells Quay and the Sheringham area. Numbers usually reach a peak during westerly gales (north-westerly and north-easterly winds have also produced good numbers). The highest counts have included 43 at Cromer Pier on 27th November 1960, 71 at Sheringham on 22nd September 1974, 22 at Hunstanton on 7th November 1976, 16 at Yarmouth on 4th February 1976, 20 at Sheringham on 13th November 1977, 32 east at Sheringham on 19th December 1979, 40 at Brancaster and 20 at Hunstanton in November 1993 and 19 at Magdalen in February 1994. When wintering has occurred, loose colonial roosts have formed on the cliffs at both Sheringham and Hunstanton, on Cromer Pier, on moored boats in Brancaster Harbour and on window ledges of the quayside granary at Wells.

Inland records of Shags have also increased in recent years. Most of the county's river systems, lakes, gravel pits, Broads and Breckland meres have hosted 'wrecked' birds. Fenland and the River Wensum in Norwich have been particularly favoured. Usually only small numbers are involved, with maximum counts including six near Foundry Bridge in Norwich on 11th December 1965, four on the Ouse Washes on 29th September 1968, at Denver Sluice five on 27th December 1977 and seven on 4th February 1996, and ten at Lynford Gravel Pit on 5th November 1998, where four remained next day. In Broadland, peak counts have included four at Hickling on 3rd December 1926, seven at Barton Broad on 3rd February 1975 and six on the River Yare between Buckenham and Hardley in April 1975. During the winter of 1962, exceptional numbers appeared throughout much of southern England. In Norwich one remained for six weeks in the Wensum Valley, whilst a group of 14 descended into a lime pit at Castle Acre. Of these, seven were caught and released at King's Lynn, while of those which departed unaided, one died after flying into an elevator. Long-stayers have included three at Breydon from 20th April to 1st June 1988, while a bird at Wells Quay stayed throughout 1994 remaining until June 1995. Mid-summer sightings have also included singles at Hickling in July 1983 and at Sheringham on 24th July 1996.

Unusual incidents involving Shags have included one shot from Attleborough Church spire on 22nd February 1883 and another shot and wounded at Yarmouth in November 1824 which regurgitated 11 flounders when approached. A wintering bird became particularly tame at Wells Quay in March 1988, often visiting a nearby fish-and-chip shop where it was hand-fed with scraps. Unfortunately on one of its visits it was killed by a passing car. Another traffic victim was noted at Drymere in 1986.

Up to the end of 1997, a total of 147 Shags ringed at British breeding colonies had been recovered in Norfolk. The vast majority had been ringed as nestlings, 94 from Scotland, 50 from northern England (mainly the Farne Islands) and three from Wales.

*Andrew Bloomfield*

# Bittern (Great Bittern)

*Botaurus stellaris*

**A very scarce resident and winter visitor.**

The Bittern breeds throughout Europe, North Africa and central eastern Asia. Juveniles in the Western Palearctic, especially from northern and eastern areas, disperse from July and migration southwards extends from September to November. There has been a general decline in much of Europe since the 19th century (Day 1981), but numbers are increasing in Sweden and Finland.

In the British Isles the Bittern is now confined to a very few breeding localities in Norfolk, Suffolk and Lancashire. The present minute population is considered to be largely sedentary, but there is some evidence of movement away from breeding sites in autumn and winter. A Cley nestling in 1950 was struck by a lorry in Cheshire in November of that year. More recently two radio-tagged birds from Minsmere, Suffolk, spent the 1997–98 winter in the Upper Thurne/Trinity Broads area and were also noted at Burgh Castle. The adult male had headed north at the end of June followed in late July by a juvenile female. The former returned to its original breeding location in February 1998, but the other bird was still present in Broadland during April 1998 wandering in the Martham, Starch Grass and Meadow Dyke area. Remarkably one of these birds appeared at Minsmere for a single night before returning to Norfolk.

Stevenson devoted over a dozen pages to detailing the history of the Bittern. It was once abundant, breeding not only throughout the Broads district but also in the Fens where they were plentiful at Feltwell and Hockwold. A Feltwell thatcher described his grandfather regularly dining off roast Bittern each Sunday. However, a steady decline in numbers took place from the opening years of the 19th century resulting in extinction as a breeding species soon after the middle of the century.

Lubbock (1845) in *The Fauna of Norfolk* remarked that Bitterns had decreased greatly in numbers during the previous 20 years. At one time four or five might be seen in a morning at Hickling Broad and Heigham Sounds; Lubbock once accounted for 11 himself in a single year. The same author remarked that prior to 1843 'a party of fen shooters would kill 20 to 30 Bitterns in one morning when they were plentiful in Feltwell and Hockwold Fens'. Near extinction was inevitable.

According to Stevenson, from 1850 until 1866, although over 100 were recorded as shot during the winter (the majority during or just before the onset of severe weather), none was recorded during the nesting season. Booming was heard at Hoveton in 1866. Two years later a nest containing two eggs was found at Upton Broad and a nestling was caught alive. Although remaining a regular winter visitor there was no further evidence of nesting until 1886 when a young female with down still adhering to its feathers was received by a Norwich taxidermist from Ludham. This specimen was undoubtedly one of a group of no less than seven Bitterns contained in the Connop collection formerly at Rollesby Hall.

For a period of 14 years Bitterns were apparently absent from the county in summer. But in 1900 one was again heard in the Broads district and from then onwards booming became an almost annual event culminating in the discovery by Jim Vincent and Emma Turner of a half-fledged young one near Sutton Broad on 8th July 1911. Historic photographs of the event feature in her classic *Broadland Birds* (1924). She described Vincent and herself 'plunging into the reedbed . . . the water was above our knees and the reeds so dense that neither of us could see the other when a few yards apart'. Ten days later two more young birds were seen and the vacated nest discovered. Evidence of nesting in the same locality was obtained during the next few years, whilst in 1917 a nest containing young was found at Hickling.

The following year two pairs of Bitterns bred at Sutton and four at Hickling; three additional males were booming throughout the season elsewhere in the Broads. Recolonisation of Norfolk and probably the United Kingdom owes much to the interest in, and protection given to, Bitterns by enlightened private landowners. Despite this, 19th century attitudes lingered: collectors were still active and 15 birds were obtained in the county during the 12 months commencing June 1917. Fortunately, numbers steadily increased and in 1923 Turner was aware of 11 nests and estimated 16–17 breeding pairs (11 at Hickling/Horsey and the rest in the Bure and Ant Valleys). Between 23 and 25 pairs were estimated by Riviere in 1928. During February 1929 severe frosts prevailed throughout the month and nine or ten Bitterns were picked up dead in Broadland. Around this period ornithologists visiting Hickling – then a private estate – were impressed by keepers who became adept at stalking and catching booming Bitterns. Usually the performer was calling again within a few minutes. During the 1930s the breeding area was further extended and nesting was proved on the north Norfolk coast at Cley in 1937.

Peak numbers were attained in the early 1950s when Bitterns were breeding regularly in seven counties. A survey in Norfolk in 1954 revealed a total of 60 booming males despite a succession of cold winters and sea flooding. This total included five on the north coast at Cley and Salthouse. The majority were in the Barton, Hickling and Horsey districts; other localities included six boomers in the Flegg Broads complex, one in the Chet Valley and two along the Waveney at Fritton and Herringfleet. At Hickling on occasions eight or nine Bitterns could be observed at the same time flying over the marshes during May. The total British population at that time was just over 80 boomers. During very cold spells wardens at Hickling and Horsey hand-fed captive Bitterns with eels and sprats. Casualties were found from time to time; three were recovered at Horsey in February 1956, the birds starving rather than moving on in freezing conditions. Bitterns in ones, and occasionally twos, have continued to visit Breckland meres as winter visitors; Thompson and Stanford Waters have been the most favoured localities. Booming was recorded at Thompson in 1958, but there was no evidence of nesting.

The first indication of an alarming drop in numbers became apparent during the late 1960s. This coincided with a loss of reed swamp in Broadland at first thought to be due to the coypu, but later found to be the effect of a complex of factors related to water quality. Also land drainage increased and pesticide use was widespread.

By 1970 the county total of Bitterns had declined to 28 boomers. The year 1976 saw a further reduction to nine regular boomers in Broadland together with an unmated male at Cley (Day & Wilson 1978). During the following decade (1977–86) and despite colonisation at Titchwell (Robson 1994), the county total varied between seven and 14 boomers. In both 1985 and 1986 more male Bitterns were present in the north coast reedbeds than in Broadland. By that time the birds were no longer breeding outside Norfolk and Suffolk except at Leighton Moss in Lancashire. After 1986 between six and 11 males were recorded regularly booming in the county each spring but by 1992 only two occupied territories were in the Broads district. By 1997 the British population had fallen to a precariously low total of 11 boomers (including three in Norfolk) in addition to an almost silent male at Cley. The following spring and summer a single male remained at Cley and two nests there each contained a single young. In addition a third nest was found in Broadland, again with one young. The radio-tagged female from that pair had fledged from Minsmere in 1997, thereby providing evidence of successful breeding in the bird's first year. One other boomer was also present in Broadland.

Lord William Percy's little-known volume (Percy 1951) contains valuable first-hand observations of nesting Bitterns studied at Catfield. His photographs confirm the birds favoured nesting sites in deeply flooded reedbeds with water lapping the nest edges. One nest built on an abandoned Coot's nest was in water so deep that the keeper had difficulty in reaching it clad in thigh-waders. Similar situations are revealed in the work produced by other eminent photographers visiting Hickling and Horsey. Sitting in tiny hides for long periods they were privileged to observe the domestic life of this mysterious bird. One discovery was that in times of a food shortage nestling Bitterns will turn cannibal and devour the smallest in a brood. One youngster, handled after wandering, readily disgorged a leg and thigh of a former brother or sister. Lord Percy's pictures show a Bittern precariously climbing the reeds before stretching wings to sun itself at their summit thus 'proving the bird a past master in the art of the tight-rope'. Ascent to the reedheads is made possible as the bird's bulk is chiefly made up of nothing heavier than feathers. It relies for support not on a single stem but a number of stems held together between huge toes. The normal progress of a Bittern through a reedbed is performed not on the ground but along the stems of the reeds, a method giving the appearance – to the hidebound photographer – of a bird walking on stilts.

During the years of abundance, between May and early June, up to six Bitterns were regularly observed performing sky dances high over Hickling: 'The birds circled round each other frequently shooting upward then planing down again. . . . Finally dispersing, two of the group would rise over the Broad before heading in a direct line to another nesting area quite three miles away. Such displays were most marked in the early morning and towards evening' (Turner 1924). The pioneer lady photographer also described Bitterns fighting in the air 'mounting in circles and endeavouring to swoop down at one another'. As she discovered over 80 years ago, male Bitterns have individually distinctive voices. Much more recently, researchers at Nottingham University have been able to exploit this by tape-recording birds. The presence of the same male between years can also be detected by this method (Tyler 1992). Similarly, it was shown by the sonograms that a female which bred successfully in a small reedbed at Weybourne in 1989–91, successfully rearing a total of eight young, was paired to the Cley male.

Present-day observers walking the Weaver's Way footpath along the southern edge of Hickling Broad are often surprised to learn that Rush Hills (where Booth had obtained his specimens of breeding Ruffs and Reeves) became completely overgrown in reed and sedge for a period of 30 years. By 1920 conversion to a reedbed was complete and it was there that Jim Vincent found three Bitterns' nests on the present-day wader ground.

Riviere described in some detail the Bittern's nesting habits. Booming formerly began in the first days of February and full clutches of eggs were expected before the end of March. But when Hickling Broad was ice-covered for 11 weeks during the 1962–63 winter, booming was not recorded that spring until 9th March. In more recent times, Bitterns often remain silent until mid-March or even fail to boom at all. The birds need very extensive reedbeds. At Leighton Moss as a result of radio-tagging, it has been discovered they may range over 70ha (although this measure includes open water and willow scrub as well as reedbed). Males may boom in several different sites during a single day. Jim Vincent, whose knowledge of Bitterns was exceptional, first considered some male Bitterns to be polygamous. On a number of occasions he found two or three nests within 30 or 35 metres of each other within an area where only a single male had been heard to boom during the spring. At Minsmere, Suffolk, in 1997 a single male was believed to have possessed a harem of five females. Any additional males putting in an appearance may well have been stabbed to death. Percy's observations and the results of radio-tagging also suggest males do not visit the nest and the young are hatched and fledged entirely by the efforts of the female.

Evidence of Bitterns leaving wintering grounds was obtained on 15th March 1995 when one headed north-west over the University Broad at Earlham followed by three moving east over Martham Broad on 22nd March 1995. The 1995–96 winter resulted in the largest arrival of displaced Continental Bitterns for many years. Almost every Broadland reedbed however small, held at least a single bird. Coastal sites between Snettisham and Weybourne were also favoured and others wandered inland to Breckland meres. Estimating numbers is difficult, but up to 50 Bitterns may have been present at this time in the county. Some lingered until mid-April, but eventually all apparently returned to the Continent. An immature male Bittern found starving in a pig-sty in Cornwall was transported to Strumpshaw where it was radio-tagged and released on 8th March 1996. It stayed until 15th April 1996 when it was seen circling high over the fen at dusk and presumably departed that night. Three other Bitterns followed the same departure pattern from Strumpshaw on 7th April that year. Other evidence of birds moving to or from the Continent has been demonstrated by the Bittern occasionally being found as a tideline corpse such as the one at Caister on 20th December 1983, and also one on the Shell Lemon gas rig on 25th November 1993.

In addition to the Cley-ringed nestling recovered in Cheshire, mentioned earlier, two nestlings ringed at Hickling have been recovered – one three months later at Kessingland, Suffolk in 1927 and the other near Yarmouth in January 1933. As well as the radio-tagged birds marked at Minsmere and found in Broadland, also mentioned earlier, two others ringed there have been found in Norfolk both in winter – a nestling at Hickling and an adult at Raveningham.

*Michael Seago*

## Little Bittern                  *Ixobrychus minutus*

**A rare vagrant.**

The Little Bittern's breeding range extends from Iberia, France, The Netherlands (where now rare) and the Baltic States eastwards to Sinkiang and south to the Mediterranean basin. Most birds winter in tropical Africa. It is an annual vagrant to the British Isles and has successfully bred on at least one occasion (in Yorkshire, 1984). More Little Bitterns have been recorded in Norfolk than in any other county. Springtime occurrences are presumably of birds overshooting Continental breeding areas.

Stevenson listed 17 or 18 authenticated records including apparent pairs summering in the county. South Walsham Broad was a favoured locality where a marshman, Samuel Ebbage, shot at least three specimens. He had become familiar with the distinctive nocturnal 'barking dog' advertising call of the male Little Bittern. This same marshman obtained a pair of Savi's Warblers at the same locality in 1840.

Riviere added a further eight specimens with sight observations of a larger number, the majority during May, June and July. His book included records of two males at Rollesby Broad, one of which was shot on 3rd July 1893, two near Watton from 21st May to 22nd August 1894 and another shot at Brettenham on 12th August 1899. The following have been recorded since 1930:

1932: One shot at Breydon Marshes on 18th September
1942: Hickling Broad on 2nd August
1952: Cley from 26th July to 6th November
Horsey on 11th August
Hickling on 20th September
1953: Mundford on 11th August
1956: Cley on 7th–24th August
1958: Buckenham on 7th May
Cley on 26th August
1963: Barton Staithe on 28th August
1967: Wells on 24th September
1968: Repps Staithe on 21st January
Holme on 1st–15th May
Hainford on 4th June where it was found dying
1970: Cley from 27th September to 14th October
1973: Weybourne on 6th–10th May
1978: Cley on 5th–6th August
1979: Cley on 20th May
1984: Eaton next Norwich from 31st May to 2nd June
1992: Holkham from 30th May to 2nd June
1996: Snettisham from 26th April to 18th May
1997: Male at Holme on 13th–16th June, probably present from 11th

*Michael Seago*

## Night Heron (Black-crowned Night Heron) | *Nycticorax nycticorax*

**A rare vagrant.**

The Night Heron breeds sporadically throughout southern Europe with colonies thinly scattered from the Mediterranean and Black Seas north to The Netherlands and Slovakia. Juveniles disperse from the breeding colonies in July and August. The majority winter in tropical Africa, but others remain in the Mediterranean region. Returning migrants in the spring are prone to overshooting and occur as vagrants in the British Isles and northern Europe.

Stevenson listed 15 or so occurrences up to 1860. These early records included one shot in an orchard at Yarmouth on 24th May 1824 and no less than three obtained during the following winter on the Yarmouth North Denes. At the time of publication of Riviere's book the county total had increased to over 20, with the most recent being one at Wroxham Broad on 22nd May 1925.

Night Herons
(Norman Arlott)

There were no further sightings until 1952 when one appeared in Holt Hall woods on 22nd–25th July. Since then and excluding birds of suspect origin, there have been single records at Acle, Blackborough End, Black Horse Broad, Breydon, Briston/Melton Constable, Brundall, East Rudham, Hickling Broad, Hoveton Great Broad, Seamere (Hingham), Sheringham, Swanton Morley Gravel Pit, Thetford, Welney and Winterton, taking the county total to 40 or more. The only localities to have received more than a single visit have been Cley with singles from 22nd May to 1st June 1983 and on 10th–11th May 1990, and Holkham with up to five in 1997 (see below) and one from 17th May to 28th July 1998. Among the other longest-staying individuals have been singles at Seamere (Hingham) from 7th July to 18th August 1952, Swanton Morley Gravel Pit from 25th September to 12th November 1972 and Briston/Melton Constable from 15th December 1982 to 25th January 1983.

In 1997 up to five were present in dykes on Holkham Fresh Marsh between 7th May, when two sub-adults were reported, and 28th August. There were confusing reports of the number and status of the birds involved with, at first, conflicting reports of adults and sub-adults being seen. In June it was established that there were five birds present including two adults. During June the party of five was seen on a number of occasions. In August the two sub-adults spent a few days in Holkham Park. This multiple arrival coincided with a similar event in north-east England. Juveniles were reported from Little Dunham on 26th–27th January and Honing Common on 2nd September 1997 with a tame adult at Garveston on 19th–22nd May.

Night Herons appearing in the Wensum Valley almost certainly originate from Great Witchingham Wildlife Park where a feral colony nests among breeding Grey Herons. Another feral colony also exists at Earsham, near Bungay on the county boundary with Suffolk. Winter records have sometimes been treated as suspect, but the finding of a Russian-ringed immature in Lincolnshire in January 1980 provided confirmation of genuine vagrancy from an unexpectedly distant source. It is also interesting to note that two Night Herons, possibly a pair, summered in Kent in 1995. This was the first such occurrence in the British Isles and may be part of an extension of the colonies less than 80km away on the Continent.

*Michael Seago*

Squacco Heron
(Robert Gillmor)

## Squacco Heron                                       *Ardeola ralloides*

**A very rare vagrant; ten records.**

The breeding range of the Squacco Heron extends from southern Spain and north-west Africa eastwards to south-west Asia. It winters in sub-Saharan Africa.

This solitary crepuscular heron has become extremely rare in the British Isles and only one has been recorded in Norfolk since 1966. Riviere listed five occurrences during the 19th century. The first county record was of a bird caught in a bow-net hanging out to dry near Ormesby Broad in December 1820. The next two were killed near Yarmouth in May 1831 'at least one of which, however, was probably obtained at Oulton, Suffolk', followed by one obtained at Ormesby, or Filby, on 12th June 1834 and an adult male formerly in Stevenson's collection and now in the Castle Museum, Norwich, taken on Surlingham Broad on 26th June 1863. In addition one was reported killed at Burlingham, but no date was recorded. Since then singles have occurred at Hickling on 6th June 1912 (which was later found shot on 26th June) and at Burnt Fen Broad on 5th July 1912. One was at Hickling on 22nd–27th July 1942 and another was filmed over three days at Rollesby Broad during late July 1966. The most recent was at Pensthorpe from 26th April to 7th May 1998.

*Michael Seago*

## Cattle Egret

*Bubulcus ibis*

A rare vagrant.

During the 20th century there has been a marked extension of the world range of the Cattle Egret with the species now breeding in Europe, Asia, Africa, Australia and the Americas. In the Western Palearctic it has a patchy breeding distribution, mainly in Iberia, France, north-west Africa and the Middle East. Some European birds overwinter in north-west Africa, others remaining in southern Europe. Prior to 1958 there had been only two British records, but it has occurred almost annually since 1980. Double-figure totals were recorded in autumn 1986 and spring 1992.

Although the species was included in Stevenson (under its old name of 'Buff-backed Heron'), the single specimen was subsequently discarded from the Norfolk list and the first county record became the male shot by Dan Banham on Breydon Marshes on 23rd October 1917. This was also only the second British occurrence and the specimen may be seen in the Booth Museum at Brighton. A second individual, obtained on West Caister Marshes in October 1934 (Seago 1977), remained in Harry Smith's little-known collection at Three-mile House on the River Bure until about 1980 when the entire collection was auctioned. An air of mystery surrounded the marshman collector and, perhaps not surprisingly, the present whereabouts of the 1934 specimen is unknown.

A further 15 examples have since been recorded:

1974: One in the Broads area visiting Horsey, Hickling and Halvergate from 27th July to 25th August
1975: Hickling on 22nd–26th April
1983: An adult at Cley and Salthouse on 28th May
1986: Two photographed at Heigham Sounds on 27th September
   One at Horstead on 30th October and at Dilham from 31st October to 2nd November. At both localities feeding among Highland cattle
1988: An adult in breeding plumage following the plough at Tunstall on 9th August, before reaching Minsmere later the same day
1990: Walpole St Andrew on 25th April .
1992: Five in the Welney/Denver Sluice/Downham Market area on 9th–15th May with one remaining on 16th–17th and two on 18th–20th. An incursion of Cattle Egrets into NW Europe at this time saw at least 18 reaching the British Isles
1995: One between Alby and Gunton on 18th May and doubtless the same bird remained in the Martham/Potter Heigham/Hickling area from 27th May to 29th December, frequently roosting on Rush Hills, Hickling
1998: Holkham 18th May

*Michael Seago*

## Little Egret     BREYDON 1·12·1992 AND 20·9·1993.

*Egretta garzetta*

A scarce visitor increasingly remaining for long periods.

The Little Egret breeds in much of southern and central Europe and north-west Africa and has increased in France, Italy and Iberia. The populations are partially migratory, wintering around the Mediterranean, the Middle East and particularly tropical Africa. It was rare in Britain until an unprecedented influx into southern England in 1989, thought to have originated from Brittany. Successful breeding was first recorded in Britain in 1996 on Brownsea Island in Poole Harbour, Dorset.

The first Norfolk record was at Cley on 7th–11th May 1952. The bird was filmed by Dick Bagnall-Oakeley, a unique event at the time. A further 26 Little Egrets put in appearances in the county up to 1988. Sightings were reported from 23rd April to 31st August. All the records were of singles apart from two at Cley, the most favoured locality, during May 1972. Apart from birds at Colney in July–August 1970, Flitcham in August 1981, Strumpshaw in July 1983, Hickling in May 1985 and West Acre, all sightings were at coastal localities.

The remarkable influx from mid-July 1989 throughout southern England was not reflected in Norfolk. However, a total of 16 appeared in the county between 1989 and 1992, including sightings at Blakeney Point, Ouse Mouth and Welney. Single birds lingered at Breydon until 13th October 1991 and 23rd December 1992. SAW IT, 1st DECEMBER 1992.

Assessing numbers became difficult from August 1993 following a further major arrival in Jersey and along the south coast from Cornwall to West Sussex. Many sightings in Norfolk referred to fly-overs and the birds wandered to a selection of feeding localities between the Wash and Cley. Apart from four in the SAW IT. Ongar Hill area, all records were of singles. One lingered at Breydon from 13th September to 4th Octo- 20.9.1993. ber. Sightings continued at Lynn Point, Snettisham and along the north coast during October with the last on 22nd November. Between 3rd December 1993 and 27th March 1994 two Little Egrets took up residence on Stiffkey saltings, the first instance of wintering in the county.

From late April 1994 ones and twos wandered extensively between coastal localities. The situation at Titchwell was complex – it attracted two roosting birds in May, up to four in August, six in September, three in October and two until the year-end. These birds fed mainly in Brancaster and Thornham Harbours and the adjacent saltings and creeks. Sightings between Holme and Stiffkey doubtless related to the Titchwell group.

The local scene during the opening months of 1995 showed a wide-ranging bird along the north Norfolk coast. Ones, twos and threes featured at many coastal sites during the spring and summer. Other Little Egrets put in appearances at Welney, Lynn Point, Snettisham, Fritton, Berney and Hickling. At Titchwell roost numbers steadily increased from one during the greater part of July to nine on 23rd–31st August. Up to eight continued roosting there until 1st December reducing to three on 2nd–9th December and two festively decorating the trees until the month-end. Almost certainly different birds visited Breydon on 16th September, Cley on 18th–19th October and Heigham Holmes on 5th December.

The pattern of an increased number of sightings continued in 1996 with at least two birds remaining at Titchwell from the previous year where there were three present on 19th–21st January. What were presumed to be wanderers from Titchwell were seen at Brancaster Harbour, Stiffkey and Cley during January to March. In April and May there were many records along the north coast from Thornham to Sheringham, mainly in ones or twos but with five at Burnham Norton on 29th May when three were seen flying east at Salthouse. There were fewer birds present during the remainder of the year but a maximum of four were roosting at Titchwell on 14th November.

In the first half of 1997 one or two birds were recorded along the north coast at a number of localities. Away from the north, singles were seen at Snettisham and Breydon on 15th and 25th January respectively and at Sea Palling, Winterton and Breydon in June. Inland records came from the Sparham Pools area on 19th May and the Nunnery Lakes at Thetford on 11th June. In the second-half of 1997 singles were reported from the usual north coast sites with five at Titchwell on 15th November where from one to two remained until the year-end. In 1998, there were again many records of one or two birds at coastal sites throughout the county with the Titchwell/Thornham area once more hosting the largest numbers, including up to four during the first winter period and a county record of 11 on 29th–30th September 1998.

*Michael Seago*

Little Egrets
(*Norman Arlott*)

## Great White Egret (Great Egret)     *Ardea alba*

**A very rare vagrant; at least ten records.**

In the Western Palearctic, the western race of Great White Egret breeds in Europe from Slovakia and Austria south to Italy and the Balkans eastwards to the Ukraine and in Asia. Small numbers also breed in Germany and The Netherlands (since 1978). Most winter in the eastern Mediterranean and the Middle East.

Following the first Norfolk sighting in 1979, nine or more Great White Egrets have occurred in the county:

1979: Hickling on 10th–18th August had been earlier noted in Lincolnshire
1983: North Wootton on 14th September, also appeared briefly at Titchwell on 2nd October and at Wells on 6th October
1985: Horsey on 11th–16th July, visiting Hickling on 15th July
1986: Titchwell on 23rd June
1989: Titchwell on 13th October followed by a lengthy stay at Minsmere, Suffolk
1990: One or two wide-ranging birds at Welney on 2nd July, Hickling on 15th, Welney again on 23rd–24th and Hockwold on 4th August
1993: Cley from 26th April to 2nd May when it headed west, appearing at Blakeney Freshes, Holkham, Brancaster, Titchwell and Holme. It returned to Cley briefly on 3rd May
Feltwell Anchor from 22nd December to 13th February 1994, when it departed at the onset of freezing conditions being subsequently seen in Cambridgeshire, Northamptonshire and Buckinghamshire
1994: One flew west at Cley on 21st January
1997: Cley on 28th December moving to Stiffkey Greens later that day, remaining in the same general area until 29th March 1998
1998: Martham Broad/Horsey Mere intermittently 3rd–14th March

*Michael Seago*

## Grey Heron    Titchwell. 8·10·1986.     *Ardea cinerea*

**A fairly common resident and scarce passage migrant and winter visitor.**

The Grey Heron breeds from Spain east across the Western Palearctic, extending north along the Norwegian coast to the Arctic Circle. Breeding fortunes in the British Isles have been better documented than those of any other species following the first national census in 1928 when 346 pairs were present in Norfolk in 21 heronries. Censuses have been carried out regularly by the BTO ever since.

British and Irish breeders are mainly non-migratory although some move from Britain to Ireland and a few from southern England to the Low Countries, France and rarely Spain. Their places may be taken by immigrants from Scandinavia. Most Grey Herons risk starvation rather than emigrating in severe winters. Heavy mortality took place in 1963 with severe frosts continuing for ten weeks with frozen ground cutting off food supplies. The county total dropped to 181 nests in the following spring, the lowest on record. Climatic factors, however, have not been responsible for the alarming decline and the collapse or near collapse of major Broadland heronries during the early 1970s (Jones 1984).

Counts of all known heronries took place annually between 1954 and 1969. The most impressive total was 430 nests in both 1959 and 1961. Further full surveys in 1990 (Jones 1991) and in 1998 (Bloomfield & Seago 1999) produced totals of 303 and 313 occupied nests, respectively.

Stevenson in 1870 could list only eight heronries then in occupation in Norfolk; all except Kimberley had fallen into disuse by the time of publication of Riviere's work (1930). Didlington heronry, long linked with the history of falconry in the county, at one time contained 60–65 nests. It was vacated in 1924 apparently remaining deserted until 1953 when three nests were reported. Between 1954 and 1997 the total did not exceed 11 apart from 13 in both 1970 and 1991. Earlham Park was colonised during the

1830s, continuing as a stronghold until 1860 and containing between 80 and 100 nests. In 1860 a severe gale 'made sad havoc with the fine firs which were strewn in all directions, several with nests still in their branches whilst the remains of many others crackled under foot . . .' From that time the numbers steadily decreased until by 1866 only two or three pairs remained to breed at Earlham. By this time, 60 pairs had colonised woodland near Costessey Hall. Two years later the Grey Herons were again on the move, 16 pairs having returned to Earlham. Here up to seven pairs continued breeding until 1928 when the woodland was deserted having been acquired the previous year by Norwich Corporation and 'thrown open to the public as a recreation ground'.

At Wolferton, considered the oldest heronry in Norfolk, Thomas Southwell was informed in 1853 that royal keepers were 'destroying the Herons as their noise disturbed the game'. Fortunately, some birds were spared with the colony containing 20 nests in 1868, but it was abandoned in 1925. Kimberley heronry, first described in 1848, was situated on the island in the park lake. Between 1911 and 1928 totals varied from 15 to 34 nests. No further information is available until 1946 when 25 nests were occupied with a peak of 29 in 1951. From 1954 until 1962 numbers ranged from 14 to 25 dropping to only three following the 1963 arctic winter. Subsequent totals until 1972 were between five and 18 nests.

The heronries currently or recently occupied are discussed in alphabetical order grouped according to habitat where relevant. Without the very considerable contribution of Tony Vine, who has visited the west Norfolk heronries each spring for a half century, this summary would have been far less complete:

**Barton Broad:** This heronry, doubtless of birds from Catfield Hall, was founded with four nests in 1960. Nesting-sites have included Heron Carr and The Island. Since 1961 between 3 and 18 pairs have bred with a maximum of 19 in 1970, but only 4 following the 1963 winter.

**Buckenham:** Situated in the mid-Yare Valley this heronry was first established with five nests in 1898. Regular nesting commenced in 1920 with three nests increasing to seven in 1928. No further details are available until 1941 when 34 pairs were in residence increasing to 40 in 1954 and 43 in 1961. The 1963 winter resulted in a decline to 27 nests. Since then the peak has been 37 in 1972, but only 16 between 1977 and 1990. The latest counts have been low – three in 1997 and 1998.

**Burgh Castle:** This new site on the edge of Breydon began with two nests in 1986 increasing to 14 in 1995 and 12 in 1998.

**Burgh Common, Fleggburgh:** A Bure Valley site where one to three pairs have nested annually since 1981.

**Burgh St Peter:** In the Waveney Valley this heronry was first reported with two nests in 1994 and again in 1998.

**Cley:** The heronry in The Hangs was first occupied with three nests in 1961. Since then the birds have nested either in the original plantation, Cop Hill or at North Foreland edging Snipe's Marsh. The highest total was seven nests in 1980, but there was only one in 1998.

**Colney Hall:** Situated in the upper Yare, this heronry was first known in 1974 attaining a peak of 14 nests in 1992–93. A total of 12 pairs was in residence in 1998.

**Denver Sluice:** In the parish of Fordham on the edge of the Ouse Washes this heronry was first recorded in 1931 when there were two nests at Bran Creek Farm with seven nests at nearby Pitcher's Farm the following year. By 1946 a total of 36 nests was found at Ouse Bridge Farm, declining to only eight in 1947. From 1950 onwards part of the colony occupied nests at White House Farm. In 1952 there was a total of 27 nests, increasing to 56 in 1961 and to a peak of 82 in 1967; the next year there were 48 nests. Only 19 pairs were in residence in 1970; numbers continued falling with the last two nests in 1977.

**Earsham:** This Waveney Valley heronry, first recorded about 1907, contained four to five nests annually until 1920. During the following four decades counts have ranged between ten and fourteen nests. Since then the birds have nested in America Wood, Holy Grove and Thorny Pit Plantation with a peak of 23 in 1998.

**Elmham Great Wood:** First recorded in 1985 this heronry in the upper Wensum Valley has varied between five and thirteen nests. The highest total was in 1991.

**Feltwell Black Dyke:** Founded in 1882 this colony overlooking Hockwold Fen and beyond to the new RSPB Lakenheath Reserve, contained three nests for several years. Despite gales blowing down nesting trees in 1895 the size increased to between 60 and 70 nests in 1924. Numbers dropped to 35 in 1928 and 28 in 1931. Between 1950 and 1958 numbers varied between two and six nests, but none thereafter. The site remained abandoned until 1992 when a single pair nested, increasing to 21 nests in 1993. Since then numbers have varied between two and five nests.

**Fritton (Waveney Forest):** Newly-established in 1976 with five nests, this heronry attained a total of 12 breeding pairs in 1989 but only two nests in 1998.

**Great Witchingham:** Situated in the Wildlife Park and complete with a viewing platform, this heronry has developed rapidly from 4 nests in 1983 to 15 in 1990, 31 in 1991, 42 in 1993, 53 in 1995 and a peak of 54 in 1996. The nests are well-concealed in Scots pines and the heronry is shared with feral Night Herons.

**Heckingham:** Overlooking the River Chet and Hardley Flood this heronry was established in 1990. The number of nests has never exceeded eight.

**Hickling, Heigham Sounds and Catfield Dyke:** In the Thurne Valley, the heronry in Sounds Wood was first occupied in 1927 by a single pair. During the 1950s there were up to 12 nests, reducing to nine in the 1960s. Fortunes improved in the 1970s with 21 nests in 1972 and 22 in 1973. A total of 17 nests was found in 1980–81, since when the colony had declined to eight by 1995. The Hundred Acre Marsh first occupied in 1997 with two nests had increased to four the following year. In earlier years up to four pairs nested on the Hickling Reserve in both General McHardy's Wood and in Whiteslea Wood. Catfield Dyke has held one or two nests each year since 1992.

**Hilgay:** On the edge of the River Wissey, Hilgay heronry was first established in 1972 with ten nests. By 1979, 30 pairs were in residence. During the 1980s counts ranged from 31 to 46 with a peak of 54 in 1989. Since then the maximum count was 48 in 1990, declining to 35 in 1995 and 1996.

**Holkham Park:** Close to Holkham Meals, this heronry had become established by 1870 in Church Wood and contained 33 nests in 1879. A decade later there were 14 nests, seven in 1890 and 26 in 1921. Up to 1910 the colony occupied both Church Wood and Obelisk Wood, but clearing out the lake that year resulted in Church Wood being permanently abandoned. There were at least 20 nests in Obelisk Wood in 1924 and 25–30 in the dimly-lit giant ilex trees in 1928. Since 1954 there have been 4–20 nests most years until 1993 when the colony deserted and occupied Decoy Wood on the Holkham Fresh Marshes, where up to 14 pairs bred until 1997. However, in 1998 Decoy Wood was abandoned and Obelisk Wood reoccupied by seven pairs. In addition, a single nest was found at Burnham Overy in a hawthorn less than a metre in height.

**Islington:** Situated almost at the extremity of Norfolk Fenland this heronry contained 50–100 nests from at least 1910 until 1953, including 80 in 1924 and 70–80 in 1928. The trees in the original nesting site were felled in 1937, but a new heronry became established nearby. High numbers of nests were attained during the 1950s – 127 in 1954 and an all-time peak of 134 in 1959. In the 1960s totals ranged between a low of 23 (following a severe winter) and 85. During the following decade, 1979 produced the highest number with 71 nests, followed by a high count of 116 in 1980. In the 1980s the lowest number was 63 nests. From 1990 onwards there were between 50 and 91 nests.

**Mautby Decoy:** This heronry overlooking the lower Bure towards Breydon was first recorded in 1874. Eight years later it held nearly 100 nests. This high total was reduced to 12 in 1887 and the site was apparently deserted in 1903. No further information is available until a single nest was reported in 1923 increasing to 11 in 1928 and to an impressive 80 by 1936. Between 1946 and 1990 this heronry was occupied continuously, ranging between one and 23 nests apart from 26 in 1962. Few if any, suitable trees now survive at this site.

**Narford:** Situated in Decoy Wood, this heronry was first recorded in 1911 with six nests. In 1924, eleven pairs were present followed by seven in 1928. The site was abandoned between 1951 and 1957, but a single pair returned in 1958. Since 1965 the peak was 17 nests in 1970 followed by 16 in 1971 and 1972. In 1998 three nests were recorded. On more than one occasion all the adult birds have been shot.

**Old Hunstanton Park:** First reported in 1984 when there were four nests, subsequent totals have been 2–11 nests.

**Quidenham:** This heronry was first known in 1985 when four nests were occupied. Subsequent counts have ranged from three to seventeen, with five in 1998.

**Ranworth and Cockshoot:** The extensive alder carrs in the Bure Valley have attracted Herons since at least 1911 when a single nest appeared beside Ranworth Broad. Four nests were recorded in 1922 and 1924, six in 1928 and 29 in 1946. During the 1950s counts varied from 26 to 28 followed by a peak of 40 in 1961. Numbers began tumbling in the 1970s with a maximum of 23 in 1973. Since then counts have ranged from one to five. An offshoot from Ranworth was established near Cockshoot Broad in 1925 increasing to three nests in 1928. The peak years were 1966 and 1969 with 14 nests, but more recently only ones and twos have appeared.

**Reedham and Wickhampton:** On the edge of Halvergate Levels the heronry adjacent to Reedham Church was first recorded in 1894 when it contained 30 nests. A considerable increase took place and 80–90 nests were noted between 1901 and 1919 with 94 in 1928, the year of the first national census. A decade later there had been a reduction to 47 nests in 1938 and to 40 nests in 1939. At this time many of the birds began taking up residence in nearby carrs and by 1941 the original wood was deserted. Wigg's Carr in Wickhampton contained 8 nests in 1941, 12 in 1942 and 30 in 1943. The site remained occupied until 1977 reaching peaks of 48 in both 1945 and 1946 and 45 in 1968 and 1969 (Jones 1983). Only fourteen nests were found in 1976 and a final four in 1977. Today the only evidence of nesting Grey Herons in Wigg's Carr are faded labels still attached to alders by the Browne family when making annual surveys. Satellite heronries with up to nine nests, have since appeared in Reedbush, Reedham Park and Decoy Carrs.

**Sennowe Park, Guist:** Newly established in 1989 with four nests, but only one in 1998.

**Snettisham:** Situated in Ken Wood close to the shore of the Wash, the heronry at Snettisham was apparently established in about 1940, but was not known to birdwatchers until 1953 when there were 18 nests. This total was not exceeded until 1959 when there were 19 nests. In the 1960s numbers varied between 7 and 21 and in the following decade between 16 and 24. From 1980 to 1989 the highest number was 17 decreasing to single-figure counts from 1991 onwards.

**Sparham:** In the upper Yare Valley, Sparham heronry dated from 1983 when there were ten nests. A peak of 20 nests was attained in 1989. All the birds subsequently moved to Great Witchingham.

**Sturston Carr:** Situated in the Stanford Training Area this heronry was first established in 1980 with three nests. It has since been occupied continuously ranging between three and seventeen nests. A recent increase may be of birds formerly at Didlington.

**Surlingham and Wheatfen Broads:** These two heronies are in the mid-Yare Valley. Wheatfen was first occupied in 1961 and Surlingham from 1988. At Wheatfen a peak of 12 nests was attained in 1974. At Surlingham one to three nests have been recorded.

**Upton Broad:** Discovered in 1953 when there were six nests in the dense alder carr known as The Doles, this heronry attained a maximum of ten nests in 1962. The latest visit, in 1998, produced three nests.

**Wimbotsham:** First discovered in 1988, this heronry which overlooks the Great Ouse and the Relief Channel contained seven nests in 1996 followed by 17 in 1997.

**Wiveton Hall:** A single pair in 1953 increased to a maximum of four by 1957 with four pairs again in 1998.

**Wolterton Park:** The early history of this heronry is unknown, but four nests were recorded in 1990 with eight the next year and 14 in 1998.

In addition to the above, single nests have appeared in Broadland alder carrs from time to time at Calthorpe, Engine House Carr (Halvergate), Horning Hall, Horning Church Marsh, Reedham Marshes (How Hill), Runham and Woodbastwick Fen.

As remarked by Riviere 'the population of heronries is an ever-changing one: old sites become vacated whilst new ones spring up'. Even so, the following list of heronries abandoned since 1955 is surprisingly lengthy, the majority of which never contained more than a dozen nests: Bawburgh, Beetley, Belaugh, Blakeney, Ditchingham, Elsing, Fishley, Gunton Park, Hemsby Common, Hockham Fen, Horningtoft, Horstead, Kerdiston, Keswick (Old Hall), Ketteringham, Kimberley, Martham Ferry, Melton Constable, Oxborough, Rackheath Springs, Shadwell, Shipdham, Sparham, Stanford, Stiffkey, Strumpshaw, Thompson Water, Tottington, Whitwell Common, Wretham Park and Wroxham Bridge Broad.

Outside the breeding season Grey Herons may be seen along the edges of rivers, streams, meres, lakes, the Broads, and gravel pits. Others feed in tidal creeks, fresh and saltwater marshes. Fish ponds in suburban gardens are regularly visited, particularly in winter. Usually only small groups are seen away from heronries and there is a lack of up-to-date information, apart from 27 at Lenwade in December 1994, a similar number at Earsham in February 1995, and 31 at Welney in August 1997. The largest groups on record have included 41 on Cley Marsh on 16th June 1924, 69 there on 12th August 1928 and 94 at Welney on 24th July 1998 due to flooding.

In the days of commercial shipping to and from the port of Norwich, Grey Herons regularly patrolled the Yare, following the coasters and readily plunging head-first into the river to seize fish damaged by propellers as the vessels negotiated bends and shoals. Often only the heron's wings, which were held high, remained in view. Grey Herons have also been observed during ploughing, the opportunists seizing earthworms. More than once a Water Rail has been recovered in the bird's stomach; moles, mice and rats all pay the price of carelessness as the heron strikes with startling speed.

A few Grey Herons are recorded annually on visible migration in spring. Most sightings have involved one to two birds flying east along the north Norfolk coast in March or April; more dramatic were two which spiralled to a great height at Weybourne on 3rd April 1998 before drifting off to the north-east. More unusual were two which flew in together from the north-east at Sheringham on 27th February 1996. Autumn passage is more marked with regular records of individuals or small groups flying west or arriving from the north between July and October. Parties of seven west at Weybourne on 19th June 1988 and six which arrived in off the sea at Sheringham on 21st June 1978 were unusually early. The largest single party consisted of 19 birds in V-formation heading west on 20th September 1980, which was noted at several points between Sheringham and Holme. Other notable day-counts, both at Sheringham, have included 20 west on 24th August 1990 and 18 west on 17th September 1992. The latest date for such arrivals was 28th December 1995, when three flew in from the sea at Overstrand.

The vast majority of ringing of Grey Heron nestlings in Norfolk was carried out between the mid-1950s and late 1970s. Over 300 Norfolk-ringed Grey Herons have been recovered, over half of which were found outside the county. Foreign recoveries have been reported from France (11), The Netherlands (2), Belgium, Spain (2) and Portugal. The recovery in Portugal was of a bird found in October 1958 which had been ringed that summer at Denver Sluice and it remains the only British-ringed Grey Heron to be recovered in Portugal. A total of 24 foreign-ringed Grey Heron nestlings has been found in Norfolk – seven each from Norway and The Netherlands, five from Sweden, four from Denmark and one from Germany. The two longest movements of nestlings ringed elsewhere in the British Isles and recovered in Norfolk involved birds from colonies in Cheshire and Staffordshire.

*Michael Seago*

Purple Heron
(Nik Borrow)

## Purple Heron                                        *Ardea purpurea*

**A rare spring and autumn vagrant.**

The Purple Heron is a summer visitor to Europe with the nearest breeding colonies in north-east France and in The Netherlands. Birds from Europe winter in sub-Saharan Africa. Despite lengthy stays in late spring, nesting has not been recorded in the British Isles. Birds arriving in Norfolk in spring are migrants which have overshot breeding areas.

Riviere recorded over 20 taken in Norfolk during May and from July to December, the most recent being shot at Barton on 8th August 1906. None was recorded in the county again until 1936 when one visited Wheatfen Broad during June, followed by another obtained on the lower Bure Marshes in September 1937 and one at Cley on 10th–12th May 1951.

The period 1953–98 produced a total of 64 records. Most observations were of singles, but two stayed at Cley on 24th–31st May 1970 with two at Burnham Norton on 11th August 1990 and another two at

Colney Gravel Pits on 3rd May 1995. A party of four, with one Grey Heron, flew in from the north-east at Salthouse on 1st June 1998. After circling over the village they departed to the south-east five minutes later. Most were recorded on a single day only, the longest-stayers being singles at Hickling from 17th August to 17th September 1974, at Horsey/Hickling for eight weeks from 4th June to 31st July 1985 and at Welney from 24th June to 31st August 1987. An often elusive bird at Brancaster Fresh Marsh from 20th April to 13th May 1993 wandered to Titchwell and Thornham; presumably the same bird was at Holkham in flight with a Little Egret on 14th May. One at Heacham on 13th–14th April 1980 is the earliest re-corded, while one at Salthouse on 3rd November 1976 and at Wells five days later is the latest.

**Table 5. The cumulative monthly totals of Purple Herons recorded in Norfolk 1953–98.**

| Apr | May | Jun | Jul | Aug | Sep | Nov |
|-----|-----|-----|-----|-----|-----|-----|
| 9 | 26 | 12 | 2 | 10 | 4 | 1 |

A high proportion of records have been at Cley, followed by six along the upper Thurne, and singles at several other Broads localities, the Tud Valley at Costessey and on the Ouse Washes.

*Michael Seago*

# Black Stork                                   *Ciconia nigra*

A rare vagrant.

The Black Stork is a summer visitor to eastern Europe as far west as France with a semi-resident population in Spain. Most birds winter in north-east and East Africa. During the period 1958–95 over 100 individuals were recorded in Britain and Ireland with a marked increase in observations during the 1980s, reflecting increasing numbers across Europe.

Riviere listed ten birds including one obtained at Breydon on 27th June 1877 now in the Castle Museum, Norwich. Since then the following have been recorded bringing the county total to 17:

1969: Castle Rising on 1st June
1970: Beetley and near Swaffham on 4th May with a further sighting of probably the same bird at Irmingham Hall on 20th May
1977: East Tuddenham on 11th September
1978: Cley on 28th April
1979: Breydon on 31st July
1990: Flitcham on 6th June
1991: Stiffkey on 16th–17th June (on the latter date it alighted in the same oak tree as a Red Kite). Presumably the same bird at Santon Downham, Thursford and Swanton Novers on 3rd–7th July and again on 16th–18th July

*Michael Seago*

# White Stork                                   *Ciconia ciconia*

A rare vagrant.

In the Western Palearctic there has been a great decline in the north-western European breeding popula-tion of the White Stork. Iberia holds the strongest population in western Europe. Western European birds winter in West Africa. Relying heavily on soaring on thermals during migration, White Storks shun lengthy sea crossings and concentrate on the well-defined route over the Straits of Gibraltar. They regularly fly straight across the Sahara without stopping.

The White Stork was known to Sir Thomas Browne as an occasional visitor to Norfolk. Stevenson listed a number of occurrences up to 1870 including one on flooded meadows at Lakenham on the out-skirts of Norwich, seen from a train. The majority appeared during the spring and summer. Riviere also recorded examples during February, March and from September to November.

Since the publication of Riviere's book, White Storks have appeared widely in the county with records in 24 of the 69 years between 1930 and 1998, covering all months. It is difficult to assess the number

131

involved accurately. Some birds are known to have appeared at several localities in rapid succession, but the total is a minimum of 34, excluding known escapes. The majority have occurred either at localities near the coast or in Broadland with a few having been seen inland, including birds at Great Cressingham on 8th May 1982 and Hillborough on 17th–19th May 1986.

A mid-winter White Stork at Whitlingham on 23rd December 1961 was found dead on 2nd February 1962. It had been caught alive, presumably in poor health, in Jutland, Denmark in 1960 and then cared for by a Danish ringer who kept it during the 1960–61 winter. It flew strongly on being released on 16th April, after it had been ringed, and was not seen again in that country.

With the exception of a remarkable series of observations during 1967 detailed below, all records have been of singles apart from two at Burnham Overy Staithe on 21st September 1979, two at Hickling, Hemsby and Horsey on 11th–20th April 1984 and two at Holkham on 16th–17th April 1996. Long-stayers have included one overwintering in the Waveney Valley between June 1975 and 20th March 1976. During 1982 one lingered in the Gunton Park area from May until 7th October.

A most unusual spring displacement took place in 1967. Two White Storks reached Halvergate Marshes on 23rd April followed by single birds over Martham Holmes on 30th, at Horsey on 8th May and over Gorleston on 20th. Along the north coast up to four appeared between Holme and Hunstanton followed by solitary wanderers at Holkham and Stiffkey. Later in that memorable year three White Storks passed over Stiffkey on 3rd July with another over Horsey on 29th October. The Halvergate pair made local history by remaining until almost the end of the year. At the beginning of their lengthy stay the birds regularly performed evening courtship displays when alighting on the sails of a derelict drainage mill. They fed all day in marsh dykes, often lost to view. With the approach of autumn the birds spent their time stalking the windswept levels seeking moles and short-tailed field voles. By early October both Storks began feeding close to the A47 Yarmouth to Acle trunk road. Highway repairers towards Christmas found the Storks readily accepting food and one day a police motor-cyclist found them both in the middle of the roadway! Sadly, disaster came on 27th December, a day of high winds, with one Stork colliding with power cables. The survivor remained close to the road until 3rd May 1968. All hope of White Storks making ornithological history by nesting on a local mill vanished following the Christmas tragedy. If road widening had not been in progress and the birds had not been tempted there in their search for food, subsequent events might have been so different (Allard 1968).

The county total does not include suspected escapes from collections. During both 1995 and 1996 a large number of spring and autumn records, mainly from the north and east of the county, apparently related to two free-flying escapees from Thrigby Wildlife Park. Although the two birds seen at Holkham in April 1996 were at first thought to be escapees, one was carrying a ring which was eventually read in the field (in Warwickshire) and the bird proved to be of Dutch origin.

*Michael Seago*

## Glossy Ibis                                                    *Plegadis falcinellus*

**A rare vagrant.**

The Glossy Ibis has shown a marked contraction of range in the Western Palearctic during the 20th century. Notoriously nomadic, the post-breeding dispersal of adults and young (often in separate flocks) is in all directions with frequent occurrences north of the breeding range. Some winter in the Mediterranean basin west to Morocco, but most European birds are considered to be trans-Saharan migrants. The species was formerly a fairly regular visitor to the British Isles but is now a rare vagrant, reflecting the declining numbers in Europe.

The earliest occurrence in Norfolk was recorded by the Pagets when a 'pair [was] shot at the mouth of the Norwich river 13th September 1824'. Remarkably, these specimens are still in existence in the Castle Museum, Norwich.

Riviere recorded 47 occurrences, the majority appearing during August and September. This included a small influx in 1926 when a total of four was noted at Holme, Hickling and Breydon; two, both immatures, were shot between 11th September and 7th October. These arrivals formed part of a northwards irruption when one juvenile travelled 2,600km from Hungary to Kuybyshev in the USSR in 23 days. Others, also ringed in the same locality, were recovered in The Netherlands (2) and west Norway.

Glossy Ibises
(*Norman Arlott*)

Details of the birds obtained by Harry Smith, a marshman, have only become known recently. Peter Allard was one of very few people to view Smith's collection and he readily recalls a case containing four Glossy Ibises. In addition to the three specimens listed below, a fourth had been taken near Breydon in September 1921.

Since 1930 at least 20 individuals have been recorded:

1935: Breydon on 22nd May and another shot on the lower Bure Marshes near Three-mile House in September
1943: Two in the Breydon area shot by Harry Smith on 6th October
One at Hickling on 12th November
1945: Six at Hickling from 25th October to 7th November with two remaining until 25th November
One shot on Breydon Marshes on 30th October by Harry Smith
1952: Cley on 24th September
1976: Wisbech Sewage Farm on 16th–19th May
1977: Hockering on 24th August
1981: Two at Horsey on 10th May and one on 30th were almost certainly the two long-staying wanderers based in Kent
1982: Holkham, Titchwell, Holme and Hunstanton on 24th October
1985: Horsey and Hickling on 15th May
1990: Welney on 19th December, and 3rd and 12th January 1991. It was first seen on the Cambridgeshire section of the Ouse Washes on 30th November
1991: Welney on 3rd and 12th January
1992: Cley and Kelling Water Meadows on 6th May
Burgh St Peter on 8th May. It had been on the Suffolk side of the River Waveney since 6th May

*Michael Seago*

## Spoonbill (Eurasian Spoonbill)                    *Platalea leucorodia*

**A scarce visitor most frequent in summer, but recorded in every month.**

In the Western Palearctic the Spoonbill is a summer migrant breeding in south-west Spain, The Netherlands and in south-east Europe, extending to central and eastern Asia. The European population winters partly in the Mediterranean basin, but mainly in northern tropical Africa. Exceptional long-distance movements have included an immature ringed in The Netherlands and recovered in the Azores (Brouwer 1964). In recent years it has become a regular visitor in small numbers to East Anglia and southern England, mostly from the colonies in The Netherlands.

According to Sir Thomas Browne, Spoonbills bred over 300 years ago in the heronries at Claxton and

Reedham, but at what date breeding ceased in the county is not known. Stevenson provided a catalogue of occurrences chiefly during May and June; the majority were 'collected' at Breydon and Hickling. He made reference to Spoonbills finding Salthouse Marshes 'as a most favourite resort' until their drainage and embankment. By the time of Riviere's book the birds had become annual visitors, but estimating numbers over a period of years is extremely difficult. Riviere remarked that 'their visits are more often than not interrupted by frequent disappearances over short periods. Their numbers when several are present, often vary from day to day and it is impossible in the case of arrivals to distinguish fresh immigrants from birds returning after an absence of perhaps a few days.' The situation is similar today, although individuals often carry a selection of colour rings. In 1991, for example, a Spoonbill ringed as a nestling in The Netherlands in 1989 was reported during the summer in Kent and Suffolk, and in Norfolk at Breydon, Hickling, Horsey, Titchwell and Holme.

**Spoonbills**
*(Richard Richardson)*

At the present time the most favoured localities include shallow floods at Titchwell, Holkham, Cley, Hickling and Berney Reserves. Breydon tidal muds have been largely abandoned since the establishment of the RSPB Reserve at the head of the estuary in 1987. Typically Spoonbills spend many hours roosting during daylight hours becoming active towards evening. Many birds appearing here are non-breeding immatures; full adults displaying a pendant crest and an ochre tinge to the base of the neck are unusual.

Early arrivals, invariably single birds, put in appearances from the second week in March. Exceptional were two at Snettisham on 7th February 1993. The majority of observations are between mid-April and early July. It is during this period that the most impressive groups have appeared. Following the establishment of the Breydon Wild Bird Protection Society, complete with a close-season warden, as long ago as 1888, the estuary attracted a flight of 16 on 13th May 1894, 12 on 5th May 1895, 17 on 27th–28th April 1911, 16 on 5th June 1929 and ten on 10th July 1954. Elsewhere in the county 13 visited Hickling on 28th April 1893 followed by a flypast of 15 Spoonbills at Cley on 4th July 1940 with 16 passing Scolt Head on 9th May 1954 and 11 at Rush Hills, Hickling on 7th July 1954.

The largest spring influx took place in 1996 as a result of adult Spoonbills deserting a main breeding site in The Netherlands where very low water levels enabled foxes to raid the colony. Between 16th April and 21st June singles and parties of between two and nine birds were reported at 17 localities. Further movements took place from 20th July until 15th November although no group exceeded four birds. Among the more interesting observations were two Spoonbills feeding flank-deep in the surf at Holme on 26th October and another heading west at Holme in company with a small herd of Bewick's Swans on 15th November 1996.

Winter occurrences of single Spoonbills and long-stayers are highly unusual, but include one shot at Wells in January 1881 and still in the Holkham Hall collection. Breydon attracted one from 8th October to 5th December 1960 which returned between 15th February and 13th April 1961 after a spell on the Suffolk Blyth estuary. Another ended its days at Terrington Marsh on 16th December 1962; it had arrived on 17th November and had been ringed in The Netherlands. One at Scolt Head during December 1970 stayed in the Brancaster area until 17th February 1971. A week later it was found dying at Titchwell. The Wash saltings at Snettisham and Wolferton attracted one from 26th November until 18th December 1982 and doubtless it was the same bird making brief visits to Titchwell and Cley. In 1984 one roamed between Hunstanton, Holme and Wells on 27th–29th December. Another mobile immature wandered endlessly between Wolferton and Cley between 21st October 1988 and 20th April 1989. Breydon attracted one on 11th–18th December 1989 and again from 26th December until 13th March 1990. For the first time two Spoonbills overwintered in the Titchwell/Brancaster area from 24th October 1996 until early March 1997. A third bird remained at Burnham Norton throughout January and February 1997.

Spoonbills have also put in appearances from time to time at Welney Washes, at Snettisham and in Broadland at Martham, Horsey, Strumpshaw and Hardley Flood. A party of four spent over a week at Cantley Beet Factory settling ponds in early June 1964 roosting in the reeds close to the railway line and feeding at Breydon at periods of low tide, while two also were present at the settling ponds on 9th October

1995. On two occasions single birds were seen at Wisbech Sewage Farm, which was reclaimed for agriculture in 1985; part of the farm was situated in Norfolk. An unlikely venue was the millpool at Gimingham visited briefly by a Spoonbill in mid-September 1988.

An interesting ringing record was of a bird seen at Rush Hills, Hickling on 9th–17th August 1992. It had been ringed as a nestling in The Netherlands in May 1988, had been seen in France in September that year at two locations and was present at a new breeding colony at Oldenico, Italy in May 1991. In addition to the three ringed Spoonbills already mentioned, three others colour-ringed as nestlings in The Netherlands have been noted at Cley, one of which was also seen three weeks later at Holkham, and another was reported at Hickling.

*Michael Seago*

## Mute Swan    HARDLEY FLOODS. (95) 1·7·1998.    *Cygnus olor*

**A common resident.**

The Mute Swan is present throughout much of Europe, often as a feral resident. The population is thought to be increasing over much of its range. It is difficult to establish the range and status of genuine wild birds following many introductions dating back to the 16th and 17th centuries. It is a migrant in the eastern parts of its range but western feral birds are largely sedentary, seldom moving far from the natal localities.

Stevenson dealt at great length with the 'domestic' nature of the Mute Swans on the Rivers Wensum and Yare and included a personal account of the annual ritual of swan upping which took place on the second Monday in August. The cygnets were collected for fattening for the table and many local birds, including those belonging to the Corporation of Norwich, were taken to the 'swan pit' which still can be traced at the Great Hospital. This brick pit, connected to the River Wensum to allow the flow of freshwater, was built by Sir Thomas Ivory in 1793 to replace an earlier pit which probably dated back to the middle of the 16th century.

What were considered to be genuine wild swans, referred to by Stevenson as Polish Swans, were treated as a separate species (*C. immutabilis*). He detailed a number which had been taken in the county. Patterson (1905) claimed to have observed three or four examples of this 'species' in Yarmouth market 'noting the green lines down the toes, the web of the foot being black' which was then considered to be a distinguishing feature. In his *Wild-life on a Norfolk Estuary*, published in 1907, he gave a graphic account of trying to rescue a foot and head of an alleged 'Polish Swan' from the saucepan at a local hostelry where the bird was being prepared for the table. He concluded that he 'found the boiled swan's foot was an awkward thing to swear the bird's identity by, and would have defied Professor Owen himself!' Pashley (1925) stated that he had had through his hands the 'so called Polish Swan with grey legs and feet and a very small tubercula on the bill'. The cygnets of this form are all white and a number have been reported from broods in the county in recent years, for example, one from a brood of seven at Titchwell in the summer of 1997 was all white. Riviere added little to the story of the Mute Swan in Norfolk, except to state that by the time he was writing few cygnets were being pinioned as a result of the annual upping.

The Norfolk Atlas recorded Mute Swans in 301 tetrads with breeding confirmed in 182. The majority of occupied squares were in the Broads district and along the main river valleys, with the Great Ouse and the Ouse Washes holding good numbers in the west of the county, where generally the species was less common. Some coastal marshes hold breeding birds with, for example, up to six pairs on the marshes between Burnham Norton and Holkham (Bloomfield 1993). Between 1955 and 1983 four full breeding season surveys have been organised by the BTO.

**Table 6. Total number of Mute Swans recorded in Norfolk during breeding season surveys.**

|  | 1955 | 1961 | 1978 | 1983 |
|---|---|---|---|---|
| Number of breeding Mute Swans | 258 | 235 | 274 | 312 |
| Number of non-breeding territorial swans | – | 8 | 114 | 182 |
| Number of grouped non-territorial swans | 656 | 642 | 675 | 916 |
| Total number of Mute Swans | 914 | 885 | 1,063 | 1,410 |

Although the numbers of non-breeding birds did not change significantly between 1955 and 1978, there was a change in distribution of some of them (Taylor 1979b). In 1958, for example, the non-breeding herd on Hickling Broad numbered 425 whereas 20 years later there were only 22. George (1992) attributed this fall to the almost complete loss of aquatic plant life on Hickling Broad resulting from the turbid water which existed at that time. By December 1997 the number of birds present had risen to 71, perhaps reflecting the improving water quality in the Broad.

The results of the 1983 survey, which indicated a 27% increase in the number of pairs holding territory and a 36% increase in the non-breeding herds, were surprising. A dramatic fall in numbers had been predicted following national trends at that time of a decreasing population; a situation which had been aggravated by lead poisoning and discarded fishing line. Len Baker of the Swan Rescue Service found that 72% of the 630 dead swans he recorded in 1982 could be attributed to angling (George 1992). Bull and Taylor (1984), in commenting on the 1983 survey results, drew attention to the possibility that the increase in numbers in the county could be partly a result of the release of rehabilitated birds collected from other parts of Britain by Len Baker and his team. Fortunately, a ban on the use of lead split-weights and improved water quality and subsequent plant growth in parts of the Broads have contributed to the steady increase in the county's Mute Swan numbers.

The Winter Atlas recorded Mute Swans in nearly all of the 10km squares in Norfolk, once again with the main concentrations in the Ouse Washes in the west and in Broadland and the Halvergate areas to the east. Recent winter counts have produced site maxima of 272 at Welney in November 1993 and 197 at Breydon in December 1989.

Although a largely sedentary species, small movements are regularly recorded along the coast with the largest party noted at Sheringham being a herd of ten which flew in from the north on 10th June 1978 (Taylor 1987a). Ringing recoveries do confirm some movements to and from the county, for example, a bird ringed at Ware in Hampshire in December 1970 was found dead at King's Lynn in March 1975; another ringed at Bedford in July 1971 was recovered near Downham Market in April 1980. From further afield was one controlled at Holme in August 1983 which had been ringed almost exactly a year earlier at East Fortune in Lothian. It was subsequently seen again at Welney on 1st January 1986. It was thought that it may have travelled south with Whooper Swans passing through Scotland *en route* to the Wash or north Norfolk. A movement in the reverse direction involved a swan ringed as a juvenile at Pensthorpe in January 1996 which was controlled at Berwick-upon-Tweed, Northumberland in July 1997. Other notable recoveries of Norfolk-ringed Mute Swans have involved movements to Cambridgeshire, Humberside and Greater London, while others ringed in Suffolk, Surrey and Yorkshire have been recovered in Norfolk. International movements are even less common but one ringed near Stockholm, Sweden in July 1962 was found at Wells the following February, and another ringed at Heacham in March 1970 was recovered in Germany in February 1972.

*Don Dorling*

## Bewick's Swan (Tundra Swan) WELNEY. 20·4·1981 (2) *Cygnus columbianus*

**A common but localised winter visitor and passage migrant.**

The Bewick's Swan breeds in the tundra regions from the Kola Peninsula east to the Kolyma Plain. Birds from the western part of this range winter in western Europe; this population has recently been estimated to contain at least 20,000 birds, of which internationally important numbers winter in Norfolk.

The early history of the species within the British Isles is confused as it was only separated from the Whooper Swan in 1830, when a paper on its identification criteria was presented to the Linnean Society by a Mr Yarrell. Stevenson regarded the species as less common than the Whooper Swan in annually varying numbers, usually occurring in coastal habitats, especially after cold weather. The largest flock he mentioned was of 23 near Yarmouth in 1855, with a total of eight 'procured' by gunners that season compared to 26 Whoopers shot. Riviere gave little information apart from stating that it was present in less numbers than the Whooper Swan, but with no indication of the actual numbers involved.

The main present-day wintering area is on the fenland washes straddling the Cambridgeshire/Norfolk border, although this was not always so. Here, only small numbers were present in the 1940s (maximum 33 in the winter of 1945–46) although by the winter of 1952–53 104 birds were present followed by 242 in 1954–55. Nisbet (1955) suggested this change in status occurred when flocks moving between The Netherlands and Ireland found favourable conditions on the Ouse Washes, this coinciding with a decrease in the Scottish wintering population and a consequential southerly shift in their migration route. As the tradition of wintering on the Ouse Washes developed the numbers wintering in Ireland dropped as birds 'short-stopped' in the East Anglian fens.

Cold weather in the winter of 1955–56 produced a record 705 birds, steadily increasing in the following decades to 1,278 in 1970–71, 3,364 in 1983–84 and peaking at 6,164 in 1986–87 with numbers later stabilising around the 5,000 mark. While these counts cover the entire Cambridgeshire/Norfolk washlands, the highest count within Norfolk was 4,641 on 13th January 1992, followed by 2,067 in 1992–93, 3,210 in 1993–94, 3,668 in 1994–95, 2,934 in 1995–96, 3,477 in 1996–97 and 3,106 in 1997–98. Since 1995 a further Norfolk wintering area has developed, a satellite of the Ouse Washes, with some interchange of birds between sites. Here, artificial grain-feeding saw numbers rise to 1,700 in February 1998.

The spectacular increases in the wintering population since the mid-1970s can be attributed to three main factors: first the acquisition of large areas of the Ouse Washes by conservation bodies thereby providing secure night-time roosts and feeding areas; secondly an almost total change in feeding behaviour since the mid-1970s when birds moved off the washes during the day onto the adjacent arable farmland where they gleaned the remains of the sugar beet and potato harvest; and thirdly the gradual establishment of a tradition. Flocks also utilised stubble fields and later in the season grazed winter cereals, most of these foods providing a higher, more easily obtained energy source than that found by traditional feeding on wetlands. This has resulted in a dawn and dusk flight each day to and from their arable feeding grounds. Early in the winter these tend to be close to their roosts but become progressively further afield during the course of the season, as local food sources are exhausted or ploughed in; consequently flocks frequently travel up to 15km each day to reach their feeding grounds. The unpredictable nature of winter flooding on the Ouse Washes sometimes produces water levels too deep for feeding or ideal roosting. This may result in part of the population temporarily moving onto the Nene Washes in Cambridgeshire until conditions improve.

Artificial feeding at Welney commenced in the late 1960s with the provision of grain and potatoes which attracted several hundred birds close to the hides. Very few Bewick's Swans now take advantage of this food source since the dramatic increase in the numbers of the larger, more aggressive Whooper Swans. Flocks still have spells of 'natural' feeding on the washes when water levels are favourable, swimming and upending in shallow flooding when they graze finer grasses such as flote grass (*Glyceria fluitans*) and marsh foxtail (*Alopecurus geniculatus*), as well as marsh yellowcress (*Rorippa palustre*) when available. Like the Whooper Swan they will also swim amongst dense stands of reed sweet-grass (*Glyceria maxima*), grubbing out the starchy white shoots.

The first autumn arrivals do not usually appear before the second week of October although late September appearances are not unknown. The larger movements gather pace in late October and through November, continuing into December. Flocks of swans migrating westward are often a feature along the north Norfolk coast at this time, hundreds being sighted on some days. Similarly the early spring return movement is apparent across the centre of the county and especially the east coast during March with the bulk of the wintering population having departed by the end of the month leaving just a handful of April stragglers. These are often lost cygnets. Two or three injured birds summer on the Ouse Washes each year, and these are invariably flightless. The timing of the main arrivals and departures is dependent upon climatic conditions. During a mild winter large numbers of swans may have left the Ouse Washes by mid-February. Later movements during March are frequently observed both in the morning and on still evenings when noisy groups depart to the east or north-east. Feeding conditions on the near Continent may also influence the timing of the main autumn immigration. During the autumn of 1997 abundant food supplies in The Netherlands resulted in record numbers (11,000+) of swans staying in that country and consequently a slow arrival on the Ouse Washes where there were just 2,259 on 1st December compared to 4,234 on 4th December 1994, 3,629 on 14th December 1995 and 3,654 on 1st December 1996.

Rapid changes in weather conditions may prompt long journeys. One Bewick's Swan family left Slimbridge in January on a mild south-westerly wind and rapidly reached the Elbe estuary in Germany. Then the temperature suddenly dropped and snow began falling. The disillusioned swan family reappeared at Welney; then, even more surprisingly, at Slimbridge the next day. It was calculated they would need to stay three weeks at Slimbridge to regain weight lost on the abortive first leg of their migration. And this was just what they did!

Annual counts of cygnets at Welney have shown rather low productivity in recent years. While there was an average of 13.2% young in the flocks between 1970 and 1984, the average in the last decade from 1988–89 to 1997–98 has fallen to 10.4% with no good breeding seasons since 1989 and 1990.

**Table 7. Percentage of first-winter Bewick's Swans at Welney from 1988–89 to 1997–98.**

| 88–89 | 89–90 | 90–91 | 91–92 | 92–93 | 93–94 | 94–95 | 95–96 | 96–97 | 97–98 |
|-------|-------|-------|-------|-------|-------|-------|-------|-------|-------|
| 10% | 18.6% | 20% | 11% | 5% | 7.2% | 8% | 12% | 8% | 5% |

Although the Ouse Washes remain the British stronghold for Bewick's Swans the species can be encountered almost anywhere in the county especially during migration periods. There are, however, a number of other regular wintering areas, the most important centred on Broadland and Breydon. Numbers here tend to peak late in the winter and almost certainly include a large percentage of Fenland birds staging on their return migration. Regular wintering of small numbers commenced here in the early 1960s (Allard 1972). Favoured areas were Breydon and Burgh Castle Levels with others visiting Halvergate, Haddiscoe and Reedham, although by the 1980s and 1990s large herds were also frequenting Broadland areas further to the north. Some of the largest more recent counts here have been 200 at West Somerton/Horsey/Waxham and 282 at Haddiscoe during February 1995, followed in 1996 by 484 at Horning/Ludham/Catfield in January and 347 at Halvergate and 752 at Breydon/Berney in February, while totals in February 1997 included 476 at Breydon/Berney Marshes, 528 at How Hill/Johnson Street/Ludham and 490 at St Benet's Level. There can be much interchange between Broadland flocks making it difficult to accurately assess the total population without specialised roost counts. Broadland birds have tended to feed on traditional habitats such as grazing marshes but during 1996 there was a marked swing towards feeding on arable land. All birds in the Breydon area, Halvergate and Wickhampton Marshes, and those towards Haddiscoe and Fritton roost regularly on the Berney Marshes Reserve except when frozen and then Breydon is used.

Smaller wintering groups (<100) periodically take up residence on the south shore of the Wash where they feed on the arable and roost on Snettisham Pits; while small groups occasionally visit Holkham Fresh Marshes and, to a much lesser degree than formerly, the Breckland meres.

The main hazard facing Bewick's Swans on the Ouse Washes is overhead powerlines, resulting in a number of fatalities each winter. Considerable lengths of powerline have been fitted with markers in an attempt to alleviate the problem, though disasters still occur, notably in the 1996–97 winter when 52 were killed on unmarked lengths of powerline. Collisions tend to occur during adverse weather conditions such as fog, strong winds or heavy rain and generally at dusk when flocks are flighting back off the arable land to roost on the washes. Although there have been instances of illegal shooting this does not appear to be a major problem on their wintering sites. Nevertheless a sample of 94 Bewick's Swans x-rayed at Slimbridge during the 1989–90 winter showed that 40% carried lead shot embedded in their body tissue. Most of this illegal shooting is believed to occur on their breeding grounds and migration routes.

A pair of leucistic Bewick's Swans accompanied by a single cygnet visited Welney on 10th March 1985. The adults had dark pink bills with a sharply defined greyish-white area replacing the yellow of a normal bird while the legs were greyish-white; the body plumage was all white. The body plumage of the cygnet was only marginally paler than a typical bird while its bill showed a little more pink. Another leucistic adult Bewick's Swan but with yellow legs and feet, and a partly orange bill was in the Breydon area from 16th January to 8th February, and on 8th March 1992.

Over 2,000 Bewick's Swans have been ringed since 1967, about 80% of these with highly visible darvic leg rings and in some instances neck-collars, all designed to be read in the field with optical equipment. Marked individuals have been returning to Welney for up to 15 years while older individuals which winter at Slimbridge occasionally visit. Ringing has confirmed the site's status as a staging area with birds stopping off, sometimes for only brief spells, on their travels to and from other wintering sites such as Slimbridge in Gloucestershire and Martin Mere in Lancashire. Over 100 Bewick's Swans ringed in Norfolk have been reported abroad, including 90 in The Netherlands between October and March, and 15 in Germany. Amongst the more distant recoveries have been two in Russia, including one in Siberia at 73°E, a distance of 4,834km, and one in Iceland in May 1981. The species is only a straggler to Iceland and this remains the only recovery of a British-ringed Bewick's Swan in that country – possibly it became attached to a Whooper

Swan flock on the British wintering grounds. Two others ringed at Welney in February 1982 were seen together on 17th April in Finland, since when there has been only one other recovery in that country. In the winter of 1996–97 a total of 137 colour-ringed Bewick's Swans was recorded at Welney, including birds marked in Russia (73) and The Netherlands (17). Marking swans has also greatly improved the understanding of their local movements within the wintering site, as well as their migratory routes. There have been many instances of multiple sightings of the same individual but surely none as remarkable as one ringed at Zeleni Island, Russia in August 1992 and subsequently reported at five localities in The Netherlands in November–December, in Kent in January 1993, at three sites in Estonia in April, at Welney in November, in Germany in March 1994, at Welney and in Cambridgeshire in November, at West Somerton in December and finally at St Benet's Abbey in February 1995.

*John B. Kemp*

| **Whooper Swan** | WELNEY, OUSE WASHES. 21·2·1982. | ***Cygnus cygnus*** |
| | HARDLEY FLOODS. (2) 31·10·1999. | |

**A fairly common but localised winter visitor.**

Whooper Swans which breed in Iceland winter primarily in the British Isles. The species also breeds across Eurasia where it occupies the taiga zone, south of the breeding areas of the Bewick's Swan with only a narrow overlap in range. The north-western European population of Whooper Swans winters primarily in the Baltic regions, while birds from northern Europe and western Siberia winter in the eastern Mediterranean/Black Sea. Other Siberian birds winter across Asia from the Caspian Sea to Japan.

The Whooper Swan, like the smaller Bewick's Swan, has shown a dramatic change both in numbers and the timing of its visits to Norfolk, where it now occurs in internationally important numbers. Stevenson regarded it as a winter visitor with numbers depending mainly upon the severity of the season. He knew of only one November record and found that most occurred between January and March. The severe winter of 1870–71 produced an influx commencing in late December when a herd of 40 passed along the coast at Horsey. Groups were later seen at numerous locations. Many fell to the gunners, up to 100 birds being sent to Leadenhall market from King's Lynn where a poulterer had a further 30 birds. Riviere provided a rather different pattern of occurrence stating 'it was a passage migrant and winter visitor, first arrivals usually seen during November travelling east to west along the north coastline. Though most abundant in severe weather, large passages of both Whooper and Bewick's Swans have been noted during more than one November which has preceded a mild winter.' This sudden change in migration pattern is puzzling, suggesting the early arrival of Continental swans, although unfortunately there is no further information as to actual numbers involved or dates, or in fact their final wintering site. It does raise the question as to whether or not these migrating flocks were being correctly identified (still a problem in the 1990s, see Kemp 1996 and Allard 1996) as large numbers of Bewick's Swans were wintering in Ireland and known to be occasionally migrating across England at that time of year. By the time the *Birds of Norfolk* was published (Seago 1967), the Whooper Swan had once again reverted to a scarce passage migrant and winter visitor, more frequent in severe weather, flocks of 20–40 being exceptional.

The fortunes of the species in the county undoubtedly changed with the founding of the Welney Wildfowl Refuge in 1968. Here, grain and potatoes provided for the more numerous Bewick's Swans began to attract a small but steadily growing herd of Whooper Swans each winter. By 1977 the revised edition of *Birds of Norfolk* stated 'the most popular haunt at the present time is Welney Wash where there was a maximum of 48 in 1975'. Rather like Bewick's Swan, once the wintering tradition became established more birds arrived each season, benefiting from secure night-time roosts and abundant food supplies on the adjacent farmland. The Whooper Swan's daily foraging radius is less than that of the more mobile Bewick's Swan, most arable feeding occurring within 5km of the washes with both species readily mixing on suitable fields. Large numbers of Whooper Swans now congregate to feed on waste potatoes tipped out on to the refuge (Kemp 1991). These large aggressive birds now dominate the feeding station to the exclusion of the Bewick's Swan which obtains its food more naturally elsewhere on the refuge or farmland. During flood conditions large numbers of swans periodically feed by swimming and upending amongst the larger areas of reed sweet-grass (*Glyceria maxima*), grubbing out the white shoots. Flocks have tended to favour the Norfolk section of washland but will under certain conditions, such as deep flooding, range into Cambridgeshire in some numbers. The Ouse Washes' flock first exceeded 100 birds in 1979–80 rising to

223 in 1982–83, 320 in 1985–86, 603 in 1988–89, 830 in 1992–93, 1,142 in 1994–95 and 1,299 in 1997–98. The largest gathering counted within the Norfolk boundary at Welney was 1,313 on 20th December 1998.

Broadland now has a regular wintering population smaller than that on the Ouse Washes but showing a similar increase. Regular overwintering, as opposed to brief visits by flocks displaced by cold weather, started in the mid-1970s with between 18 and 54 birds present each winter, increasing in 1985–86 to 70, reaching 105 in 1990–91, 176 in 1995–96 and 250 in 1996–97. Broadland birds have tended to be in two main groups centred on Ludham/Wood Street/Catfield and Hickling/Horsey/Waxham, the latter group roosting on Hickling or Horsey Broads. These birds now feed to a large extent on arable land. It remains scarce in the Breydon area.

With such large numbers of Whooper Swans now wintering in the county, small groups are encountered for brief periods in many locations, especially at migration times. Small herds have occasionally wintered at Holkham and the south Wash, the latter roosting on Snettisham Pits.

The cold-weather movements and influxes of Stevenson's day were probably due to the arrival of Continental birds, although the ringing to date of over 1,000 birds in the British Isles (together with over 3,200 ringed in Iceland) has shown that the Ouse Washes flock is composed primarily of Icelandic breeders. For instance, of 145 colour-ringed Whooper Swans identified at Welney in the 1996–97 winter, 118 had been ringed in Iceland, six in Finland and 12 at Caerlaverock, Scotland. These birds now start to arrive at Welney at the end of September or early October. An exceptionally early build-up occurred during the autumn of 1996 with counts of 544 by 31st October and 924 by 17th November. In most years the rate of arrival is much slower. Ringed Icelandic swans are also regularly noted in Broadland but recent winters have also seen a small number of Finnish-ringed birds both in the Broads and at Welney. It seems highly likely that some Continental birds will continue to arrive especially during spells of cold weather.

The spring exodus of Whooper Swans takes place later than that of the Bewick's Swans. The former travel about 1,600km to reach their breeding grounds while the latter may fly 4,000km. Large numbers of Whooper Swans remain on the washes throughout March, with still 200–300 into the first week of April. Most will have departed by the end of the third week of the month. Flocks often depart shortly before dusk, flying off over the fenland to the north-west. There are invariably a handful of injured birds remaining to oversummer each year, although in 1995 only one out of six birds present was unable to fly. This particular individual was resident from 1984 to 1998. There has never been any suggestion of breeding on the Ouse Washes. However, in 1928 a nest was found at Merton, but this was not successful.

Whooper Swans have on average enjoyed better breeding success than Bewick's Swans over the past decade, as shown by cygnet counts at Welney between 1988 and 1998.

**Table 8. Percentage of first-winter Whooper Swans at Welney from 1988–89 to 1997–98.**

| 88–89 | 89–90 | 90–91 | 91–92 | 92–93 | 93–94 | 94–95 | 95–96 | 96–97 | 97–98 |
|-------|-------|-------|-------|-------|-------|-------|-------|-------|-------|
| 10% | 11% | 16% | 24% | 16% | 13% | 17% | 15% | 20% | 15% |

The recent increases in the wintering population cannot be accounted for by breeding success alone and there has clearly been some recruitment from other areas. Ringed individuals previously wintering in Northern Ireland have been recorded at Welney. At the same time there have been recent declines at some Scottish sites.

A small number of Whooper Swans are killed by striking overhead powerlines each year on the Ouse Washes, usually between five and ten individuals. An additional hazard was fireworks being set off close to the main roosts on two evenings in early November 1997. The worst occasion was on the evening of 1st November when about 1,000 mixed Whooper and Bewick's Swans were panicked off their roost by a prolonged fireworks display, resulting in them flying around the area calling for several hours. A number of birds collided with overhead powerlines causing localised blackouts. Only 400 Whoopers/Bewick's Swans remained the following day; it seems possible some birds deserted the area completely, later increases being due to the normal arrival of more wintering swans. With much of the migration route over the sea this species has suffered less than the Bewick's Swan from illegal shooting. A sample of birds x-rayed in the winters of 1988–89 and 1989–90 showed that 10% carried lead shot embedded in body tissue.

As with the Bewick's Swans, the colour-ringing of Whooper Swans enables their winter movements to be tracked. A cygnet ringed in Iceland in 1988 was at Lough Neagh in Northern Ireland in February 1989 and from January to March 1990, at Welney from November 1990 to January 1991, back at Lough Neagh from February to March, and finally at Welney from November to January 1992. Another family party ringed in southern Finland during summer 1995 was seen in Broadland, mainly in the Catfield area, during the winters of 1995–96 and 1996–97. Its members were also seen together during their various migrations in The Netherlands, Germany, Sweden and the Baltic States.

*John B. Kemp*

| **Bean Goose** | WELNEY (14) 21-2-1982. | ***Anser fabalis*** |
| **Taiga Bean Goose** | BUCKENHAM MARSHES (c.100) 5-1-2000. | ***A. f. fabalis*** |

A fairly common but highly localised winter visitor.

### Tundra Bean Goose
***A. f. rossicus***

A scarce winter visitor.

The breeding range of the Taiga race of Bean Goose *T. f. fabalis* extends from Fennoscandia eastwards to the Ural Mountains. The main western wintering grounds are in the Low Countries and central Europe. The Tundra race *A. f. rossicus* breeds in the high Arctic tundra of northern Russia and north-west Siberia from the Kanin to the Taymyr Peninsulas. This population winters mainly in Sweden, Denmark, Germany, the Low Countries and France.

As elsewhere in Britain, the early history of the Bean Goose is obscured by confusion with the Pink-footed Goose. Stevenson referred to several localities which had been gradually abandoned including 'wild country about Thetford and Wretham' and 'about Westacre'. Riviere considered the Bean Goose regular but only in small numbers and was apparently unaware of the mid-Yare Valley location during the 1920s when many of the marshes flooded each winter. Fortunately, Robin Harrison obtained details from Frank Ward, a marshman who occupied a cottage overlooking Buckenham Station Level until 1950. The first Bean Goose was shot by Ward in mid-December 1924 when between 200 and 300 fed regularly on Claxton and Langley Ham Marshes. Similar numbers arrived in 1925 and 1926. In the 1927–28 severe winter an exceptional total of over 5,000 Bean Geese put in an appearance. Very cold conditions commenced on 15th December 1927 'with continuous hard frosts . . . and the year closed with the country under deep snow and with the flooded river valleys vast sheets of ice' (Riviere 1928). The first year in which Bean Geese fed regularly on the north side of the Yare was 1930; 200 or more arrived each winter during that decade. A single Bean Goose was shot as early as 28th September 1935 on the adjoining Strumpshaw Marshes. The remarkably high 1927–28 assembly was never repeated. However, in the 1936–37 winter over 1,000 Bean Geese and 2,000–3,000 Whitefronts were present. Subsequently numbers decreased annually until Ward's departure.

It is interesting to note that the Castle Museum, Norwich contains a Bean Goose shot at Rockland during severe weather in February 1929 and the Riviere skin collection includes a Bean Goose obtained at Cantley in January 1935. The Buckenham and Cantley Marshes were abandoned by the geese during the 1940–41 winter when part was ploughed. The birds favoured the levels at Claxton and Langley for six winters. In 1946 following reseeding they returned. During the following half century the marshes on the north side of the River Yare have remained the most favoured area for the only regular flock of wintering Taiga Bean Geese *fabalis* in England.

During recent winters Cantley Marsh has assumed the greater importance. Its hollows and patches of *Juncus* and *Phragmites* have enabled the feeding birds to become surprisingly well-hidden. Buckenham Marsh, for long the traditional site, is now resorted to mainly when the birds are disturbed at Cantley. As elsewhere, sheep have partly replaced cattle and more intensive grazing has led to a shorter sward, more suited to the thousands of Wigeon. Within the valley site usage varies little from winter to winter according to livestock patterns, disturbance and weather conditions; there is also an apparent need for the geese to occasionally explore pastures new. On first arrival the same marshes at Buckenham and Cantley are se-lected. These areas are where the birds feel safest – close to their roost and containing or edged by taller vegetation where even a large number can remain surprisingly well-hidden. Later in the season the more favoured marshes are largely deserted and the geese may be found at Rockland/Claxton, Langley Green, Langley/Hardley or Halvergate. Both Postwick and Haddiscoe Island seem to have lost their attractiveness. The numbers wintering in the Yare Valley are shown in the table below.

**Table 9. Peak numbers of Taiga Bean Geese in the mid-Yare Valley from 1939–40 to 1997–98.**

| | | | | | | | | | | | |
|---|---|---|---|---|---|---|---|---|---|---|---|
| 1939–40 | 180 | 1949–50 | 54 | 1959–60 | 80 | 1969–70 | 66 | 1979–80 | 155 | 1989–90 | 360 |
| 1940–41 | 196 | 1950–51 | 120 | 1960–61 | 30 | 1970–71 | 73 | 1980–81 | 168 | 1990–91 | 485 |
| 1941–42 | 200 | 1951–52 | none | 1961–62 | 52 | 1971–72 | 67 | 1981–82 | 329 | 1991–92 | 405 |
| 1942–43 | 158 | 1952–53 | 75 | 1962–63 | 48 | 1972–73 | 77 | 1982–83 | 197 | 1992–93 | 410 |
| 1943–44 | 250 | 1953–54 | none | 1963–64 | 38 | 1973–74 | 109 | 1983–84 | 236 | 1993–94 | 475 |
| 1944–45 | 250 | 1954–55 | none | 1964–65 | 25 | 1974–75 | 102 | 1984–85 | 375 | 1994–95 | 310 |
| 1945–46 | 187 | 1955–56 | 101 | 1965–66 | 36 | 1975–76 | 91 | 1985–86 | 340 | 1995–96 | 310 |
| 1946–47 | 227 | 1956–57 | 54 | 1966–67 | 46 | 1976–77 | 127 | 1986–87 | 310 | 1996–97 | 350 |
| 1947–48 | none | 1957–58 | 78 | 1967–68 | 48 | 1977–78 | 96 | 1987–88 | 420 | 1997–98 | 250 |
| 1948–49 | 150 | 1958–59 | 122 | 1968–69 | 40 | 1978–79 | 141 | 1988–89 | 370 | | |

Until recently the main roost of the Taiga Bean Geese has been a small wooded lake on a private estate no distance from the most attractive feeding areas. If frozen or disturbed by occasional shooting, Surlingham Broad formerly provided an alternative. During the 1997–98 winter, roosting on the marshes became equally attractive. Exceptionally the birds have roosted at Breydon (in 1964), at the well–wooded Fritton Lake (in February 1979), Rockland Broad or on the River Yare (Parslow-Otsu 1991, 1992).

During the 1950s and 1960s, when numbers were low, arrivals were frequently as late as January and never earlier than December. However, in the last two decades the first arrivals have been as early as 23rd October (1981) and as late as 6th December (1986), but have been most often during the second and third weeks of November. The bulk of the birds have usually put in an appearance between late November and mid-December. Three arrival phases are noted in most years. The first comprises mainly or wholly birds which have failed to breed, followed by a second phase of arrivals including family groups. A final influx may take place during cold weather. An exceptionally early arrival of the entire wintering group occurred in the 1987–88 winter following a cold spell in the Baltic in late November.

Bean Goose departures are usually between 15th February and 10th March. Migration is somewhat earlier in mild seasons, somewhat later in cold ones. In 1987 two lingered until 6th April. Following very mild weather almost all left the Yare Valley before the end of January in both 1989 and 1994. Most cross the coast, at no great height, north of Caister.

It is intriguing to read in BWP that Taiga Bean Geese rarely appears in Britain before early January, suggesting a secondary movement from another wintering area, possibly Denmark. During the closing weeks of 1987 a total of 22 Bean Geese, carrying coded blue neckbands, reached the Yare Valley. These birds, among 36 captured in a moulting flock of some 300 non-breeders or failed breeders in central Sweden earlier that year, had indeed staged through Denmark and provided the first evidence of the origin of at least part of the flock visiting Norfolk. Ten banded birds returned to the same remote Swedish site during the 1988 summer. In the 1988–89 winter all but one of the 22 reappeared in Norfolk; the missing bird was located in north-west Jutland in March 1989. During 1989–90 only 14 birds returned, but three of the missing individuals were seen in north-west Denmark in February. It seems likely that many of the Yare Valley Bean Geese in these three winters derived from the Swedish moulting flock. Other individuals must have been involved, however, since at least in 1987 total numbers were higher than at the moulting site. The survival rate of the neck-banded birds wintering here has been high; a single banded survivor appeared in the 1997–98 winter.

During the second half of September most Bean Geese leave Sweden heading for north-west Jutland. Here a 4,000ha reserve contains a score of small lakes surrounded by heathland and dunes. Up to a third of the autumn flock moves to Norfolk at intervals from mid-November. Historically, the Bean Goose population in Jutland has fluctuated in parallel with the Yare Valley birds, albeit at a higher level, reaching a similar low point between the 1940s and 1960s. The decline in Denmark and this country coincided with a drastic contraction in the breeding range in central Sweden and Norway.

At dawn on 14th February 1992 the last 65 Bean Geese of the winter in the Yare Valley headed north-east from their roost. Exactly seven hours 22 minutes later, 650km away on the coast of Jutland they arrived from the North Sea passing over Mariko Parslow-Otsu's head. All landed a short distance inland joining other birds which had wintered with them in Norfolk and which had travelled as several units during the previous two weeks. By late April they would be on their way north again to the central Swedish breeding grounds.

Elsewhere in the county Peter Scott recorded a flock of 109 Bean Geese off Terrington Marsh in the Wash on 1st–9th March 1930 (Scott 1935). In north Norfolk small numbers appear on Holkham Fresh Marshes. The largest group of 60 remained between early January and mid-February 1979. In the upper Thurne area of Broadland where visits have become regular since 1988, especially to Heigham Holmes, the largest flocks (all considered to be of the Tundra race *rossicus*) have included 28 during the 1988–89 winter, 80 on 11th January 1994, 43 on 25th February 1996 and 62 in January 1997.

The Tundra Bean Goose *rossicus* was first recognised in Norfolk during the 1987–88 winter when up to seven visited Buckenham, remaining separate from the Taiga flock. However, all previous Bean Goose records away from the mid-Yare Valley may well have related to *rossicus*, as is the case nowadays. During the same winter this race was detected at Waxham where 19 appeared on 25th December. At Welney 21 arrived on 20th December 1987 and up to 40 have since put in appearances. During a large-scale arrival of grey geese along the East Coast from Northumberland south to Essex in mid-February 1993, a flock of the increasingly successful Tundra race totalling 104 birds reached Heigham Holmes with an additional 39 at Berney Marshes. Small numbers have appeared at a number of sites near to the north and east coasts of Norfolk, the largest party being 62 at Catfield in early 1997.

*Michael Seago*

## Pink-footed Goose WELNEY. (40) 21·2·1982. *Anser brachyrhynchus*

**An abundant winter visitor.**

The Pink-footed Geese wintering in Scotland, northern and eastern England represent the whole of the population breeding in Iceland and Greenland. The latest estimate totals 225,000 birds. A recent expansion into lowland nesting areas in Iceland has corresponded with a dramatic increase in the numbers wintering in the British Isles. Those appearing in Norfolk represent the most southerly group in the country. The Svalbard breeding population, currently estimated at 34,000, wintering in Denmark, Germany, The Netherlands and Belgium, migrates through Norway.

The principal haunts in Norfolk and the adjoining Fenland areas feature in the following account:
**Holkham:** The first Norfolk specimen, still in the Holkham collection, was identified in 1841 'since which time this goose has proved to be by far the most common species frequenting Holkham Marshes' (Stevenson 1890). This situation continued for at least a century, the birds roosting on Stiffkey High Sands. A peak between 5,000 and 8,000 was attained in the 1930s. However, following the establishment of an anti-aircraft firing range at Stiffkey, the numbers decreased rapidly after 1938. Wartime ploughing of the fresh-marshes followed and very few geese appeared after 1941.
Riviere recorded the scene:

> The first flocks begin coming in during the latter half of September, the earliest date being the 10th. The main body has usually arrived by the end of October. Throughout the winter the numbers run into many thousands. The return journey to northern breeding grounds takes place in March. When they can do so undisturbed and particularly early in the season, Pinkfeet will feed upon stubbles and new leys at some distance inland, but for many years Holkham Marshes – where they are never disturbed – have been the favourite feeding ground. There are few more wonderful sights or sounds than their arrival from the sea at dawn or their return at dusk. Here, lying up before daylight behind the range of sandhills, generations of Norfolk gunners have shot at them as they pass over and instinctively as they cross the danger zone the flocks lift high in the air. But from time to time in wild or foggy weather the gunners reap their reward.

Pinkfeet remained almost absent from Holkham until the 1976–77 winter when 250 made a brief appearance in December. The two succeeding winters provided a similar pattern, but during 1980–81 regular wintering began. Following controlled flooding of part of the grazing marshes from 1986, this National Nature Reserve has become greatly attractive to wildfowl.

Despite the nearness of Scolt Head, the Holkham contingent has remained attached to an area off the Lodge and Warham Marshes and on the Stiffkey High Sands as a night-time roost thus continuing the habits of the pre-war battalions.

**Table 10. Peak winter counts of Pink-footed Geese at the Warham/Stiffkey roost from 1980–81 to 1984–85.**

| | | | |
|---|---|---|---|
| **1980–81** | 206 | **1983–84** | 1,500 |
| **1981–82** | 90 | **1984–85** | 1,500 |
| **1982–83** | 300 | | |

**Lower Bure and Halvergate:** Pinkfeet began wintering in south-east Norfolk during the 1913–14 winter when 30–40 were using the marshes to the west of Breydon. It was at about this time that Scroby Sands off Yarmouth began remaining high and dry at high tides, thus offering a safe roost. Numbers increased annually and 1,500 were present in January 1922. The impressive skeins passing over the town as the birds came in from the sea in early morning and returned at night, became a winter feature. The birds normally favoured the marshes adjoining the lower Bure, although the Halvergate Levels were also visited. It was not unusual to see both Pinkfeet and Whitefronts feeding together. The maximum numbers were attained between 1938 and 1946 despite a wartime network of tubular steel barriers erected on the marshes to prevent an airborne invasion. The peaks were obtained in 1943 and 1946; on both occasions 3,000 were estimated by Robin Harrison. The earlier total was recorded on 26th December 1943 on the Mautby/Runham Marshes. Earliest autumn arrivals were recorded during the latter part of September, but the first parties seldom stayed any length of time. There was a gap until late October when the main flights arrived. In 1936, for example, 1,000 Pinkfeet were feeding on the lower Bure Marshes on 30th October.

After spending the short winter day on the marshes, the Pinkfeet normally returned to Scroby to roost. During periods of fog, exceptional high tides and gale force winds, however, the birds avoided heading out to sea. In these conditions Breydon was favoured despite disturbance. Normally diurnal feeders, at the times of full moon the Pinkfeet regularly fed at night.

After 1948 Halvergate and the lower Bure Marshes steadily declined as a wildfowl resort. The introduction of electric pumps resulted in the drainage mills falling into decay. Each succeeding winter saw less and less flooding and greater disturbance. Inevitably Pinkfeet numbers fell each winter and had declined to 450 in 1950–51, 150 in 1952–53 and 100 in 1955–56. During the following decade winter totals did not exceed 40 birds. Since then small groups have put in only very brief and occasional appearances. Distribution changed dramatically during 1997–98 when up to 5,500 began feeding and roosting on the lower Bure and Breydon Levels after an absence of three decades. Earlier that winter these birds had doubtless formed part of the Heigham Holmes assembly.

**West Wash/Fens:** Withdrawal from north Norfolk by 1941 and from the Broads grazing levels during the 1950s was fully offset by an increase along the Lincolnshire shore of the Wash. This was a new tradition; at the same time feeding habits changed completely. The pattern of these movements is included for the sake of completeness and because it also sheds light on today's habits. Research by Cambridge Bird Club confirmed that during the late 1940s and 1950s a regular Pinkfoot arrival and build-up to 7,000 and even 10,000 birds took place each autumn on the west Wash at Wainfleet from October, before a move was made to Holbeach by mid-November or December. From here over 5,000 moved inland to the Cambridgeshire Fens from January until early spring. This pattern varied little up to 1962. The Pinkfeet used the Nene Washes (some 20 miles inland) as an over-night roosting area, moving out to farmland to feed during daylight hours. Luckily farmers welcomed these wandering flocks. These geese gathered on fields of harvested potatoes, where the tubers left formed a major part of their diet; otherwise they grazed on winter wheat. The first activity greatly reduced the number of potatoes growing in following cereal crops as weeds. Feeding on main shoots of growing corn produced more side tillers, beneficially thickening the crop.

Just how important the Nene Washes had become was all too clear in 1963 when much of the grassland along the eastern half was ploughed and the geese failed to return. This sudden conversion to arable came at the time The Wildfowl Trust was negotiating the possibility of setting up a wildfowl refuge on the Nene Washes. The inland roosting habit which had developed on the Nene has rarely extended to the Ouse Washes. At the latter site a combination of unpredictable flooding covering feeding areas on the washes themselves and shooting pressure levelled against geese using arable for feeding (and the washes for roosting) has prevented any traditional use becoming established.

**East Wash/Snettisham:** There were scattered reports of geese visiting the east coast of the Wash from the early years of the 20th century, including an intriguing reference by Riviere to 2,000 Pinkfeet and Whitefronts feeding on Snettisham fresh-marshes during very hard weather in February 1929. In 1956, 329 Pinkfeet were recorded in January. During later years flocks of 200–300 were frequently seen. But it was not until the 1968–69 winter that monthly figures first became available, including a peak of 843 birds in February.

**Table 11. Peak winter counts of Pink-footed Geese at the Snettisham roost from 1969–70 to 1984–85.**

| | | | | | | | |
|---|---|---|---|---|---|---|---|
| 1969–70 | 1,348 | 1973–74 | 1,784 | 1977–78 | 4,572 | 1981–82 | 10,500 |
| 1970–71 | 1,093 | 1974–75 | 2,400 | 1978–79 | 2,370 | 1982–83 | 5,400 |
| 1971–72 | 1,274 | 1975–76 | 2,731 | 1979–80 | 3,720 | 1983–84 | 7,000 |
| 1972–73 | 1,816 | 1976–77 | 3,700 | 1980–81 | 2,450 | 1984–85 | 9,500 |

**Scolt Head:** A full decade after the commencement of the Snettisham build-up, 90 Pinkfeet began roosting at the western end of the island, between 20th November 1979 and 19th January 1980. As the site became more 'traditional' so the numbers rapidly increased.

**Table 12. Peak winter counts of Pink-footed Geese at the Scolt Head roost from 1981–82 to 1984–85.**

| | | | |
|---|---|---|---|
| 1981–82 | 3,500 | 1983–84 | 13,000 |
| 1982–83 | 5,600 | 1984–85 | 9,300 |

**Upper Thurne:** The extensive Heigham Holmes Marshes began attracting Pinkfeet during January and February 1991. Numbers have steadily increased and the birds now feed in sugar-beet fields as far south as Scratby, Filby and Runham. At other times this group almost certainly accounts for wandering flocks in the mid- and lower Yare Valley.

**Table 13. Peak winter counts of Pink-footed Geese at Heigham Holmes from 1990–91 to 1997–98.**

| | | | |
|---|---|---|---|
| 1990–91 | 374 | 1994–95 | 2,000 |
| 1991–92 | 150 | 1995–96 | 1,400 |
| 1992–93 | 1,000 | 1996–97 | 5,000 |
| 1993–94 | 850 | 1997–98 | 10,000 |

The presence of very substantial numbers of Pinkfeet in north-west Norfolk warranted co-ordinated counts at dawn. This arrangement commenced in December 1985 and the count of 76,355 on 14th December 1998 exceeded any of the previous counts given in Table 14.

**Table 14. Combined peak totals of Pink-footed Geese at Snettisham, Scolt Head and Warham/Stiffkey roosts from 1985–86 to 1997–98.**

| | | | | | | | |
|---|---|---|---|---|---|---|---|
| 1985–86 | 19,900 | 1989–90 | 26,920 | 1993–94 | 68,560 | 1997–98 | 76,355 |
| 1986–87 | 19,800 | 1990–91 | 42,950 | 1994–95 | 53,540 | | |
| 1987–88 | 18,800 | 1991–92 | 35,060 | 1995–96 | 54,760 | | |
| 1988–89 | 13,500 | 1992–93 | 33,880 | 1996–97 | 55,500 | | |

The roosts within Britain are not self-contained. A continual shifting of birds from roost to roost around the country has been confirmed by counts, by numerous ringing results and by radio tracking. Recoveries of geese ringed near particular roosts have come within the following three months from all parts of the winter range. Movement may take place on any date and not only in response to hard weather or food shortages. As might be expected, interchange is greatest between adjacent roosts. There is evidence that this is the situation locally, particularly as the Snettisham and Scolt Head roosts are only 20km apart.

Observation has shown that the Snettisham-based Pinkfeet feeding at Babingley may be joined by others flighting in from the north, presumably from Scolt. During the 1989–90 winter a morning flight count at Scolt on 10th November, for example, revealed a one-off total of 7,000 birds compared with 2,200 the previous day. Peak numbers at Scolt were attained during the second and third weeks of January 1990, but by 29th a high proportion had shifted allegiance to Snettisham where 19,000 assembled. During the same winter, interchange was first noted between the Pinkfeet roosting on Scolt and those spending the night off Wells/Stiffkey; at 16:00 hrs on 26th December a flight of several thousand south of Burnham Market separated with 1,500 heading towards Wells and the remainder alighting on the Far Point at Scolt (Gill 1991).

The factors that influence roost preference must remain a matter of speculation. But a spring tide and a strong northerly wind certainly make the Wash uncomfortable for wildfowl. It may well be that the relative shelter offered by the shingle ridges of Scolt Head's Far Point provides calmer conditions.

Throughout the 1950s The Wildfowl Trust ringed large numbers of Pinkfeet both in Iceland and in Britain. But it was not until 28 years later that a new marking programme commenced. One of the early results was that the long-suspected link between the Lancashire geese and the Norfolk gatherings was confirmed by a Pink-footed Goose ringed in April 1987, resighted at Martin Mere in December 1987 but which subsequently moved to spend the mid-winter period at Holkham.

Some Pinkfeet flocks within the wintering population are quite mobile, often staying in Grampian, Tayside or Lothians before heading south to Dumfries, Lancashire and eventually to Norfolk. Yet others are remarkably site-loyal perhaps not straying far from the same roost and feeding in the same fields all winter. It is known that some flocks make the trip from Lancashire to Norfolk, staying during December and January before heading back north. A record 76,170 birds (almost a third of all the Pink-footed Geese in the world) was present in the county during December 1997.

Until the late 1970s the first arrivals appeared towards the end of October, but more recently groups have begun putting in an appearance in the second and third weeks of September. The main arrivals are expected by late November. Peak numbers are attained during December often remaining well into January. The numbers may still be high during February and exceptionally until late March. In April, flocks of up to 760 birds have become a regular feature; 160 lingered at Holkham until 2nd May 1996 with a similar number at Scolt Head on 2nd May 1997. The latest spring birds were noted on 24th May 1996. These late-stayers often resort to the most isolated saltings.

When undisturbed, Pinkfeet feed during the day and flight to their roost any time from near sunset until an hour or so afterwards. On occasions, however, departure may be delayed until conditions of practically total darkness, at least as far as the human eye is concerned, are reached. The only time navigating ability breaks down is in mist and fog. Gales do not deter them. For example, on 25th January 1990 the geese – despite being swept well off course – continued battling against west-north-west storm-force 12 winds to reach the Scolt roost at dusk.

At periods when the moon is of any extent and is riding in the night-time sky the geese may be heard flying to and from the roost throughout the night, often flighting in as the moon rises in the evening. Particularly in mid-winter when the moon is full they are liable to stay in the fields all hours of the night, only returning to the roost when it pleases them. Moonlight feeding sites need to be very secure having almost always been used during the previous days. The birds are well aware which flight paths and farms are 'safe'.

The Pinkfeet roost-site off Snettisham occupies the centre of a 3,000 acre wildfowl refuge and offers relative safety and no enemy can approach undetected. The high tides at night cause the geese to float on the water before settling later on the mud and sandbanks. Ever wary, they may stand up to 2km offshore on Peter Black Sand and Ferrier Sand. At Scolt Head the most regularly used area is amongst the sand and shingle ridges at the extreme western end of the island. Depending on the tide, the geese remain on the ridges avoiding the dunes. The muddy Cockle Bight area is occupied during strong northerly winds when the dunes provide shelter. During calm conditions the birds are content to roost on the open sea off the Far Point and Cockle Bight.

The Wells roost is situated on very exposed sandbars and shingle ridges off the Lodge and Warham Marshes and on Stiffkey High Sands. This roost-site attracts the 'meadow' feeders from Holkham Fresh Marshes and also the Pinkfeet attracted to inland fields west of Wighton.

As the light fades the evening flight commences, and small and large formations begin arriving – often from more than one direction. On windy nights arrival is often more prolonged than on calm ones. Each flight turns upwind before side-slipping and tumbling out of the sky. After the first geese are settled, late arrivals fly in without the hesitation often displayed by the first arrivals. Coming in to roost there is usually a great clamour, redoubled whenever a fresh assembly arrives with greeting calls from the new arrivals. Sometime after the last flight comes in the chorus steadily falls to a low level which is often maintained until an hour or so before the dawn flight, when it increases again.

At daybreak the geese return to the fields chosen as feeding grounds. The vanguard alights usually as near the centre as possible after circling several times and after more than one 'failed' attempt to settle before actually doing so. The build-up then becomes rapid with a succession of newcomers settling without hesitation. Roosting Pinkfeet usually separate into several feeding flocks travelling at varying distances and directions from the roost. During the day groups move between flocks and also between feeding and roosting places, following disturbance inland during Pheasant shoots and movements of farm vehicles. The birds feed least around midday.

Morning flight usually lasts between 30 and 45 minutes, but may extend for well over an hour depending on the state of the tide and the moon. Delay in departure from the Scolt Head roost following moonlight feeding is most noticeable on a rising tide at high water. These conditions enable the geese to bathe readily and to preen. Off Snettisham they may be observed splashing in the creeks before flighting. In addition, there are occasions when birds are still returning to roost at dawn. These late arrivals perhaps 'encourage' the main assemblies to linger (Seago 1990).

Newly arrived, Pinkfeet favour feeding on germinated spilt grain in stubble, but the principal diet between October and January-February is sugar-beet tops. This habit was first recorded locally in February 1966. After the remaining beet tops are ploughed in the Holkham-based birds feed mainly on permanent grassland and on winter cereals. At Snettisham during February–March the Pinkfeet have favoured old water meadows for feeding. But early in 1990, following the close of the wildfowling season, up to 8,000 regularly fed on saltmarshes (Gill 1996).

Usually the most extensive fields are favoured and especially those nearest to roost-sites. Small fields and also tall hedges which restrict the view are avoided. The uneasy coexistence with the farming community invariably results in some disturbance. Fortunately, individual farmers are extremely tolerant and are prepared to considerably delay ploughing in sugar-beet tops so that they may enjoy one of winter's finest wildlife spectacles, that of flighting geese (Cross 1994).

The main feeding area in north-west Norfolk extends eastwards as far as the Holkham Estate. Normally, the southern limit is the main A148 Fakenham to King's Lynn Road but flights have appeared towards the B1145 in the vicinity of Peddar's Way.

At the onset of a heavy snowfall the vast majority of Pinkfeet depart, failing to return until the following autumn. During the 1986–87 winter, for example, severe frost on 9th January quickly followed by snowfalls with drifts in the Brancaster district of 3–5m , caused complete abandonment of the Scolt roost. Yet at Snettisham up to 2,300 Pinkfeet continued roosting until mid-March.

A Pinkfoot disaster took place soon after dawn on 3rd January 1978 when a violent storm complete with thunder, lightning and hailstones, crossed East Anglia. In its wake 140 wild geese (mainly Pinkfeet) lay dead in fields, along hedgerows and on roads. It is highly probable that the birds involved formed part of the Snettisham flock. The most likely sequence of events was that the geese were flighting along the southern perimeter of the Wash at dawn – or panicked into the air by the approaching storm – and were overtaken by a tornado or funnel cloud and forcibly sucked upwards to a considerable altitude like toy balloons. Death or unconsciousness quickly followed. Their involuntary return to earth became only a matter of time and occurred along a 50km path extending from near Castle Acre to just south of Norwich (Thrower 1980). The numbers of Snettisham-based Pinkfeet declined that day from 4,540 to 640 thereafter, dispersed by the high winds.

The presence in Britain of a very few Pink-footed Geese known to have originated from the Svalbard population (and ringed in Denmark) is intriguing. One individual appears to have switched between populations and by 1996 was probably summering in Iceland. Between March 1994 and February 1996 it was detected in Denmark, Lancashire, Tayside, Merseyside and north Norfolk. Another Svalbard bird, ringed in Denmark in 1989, appeared in The Netherlands in the 1993–94 winter, in Lancashire in the spring of 1994, and later that spring had returned to its original flyway and was reported from northern Norway. Surprisingly it was next seen in north Norfolk in January 1996 (Mitchell 1997).

*Michael Seago*

HARDLEY FLOODS. 30·11·1992.

## White-fronted Goose (Greater White-fronted Goose) | *Anser albifrons*

**A fairly common but localised winter visitor and passage migrant; Greenland White-fronted Goose**
***A. a. flavirostris* is a rare visitor.**

The White-fronted Goose of the nominate race *A. a. albifrons* breeds in the northern Russian and Siberian
tundra from the Kanin Peninsula to the Kolyma River. The species winters on the steppes, farmland and
marshland of temperate Europe and Asia. Movements further south take place in severe winters.

There has been an enormous increase in numbers in north-west Europe during the past three decades.
The reason appears to have been a substantial shift in population. Formerly the large numbers wintered in
central Europe. The decline there has coincided with a massive build-up of the Baltic/North Sea group to
an estimated total of 750,000 in most recent winters, but numbers in Britain have not followed this trend
and have declined during past decades with no sign of a recovery.

Earlier Norfolk writers considered the Whitefront an uncertain visitor locally, except during spells of
severe weather. The birds favour wet meadows close to a secure roost. It was not entirely coincidental that
a safe night-time refuge on Scroby Sands began remaining high and dry at all tides shortly before Whitefront
numbers began building up in south-east Norfolk. The vast acreage of marshland extending westward
from Breydon attracted ever-increasing numbers from the early 1920s. Robin Harrison documented the
scene during the 1930s. On many occasions during that period, thousands of acres became flooded for
weeks at a time, particularly at Halvergate which became the Whitefronts' stronghold. After feeding each
short winter day the Whitefronts flighted over Yarmouth Town to Scroby to roost. During spells of fog
and storms the birds avoided heading out over the North Sea, resorting to Breydon or to the more isolated
marshes. Halvergate always remained the most important level, but for days or even weeks skeins fed at
Wickhampton, St Benet's, Norton, Thurlton, Buckenham, Claxton, Langley and Haddiscoe Island.

During the 1935–36 winter a maximum of 2,000 was attained followed by a peak of 3,000 during
December 1938. Wartime restrictions made it impossible to obtain regular estimates of numbers between
1939 and 1945, but in 1946–47 over 2,000 Whitefronts overwintered. The year 1948 marked the beginning of a slow but steady decline for Halvergate as a wildfowl resort. The six drainage mills spaced along
the length of The Fleet were replaced by a powerful electric pumping station. Inevitably, each succeeding
winter saw less and less flooding. A total of 800 spent the 1954–55 winter in the traditional haunt, but
during the following decade numbers never exceeded 500 apart from 1,200 between 18th January and
late February 1958. Ever-reducing numbers put in appearances each winter between 1964–65 and 1973–
74. Then the marshes were abandoned by resident gaggles. So far as the Breydon area is concerned the
Whitefront has reverted to its earlier status and become an uncertain visitor often associated with Continental cold spells. A reminder of former glory returned after the shooting season in February 1989 when
240 Whitefronts frequented Berney Reserve, roosting nightly on the main flood.

Three exceptional movements are on record. Early one morning towards the end of January 1947 (and
only a few days before the county was to endure six weeks of unbroken frost and deep snow) flight after
flight of Whitefronts reached Halvergate Marsh. Arrivals took almost an hour and the birds, approaching
4,000 in number, appeared to cover two marshes. Their stay was very brief. Another abnormal movement
was recorded on 25th January 1964 when a total of over 4,000 headed westward across Halvergate. That
winter the peak number of local birds was only 320. A large-scale influx into the county commenced on
the night of 13th–14th February 1993 when presumably lost birds were heard over Yarmouth. It is thought
east winds and dense fog over the North Sea disorientated numbers of Continental geese moving at the
time. These conditions led to a total approaching 3,000 arriving in Norfolk and many remained here until
well into March. The largest groups included 590 at Breydon and Burgh Castle, 600 on Heigham Holmes,
400 at Salthouse/Cley and Blakeney Freshes and 350 at Holkham. This large-scale influx along the East
Coast of England extended from Northumberland to Essex. Adding variety were small numbers of Bean,
Pink-footed and Barnacle Geese. At Holkham the Barnacle Geese included two colour-ringed birds from
Novaya-Zemlya normally wintering in The Netherlands (Eve 1993).

Following severe weather or during foggy conditions White-fronted Geese make brief visits to a wide
selection of coastal and Broadland marshes. In addition, wandering groups have long been a feature during
most winters at Cley and Blakeney. The following summaries provide details of the peak numbers appearing at the main localities (Seago 1991):

**Mid-Yare Valley**: By far the largest number of Whitefronts reported between Cantley and Strumpshaw was a total of over 2,000 during the 1936–37 winter. Unusually high numbers of wildfowl were recorded in January 1937 during severe weather conditions. No detailed information for the Buckenham area is available until 30th December 1950 when there were 200 on snow-covered Buckenham Marshes. During the remainder of the 1950s the largest Whitefront groups there were 250 sitting in snow 25cm deep on 21st February 1956 with 160 still present on 3rd March.

In the 1960s small groups of Whitefronts remained occasional visitors. It was only in January 1969 when the marshes were deeply flooded due to a pumping breakdown that 180 put in an appearance. During the next decade numbers again remained low, but at least visits became annual from 1973. A peak of 56 was attained between 18th February and 5th March 1978 with 13 lingering until 9th March.

**Table 15. Peak winter counts of White-fronted Geese between Cantley and Strumpshaw from 1982–83 to 1997–98.**

| 1982–83 | 135 | 1988–89 | 310 | 1994–95 | 265 |
|---------|-----|---------|-----|---------|-----|
| 1983–84 | 44  | 1989–90 | 255 | 1995–96 | 220 |
| 1984–85 | 140 | 1990–91 | 296 | 1996–97 | 178 |
| 1985–86 | 200 | 1991–92 | 338 | 1997–98 | 245 |
| 1986–87 | 45  | 1992–93 | 355 |         |     |
| 1987–88 | 252 | 1993–94 | 311 |         |     |

On occasions part of this group visits marshes on the south side of the Yare at Rockland, Claxton and Hardley Flood; others travel down-valley to Berney and Haddiscoe Island. Completing the picture is evidence of some interchange between the groups in the Yare Valley and Heigham Holmes.

**Upper Thurne**: White-fronted Geese first became attracted to Heigham Holmes during the 1975–76 winter. From time to time some appear at nearby Potter Heigham, Hickling, Horsey, Ludham and St Benet's.

**Table 16. Peak winter counts of White-fronted Geese on the upper Thurne from 1991–92 to 1997–98.**

| 1991–92 | 300 | 1995–96 | 1,043 |
|---------|-----|---------|-------|
| 1992–93 | 28  | 1996–97 | 900   |
| 1993–94 | 260 | 1997–98 | 308   |
| 1994–95 | 165 |         |       |

**Holkham**: One of the first Whitefront occurrences recorded here was during December 1851 when 20 arrived. Their status here apparently remained unaltered up to the time of publication of the final volume of Stevenson in 1890. Subsequent information for Holkham is tantalisingly brief, although during the mid-1930s over 250 were present. Shortly after the Second World War, 200–300 Whitefronts were regularly present, declining to 100 by 1951. From then until the 1967–68 winter there were only occasional records of up to 50 birds. Subsequent peak counts have been as follows:

**Table 17. Peak winter counts of White-fronted Geese at Holkham from 1968–69 to 1997–98.**

| 1968–69 | 84  | 1976–77 | 234 | 1984–85 | 270 | 1992–93 | 350 |
|---------|-----|---------|-----|---------|-----|---------|-----|
| 1969–70 | 132 | 1977–78 | 93  | 1985–86 | 326 | 1993–94 | 284 |
| 1970–71 | 90  | 1978–79 | 250 | 1986–87 | 232 | 1994–95 | 270 |
| 1971–72 | 129 | 1979–80 | 154 | 1987–88 | 290 | 1995–96 | 800 |
| 1972–73 | 132 | 1980–81 | 145 | 1988–89 | 376 | 1996–97 | 570 |
| 1973–74 | 150 | 1981–82 | 300 | 1989–90 | 255 | 1997–98 | 400 |
| 1974–75 | 50  | 1982–83 | 225 | 1990–91 | 290 |         |     |
| 1975–76 | 150 | 1983–84 | 280 | 1991–92 | 350 |         |     |

After spending each day on the fresh-marshes the Whitefronts formerly flighted to roost either on the open sea or on exposed sandbars off Wells and Warham. More recently, however, all have remained on the marshes, attracted by shallow floods.

**Ouse Washes**: Since the mid-1950s Whitefronts have put in appearances on the Washes at Welney. However, these visits may last for only a few days due to unpredictable flooding covering the feeding areas and shooting pressure levelled against the geese when feeding on nearby winter cereal fields. Most arrivals are of 40 or fewer birds, but flights of up to 130 are on record.

The first autumn arrivals of White-fronted Geese in Norfolk usually appear during the second week of October, but the main numbers seldom put in an appearance until December. By the second week of March all have departed unless the winter is severe in which event some linger until almost the month-end. Feral and injured birds oversummer and one or two pairs have bred in most recent years at Cley. A summer survey during 1991 revealed 40 Whitefronts in the county including 26 at Blakeney Fresh Marsh (Delany 1993).

Five White-fronted Geese of the nominate race *albifrons*, ringed in The Netherlands between December and March, have been shot in Norfolk in December–January, up to eight years after ringing.

The Greenland White-fronted Goose *A. a. flavirostris* migrates to Iceland before wintering in Ireland and western Scotland, and is occasional on the eastern seaboard of North America. Following the first Norfolk record at Cley in 1960, a further 11 individuals have been identified in the county:

1960: Cley from 8th November to 4th December

1984: Five at Welney from 27th October to 2nd December

1990: Breydon on 16th–25th November

1991: Snettisham on 27th January

1992: One shot at North Wootton on 27th January had been ringed on the North Slob, Wexford, Eire in November 1987.

1995: Houghton on 1st January, amongst Pinkfeet, and almost certainly the same, again with Pinkfeet, at Holkham on 8th February

1996: Two with Pinkfeet at Burnham Market on 16th November

*Michael Seago*

# Lesser White-fronted Goose          *Anser erythropus*

**A rare vagrant.**

The Lesser White-fronted Goose breeds in a narrow band from northern Fennoscandia eastwards across northern Russia and Siberia. The lightly wooded tundra near the taiga zone is favoured. The main wintering areas are on the coastal plains of the Caspian and Black Seas eastwards in isolated pockets to China. Occasionally it occurs much further west. The Fennoscandian breeding population has almost disappeared due mainly to widespread shooting on the migration routes and wintering grounds and to disturbance by humans and reindeer. It has always been a rare vagrant to the British Isles with most sightings in the Yare Valley or at Slimbridge in Gloucestershire.

The first county record was one, now in the Castle Museum, Norwich, shot by R. F. Porter on the Breydon Marshes on 24th January 1949. Between 1949 and 1971 a total of 17 or more wild Lesser White-fronted Geese have been recorded (those identified at Buckenham were in company with overwintering Bean Geese):

1949: An adult male now in the Castle Museum, Norwich, shot on Breydon Marshes on 24th January

1955: One, now in the Castle Museum Norwich, shot on the Bure Marshes near St Benet's Abbey on 17th January
Buckenham from 22nd January to 6th March

1956: Buckenham from 1st January to 5th March

1958: Buckenham on 19th January and 2nd March

1960: Buckenham on 4th–13th February

1961: Cley, one amongst Brent Geese, on 3rd–8th February
Two at Buckenham from 26th December to 13th January 1962, one of which was at Wickhampton with Bean Geese on 4th February 1962

1962: Another with Pink-footed Geese near Six-mile House along the lower Bure on
20th and 27th January
Buckenham on 31st December

1963: Two at Buckenham on 4th–26th January with one remaining until 27th
One with White-fronted Geese at Halvergate Marshes on 11th January
An immature at Stracey Arms Marshes on 25th February

1964: An immature at Breydon on 5th January
An adult with White-fronted Geese at Halvergate on 15th January

1966: Holme on 20th–30th March

1967: Buckenham on 1st–21st January

1969: Buckenham on 11th January

1971: An immature at Buckenham from 16th January to 14th March

There were no further observations of Lesser White-fronted Geese until 1983 when one appeared amongst White-fronted Geese at Holkham from 21st February to 8th March and another joined Pinkfeet in the Holkham/Docking/Stanhoe area on 9th–23rd November 1991. But what of their credentials?

To compensate for the dramatic decrease in the local breeding population there have been a number of reintroduction schemes in Fennoscandia using Barnacle Geese as foster parents. These schemes have led to regular wintering of Lesser Whitefronts in The Netherlands. As a consequence, however, the true status in Britain has become impossible to determine. Details are available of a captive-bred Lesser Whitefront released on 12th July 1993 in Finnish Lapland which appeared at Buckenham on 17th November 1993 remaining with Bean Geese until 15th January 1994. It was reported back in Denmark between 10th February and 10th April, in Sweden on 17th April and in Finland five days later (King 1997).

Most recent reports of Lesser Whitefronts have been of singles which regularly join wild geese, but nine appeared at Pentney Gravel Pits in two family groups on 16th January 1993 and their origin may have been a wildfowl collection. An adult with White-fronted and Pink-footed Geese at Holkham in January 1997 was perhaps a genuine vagrant.

*Michael Seago*

## Greylag Goose HARDLEY FLOODS. (110) 7·2·2000.     *Anser anser*

**A common resident.**

The Greylag Goose breeds across northern and central Europe, including Iceland. Birds breeding in Continental Europe winter in southern Europe and North Africa, while the Icelandic population winters in the British Isles. Within Britain, the native population breeds only in north-west Scotland where it is sedentary. Birds breeding elsewhere in Britain, including Norfolk, originated from the Hebridean birds but were introduced during the 20th century.

Greylag Geese undoubtedly bred in Norfolk up to the 18th century when the drainage of Fenland was substantially completed. Reintroductions started in 1933 with the arrival of eight birds and continued to the early 1960s, the later birds being released by wildfowlers as part of a major programme throughout the British Isles (Ellwood & Ruxton 1970). The first breeding record in Norfolk in recent times was of a single pair at Hickling in 1960.

Despite the programme of releases, the increase in numbers has been poorly documented. The only count for the whole of the county was in July 1991 (Delany 1993). Then, including juveniles, a total of 5,083 birds was recorded.

Although the majority of birds were on the Broads, the largest concentration was at Holkham Park and Holkham NNR where 576 were present. This has long been one of the major sites for moulting Greylag Geese in the county. The geese have continued to breed very successfully in the Park, nesting in a dense colony on the island in the lake. On the Broads the main concentrations of moulting birds were associated with areas where they were fed by the public (Salhouse Broad, Horning, Wroxham/Hoveton) or where they could find extensive secure grazing on adjacent grass (St Benet's, Heigham Sound, Hardley Flood, mid-Yare Valley).

**Table 18. The distribution and age structure of Greylag Geese in Norfolk in July 1991.**

| Area | adults | juveniles | unaged | total |
|---|---|---|---|---|
| River Ant | 143 | 3 | 0 | 146 |
| River Bure | 1,072 | 325 | 0 | 1,397 |
| River Thurne | 119 | 73 | 0 | 192 |
| Trinity Broads | 154 | 25 | 0 | 179 |
| Breydon Water | 49 | 34 | 0 | 83 |
| River Yare | 377 | 250 | 0 | 627 |
| River Chet | 119 | 37 | 0 | 156 |
| River Waveney | 5 | 13 | 0 | 18 |
| Broadland | 2,038 | 760 | 0 | 2,798 |
| North Norfolk | 593 | 308 | 96 | 997 |
| W & S Norfolk | 369 | 213 | 183 | 765 |
| River Wensum | 383 | 140 | 0 | 523 |
| **County total** | **3,383** | **1,421** | **279** | **5,083** |

Breeding birds are more scattered throughout the reedswamps of the Broads and the north Norfolk coast or on islands in gravel pits and lakes of the large estates throughout Norfolk. They nest early, often being on eggs by early April, with small goslings by early May. Nests which are of relatively easy access are often predated by foxes, and even sitting adult females have been taken on the Thurne Broads. After the end of the moult and when the young can fly, in late July, large concentrations gather in the Broads. Up to 900 have been seen on the Hickling NNR, indicating that some movements take place, but to date little is known about them. They are thought to involve only short distances as the few colour-ringed birds on the north coast and on the Broads have only been recorded within 30km of the ringing site; most remain at the site of ringing. However, a bird from a feral population ringed at Harrogate, Yorkshire in June 1982 was recovered at Titchwell in September 1993. There have also been two foreign-ringed birds recovered in the county – an adult ringed in Germany on 5th July 1961 was found at Wroxham on 1st November and the ring number of a nestling ringed in The Netherlands in June 1972 was read at Narborough in July 1976.

Annual counts giving the peak winter numbers at Hickling Broad between 1976 and 1992 have been provided by Stewart Linsell. A single bird in 1976 increasing to 82 by 1983, 202 by 1985, 311 by 1988, 472 by 1989 and 589 by 1991. Elsewhere little is known concerning changes in numbers over the last 60 years. Detailed counts of the birds in the northern and eastern Broads, the north Norfolk coast and the Wensum Valley between 1989 and 1993 have shown that numbers were increasing steadily over that period at a linear rate of 6.2% per annum (Prater 1995). However, more recently a combination of increased winter shooting and control by egg-pricking being extended to a much greater area, under licence from English Nature, suggests the numbers are beginning to decline. Even so, during December 1997 346 were recorded at Attleborough/Swangey Gravel Pits, 350 at Heigham Holmes, 750 at Holkham Lake, 355 in Raynham Park, 400 in Sennowe Park, 380 at Thetford Nunnery Lakes and 500 in Wolterton Park. These totals were followed by a massive count of 1,300 at Hickling in December 1998.

As a result of the now common introduced population it is very difficult to detect genuine wild birds in the county. The Icelandic birds have the same bill colour and are thus of identical appearance to local birds. Occasionally small parties have arrived on the coast on cold north or north-westerly winds in midwinter and appeared 'wild'; such birds were noted on Breydon on 21st November 1975 and 9th January 1987 (Allard 1990). The Continental birds of the race *A. a. rubirostris* have pinkish bills, and only one group of this race has been identified at Breydon; they arrived on 26th January 1976 and stayed for four days (Allard 1990). Other recent sightings have included an adult and a first-winter bird at Sheringham on 18th–20th February 1993, which arrived with eight of the nominate race and which might also have been genuine migrants. In 1996, up to three at Stiffkey on 21st–24th January, up to two at Flitcham on 1st–3rd February, and at Scolt Head one on the sea on 14th February and six west with Brent Geese on 23rd October, were all considered to have been birds of the race *rubirostris*. Adding to the difficulty, Greylag Geese using the west European flyway between the Baltic and Spain have been infiltrated by feral birds from the Low Countries.

*Tony Prater*

## Snow Goose    *TITCHWELL (20) 19·9·1993.*    ***Anser caerulescens***

**A very rare vagrant; at least three records are considered to have involved wild birds.**

The Snow Goose breeds in extreme north-east Siberia (mainly on Wrangel Island) eastwards across the whole of Arctic North America to north-west Greenland. Ones and twos are seen almost annually in Iceland. It is a vagrant to the British Isles, but it is impossible to determine the true status as Snow Geese are kept in many British and European waterfowl collections and escapes are frequent. Recently, small feral populations have become established.

The first county record, thought to be of a genuine wild Snow Goose, was an adult white-phase in north-west Norfolk, mostly in the Docking area, from 17th November 1985 to 14th January 1986. Thought to be a Greater Snow Goose *A. c. atlanticus*, it ranged widely with Pinkfeet feeding on sugar-beet tops. Another adult white-phase Greater Snow Goose was present with Pinkfeet in the Docking/Scolt Head/ Burnham Norton area from 6th December 1996 to at least 25th February 1997. Previously seen in Lancashire in November 1996, it was highly mobile and towards the end of its stay moved to the Snettisham area. It was relocated in Lancashire on 28th February 1997. An adult white phase bird which was almost certainly a Lesser Snow Goose *A. c. caerulescens* remained at Welney from 1st December 1996 until 30th March 1997. This bird arrived, associated throughout its stay and departed with Whooper Swans and was considered to be a wild individual. The Lesser Snow Goose is a long-distance migrant and its capability to reach Europe has been proven by a colour-ringed bird seen in The Netherlands (amongst a flock of 18), which had been ringed at La Perouse Bay, 40km east of Churchill, Manitoba in Canada.

Other sightings which may have related to wild birds have been :

> 1909:  One shot at Cley on 9th January
> Three with Pink-footed Geese at Holkham from October to January 1910
> 1912:  Six in off the sea at Cley on 12th October
> 1973:  An adult blue-phase, which was exceptionally wary, with Bean Geese in the Yare Valley from 13th November to 26th February 1974

Other records of particular interest are a gaggle of eight adults and four juveniles which arrived at Cley on 21st September 1982 following strong westerly winds, and an adult white-phase in flight with 2,000 Pinkfeet at Wells on 18th February 1984.

Feral populations in Norfolk include up to 38 in the Holkham area where breeding first took place in 1990.

*Peter Allard*

## Canada Goose    *HARDLEY FLOODS. (6) 27·2·2000.*    ***Branta canadensis***

**A fairly common introduced resident.**

The Canada Goose is an introduced species to the Western Palearctic, initially brought into the British Isles in the 17th century. In addition to the British population, there are also feral breeding populations in Norway, Sweden, Finland and probably Germany. The British population is still expanding at an estimated rate of 8% per annum.

Stevenson classified the Canada Goose with 'other fancy fowl' which had been introduced to the county. He considered that it was more plentiful 'as an acclimatised species' than the Egyptian Goose, for example, and mentioned a flock of 150 at Gunton Park (where 148 were reported 100 years later in 1994!). They were already wandering from their protected areas by the second half of the 19th century with records of single birds being shot on Breydon in 1878 and 1889 (Allard 1990).

The status had changed little by the time of Riviere, who included this species in square brackets. At this time the largest flock was at Holkham where 100 or so could be found on the lake. Despite the proximity to this favourite haunt, the first record along the coast at Cley was not until November 1949 (Gantlett 1995a) and breeding was not noted at Sheringham until 1986.

By June 1958 a countywide census gave a total of 1,277 adult birds with breeding being recorded from the Broads, Brecks and flooded gravel pits in the river valleys. During fieldwork for the Norfolk Atlas

(1980–85) the Canada Goose was recorded in 201 tetrads, well spread throughout the county, with breeding confirmed in 112. Prater surveyed the Broadland population in 1989 and found 742 in the area, including 576 adults. A further survey in July 1991 gave a total for the entire county of 2,636 birds, including 429 juveniles. Bloomfield (1993) stated that there was some evidence of a decline at Holkham, one of the traditional haunts, possibly as a result of the local birds switching their summer moulting-site westwards along the coast to Titchwell. The largest party recorded in 1996 was one of 418 at Titchwell in July. The WeBS total for the north coast was 497 in August 1996 with 78 at Breydon at the same time. There were many records of three-figure counts in 1997 with the larger ones occurring at Thetford Nunnery Lakes (360 in January and September), Titchwell (300 in June), Whitlingham Lane Gravel Pit (285 in September) and a record 600 at Wolterton Hall in December.

In east Norfolk skeins are regularly seen migrating north in the first half of June, presumably on moult migration. Further around the coast similar movements have been noted. In 1996, for example, 30 passed Sheringham in a northerly direction on 31st May and 220 flew east there on 5th June with small parties passing east at Scolt Head between 31st May and 8th June 1997.

Single examples considered to be of the Cackling Goose *B. c. minima*, the darkest of the small forms and smallest of all with a tiny bill and a short neck, have been reported on three occasions. The race breeds in coastal western Alaska, wintering chiefly in the interior of California south to northern Mexico. Genuine vagrancy is a possibility. The first in Norfolk appeared at Brancaster on 16th January 1984, at West Rudham on 5th February, over Wells on 18th February and finally at Heacham fresh-marsh on 3rd March. On each occasion it was in the company of Pink-footed Geese. Another was at Welney on 15th–17th December 1984 and again from 14th February to 24th March 1985. It was always in company with Bewick's Swans and departed with them. A third example, associating with Canada Geese, appeared at Holkham on 3rd February 1985.

During the late 1970s and early 1980s large numbers of moulting Canada Geese were ringed at Holkham Park Lake in July. As a result over 350 recoveries were reported, almost 300 of which were within Norfolk. There were only seven movements of over 100km – five to Suffolk and one each to Hertfordshire and Staffordshire. However, controlled amongst the flock of moulting birds in July 1981 was an adult ringed on the Beauly Firth, Highland Region on 2nd July 1978 and a nestling ringed in North Yorkshire on 9th July 1978. Amongst those that died during a severe storm at Castle Acre in January 1978 were four that had been ringed in Nottinghamshire.

*Don Dorling*

## Barnacle Goose | HARDLEY FLOODS (1) 1·1·2000.  *Branta leucopsis*

**A scarce passage migrant and winter visitor; an increasing feral resident.**

The Barnacle Goose has breeding ranges in Svalbard (Spitsbergen), Novaya Zemlya and eastern Greenland with each population having its own wintering location. Since the early 1980s a small but growing population has broken away from the Russian group and established itself in the Baltic off Sweden. The birds from Svalbard spend the winter in the Solway Firth area, those from east Greenland in Scotland and Ireland, while the Russian and Baltic geese visit The Netherlands.

In the middle of the 19th century both the Pagets (1834) and Gurney and Fisher (1846) described this species as being 'not uncommon' and there are records of birds being shot at Salthouse and Blakeney on the coast and Burlingham, Hickling and Kimberley inland. But when Stevenson wrote later in the century, he had not known of a Norfolk specimen taken for ten years, even during the severe winter of 1870–71. They were still described as 'scarce' by Riviere although he mentioned that unusual numbers were seen in the winter of 1899–1900 with 8–10 being reported killed.

Their appearance continued to be irregular and in small numbers for the first half of the 20th century, with 24 at Salthouse on 16th March 1935 and 12 at Cley on 20th January 1951 being the largest parties recorded. In 1970 unusual numbers arrived on 1st January with at least 60 birds in north Norfolk, some wintering at Holkham, and flocks of 38 seen off Weybourne and 45 feeding at East Runton. Five years later parties of 25 were at West Caister and 49 at Cley. This pattern of small parties appearing annually continued until 1st March 1981 when 116 arrived at Blakeney Eye with 75 remaining for a further three days. During the next two years the largest sighting was a group of 49 at Horsey in December 1982. On

23rd January 1984 another notable influx occurred, including up to 155 in the Wiveton/Cley/Salthouse area, with many other smaller parties around the coast from Lynn Point to Horsey. A flock of 32 Barnacle Geese reached the north coast in thick fog on 21st October 1988.

It is thought that birds from all three main wintering populations visit Norfolk from time to time (Kemp 1984, Rooney 1994c). The occasional birds that arrive with the large flocks of Pink-footed Geese most probably come from Greenland, whilst one seen in the Holme and Thornham area early in October 1988, had been ringed during the previous winter in Denmark. A party of 15 which appeared at Cley in October 1990 included six birds carrying Spitsbergen rings. One of these had been ringed in July 1979 and had been present at Caerlaverock every winter since; it was still at Cley on 20th October but was back at Caerlaverock by 14th November 1990. The following October saw a party of 21 at Cley containing three Spitsbergen-ringed geese which had also returned to Caerlaverock later in the autumn.

In December 1991 a flock of 59 was in the Lound/Haddiscoe area. Heigham Holmes has been a favoured locality in recent years with a flock of 65 in February 1992, 68 in February 1993, 80 in January 1994 and 65 in December 1995. Many smaller parties arrived during these four years including six at Holkham, four of which were carrying coloured rings. These came from the new breeding area on the island of Gotland, Sweden, which was established from the Russian population in the early 1980s.

There was a notable influx in December 1995 with many remaining in the county into 1996. The larger counts included 53 at Holme, 67 at Holkham, 53 at Horsey/Heigham Holmes, 54 at Breydon (including a Russian-ringed bird) and 60 at Haddiscoe. No doubt there was some duplication in these counts as the birds roamed from site to site before the majority moved on in February, with 11 remaining at Holkham until 14th April 1996. In early 1997 there were small parties at several sites along the coast usually associating with flocks of other species of wild geese; the largest party numbered 67 at Hickling/Heigham Holmes. In October 1997 there were reports of small parties from five coastal sites between Holme and Yarmouth, which were considered to be of wild origin; a flock of 16 at Cley on 13th–16th October contained two birds ringed in Spitsbergen.

By 1986 reference was made in the *Norfolk Bird Report* to the increasing numbers of feral birds present in the county. A survey of the Broads area carried out by Prater in 1991 produced a total of 18 feral birds. The New Atlas covering the years 1988–91, only showed 10km squares occupied on the periphery of Norfolk. Since those data were collected, breeding has certainly occurred in the county. It was first confirmed at Hethersett, for example, in 1995 with two pairs and in the following year three pairs raised seven young between them. These were joined by a wandering flock from time to time in late summer and early autumn, usually feeding on stubbles, and which probably came from the Yare Valley. The maximum number in this flock had been 57 in the autumns of 1996 and briefly in 1998. They have rarely been noted at Hethersett in the winter months. Elsewhere there are records of 67 presumed feral birds at Gunton Park in December 1995 with many parties in the Yare Valley at sites such as Buckenham, Cantley and Strumpshaw (where there were 49 in October 1995).

However, the situation is not clear cut, as was demonstrated by a bird at Lound in April 1993 which had been ringed in Spitsbergen in 1986. Another at Fritton Lake in June 1993, April 1994 and April 1995 had been ringed in Sweden in 1989. It was still present in 1998 when it bred with a presumed feral female rearing five goslings. But perhaps the most extraordinary report of a ringed bird came from Bessingham, where one ringed in Donegal, Eire in November 1985 (and presumably from the Greenland population) was feeding with domestic animals and captive birds on 15th April 1986. To further cloud the issue, a flock of 100 feral birds based at the Otter Trust at Earsham in the Waveney Valley regularly disappear for several weeks at a time (P. Wayre *in litt.*). Likewise, the feral flock of up to 60 at Fritton Lake Country Park often disappears.

*Don Dorling*

## Brent Goose    *BREYDON WATER. (5) 1-12-1992.*    *Branta bernicla*

### Dark-bellied Brent Goose    *B. b. bernicla*

A very common passage migrant and winter visitor; very scarce inland.

### Pale-bellied Brent Goose    *B. b. hrota*

A very scarce winter visitor and passage migrant.

### Black Brant    *B. b. nigricans*

A rare winter visitor.

The Brent Goose has a limited breeding range in the Western Palearctic but is a widespread passage migrant and winter visitor to the area. The three races, taken together, have an almost circumpolar, high Arctic, breeding distribution. The Dark-bellied race *B. b. bernicla* which winters along the coasts of eastern and southern England, The Netherlands, Germany and western France, breeds in Siberia, mainly on the Taimyr Peninsula. There are two populations of the Pale-bellied race *B. b. hrota* – those breeding in north and north-east Greenland and the Canadian Arctic islands, which winter in Ireland, and those from Svalbard which winter in Denmark and north-east England. The Black Brant *B. b. nigricans* of the Canadian Arctic and eastern Siberia, winters on both sides of the Pacific Ocean.

In Stevenson's day the Brent Goose was a regular winter visitor to the county, with the largest parties occurring along the north coast, arriving generally at the end of October with the majority departing by the end of March. Flocks at Blakeney ranged between 100 and 300. Severe winters greatly increased the numbers appearing on the coast and consequently on the local market stalls. These visitors were entirely maritime in their habits, only very rarely being seen inland. The existence of both pale and dark bellied individuals was recognised, the former being known locally as 'stranger' Brents, but the fact that these differing birds represented two races coming from separate breeding populations was unknown at that time.

By the time Riviere prepared his book, the three races with their discrete breeding ranges had been recognised. Both Dark-bellied and Pale-bellied regularly appeared on the Norfolk coast in winter 'apparently in about equal numbers', although he considered the species as a whole to be less abundant than of late. Riviere examined a number of skins, including those of three birds shot on the Wash in 1909 which had been claimed as *nigricans,* but reached the conclusion that they were all typical Dark-bellied birds; a view confirmed at the time by Harry Witherby.

The worldwide populations of the Brent Goose, particularly the Dark-bellied race, decreased substantially in the 1930s as a result, it was thought at the time, of the failure of a favourite winter food source, the eel-grass *Zostera marina*. Subsequent investigations have thrown doubt on this failure as being the only reason for the species' rapid decline. Poor breeding success and hunting pressures are now thought to have played a significant part. It has been suggested recently that large numbers of eggs and of moulting, flightless, geese were collected each year to help feed the inmates at Stalin's Siberian gulag camps (Vickery & Sutherland 1996).

A result of the drastic drop in the population was the introduction of almost universal protection in the breeding and wintering areas and on migration. This, together with a number of good breeding seasons and the goose's ability to adapt to a wider range of food on the wintering grounds, has resulted in a steady and substantial increase in the size of the world population of the Dark-bellied race. This was thought to total around 22,000 in the early 1960s and is now estimated to be in the region of 250,000–300,000 birds.

The recovery of the population is demonstrated by the gradual increase in numbers spending the winter on the Norfolk coast. In 1953 the maximum flock recorded was one of only 150–200 at Blakeney. By 1958 Blakeney had a flock of 1,100 with another 700 at Brancaster. Five years later, in 1963, the wintering parties along the north coast had reached 2,500–3,000 at Blakeney with 500 at Brancaster and 1,500 in the Wells area. While these were not co-ordinated counts, so there could have been some duplication as the parties moved around the favoured feeding and roosting locations, they demonstrated the substantial increase in numbers recorded when compared with those of ten years earlier. The growth in the wintering population of the Dark-bellied race continued and co-ordinated counts in 1985 gave totals of 10,355 in January and 12,592 in December. By 1994 the north coast was home to nearly 15,000 with another 22,000 on the whole of the Wash, only part of which is in Norfolk. Similar counts in 1996

Brent Geese
(*Nik Borrow*)

produced a maximum of 14,803 in February between Holme and Salthouse and the Wash total reached 21,023 in March. A total of 14,088 was counted along the north coast in February 1997. A record flock for the east coast numbered 285 at Breydon in February 1996.

The rapid and sustained growth has occurred despite considerable fluctuations in the breeding success from year to year. The percentage of young appearing in the wintering flocks in north Norfolk varies from almost nil to 60% (1982–83). A ratio of 30% of young birds in the winter of 1993–94 was followed by two almost blank years with many first-winter birds appearing again in the autumn of 1996. Evidence for 1997 was conflicting with estimates ranging between 7% and 25% for two flocks counted on successive days. The successful years frequently follow a three-year cycle which has been shown to coincide with the years of high numbers of lemmings in the breeding grounds which result in low predation of the geese by the arctic foxes. The prevailing winds in the Baltic at the end of May affects the condition of the birds on arrival in Siberia and consequently the breeding success (Ebbinge 1988).

The main autumn arrivals of the Dark-bellied race take place in October and November when numbers can be seen on passage all along the Norfolk coast. Occasionally these movements can be spectacular. Early in November 1982 high pressure over northern Europe with a fresh south-east wind and poor visibility over the North Sea, brought about one particularly notable movement. On 5th November 14,500 Brent Geese were counted passing south off Yarmouth in one hour. The day's total was estimated to be 25,000 Brents accompanied by large numbers of other wildfowl. The move-ment continued for another two days but with much reduced numbers of geese (Allard 1983, 1990).

A recent detailed study of one north Norfolk flock has shown that on arrival the birds feed on the algal beds and saltmarshes, then by November are moving inland to grass pasture and arable crops. There is historical evidence that the algal beds and saltmarshes were used throughout the winter; the move to inland areas being first noted in the 1970s. This change in habit has removed one of the restrictions on population growth (Vickery & Sutherland 1996). The majority of the flocks move off eastwards again in March, leaving smaller parties lingering in the north coast estuaries until May where a few birds can now be seen in any month of the year. Exceptional numbers were present in May 1995, including 1,500 at Blakeney on 1st, with 2,387 at Terrington and 660 at Brancaster on 4th. A count covering the whole of the Wash in May 1996 produced a total of 7,220 birds still present. In 1997, 700 were recorded at Lynn Point on 24th May with parties of up to eight appearing at ten sites from Titchwell to Yarmouth in June.

Brent Geese mainly occur at the coast but occasionally small numbers have been seen inland at locations such as Welney, the beet factory settling ponds at Wissington and Cantley and the Broads, where 17 were present at Wroxham on 24th March 1996 and one a year later.

The appearances of the Pale-bellied race *B. b. hrota* has not followed the same pattern. Instead of the 'equal numbers' of earlier times, *hrota* is now only recorded annually in small numbers. There were 29 at Blakeney in 1954 and 'many considered pale-bellied' there the following year with a few at Cley. In 1966, 1–2 appeared at Salthouse with no others reported until 1979 when there were 15–20 at Cley/Salthouse and two at Wells in January–February. In 1982 up to 13 were seen at Lynn Point. In January and February 1985, 15 were at Lynn Point again and parties of 20 or more between Stiffkey and Salthouse with a maximum of 38 at the latter site. A lone bird was on the east coast at Horsey at the same time. This pattern has continued with small parties being seen annually at various coastal locations; the recent maximum being 23 at Salthouse between 17th January and 1st March 1996. It is believed that these birds come from the Svalbard population wintering in Northumberland and Denmark. In support of this view was a very early party of 13 seen passing Horsey, Sheringham, Weybourne and Cley on 30th August 1996. The next day they were seen flying north past Flamborough Head in Yorkshire. A programme of colour-ringing at Lindisfarne in Northumberland gives further confirmation. Two birds in a group of 11 at Holkham from 27th February to 6th March 1996 were ringed at Lindisfarne in December 1991 and had been seen in Northumberland in January 1996, The Netherlands on 12th March and Denmark by 4th April returning to Northumberland again by the year-end (Bloomfield 1998).

The Black Brant *nigricans* has occurred almost annually since 1982 when one appeared with the Dark-bellied flock at Cley Eye Field on 7th November staying in the area until 13th March 1983. What is possibly the same bird returned to the Cley/Salthouse area during the next six winters being finally seen on 12th March 1989; an additional bird was also present in early 1988. It, or another, put in a brief appearance at Salthouse for two days in January 1990. Another bird appeared in the Kelling to Cley area in 1996 remaining until 22nd January 1997. In September–November 1998 one was at Wells Harbour, in November another at Lynn Point and in December one was at Titchwell, while in November–December up to three adults were present in the Cley area; it is likely that at least five birds were involved. Other favourite localities for this wanderer from the Canadian Arctic have been the Holme/Thornham/Titchwell and Brancaster/Burnham Overy Staithe areas. More unusual was the bird that spent seven weeks at Breydon in November and December 1990. It has usually been assumed that these birds were transatlantic wanderers but a recent visit to breeding grounds in eastern Siberia has proved a westerly spread of *nigricans* to a point where they meet the nominate race *bernicla*. This makes it a distinct possibility that the Black Brants visiting Norfolk in winter have joined the Dark-bellied birds and migrated westwards in the autumn (Syroechkovski *et al.* 1998).

Following the earlier drop in population and subsequent threats to a major wintering area in Essex, the Dark-bellied race has been the subject of much scientific attention for many years. One result of this has been that a number of birds carry large coloured rings easily readable in the field. The information gleaned from this exercise has confirmed that our wintering birds breed in the Pyasina and Taimyr Deltas of the Taimyr Peninsula in northern Siberia. It has also shown that the Dutch Islands and Schleswig-Holstein are used as important feeding and stop-over points during April and May before making the non-stop return journey to Siberia.

Site fidelity on the wintering grounds is also demonstrated by the record of one bird seen on the Wells Pitch and Putt Course in mid-March 1993 which had returned to the same location by November that year. Another has been seen on Cley Eye Field in three consecutive winters. These records are surpassed by two first-winter birds ringed at Salthouse in February 1974 which were seen at Cley in January and February 1995, with one appearing again in 1997. Two leucistic birds were seen flying west at Cley in October 1982. In 1988 one was reported back at Scolt for its seventh winter and what was almost certainly the same silvery-grey bird was still present in a flock at Burnham Norton into 1999. However, there is some interchange between wintering sites as was shown by one ringed at Farlington Marshes, Hampshire in February 1980 which was found at Brancaster in February 1984.

*Don Dorling*

## Red-breasted Goose | *Branta ruficollis*

**A very rare vagrant; seven records.**

The Red-breasted Goose breeds in decreasing numbers in northern Siberia and winters near the Black Sea and Caspian Sea south to Greece and Turkey. It is a rare vagrant to the British Isles.

Stevenson and Riviere both recorded one early and dubious record of a bird shot at Halvergate in 1805 which was bought on Yarmouth market by a Mr Wigg, a well-respected botanist. He promptly ate the specimen 'as he had never tasted one before'. When he subsequently realised the significance of his action he could only recover a few feathers for others to see!

The first definite record for the county was a bird found by Peter Allard which accompanied White-fronted Geese on the Halvergate Marshes on 2nd–28th January 1962. Nearly 22 years were to pass before the second record – a first-winter bird which appeared at Stiffkey on 10th November 1983. It was usually with a flock of Brent Geese and was also seen at Holme, Brancaster Staithe, Holkham and, finally, Wells Quay, until 23rd March 1984.

The next record was another bird with Brent Geese in the Wiveton, Blakeney and Cley area on 10th–14th January 1986. The fourth record, a year later, was also with Brents in the same general area – Langham, Blakeney, Cley and Salthouse from 7th December 1987 to 2nd March 1988. A first-winter bird was present, again with Brent Geese, in the Wells and Warham area from 23rd October to 6th November 1994 when it was seen to fly east. Later that day it was seen flying south at Winterton with Brent Geese.

The latest two occurrences were in 1995 when a first-winter was at Welney on 12th November and an adult was with Pink-footed Geese at Sea Palling and Waxham from 28th November to 9th December 1995, having been seen earlier at Ludham.

*Don Dorling*

## Egyptian Goose

BY HARDLEY FLOODS. (2)
23-12-1999.

### *Alopochen aegyptiacus*

**A fairly common introduced resident.**

Egyptian Geese
(Bryan Bland)

In Europe, the Egyptian Goose is restricted as a feral breeding bird, mainly to the lowlands of eastern England, Belgium and The Netherlands. It had probably been introduced into the British Isles from Africa by the late 17th century, as there is a painting of this species in Willughby and Ray (1676–8) although it is labelled as a 'Gambo-Goose or Spur wing'd'. By the late 18th century it was stated that numbers have been brought to England: 'and they are now not uncommon in gentleman's ponds in many parts of this kingdom' (Latham 1785). Thus, although this species is widely perceived as a newcomer, it was established well before the Victorian introductions of Little Owl and Gadwall (Lever 1987). It was placed on the British list in 1971.

Within Britain, the Egyptian Goose is very much a Norfolk speciality. The first known record for Norfolk was in 1808 and by the middle of the 19th century there were known to be large flocks at Blickling Hall, Gunton Park, Holkham Hall and Kimberley Park. There were also large flocks in Devon, Bedfordshire and East Lothian, but even two hundred years ago the distribution was concentrated in Norfolk. The large populations outside Norfolk have disappeared and, although scattered birds have bred in a wide range of counties, these populations seem unsustainable. The exception is Suffolk, where the species is gradually increasing.

Evolutionary biologists have suggested that, as a result of humans evolving in the African savanna, their innate ideal of landscape beauty is a lush savanna landscape. These evolutionary biologists suggest that this is why, when given the opportunity to determine their own landscape, humans create a habitat of scattered large trees, short grass and water, of which the parkland linked to stately homes is the most extreme example. It seems entirely appropriate that these recreated savannas should also be occupied by Egyptian Geese, which are so typical of their natural habitat. Of the total of 144 pairs in Norfolk, located in a survey of suitable sites in East Anglia in April 1988 by Sutherland and Allport (1991), 98 were in parkland, 24 in river valleys, eight on gravel pits and two on Breckland meres. Most areas of parkland in Norfolk contained birds with particular concentrations at Sennowe, Holkham, Hunstanton, Sandringham, Raynham and Kimberley. Outside the parks, the main concentrations were on the Rivers Bure, Wensum or the lower reaches of the Waveney. During the fieldwork for the Norfolk Atlas, carried out in 1980–85, it was recorded in 91 tetrads. These covered 30 of the 10km squares in Norfolk, compared with only 13 during the 68–72 BTO Atlas, an indication of the expansion of its range during the intervening period. It is of interest that during the fieldwork for the New Atlas in 1988–91, Egyptian Geese were again recorded in 30 of the 10km squares in Norfolk, but showed a different distribution to that in the Norfolk Atlas. The highest concentrations of breeding pairs in recent years have been 13 pairs in the Stanford Training Area in 1995, up to 12 pairs at Holkham Park and six pairs at Wroxham in 1994. Egyptian Geese breed extremely early in the year with broods of small young not infrequently reported in January – up to eight pairs were found nest-building at Holkham Park in December 1994. Many of these early broods perish due to the adverse weather. The extended breeding season was well-demonstrated in 1991 when broods of downy young were reported from Taverham on 26th February and Lenwade on 25th November.

The Norfolk population was estimated at 350–400 in 1988, whereas during a county-wide goose survey in July 1991 a record total of 846 Egyptian Geese were counted of which 610 were adults. In addition to 121 at Holkham Lake and 48 at Holkham Fresh Marshes, other counts included 91 along the River Bure in Broadland, 90 at Cranwich Gravel Pit and 63 at Lyng Easthaugh Gravel Pit. Other notable counts since then have been of 98 at Catfield in 1994, 84 at Ludham Hall and 78 at Lynford in 1996, and 83 at Pentney Gravel Pit, 53 at Middleton Gravel Pit, 69 at Sennowe Park, 76 at St Benet's Level and 80 at Blickling Park all in 1997. The highest counts at Breydon were in 1998 with 17 in June and 25 in November.

During the summer they largely feed on permanent grassland, often within parks, but in the winter birds wander away from waterside habitats and regularly feed on winter wheat, sugar beet and potatoes (Sutherland & Allport 1991). They moult in July and August, often collecting in considerable flocks in sites with large lakes and adjacent grassland, such as at Holkham Lake and more recently, the grazing marshes (Bloomfield 1993), where maximum counts of 200 in 1979 and 169 in 1991 have been made. A survey in 1988 indicated that breeders from the River Wensum and upper Bure moulted at Sennowe and Blickling (Sutherland & Allport 1991). Adults, with flightless young at this time, moult while caring for them at the breeding site.

They typically nest in old trees, usually in holes but also sometimes on the epicormic shoots, within walking distance of open water, although this may be over a kilometre away. The combination of restricted breeding habitat, strong territoriality, relatively low productivity and remarkably little change in numbers over the last 150 years all suggest that this species is unlikely to be a problem on the scale of Canada or Greylag Geese. A change from, say 100, to perhaps 800, over 150 years is an annual increase of less than 1.4%. There is some indication of a general spread and increase in numbers (New Atlas) and there does seem to be much suitable but unused habitat, especially outside Norfolk, so providing the opportunity for a continued expansion.

With increasing concern over introduced species, following the disaster of the Ruddy Duck, and increasing problems involving Canada and Greylag Geese, there are calls for introduced species such as the Egyptian Goose to be controlled. This species is already shot as part of control programmes for other feral species and it may also be shot for sport.

*William J. Sutherland*

## Ruddy Shelduck    TITCHWELL. 11-9-1993    *Tadorna ferruginea*

**A very rare vagrant; most, if not all, recent records relate to feral birds.**

The Ruddy Shelduck is a Southern Palearctic species with a decreasing population in Rumania, Bulgaria and Greece, eastwards into central Asia. There is also a small isolated population in North Africa. It is mainly dispersive or nomadic with some groups being migratory. Since the late 1960s feral populations have become established in Germany and The Netherlands.

Stevenson mentioned that this species had been taken in Norfolk more than once but, to his knowledge, had not occurred in an undoubtedly wild state. An adult male shot at Snettisham on 26th March

1869 and sent to him for identification was established as having been an escape from nearby Anmer.

Riviere recorded one that had been washed up on the beach at Snettisham in September 1892 and listed another 11 birds shot at various coastal localities between 1893 and May 1926. The record of a female obtained at Thetford in February 1906 was perhaps one of the pair flushed at Langmere by W. G. Clarke in April 1906 (Clarke 1937). In addition, a party of four was seen at Hickling at the end of October 1916 with another, or the same, four at Breydon in January 1917. Riviere considered that some of these records may have been genuine migrants, although all must be under suspicion of being escapes from collections. The 1892 bird could well have been associated with a major influx of Ruddy Shelducks into western Europe that year, following an exceptionally dry summer and autumn in southern Europe when two or three birds reached as far as eastern Greenland (Rogers 1982), and thus may be the county's only wild bird.

After 1926 there were no further sightings reported until two appeared in Holkham Park in 1963 with one still present in 1966. In 1971 there were five at Wisbech Sewage Farm on 25th August and ten days later perhaps the same five at Cley. An adult female in the Cantley and Breydon areas in July and early August 1977 were the next records, followed by occasional autumn and winter sightings in 1978, 1979, 1980 and 1983.

A spring record from the Breydon/Berney area on 28th–29th May 1988 was notable. From 1990 onwards Ruddy Shelducks have appeared annually, at first mainly in the autumn, with the largest parties being seven which were seen departing westwards from Holkham beach on 10th October 1992 and eight at Sennowe Park on 24th October 1993. More recently the increasing number of reports have related to spring and early summer with pairs breeding at separate north Norfolk sites in 1996 and 1997. In the latter year a brood of 11 was seen but no young were thought to have survived.

It is impossible to assess the origins of birds observed in the county. There was a minor influx into north-west Europe from late 1994 (including between 75 and 100 in Denmark, 100 in Finland and 40 in Sweden), but German feral birds, escapes and releases continue to create confusion. Rogers (1982) concluded that there were no grounds for presuming that any records of Ruddy Shelducks appearing in Britain during the last 50 years could have definitely related to wild vagrants. This opinion must be valid for the majority of Norfolk's records this century, which must be assumed to have come from collections or feral populations here or on the near Continent. After reviewing the status of this species in 1993, the BOURC decided that the Ruddy Shelduck should remain on their list in Category B, that is, no recent records are considered to be of genuine wild birds (Vinicombe *et al.* 1993).

*Don Dorling*

## Shelduck (Common Shelduck)    *Tadorna tadorna*

BY MY GARDEN
12-6-2000.

**A common breeder, passage migrant and winter visitor.**

The Shelduck breeds in the coastal regions of north-western Europe from Scandinavia, the British Isles, south to the Atlantic coast of France with pockets along the Mediterranean coasts of France, Sardinia and Tunisia. In the east it breeds from the shores of the Black Sea eastwards into central Asia. The majority of adults from the western European populations migrate in late summer to moult in the Wadden-zee area of Germany, leaving only a few adults with the year's juveniles on the breeding grounds.

In Norfolk the Shelduck was a widespread breeder along most of the coastal dunes at the beginning of the 19th century. Their demise was because they 'were supposed to disturb the rabbits'. Sir Thomas Browne in the 17th century knew of them breeding away from the coast in 'coney burrows in the vicinity of Norrold [thought to be Northwold] and other wild places'. By the middle of the 19th century they had become much less common as a resident and winter visitor. Stevenson thought that this was undoubtedly a result of the persecution by the gunners, particularly in the early months of the year.

Riviere was able to report a considerable increase during the early decades of the 20th century with breeding becoming abundant in all suitable localities along the coast between Kelling and King's Lynn. By then they had also returned to Breydon where they first bred in 1920 at the Burgh Castle end and on the north side of the estuary in 1935. Shelducks soon adapted to the disappearance of the rabbits as a result of the outbreak of myxomatosis in 1953, by using alternative nest-sites, and at the same time began to move further inland. In the Brecks they first nested at Stanford Water in 1976.

Shelducks
(Nik Borrow)

During fieldwork for the Norfolk Atlas, the species was recorded in 286 tetrads (20%) with breeding confirmed in 115. The main concentrations were in the north-west corner of the county and the Breydon and Broads area in the south-east. The New Atlas confirmed that the most abundant populations were still sited around the Wash and the Breydon areas but also disclosed a continuing spread inland with many new squares being occupied across the centre of the county. Norfolk had more inland squares with breeding Shelducks than any other county.

The settling ponds at Cantley Beet Factory have been a favoured locality for concentrations of young birds with regular counts of 200–300 juveniles. In the west, 230 young were seen at Lynn Point in June 1972. Since 1988 numbers using Breydon have declined both during the breeding season and the winter months.

Most adults leave Norfolk in mid-summer for their moulting grounds on the estuaries in north-west Germany returning from the end of October. Before departure large flocks gather at favoured localities with totals of 5,748 and 6,264 being counted in the Norfolk section of the Wash in July 1990 and 1994, respectively. A recent trend has been for an increasing number of birds to remain on the Wash for their moult (Bryant 1981). In a flock of 2,268 seen between King's Lynn and North Wootton on 1st August 1980, 1,000 were in full wing-moult. It was estimated that 4,000 were in the Wash moulting flock in 1988 and 1,000 were noted as flightless there in 1994.

The passage to and from the German moulting areas can be witnessed along the county's coast with parties of birds regularly seen passing eastwards at Holme and Sheringham in June and early July. The return passage is noted from early September to the year-end with recent maximum numbers at the same localities being 150 flying west at Holme on 9th September and 210 off Sheringham on 8th November 1996, with a maximum of 240 there in October 1997. The largest day-count recorded at the latter site was 780 flying west on 29th October 1974 (Taylor 1987a). As can be seen from these figures, there has been a noticeable decrease in the numbers passing initially east and then west later in the autumn off the north Norfolk coast, presumably a result of more birds using the moulting area in the Wash.

The British Isles is an important wintering area for this species with 50% of the European population spending the winter months on our estuaries – some 60,000–65,000 birds. Norfolk, at times, holds a significant proportion of this total with January counts of over 11,000 birds being recorded in the county's section of the Wash in both 1988 and 1992, the maximum winter count being 14,560 in December 1985. In addition, Breydon and the estuaries along the north coast also hold important numbers throughout the winter months. For example, there were 1,357 on Breydon in January 1979 with 1,307 there eight years later (Allard 1990) and, also in January 1987, a maximum of 1,420 at Warham (Bloomfield 1993).

Shelduck ringed in Norfolk both as nestlings and adults have been recovered in The Netherlands (3) and in autumn in the moulting area in the Helgoland Bight, Germany (3), including one in its seventeenth year. A total of 23 foreign-ringed Shelducks has been found in Norfolk from Germany (17), France (3) and The Netherlands (2), while an adult ringed in Lithuania in June 1986 and found at Holkham in April 1991 was only the second recovery of a Shelduck from the Baltic States. One ringed while moulting on the

River Weser Estuary in Germany on 29th July 1956 was controlled while breeding at Blythburgh, Suffolk in 1960, and was subsequently found dead at Terrington in January 1963. Other notable recoveries have included an adult ringed at Teesmouth, Cleveland in December 1977 which was found dead at Blakeney Point in January 1985, while one controlled at Teesmouth in January 1984 which had been ringed at North Wootton in August 1968, was also in at least its seventeenth year.

*Don Dorling*

## Mandarin (Mandarin Duck)           *Aix galericulata*

**A scarce but increasing introduced resident.**

The native range of the Mandarin is in the Far East, mainly Japan, China, Korea and the former USSR. Although it was first introduced into Britain before 1745, the first concerted attempts to establish a free-living population was not until the early 20th century, at Woburn Park in Bedfordshire. Nowadays the British stronghold is in Surrey and east Berkshire, with most of the 3,500 breeding pairs in southern England. This total equals that in Japan and exceeds that in the rest of Asia, where it has declined as a result of deforestation. Thus the British population is of major conservation importance.

The species was added to category C of the British and Irish List in 1971. The status of the Mandarin in Norfolk has always been beset by the problem of escapes from wildfowl collections. At Salhouse, a pair believed to have escaped from a nearby collection bred annually between 1965 and 1971, while at Smallburgh a pair nested in a nest box 4m from the ground on an oak in 1977, but the eggs failed to hatch. During the late 1970s the majority of sightings, of up to four birds, were in Broadland and during fieldwork for the Norfolk Atlas (1980–85) the only record of confirmed breeding came from the Yare Valley at Bramerton, where a pair nested under tree roots on a slope. Earlier, in 1973, the head gardener at the Sandringham Estate introduced eight ducklings which he had obtained from Windsor (M. Woods *in litt.*). Numbers appeared to increase there quite dramatically for a time, although as they were free-flying birds, the number present also fluctuated, reaching 100 by 1993 if not earlier. By the mid-1980s most records came from west Norfolk, no doubt of birds originating from Sandringham or possibly, Pensthorpe.

The next breeding record was of a pair which hatched six ducklings at Felbrigg in 1986, but none of them reached the free-flying stage (Taylor 1987b). Since then single pairs have bred at Gunton Park in 1989, Hillington Park in 1990, in the Wensum valley between Guist and Bintree in 1992, at Castle Rising in 1993, at Flitcham in 1993 and 1994, at Babingley in 1995, at Little Snoring in 1996 and at Ken Hill Marsh and Framingham Pigot in 1997. Because of their secretive behaviour during the breeding season and their habit of nesting in holes in trees, up to 18m off the ground (European Atlas), most breeding records relate to females found with ducklings, and it is likely that other feral pairs have bred elsewhere in the county.

Until 1995 Mandarins remained relatively scarce birds in Norfolk. Away from known collections, no more than four together were generally recorded at up to about a dozen sites annually. However, the species appeared to become more widespread in 1995 with sightings from at least 25 well-scattered localities, increasing to 28 in 1996. During the autumn and winter, Mandarins feed on acorns, chestnuts and beechmast, which may account for the fact that in recent years Felbrigg Park has been one of the more reliable sites at which to see the species, with a maximum of 20 in October 1995. One of the highest winter counts, 102 at Dersingham on 8th January 1996, consisted of displaced birds from Sandringham. While the vast majority of records come from inland sites, a male was seen on the shore at Old Hunstanton on 3rd January 1990 and a pair were resting on groynes at Yarmouth Harbour entrance, throughout the day, on 29th March 1997. Another unusual record concerned a pair displaying on rooftops in Cromer on 16th April 1995.

Over 30 have been ringed at Pensthorpe, from where an adult male trapped in December 1986 was seen at Grovelands Park, Southgate, Greater London on 16th February 1991 – perhaps a surprising distance for a species generally thought of as fairly sedentary.

*Moss Taylor*

## Wigeon (Eurasian Wigeon) | CLEY. 7·9·1985.    *Anas penelope*

A very common passage migrant and winter visitor; small numbers oversummer and occasionally breeds.

Wigeon
(Nik Borrow)

Wigeon breed throughout the northern parts of the Palearctic region. The British wintering population, which originates from Iceland, Fennoscandia, and central and northern Russia, has shown a marked increase in numbers since the 1960s and comprises nearly half of the estimated north-western European wintering population.

Stevenson noted the Wigeon as an abundant winter visitor arriving towards the end of September and departing by the end of March. Thousands of Wigeon were caught annually at a number of decoys in the region; the figures from Langham showed that three Wigeon were caught for every two Mallard and one Teal, these birds being sent to the London markets. Holkham Lake was also a favoured wintering site at the time and held thousands of birds. Stevenson could find no well-authenticated instances of breeding in the county and this did not occur until 1944 when a pair bred at Hickling and again in 1946 and 1947. This was followed by breeding at Brancaster in 1959 (two nests), and Cley in 1953, 1963 and 1965, although some cases may have involved 'pricked' birds. During fieldwork for the Norfolk Atlas it was recorded in 17 tetrads, with confirmed breeding in four. However, the pairs at South Creake and Shotford Pits were known to have been escapes from collections. While the pair on the Ouse Washes may have been genuinely wild, the status of the pair at Hockwold Fen was unknown (Kelly 1986). More recently two pairs bred at Holkham in 1994, one of these fledging three young, followed by another breeding attempt in 1996 when one brood was seen. In addition a small number of non-breeders oversummer annually. For instance a total of 60 were present in June–July 1997, including 12 at both Welney and Holkham, but with no evidence of breeding at any site.

Wigeon begin to arrive in the county during August when westerly movements occur along the north coast, continuing through to mid-November. At times the Wigeon are mixed in with other wildfowl. Maximum day-counts at any one site are usually in the hundreds, but in 1977 there were 1,300 west at Sheringham on 28th September, and 2,520 west on 19th October and 3,000 west on 6th November both at Scolt Head. A similar passage of southward moving birds is observed off the east coast although usually involving smaller numbers. Hard-weather movements may also occur during the winter months, one of the highest counts being 7,300 west at Sheringham on 30th December 1978. Spring departures occur especially during March although some substantial numbers now linger on the Ouse Washes at Welney, depending upon the suitability of conditions. Late counts here have included 1,517 on 11th April 1994. On clear calm evenings noisy flocks can be seen departing from this site in straggly line-abreast formation high to the north-east.

The species was largely confined to coastal sites early in the 20th century but modern times have seen substantial numbers move inland especially to locations where protected areas exist and land management, such as summer grazing with livestock and the raising of water levels, has created areas of ideal feeding and safe roosting. The Ouse Washes (Cambridgeshire/Norfolk) rarely held more than 5,000 Wigeon prior to the mid-1960s when conservation organisations first started to acquire large blocks of land on the site. However, favourable management regimes resulted in spectacular increases in the numbers of wintering Wigeon, peaking at 53,615 in the 1989–90 winter. The highest modern count in just the Norfolk section of the Ouse Washes was 15,353 in January 1992. Some older published figures have quoted between 20,000–35,000 Wigeon in the Welney area (1973–74, 1976–77) but it is not clear if this also includes birds from within parts of the Cambridgeshire section of washland. Birds wintering on the washes prefer to feed in areas of shallow flooding but will adapt to local conditions as water levels rise, first grazing the high river banks but then making night-time excursions in large numbers on to the adjacent arable fields to graze emerging winter wheat. This may result in large areas within the affected fields appearing bare although most crops seem to recover within a few weeks. Nevertheless, local farmers sometimes resort to deterrents such as flashing lights placed overnight in the worst affected fields in order to prevent further nocturnal feeding forays.

Other favoured Wigeon sites in the county include the Broads ESA first established in 1987 and covering around 400km$^2$ of river valley wetland in Norfolk and Suffolk where the raising of water levels and continuation of summer grazing have greatly benefited wintering wildfowl. Some of the larger concentrations in this area occur at Buckenham/Cantley where there were over 13,000 in 1995 and Berney/Breydon where there were 10,200 in December 1997, although many other sites within Broadland hold smaller gatherings. A similar situation is found at Holkham where the raising of water levels, which commenced in 1986, has resulted in dramatically higher numbers of Wigeon, increasing from a few hundred in the early 1980s to over 11,000 in 1995–96. Raising of the water table has also seen Wigeon numbers rise at Holme Dunes to reach 2,410 in January 1995 at a site not previously important for the species.

**Table 19. Peak winter counts of Wigeon at some main Norfolk sites from 1988–89 to 1997–98.**

|  | 88–89 | 89–90 | 90–91 | 91–92 | 92–93 | 93–94 | 94–95 | 95–96 | 96–97 | 97–98 |
|---|---|---|---|---|---|---|---|---|---|---|
| Welney | 10,980 | 14,285 | 10,683 | 15,353 | 10,160 | 11,635 | 15,146 | 9,782 | 9,275 | 11,118 |
| Wash | 1,431 | 942 | 1,009 | 1,412 | 1,254 | 1.528 | 248 | 836 | 1,394 | 1,273 |
| Holme | 800 | 800 | 1,175 | 1,120 | 1,500 | 1,725 | 2,410 | 2,050 | 2,200 | 1,010 |
| Holkham | 1,500 | 3,000 | 5,810 | 7,700 | 7,020 | 9,185 | 9,210 | 11,000 | 11,000 | 13,030 |
| Cley/ Blakeney | - | - | 6,000 | 6,250 | 4,500 | 2,524 | 7,080 | 6,300 | 6,035 | 2,666 |
| Berney/ Breydon | 1,500 | 1,981 | 1,950 | 3,500 | 3,800 | 5,100 | 4,900 | 4,300 | 7,000 | 10,200 |
| Buckenham/ Cantley | 8,700 | 7,300 | 8,000 | 5,800 | 5,880 | 10,000 | 4,743 | 13,525 | 7,189 | 6,290 |
| Ranworth/ Cockshoot | 162 | 193 | 385 | 290 | 751 | 1,010 | 704 | 485 | 700 | 640 |

The south shore of the Wash between Terrington and Snettisham holds the largest salt-water wintering population of Wigeon in the county. The highest count recorded here was 7,000 in January 1982 and although there are enormous annual fluctuations there has been a general decline in peak counts in recent years possibly reflecting the increased habitat now available elsewhere. Nearby at Ken Hill grazing marsh the raising of the water table and improved livestock grazing has seen regular usage of the area by up to 450 Wigeon by 1997, from almost nil previously.

Over 1,000 Wigeon have been ringed in Norfolk, mainly at Snettisham in the 1970s or at Pensthorpe in the 1980s, where more were being ringed than at any other site in the British Isles. These have resulted in over 150 foreign recoveries. The majority were found between April and October in the species' extensive breeding range from Sweden and Finland, and across central and northern Russia. Over half (89) were found in Russia, including the most easterly ever from the British ringing scheme recovered in June near Khatanga, Krasnoyarsk at 102°E, a distance of 5,456km. Others have been recovered in autumn or winter in The Netherlands and France, while one ringed at Pensthorpe on 1st February 1992 was found in December in Venezia, Italy. An adult male ringed at Snettisham in 1970 was shot in at least its tenth year in Russia (the longevity record for a British-ringed Wigeon is 24 years). A total of 29 foreign-ringed Wigeon has been recovered in Norfolk, the majority having been ringed in autumn or winter in The Netherlands, but two ringed as ducklings in Iceland and one in Russia.

*John B. Kemp*

## American Wigeon

*Anas americana*

**A rare vagrant.**

The American Wigeon is a highly migratory species breeding across much of North America, moving south to winter along both Pacific and Atlantic coasts as well as the Gulf of Mexico, Central America and into Colombia. In recent years it has become an annual visitor in varying numbers to the British Isles.

The first record for Norfolk was of a drake shot on Rush Hills, Hickling on 15th September 1931. It was sent by Jim Vincent to the Castle Museum, Norwich but enquiries and searches there for the specimen in 1990 were unsuccessful. A second drake was found by Bill Oddie and Richard Richardson at Cley on 15th November 1967. Occurrences are marred by the possibility of some being escapees. However, the recovery within the British Isles of a number of birds ringed in North America suggests that most are genuine vagrants. Visits to the county have a bias towards winter and spring when the drakes are in distinctive breeding plumage. The female, however, is difficult to locate and identify amongst flocks of Wigeon, its usual companions. Hence, despite the massive increase in ornithology as a pastime, there is just one record of a female in Norfolk, an individual which was shot in 1988. Hybrids with both Wigeon and Chiloe Wigeon create an identification problem and both have occurred in the county.

There have been 17 records, some possibly involving returning individuals:

1931:  A drake shot at Rush Hills, Hickling on 15th September
1967:  A drake at Cley on 15th November
1969:  An immature drake at Cley on 4th November
1977:  A drake at Welney on 23rd October
1979:  A drake at Breydon on 19th February
1987:  A drake at Welney on 13th March
      A drake at Cley on 22nd June
1988:  A female shot near Holkham on 2nd February
      A drake at Berney Marshes on 23rd–24th May
      A drake at Welney from 10th December to 16th January 1989
1989:  A drake at Welney on 19th December
1990:  A drake at Cley on 14th–18th March
      A drake at Berney Marshes on 10th April
1995:  A drake at Berney Marshes on 15th–16th May
1996:  A first-summer drake at Welney on 22nd–28th April
1997:  A drake at Welney on 24th January
1998:  A drake at Cley and Blakeney from 1st January to 27th March
      A drake at Berney Marshes on 25th November

*John B. Kemp*

## Gadwall   *E.G. HARDLEY FLOODS. 22.2.2000. (♂♀)*

*Anas strepera*

**A fairly common resident, winter visitor and passage migrant.**

The Gadwall breeds both in North America and across Eurasia where it is commoner towards the east of its range. The north-western and north-eastern populations winter in the Mediterranean and Black Seas. The increasing British wintering population, which now exceeds 10,000 birds, primarily inhabits freshwater habitats.

According to Riviere the Gadwall was long known in the county as a winter visitor in small numbers although its occurrence as a breeding species stems from the release of a pinioned pair onto Narford Lake around 1850. This wild pair of Gadwall had originally been caught at Dersingham decoy and by 1875 their descendants were present in flocks of up to 70 birds. The species later spread throughout the south-west of the county, favouring the Breckland meres where it remained common during the winter months. It was initially scarce in the Broads where the first breeding was proven in 1916 on the Yare at Bramerton. Its continuing scarcity throughout the north and east of the county is best shown by the 'bag' records from a number of sites. At Cley in the 1923–24 winter, of 768 ducks shot just four were Gadwall followed by only one out of 493 ducks shot during 1927–28. Just one was found amongst 1,684 ducks killed at Hoveton between 1912 and 1920 and of 7,132 ducks caught or shot at Ranworth/Woodbastwick between 1920 and 1928 only five Gadwall were obtained. During the 1927–28 season, not one Gadwall was found amongst 907 ducks of 11 species shot at Hickling. This contrasts with 140 Gadwall, out of 1,369 ducks shot on the Breckland Merton estate during 49 days shooting between 1913 and 1927.

There were further signs of spread by the early 1930s when a flock of 30 was found in Gunton Park in 1932, followed by 'good numbers' in the winter of 1935 at Hickling, where breeding occurred the next year. By 1958 the species was extending its range throughout the Broads and into the north of the county with a dozen broods found at Raynham Park. Further expansion in range and numbers continued throughout the 1960s with flocks of up to 250 becoming regular in Breckland during the autumn and winter. Especially favoured sites were Narford Lake, Westacre, Mickle Mere, Thompson Water, Stanford Water and Fowl Mere. The largest gathering at the time was 324 on Stanford Water on 15th October 1966. Flocks of Gadwall were also reaching Fenland areas such as the Ouse Washes and Wisbech Sewage Farm but the species remained scarce on the Wash. The Gadwall seems able to exploit deeper waters better than most other dabbling ducks as it feeds by swimming and immersing the head and neck or upending to locate aquatic plants, sometimes indulging in kleptoparasitic behaviour as it robs Coots of waterweeds they have brought to the surface.

The species continued its range expansion throughout the 1970s and 1980s, being found in 112 tetrads during fieldwork for the Norfolk Atlas (1980–85) and an estimated 150–200 pairs were breeding in the county by 1987. Substantial flocks were also being found outside Breckland, particularly in the Broads where some of the largest gatherings included 100 at Horsey in January 1973 and 1984, 196 at Hickling in November 1982, 120 at Martham Broad in November 1989, 210 at Strumpshaw and 147 at Surlingham in December 1989, 198 at How Hill in November 1983 and 106 at Hardley Flood in October 1986. Other areas were also attracting increasing numbers with peaks of 113 at Welney in March 1988, 135 at Hillington in November 1984, 216 at Snettisham in February 1985 and 180 at Titchwell in September 1983. However, Gunton Park in the north-east of the county became by far the most important site regularly holding autumn flocks of between 300–500 and peaking at 680 on 29th September 1979 and 630 in September 1981. The Breckland meres still remained as a major stronghold, especially Stanford Water which held 500 in September 1970 and 400 in both August 1978 and October 1983. Counts at some other waters included 300 at Mickle Mere in October 1972, 90 at Didlington Lake in December 1972, 65 at Fowl Mere in September 1976, 150 at Thompson Water in October 1973 and 105 at Gooderstone in November 1977. Increasing numbers at Narford Lake peaked at 450 in November 1986 and 525 in September 1988.

There has been a redistribution in the non-breeding population during the course of the 1990s with much lower numbers now frequenting the Breckland meres and Gunton Park, compensated for by many more new sites around the county now holding sizeable gatherings. Areas holding over 200 birds for the first time now included Hardley Flood with 373 in September 1992, Welney with 343 in March 1994, Colney Gravel Pit with 209 in December 1995, Wroxham Broad with 210 in January 1996 and Raynham Lake with 246 in September 1997. Only two Breckland waters have exceeded 260 birds since 1990. At least another 15 sites have now had flocks of over 100 Gadwall, ranging over a wide spectrum of habitats including gravel pits, artificial scrapes and lagoons, broads, park lakes and Breckland meres.

**Table 20. Peak winter counts of Gadwall at some regular Norfolk sites from 1988–89 to 1997–98.**

|  | 88–89 | 89–90 | 90–91 | 91–92 | 92–93 | 93–94 | 94–95 | 95–96 | 96–97 | 97–98 |
|---|---|---|---|---|---|---|---|---|---|---|
| Welney | 80 | 149 | 137 | 184 | 172 | 343 | 154 | 122 | 141 | 122 |
| Wash | 60 | 51 | 70 | 48 | 32 | 112 | 48 | 94 | 53 | 70 |
| Stanford | 81 | 118 | 141 | 200 | 255 | 220 | 95 | 142 | - | - |
| Titchwell | - | - | 140 | 46 | 40 | 66 | 28 | 43 | 111 | 36 |
| Holkham | 6 | 32 | 64 | 40 | 55 | 64 | 125 | 56 | 74 | 114 |
| Gunton Park | 461 | 496 | 496 | 450 | 75 | 186 | 67 | 234 | 58 | - |
| Breydon/ Berney | 54 | 68 | 93 | 25 | 58 | 76 | 51 | 46 | 129 | 161 |

The species is now widely distributed as a breeder in suitable habitats around the county with Welney (17 broods in 1992), Holkham Lake (nine broods in 1997), Holkham NNR (16 broods in both 1996 and 1997, although over twice as many pairs present) and Strumpshaw Fen (nine pairs in 1997) being amongst the more favoured areas. There are no recent estimates for the breeding population in the county; the 70 pairs reported from 21 locations in 1995 is clearly well below the true figure. As a passage migrant very few Gadwall are recorded in autumn and even fewer in spring, day-counts reaching double figures are unusual at any of the regularly-watched migration points.

Over 400 Gadwall have been ringed in Norfolk, mostly at Pensthorpe, which have resulted in 21 foreign recoveries of which 18 have been in France between August and February. The most distant was one recovered in Kaliningrad, Russia. Ten foreign-ringed Gadwall have been found in Norfolk – eight adults from The Netherlands, and nestlings from Germany and Czechoslovakia.

*John B. Kemp*

## Teal (Common Teal)   E.G. HARDLEY FLOODS. 1·1·2000.     *Anas crecca*

**A common winter visitor and passage migrant, but a rare breeder.**

Teal breed across all parts of northern Palearctic Europe and Asia, wintering further south in the more temperate regions, as well as into tropical Asia and with smaller numbers in parts of Africa. Birds wintering in the British Isles originate mainly from Fennoscandian, and western and central Russian breeding populations. The species is found in a wide range of coastal and freshwater habitats, at times occupying even tiny patches of wetland.

Teal have always been common visitors to the county, Stevenson mentioned large arrivals in October and November with many being caught in the decoys. The 1834–35 winter saw over 1,000 Teal taken at the Hempstead decoy by January, while in another year at the Winterton decoy 1,010 were caught in six consecutive days. However, it was rather scarce as a breeder with just a few pairs frequenting mainly Breckland and the Broads. Riviere described the Teal as occurring in large numbers as a passage migrant and winter visitor while it had become more abundant as a breeder having previously been scarce at the end of the 19th century. The Teal has once again reverted to the status of 'rare breeder' with successful breeding occurring in just seven of the years between 1988 and 1997, this despite the fact that it was recorded in 101 tetrads during the years 1980–85 for the Norfolk Atlas. Welney, at present the most regular site, recorded five broods in 1992.

Flocks of immigrant Teal travelling westward are a regular feature off the north coast from August onwards. Well-watched sites such as Holme and Sheringham occasionally record impressive movements such as 1,169 off Holme and 890 off Sheringham on 1st September 1994. These passage movements are observed through the autumn and into early winter although later flights may be cold-weather movements. Examples of day-counts have included 545 off Holme on 2nd December 1995 and 410 off Paston on 6th January 1995.

Wintering Teal are found, sometimes in considerable numbers, in a variety of habitats throughout the county including coastal marshes, saltings, inland rivers, lakes, ponds, gravel-pits, beet factory settling ponds, Breckland meres, the Ouse Washes and flooded freshmarsh grazing as found throughout Broadland and the north coast marshes. Substantial numbers depart at the onset of severe weather when favoured water bodies freeze over. Ringing recoveries and an analysis of hard weather movements show that large numbers of Teal move south into western France and Spain. Deep flooding at sites such as the Ouse Washes may also result in mass departures due to the species' inability to feed efficiently in water deeper than 25cm. National wildfowl counts have shown that 40% of Teal wintering in the British Isles occur in flocks of less than 200. Nevertheless many sites within the county regularly attract flocks of between 200–500 Teal, although just six areas have produced peak counts exceeding 1,000 birds in recent years – Welney, Holkham and Cley Marsh/Blakeney, and in the Broads – Heigham Sounds, Horsey and Cantley Beet Factory. Autumn numbers have been very high at Horsey where artificial feeding resulted in 2,000 in November 1995 and 2,100 in November 1996 while Cantley Beet Factory attracted 1,000 in March 1993, 1,300 in November 1995 and 1,000 in November 1996. There were also 1,000 Teal at Heigham Sounds in January 1995, 970 at Hickling in October 1992 and 925 at Berney Marshes in March 1995. Three other sites with notable counts have been Tottenhill Gravel Pit with 500 birds in November 1988,

How Hill with 650 in November 1993 and Buckenham/Cantley with 566 in November 1997, although numbers are typically much lower. The largest gathering of Teal ever recorded in the county was 4,102 at Welney on 29th December 1997 although numbers fell to just 35 birds three weeks later when rising water levels rendered the site unsuitable.

**Table 21. Peak winter counts of Teal at some main Norfolk sites from 1988–89 to 1997–98.**

|  | 88–89 | 89–90 | 90–91 | 91–92 | 92–93 | 93–94 | 94–95 | 95–96 | 96–97 | 97–98 |
|---|---|---|---|---|---|---|---|---|---|---|
| Welney | 2,010 | 2,950 | 1,270 | 1,911 | 1,145 | 1,205 | 2,302 | 1,892 | 1,296 | 4,102 |
| Wash | 266 | 365 | 634 | 298 | 597 | 792 | 480 | 413 | 646 | 611 |
| Holme | - | 380 | 310 | 153 | 211 | 268 | 395 | 240 | 158 | 286 |
| Holkham | 831 | 1,000 | 917 | 1,506 | 979 | 1,279 | 1,621 | 715 | 632 | 786 |
| Titchwell | - | - | 250 | 671 | 277 | 376 | 400 | 217 | 229 | 884 |
| Cley/ Blakeney | - | - | - | 2,000 | 1,500 | 1,250 | 1,616 | 1,558 | 1,543 | 1,400 |
| Berney/ Breydon | 271 | 286 | 200 | 420 | 700 | 750 | 925 | 330 | 500 | 779 |
| Ranworth/ Cockshoot | 196 | 183 | 276 | 165 | 352 | 504 | 440 | 301 | 190 | 313 |

There have been over 20 records of the North American race *A. c. carolinensis* since the first at Cley on 7th–11th April 1964. All have been drakes with the majority in March and April. Apart from two at Cley on 19th–22nd April 1981, all refer to single birds and most have only made short stays. However, one found at Blakeney on 11th February 1990 was relocated at Cley and was seen intermittently until 25th April. Many of the sightings have been at Cley or Welney, and may well have involved the same bird returning in subsequent years.

Over 700 Teal have been ringed in Norfolk, of which 92 have been recovered outside the British Isles and a further 22 in Ireland. Of the foreign recoveries over 40 involved birds on autumn passage in Denmark, Sweden or Finland, while 13 were found during the winter in The Netherlands or France. Nine have been recovered in Russia, but only one during the breeding season and the most easterly concerned one which had flown almost 3,000km to the east after being ringed at Pensthorpe. A total of 54 foreign-ringed Teal has been found in the county, of which 33 were ringed in The Netherlands between August and March, and eight ringed on passage in Denmark. Birds from further east have come from Poland (2) and Czechoslovakia.

*John B. Kemp*

**Mallard** MY GARDEN. 6-3-2000.   *Anas platyrhynchos*

**A common resident, winter visitor and passage migrant.**

The Mallard occurs throughout the Holarctic region, being the most abundant and widespread duck species in Europe. Although mostly migratory, some populations in southern and western Europe are sedentary. The winter population in Britain and Ireland consists of birds from the large native stock, supplemented by an influx of winter visitors from Fennoscandia and Iceland (Winter Atlas).

This, the most familiar and widespread of all ducks in Norfolk, occupies an extensive range of habitats which includes gravel pits, grazing marshes, Broadland and Breckland meres, saltings and tidal estuaries. During fieldwork for the Norfolk Atlas it was recorded in 71% of the tetrads visited. During the early autumn Mallard regularly flight out to feed on stubble fields in the evenings, while harvested potato fields may be visited later in the season. It readily mixes with domesticated varieties on village ponds and in parks where its sexual activities may produce a bewildering selection of colour schemes. One of the more familiar variants is predominantly blackish with a conspicuous white patch on the breast.

During the age of the commercial decoy large numbers of Mallard were caught annually and sent to the London markets. However, the increasing popularity of shooting coupled with competition from imported, Dutch-taken fowl resulted in the closure of many of the 30 known decoys in Norfolk, only five of which remained active by 1890. Riviere gave details from the Ranworth and Woodbastwick decoy for the winters from 1920–21 to 1928–29 when the annual Mallard catch ranged between 381 and 1,737 birds. The Hickling shoot also accounted for a large number of Mallard between 1920–35 when the annual 'bag' varied between 69 and 1,418 birds. Also at Hickling, an estimated 10,000 Mallard (the largest number ever recorded there) were present between Turner's Island and Swim Coots on 15th February 1947, during the spell of exceptionally hard weather, and they were occasionally disturbed by the ice-skaters on the frozen Broad. The Dersingham decoy, which operated between 1818 and 1870, was partly restored in 1968 and used to catch wildfowl for ringing purposes. Figures for this period show catches of Mallard reaching 888 in 1968 and 993 in 1969.

At present only two sites in the county, Welney and the Norfolk section of the Wash, regularly host gatherings in excess of 1,000 birds. Numbers at both localities have fallen in recent years in line with a general decline throughout Britain since the late 1980s and early 1990s.

**Table 22. Peak winter counts of Mallard at Welney and the Norfolk section of the Wash.**

|  | 88–89 | 89–90 | 90–91 | 91–92 | 92–93 | 93–94 | 94–95 | 95–96 | 96–97 | 97–98 |
|---|---|---|---|---|---|---|---|---|---|---|
| Welney | 1,630 | 2,862 | 2,022 | 2,161 | 2,534 | 1,849 | 1,814 | 1,911 | 1,206 | 1,153 |
| Wash | 1,604 | 1,697 | 1,297 | 1,745 | 632 | 1,752 | 1,159 | 953 | 1,273 | 1,321 |

Many other areas occasionally hold smaller flocks in the region of 200–400 birds, but larger counts are infrequent. A selection of peak counts in recent years have included:

1993:  213 at Blickling in January, 244 at Pensthorpe and 279 at Thetford Nunnery Lakes in February

1994:  506 at Cley/Blakeney and 512 at Berney Marshes/Breydon in January and 270 at Stanford Water in December

1995:  295 at Titchwell in August, 200 at Sparham Pools in November and 340 at Holme and 658 at Ranworth/Cockshoot in December

1996:  445 at Holkham Park, 454 at Sennowe Park and 310 at Lynford Gravel Pit in January, 400 at Raynham Lake in July and 235 at King's Lynn Docks in December

1997:  558 at Buckenham/Cantley and 800 at Horsey Mere in January, and 408 at Scolt Head/Brancaster, 362 at Holkham NNR and 334 at Hickling Broad in November

Considering the numbers present in the county in winter, surprisingly few are seen arriving in autumn. The passage peaks in October and November with maximum counts in recent years, all of birds flying west at Sheringham, of 160 on 21st November 1975, 135 on 3rd November 1990 and 140 on 15th October 1993.

Several thousand Mallard have been ringed in Norfolk, mainly around the Wash and at Pensthorpe. Of these, almost 1,200 have been recovered, including 370 outside the British Isles. Most of the recoveries have been between August and February with the highest number of birds being recovered in France (22), The Netherlands (55), Germany (41), Denmark (85), Sweden (64), Finland (37) and Russia (29). One of the most distant was one ringed at Welney in March 1984 and found at Tyumen, in western Siberia in September 1989, a distance of almost 4,000km and at a locality beyond the Ural Mountains. A total of 112 foreign-ringed birds has been found in Norfolk, including Mallard from Belgium (26), Denmark (36) and Sweden (17), some of which were marked as ducklings.

*John B. Kemp*

## Pintail (Northern Pintail)  OFF CLEY-ON THE SEA. 26·11·1988.  *Anas acuta*

**A common winter visitor and a fairly common passage migrant; a very rare breeder.**

The Pintail is a highly migratory species breeding throughout the northern parts of Eurasia and North America. The main wintering sites for the European population are in the British Isles, The Netherlands, Belgium and France, although cold weather forces the birds south to the Mediterranean. Ringing recoveries suggest that the majority of birds wintering in the British Isles originate from western Siberia although others also arrive from Iceland, Fennoscandia and other western European countries.

Pintails
(Nik Borrow)

The early accounts of status in the county are conflicting, possibly suggesting annual fluctuations in numbers. Rather surprisingly, Stevenson described the Pintail as 'sparingly met with in most years from October to March' adding that it 'is at no times numerous in Norfolk'. However, it was not uncommon on the marshes at Blakeney 30 years earlier according to the Revd. E. W. Dowell. Others such as the Pagets (1834) described it as not uncommon at Yarmouth, while Gurney and Fisher (1846) said it was not uncommon in early autumn, winter and spring. Riviere stated that although the Pintail had been scarce it was undoubtedly on the increase, especially since the hard winter of 1923–24 when between 20–30 birds were reported to him. This was followed in 1929 by the first authenticated breeding record for England when two pairs bred in Breckland at Roudham Heath. Later breeding took place in east Norfolk at Breydon for the first time in 1949. Further largely unsuccessful breeding attempts were made at Breydon between 1950 and 1953, and from 1956 to 1958. One or two pairs also bred at Cley between 1958 and 1960. The Pintail remains a very rare breeder, and despite instances of pairs lingering well into the spring and occasional birds into the summer, the only proven cases of breeding in recent years have been from Welney in 1977 when two broods were seen, one record of confirmed breeding at the Ouse Washes during the Norfolk Atlas and at Cley in 1993 when two young were seen.

One of the main wintering sites for Pintail is on the Ouse Washes. About 9km of this 35km-long flood plain lies within Norfolk. Here, numbers of wintering Pintail began to increase noticeably in the early 1940s. Later counts included 2,150 in March 1954, 3,000 in March 1961 and 2,000 in January 1974 although there were marked annual variations in numbers. Many of these wintering Pintail visited the surrounding farmland, often in the company of Mallard, to feed on stubble and waste left behind after the sugar beet and potato harvests. When feeding on the flooded washlands, seeds, especially those of the common spike-rush *Eleocharis palustris* make up 80% of the diet. In more recent years there has been a distinct October peak at Welney, numbers later dropping off to leave a smaller wintering population although a secondary mid-winter peak sometimes also occurs. These October birds appear to feed on the coast, probably the Wash, and use Welney as a roosting site as they arrive high from the north each day, often all appearing within a few minutes. The timing of these daily visits varies and appears to be influenced by the tides. This autumn passage is in decline at present with a peak of 436 in October 1997 compared to a high of 1,969 in October 1991. Although some Pintail still flight to the arable land to feed, this habit is not as prevalent as it was 30 years ago.

One of the other major Pintail wintering sites is on the intertidal zone on the shore of the Wash between Terrington and Snettisham, with a peak count of 5,453 in January 1988, although numbers here have tumbled in recent years in common with several other British sites. These birds tend to feed at the water's edge on the incoming and outgoing tides when their main diet comprises small snails of the genus *Hydrobia*. The only areas attracting large numbers of Pintail along the north coast are Cley Marsh and Blakeney Harbour, where there is much movement between sites, the birds increasing here during the 1970s to peak at 400–500 in February 1977, 1,000 in January-February 1982 and 1985, 915 in December 1994 and 1,519 in December 1997. Relatively few are found at Holkham where the largest counts were 50 in February 1995 and 69 in January 1996. Counts of 120–184 between December 1996 and February 1997 at Brancaster/Scolt Head were well above average for the site. The only other intertidal/coastal site with a long history of regular flocks of wintering Pintail is Breydon where counts reached 173 birds as long ago as March 1954. Numbers here have fluctuated between 104 and 286 birds during the period 1973–97, peak numbers usually being present in January or February.

Two inland waters in west Norfolk have attracted large flocks of Pintail in recent years, although the birds appear to be using both sites for loafing or roosting rather than feeding, for which they are probably unsuitable. It is highly likely that these Pintail flocks are flighting to the coast to feed on the Wash. Narford Lake, which is largely surrounded by woodland, attracted autumn gatherings of Pintail from 1984 when 54 were counted in September, followed by 90 in November 1986, 174 in October 1987, 866 in September 1988 and 300 in September 1989. No further details are available from this private water. The other site, Tottenhill Gravel Pit, held 70 birds in November 1988 increasing to 570 in October of the following year and peaking at 735 in January 1997; large gatherings may appear here both in autumn and winter.

**Table 23. Peak winter counts of Pintail at some main Norfolk sites from 1988–89 to 1997–98.**

|  | 88–89 | 89–90 | 90–91 | 91–92 | 92–93 | 93–94 | 94–95 | 95–96 | 96–97 | 97–98 |
|---|---|---|---|---|---|---|---|---|---|---|
| Welney | 1,200 | 932 | 1,780 | 1,969 | 1,765 | 866 | 642 | 1,092 | 502 | 1,728 |
| Wash | 5,440 | 2,125 | 1,671 | 269 | 221 | 248 | 122 | 153 | 49 | 28 |
| Cley/ Blakeney | 510 | 974 | 410 | 700 | 400 | 840 | 915 | 898 | 740 | 1,519 |
| Breydon | 163 | 113 | 170 | 171 | 161 | 218 | 203 | 172 | 227 | 192 |
| Tottenhill GP | 70 | 570 | 530 | 500 | 600 | 350 | 371 | 670 | 735 | 500 |

Small flocks of migrating Pintail are regularly seen flying westwards along the north coast during the autumn. Some of the larger movements in recent years have been 400 off Blakeney Point on 10th October 1991, 185 off Holme on 28th September 1993, 350 off Sheringham on 20th September 1994 and 305 off Holme on 16th September 1995, while there was a westerly cold-weather movement of 205 off Paston on 6th January 1995. In spring, most birds have departed by mid-April.

Over 100 Pintail have been ringed in Norfolk, from which there have been eight foreign recoveries – three each from France and Russia, and two from Finland. One of the Russian recoveries was of a bird from western Siberia in mid-May. A total of 13 foreign-ringed Pintail have been found in Norfolk, nine from The Netherlands and singles from Denmark, Sweden, Estonia and Russia. The bird from Estonia was ringed as a nestling and that from Russia was ringed in August on Velikii Island in the White Sea. Others have been ringed at Abberton Reservoir, Essex and Slimbridge, Gloucestershire, including one shot at North Wootton four days after being ringed at Slimbridge.

*John B. Kemp*

## Garganey                                                    *Anas querquedula*

**A very scarce summer visitor and scarce passage migrant.**

The Garganey breeds throughout Eurasia as far east as Kamchatka although always south of the Arctic Circle. Apart from small flocks wintering in the Mediterranean area, most European birds winter in sub-Saharan Africa. The British Isles is at the extreme western edge of its range with a maximum of 100 pairs breeding in a good year.

In Stevenson's day the Garganey was regarded as widely, though sparingly, distributed in the county, while earlier in the 19th century it had not been fully appreciated that it was a summer visitor. Riviere (1930) stated that although it appeared to have been fairly abundant 50 years earlier it was now a scarce and very local summer visitor, although he did notice increased numbers during 1928 and 1929 when eight pairs bred at Hickling (following an arrival of over 50 there on 26th March 1928), four or five pairs at Ranworth and one pair at Cley, apparently for the first time. Nests were also found at Holme and Burnham Overy in the latter year.

**Table 24. Annual numbers of Garganey shot at Hickling and caught at the Ranworth and Woodbastwick decoy 1926–35.**

|  | 1926 | 1927 | 1928 | 1929 | 1930 | 1931 | 1932 | 1933 | 1934 | 1935 |
|---|---|---|---|---|---|---|---|---|---|---|
| Hickling | 22 | 138 | 121 | 81 | 56 | 58 | 51 | 119 | 29 | 42 |
| Ranworth & Woodbastwick | 1 | 15 | 52 | 66 | 70 | 48 | 142 | - | 40 | 47 |

Hickling remained the breeding stronghold for the species with 12 pairs in 1949 and 1950 although declining to about six pairs later, with mainly single pairs at a further nine Broadland sites.

Since the 1970s the species has shown further declines with proven breeding, as opposed to 'pairs present' being reported in only 16 years between 1975 and 1997, and mostly concerning just one or two instances a year. The centre of breeding has swung away from Broadland and now includes Cley and Welney. Nevertheless a small number of pairs are present at a few other potentially suitable breeding sites each year with the likelihood that at least some result in successful breeding. Despite few cases of proven breeding, the species has been seen more frequently in recent years at many sites around the county, no doubt benefiting from the more sympathetic management regimes and raised water levels now found on many grazing marshes. Small numbers, between one and six birds, are encountered each year at a number of favourite localities – Welney, Titchwell, Holkham, Cley, Hickling and Berney Marshes especially during the main migration periods April–May and August–September.

Spring arrivals normally appear during March although first dates have varied between 24th February and 5th April in the years 1980–98 with the average arrival date being 13th March. Most Garganey have left the county by the end of September with a few stragglers in October and, rarely, into November. Winter records are exceptional and have involved one shot at Martham on 9th December 1915, one shot at Ranworth on 12th December 1930, three shot at Hickling in January 1940 and one present at Welney from 17th November to 7th December 1997.

Sizeable gatherings of Garganey are an event of the past, the largest flock recorded being 50 at Hickling in August 1936; nowadays a flock of ten is rare. The largest counts in recent years have both been at Welney with 16 on 30th July 1992 (after a successful breeding season) and in July 1998 with up to seven regularly throughout the month peaking at 19 on 26th with 18 still present on 29th, suggesting local breeding.

Very few Garganey have been ringed in Norfolk but a male ringed at Dersingham decoy on 3rd September 1967 was found at Sultanky, Ipsala, Turkey on 27th March 1969, only the second British-ringed Garganey to be recovered in that country, although the species is known to migrate through south-eastern Europe and the Middle East. One ringed on Friesland, The Netherlands in August 1947 was recovered at Buxton in November, and another also ringed on Friesland in mid-August 1958 was shot at Burnham Overy in early September; while two other August-ringed birds from Abberton, Essex and Frodsham, Cheshire were found in Norfolk the month after ringing.

*John B. Kemp*

# Blue-winged Teal                                     *Anas discors*

**A rare vagrant.**

The Blue-winged Teal is a highly migratory species breeding across much of North America, wintering from the southern USA down into South America. In recent years it has been recorded annually in small numbers in the British Isles.

The first record for Norfolk was one found by Chris Goate at Hardley Flood on 12th December 1971. Escapes from captivity potentially confuse status but there are a number of ringing recoveries from within the British Isles confirming its position as a genuine vagrant. Occurrences have tended to peak during the spring and especially autumn passage periods, suggesting most records are valid. Vagrant Blue-winged Teal often seek the company of Shoveler and have been known to form mixed pairs. A drake Shoveler x Blue-winged Teal hybrid was at Welney in November 1986.

A total of 14 individuals has been recorded, all single birds apart from two together at Wisbech Sewage Farm in 1978:

> 1971: A drake at Hardley Flood from 12th December to 12th March 1972
> 1972: Presumed same drake at Hardley Flood on 5th–26th November 1972
> 1975: Female shot at Hickling on 27th September
> 1978: A drake at Welney on 5th–12th March
>        An eclipse drake at Cantley from 6th August to 4th October, also visiting

Hardley Flood between 14th August and 27th September

Two eclipse drakes at Wisbech Sewage Farm from 11th September to 8th October

1984: A drake at Titchwell on 11th–15th June 1984

An eclipse drake at Welney from 30th September to 5th October

1986: An eclipse or immature female at Welney on 5th–9th November

1987: An eclipse drake at Cley on 16th–19th September and again on 10th–13th October (Kightley 1987)

1990: A drake at Cley from 22nd June to 12th July, presumed same at Titchwell on 20th–30th August and from 20th September to 4th October

1994: A female at Cley on 12th May

1996: An eclipse or immature female at Welney on 28th October

1997: A drake at Stiffkey Fen on 22nd–23rd December

*John B. Kemp*

## Shoveler (Northern Shoveler)  HARDLEY FLOODS. 9·4·2000. (♂) *Anas clypeata*

**A fairly common passage migrant and winter visitor, a scarce breeding summer visitor.**

The Shoveler breeds across the whole of the northern hemisphere, except for Arctic regions, moving south in winter to more temperate areas. British-breeding Shoveler depart in the autumn for France and Spain to be replaced by immigrants from as far afield as western Siberia.

It is clear from the accounts by Stevenson and Riviere that the Shoveler was at times an abundant breeder in the Broads, Breckland meres and parts of the north coast during the 19th and early 20th centuries, with a surprising number occasionally being taken in the decoys from the late 1920s to early 1930s.

**Table 25. Annual numbers of Shoveler shot at Hickling and caught at Ranworth and Woodbastwick decoy 1927–35.**

|  | 1927 | 1928 | 1929 | 1930 | 1931 | 1932 | 1933 | 1934 | 1935 |
|---|---|---|---|---|---|---|---|---|---|
| Hickling | 25 | 21 | 18 | 10 | 24 | 42 | 44 | 39 | 58 |
| Ranworth & Woodbastwick | 5 | 197 | 152 | 156 | 144 | 111 | - | 26 | 25 |

During present times there is still a bias towards these areas though fewer now nest on the Breckland meres, while the Ouse Washes has become an important breeding area. During fieldwork for the Norfolk Atlas it was found in 104 tetrads (7%). Numbers of breeding pairs show marked annual variations, those on the Ouse Washes at Welney fluctuating in relation to springtime water levels. For example, from 1992 to 1997 the annual number of potential breeders at Welney varied between 12 and 37 pairs. Other strongholds, such as Holkham (where the habitat has improved since 1986) and Strumpshaw had 35 and 21 pairs, respectively, in 1996, while in 1993 ten broods were seen at Cley and five at Titchwell. The county's breeding population does not exceed 100 pairs.

A large proportion of the sites holding sizeable non-breeding flocks of Shoveler are in the ownership of conservation bodies and include areas such as Welney, Titchwell, Holkham, Cley Marsh, Ranworth Broad, Hickling Broad, Strumpshaw Fen and Berney. A variety of other habitats also attracts smaller flocks and includes gravel-pits and Breckland meres, as well as semi-tidal areas such as Hardley Flood. Since 1980 there have been 15 sites recording gatherings of over 100 Shoveler, though just nine of these sites have ever exceeded 200 birds. The largest concentrations recorded in the county were 1,500 on the Ouse Washes near Welney in January 1975, although it is not clear if all were within the county boundary, while a remarkable 1,280 were counted at Narford Lake in October 1988. The Shoveler is very susceptible to severe weather and flocks seeking open water may form sizeable temporary gatherings wherever conditions are suitable. Harsh weather in the winter of 1996–97 resulted in flocks of 295 at Rollesby Broad in December and 250 at Filby Broad in January, both figures well above normal for theses sites.

**Table 26. Peak winter counts of Shoveler at some regular Norfolk sites from 1988–89 to 1997–98.**

|           | 88–89 | 89–90 | 90–91 | 91–92 | 92–93 | 93–94 | 94–95 | 95–96 | 96–97 | 97–98 |
|-----------|-------|-------|-------|-------|-------|-------|-------|-------|-------|-------|
| Welney    | 157   | 201   | 260   | 209   | 257   | 621   | 536   | 240   | 181   | 309   |
| Holkham   | 21    | 35    | 75    | 64    | 84    | 99    | 129   | 97    | 111   | 32    |
| Berney/   |       |       |       |       |       |       |       |       |       |       |
| Breydon   | 120   | 163   | 136   | 216   | 120   | 120   | 213   | 46    | 172   | 183   |

The Shoveler does not feature strongly in the westerly movements of wildfowl along the north coast during the autumn; therefore a passage of 77 off Holme on 2nd September 1995 was noteworthy.

Over 100 Shoveler have been ringed in Norfolk, of which five have been recovered abroad – three in France and singles in The Netherlands and Finland, from where only three British-ringed Shoveler have been recovered. A total of 14 foreign-ringed Shoveler has been found in Norfolk, including ducklings ringed in Belgium, The Netherlands (2), Sweden, Finland and at Lake Engure, Latvia (3). Another duckling ringed at Lanker See, Germany and recovered at Wiveton in 1991, was the first German-ringed Shoveler to be found in the British Isles.

*John B. Kemp*

Gadwall & Shovelers
(Nik Borrow)

**Red-crested Pochard**   MERTON HALL, WATTON. 23·3·1976. ♂   PENSTHORPE. 29·11·1992 ♂   *Netta rufina*

**A rare vagrant; increasing numbers of records in recent years most probably relate to feral or escaped birds.**

The Red-crested Pochard is primarily an Asiatic species, and has its stronghold around the Caspian and Aral Seas, with a further scattered population extending westwards throughout most of Europe. It is a migratory duck, with European birds wintering mainly throughout the Mediterranean basin and Black Sea. The north-western European population is, however, very small. In The Netherlands, about 60 breeding pairs in the 1970s had declined to only ten pairs by 1990, while at the same time in Denmark only five wild pairs and three feral pairs were nesting (Harrop 1991).

The first British example was a female taken on Breydon in July 1818. Further early dated county records were two killed on Breydon in the winter of 1826, a drake shot at Surlingham in December 1827, one shot at Horsey on 12th January 1844, a drake obtained at Yarmouth on 8th July 1859 and a female shot at Hickling in December 1867. During a heatwave in 1906 a flock of 13 arrived on Breydon from the direction of the sea on 4th September, of which nine were promptly shot the same day. Presumably it was the four survivors which were later seen at Hickling Broad on 8th September, a pair of which were also shot, the remaining two staying until 12th September. Another drake was shot at Potter Heigham on 23rd October the same autumn. Further drakes were shot on Breydon on 20th December 1925, and at Rockland Broad on 6th February 1929 (Stevenson, Riviere, Allard 1990).

None was recorded in the county between then and March 1954 when possibly the same drake was at Blickling, Hickling Broad and Rockland Broad until May, followed by a drake at Bayfield, Brinton and Kelling Hall Lakes in winter 1959-60, until it was shot near Holt on 26th January 1960. Another was also shot at Hickling on 23rd January 1960. Annual records of 1-2 followed in the periods 1964-66, 1972-74,

1978, and throughout the 1980s, from a wide scattering of localities. Records have become frequent in the 1990s, with highest counts of 17 at Oulton and 13 at Melton Constable both in November 1993, up to ten at Sennowe Park in 1994 and 1995, and up to nine at Felbrigg from October to December 1995. Most records are in the spring, autumn and particularly winter, with very few mid-summer observations.

There is a noticeable late autumn moult migration on the Continent, with a few small gatherings in The Netherlands and larger concentrations in north-west Germany and Switzerland, with birds coming from as far afield as the Camargue and the Black Sea. (Gooders & Boyer 1986, Harrop 1991, BWP). It is from these sources that some autumn records must no doubt derive. However, Red-crested Pochard are widely kept in captivity and breed freely. Many full-winged young escape on a regular basis each autumn, confusing any natural pattern of migration or colonisation. Indeed many of these birds breed ferally in Britain, and within the county there is a large and successful colony at Pensthorpe, with an estimated free-flying feral population of 40 birds in 1998. This no doubt is the origin of birds now seen regularly at Sennowe Park and other nearby localities. Birds are known to have escaped from a collection at Great Fransham from at least 1954 and many recent records are of known escapes, obviously tame, or even pinioned birds. It is estimated that there are currently about ten times as many pairs in captivity in Britain as there are wild pairs in The Netherlands and Denmark, and that the captive and feral British population probably exceeds the total wild populations in The Netherlands, Denmark and northern Germany (Harrop 1991). Although some birds recorded in the county over the last 40 years may be from the nearby small Danish and Dutch populations, or even from further afield, it would be futile to try to make any attempt to separate genuine immigrants.

Two ringed at Pensthorpe have been recovered – one was shot at Burnham Norton Marshes and the other was found dead at Elveden, Suffolk.

*Phil Heath*

## Pochard (Common Pochard) E.G. HARDLEY FLOODS. 1·1·2000. *Aythya ferina*

**A scarce breeding resident, common winter visitor and scarce passage migrant.**

The Pochard breeds widely across central Eurasia with wintering grounds stretching from the west of Africa through to Japan. Pochards wintering in Britain originate from central Europe and from as far east as central Russia.

Both Stevenson and Riviere mentioned large numbers of wintering Pochards in the county, the former referring to 'immense flocks' resting during the day at Rollesby decoy, while Hickling Broad was also a 'great resort'. Unfortunately there is no indication of the numbers involved, while records of catches from the decoys do not represent its true status due to it being very difficult to successfully lure into the pipes. It was recorded as breeding in the county at Scoulton Mere in 1815 and Stanford in 1836 followed by breeding at a number of Breckland sites in later years. Odd pairs nested at Cley in 1923, 1924 and probably 1929, at Hickling between 1928 and 1940, and Hoveton Great Broad in 1944, 1945 and 1954. Up to four pairs bred in the Yare Valley from 1956 with two nests at Cantley in 1966. Further increases saw 31 broods in Breckland in 1969 and 17 broods elsewhere in 1975 including the Fens at Welney.

More recently, since the early 1980s, breeding has been recorded from many more Broadland sites including a remarkable 49 pairs on the Flegg Broads (Filby, Rollesby, Lady and Ormesby) in 1984 and 16 pairs at Ranworth in 1997. The raising of water levels on Holkham Fresh Marsh attracted two breeding pairs in 1988; this site is now the most important along the north coast with 15 broods seen in 1996 and 19 in 1997. Nearby at Holkham Lake, one or two pairs first bred in 1984 and 1985. Curiously, unlike the Tufted Duck, Pochard have been slow to colonise and breed regularly on flooded gravel pit complexes. One notable exception is Pensthorpe where 10-13 pairs were present in 1993. It remains a rare breeder in the Fens. An incomplete breeding survey conducted in 1994 located 65-68 broods with a similar figure of 60 broods from nine localities in 1996. The breeding population in the county is probably approaching 100 pairs.

The major wintering site is on the Ouse Washes at Welney where internationally important numbers gathered for the first time during January 1998. Here, a proportion of the birds partake in daily artificial feeds of corn and waste potatoes. The majority of the Pochards use the site as a secure daytime roost and flight out to feed each evening; where to is not known. There is a marked imbalance in the proportion of the sexes present. Recent mid-winter counts have shown the male:female ratio to vary from 8:1 to 11:1. It is believed that most females winter further south in Europe. First autumn arrivals may appear in late September, gathering pace through October to December and invariably peaking in January or February. In contrast to most other wildfowl, the largest numbers are present during deep flood conditions. During the 1996-97 winter, severe weather conditions with extensive icing disrupted the normal influx. Large numbers of Pochard temporarily deserted the washes and moved onto areas of unfrozen water at Wissington Beet Factory where counts reached 768 on 5th January. The main departure is generally in March, relatively few remaining into April.

**Table 27. Peak winter counts of Pochards at Welney from 1988-89 to 1997-98.**

| 88/89 | 89/90 | 90/91 | 91/92 | 92/93 | 93/94 | 94/95 | 95/96 | 96/97 | 97/98 |
|-------|-------|-------|-------|-------|-------|-------|-------|-------|-------|
| 1108 | 1907 | 1240 | 1442 | 2272 | 1960 | 2009 | 2188 | 1404 | 4758 |

Numerous sites, especially gravel-pits or areas within Broadland, have occasionally attracted flocks of between 100-200 birds. Larger gatherings are infrequent and are often the result of severe weather; such flocks tend to disperse again once conditions improve. Notable concentrations have included 425 at Pentney Gravel Pits in January 1989, 310 at Stowbridge in March 1991, 240 at Barton Broad in January 1994 and 480 at Ranworth Broad in December 1995. The early part of 1996 saw flocks of 500 at Earsham Gravel Pit and 548 at Wroxham Broad during January, 314 at Tottenhill Gravel Pit in February and 332 in King's Lynn Docks in March.

Pochards are occasionally observed migrating westwards off the north coast in autumn and early winter. Numbers tend to be mostly small, the highest recorded counts referring to 130 west at Sheringham on 21st October 1994, 60 off Holme on 10th December 1995 and 73 west at Holme on 12th January 1997. Apart from migrants, Pochards are only rarely encountered on salt water, and then usually only during severe weather when forced to leave ice-bound inland habitats.

Over 500 Pochards have been ringed in Norfolk, the majority at Pensthorpe. These have produced 35 foreign recoveries, including birds found on passage or in winter in France (10) and in Russia (13). Most of the Russian recoveries were in April-May or August-October, in north-western Russia, with the most easterly reaching the Urals, at 61°E. Other birds have been recovered in winter in Alicante, Spain and on the Danube Delta in Romania. A total of 14 foreign-ringed Pochards has been found in Norfolk from the Baltic States (8), Russia (2), Denmark (3) and Switzerland. All seven recoveries from Latvia involved birds ringed as ducklings at Lake Engure. There have been many recoveries in the county of birds ringed elsewhere in England, the most rapid movement being one ringed at Slimbridge, Gloucestershire on 26th January 1980 and found at Rockland Broad ten days later.

*John B. Kemp*

# Canvasback                                    *Aythya valisineria*

**A very rare vagrant; one record.**

The Canvasback is a North American duck with a breeding range extending from central Alaska southwards to north-eastern California and Nebraska, and east to Minnesota. It winters from British Columbia and the Great Lakes region southwards along both coasts to central Mexico. It is a very rare vagrant to the British Isles with a single record involving a drake returning in two successive winters, although the BOURC is currently examining a record from Kent in 1996.

A first-winter drake Canvasback was discovered amongst Pochards by Carl Donner on pools at Wissington Beet Factory on 18th January 1997. This was the first British and second Western Palearctic record. It was then relocated by John Kemp at Welney on 21st January and thereafter commuted regularly with Pochards between Welney and Wissington until 28th January, although at times it could not be found at either site. It then became more erratic and elusive but appeared again at Welney on 1st, 6th and 22nd February and finally on 7th-10th March. Throughout its stay it closely associated with Pochards, its closest congener on this side of the Atlantic. Its arrival at Welney attracted well over 4,000 visitors during its stay. At first the Canvasback was very shy, flying off when grain was fed each day to the Pochard flock. However, by the end of its stay it became partly adjusted to the feeding regime and simply swam off to the further reaches of the lagoon, at no time attempting to join the hundreds of Pochards at the feed (Kemp 1997b, Millington 1997a).

What was considered to be the same individual, now in adult plumage, appeared at Abberton Reservoir, Essex on 23rd-30th November 1997. It returned to Welney on 3rd December 1997 but was not seen again until 8th and was then present most days in company with up to 4,000 Pochards on the deep floods in front of the observatory, until 29th December after which it was present daily until 22nd February 1998, with a final visit on 9th March. It initially remained shy but by late January it came close to the main hide at feeding times (Kemp 1998).

*Peter Allard*

# Ring-necked Duck            *Aythya collaris*

**A rare vagrant.**

The Ring-necked Duck breeds in Canada and many of the northern States of North America. It winters in coastal lowlands and southwards through Mexico to Guatemala and the West Indies. In recent decades it has been increasing in numbers and extending its breeding range eastwards. Since 1955 there have been regular records in Britain, Europe and North Africa, no doubt linked to the species' population and range expansion and its southerly winter migration. Nationally there is an autumn peak to arrivals with the majority remaining to overwinter. There is another peak of records in April-May suggestive of overwintering birds undertaking a northerly spring passage. Some birds winter at chosen localities for several years running.

The first Norfolk, and third British record, was a drake found by Colin Kirtland which visited Stanford Water and Tottington West Mere in the Stanford Training Area between 1st and 22nd April 1962. The second county record was of a drake frequenting Hardley from 23rd April to 2nd June 1969. This bird returned to the same area from 15th March to 5th June 1970, and presumably again in 1971 from 13th March to 25th April. A further ten individuals have since been recorded as follows:

1978: A drake at Ranworth Broad on 9th March.
1979: A drake at Bayfield Hall Lake on 26th December.
1980: A drake at Breydon on 27th May.
1987: A drake at Hardley Flood on 2nd–29th May.
1991: A drake first seen during freezing conditions on an area of open water on the River Bure by the Acle Way Bridge on 10th February, was refound at Ranworth Broad on 16th, Wroxham Broad on 17th–25th and Belaugh Broad on 26th February. The same bird returned to the upper Bure Valley for a second winter, being recorded at Ranworth Broad on 17th December and Wroxham Broad on 24th December. It remained in the upper Bure Valley until 9th April 1992, being seen variously at Ranworth, Salhouse and Wroxham Broads.
1992: The same drake reappeared for its third winter at Ranworth Broad on 31st December. At the start of the New Year it put in appearances at Wroxham Broad on 8th–9th, 23rd–24th and 29th January, and on 14th February 1993. Then what was presumably the same drake was seen erratically at Strumpshaw Fen between 3rd and 26th March, returning to Wroxham Broad briefly on 21st March.
1993: Another drake, the eighth individual for Norfolk, was at Welney on 13th and 16th April, and probably the same bird was at Titchwell on 25th April. The regular drake returned to Wroxham Broad for the fourth successive winter on the early date of 1st December, with further sporadic sightings on 28th (on which date it was also seen at Hoveton Great Broad), 31st December and 1st January 1994, and then on 4th, 6th, 15th and 21st–23rd February.
1994: A drake was seen on the River Bure east of Horning at St Benet's on 18th and 20th–21st April. What was presumed to be a different drake was at Hockwold Flood on 24th–25th March. The usual drake returned to the upper Bure for a fifth winter, putting in a Christmas Day appearance at Wroxham Broad. It was seen at Wroxham Broad on 2nd–8th January 1995, but failed to return the following winter.

1996:  Two, a female and an immature drake, were at Welney on 27th-28th October, the
       immature drake remaining until 29th.
1997:  An immature drake was at Pentney Gravel Pits on 19th October.

A bird showing the characteristics of a first-winter drake Ring-necked x Tufted Duck hybrid was present at Wroxham Broad on 20th-22nd February 1994, possibly the result of the drake Ring-necked Duck, which had frequented this area for a number of winters, breeding in northern Europe with a female Tufted Duck which had also wintered at Wroxham (Bowman 1994).

*Phil Heath*

## Ferruginous Duck                                          *Aythya nyroca*

**A rare visitor, or escape from captivity.**

Often known in the past as the White-eyed Pochard, the Ferruginous Duck is a species with a principally eastern European and Asiatic distribution. It formerly bred in small numbers in most Mediterranean countries, but has disappeared from North Africa and Italy, with only a handful of pairs remaining in Spain, France and Greece. Most European birds winter in North Africa, while a few cross the Sahara to central Africa. It is a very scarce vagrant to western Europe and the British Isles, with birds assumed to come from the eastern population, either as they depart the breeding grounds in September and early October, or when displaced in the winter by severe weather conditions.

The first known Norfolk record would seem to be one illustrated in May 1805 by Sowerby, from a specimen sent from Yarmouth (Sowerby 1804-06). Stevenson recorded over 20 further instances of Ferruginous Ducks being shot or caught in decoys in the county up to 1890. Riviere stated that about a further 40 had been obtained or seen up to 1929, although apart from a 1903 influx he does not detail them. He was unaware of five drakes at Hickling seen by Jim Vincent on 18th October 1920. Since then an additional 32 individuals have been identified up to and including 1998, giving a county total of about 95 records.

Stevenson regarded it as a 'rare and uncertain visitant' to the county and its status has changed little since then. Records are far from annual, although up to four have been recorded in some winters. A major exception to this was the remarkable influx of 20 on 15th April 1903, when a flock of ten drakes was recorded on Hickling Broad, most of which were shot, with an additional ten birds on Rollesby Broad. As with many duck species, individuals sometimes return in successive winters to favoured localities. Thus a drake wintered at Cawston Manor Lake in 1956 and 1958-60, and a drake lingered at Hardley Flood in the springs of 1983 and 1984. The vast majority of records have been from the Broads, with smaller numbers from park lakes, and in recent decades from the newly-created gravel pits around the county, with only a scattering of records from other localities.

Small numbers are kept in collections, both here and on the Continent, and some records may be of escaped birds migrating, though displaced in longitude and latitude. However, few of the county records are thought to relate to such escapees. Of the dated Norfolk records virtually all fall between November and April, with the earliest on 24th September, and with the odd one or two lingering into May or even June. This conforms well with established patterns of vagrancy for ducks and most are probably wild birds.

Exceptions to this pattern are two records from July mentioned by Riviere, and a highly unusual series of recent summer records from Holkham, where an approachable pair seen on 27th April 1992 was joined by a second pair on 12th June, remaining until mid-July, the original female reappearing on 26th September. The following year there were erratic sightings of singles from 12th March to 2nd August, followed by a wary pair seen at Longlands Farm in Holkham Park on 20th August. The habitat at Holkham fits well with their breeding requirements of shallow freshwater rich in aquatic vegetation and with a strong growth of emergent plants such as reeds, and it is not impossible, whatever the origin of these birds, that breeding may have been attempted. A pair were also seen at Syderstone Common on the late dates of 21st–22nd May 1995.

*Phil Heath*

**Tufted Duck** *E.g. HARDLEY FLOODS. 1-1-2000.*                    ***Aythya fuligula***

A fairly common resident, common winter visitor and scarce passage migrant.

Tufted Ducks & Pochards
(*Norman Arlott*)

The Tufted Duck breeds widely across northern Palearctic Europe and Asia. It retreats southwards in winter, occurring throughout temperate western Europe and the Mediterranean, as well as further east. Its range expanded westwards throughout the late 19th and early 20th centuries, with further increases in the last 40-50 years. In Britain there was a corresponding increase and spread until the late 1930s with a further spread since, boosted by the creation of new reservoirs and gravel pits.

The Tufted Duck has long been known as a regular and common passage migrant and winter visitor in Norfolk. Lubbock (1845) and Stevenson gave evidence that it may have oversummered sporadically or even bred in the Broads during the early to late 1800s. It first began nesting regularly in the county on the Breckland meres in the 1870s, with the first nest found at Merton in 1873; and 30-40 pairs were breeding at Thompson Water and on Stanford Mere by 1889 (Stevenson). It is described as abundant in the Breckland district by Riviere in 1930.

By the time of the publication of the *Birds of Norfolk* (Seago 1967), the only appreciable extension of range which had taken place was to the Fenland borders at Stow Bardolph, Hilgay and Runcton Holme in 1958. Further colonisation in the Fens included Wisbech Sewage Farm in 1969, followed by Welney in 1974. In north Norfolk pioneer pairs bred at Blickling and Ingworth in 1957, with a gradual increase thereafter. Salthouse was colonised in 1978; Melton Constable Park, Holme and Titchwell in 1980; Brancaster in 1982 and Holkham Fresh Marsh in 1987.

In the Broads, Riviere noted breeding at Hickling in 1912 and Salhouse in 1913, while in 1926 four pinioned females were released onto Hickling Broad as mates for four summering pricked drakes. In the following year three of these pairs raised broods, with several wild pairs also nesting in 1928, but not again, it seems, for another 39 years until a brood was found at Hickling in 1967. Most of Broadland had been colonised by the mid-1980s.

Large scale expansion throughout the whole county only started from the late 1960s as birds began wintering on the numerous newly-created sand and gravel pits. As these pits 'matured' birds began summering, and in 1970 there were broods at Colney, Bawburgh, Sparham and Corpusty, and subsequently at many other gravel pits around the county. The most recent extension of range has been on the edge of the Wash, with pairs nesting at Snettisham since 1985.

It is now a widespread and fairly common breeder throughout the county, having colonised nearly all suitable inland waters, sluggish stretches of rivers, grazing marsh dykes, the Ouse Washes and coastal floods. The Norfolk Atlas recorded the Tufted Duck in 270 tetrads (18.6%), with confirmed breeding in 133. The total county breeding population is hard to estimate as not all localities are monitored each year, but is probably around 180-230 pairs, with 30-60 of these at Pensthorpe; while 25-30 pairs at Holkham in 1997 reared a total of 14 broods.

Spring and autumn passage usually passes unnoticed as it seems to be mostly overland. This species is infrequently noted among wildfowl movements along the coast and then usually only in single figures. Autumn passage commences in mid-September and the highest counts, both at Sheringham have been 30 east on 23rd October 1979 and 42 west on 9th November 1992. Peak numbers of wintering birds are usually found in January-February as further birds are driven from the Continent. Spring departure is largely during March, and is usually complete by mid-April.

Today flocks of Tufted Duck are a familiar winter sight. They utilise almost every suitable sheet of water or river course, and can even be found in the towns and cities, such as on Diss Mere, the River Wensum in Norwich and King's Lynn Docks. Although smaller groups are more usual, flocks of 100-200 are normal on favoured gravel pits and broads, with concentrations of 300-600 on those that remain open during freezing conditions. Maximum site-counts in recent years have included 300 at Colney in February 1991, 320 at Sennowe in December 1992, 760 at Ranworth/Cockshoot Broads in December 1995, 358 at Wroxham in January 1996, 418 at Hickling Broad in November 1997 and 419 at Welney in February 1998. Other sites to have held over 200 are Pensthorpe, Swanton Morley Gravel Pit, Sparham Gravel Pit, Pentney Gravel Pit and Rollesby Broad.

Over 2,500 Tufted Duck have been ringed in Norfolk, the vast majority at Pensthorpe since 1982, of which 41 have been recovered abroad. Most of the 13 recoveries in Russia have been in May and June, some almost 4,000km to the east in western Siberia well beyond the Ural Mountains. Others have been found on autumn passage in Finland, Denmark and The Netherlands, while six have been recovered further to the west in Ireland. One of the longest-lived from Norfolk ringing involved a female ringed at Pensthorpe in November 1982 which was found freshly dead at Myvatn, Iceland in August 1990. Eight foreign-ringed birds have been found in Norfolk; five of which were ringed as ducklings in Czechoslovakia (two), The Netherlands, Finland and Germany, and the others as adults in Denmark (two) and Estonia.

*Phil Heath*

## Scaup (Greater Scaup)                                    *Aythya marila*

**A scarce or fairly common winter visitor and passage migrant, numbers varying annually; very scarce in summer and inland.**

The Scaup is the most northerly breeding member of the genus *Aythya*, nesting among the northern tundra. It has a circumpolar distribution, in Europe breeding from Iceland and Fennoscandia eastwards across northern Eurasia to Siberia. It migrates south in autumn and during winter it is present in most European countries, 90% of the population being concentrated along the coasts of Denmark, Germany and The Netherlands. In the British Isles very small numbers have bred sporadically in northern Scotland and Ireland since the end of the 19th century (Ogilvie 1975, New Atlas). About 5,000-10,000 currently winter around the British coast, principally off Scotland (Winter Atlas).

Earlier writers do not have much to say about the Scaup, and its status within the county seems to have remained fairly constant. It has been generally uncommon, being most numerous in winters of severe weather, and with inland occurrences very scarce.

Although odd individuals are sometimes noted returning from as early as August, most autumn passage is from late September through to early November, although daily numbers at any one site rarely reach double figures.

Wintering flocks can occur anywhere around the coast in response to the availability of food. However, their principal wintering grounds are the mussel beds or 'scaups' in The Wash and off the north-west coast, from Snettisham around to Titchwell. The numbers present vary greatly from year to year, ranging from virtually none in some mild winters, up to 200 and very occasionally 600. During the first two weeks of 1997, for instance, numbers built up rapidly to peak at 465 off Holme on 12th January, only to decline rapidly in early February, with all birds having departed by mid-month. Highest numbers usually coincide with periods of harsh wintry weather. Thus during severe freezing conditions in late February to early March 1963 the exceptional total of 2,500 was recorded off Heacham, while from January to March 1942 there were apparently 'thousands' in the Yarmouth Roads (Ley 1943). It is usually only in winters of severe weather that large flocks of up to 200 birds are recorded away from the north-west coasts. At such times hard weather movements of birds presumably displaced from the Continent or further north in Britain are often noted passing along the coast. Examples have included 410 west past Sheringham on 11th February 1991 and 280 east at Sheringham on 31st Dec 1995.

Although most winter on the sea, they are quite tolerant of brackish and even freshwater, and can be

181

found in small numbers on coastal gravel pits. Up to 40 overwintered at Breydon in the winters between 1972-73 and 1976-67 (Allard 1990), and since the late 1980s up to 20 have regularly wintered on the coastal gravel pits at Snettisham, with an exceptional 30 in February 1994.

Although inland records were considered unusual by Stevenson, Riviere and Seago (1977), they have become much more frequent in the last couple of decades. This is quite probably a result of greater observer coverage and better optical equipment rather than a genuine increase in occurrence. Odd singles or very small groups can appear on any inland water, ranging from coastal docks, ponds and floods to rivers, gravel pits and broads, although they rarely linger. Again most records coincide with severe winter conditions, such as the particularly high inland counts of 19 on the Magdalen Relief Channel in February 1991 and February 1996, 17 at Denver Sluice in February 1996, and 16 at King's Lynn Docks also in February 1996. During adverse wintry weather Breydon is often a favoured refuge – 138 were there in February 1963 and 150 on 3rd March 1956.

Most birds depart during March or early April, and small numbers are recorded passing coastal localities during this period. Very small numbers can linger into May and even June. Almost annually since 1952 small groups of up to nine birds have visited Breydon and recently other coastal sites such as Cley, Titchwell and Snettisham, in July and early August. Most of these records seem to be of moulting drakes. These overlap with the first returning migrants, and in some years (1993, 1995 and 1996), this species has been recorded in every month of the year.

There have been three ringing recoveries affecting the county – a hand-fed, rescued bird released at Cley on 28th February 1954 was recovered at Ust-Tsilma, Russia on 25th May 1958 and one ringed at Sandvatn, Iceland in June 1982 was found at Terrington Marsh on 13th February 1983 (one of over 75 Icelandic-ringed Scaup that have been recovered in the British Isles). The third, ringed at Pensthorpe in December 1990 was shot near Aylmerton the following March.

*Phil Heath*

## Eider (Common Eider)   *TITCHWELL (9) 19.9.1993*    *Somateria mollissima*

**A fairly common winter visitor and passage migrant, varying numbers of non-breeders oversummer; rare inland.**

The widespread breeding range of the Eider encircles the North Pole, with birds nesting along most Arctic and sub-Arctic coasts. In Europe their range extends south to the British Isles, north-west France, The Netherlands, Germany and Poland. They are robust birds, and most populations are resident, with winter displacement largely within the breeding range. The bulk of the British population is found in northern Ireland and Scotland, with the nearest east coast colony to Norfolk on Coquet Island off Amble in Northumberland. Birds occurring further south, including Norfolk, are non-breeders (New Atlas). Eiders have not always been so numerous. They first colonised the Scottish mainland in about 1850 and gradually expanded their range following protection in the late 19th century, colonising Ireland in 1912.

When Stevenson wrote his *Birds of Norfolk* the Eider was considered a very scarce but just about annual winter visitor to the Norfolk coast. Then, as now, most were in various immature plumages and adults were rarely recorded. He only recorded a single instance of oversummering, off Blakeney Point from July to October 1885. Riviere reiterated Stevenson, but added another summer record at Cley on 2nd August 1907.

The Eider's fortunes had greatly changed by the time Seago wrote his *Birds of Norfolk* (1967). It remained very scarce until the late 1940s, but in 1954 parties of up to 45 were recorded along the north coast in every month. The following year, 200 collected off Hunstanton in December; no previous Wash record had exceeded six birds! Records and numbers became gradually more frequent in the late 1950s and early 1960s, although summer records remained rare, with maximum winter counts from The Wash of 350–500. Birds occurring around Norfolk are assumed to originate primarily from the Dutch population, which was undergoing a spectacular rise in numbers at that time, along with some from the Baltic, rather than from British colonies (Winter Atlas).

Westward autumn passage has been noted as early as August, but is chiefly from late October to early December, with a peak in mid-November. On occasions this movement can be spectacular, such as 256 west at Paston on 12th November 1983, 500 west at Sheringham on 20th November 1991 and 300 west at Sheringham on 4th December 1996. Winter movements are uncommon, but 102 passed west off Paston on 8th January 1982.

From 1964 to 1979 the Wash lost its dominance as the favoured wintering locality, and flocks were widely recorded around the coast from Snettisham to Cromer, and occasionally the east coast (most regularly off Gorleston), with the annual winter/early spring maxima fluctuating between 20–250 birds. Eider feed principally on mussels and crabs, and such changes in wintering locations reflect the availability of food. The Wash returned to prominence from 1980 to 1985, with winter peaks of 200–500, with a particularly high count of 750 off Heacham in February 1985. Since then flocks have occurred anywhere from Snettisham to Brancaster, with winter maxima of 60–280. An exceptional build-up commenced in late autumn 1992, reaching 1,000 off Hunstanton by 31st December and peaking at 1,300 off Holme/Hunstanton in January 1993, with 1,090 still there in February. Exceptionally large numbers again built up off Snettisham in late 1996 with 1,000 in December, peaking at a new county record of 1,400 in January 1997. Birds remain generally scarce off the east coast, where feeding conditions are presumably less favourable, but flocks of 20–100 have occurred in each winter since autumn 1993, with maxima of 120 off Winterton in January 1994 and 158 off Winterton/Hemsby in January 1996.

Return movements in the spring are much less pronounced, with no obvious peak, and passage is probably protracted from late February to late May. Variable numbers of birds now remain off Norfolk throughout the summer, and moulting birds have been noted regularly since 1960 (Seago 1977), chiefly off Snettisham, Hunstanton/Holme/Titchwell and Brancaster/Scolt, with gradually increasing peaks of 122 at Snettisham in June 1981, 150 off Scolt in summer 1986 and up to 215 off Hunstanton/Holme in July 1993.

The Eider is very much a maritime duck, and although singles and small parties very occasionally put in appearances in harbours such as Yarmouth, and on estuaries such as Breydon, it is rare elsewhere inland. An unusual spate of inland records, particularly in the Midlands, occurred from 30th October 1993, when strong north to north-east winds over Denmark and days of extensive low cloud over England and the North Sea appeared to disorientate birds returning from Baltic moulting areas. As well as unusually high numbers around the coast, about 16 birds appeared inland at Strumpshaw, Rockland Broad, Buckenham, Colney, Lyng Easthaugh and Pentney Gravel Pits, Ousebridge (near Ten-mile Bank) and Welney. In addition 18 arrived at Breydon where two stayed until 27th December.

Although Eiders are generally very faithful to their natal areas, a female successfully nested within Lowestoft Harbour in Suffolk in 1996. With more birds summering as the population continues to gradually increase, breeding in Norfolk is a real possibility.

There has been just one recovery of a ringed Eider in Norfolk: marked as a young bird at Terschelling, The Netherlands on 6th July 1983, it was found at Heacham on 24th November 1984, providing evidence of the limited winter contact in the North Sea between the British and Dutch populations. It remains the only Dutch-ringed Eider to have been recovered in the British Isles.

*Phil Heath*

# King Eider                                    *Somateria spectabilis*

**A very rare vagrant; four records.**

The King Eider is a northern Holarctic species with a breeding distribution encompassing Spitsbergen, Arctic Russia and Siberia, Alaska, Canada and Greenland. It has occasionally bred in Arctic Norway. It is largely sedentary, but in winter moves south to the Norwegian fjords with small numbers regularly appearing as vagrants south to Scotland.

An immature drake which was obtained off Hunstanton on 7th January 1888, constituted the first Norfolk record and is on display at the Castle Museum, Norwich. An immature female was shot off Hunstanton on 3rd November 1890 with surprisingly another, an adult female shot there on about 10th November. Unfortunately both birds' present whereabouts are unknown.

There is one recent record, an eclipse drake which attracted large numbers of admirers to Scolt Head on 5th–15th September 1986 where it was present with up to 200 moulting Eiders.

*Peter Allard*

## Steller's Eider                                          *Polysticta stelleri*

**A very rare vagrant; one record in 1830.**

Steller's Eider breeds primarily along the arctic coastlines of eastern Siberia, from Khatanga Bay to coastal Alaska and occasionally further west in Siberia, even reaching extreme northern Norway. In winter and during the post-breeding moult in late summer, large numbers gather in the southern Bering Sea with smaller numbers in the Baltic and arctic waters of Scandinavia. Vagrants from this region regularly wander as far south as Denmark, but it is an extremely rare vagrant to the British Isles.

A magnificent drake, though not quite fully adult, was obtained on Caister Marshes on 9th February 1830. It was shot during a period of harsh weather by George Barrow who first saw it sitting on a pool of water close to the River Bure. It constituted the first British record and is on display at the Castle Museum, Norwich.

*Peter Allard*

## [Harlequin Duck                                     *Histrionicus histrionicus*

**One record, involving five individuals, not now considered acceptable.**

The Harlequin Duck has two distinct populations, one breeding in the Atlantic and the other in the Pacific. The Atlantic population breeds throughout eastern Canada, southern Greenland and Iceland, while the Pacific range extends from eastern Siberia eastwards to Alaska. It is a rare vagrant to Britain.

Seago (1967) included a record of a party of five Harlequin Ducks, including three drakes, at Cley on 19th February 1947. These five birds were seen in a tidal drain sheltering under a wall of ice by Billy Bishop, the warden of the Norfolk Naturalists Trust's Reserve at Cley Marsh. Their appearance occurred during a period of very severe weather including ice-floes on the sea at Cley.

The writer later discussed this sighting with Billy Bishop, who had seen the species a few years earlier during naval service in Iceland during the Second World War, and was shown the brief entries in his diary. Unfortunately, because of the lack of a written description or any other corroboratory evidence, this record has not been accepted nationally and consequently is not now included in the accepted total of species recorded in Norfolk.]

*Michael Seago*

## Long-tailed Duck   OFF TiTCHWELL. 26·11·1988·          *Clangula hyemalis*

**A scarce winter visitor and passage migrant; rare inland.**

Although only a scarce winter visitor to Norfolk, the Long-tailed Duck is probably the most numerous of the arctic-breeding sea ducks. It has a circumpolar distribution, breeding in Iceland, and from Fennoscandia right across northern Siberia to the Bering Straits, and from Alaska across arctic Canada and the ice-free coasts of Greenland. Birds withdraw southwards in winter from those areas subject to freezing. Birds are widespread in small numbers around the coasts of the British Isles in winter, the majority located around the Outer Hebrides, Shetland, Orkney and along the east coast of Scotland (Winter Atlas).

The maritime nature of the Long-tailed Duck was commented on by Stevenson and Riviere, both noting its tendency to remain well out to sea and its ability to shrug off the stormiest weather. Its status may have changed. Both these early authors considered the Long-tailed Duck to be a regular but scarce winter visitor, but gave few indications of actual numbers. In the 1950s the largest party reported was one of 30–40 off Sheringham on 28th–29th October 1958, while Hunstanton hosted a maximum of nine on 13th April that year. From the early 1960s the number wintering off north-west Norfolk gradually increased and it became clear that there was a variable but regular wintering population in that area. Although Seago (1977) considered this to be a genuine increase, it could well have been due to the steady rise in the numbers of observers and the proliferation of high-quality optical equipment, leading to more birds being detected out at sea.

The bulk of the western European population winters in the Baltic, although reasonable numbers also winter north of the Arctic Circle around northern Norway. They remain close to their breeding grounds until forced to depart by freezing conditions and only arrive in the western Baltic in November and December

184

(BWP). Although occasional singles have arrived off the Norfolk coast in August and September, and others during October and November, most do not appear until December. Excluding an adult male at Sheringham on 13th July 1992, the earliest records have been at Holme on 18th August 1972, two at Breydon on 18th August 1985, at Winterton on 26th August 1961 and at Waxham on 27th August 1974. Their robust nature and maritime habits mean that few are noted on passage from coastal localities, and day-counts rarely reach double figures, even during severe onshore winds, the highest count being 20 west at Cley on 23rd October 1990.

Numbers wintering in the county vary from year to year, and can range from less than 40 to perhaps 300. Like the other sea-ducks their principal wintering area is from Hunstanton to Holme, with smaller numbers eastwards to Holkham Bay. Apart from this area of the Wash and north-west Norfolk they are very scarce elsewhere. Numbers seem to gradually rise throughout the winter, with peak counts usually in March. At Hunstanton/Holme the highest counts have been 175–200 in March 1986, 150 in January 1987, 120 in December 1993 (when a county-wide sea-duck survey on 5th December produced a total of 220 Long-tailed Ducks between Hunstanton and Scolt Head) and 141 in January 1997. Counts of 40–100, however, are more usual in the Hunstanton area. The origin of this March peak is unknown, but it could be the result of late onward migration, or hard weather movements from the Continent, although there are no significant observations from around the coast to confirm this. Long-tailed Ducks regularly undertake overland passage (BWP), and it could be a pre-migratory concentration of birds that have wintered elsewhere off England or even Ireland. Peak counts elsewhere, have been 70 at Scolt Head on 3rd March 1982 with some of the drakes performing 'parachute' displays, 60–70 at Brancaster in March 1983 and 20 in Blakeney Harbour on 22nd April 1989. In recent years very few have been reported from east Norfolk, although up to 12 wintered at Gorleston in 1972–75 and again in 1980–85.

Return passage is rarely noted from coastal localities. Birds depart very rapidly in April, with odd stragglers lingering into May. Although non-breeders often oversummer in wintering areas (Madge & Burn 1988), summer records are rare in the county, probably reflecting the comparatively small wintering population. These summer records are usually of singletons, but two were killed in Blakeney Harbour on 19th June 1907 and there were three at Titchwell on 5th June 1958, two at Sheringham on 28th June 1991 and three on Titchwell Reserve on 16th–17th June 1992. One remained on Arnold's Marsh, Cley until 20th June 1983.

Inland records are now almost annual. These occurrences usually involve short-staying single birds, although twos or threes are sometimes noted. On occasion, where they find suitable feeding conditions, inland birds can linger for a few weeks or exceptionally even months, such as a female which remained at Holkham Park Lake and then Holkham from 20th January to 13th May 1996. Long-tailed Ducks are not usually affected by inclement weather and individuals can turn up inland at any time of the winter, regardless of weather conditions. The majority of inland occurrences are on the various coastal pits and lagoons, and the Broads.

*Phil Heath*

## Common Scoter (Black Scoter) HUNSTANTON. 8·9·1985. (12) *Melanitta nigra*

**A common winter visitor and passage migrant, varying numbers of non-breeders oversummer; rare inland.**

The nominate race *M. n. nigra* of the Common Scoter breeds in a broad band from Iceland and Scotland eastwards across the tundra to the River Olenek in Siberia. The entire population withdraws west-south-west to winter along the western Atlantic seaboard, from northern Norway as far south as Mauritania. In the British Isles about 65–70 pairs nest atypically on large limestone lakes in Ireland, with about a further 100 pairs in Scotland (New Atlas).

The status, range and habits of the Common Scoter do not seem to have changed much over the years, and Stevenson's and Riviere's accounts of its standing in the county are as true now as then. Thus Riviere described the Common Scoter as 'a winter visitor to the north Norfolk coast in very large numbers, the attraction to this and other species of diving ducks being the extensive mussel-beds lying off the western portion of our coastline and within the area of The Wash. The habits of this species during the winter are wholly oceanic, and however severe the weather they are extremely rarely driven inshore. Although the majority depart in March a number of Common Scoter, as noted by Stevenson, are often present off the coast throughout the spring and summer...'.

Birds wintering off the North Sea coasts are thought to be from the Swedish, Finnish and Russian breeding populations. After moulting off the Continent, immatures and males start to disperse west in September, with corresponding movements off the Norfolk coast gradually increasing from then to peak in November and early December. The proportion of females and juveniles gradually increases until passage ends in December. Numbers passing coastal localities vary considerably from year to year, but day-counts of several hundred are not unusual and on occasions passage can be considerable, such as in October 1991 when westerly movements included 2,645 at Holme and 2,000 at Blakeney Point on 20th, 1,500 at Cley and 1,100 at Holme on 21st, and 1,500 at Sheringham and Cley on 22nd.

Common Scoters feed mainly on molluscs during the winter, principally on the blue mussel (BWP), and the largest winter concentrations have traditionally been around the mussel scaups off the Wash and north-west coast of Norfolk. They are sociable ducks and tight flocks of 200–600 are regular each winter anywhere from Snettisham around to Holkham, favoured localities varying from winter to winter depending on feeding conditions. Exact numbers present around the county are difficult to determine, as flocks drift around the coast and also out to sea at times. In some years individual flocks may total as many as 3,000–3,500, and exceptionally 6,000. Elsewhere around the north and east coasts of the county winter flocks are usually small and transitory. However, during the 1950s exceptionally high numbers appeared in Gorleston Bay, with a peak of 5,000 in January 1955. Numbers gradually declined from the 1960s, and no significant numbers have been recorded there since 1983 (Allard 1990). Following a large influx in autumn 1991, 1,500 were off Waxham/Horsey in early November, with 400 still present in December, and 300 off Horsey/Winterton during January 1992.

With flocks present throughout the year, coastal movements can occur at any time, particularly during spells of strong onshore winds. To some extent such movements mask return easterly passage in the spring which probably lasts from late February until April. Thus a notable spring movement of 1,500 east off Morston on 15th May 1995 could have been a late passage or local movement. Many immature birds remain off the Norfolk coast throughout the summer and presumably moult here. Their summer distribution mirrors that of the winter, with most off the north-west coast and far fewer off the north-east and east coasts. Numbers summering vary from year to year and individual flocks can range from a few dozen to over 2,500. During the summer months Common Scoter flocks are occasionally noted several kilometres out to sea, with recent counts of 500+ about 4km north-west of Brancaster Harbour on 16th May 1995 and 400 at the same distance north of Scolt on 25th June 1996.

Common Scoters are occasional on inland waters, and although not annual, in some years there can be a dozen or more records. As noted by Stevenson and Riviere, autumn and winter records are the exception. Between 1925 and 1948 a total of nine was shot at Hickling during the period November to February. Nowadays, most inland occurrences are between March and July, but principally April to June. Birds rarely linger for more than a day, and these records probably relate to individuals undertaking overland spring passage. Although most inland records are usually of singletons, small flocks are sometimes involved, and occasionally these can reach double figures, such as at least 14 on Hickling Broad in July 1875 and 12 on 13th April 1928, 12 at Breydon on 10th June 1990 and 18 at Welney on 20th April 1992.

*Phil Heath*

# Surf Scoter                                            *Melanitta perspicillata*

**A rare vagrant.**

The North American Surf Scoter is an abundant species which breeds in Alaska and northern Canada, wintering on both the Pacific and Atlantic coasts, as well as the Great Lakes.

It is the commonest Nearctic duck occurring in Europe, and as Surf Scoters are almost unknown in wildfowl collections, there is no reason to doubt that all are wild birds. It is remarkably regular in its appearances in the British Isles, currently averaging about ten new records each year, as well as established birds returning in successive years to winter at favoured localities. Most occur among flocks of Common or Velvet Scoters, and most records are of the far more distinct drake. While most occurrences are in autumn and winter, a few are in spring, and these are probably of birds which have wintered with other scoters off

Atlantic coasts further south and are undertaking a northerly spring movement. There are also a few inland records of individuals appearing in association with overland movements of Common Scoters.

Although most records in the British Isles are from Shetland, Orkney and western Ireland, birds in the North Sea are not uncommon. It, however, remains a very rare bird in Norfolk with the county total standing at ten:

1925: Three drakes were seen by Emma Turner close inshore off Scolt Head on 2nd October. Another four scoters in the same flock were also claimed as Surf Scoter, but as no description was provided for them, their identity must remain unproven (Turner 1926).

1927: A party of three drakes close inshore off Hemsby on 16th November.

1981: An immature female made a prolonged stay off Heacham and Old Hunstanton from 2nd March to 9th May.

1988: An adult drake off Holme beach on 19th–24th June.

1991: A drake flew west past Cromer, Weybourne and Cley on 20th October. This was associated with a particularly heavy westerly passage of several thousand Common Scoters along the north Norfolk coast at that time.

1997: A first-summer drake off Titchwell on 2nd–15th April, was joined by an adult drake on 9th April.

*Phil Heath*

## Velvet Scoter                                                 *Melanitta fusca*

**A scarce winter visitor and passage migrant; rare in summer and inland.**

Velvet Scoters
(*Norman Arlott*)

The Velvet Scoter has an extensive almost circumpolar summer distribution. Although absent from eastern North America, Greenland and Iceland, it breeds from Norway eastwards right across Eurasia to Kamchatka, and from Alaska eastwards to Hudson Bay. In the winter it withdraws southwards, with the Eurasian population dividing between European waters and the Pacific (Winter Atlas).

Status in the county seems to have changed little over the years, with both Stevenson and Riviere having recorded it as a regular but scarce winter visitor, with single-figure flocks around the coast in most years, but with higher numbers in winters of exceptional severity. The winters of 1829–30, early 1832, early 1855, 1859–60 and 1870–71 all produced notable numbers. Although there has been a higher frequency of observations in recent years, with slightly higher numbers recorded, this is most likely to reflect increases in observer coverage and optical performance, and the ability of observers to pick out birds among the large flocks of Common Scoter, with which they often mingle. The only change in status would seem to be that while both Stevenson and Riviere noted most birds to be immatures, and regarded adult drakes as a rarity, today they are by no means unusual.

Autumn passage off the coast commences in September, and continues through to early December, with further winter movements into January. Usually only noted during periods of strong onshore winds, movements are far from daily, and rarely reach double figures. Counts from Sheringham of 35 west on 26th November and 36 west on 20th December 1993 were notable.

Total numbers wintering around the county are usually in the order of 20–80, but this is variable and in poor years it can be fewer than ten; while in other winters over 100 may be present. Birds continue to arrive during the winter, and numbers usually peak in January or even February. Particularly large flocks noted recently include an exceptional 325 off Heacham/Hunstanton in March 1961, 140 in the same locality in February 1989, and 160 in Holkham Bay from December 1991 to January 1992, with 125 still there in February. Neither Stevenson nor Riviere gave any indication that Velvet Scoters favoured any particular section of coast. Today, although on occasions they can be met with anywhere, they show a distinct preference for the north-west coast from Heacham around to Holkham. In some winters 10–40 can occur off the east coast, while in 1962 there were 80 in Gorleston Bay on 15th April, and in 1972 there were up to 102 in the same locality in early November. A flock of up to 95 off Blakeney/Cley in February, and 120 off West Runton in March 1956 is also unusual for that section of the coast.

Return spring passage is rarely noted. A count of 80 south at Gorleston on 15th April 1962, with 12 south the following day was exceptional. Birds may start moving from as early as March, but passage is principally during April, with stragglers until late May. Odd singles or very small groups are occasionally noted during the summer months and birds were recorded in every month of the year in 1984 and 1989. Some are likely to be tardy non-breeders, late in crossing the North Sea. However, on rare occasions a very few certainly do oversummer and moult here, such as a drake off Hunstanton in 1967. Summer records of nine close to Scroby Sands on 5th July 1956 and 17 there on 4th–23rd July 1963 were noteworthy (Allard 1990).

Stevenson noted several inland occurrences, and said that in hard weather '... they not uncommonly resort to inland waters, and have been met with far from the sea'. This is still the case, and although not annual, there are often one or two inland records in the course of a winter. In 1979 there was an unusual series of inland records between 28th January and 2nd March, with nine individuals at seven localities including Denver, Lound, Gillingham, Burgh Castle and Ranworth Broad. This propensity initially appears unusual for what is essentially a scarce sea-duck. However, Velvet Scoters use brackish and freshwater lakes far more than Common Scoters, in summer, winter and on passage, and perhaps as a consequence they are notably more prone to occur inland.

*Phil Heath*

# Bufflehead                                    *Bucephala albeola*

**A very rare vagrant; two records, both currently under review.**

The Bufflehead is an abundant and widespread North American sea-duck breeding from central Alaska across Canada with occasional sporadic breeding south to California. Most winter from south Alaska to northern Mexico, being widespread across the southern USA to the Gulf coast and north along the Atlantic seaboard to New England. It is an extremely rare vagrant to Britain.

The first British record of Bufflehead was of an adult drake alleged to have been shot near Yarmouth, almost certainly on Breydon, in about 1830. It was initially kept in Stephen Miller's collection at Gorleston and then passed to Robert Rising's collection at Horsey. This collection was auctioned in September 1885 and the specimen was purchased by the Castle Museum, Norwich. However, a second adult drake claiming to be the above bird, is in the Museum at Saffron Waldon, Essex. A third specimen, also an adult drake and labelled as shot at Yarmouth in about 1830, is understood to be at the Natural History Museum, Kensington Gardens, London.

The second county record concerned a female seen by C. T. M. Plowright and N. Tracey off Hunstanton on several days in February 1932. Both these records are highly unlikely to be accepted by today's standards (Allard 1997). Relevant details of both occurrences have been sent to the BOURC and a decision is awaited.

Additionally, there is an interesting but unconfirmed report in Jim Vincent's Hickling diary for 1913 that whilst punting across Hickling Broad he came upon a pair of Buffleheads on 11th February. He was an extremely careful observer and his notes mentioned the conspicuous white patch in the centre of the green on the drake's head.

*Peter Allard*

HARDLEY FLOODS. c6. 5-11-2000.

## Goldeneye (Common Goldeneye)

*Bucephala clangula*

**A fairly common winter visitor and passage migrant; scarce inland.**

The Goldeneye breeds from Scotland, Fennoscandia and the Baltic eastwards across northern Russia to Kamchatka and Japan. In the New World it breeds from Alaska to Newfoundland, southwards to the USA border. In Europe the Goldeneye winters in the British Isles, along the coasts of the North and Baltic Seas, in Switzerland, on the Adriatic and Greek coasts to the Black and Caspian Seas. Scottish breeders are thought to winter near their breeding sites. The limited number of ringing recoveries suggests that the majority of those wintering elsewhere in the British Isles are from Fennoscandia and western Russia (Winter Atlas).

Goldeneyes
(Nik Borrow)

Known as the 'Rattle-wing' by the gunners of Stevenson's and Riviere's time, the Goldeneye seems always to have been a fairly common winter visitor, both around the coast and on larger inland rivers and water bodies. Somewhat surprisingly Stevenson stated that 'it seldom appears far inland'. Riviere, however, considered it frequent on inland waters and today they are regularly encountered in small numbers throughout the county. Numbers visiting Norfolk have possibly been increasing over the last few decades, as the excavation of numerous gravel pits throughout the county provides a steadily increasing amount of new habitat for birds to utilise.

Following their moult, autumn migration begins in August, reaching a peak in the North Sea in November, and is virtually completed by early December (BWP). Thus in the county there can be odd returning singletons from mid-August through September, but the main return passage is from mid-October to mid-November. Single-figure counts are regular from coastal localities during this period, and can be much higher during spells of onshore winds. Notable counts have included 110 west off Cley in $2^{1}/_{2}$ hours on 18th November 1972, 125 west off Paston on 2nd November 1986, 88 west at Sheringham on 4th November 1990, and 105 west at Holme and 98 west at Sheringham on 2nd November 1995, these two counts being part of a significant westerly passage in the first few days of November that year. The majority of these passage birds are immatures and females, the adult males generally migrating less far and predominate in the Baltic wintering sites. Severe freezing weather sometimes forces these birds westwards, and large numbers of adult males are usually only seen in the county later in the winter after such hard weather movements.

Although primarily viewed as a sea-duck, Goldeneyes winter in small numbers on most large rivers and water bodies throughout the county, as well as coastally. The most favoured section of coastline is from Snettisham on the Wash around to Blakeney Harbour on the north coast. Although wintering numbers vary, site-counts here of up to 200 are not unusual. They are much scarcer off the north-east and east coasts, where feeding conditions are presumably less suitable. Although single-figure counts are usual for most inland sites, favoured inland localities such as the coastal gravel pits at Snettisham, the Fenland rivers and drains, and the larger Broads can hold 10–30 birds. Particularly notable counts have included 90 on Hickling Broad on 6th March 1954 with 100 there on 24th February 1959, 100 at Breydon on 31st March 1971, 80 at Snettisham Pits in January 1994 and 60 at Saddlebow/Magdalen in January 1997. In freezing weather higher numbers of birds may be concentrated on those areas of water that remain open.

Spring passage is unremarkable, and often goes unnoticed. Return movements start as early as mid-February, and most birds have left by the end of March. A few linger throughout April, and as Stevenson and Riviere both remarked, it is not unusual for odd birds, possibly first-years, to be noted in the first couple of weeks of May. A few birds have been recorded as late as June, such as singles at Acle Bridge on 1st June 1991, at Snettisham Pits on 4th June 1960, at Tottenhill Gravel Pits on 5th–10th June 1985, at Hickling Broad on 16th June 1985 and at Kelling Water Meadows from 26th June to 18th July 1998. There have also been a few other unusual mid to late summer records. In 1960 one was at Snettisham Pits from 1st August, and one was between King's Lynn and Saddlebow on 16th July 1975 (possibly since 31st

May), while in 1995 a female was recorded at Surlingham on 29th July and at Bramerton Woods End on 13th August. In the same year a single bird was variously recorded at Titchwell, Holme, Brancaster and Snettisham between 15th July and late September. The following year an immature female summered at Breydon from 21st April to 20th October 1996.

Despite only 11 having been ringed at Pensthorpe, two from February 1990 were recovered abroad – one at Koudum, The Netherlands on 15th January 1991 (the only Dutch recovery of a British-ringed Goldeneye) and the other at Nykoping, Sweden on 8th December 1991, an area of Sweden in which small numbers of Goldeneyes are known to winter. Another ringed at Pensthorpe in February 1994 was found at Mala in northern Sweden on 10th October. An adult female ringed near Sarkisalo, Finland on 26th May 1963 was found dead at Hickling Broad on 31st January 1964.

*Phil Heath*

## Smew | *Mergellus albellus*

**A scarce or very scarce winter visitor, numbers varying annually.**

Smews
(*Norman Arlott*)

The smallest of the European sawbills, the Smew is a tree nester, and is intimately associated with the boreal zone where mature trees offer suitable nest holes. The breeding range extends in a wide belt from northern Fennoscandia right across Europe to Asia. It is a rare breeder in Fennoscandia, and many of the birds wintering in temperate Europe must be from the Russian population. During the winter months Smew can be found scattered around the North Sea, central Europe and the eastern Mediterranean. Apart from up to 10,000 on the Dutch polders, numbers at these localities are small, but many thousands winter further east. These birds are displaced westwards only by exceptionally severe weather (Winter Atlas).

Earlier authors agreed that the Smew was a 'hard-weather fowl', and that although small numbers were seen annually, it only occurred in numbers in severe winters. Stevenson noted that they were particularly abundant in the following years: 1819–20, early 1855, early 1861, 1867–68 and 1870–71. As with many migratory duck, immature and/or female redheads move further afield than adult drakes in the winter, and the latter are only seen in any number in influx years.

Small numbers of birds can start arriving as early as October and ones or twos are very occasionally recorded passing coastal stations at this time. A drake off Scolt Head on 12th September 1934 and another referred to by Ticehurst (1932) as being obtained at Yarmouth on 17th September 1843 were unusually early. Further arrivals can take place at any time during the late autumn and winter, their appearance almost always triggered by the onset of severe freezing conditions in Europe and particularly The Netherlands. The main arrival is often not until January or February. Again at these times small numbers can be noted moving westwards along the coast. During a late winter influx in 1985 an exceptional 21 moved west at Cley on 17th January. Numbers arriving in the county vary considerably from winter to winter. Although conspicuous, Smew are very mobile and accurately estimating true numbers is tricky. In mild winters there may only be a dozen or so records, while in years of severe wintry weather perhaps 100 may be present within the county. There has been a considerable reduction in the number of Smew regularly wintering in Britain since the 1950s (Winter Atlas), although this trend is hard to discern within the county. Singles and small single-figure groups are currently the norm and even in recent influxes flocks of more than ten are particularly notable. Seago (1977) gave several records of groups of 30–40 birds, which today would be considered exceptional.

Marked influxes occurred in 1947, early 1954, February 1956, 1963, and more recently in early 1985, early 1986, early 1987, February 1991, January 1996 and 1996–97. Peak counts have included 21 on the lower reaches of the River Yare on 6th February, 35 on the Denver/Welney Washes on 7th February and 32 at Rockland Broad on 20th February 1954, 32 at Breydon on 11th February and 35–40 on the Ouse Washes on 12th February 1956, up to 40+ at Rockland Broad in February and 28 on the River Ouse at South Lynn on 24th February 1963. The only counts of any size in recent years, until January 1997, have been 24 between Denver Sluice and King's Lynn on 19th January 1985, with individual counts of 18 at Denver and 18 at Wiggenhall St Peter around that time, and 16 on the River Bure by the Stracey Arms in February 1986. However, a major influx occurred in January 1997, involving about 250 birds in Norfolk. Maximum site-counts in January included ten at Magdalen Relief Channel, 16 at Saddlebow, 12 at Tottenhill Gravel Pits, 11 at Stowbridge Pits and ten between Stowbridge and King's Lynn, while in February there were 14 at Eau Brink, 13 at Pentney Gravel Pits and ten at Lound.

Smew can occur on any moderately large lake, mere, broad, gravel pit or river throughout the county. Their visits are often brief, with birds only remaining a day or two, but where they find conditions to their liking, singles or small groups can linger for weeks or sometimes months. Although showing a preference for freshwater, they are not averse to brackish coastal pits or the estuarine conditions at Breydon. During passage they can be noted resting on the sea. In freezing conditions some birds are presumably forced further west out of the county. Those that stay are then found on remaining areas of open water, usually the Fenland rivers and drains, coastal pits, the larger rivers of the Broads and Breydon.

Other than the appearance of short-staying individuals in March, return passage is inconspicuous. In mild winters most have departed by the third week of March, but particularly in influx years odd singles regularly linger until mid-April. These are presumably non-breeding immatures lacking the urgency of full adults to return to the breeding grounds. Latest records were of a 'redhead', thought to be injured, which stayed at Sparham Pools until 8th June 1986, and a particularly tardy 'redhead' which stayed at Cley from early February until 7th June 1994. During the latter part of its stay it seemed to have paired with a female Shelduck and was often noted trying to drive off this bird's mate!

*Phil Heath*

## Red-breasted Merganser | *TITCHWELL. (1) 26·11·1988.* | *Mergus serrator*

**A fairly common passage migrant and winter visitor; rare in summer.**

The Red-breasted Merganser is a highly successful species, and has an unbroken circumpolar distribution. Unlike its close relatives the Smew and Goosander, it nests on the ground and is not tied to woodland areas, it will also nest on estuaries and sea inlets as well as freshwater rivers. In the Western Palearctic, the breeding range covers Iceland, the north of Britain, Denmark and a broad band across Fennoscandia and Russia. In winter the species is predominately marine, and withdraws south to more temperate coasts (Winter Atlas). The bulk of the British and Irish populations are thought to winter around the coasts close to their breeding areas, with additional birds joining them from Iceland. Those Red-breasted Mergansers found on the east coast of England, from the Wash southwards, are assumed to be principally birds from Fennoscandia, Poland, the former Baltic States and north-west Russia (Winter Atlas).

Both Stevenson and Riviere considered Red-breasted Mergansers to be irregular winter visitors, generally more frequent in hard winters, and both make particular mention of a single summer record. These views are at slight variance with its status today as a regular winter visitor, if in varying numbers, with occasional records of small numbers around the coast throughout the summer. Rather than these differences merely reflecting greater observer coverage and the greatly improved performance of optical equipment, there does seem to have been a genuine change of status. Red-breasted Mergansers underwent a marked population increase in Scotland between 1885 and 1920, and subsequently colonised northern England in 1950 and Wales in 1953 (BWP). However, most birds off the Norfolk coast are thought to be from the Continent rather than British breeding birds. The Fennoscandian population seems to be fairly stable, but that in the Baltic is increasing following protection (BWP). The change in status is perhaps most likely to relate to increased numbers of birds originating from this region, and/or a slight westward shift in the wintering area.

Although a few birds can arrive earlier, autumn passage is mainly from late October and numbers build up rapidly from then. Single-figure numbers are regularly noted passing coastal sites throughout the late autumn and early winter, and counts can sometimes exceed 20, especially during spells of onshore winds. A count of 48 west at Sheringham on 9th November 1992 was particularly high and 37 east at Holme on 25th October 1997 was noteworthy. The onset of severe weather on the Continent can push additional birds across the North Sea, and such arrivals can continue well into the winter. These movements, such as 25 west at Cley in half an hour and ten west at Sheringham on 2nd January 1995, probably involve Baltic and Russian wintering birds.

Neither Stevenson nor Riviere suggested that any particular section of the coast was favoured. However, by the time Seago wrote *Birds of Norfolk* in 1967, the bulk of those wintering around the county were concentrated in the Wash, with very few on the north or east coasts. This has changed slightly and today they are commonly found from the Wash around to Blakeney Harbour, although other than passage birds records from the north-east and east coasts are still decidedly scarce. Numbers do vary from winter to winter, but current counts would seem to estimate a county wintering population of 100–200. The Winter Atlas stated that winter flocks were usually small and that only about one in eight reports involved flocks of over 30 birds. Counts from localities around the county now regularly reach 40–60, and notable concentrations have included 110 off Hunstanton on 8th December 1963, 154 off Heacham on the early date of 9th October 1965, 150–200 off Heacham following severe weather on 4th March 1979 and 132 off Heacham/Hunstanton in November 1997.

Although principally maritime in the winter months, they will utilise other habitats. Many of those feeding in the Wash currently roost on the adjacent coastal pits at Snettisham and variable numbers of Red-breasted Mergansers regularly appear and sometimes winter on the Fenland drains and rivers. Numbers here range from less than a dozen records in mild winters to notable counts in more severe weather, such as up to 70 on the Welney Washes in February 1956, 58 between Downham Market and Lynn Point in February 1985, 54 between Denver Sluice and Ten Mile Bank on 13th February 1991, 74 between Ten Mile Bank and King's Lynn on 29th January and 52 between Denver and King's Lynn on 11th February 1996, and 55 between Stowbridge and King's Lynn on 5th January 1997, the day after 75 were in King's Lynn Docks. Elsewhere it is not unusual for small numbers to penetrate inland along the lower reaches of the larger rivers and Breydon estuary, and there are usually also 1–6 records each winter from lakes and rivers well inland. These inland records often coincide with spells of severe weather and probably involve birds displaced from the Continent (Winter Atlas). Many were recorded inland in early 1979 and included notable counts of 20 at Hickling Broad from 18th February to 19th April and 13 at Horsey Mere on 3rd March.

Return passage probably starts in late February, but is chiefly in March, when there are occasional counts of up to 12 passing coastal sites. A movement of 35 west in $1^1/_2$ hours at Titchwell on 5th March 1994 was particularly high. Most have departed by early April, but stragglers may linger into May and even June.

Summering records are becoming more regular. Stevenson and Riviere considered a summer record in late July at Lowestoft North Denes, Suffolk to be exceptional, but Red-breasted Mergansers were noted as 'occasional in summer' by Seago (1967). A few summer records were recorded in 1977 and, most unusually, two moulting males were noted well inland at Denver on 15th–18th August 1985, where two had earlier lingered into late June. An injured bird summered in the Breydon/Berney area in 1987 and one was off Wells on 25th July 1992. Since 1993 there have been occasional records of 1–10 off various coastal localities from June to September, presumably of lingering non-breeders.

*Phil Heath*

| **Goosander** | HARDLEY FLOODS. (♀) 25·11·1991. | *Mergus merganser* |

**A scarce winter visitor and passage migrant; rare in summer.**

The largest of the sawbills, Goosanders are mostly tree nesters along upland rivers, and their distribution is closely linked with the boreal zone. The nominate race *M. m. merganser* breeds in Iceland, Scotland and Fennoscandia eastwards in a broad band across northern Russia and Asia. The Icelandic, Scottish, and north-western European breeders are largely sedentary, but those that breed further east are forced by freezing conditions to move either west, to winter in north-western Europe, or south (Winter Atlas).

From Stevenson's and Riviere's accounts, it is clear that small parties of up to about ten Goosanders were regular winter visitors to Norfolk, particularly favouring the estate lakes at Antingham, Gunton and Holkham. Elsewhere they were occasional on most rivers, lakes and broads around the county, most numerous in severe winters.

The first birds of the autumn do not normally arrive until late October and most not until freezing conditions drive birds westwards from December onwards. Exceptionally, birds may arrive in September, such as an immature drake which arrived at Stiffkey on 9th September 1997 and remained until the end of the year, one at Snettisham on 17th September 1994, two singles south past Winterton on 21st September 1997 and two at Breydon on 25th September 1883. The idea that most of our wintering birds arrive from the east is supported by numerous autumn and early winter observations of passage Goosanders, which are invariably of singles or single-figure parties arriving from the sea on the east coast, or passing west along the north coast. Arrivals can continue through January and February, depending on weather conditions on the Continent. Cold weather at the start of 1996 produced a notable influx with impressive visible migration, including counts of 22 off Heacham, six west at Wells, 19 west at Cley and nine west at both Weybourne and Sheringham, all on 3rd January, with 30 west over Burgh Castle the next day. A similar influx occurred in early 1997 with nine west at Brancaster on 2nd January, 17 south at Snettisham and ten north at Sea Palling the following day, and eight south at Eccles on 18th January.

Goosanders usually favour freshwater and can occur throughout the county on any reasonably sized river, broad, lake or gravel pit, but they will also frequent estuaries such as Breydon, and on rare occasions sheltered coastal waters, for example one which lingered off Sheringham from 3rd November to 31st December 1989. Ones and twos are most frequent, but larger parties of 10–20 are regular. Many of these birds only stay for a few days and then presumably carry on westwards. The numbers passing through and overwintering in the county vary considerably

Goosanders
(John Wright)

from year to year, with significantly higher numbers during severe weather. During such cold spells far larger groups of 20–40, and even 60, can gather on undisturbed and unfrozen areas with suitable feeding. The Fenland drains are especially productive at these times, with groups of over 50 recorded. The highest counts were a spectacular 98 along the Great Ouse Relief Channel between Ten Mile Bank and King's Lynn on 19th January 1985 and 100+ between Denver and St Germans on 31st January 1987. Certain locations can become favoured and used as regular wintering sites for several years running. Thus both Holkham and Kimberley Park Lakes had regular wintering groups in the 1880s, while Gunton Park Lake and Antingham Lake were used regularly by a dozen or so birds from the late 1850s till at least the late 1880s, and during the late 1970s and early 1980s. During the 1960s Narford Hall Lake was a regular haunt, with a maximum count of 38 in 1963. Most recently, since the 1993–94 winter the UEA Broad on the outskirts of Norwich has up to 22 regularly roosting there, with birds dispersing during the day to feed on the adjacent River Yare and nearby Colney Gravel Pits. In January 1997 up to 32 were on the River Yare at Cantley.

Return migration starts in early March and most have departed by late April. There are occasional records of 1–2 passing coastal sites during this period, particularly during influx years, as birds return to the Continent. An interesting count of 20 at Breydon on 29th–30th March 1992 was presumably of birds on return passage.

On odd occasions stragglers can linger into May, but summer records are rare and none was mentioned by Stevenson or Riviere. Seago (1967) recorded a moulting drake at Rockland Fleet on 23rd July 1962, with perhaps the same at Rockland Broad in June the following year. An injured individual summered at Welney in 1985, an injured drake remained at Breydon from 7th February to 14th July 1987 and another injured bird summered in the King's Lynn Docks area from 7th May to 19th August 1989, while one was seen on Hickling Broad on 10th July 1993. During 1995 a pair lingered at the UEA Broad until at least 21st May, with the female staying on until late August, an injured drake remained at Breydon from 21st

April to 13th June and one was at Magdalen Bridge, Norwich on 15th July. Additionally, an injured or escaped female summered on the River Yare at Brundall during August 1995, moving to Whitlingham and then the River Wensum in Norwich in October, where it remained, occasionally visiting Whitlingham, into 1996. It attracted a drake from 17th May 1996 (at Whitlingham), both moving to Friar's Quay in Norwich City centre from 24th May until at least 11th September. Amazingly, both a male Goosander and a male Red-breasted Merganser were present at Snettisham Reserve throughout June and July 1998.

The few ringing recoveries nationally suggest that most birds wintering in the south of England are from central and northern Fennoscandia, the former Baltic States and Russia. The only recovery affecting Norfolk involved one ringed as a nestling at Uuiskaupunki in south-west Finland in June 1955 and recovered at Breydon in February the following year. It remains the only Finnish-ringed Goosander to have been recovered in the British Isles.

*Phil Heath*

## Ruddy Duck — *Oxyura jamaicensis*

**An increasing but scarce introduced resident, first recorded in 1977; a few pairs have bred annually since 1995.**

It is the nominate North and Central American race of the Ruddy Duck *O. j. jamaicensis* which is ferally established in Europe. The principal breeding range of this race is through much of western Canada and the USA. The population is largely migratory, spreading southwards into Mexico and eastwards across the USA in the winter.

Ruddy Ducks were first imported to Slimbridge by the (then) Wildfowl Trust in 1948. These began breeding, and between 1952 and 1973 about 70 unpinioned juveniles escaped, and feral breeding was first recorded in 1960. Until the early 1970s it remained a fairly scarce bird, with the population centred on the Midlands and Somerset. Since then their range has consolidated and expanded considerably (New Atlas).

The first record for Norfolk was one seen at Welney by G.H.Scott on 10th–18th January 1977. This was followed by one at Lyng Easthaugh Gravel Pits on 9th July 1978. The British population is particularly dispersive in severe weather (Vinicombe & Chandler 1982, Winter Atlas), and the winter of 1978–79 produced three further individuals in the county, with four more in late 1979, including the first multiple count of three at Breydon on 3rd November.

Observations gradually increased throughout the 1980s, rising from a single occurrence in 1980 to records of 1–3 birds at 19 localities scattered throughout the county in 1989. This steady increase has continued during the 1990s, with numerous observations throughout the year of 1–5 birds at 26 localities in 1996 and up to six at 32 localities in 1997. Although there have been records from most areas of the county, the bulk are from the Breckland meres, Welney, various inland gravel pits and the Broads. In recent years Welney and Tottenhill Gravel Pits have been greatly favoured, with presumably some movement between the two. Here counts have risen from a maximum of eight at Tottenhill and five at Welney in late 1992, to regular double–figure counts in 1993–95 and 1998. Peak counts have been during the winter months, with 16 at Welney in February 1993, 22 at Tottenhill in November 1993, 25 at Welney in January 1994 and up to 24 at Tottenhill from November 1994 to January 1995. Up to 13 were again at Tottenhill in March 1996 and up to 16 in January–February 1998. Other counts around the county worthy of mention have included six at Narford Hall Lake on 22nd May 1981 and 20 at Pentney Gravel Pit on 17th January 1998. Ten or more have also been reported in 1996–98 at Sennowe Lake, Holkham Park Lake, Pensthorpe and Hickling Broad.

Kelly (1986) mentioned records of probable breeding at Hardley Flood and at one of the Trinity Broads, and one of possible breeding from Hillington Lake during the 1980–85 fieldwork for the Norfolk Atlas. However, the first confirmed breeding in the county was not until in 1988 when a pair was noted with a brood of five ducklings at Stanford. There was then a gap of seven years until 1995 when breeding again took place, this time at four sites – at Fowlmere, where three large ducklings were seen on 2nd September, Ringmere where a pair reared five young, Little Broad at Filby where there was a female with a duckling on 9th August (and where a drake had been displaying to two females in 1994) and at a central county locality where 11 young were reared from three broods. Although there were no breeding records in 1996, five pairs bred at three sites in 1997 – two pairs at Cockley Cley, two pairs at Holkham Fresh Marsh and one pair at Cantley Beet Factory lagoons which reared two broods. Pairs were also present in May–June at Ormesby Broad and Ormesby Little Broad, but with no evidence of breeding. In 1998 a total of five pairs bred successfully at Cockley Cley, Holkham Park Lake, Pensthorpe, Cantley Beet Factory andMautby decoy.

Although there are now regular records in every month of the year, numbers in the county rise rapidly from September to peak in December–February, presumably as birds disperse from the Midland reservoirs, although birds could also come from expanding populations in the London area, Cambridgeshire and Essex. Passage seems to be principally nocturnal, but six were noted passing south-west off Hunstanton on 26th October 1986 and three passed south-west there on 17th October 1991. As well as a late-summer moult, Ruddy Ducks also have a complete pre-breeding moult, mainly in February–March, and a drop off in numbers around this time suggests that many return to their breeding areas just prior to this moult.

Although Ruddy Ducks prefer freshwater, they will frequent brackish estuaries and sheltered coastal bays in the winter, and there have been three county records of birds on the sea, including the previously mentioned second county record of one off Cley/Salthouse on 30th January 1977, one off Overstrand in 1988 and one off Gorleston on 19th November 1994, as well as a few records from Breydon.

*Phil Heath*

## Honey Buzzard (European Honey Buzzard)     *Pernis apivorus*

A rare summer visitor and very scarce passage migrant. CANTLEY. 2-10-1999.

In the Western Palearctic, the Honey Buzzard breeds throughout most of Europe east to Russia with the largest populations, numbering thousands of pairs, in Sweden, France, Germany and Poland. It winters in sub-Saharan Africa. On the edge of its breeding range in Britain, it remains a scarce breeder with up to 15 pairs (New Atlas).

Riviere recorded the Honey Buzzard as an irregular passage migrant, usually in small but occasionally in considerable numbers. Exceptionally large movements took place in 1841 and also in 1881 when between 20 and 30 were killed in September. A Honey Buzzard egg from a collection of Sir Vauncey Crewe sold in the 1920s was supposedly taken at Two Mile Bottom, Thetford in June 1889. However, the authenticity of its origins remains doubtful. Among the mounted birds in Felbrigg Hall are two cases of Honey Buzzards. Unfortunately there is no catalogue providing details, but it is quite possible the specimens were obtained on the estate bearing in mind subsequent events.

One shot at a wasp's nest at High Kelling on 7th October 1959, in mistake for a crow, was only the fourth county record since 1930. Another found trapped at Gresham on 17th September 1960 had to be destroyed and the skin is preserved at the Castle Museum, Norwich. Between 1959 and 1973, the species was reported annually in the county with 29 records, the highest numbers being in May and September.

The first recorded successful breeding for Norfolk was in 1974 when three young were reared at Felbrigg Park. Subsequently a pair was present annually each summer up to 1978, although there was no proof of successful breeding. A single bird was also present in 1979, the year in which a pair summered at nearby Sheringham Park. A pair summered in the county again in 1983 and on the Sandringham Estate in 1987–89, with one seen displaying at Dersingham in 1990.

Successful breeding had resumed in 1989 when two pairs were present in the county and young were reared again in 1990, 1992, 1993 and 1996. On 28th August 1993 a total of six Honey Buzzards was on show at one site, including two juveniles. Pairs summered in the intervening years and in 1997 but with no evidence of breeding. Since 1989 the favoured nesting site has been in the Swanton Novers/Fulmodeston area. Recently birds have moved from the Great Wood following the appearance of Common Buzzards in the area. It is believed that this displacement of the nest-site has occurred because the two species will not exist in close proximity.

Honey Buzzards leave their wintering grounds from mid-April to the end of May with birds returning to their northern breeding territories from mid-May to early June. In Norfolk, spring sightings peak in May and June with birds generally being seen back at the breeding site in the third week of May. Away from the breeding localities most sightings are on or near the coast, although inland records of birds on passage have been made in May at Norwich, Strumpshaw, Thetford and Bagthorpe/Syderstone, and in June at Norwich, Great Witchingham and the Little Ouse Washes.

Return migration in the autumn begins from mid-August through September, which has been the peak month in Norfolk with 43 records since 1960. Inland sightings in autumn have come from Walpole Island, Stanford Water, Welney, Massingham, Hempstead and Hoveton. An impressive autumn passage occurred in 1993 with the first at Wootton Marsh on 21st August. Mid-September saw an abundance of records with Continental migrants crossing the North Sea in large numbers. At least ten different birds were reported in Norfolk at many well-scattered, mainly coastal, localities from Wells in the north to Yarmouth in the south. Mostly single birds were involved but there were three at Wells East Hills on 14th September and two at Weybourne on 13th and Cromer on 16th.

**Table 28. Cumulative monthly totals of all migrant Honey Buzzards recorded in Norfolk 1953–97.**

|         | Apr | May | Jun | Jul | Aug | Sept | Oct | Nov |
|---------|-----|-----|-----|-----|-----|------|-----|-----|
| 1953–59 | -   | -   | -   | -   | -   | -    | 1   | -   |
| 1960–69 | -   | 2   | 2   | 1   | -   | 7    | 3   | -   |
| 1970–79 | -   | 5   | 1   | 5   | 3   | 8    | 4   | 1   |
| 1980–89 | 4   | 5   | 10  | 1   | 4   | 2    | 2   | -   |
| 1990–97 | -   | 22  | 9   | 4   | 11  | 22   | 3   | -   |
| Total   | 4   | 34  | 22  | 11  | 18  | 39   | 13  | 1   |

The earliest spring sighting for Norfolk was at Holme on 23rd April 1983 and the latest autumn records involved one shot at Downham Market on 5th November 1876 and one at Cley and Blakeney on 7th November 1976. There are two old winter records of birds shot near Yarmouth in December 1850 and at Cawston on 23rd December 1927.

*Phil Lockwood*

## Black Kite                                                         *Milvus migrans*

**A rare vagrant, mainly in spring.**

The Black Kite is a scavenging and often gregarious raptor which breeds throughout Europe (except for the British Isles and at only a few sites in Fennoscandia), Africa, Asia, Arabia and Australia. The European population is mainly migratory, wintering in Africa south of the Sahara. Regarded as the world's most numerous raptor, but with Europe holding only a small proportion of the total population, the species has increased in some areas of central Europe because of increasing numbers of dead fish due to pollution. Elsewhere numbers are decreasing.

It was added to the county list in 1966 when one was observed by David Butt flying over West Runton on 14th May. The bird was brought to his attention by the inquisitive gaze of his three-year-old daughter looking up from her pushchair in the garden (Taylor 1987a). There had been only five previous British records. Since then more than 20 have been recorded in Norfolk:

1966: One flying west at West Runton on 14th May, later seen at Cley and Salthouse.
1971: Cley and Salthouse Heath area on 6th–10th May.
1974: Ringstead Downs on 11th May.
1976: Horsey on 2nd May.
      Holkham Gap on 12th October and at Holkham Park on 17th October, probably the same individual.
1978: Cley on 15th October.
1979: Cromer on 28th May.
1980: Burnham Deepdale on 24th August.
1984: Loddon and Great Hockham on 1st June.
1985: Langham, Wells, Holkham Park and North Creake area on 12th July, Brancaster on 13th and Snettisham on 24th.
1987: Hickling on 11th April and Blofield on 12th.
      Castle Acre on 3rd May. Repps on 9th May.
1988: Dersingham on 12th May, in company with a Red Kite.

1989: Kerdiston and Reepham on 24th June.

1992: Stiffkey on 24th August.

1993: Blakeney on 20th April, High Kelling on 22nd, Wells, Burnham Norton and Burnham Deepdale on 23rd, Great Snoring and Pensthorpe on 25th. Wells, Holkham and Burnham Norton on 16th May, Brancaster, Titchwell, Sedgeford and Ringstead on 17th, seen heading south over Wolferton on 18th.

1994: Beeston and Blakeney on 29th April. Cromer and Paston on 2nd May. Attleborough on 15th May.

1997: Burnham Norton on 31st May.

1998: Sheringham 18th May.

As might be expected from such a pronounced migrant, Black Kites are seen north of their breeding range but relatively few make it to Britain. Most records are in May which is also the peak month for Norfolk sightings. A Black Kite flying over Yarmouth Haven bridge on 22nd February 1975 appeared the following day at Ormesby East End. It showed the characteristics of one of the southern forms and in view of its tameness and the unusual date, was almost certainly an escape from captivity (Allard 1990). In 1981, an escaped individual bearing a green colour ring was at large in the Broads area and north Norfolk between January and May (Rogers *et al.* 1982).

*Phil Lockwood*

## Red Kite                                                                       *Milvus milvus*

**A scarce, but increasing, passage migrant and year-round visitor, involving birds from the Continent and the British reintroduction projects.**

The Red Kite is essentially a European raptor, elsewhere it only breeds in small numbers in North Africa and islands in the Atlantic. It is decreasing in many areas due to human persecution. The largest populations, numbering thousands of pairs, are in Germany, Spain and France. In 20th century Britain it was, until recently, confined to central Wales as a breeding species. However, in 1989 a reintroduction scheme began in England and Scotland to return the Red Kite to some of its former haunts. The first successful breeding outside Wales occurred in 1992.

Both Stevenson and Riviere described the Red Kite as abundant on the heaths and warrens of Thetford and Elvedon between 1770 and 1780, where it was hunted by falcons of the Earl of Orford. It remained 'rather common' in Breckland up to the end of the 18th century, but had ceased to breed in Norfolk by about 1830. There were only eight records between 1852 and 1881 when one, displayed in the Castle Museum, Norwich, was killed at Winterton on 7th October. A further 77 years were to pass before the Red Kite was again identified in Norfolk, with three sightings in 1958 – at Ridlington Common on 3rd March, Kelling Heath on 22nd March and Woodbastwick on 26th May. Since then, the Red Kite has been recorded annually except in 1962, 1964–66, 1968 and 1985.

During the 1960s, a total of 16 Red Kites was recorded, mostly in the spring. Notable amongst these was one seen at Winterton on 19th February 1967 involved in an aerial encounter with a Rough-legged Buzzard and two at Ludham on 16th April 1969. Spring sightings such as these are considered to be Continental birds deflected west (Seago 1998).

The 1970s produced 34 records with both spring and winter sightings, the latter thought to be wandering Welsh birds. The skin of a bird found dead at Wells on 23rd March 1972 is now in the Castle Museum, Norwich. A further increase in records occurred during the 1980s when 43 were reported. The bird seen at Hedenham in early December 1982 which remained in the area until the first week of March 1983, was the first Red Kite in the 20th century to have made a prolonged stay in the county. An unusual record was of an exhausted bird, flown by helicopter to Yarmouth from a North Sea drilling rig 65km north of Blakeney, on 15th March 1986. Another long-stayer, wandering widely between Cromer in the east and Snettisham in the west, was present from 4th January to 8th March 1987. Early spring 1988 produced a spectacular movement of Continental migrants moving from their winter quarters. Commencing with four at Ringstead and Holme on 18th March, a total of 11 birds passed through the county between then and 17th April.

Following the reintroduction scheme it was not surprising that reports of sightings increased from 1990 as birds wandered from their release areas. A wing-tagged bird with a radio transmitter was seen on 25th July at a number of north Norfolk sites between Paston and Blakeney, which had been released in the Chilterns in early July. A sighting at Burnham Market on 2nd August possibly involved the same bird. During 1991, Red Kites were reported in seven months of the year and in 1992 in each month from March to July and again in November. An unusual offshore report on 19th July 1992 was of a wing-tagged juvenile alighting on a gas platform 45km off Cromer. This bird had been ringed as a nestling in June in central Wales. 1993 produced seven spring sightings, mostly coastal and ranging from Wells in the north to Yarmouth in the east. The first autumn sighting was of a wing-tagged bird seen on 1st September at South Walsham and Plumstead Green, before being relocated in the Saxthorpe area three days later and the annual total rose to 13.

In 1994, there were sightings in all months except February, July and September, with autumn providing a good series of records, including up to two in Melton Constable Park for several weeks after 1st August. Birds were recorded in all months except June and September during 1995 and amongst the more interesting reports were of one eating a dead hare on a road at Anmer and another at Woodton on 28th–30th July which was identified from its wing-tags as a female fledged in southern England in 1994.

1996 saw the Red Kite being recorded in every month from January to August. There was a scattering of records of single birds during the first winter period, with two at Ringstead on 2nd January. A record number of spring migrants was seen between 9th March and 1st June, with about 45 individuals being involved, none of which was seen to be wing-tagged. A pair, neither of which carried wing-tags and which were believed to have been of Scandinavian origin, successfully reared two young just across the county border in Suffolk and a juvenile seen some distance away in Norfolk on 31st July may have been associated with this breeding occurrence. In contrast to the spring passage, only two birds were seen in autumn and none in the second winter period. Good numbers were once again recorded in spring 1997, mainly single birds but two at Weybourne, Sheringham, Shotesham, Hickling and Bradwell, with three at Yarmouth on 15th March. Although some of the birds carried wing-tags, many were unmarked. At least five and possibly seven different wing-tagged individuals moved through Horsey in March. There were far fewer records after July, in fact August was the only month of the year in which the species was not noted in the county. Two birds took up residence at Hoveton on 5th December and remained until the end of January 1998. One was an untagged first-winter bird, the other older bird carried wing-tags which identified it as one of the Suffolk-bred young fledged in the summer of 1996. This bird had left its natal area in the autumn of that year only to be relocated at a Midlands roost, remaining there until February 1997. Spring passage in spring 1998 was disappointing, apart from three at Winterton on 17th February 1998.

At least two Red Kites from the Midlands reintroduction project, which began in 1995, have already been recorded in Norfolk. The first involved a bird released in 1996 that was rescued near Dersingham in June. It had returned to the Midlands by the autumn and was still present there in January 1998. The second, the bird in the West Raynham/Great Massingham area in November, was one of eight young fledged in the Midlands in 1997. This was one of four chicks reared by another untagged pair of kites, birds that were certainly not released in the Midlands and were most likely to have been wild migrants.

With sightings of Continental migrants in spring and Welsh birds in autumn and winter, interspersed with wandering birds from the reintroduction scheme, it is now possible to see Red Kites in any month of the year in Norfolk. Now that the species is nesting on the Suffolk/Norfolk border, hopefully it will not be too long before the Red Kite, arguably the most beautiful raptor in Britain, breeds again in Norfolk.

*Phil Lockwood*

## White-tailed Eagle OVER NORWICH. 1-4-2000. *Haliaeetus albicilla*

**A rare vagrant, mainly in winter.**

The White-tailed Eagle is largely confined to northern areas as a breeding bird ranging from Greenland, Iceland, northern Europe and Fennoscandia to north-east Asia. In Norway, Germany, Poland and Russia the population is thought to number hundreds of pairs (Gensbøl 1984) but elsewhere in eastern Europe it can be described as scarce. This huge raptor was distributed throughout most of Europe in the 19th century but was exterminated by shooting and poisoning in many areas including Scotland. In an effort to re-establish a breeding population in western Scotland young Norwegian birds were introduced from 1968 and this species now breeds in small numbers once again in Britain.

Stevenson writing in the 1860s stated 'Nearly every autumn or winter affords specimens of this eagle in immature plumage, and it appears also at times late in spring'. The first six dated records are all from east Norfolk between 1811 and 1829 (Patterson 1905). Severe weather prevailed in the 1828–29 winter and White-tailed Eagles were unusually numerous. Five were observed at the same time over Horsey Warren, a favoured locality with its abundance of rabbit warrens. On one occasion during very cold conditions, one of these huge and ponderous birds '... approached as near the city as Postwick Grove ...searching for Coot or wildfowl in the wakes which remained unfrozen' (Lubbock 1879).

The details surrounding the capture of one at Winterton in 1840 make fascinating reading 'Some boys having thrown out a line and hook into the sea, baited with a herring, for the purpose of catching a gull, the bait was spied and pounced upon by the eagle, and the hook becoming fixed in the inside of his foot, he was found by the boys, upon their return to examine their line, floating on the surface of the water. They immediately went off in a boat, and completed their capture without much difficulty. This bird was subsequently kept in confinement for some years, but accidentally escaping, was shot a few days afterwards by a gamekeeper in the neighbourhood' (Gurney & Fisher 1846). The specimen, by then in adult plumage, was presented to the Castle Museum, Norwich where it remains to this day. In total, there are just over 30 dated records for the 19th century, all of immature birds and the majority during the winter months, although one, formerly in Stevenson's collection, was obtained at Rollesby on 27th April 1873. Between 27th October and 31st December 1875 no less than seven were obtained in the county including two at Northrepps and two at Herringfleet.

During the 20th century, approximately 25 White-tailed Eagles have been recorded in Norfolk, of which six have occurred since 1980. The majority have been found between December and March, mainly in north Norfolk or Broadland. There have been two records of adults – one shot at Hanworth on 18th June 1905, after five days of continuous north-easterly gales (Riviere) and one at Hickling on 25th–29th October 1945.

The six most recent records concern an immature found shot between Crabbe and Wighton, near Wells on 11th May 1984, which subsequently died. It had earlier been reported in Broadland and at Winterton after initially being found in coastal Suffolk on 14th April. It had been ringed as a nestling on 5th June 1983 at Warder See, Schleswig-Holstein, Germany and was the first foreign-ringed White-tailed Eagle to be found in the British Isles. In 1985 an immature was present between Holme and Scolt Head on 16th – 19th November. During its stay it was observed pursuing an overwintering Chilean Flamingo and Cormorants at Titchwell and attacking a Shag at Scolt Head.

In 1990, no less than three White-tailed Eagles were seen in Norfolk and the following details are all taken from Williamson (1991). An immature, probably a second-year bird, was first seen at Westacre Trout Farm, near King's Lynn on 1st January and remained in the county until at least 15th March. Whilst at Westacre it regularly roosted in Sigone Wood, but it left the area on about 1st February and was relocated in Suffolk three days later. Between then and 15th March, it was seen on various dates in both counties. During its stay in Norfolk it frequented Haddiscoe Island where it was seen from a Lowestoft to Norwich train by a lucky observer on 10th February. It was present in this area from 20th February to 7th March. On the day of its last confirmed sighting in Norfolk, it flew over the Halvergate and Mautby Marshes before gaining height and drifting eastwards, over West Caister.

Another immature was also reported, battling against gale force winds along the north-west coast, moving from Scolt Head to Snettisham on 10th January. While off Titchwell, it made repeated strikes at a Goldeneye, hovering over the sea in a stiff wind. The Goldeneye escaped capture by both diving and swimming in circles, ducking its head at each attempted strike.

Amazingly, a third individual, a first-year bird, was first seen at Snettisham on 27th October, before taking up residence in east Norfolk until December. It remained near Eastfield Farm, Hickling from 30th November to 2nd December. Whilst feeding, the bird was permanently accompanied by local Magpies which seemed to take delight in harassing the eagle by pulling its tail feathers in an attempt to steal food. On 2nd December, it was noted at sea off Waxham and the following day it was seen heading out to sea over Winterton dunes. The final sighting came from Walcott and Happisburgh on 14th December. Both long-staying birds favoured extensive open areas with nearby woodland and although they were frequently observed eating carrion, no kills were witnessed. The most recent record concerned an immature flying west over Burnham Overy dunes on 28th October 1997. It was later seen heading west in the Midlands and finally at Tregaron in central Wales.

Although White-tailed Eagles breeding in Europe are non-migratory, young birds move around, with immatures from Fennoscandia reaching France, Spain and Italy (Gensbøl 1984). It is probably these birds that are recorded in Norfolk.

E.G. HARDLEY FLOODS. (♀) 17·5·1991.    (♂) 20·6·1991, 4·7·2000.

*Phil Lockwood*

## Marsh Harrier (Eurasian Marsh Harrier)          *Circus aeruginosus*

**A scarce breeding summer visitor, passage migrant and resident; bred in the Fens at Welney in 1997 for the first time since the early 19th century.**

Marsh Harriers
(*Norman Arlott*)

In the Western Palearctic, the Marsh Harrier disappeared from many areas in the 20th century due to drainage and persecution, but from the mid-1970s some northern European populations, including that in Britain, started to increase rapidly. Northern and eastern populations are migratory with birds wintering in the Mediterranean area and in sub-Saharan Africa. In Britain, the Marsh Harrier became extinct by the end of the 19th century. The last record was of a nest built in Norfolk in 1899 and photographed by the Kearton brothers, but the adults were trapped before any eggs were laid (Historical Atlas). Numbers are now increasing with 87 breeding pairs reported in 1990 (New Atlas), mostly in eastern England, and a count of about 160 pairs in 1995 (Stone *et al.* 1997).

Lubbock called it the 'Norfolk Hawk' as it was so generally dispersed amongst the Broads. It was abundant in the Fens and Broadland as a breeding species in the early 19th century but between 1878 and 1926 breeding was reported on only six occasions. By 1930, it was one of the rarest breeding birds in Norfolk and was confined to the Broads (Riviere). Early photographers all failed with the Marsh Harrier, but under the guidance of Jim Vincent, the Lancashire photographer Walter Higham took the first pictures of the species in Britain – a female at a nest of young chicks at Hickling in the early 1930s (reproduced in his 1949 book *Birds in Camera*).

Marsh Harriers bred annually in the Hickling/Horsey area from 1927 to 1959, where up to six pairs nested in their traditional reedbed habitat. Although birds were present each spring, successful breeding did not take place again until 1967 when one young was fledged in west Norfolk and a single pair raised four young in 1972. In 1975, a pair once again bred successfully in the Hickling/Horsey/Martham area and thereafter the number of nesting pairs slowly increased at various locations throughout the county. This recolonisation may well have been assisted by the spread of birds from the polders in The Netherlands. The largest polder, Southern Flevoland, was reclaimed in 1968 and rapidly colonised throughout the 1970s. Marsh Harrier numbers built up to about 400 nests, but rapidly fell to about 100 nests by 1990 as much marshland was reclaimed for agriculture. By 1995 up to 69 nesting females were recorded in Norfolk, raising over 100 young. Breeding is now firmly established at reserves such as Titchwell, Cley, Strumpshaw and Hickling, and also in the Yare, Bure and Waveney Valleys, at other Broadland sites and in north-west Norfolk around the Wash. In 1997 a male summered for the first time at a suitable breeding location in the Wensum Valley. Sills (1984, 1985) provided a detailed and fascinating account of breeding Marsh Harriers at Titchwell in 1980–83.

1982 marked a further landmark in the revival of the Marsh Harrier when three young fledged from a nest in arable crops, the first such record in Britain. The nest, containing three nearly-fledged young, was saved from probable disaster by a vigilant combine harvester driver who can vouch for the lightning re-flexes and razor sharpness of the bird's talons! The young were removed to a nearby ditch where the parents continued to feed them. All were on the wing a few days later (Image 1987). This practice has increased to such an extent that in 1991, a total of 18 nests in Norfolk were in cereals. The number nesting in arable crops in Norfolk in 1987–91 had more than quadrupled compared with the previous five-year period (Image 1992). Examples of the polygamous behaviour of the Marsh Harrier were provided from two sites in 1990 and one in 1992 and 1993, where single males each paired with three females. Six of the young fledged at three sites in 1989 were strikingly patterned in white and similar birds were also raised at three sites in Suffolk.

**Table 29. Total number of Marsh Harriers fledged annually in Norfolk 1975–97.**

| 1975 | 4 | 1980 | 24 | 1985 | 36 | 1990 | 90 | 1995 | 112 |
|------|---|------|----|------|----|------|----|------|-----|
| 1976 | 8 | 1981 | 27 | 1986 | 43 | 1991 | 75 | 1996 | 87 |
| 1977 | 19 | 1982 | 42 | 1987 | 60 | 1992 | 114 | 1997 | 88+ |
| 1978 | 18 | 1983 | 49 | 1988 | 82 | 1993 | 105 | | |
| 1979 | 15 | 1984 | 33 | 1989 | 88 | 1994 | 71 | | |

Marsh Harriers are recorded regularly on spring passage between April and June, mostly from coastal marshes and the Ouse Washes. Highest spring passage counts have been from Cley, where a total of ten in 1964, 14 in 1967 and 16 in 1968. As the number of breeding pairs has increased in the 1990s, so have the numbers seen on spring passage with eight in April and eleven in May 1994 at Sheringham and no less than eight at Cley on 30th May 1994. Six flew over Swanton Novers on 2nd June 1995. During April 1996, a total of 22 Marsh Harriers passed Holme including a maximum count of 13 west on 27th April. Another recent feature has been a tendency for Marsh Harriers to be recorded earlier on spring passage; for instance in 1996, the species was noted at three north coast localities in February and at many coastal sites in March. As a result of widespread post-breeding dispersal from late July, the species is now recorded from many parts of the county in early autumn. The highest autumn total has been ten at Welney in 1993, including three on 30th August. An unusual record of a melanistic-type male, a very dark bird with grey tail and pale patches under the primaries was noted at Welney on 10th September 1988.

A highlight of the autumn period, believed to involve local breeders and their fledged young, is the communal roosting of Marsh Harriers in crops and, after harvesting, in a reedbed at a coastal site in north-west Norfolk. This was first recorded in 1976, with a maximum count of 15 birds roosting on 31st August, since when spectacular counts have included up to 32 birds in early September 1983, 36 on 1st September 1991 and 18 on 28th August 1993 (Image 1994a). The Marsh Harriers are often joined by Montagu's Harriers with four present on 13th August 1986 and occasionally by an early Hen Harrier, as on 12th September 1992.

Formerly rare in winter, small numbers of Marsh Harriers now overwinter in the county at favoured sites. Since the mid-1950s the main Broadland roost has been in the Horsey/Hickling area, with a maximum of 11 in December 1958 and up to ten annually in the 1990s. From the mid-1980s, birds were also roosting at two additional sites in the Waveney and mid-Yare Valleys with up to a total of 20 birds recorded in 1994 and 1995.

Whilst the revival of this species continues, it is distressing to report that examples of persecution continue with poisoning at one nest in 1986 and a brood removed by a gamekeeper from another nest in 1991.

A total of 23 Marsh Harriers ringed as nestlings in Norfolk has been recovered, of which five have been found abroad. The first concerned one ringed at Horsey in 1935 which was found long-dead in Morocco two years later. Another early recovery involved a nestling ringed by Jim Vincent at Hickling in June 1943 which was found at Felixstowe, Suffolk in August. Of the nestlings ringed at Hickling in the 1950s, one was recovered at Amiens, France in August the following year and others were found at King's Lynn and in Suffolk, Lincolnshire (2) and Berkshire. More recently-ringed Norfolk nestlings have been found in Yorkshire and Humberside, and singles in France in April and in Algeria in October. Nestlings ringed at Walberswick, Suffolk have been recovered in the county, as was one from the Isle of Sheppey, Kent, only a few weeks after ringing. Four foreign-ringed Marsh Harriers, all marked as nestlings, have been found in Norfolk – two from The Netherlands and one each from Sieversdorf, Germany and Odense, Denmark.

*Phil Lockwood*

## Hen Harrier | *HARDLEY FLooDS.* ♂. 1-5-2000.        *Circus cyaneus*

**A scarce passage migrant and winter visitor, very rare in mid-summer; last bred in 1861.**

During the 20th century, the Hen Harrier has suffered a decrease in numbers due to habitat loss and disturbance, and in the early years due to shooting. About 95% of the breeding pairs in the Western Palearctic (excluding those in Russia) are to be found in Sweden, Finland, the British Isles, France and Spain (Gensbøl 1984). Prior to 1939, in Britain it was confined to Orkney and the Outer Hebrides but has since spread to the Scottish mainland, northern England and Wales. It continues to be persecuted, particularly by gamekeepers on grouse moors, and numbers are thought to be declining with currently less than 700 breeding pairs (Wynne 1997).

In Norfolk, it formerly bred in the Fens and Broads with the last recorded breeding at Horsey in 1861 (Stevenson). Riviere recorded the Hen Harrier as a scarce winter visitor to Norfolk with no summer records for 50 years.

Nowadays, most Hen Harriers occur on coastal grazing marshes, saltings, sand dunes, reedbeds and heaths, and also in Breckland and the Fenland washes. Winter visitors generally start to arrive in late September, with the earliest at Bradwell on 13th August 1961, peaking in October and passage can continue into early November, as demonstrated by one seen coasting north-west 2km offshore at Winterton on 9th November 1981, and birds coming in off the sea in 1982 at Hunstanton on 5th November and at Yarmouth on 7th November.

A habit common amongst harrier species is that of communal roosting. At favoured locations, Hen Harriers gather at the end of the day to provide an unforgettable winter spectacle. This habit was known at Hickling in 1912 and referred to in Jim Vincent's diaries as 'the birds sleeping amongst the sedge'. Few roosts were known before 1974, but by 1996 a total of 18 sites had been identified in Norfolk. Communal roosting was first mentioned in the *Norfolk Bird Report 1972*, although multiple sightings in 1962 of three birds in the Brecks at Gooderstone and three 'ringtails' at Cley on 1st January 1964 may provide earlier pointers to the habit. Norfolk is thought to hold around 15% of the country's winter population of Hen Harriers (Clarke 1986, 1987).

The 1978–79 winter provided unprecedented numbers of Hen Harriers with birds reported from 140 locations, including many inland sites, and the main six roosts held a total of 45 birds. The largest roost recorded in the county was at Titchwell on 5th March 1982, when 22 birds, including 7 grey males, were present. Observations at two roosts in north-west Norfolk during the 1979–80 and 1980–81 winters (Brown 1981) found an increase in the number of males during late winter and early spring, perhaps a reflection of a westerly movement of males from the Low Countries in January–February. The highest number of males at a Broadland roost in 1990–91 was also in late February (Hampshire & Lockwood 1992).

**Table 30. Total number of Hen Harriers at roosts in Norfolk 1984–97, as recorded in January (one of the peak months) during coordinated counts (figures supplied by Roger Clarke).**

| Winter | Total | Ringtails | Grey males | Sites watched | Sites occupied |
|--------|-------|-----------|------------|---------------|----------------|
| 15.1.84 | 37 | 25 | 12 | 8 | 7 |
| 13.1.85 | 51 | 37 | 14 | 14 | 11 |
| 21.1.86 | 36 | 23 | 13 | 12 | 10 |
| 18.1.87 | 24 | 15 | 9 | 10 | 6 |
| 17.1.88 | 22 | 13 | 9 | 11 | 8 |
| 15.1.89 | 22 | 13 | 9 | 13 | 6 |
| 14.1.90 | 28 | 21 | 7 | 12 | 9 |
| 31.1.91 | 21 | 13 | 8 | 12 | 8 |
| 12.1.92 | 21 | 16 | 5 | 9 | 5 |
| 17.1.93 | 19 | 12 | 7 | 8 | 6 |
| 16.1.94 | 20 | 14 | 6 | 9 | 5 |
| 15.1.95 | 26 | 18 | 8 | 8 | 7 |
| 14.1.96 | 27 | 17 | 10 | 8 | 6 |
| 12.1.97 | 34 | 23 | 11 | 7 | 7 |
| Total | 388 | 260 | 128 | | |
| % | 100 | 67 | 33 | | |

Hen Harriers are regularly seen on spring migration on the coast in April and May. Records have included reports of birds flying out to sea at Winterton on 12th April 1981 and at Cley on 23rd April 1963 and 2nd May 1960. More unusual records were of singles coming in from the sea at Titchwell on 10th May 1993 and at Cromer on 19th May 1997. The highest spring day-count was five south at Winterton on 22nd April 1979. On 19th May 1983 a female at Horsey was seen carrying nesting material into the reeds and in 1992, an adult male was seen at Welney on 19th May and later in the summer in Cambridgeshire. June records are unusual, but include a male in 1985 giving spectacular aerial displays and on occasions attracting a wandering female, until as late as 26th June. In 1994, there were a number of sightings in June at three coastal sites with the last at Welney on 30th. An even more unusual record was one in the Brancaster Harbour/Burnham Norton area on 19th July 1995. It is perhaps wishful thinking that these beautiful birds will ever again breed in the county.

A unique record is that of an immature bird resembling the American race *C. c. hudsonius*, originally called Marsh Hawk but now known as Northern Harrier, which spent the winter at Cley from 26th October 1957 to 13th April 1958. Full details including field sketches appear in *British Birds* (Wallace 1971).

Norfolk's Hen Harriers arrive from Scotland, Wales and the Continent with cold-weather influxes thought to involve birds from Sweden in particular. Evidence to support this comes from a recovery of a bird ringed in Belgium on 11th November 1961 and found at Wretham in February 1962, and a nestling ringed in The Netherlands found dead at Tunstead four years later. Ringed nestlings and more recently those with wing-tags have originated from breeding pairs in Wales (6) and Scotland (5).

*Phil Lockwood*

| **Montagu's Harrier** | CHEDGRAVE - ♂ 23-5-2001. (JuE)<br>CHEDGRAVE - ♂ 26-5-2001 (mE) | ***Circus pygargus*** |

**A very scarce breeding summer visitor and scarce passage migrant.**

The Montagu's Harrier breeds across the middle latitudes of the Western Palearctic to the low lying steppes of south-west Asia. Following a decline during the 19th century some recovery occurred in the first half of the 20th century but further sharp declines occurred from the late 1950s. The only countries where the breeding population numbers at least a thousand pairs are France, Spain, Portugal, Turkey and Russia (Clarke 1996). The species is entirely migratory with the European population wintering in sub-Saharan Africa. In the British Isles, the 'Ash-Coloured Falcon', as Montagu called it, has always been scarce and may have reached a maximum of 50 pairs in the 1950s (Gensbøl 1984). In the last 20 years numbers of breeding pairs have never exceeded 15.

In the 1830s, the species was widely distributed as a breeding bird in the Broads and Fens, but was almost entirely confined to eastern Broadland by the middle of the 19th century. The species was heavily persecuted although a pair bred at partly-flooded Northwold Fen in 1924. In 1910 the birds breeding area at Horsey and Hickling was afforded special protection resulting in six nests in 1921 and 1922. A peak of nine nests was attained in 1924 when Jim Vincent, Whiteslea estate headkeeper, wrote as follows 'After all the young hatched and could fly one could see 30 with one sweep of the glasses. Montagu's is the most colonial of harriers; I have known four nests in a 200 yard circle. On another occasion two nests were only ten yards apart'.

The main Broadland area held five nests in 1930 and 1931, and breeding continued, but in ever-decreasing numbers, until 1956. A pair also nested at Wheatfen in the Yare Valley each year from 1948 to 1954. A pair returned to Horsey in 1968 and may have bred, as a bird of the year was seen in July. A final pair returned to Horsey in 1973, but the clutch of eggs was deserted.

Elsewhere two pairs nested in Breckland, in young conifer plantations, in 1931 and breeding was suspected on the Sandringham estate in 1954 when four birds were observed on 8th August at Snettisham. Further success in Breckland followed in 1957 when a pair nested at Foulden Common and another pair summered at nearby Hilborough. The following year two nests were recorded at Foulden and a third pair summered at Bodney. In 1963 a pair bred in the Fens close to Breckland and were again present in 1964. A pair bred in west Norfolk in 1965 increasing to three pairs the next year and still two pairs in 1967.

Two nests in wheat fields in 1968 in the vicinity of the Wash became the first record of crop-nesting by Montagu's Harriers in Britain. Between 1970 and 1972 a pair bred annually at Titchwell fledging a total of 13 young. In addition, another pair at Brancaster reared five young in 1972. No further instances of summering occurred until 1978 when a pair in the Brecks raised three young at Bridgham Heath. Four years later, in 1982, successful breeding occurred at a site in north-west Norfolk bordering the Wash. It was here that the Montagu's Harrier was afforded special protection as a rare breeding bird and the RSPB provided summer wardens. This site is now the stronghold of Britain's small breeding population.

**Table 31. Total number of Montagu's Harrier's nests and young fledged in Norfolk 1982–97.**

|       | 1982 | 1983 | 1984 | 1985 | 1986 | 1987 | 1988 | 1989 | 1990 |
|-------|------|------|------|------|------|------|------|------|------|
| Young | 4    | 9    | 3    | 7    | 3    | 9    | 6    | 13   | 13   |
| Nests | 2    | 3    | 2    | 2    | 4    | 3    | 3    | 5    | 5    |

|       | 1991 | 1992 | 1993 | 1994 | 1995 | 1996 | 1997 | 1998 |
|-------|------|------|------|------|------|------|------|------|
| Young | 7    | 10   | 13   | 11   | 12   | 10   | 6    | 4    |
| Nests | 2    | 4    | 4    | 9    | 4    | 3    | 7    | 1    |

1984 provided a unique breeding record of polyandry with two males and one female successfully fledging 3 young. In 1985, this was the only site in England where successful breeding occurred. It is only with the close cooperation of local farmers that successful breeding in arable crops has been achieved (Image 1987). The only other locality at which Montagu's Harriers have bred in Norfolk in recent years has been Burnham Deepdale in 1986.

After leaving their winter quarters, birds arrive back in Britain between the second half of April and the end of May, the period during which spring passage peaks in Norfolk. The earliest records have been at Wheatfen on 11th March 1948, Ludham on 6th April 1997, Cley on 11th April 1964 and Horsey on 14th April 1963. Most sightings come from coastal localities, the Broads, Brecks, Fens and the Wash area. The total of 37 records during the spring of 1983, was unusually high, with the majority seen in May on the coast or in Broadland. On 24th April 1994, after a few days of southerly winds, a multiple arrival of three males and two females was recorded at the breeding area in west Norfolk. This suggested that birds had 'met up' at a favoured traditional roost or hunting ground in England or the near Continent, before arriving in Norfolk. In most years, the male and female of a pair arrive almost simultaneously with court-ship commencing immediately on arrival, indicating that the birds probably also pair up beforehand (Image 1994a).

Return migration starts in August and continues into September. The latest records have been at Titchwell and Thornham Point on 6th November 1995 and at Cley on 16th November 1918, while a juvenile harrier at Warham Green/Stiffkey on 24th–27th November 1995 was almost certainly a Montagu's and not a Pallid Harrier (Forsman & Millington 1996). There have been two mid-winter records – singles at Horsey on 28th December 1866 and at Melton Constable on 19th January 1876.

There have been several records of melanistic birds, the first, a female shot near Yarmouth in September 1853, is in the collection at the Castle Museum, Norwich. More recently, singles were at Cley on 29th August and Scolt Head on 3rd–9th September 1956 and at Bargate Fen on 11th September 1959.

Evidence that fledged birds, both male and female, return to breed in their natal areas comes from colour-ringing the young harriers. A female fledged in 1986 was back breeding in 1988, while another rearing young in 1990 was only ten months old, having fledged the previous summer (Image 1992). Four Norfolk-ringed nestlings have been recovered in autumn in France, the first two ringed at Hickling in 1930 and 1955 respectively, while the remains of one from west Norfolk was found in an Eagle Owl's nest in the south of France on 1st September 1986, the year after ringing. Another was reported from Zeeland, The Netherlands and one from the wintering area in Senegal in February 1995, the first recovery of a British-ringed Montagu's Harrier south of the Mediterranean. Another unprecedented movement concerned one recovered at Pitlochry, Tayside in May 1996, the year after ringing, although the bird was long-dead when found. The earliest recovery, however, involved a nestling ringed at Waxham in 1927 which was found in Northamptonshire the following May.

*Phil Lockwood*

## Goshawk (Northern Goshawk)

*[handwritten: CHEDGRAVE MANOR 13-2-2000 (PLUCKING WOODPIGEON)]*

*Accipiter gentilis*

**A very scarce resident and passage migrant.**

The Goshawk is an abundant breeding species throughout the boreal and temperate zones of the northern hemisphere. It occurs as a resident in most of Europe, although northern Fennoscandian juveniles may be partial migrants. The population has been stable since the 1960s, except for the British Isles where it has been expanding. It was exterminated as a British breeding species in the late 19th century, as a result of deforestation and persecution. Sporadic breeding attempts only occurred until the mid-1960s, after which it once more bred regularly, with 60 pairs by 1980 (New Atlas) and 400–450 pairs by 1993–94 (Stone *et al*. 1997). The British breeding population has largely, if not wholly, been derived from imported birds which have escaped or have been deliberately released, with concentrations in Wales, the Scottish borders, and northern and central England.

Until recent times, the Goshawk had always been a rare vagrant to Norfolk. The first record concerned an adult male shot at Colton in 1841, which is still in the collection at the Castle Museum, Norwich. It remained the only example of one in adult plumage for over a hundred years. In fact Stevenson and Riviere were able to provide details of only a further 12 records up to 1901, and only six more reported between 1942 and 1956 (Seago 1967). Between 1967 and 1975, there were an additional 17 records, including a pair which bred in the Brecks in 1975, the female of which carried a falconer's bell. The continuing persecution of the species is illustrated by the fact that three of the 17 records concerned birds found shot (Seago 1977).

Between 1975 and 1980, a pair of Goshawks bred annually in the Brecks, and at another Breckland locality in Norfolk between 1985 and 1987, but the nest was robbed in the last year. A pair also summered in north Norfolk in 1985 and 1986, but with no evidence of breeding. From 1988 there was an increase in the number of Goshawks reported in the county, with records from three main areas, and by 1990 at least four pairs had successfully fledged young. Since then up to 5–6 pairs have probably bred annually, with the huge coniferous tracts of Breckland remaining the centre of activity. However, a more recent trend has been for an increase in records away from Breckland, almost exclusively in large, undisturbed areas of mixed and deciduous woodland. It remains a possibility that a combination of the Goshawk's secretive nature and an understandable reluctance by observers to reveal breeding locations, continues to mask the species' true county status. Most sightings have related to birds seen in display flight between February and April, as Goshawks spend much of their time in woodland. In view of their vulnerability it is clearly inappropriate to disturb birds simply to prove breeding or to disclose the exact localities of breeding pairs.

A few migrant Goshawks have been reported in the spring between 13th April and 2nd May, including birds heading out to sea at Mundesley and Winterton, while at the latter site one was associated with a movement of 17 Sparrowhawks on 13th April 1979. One or two have been noted on autumn migration almost annually in recent years, between mid-October and mid-November. These have included birds seen to arrive in off the sea at Brancaster, Overstrand, Waxham and Winterton.

*Moss Taylor*

*[handwritten: MY GARDEN - CHEDGRAVE. EG 6-2-2000 CAUGHT JUV B-H GULL - (WE RESCUED THE GULL)]*

## Sparrowhawk (Eurasian Sparrowhawk)

*Accipiter nisus*

**A fairly common resident, passage migrant and winter visitor.**

The Sparrowhawk is widely distributed in the Western Palearctic eastwards as far as the Pacific Ocean. Historically the species was heavily persecuted to protect game interests and numbers also decreased markedly in the 1950s due to pesticides, since when numbers have recovered to their former levels. Because the Sparrowhawk is difficult to record in the breeding season, the populations tend to be underestimated but it is now common over much of Europe, where it is one of the most widespread raptors below the treeline. British birds are non-migratory and numbers increase in winter as a result of visitors from Fennoscandia.

Riviere recorded the species as a very scarce breeding bird prior to 1914 but with a considerable increase during the First World War, when the persecution from gamekeepers was reduced. Up to the mid-1950s, it was not an uncommon resident in well-wooded areas and on migration but thereafter numbers reduced to such an extent that only a very small breeding stock remained in Breckland and possibly Broadland (Seago 1977).

Between 1954 and 1960, the Sparrowhawk had become extremely rare in Norfolk, with no definite proof of breeding. However, during the 1960s the number of sightings increased with birds seen at up to 45 localities and successful breeding was recorded in 1962, 1963 and 1965 (involving up to two pairs). During 1966–68, pairs bred at up to three known nest sites. Successful breeding took place in most years in the 1970s, involving up to five pairs. During this same period, the number of sightings increased with birds recorded annually from up to 65 localities.

During fieldwork for the Norfolk Atlas (1980–85), it was recorded in only 9% of the tetrads visited although it was present in 43 of the 10km squares in the county. During the 1980s, the numbers of breeding pairs had increased to 15 by 1988, although confirmation of breeding was not reported in 1986, 1987 nor 1989. During this period, the Sparrowhawk was increasingly widely reported. Recovery continued into the 1990s and it was not unusual to record the species on most birding trips. Records even included sightings within the City of Norwich boundaries. In 1996, as more breeding details emerged, a total of up to 48 pairs was noted at 27 sites, although this still was thought to represent only a small proportion of the total breeding population in the county. During the 1994–97 BBS it was found in 29% of the 1km squares covered in Norfolk in the first year, but in only 11–14% in the three subsequent years, figures which do not accord with the apparent increase noted by most observers. Despite experiencing the highest mortality rate of any of our birds of prey, the future of the Sparrowhawk looks promising. Evidence of its recovery from the effects of pesticides in the 1950s can be seen, as Sparrowhawks colonise our cities, including Norwich, and the reports of sightings increase.

As a spring migrant the species is regularly recorded from coastal locations during March, April and May. Favoured localities include the Winterton/Horsey Gap area in the east of the county where maximum day-counts have included ten on 4th April 1976, 17 birds south on 13th April 1979, ten on 27th April 1980 and 13 on 3rd May 1981. Other locations include Snettisham, Holme, Wells East Hills, Sheringham and Paston, where up to eight birds have been observed in a single day on spring migration.

Numbers on autumn migration have been less spectacular but maximum day-counts have included four at Welney, Holme and Wells East Hills, with six at Burnham Overy Dunes on 31st October 1995. Between 27th September and 14th November 1996, there were many reports of birds coming in from the sea at Holme, Titchwell, Salthouse, Weybourne and Sheringham. An interesting observation, which may have involved winter visitors, comes from the north of the county where four birds entered a wood, possibly being used as a communal roost-site, on 8th November 1993.

Whilst usually regarded as a woodland bird, female Sparrowhawks, in particular, regularly hunt over saltings, fens, marshes, dunes and estuaries. Figures from the RSPB Set-aside Survey involving ten farms in the county have indicated that, at least at these sites, the bird is more numerous than the Kestrel. Over 34 species of birds have been recorded as prey items of the Sparrowhawk. As well as the more common residents, they include Grey Partridge, Moorhen, Water Rail, Snipe, Woodcock, Wood Sandpiper, Cuckoo, Green Woodpecker, Red-breasted Flycatcher, Brambling, Crossbill and Snow Bunting. Observations of the species preying on Snipe at Welney record the flight as low and slow, just a metre or so above the ground, with the prey taken as it leaps into the air on take-off, a technique similar to harrier-type quartering.

An interesting record in 1994 concerned a leucistic, pale buff-coloured bird raised from a brood of six at Gooderstone, while a melanistic Sparrowhawk was at Breydon on 14th September 1997.

Over 250 Sparrowhawks have been ringed in Norfolk but very few have been recovered away from the area of ringing, indicating just how sedentary is the local breeding population. Singles have been found in Essex, Kent and Nottinghamshire, while two have been recovered abroad. A first-winter female ringed at Weybourne on 19th October 1994 (presumably an autumn immigrant) was found dead at Brobderslev, Jyland, Denmark on 15th July 1995 and an adult female ringed at Banningham on 17th February 1996 was controlled on Helgoland, Germany on 21st April 1997. Eight foreign-ringed Sparrowhawks have been found in the county, all between September and January – two from Belgium, three from Norway (including two ringed as nestlings), one from southern Finland and two from Helgoland, Germany (including one which died after striking the window of a ringer's house at Sheringham). In addition, a nestling ringed in Sweden was picked up alive 120km off Yarmouth two months later in September.

*Phil Lockwood*

# Common Buzzard                                          *Buteo buteo*

**A scarce passage migrant and winter visitor; very small breeding population of uncertain origin.**

The Common Buzzard is widespread throughout the Palearctic and in Europe it is regarded as the second-commonest raptor (Gensbøl 1984). The western European population, including that in Britain, is sedentary but northern populations migrate south as far as the Mediterranean. In Britain human persecution reduced its range up to the early 20th century so that by 1915 it was restricted to the north and west. By the mid-1950s, there had been some recovery, due to reduced gamekeeping, but then a fall in the number of rabbits, as a result of myxomatosis, affected Buzzards in southern and central England. Although it has once more recovered, the main breeding population is largely confined to western and northern Britain.

Riviere recorded the Buzzard as a spring and autumn passage migrant in small numbers and an occasional winter visitor. An unusually large immigration in association with Honey Buzzards took place in September 1881. The next recorded notable immigration occurred in 1931–32 when ten birds wintered in Holkham Park (Seago 1967).

As a breeding bird there were records from large woods at Hethel and Ashwellthorpe dating from the 19th century. During the 1950s the Common Buzzard was recorded in Norfolk on no more than six occasions annually, mostly in spring and autumn from coastal localities and the Brecks. In 1963, the annual total reached 16, again mostly single birds on migration. Up to two birds were present in the Brecks at Stanford in early September 1965, where one fortunate observer saw a Buzzard being chased by two Ospreys.

In 1966 and 1968 up to two birds spent the first half of the year in the Brecks, first at Tottington and then at Stanford but with no proof of breeding. A notable passage occurred in the spring of 1969 when eight Buzzards passed over Breydon in the course of an hour on 28th March. Most records continued to relate to birds on spring or autumn passage.

During the 1970s, records suggested an increase in migrant birds. In mid-November 1971 up to four Buzzards were observed feeding on rabbits at Sandringham, where they were joined by a Rough-legged Buzzard and a Red Kite. Spring migration in 1973, included six soaring over Ebridge Mill on 25th April. A total of 21 records in 1979 was the highest annual total on record and included many multiple sightings of birds on spring migration, mostly from Winterton where up to five were seen on 18th March, four on 24th March, eight on 1st April and three on 13th April. In addition, up to four birds had spent the late winter and spring at a now favoured location in the Lound/Fritton area, where two birds had been present in March 1978, while there were three in January 1980.

During the 1980s, the number of winter records increased, in particular in December 1984 with eight records at both coastal and inland sites. In 1984 a pair summered at one site and nest building was observed although with no other evidence of breeding. A pair also summered the following year but without any attempt at nesting. Another favoured site was Massingham Heath, where up to two birds were present for most of 1991, peaking at seven in September. Pairs also summered at Swaffham and West Acre. Most of the 31 reports for 1991 continued to relate to migrants during March–May and September–October.

The first successful breeding in the 20th century took place in 1992, at a site in central Norfolk, where a pair raised two young. The origin of the adults was unknown but they may have been from an illegal release. Further successful breeding took place the following year, with six young fledged from three localities. The autumn of 1993 was notable for an arrival of Continental drift migrants which included an unprecedented passage of Honey Buzzards and up to six Common Buzzards.

Since 1994 the Institute of Terrestrial Ecology has been undertaking a Common Buzzard release scheme in Norfolk, to study the habitat requirements of the species in unpopulated areas. In the first year, two artificial nests were constructed at a site in north Norfolk, in each of which were placed two siblings, and in one an additional unrelated bird. All five had earlier been fitted with a radio transmitter. To avoid human imprinting, the nests were rigged with a pipe-and-plunger feeding system, operated from below the nest. One bird subsequently died and the four survivors dispersed from the release area together as a group, three of which settled to winter together about 15km from the release site. A further eight birds were released in Norfolk in 1995 (Williamson 1997a)

In 1994, over 40 Buzzards were recorded in the county, the numbers swollen by an influx between 20th October and 6th November when at least eight arrived along with Rough-legged Buzzards. It is probable that some of these birds overwintered in Norfolk, as Buzzards were reported from 27 localities in January and February 1995.

The spring migration of Buzzards in 1995 was unprecedented. It started on 23rd March with a southerly movement of birds including five at Winterton, three at Yarmouth and four at Salthouse Heath. Movement continued into April with three main peaks. The first was between 2nd and 9th April, which included six birds at Lound and a total of 12 at Winterton, the second peak was on 14th April and included five at Felbrigg and West Runton, and the third from 20th to 29th April. On 20th April, alone, 32 flew west at Sheringham (including a flock of 21), 11 west at Holkham and 20 west at Thornham. The pattern of records suggested that the birds had arrived from the sea between Mundesley and Sheringham. While pairs summered at a minimum of three locations in 1995, breeding was only proved at a single site, where the long-standing resident pair fledged one young. The autumn migration was less spectacular but did include up to six birds at Cley and West Acre.

Buzzards were recorded in all months during 1996. At least 45 birds were recorded on spring migration in March and April, including 13 west at Walsey Hills, Cley on 30th March, nine east at Sheringham on 1st April and nine at Waxham on 18th April. Breeding occurred at two sites, each pair raising one young; adults were noted displaying at five other sites and at least two birds summered at two other localities. Evidence that the small breeding population is gaining a foothold in Norfolk was confirmed in 1997 with breeding confirmed at four locations and a minimum of seven young fledged. Birds were noted in display at a further four sites, one of which held six birds in September, some of which may have been juveniles. Two further sites held summering birds, one of which (on the county border with Suffolk) may hold breeding birds just outside the county limits. Counts of five at Cockley Cley on 24th January 1998 and seven at Fritton on 7th March 1998 auger well for the future.

**Table 32. Total number of pairs of breeding Common Buzzards and the minimum number of young fledged in Norfolk 1992–97.**

|  | 1992 | 1993 | 1994 | 1995 | 1996 | 1997 |
|---|---|---|---|---|---|---|
| Confirmed breeding pairs | 1 | 3 | 2 | 1 | 2 | 4 |
| Probable breeding pairs | - | 1 | 1 | - | 5 | 4 |
| Possible breeding pairs | 1 | 1 | 2 | 1 | 1 | 1 |
| Maximum breeding pairs | 2 | 5 | 5 | 2 | 8 | 9 |
| Minimum fledged young | 2 | 6 | 2 | 1 | 2 | 7 |

*Phil Lockwood*

## Rough-legged Buzzard

*Buteo lagopus*

**A very scarce passage migrant and winter visitor, with larger influxes in some years.**

As a breeding species, the Rough-legged Buzzard is confined to the northern part of the Western Palearctic, nesting in the tundra zone of Norway (where it is the commonest raptor), Sweden, Finland and northern Russia. The species is migratory, leaving its breeding grounds between August and October, the timing dependent on the availability of rodents, mainly lemmings and voles. Birds spend the winter in a broad belt extending across northern Europe and eastward to southern Russia, with Britain on the western edge of this range. Birds begin to return to their breeding areas from February onwards.

Both Stevenson and Riviere described it as a regular winter visitor in varying numbers, occurring from the end of September to early May. Exceptional influxes were recorded in the winters of 1839–40, when 47 Rough-legged Buzzards were killed within eight miles of Thetford, and 1858–59, when about 20 specimens were obtained principally in the Thetford and Yarmouth areas.

The species has been recorded almost annually since 1953 and in every year since 1978. The majority of autumn arrivals occur from October onwards, with a few in September. The only August sighting was of one at Winterton on 3rd August 1975, which was believed to have been the oversummering bird last officially seen at Heigham Holmes on 22nd June but reported in July (see below). Most overwintering and spring passage birds have left the county by May, although there have been June records in 1975, 1979, 1993 and 1998.

At irregular intervals impressive influxes of Rough-legged Buzzards occur during the autumn in eastern England. These influxes are probably linked to breeding success, weather-conditions and the availability of prey. Norfolk's flat and open landscape with an abundance of rabbits, help to attract these birds to favoured coastal marshes, saltings, heaths and Breckland, with some overwintering in the county. In the 1966 influx, the largest for 50 years, there was an unusual number of records from 6th October, mainly at coastal localities and in the Brecks. One was present in the Horsey/Winterton Dunes/Martham Broad area from 30th October to 26th February 1967. The next invasion occurred in 1973 with numerous reports from coastal or near-coastal locations of single birds from 20th October. At Cley nine were recorded on 26th October, including six moving west and another six on 28th October, while four were at Winterton on 4th November. Sightings of wintering or passage Rough-legged Buzzards continued up to 4th May 1974 including parties of up to three birds.

An exceptional arrival was again recorded in autumn 1974, the largest-ever recorded in the British Isles with over 50 county records from early October. Up to four birds were regularly reported in the Winterton/ Horsey Gap area of east Norfolk from 24th October 1974 into early 1975. Following the large autumn arrival, it was perhaps not surprising that an exceptional spring movement produced unprecedented numbers in April and May 1975. In the Winterton/Horsey Gap area numbers increased to ten by 19th April with birds observed at some height drifting to the north-east but always returning. By 1st May, 12 were in the area including a pair displaying at West Somerton. This pair remained until 15th May when a mechanical bird scarer was set up, after which one lingered until at least 22nd June. However, Holme provided the highest count with 15 on 28th April when birds arrived from the north-east and soared away to the south-west.

Exceptional numbers of Rough-legged Buzzards again occurred during the period January to May 1979 with reports from the Brecks, and many inland and coastal locations, with maximum counts of five at Winterton on 22nd April and nine at Holme on 13th May. Six years were to pass before the next large scale-influx was recorded in autumn 1985. Maximum counts were up to four in the Horsey/Hickling area from 4th November to mid-December, three at Brancaster on 30th December, up to three at both Winterton/Horsey and Massingham Heath, and four at Fritton.

The most recent invasion (second-only in size to that in 1974–75), which was part of an influx along the east coast of Britain, commenced on 17th October 1994 and reports included many sightings of birds in from the sea at Holme, Titchwell, Burnham Overy Dunes, Wells and Yarmouth. Almost daily sightings of Rough-legged Buzzards continued to the end of the year, including four at Wells on 2nd November, increasing to seven on 4th. Unusual numbers overwintered with up to three at Great Snoring during January, four at West Acre on 14th January, up to four at Flitcham throughout February and up to three at Wells. During March, one or two were resident at Flitcham and up to three were present in the Docking/Choseley area. About 15 were recorded in April but none lingered, with the last two at Sheringham on 2nd May and Horsey on 6th May (Hibberd 1995). Most interestingly the departing Rough-legged Buzzards began to appear at coastal sites at the same time as the county was recording its largest-ever movement of Common Buzzards.

*Phil Lockwood*

| Golden Eagle | *Aquila chrysaetos* |

**A very rare vagrant; one record in 1868.**

The Golden Eagle has a limited and much fragmented range in the Western Palearctic. In the British Isles, it has long been mainly restricted to the Scottish Highlands. One, probably an adult male, was found long-dead on the saltmarshes at Stiffkey, in November 1868 and is the sole record for Norfolk.

*Peter Allard*

# Osprey

*Pandion haliaetus*

**A scarce passage migrant; has oversummered.**

Primarily a fish eater, the Osprey is mainly a summer visitor to the Western Palearctic. It breeds in northern and eastern Europe, in some Mediterranean countries and in Asia east to the Pacific. Birds migrate over a broad front across seas and deserts to their central and southern African winter quarters, although some birds winter around the Mediterranean. The Osprey bred commonly in Scotland until the early 19th century but persecution and collection reduced the population to one nesting pair by 1916. It then became extinct as a breeding species and nearly 40 years were to pass before a pair reared young again in Britain, from a site near Loch Garten in 1954 (Dennis 1991a).

Riviere recorded the Osprey as a fairly regular migrant to Norfolk's coastal and inland waters in spring and autumn, occurring in most years. There were also two winter records – at Rockland Broad in mid-February 1868 and at Hickling on 1st January 1905.

Since 1953, the Osprey has been recorded annually in the county with the majority of sightings in the periods April to June and August to October. The earliest recorded spring migrants were at Cley on 15th March 1909 and at West Acre on 18th March 1988. The latest autumn records have been at Denver on 23rd November 1997 and Ickburgh on 25th November 1994. With its specialised diet the species is closely associated with water and most sightings come from coastal locations, the Broads, inland lakes, trout farms and gravel pits, each having a plentiful supply of fish.

During the 1950s, the average number of annual records was six, although at least 13 were recorded in 1956 with more than usual in September and included long-staying birds at Gunton Great Water on 15th–28th August and another at Hoveton on 4th–25th September. Since then the average number of annual records has nearly doubled each decade with 13 in the 1970s, 22 in the 1980s and 41 in the 1990s. The growth in the Scottish population may explain the increasing numbers of spring and autumn passage sightings in Norfolk in recent years.

Most spring records have involved single birds but there were two together at Hickling on 23rd May 1985 and one week later at Narford and West Acre, at Hickling on 30th May 1988 and at Stanford on 31st July 1988, while two flew west at Cley on 28th April 1993. In 1970, two Ospreys remained at Holkham for over three weeks in May.

The first record of an Osprey oversummering in the county was in 1962 when one was present at Hardley Flood through July until 3rd August. Another oversummered in the Ant Valley from 30th May to 27th July 1985 with sightings at Ranworth and Cockshoot. More recently, one was present in the mid-Yare Valley from 18th May to 4th September 1993, during which time it was frequently seen between Thorpe St Andrew and Cantley. Two years later, and again in the Yare Valley, a bird was present from 3rd July to 24th August, favouring Strumpshaw and Cantley but seen as far afield as Breydon and Potter Heigham. In 1998 at least three and probably five birds visited the mid-Yare Valley and were often watched fishing at Rockland Broad. Extreme dates were 26th April and 11th October.

In autumn some Ospreys have lingered in the county. Such extended stays have involved single birds remaining at Upton, Stanford, Ketteringham Lake, Lound, where one was present from 30th August to 6th October 1983, and Strumpshaw, from 22nd August to 10th October 1997. Occasionally two birds remain together for these longer autumn visits such as at Stanford from 14th September to the end of October 1968, from 31st August to 11th September 1992 and two immatures from 27th October to 6th November 1994, during which time they also visited Buckenham Tofts; while another two were at West Acre on 3rd–20th November 1994. One which lingered at Holkham Lake from 4th September to 3rd October 1998 was joined by a second bird on 7th–27th September. Three birds present at Horsey Mere in early August 1944 and three at Rollesby and Barton Broads in mid-September 1994 are unprecedented.

Three Ospreys ringed as nestlings have been reported in Norfolk. One ringed on 5th July 1945 at Veckholm, Sweden was found at Woodbastwick in spring 1947 and another ringed in 1989 in northern Scotland was trapped in protective netting at a trout farm at West Acre on 5th May 1991 and was released, after care, three days later. The third ringed on Tayside on 8th July 1998 was seen at Strumpshaw on 13th September.

*Phil Lockwood*

# Kestrel (Common Kestrel) HORSEY MERE. 25-6-1986. *Falco tinnunculus*

**A fairly common, but declining, resident and scarce passage migrant.**

The Kestrel is the most widespread and often the most abundant diurnal bird of prey in the Western Palearctic. Numbers fluctuate because of changes in the rodent population and the effects of severe winters. In northern and eastern regions the birds are mainly migratory but elsewhere in Europe Kestrels are only partially migratory or dispersive.

Riviere described the Kestrel as 'still fairly abundant as a breeding species' in Norfolk up to 1930 and unusual nesting sites were on the ground in the Broads and in 1900 in the tower of St Benedict's Church, Norwich. Seago (1967) recorded the species as fairly abundant in Broadland, in the south-east of the county, the Brecks and along the coastal strip, but very scarce in agricultural areas. During fieldwork for the Norfolk Atlas, it was recorded in 72% of the tetrads visited, although during the breeding season birds will often search for food well away from the nest site. It was the commonest raptor in the county, being widespread in farmland with plenty of trees, in woodland, and in both the Brecks and the Broads. Breeding pairs were also found in Yarmouth, although none was proved to breed in inner Norwich during the survey period. It was scarce or absent in the more open Fens and in the intensively-farmed districts with a paucity of woodland, such as between Hindringham and Wells (Kelly 1986).

Sadly, at both county and national level, the species is in decline. The BTO Common Bird Census maps a steady decline in numbers over the last 25 years. At a national level the BBS results have shown a 21% reduction between 1994 and 1996, while in Norfolk, Kestrels were recorded in 33–45% of the 1km squares visited during the four years 1994–97, with no clear trend apparent. Agricultural methods, however, continue to be an important factor affecting the Kestrel population today. Although it is almost certainly under-recorded, only 50 breeding pairs were reported in the county during 1996 and we should not be complacent about the future of the species in such an agriculturally-based county as Norfolk.

The choice of nesting sites is varied. In 1954, a pair bred in the tower of Norwich Cathedral and on several occasions nests have been known in the tower of St Nicholas Parish Church in Yarmouth, a town in which up to six pairs now nest, the sites including the Nelson's Monument, the main stand at Yarmouth Racecourse and up to 1997, Lacon's old brewery stores on North Quay. The old windmills in Broadland have proved popular as nest sites. Since the late 1980s, the Stanford Training Area has supported a steadily growing population with nests in boxes, trees and churches, where in 1996, 16 pairs raised 71 young, helped by a vole plague. Prey items have included birds such as Snow Bunting, Avocet, Little Ringed Plover and various wader chicks. The Little Tern colonies at Scolt Head, Holkham, Winterton and Yarmouth have also been raided, with chicks being taken as prey by Kestrels.

The species is also recorded at coastal localities in small numbers on spring and autumn passage. Unprecedented spring movements were a feature of the early 1980s with an impressive count of 23 birds flying south at Winterton on 12th April 1981, and at Holme 30 flew west on 16th April 1983 and 25 west on 25th May 1985. Autumn passage is recorded between July and October with a maximum count of 15 birds at Cley on 2nd August 1965, where three were seen to arrive from the sea on 25th October 1955.

In autumn, large concentrations of Kestrels have been reported from the north and west of the county. First noted in 1953 on areas reclaimed from the sea around the Wash at North Wootton, up to 30 birds were present in the second week of August. During the 1980s the favoured area has extended from King's Lynn across saltings and sea walls towards Snettisham and peaked at 96 on 28th August 1984. As recently as 1994, up to 40 Kestrels were present at North Wootton in August, but the large concentrations which regularly assembled are probably a thing of the past. However, an impressive post-breeding gathering of 20 birds at Horsey on 13th August 1993 and 19 at Winterton on 3rd July 1994 were notable. Peak counts for 1995 and 1996 involving only six birds came from Holkham and Welney in the autumn and winter periods.

About 500 Kestrels have been ringed in the county resulting in over 100 recoveries, of which 70% have been within Norfolk and over 20% in southern England, with very few moving north. Only one has been recovered abroad – a nestling ringed near Watton in 1988 was found near the Channel coast in France, at Yvetot in February 1990. However, ten foreign-ringed nestlings have been recovered in Norfolk – seven from The Netherlands, two from Sweden and one from Denmark, the oldest eight years after ringing. Random dispersal is characteristic of juvenile Kestrels, well illustrated by two siblings ringed in the nest at

Southam, Warwickshire in June 1979, one of which was recovered in August at East Runton and the other in September at Matlock, Derbyshire. A rapid movement was shown by one ringed at Spurn Head, Humberside on 27th October 1995 which was found freshly dead near Burnham Market the following day, having travelled a distance of 84km.

*Phil Lockwood*

## Red-footed Falcon                                         *Falco vespertinus*

**A rare vagrant, mainly in spring.**

Red-footed Falcons
(*Norman Arlott*)

A summer visitor to the Western Palearctic, the breeding populations of the Red-footed Falcon are centred in Hungary (with over 2,000 pairs), Romania and Russia. The species nests in rookeries, in colonies of up to 50 pairs (Gensbøl 1984). The entire population winters in semi-arid habitats in southern Africa where the species forms large nocturnal roosts. Whilst autumn migration occurs almost entirely through the eastern Mediterranean, the return in spring is more westerly oriented with large numbers passing through West Africa, thus explaining why most birds from western Europe are recorded in spring. Very occasionally, large influxes occur, as in 1973 when 42 birds reached Britain in spring and in 1992 when 150 birds arrived between mid-May and the end of June.

The first Norfolk records were in 1830 (probably all in May) – three obtained at Horning and one at Yarmouth, and a female killed at Holkham which is present in the collection at the Castle Museum, Norwich (Stevenson and Riviere). There were a further eight records in the period 1843–1927. Of all the records prior to 1930, only one was not taken by a collector (Riviere). Following an autumn record from Hickling in 1931, a further 27 years were to pass before Red-footed Falcon was again recorded in the county, with singles at Hickling in June and at Holme in September 1958. The following year Fred Ashton, one-time Norwich taxidermist, identified a flattened casualty on the Acle New Road near the Stracey Arms on 27th September.

Since the late 1950s, the species has been recorded on average in three out of every four years with over 80% in May and June. Between 1984 and 1997 this enchanting falcon from eastern Europe has appeared annually, except in 1996. The total number of records exceeds 100.

The earliest arrival was an adult male at Winterton on 3rd April 1979 (which remains the second earliest British record), while an immature bird at the same location on 30th September 1979, is the latest record. The majority of sightings have come from coastal or near-coastal locations although birds were recorded inland at Welney, Guist, Norwich and Fakenham in the large influx of 1992 and at the Warren Wood/Gallows Hills area of Thetford in June 1995. Often only present briefly, some birds linger for a few days. The longest-stayers have been an immature male at Cley on 17th–27th July 1978 and a female at Buxton from 24th May to 3rd June 1981.

The large influx of the species in 1992 was unprecedented with over 40, out of a total of 150 in Britain, passing through Norfolk in a six-week period from mid-May. Above average temperatures and surges of warm air caused by a vast anticyclone over Scandinavia resulted in birds travelling far to the west of their normal route from West Africa to their eastern breeding grounds. The influx commenced on 14th May with records from the east and north of the county. Included were multiple sightings at Winterton (a male and two females) and at Blakeney Point (two males and two females). A second and much larger influx, commenced on 25th May during which birds were seen almost daily to the end of June, with reports from Welney, Holme, Titchwell, Brancaster, Holkham, Blakeney, Happisburgh, Hickling (where two males were present on 28th June), Horsey, Winterton, Martham Broad, Potter Heigham, How Hill and Hindolveston.

An analysis of all the county records since 1958, shows that just over half have been females. In the 1973 influx, the females arrived first, outnumbering the later-arriving males. In the 1992 influx both sexes arrived together with over half aged as first-summer birds, and females constituted 64% of the total.

*Phil Lockwood*

## Merlin

*Falco columbarius*

**A scarce passage migrant and winter visitor.**

The Merlin, the smallest European bird of prey, breeds in the northern part of the Western Palearctic, in Iceland, the British Isles, Fennoscandia and Russia. Although some birds are resident, the species is mainly migratory, with many moving south, down from the hilly moorland breeding areas, to winter in the warmer coastal or valley sites (Gensbøl 1984). In the British Isles, this fierce and diminutive falcon breeds in the uplands of Wales, Scotland, northern England and Ireland with an estimated breeding population of up to 800 pairs.

Both Stevenson and Riviere recorded the Merlin as a regular autumn passage migrant with considerable numbers passing along the coast during October in some years. The number of localities at which Merlins were recorded increased from only a few in the 1950s to over 30 annually by the late 1970s. By the mid-1990s, Merlins had been recorded in every month but with the majority in the January–May and September–December periods.

Autumn migration usually commences in September although one was present at the Scolt Head ternery on 14th–17th July 1956 and again on 30th July 1958, and since 1991 there have been July records almost annually. The autumn of 1996 produced a considerable number of records. Apart from one at Snettisham on 28th July, reports from coastal locations commenced in the last week of August and continued into September. Multiple sightings included two at Scolt Head on 18th September, three at Horsey on 24th September, two at Warham on 26th September, three at Sheringham on 28th September and two at Breydon on the last day of the month. At Scolt Head a Merlin was observed 1km offshore intercepting incoming migrants.

Winter diet consists solely of birds with Skylarks accounting for over half of the prey items (Clarke & Hewson 1993). The coastal fresh marshes, saltings, marram dunes and heaths of Norfolk are favoured wintering areas. At this time, Merlins roost communally at favoured sites, often in association with Hen Harriers. There are five known roost-sites in the county. The first, a heathland site in west Norfolk was discovered in 1976 and has held up to five birds (in the first winter period of 1986). The second and smaller roost in marram dunes in the north of the county dates from 1978 and has held up to three Merlins. The main Broadland roost on a freshwater marsh, where Merlins were first observed roosting with Hen and Marsh Harriers in 1984, has held up to ten birds (in March 1987). A fourth, in willows in the Fens, which was known to be occupied from 1986–92, held up to four birds, but as Merlins continue to be reported from the area they may well be roosting nearby. In 1991, a fifth site, in marram dunes next to saltings on the north Norfolk coast has been used by up to five Merlins roosting with Hen Harriers. Most of these roosts are not occupied until October when the first overwintering birds arrive and numbers have generally peaked in December and January. Merlins start to move back to their breeding grounds in March and usually by April the roosts are empty.

Merlins are regularly observed on migration in April and May mainly from coastal locations. Notable spring sightings have included ten migrants in May 1985, while in 1995, following the first migrant at Holme on 24th March, six inland and 20 coastal sites recorded birds moving west in April, with sightings continuing up to 28th May. Most Merlins have usually left Norfolk by the end of May, although there are a number of unseasonal June records, including singles at Scolt Head on 12th June 1986, Great Bircham on 25th June 1986, Cley on 16th June 1990 and one passing offshore at Horsey on 13th June 1992.

A single Merlin recovery affects Norfolk – a nestling ringed in Northumberland in 1971 was found four months later in the Brecks at Feltwell on 15th October.

**Table 33. Maximum counts of Merlins at winter roost-sites in Norfolk 1984–97.**

| Year | Number of roosts observed | Month | Total number of birds present |
|---|---|---|---|
| 1984 | 2 | December | 7 |
| 1985 | 2 | - | 9 |
| 1986 | 3 | March | 15 |
| 1987 | 3 | January/March | 15 |
| 1988 | 3 | January | 12 |
| 1989 | 1 | November | 8 |
| 1990 | 3 | January/December | 10 |
| 1991 | 4 | January | 15 |
| 1992 | 2 | January | 8 |
| 1993 | 4 | January | 14 |
| 1994 | 5 | January | 14 |
| 1995 | 3 | February/December | 12 |
| 1996 | 4 | February/December | 6 |
| 1997 | 2 | January | 10 |

*Phil Lockwood*

## Hobby (Eurasian Hobby)                    *Falco subbuteo*

A very scarce summer visitor and scarce passage migrant.

Hobby and Honey Buzzard
(*Norman Arlott*)

The Hobby is a summer visitor which breeds in much of the Western Palearctic, through Asia to the Pacific Ocean, with over 2,000 pairs each in Finland, France, Spain and Russia. It is a long-distance migrant which winters in tropical Africa, feeding on swarms of flying termites. By the late 1970s there were no more than a hundred or so pairs breeding in southern England but in recent years there has been a marked increase and an extension of its range northwards. The species favours damp meadows, marshes and heaths where it preys on aerial insects and small birds. During the breeding season Hobbies lead a secluded existence and are difficult to record. However, during August and September they are more conspicuous when they feed on roosting hirundines (Gensbol 1984).

Both Stevenson and Riviere recorded the Hobby as a regular summer visitor and passage migrant, but only as an irregular breeding species. When pairs did attempt to nest they were invariably shot and the nests robbed. The last breeding record up to 1930 was at Rushford in 1903, but as usual the pair and one of the three fledged young were shot. Stevenson also recorded an instance of a Hobby apparently pairing with a Sparrowhawk at Witchingham, but both adults were shot at the time that hatching occurred and the young perished. The next successful breeding was not until 1933 at Brettenham Heath, and again there in

1934 and near Weeting in 1951 but without success (Seago 1967).

The increase in the species in Norfolk over the second half of the 20th century is surprising. During the 1950s and 1960s, there was an average of only eight records annually, 70% occurring in the periods May–June and August–September. The 1960s, however, produced an increasing number of July records, as non-breeding birds wandered more widely. Hobby records increased by over 70% during the 1970s and a further significant increase occurred from the mid-1980s, such that by the end of that decade the species was frequently and widely reported. By 1995, over 200 sightings were recorded annually with the majority between May and September. Inland records, away from breeding areas, came from Thetford, Barnham Broom, Hethersett, Poringland, Welney and Norwich.

Hobbies start to leave their wintering grounds in March and passage continues through April and May. There have been regular April records since 1982, and three earlier ones in March – at Belaugh on 3rd March 1866, at Yarmouth on 20th March 1858 and at Northrepps on 25th March 1863. The earliest arrivals since were singles at Wootton on 11th April 1991 and at Lynford Arboretum on 11th April 1997. Peak passage occurs in May – in 1995 over 100 birds were recorded that month from 42 sites, mainly coastal and there were 65 birds at 50 localities in 1996. Passage often continues into June. Most sightings on passage involve single birds but two have been recorded at Thetford Nunnery Lakes, Lynn Point, Holme, Holkham, Cley, Sheringham and Winterton, with three at Roydon Common on 25th April 1995, three west at Cromer Golf Course on 22nd April 1997 and four east at Blakeney Point on 20th June 1994.

Early indications that Hobbies might once again breed in the county came in 1976 when up to two birds were present at Cley throughout the summer. Later, in 1981, three birds were observed at another site in July. Hobbies may have nested for the first time in Norfolk for over 30 years in 1983, and again in 1984 and 1985, but without success. The first confirmed successful breeding was in 1986 when three pairs bred in the county. Numbers are now slowly increasing and between 1993 and 1997, between six and ten young have fledged annually.

**Table 34. Total number of pairs of Hobbies and fledged young in Norfolk 1986–97.**

|                 | 1986 | 1987 | 1988 | 1989 | 1990 | 1991 | 1992 | 1993 | 1994 | 1995 | 1996 | 1997 |
|-----------------|------|------|------|------|------|------|------|------|------|------|------|------|
| Confirmed pairs | 3    | 2    | 2    | 1    | 3    | 4    | 7    | 6    | 7    | 8    | 4    | 5    |
| Possible pairs  | -    | -    | -    | 2    | 2    | 4    | -    | 4    | 1    | 1    | -    | 5    |
| Fledged young   | -    | 5    | -    | -    | -    | -    | -    | 10   | 6    | 8    | 10   | 6    |

Autumn migration occurs during August and September. Migrants observed coming in from the sea have included a very early bird at Cromer in July 1954, two at Winterton on 29th August 1993 and one at Yarmouth on 6th September 1995. An increasing number of Hobbies pass through the county in autumn, mirroring the recent upsurge of the species in Britain. Some birds, including juveniles, often linger at coastal localities to feed on migrating hirundines. In 1984, a bird was present in the Winterton/Horsey area for nearly a month from 8th September to 2nd October and up to two were present at Holkham from 22nd September to 13th October 1989. The latest dates for Hobby have been 23rd October 1992 at Holme and 23rd October 1995 at Titchwell.

Examples of the variety of prey items come from observations of Hobbies pursuing Swifts and taking a Little Tern at Scolt Head, bats at Felbrigg, House Martins and Swallows at Cley, and peacock and small tortoiseshell butterflies at Welney. Sand Martins and freshly emerged four-spotted chaser dragonflies have also been taken.

Only two Hobbies have been ringed in Norfolk and amazingly one of them was recovered – ringed at a Swallow roost in the reedbed at Hardley Flood on 1st August 1987 it was found freshly dead at Zaandam, The Netherlands on 7th May 1988 and remains the only Dutch recovery of a British-ringed Hobby. Another ringed at Alvkarleo, Sweden on 20th July 1953 was recovered at Hickling two months later, the first foreign-ringed Hobby to be found in Britain and still the only one from Fennoscandia.

*Phil Lockwood*

# Gyr Falcon                                          *Falco rusticolus*

**A very rare vagrant; three records.**

The Gyr Falcon has a circumpolar breeding distribution, extending from Iceland and northernmost Fennoscandia, eastwards to the Bering Straits, and in arctic North America from Alaska to Labrador. It also nests on both sides of Greenland. In winter, it wanders south in Norway, Finland and Siberia, and in Canada south to about 50°N.

An adult male of the Greenland race *F. r. candicans* shot at Beeston in February 1848 is on display at the Castle Museum, Norwich. Another, considered to be of the Icelandic race *F. r. islandus,* was seen at Blakeney Point on 20th December 1953. What was undoubtedly the same bird appeared over Blakeney Harbour on 26th and near Stiffkey Channel on 29th. It remained in the area until 8th January 1954. It was seen by several observers including Dick Bagnall-Oakeley, Archie Daukes and Billy Bishop. Another at Blakeney Point on 1st October 1954 was described as a very large, pale grey falcon with no 'moustaches' and pale greyish underparts.

*Peter Allard*

## Peregrine (Peregrine Falcon)   NEAR HARDLEY FLOODS. *Falco peregrinus*
2·4·2000.

**A scarce winter visitor and passage migrant; formerly bred.**

The Peregrine Falcon is found in most countries of the Western Palearctic. The largest European breeding populations are to be found in Russia, Spain, France and the British Isles. Most Fennoscandian and Russian populations are migratory with birds moving south and west, whilst those elsewhere in its range are resident although some younger birds wander (Gensbøl 1984).

In Britain the Peregrine declined during the Second World War through official control by the Air Ministry, but by 1954 the species was protected and some recovery had occurred. However, a severe population decline followed due to persistent pesticides and it was not until after 1963 that a recovery commenced. Currently in Britain there are thought to be over 1,000 breeding pairs (Dennis 1991b). The British population is largely non-migratory although some birds (including juveniles) wander in autumn and winter. Preferring cliffs for nesting, Peregrines are found around the coasts, on moorland and in mountainous areas.

Riviere recorded the Peregrine as a fairly regular passage migrant and winter visitor to Norfolk. Until 1815 the species regularly nested on Hunstanton cliffs and for eight successive winters one frequented the spire of Norwich Cathedral (Stevenson), although by the middle of the 19th century it had disappeared as a breeding species from the county.

The species is now regularly recorded on spring migration through March to May, mostly at coastal localities and in the Fens. In 1993, there were eight records from 21st March to 19th May. A particularly heavy passage in March 1994 resulted in 16 records, three were at Welney on 9th–19th April and one was seen to arrive from the sea at Cley on 8th May. Between March and May 1995, a total of 22 birds was noted with Welney playing host to 2–3 on 20th March. On 13th April 1996 one was recorded flying out to the north at Cley. Records in June and July are unusual, and a number have related to escaped falconer's birds carrying jesses, as at Wisbech Sewage Farm on 12th July 1977 and at Horsey on 30th June 1985, while another was present at Holkham for over a month from 2nd May to 5th June 1995.

Autumn passage generally commences in August and continues through to October. However, a sub-adult appeared at Welney on 28th July 1995, roosting on pylons and it remained in the area until 15th August; while birds were recorded at Kelling, Cley, Lakenheath, Welney and Snettisham in July 1996. In August 1993, the unusually high total of 22 was reported at various sites in the county and 19 seen in September 1995, including two at Holme on 12th September. An interesting report of a late migrant at Titchwell involved a Peregrine seen to arrive from the north on 5th November 1995.

Peregrine sightings have not always been so numerous as in the 1990s. Up to the early 1980s, the maximum number of annual records was 13 with the majority from coastal locations, the Brecks and the Fens. By the end of the 1980s, the number of annual sightings had increased to up to 30. From 1993 the number of Peregrine records had risen dramatically with birds increasingly reported on migration.

The first record of a Peregrine overwintering in recent years was at Scolt Head where one was present up to mid-March 1967 and again from the end of November. Since 1984 Peregrines have regularly overwintered in the county at an increasing number of sites. Favoured localities have included the Wolferton/Sandringham/Snettisham area, Holkham/Wells, Welney and the lower Waveney Valley, including Breydon and the marshes of Berney, Fritton and Haddiscoe. At all of these sites up to two birds have regularly been present in recent winters with three different birds wandering the coastal strip between King's Lynn and Scolt Head from January to mid-April 1997 and up to three at Chedgrave/Fritton Marshes during February 1998.

Observers have recorded Peregrine attacks on Gannets, White-fronted Geese, Gadwall, Pochards, Oystercatchers, Knots, Dunlins, Black-tailed Godwits, Redshanks, Greenshanks, skuas, Collared Doves and Starlings. In 1993 one was seen stooping at pigeons over Norwich City centre on 14th May and in 1996 chasing migrant thrushes up to 1km out to sea from Scolt Head. In the Blakeney area, Tim Lubbock had seen them sitting on offshore buoys, chasing a Leach's Petrel over the sea and had witnessed an impressive list of kills, including Bar-tailed Godwit and Brent Goose (McCallum 1998c). With the recent report of a bird roosting regularly on Hunstanton cliffs, perhaps Peregrines may once again return to this former nesting site to breed.

*Phil Lockwood*

## Red-legged Partridge  *MY GARDEN. CHEDGRAVE(3) 17·7·2000.*  *Alectoris rufa*

**A common introduced resident.**

The Red-legged Partridge is a resident of south-west Europe, occurring naturally in Iberia, France, northern Italy and some of the Mediterranean Islands. It has been introduced successfully into Britain, the Azores, Madeira and the Canary Islands but has failed to become established in central Europe. Introduced into Suffolk initially in the late 1700s, its spread has been aided by further introductions but has been complemented by introductions of the similar Chukar and their hybrids from 1970. Although present in Scotland and Wales it is concentrated in south and east England (New Atlas).

Stevenson commented that they had spread rapidly through East Anglia, aided by further introductions, but had become unpopular as gamebirds. In some places nests were destroyed in an attempt to control numbers because it was believed that they were antagonistic towards Grey Partridges, were uncooperative in front of the guns and did not make good eating. Stevenson commented, however, that despite this they were frequent in Norfolk in his time, especially on heavy land where the Grey Partridge was scarcer.

Kelly (1986) remarked that by 1960, the Red-legged Partridge population was probably greater than that of the Grey Partridge and at the time of the Norfolk Atlas it was found in 90% of the tetrads, compared with 37% for the Grey Partridge. Many of the tetrads in north-west Norfolk had both species present. It is generally more confined to arable areas than Grey Partridge but it is more tolerant of wooded landscapes. It is difficult to determine whether its natural population is now stable, declining or increasing as reared birds are still released. Results from the BTO's Common Birds Census indicated a national decline of 17% over 25 years and Potts (1986) suggested a marked decline since 1985 (New Atlas). Results from the Norfolk Partridge Group and the Game Conservancy Trust have shown that, in Norfolk, populations have recently been relatively stable, and this has been confirmed by the 1994–97 BBS, during which it was recorded in 84–86% of the 1km squares covered in Norfolk. In contrast to the Grey Partridge, its newly-hatched chicks are not so dependent on insect food and have therefore not suffered to the same extent through the intensification of farming. They do, however, suffer from the increased attentions of predators due to the reduction in the control of the latter. This is offset to a degree because a pair of Red-legged Partridges can brood two clutches (New Atlas). The largest coveys reported in autumn 1997 included 155 at Swanton Abbot and 80 at Horsey, although these may have involved released birds. The 1998 autumn survey by the Norfolk Partridge Group which covered 19,800ha, found 4,981 adult and 2,115 young Red-legged Partridges, compared with 2,199 adult and 2,624 young Grey Partridges (T. Cook *in litt.*).

The species is thought to be largely sedentary but, as with Grey Partridge, Stevenson remarked that many people thought it might be migratory because exhausted birds were sometimes found in spring on the coast. He attributed this to movements of English birds out to sea (where they had been observed) before turning round and returning to the coast. These coastal sightings were only observed after the introductions had occurred, and thus there was no evidence of birds from the Continent migrating to England. Interestingly, in 1989 a young bird was seen to land on the sea at Overstrand and then drown.

*Nick Carter*

## Grey Partridge CHEDGRAVE COMMON (2) 23·3·1999.          *Perdix perdix*

**A common resident.**

The Grey Partridge occurs throughout much of the Western Palearctic, especially in the middle latitudes. It also occurs in Asia, reaching eastern Mongolia. In Britain it is widely distributed across central and eastern parts, being local or absent from much of south-west England, Wales, north-west Scotland and the Scottish Isles (New Atlas).

Stevenson noted the high numbers in the county and indeed even referred to it as the Common Partridge. It was widely distributed although the western and south-western areas, on the light soils, was where it reached its highest numbers.

The Grey Partridge is still a relatively familiar site on arable farmland in Norfolk, especially in the north-west of the county. Here high densities (amongst the highest in the world) have been maintained through dedicated management to ensure shootable surpluses (Dowell 1991). During fieldwork for the Norfolk Atlas the Grey Partridge was noted in 37% of the tetrads. It also clearly demonstrated the concentration in the north-west of the county.

Grey Partridges
(*Norman Arlott*)

The decline in the Grey Partridge, both locally and nationally, and indeed internationally, is well known. Since the Second World War numbers have declined nationally by 80% (Potts 1986). Results from the BTO's Common Birds Census for the period 1969–94 showed an 82% decline nationally. Data from spring and autumn counts by the Norfolk Partridge Group and the Game Conservancy Trust are insufficient to conclude whether the Grey Partridge is still in decline across the county or showing a sustained recovery. However, it is encouraging that in three of the four years 1994–97, the number of 1km squares in Norfolk covered for the BBS in which the Grey Partridge was found has steadily increased from 36% in 1994 to 48% in 1997. The largest covey reported in 1997 was one of 40 at Docking in January. The 1998 autumn survey by the Norfolk Partridge Group which covered 19,800ha, found 2,199 adult and 2,624 young Grey Partridges compared with 4,981 adult and 2,115 young Red-legged Partridges (T. Cook *in litt.*).

Various hypotheses have been proposed to explain the decline but it is now generally accepted that herbicides are the major cause of the recent decline, at least in England (Potts 1986). Herbicides remove the weeds that are fed on by the insects, which are the food of partridge chicks in their first two weeks of life. Summer use of insecticides to control aphids and other cereal pests remove crop and ground-living insects. As a consequence, survival of the chicks falls to such a low level that the population goes into decline. This decline may be hastened by the activities of predators such as crows and foxes, which have increased because there are fewer gamekeepers controlling them (Dowell 1991).

Various measures have been proposed to try to reverse these declines. Conservation headlands, where the edges of fields are left largely unsprayed in summer, have been particularly successful in raising chick survival rates. The introduction of beetle banks (raised earth banks in fields which are sown with grasses), provide habitats not only for beetles, but for nesting partridges also.

The Grey Partridge is largely sedentary in this country. Stevenson commented on reports of coveys of Grey Partridge being found on the beach at Yarmouth but attributed this to displacement from shooting rather than migration. There are no recent recoveries although small numbers of Grey Partridge are now ringed in the county.

*Nick Carter*

# Quail (Common Quail)                               *Coturnix coturnix*

**A scarce summer visitor; very rare in recent years in winter.**

The Quail breeds throughout Europe, except for Iceland, the northern part of the British Isles and northern Fennoscandia, but due to its small size and cryptic habits, much about its distribution and migration remains unknown. Although it occasionally overwinters in the British Isles, and occurs in moderate numbers in the Mediterranean basin in winter, most Western Palearctic birds are thought to migrate to the arid zone south of the Sahara from Senegal to Sudan. In the British Isles its occurrence and distribution are very erratic. The species was probably common until the end of the 19th century, but subsequently declined and numbers remained low until 1942, since when there has been an upward trend. During the fieldwork for the New Atlas (1988–91) it occurred in over 838 of the 10km squares, compared with 438 squares in the 68–72 BTO Atlas. This widespread distribution was largely because 1989 was a mass invasion year, probably the highest on record (New Atlas).

Quail
(*Richard Richardson*)

The Historical Atlas noted Quail as being rare in Norfolk and across much of the British Isles. Population declines in the 1800s were thought largely to be due to hunting and the taking of eggs, although changes in farming practice cannot be ruled out. Stevenson also remarked on this decline and the scarcity of Quail in Norfolk, noting the Fens in the south-west near Feltwell to be the stronghold. He also described the Quail invasion year of 1870, during which 200–300 were shot in the Fen districts alone, while over 1,000 eggs were taken. Pashley (1925) noted that Quail bred every year in the Cley area. The regulation of spring hunting in 1937 in Mediterranean areas and the extension of arable farming during and after the Second World War probably led to a subsequent increase in numbers. Between the early 1950s and the late 1980s, the number of calling males heard in Norfolk varied from one to 18, except during the influx in 1964. In that year birds were recorded at 35 sites with successful breeding confirmed at Brancaster, Walsingham and Glandford. The Norfolk Atlas included only two confirmed breeding records for the 1980–85 period, but the species was recorded in 38 tetrads, the majority in north and north-west Norfolk. In 1989 birds were recorded at 40 localities, many along the north Norfolk coast, including twelve calling birds in the Choseley/Ringstead area and four others within 3km. In each of the summers 1993–95 Quail were unusually plentiful and widespread with over 50 recorded each year. The highest concentrations of calling birds were five at Haveringland in 1993, eight at Kelling and four at Hockwold in 1994, and seven at Docking/Choseley, six at Metton and five at Ten Mile Bank in 1995. While at least 16 calling birds were recorded within a 3km radius at Choseley on 15th–16th July 1998. There is a strong tendency for Quail to concentrate in small areas, late males presumably being attracted by the calling of earlier arrivals (68–72 BTO Atlas). Because of their late arrival, many of the records of confirmed breeding concern pairs seen with young during or after harvesting in August. In 1959 a nest containing nine eggs was found as late as 21st August at Kirstead Ling, near Brooke.

In March Quail start their migration, crossing the Mediterranean in April and mid-May. The first birds are generally not heard in Norfolk until the second half of May, with peak numbers reported in June. The earliest records have been on 12th March 1993 at Sheringham, on 16th March 1983 at Holme and on 25th April 1997 at Sheringham. While many of the birds heard calling in May are probably still on passage, Quail are very rarely recorded at coastal migration sites in spring. Five have been reported at Blakeney Point, all in the period 16th to 30th May, including one which was seen to arrive in off the sea on 29th May 1992; two at Holme including a tideline corpse on 4th June 1964 and one at Scolt Head on 25th May 1989.

The autumn migration starts in August, with the peak movement across the Mediterranean in mid-September. As in spring, the species is very rarely noted on autumn passage in Norfolk. Singles have been recorded in September at both Holme and Scolt Head, two were at Blakeney Point on 20th–21st July

1959, one flew on to Cley beach from the north-east on 26th September 1964 and singles were at Weybourne on 5th October 1989 and at Sheringham on 8th October 1994, which constitute the latest autumn dates for the county. Winter occurrences appear to have been fairly frequent during the 19th century. Gurney and Fisher (1849) recorded an unusual number killed in December 1847, while Stevenson obtained a few in the months November to February, almost invariably during severe weather. In recent years, despite the increase in the number of observers, there have been only four records in winter – one at Caister on 28th November 1986, three, of which one was a casualty, disturbed during beet lifting at Antingham on 19th December 1995, and singles at Cley on 25th–26th December 1995 and at Old Hunstanton on 31st December 1997.

*Nick Carter*

## Pheasant (Common Pheasant)       *Phasianus colchicus*

**An abundant resident.** *MY GARDEN, CHEDGRAVE. ♀ 8·7·1999.  ♂ 9·7·1999.*

The native European range of the Pheasant is confined to the eastern part of Russia. Its introduced range, however, covers much of Europe except for northern Fennoscandia and the Iberian Peninsula. Although the Romans introduced it to Italy, Germany and France, it was almost certainly the Normans who first brought the species to the British Isles in the late eleventh century. However, it was not until the late 18th century that it had become widespread throughout Britain. Nowadays, Britain has the highest population of any European country, representing 25% of the total of Pheasants in Europe, reflecting the fact that an estimated 15 million are released here for shooting each year.

The use of artificial methods for rearing large numbers of Pheasants for shooting has been common practice in Norfolk for over 200 years and accounts for the fact that East Anglia, along with Sussex, held more Pheasants than any other part of Britain, as long ago as the early 1800s (Historical Atlas). The earliest game book held in the Holkham Estate Office is for the period 1793–94 to 1797–98. During those five seasons a total of 1,618 Pheasants was shot. The game book reveals that a great deal was given away. On two occasions the recipient was Sir Horatio Nelson of nearby Burnham Thorpe. Both times he received six partridges, a Pheasant and a hare. Another Holkham game book for the 30 seasons 1900–30 produced a 'bag' of 104,660 Pheasants. More recently the 27 seasons 1930–56 resulted in a 'bag' of 88,285 Pheasants. The gamebooks for the Hilborough estate in Breckland which included Clermont and Bodney reveal that for the 14 seasons from 1866–67 to 1879–80 a total of 46,691 Pheasants was shot. A later gamebook for the same estate shows that during 15 seasons from 1959–60 to 1973–74 a total of 84,561 Pheasants was obtained. Up to the end of the 19th century, the largest 'day-bag' of Pheasants was 3,114, shot at Sandringham on 4th November 1896 (Riviere).

Even excluding introductions, there is undoubtedly a widespread, thoroughly naturalised and self-supporting feral population of Pheasants in Norfolk. During the fieldwork for the Norfolk Atlas the species was recorded in 93% of the tetrads, being the most widespread non-passerine after the Wood Pigeon. Its favoured habitat is wooded, agricultural land and it was absent only from the Halvergate Levels, the exposed coastal tetrads and the heavily built-up areas of Norwich and Yarmouth (Kelly 1986). Even in the treeless Fens the dykes provide the necessary cover for nesting. More recently it was recorded in 94–100% of the 1km squares covered in Norfolk during the 1994–97 BBS, compared with a national average of only about 60%.

The early introductions into Britain involved the race *P. c. colchicus* from the Caucasus, the so-called 'Old English' variety, whereas since the 18th century most have been the 'Ring-necked' type *P. c. torquatus* from China and this is the variety most often seen in Norfolk. Apparently melanistic birds may actually be distant hybrids with the Green Pheasant *P. versicolor* from Japan. Pure white birds are not infrequently reported, but 22 seen on the Burnley Hall Estate at Winterton on 24th September 1995 was a surprisingly large number.

*Moss Taylor*

# Golden Pheasant                                         *Chrysolophus pictus*

**A scarce and localised introduced resident.**

The Golden Pheasant is rare in its native mountains of central China. The only feral populations in Europe are in the British Isles, with the species' stronghold around Breckland, on the South Downs, on Anglesey in Wales and in Galloway, Scotland. It was first imported into Britain in the 18th century and the first releases took place in the west Highlands of Scotland in the 1880s. The present distribution probably reflects the areas where introductions and releases were successful.

Although the earliest record of a Golden Pheasant in the wild was one seen in Norfolk in 1845 (Browne *et al.* 1997) they were not turned down in Breckland until the late 1890s. By 1950 they were common and increasing there as new conifer plantations were established (68–72 BTO Atlas) and up to 100 were seen together in Thetford Forest in the 1950s by Ron Hoblyn. By the mid-1960s, the species was well-established in many localities in Breckland, especially in the Fowl Mere/Hockham/Thompson Water/West Tofts area, where flocks of up to 60 had been recorded (Seago 1967). During fieldwork for the Norfolk Atlas, in the early 1980s, Golden Pheasants were recorded in 50 tetrads, the vast majority in the Brecks but with a smaller concentration in the Sandringham/Wolferton area, where a separate introduction had taken place in about 1967. Birds had also been noted in the areas near Ringstead, Syderstone, Sculthorpe and Corpusty, but these were considered to have been locally escaped birds. Golden Pheasants are commonly kept in collections. The species was admitted to Category C of the British and Irish List in 1971 and in that year records first appeared in the *Norfolk Bird Report*.

Despite their brightly-coloured and attractive appearance, Golden Pheasants are not easy birds to see, living as they do in the darkness of 10–20 year-old coniferous thickets. Their stronghold continues to be in Breckland and Thetford Forest, although anecdotal evidence suggests that numbers are declining probably due to the cessation of large-scale releases, inbreeding and increased predation (especially by foxes) as gamekeepers become fewer (European Atlas). Also, scrub clearance in dense woodland can cause considerable disturbance. Certainly flocks of 60 are no longer seen and the maximum counts in recent years have been at Wayland Wood with 28 in 1993, 23 in 1995 and 14 in 1998. In the East Wretham/Hockham area, where 13 were present up to 1993, only two were reported in 1996; similarly at Brettenham Heath 30–40 were located in November 1976, but only seven in 1993. During the 1980s other favoured sites included Cockley Cley, Santon Warren, Drymere and Warren Lodge, but few records are now forthcoming from these localities. A few continue to be reported annually from the Wolferton/Sandringham/Dersingham area, where six were counted in 1997, in addition to at least one hybrid male. Elsewhere in Norfolk, Golden Pheasants have been reported occasionally from Holkham, Wells and Kelling in north Norfolk, and at How Hill in Broadland, but as with the records in the Norfolk Atlas, these must relate to escapes from collections. Evans (1996) estimated the Norfolk population at 110–115 birds, but this appeared to have been based on the maximum counts at each site during the 1990s.

*Moss Taylor*

# [Lady Amherst's Pheasant                           *Chrysolophus amherstiae*

**A very rare introduced, but not established, resident or escape from captivity.**

Lady Amherst's Pheasant is a colourful introduced species from the mountains of south-west China and adjacent areas of south-east Tibet and upper Burma. In the British Isles various attempts at introduction have been made since 1900 and small, self-perpetuating populations exist in Bedfordshire and adjacent parts of Buckinghamshire and Hertfordshire. However, a survey in 1998 by the Bedfordshire Bird Club revealed that the species is at a very low population level with no more than 50 birds remaining. A Category C species since 1971, Lady Amherst's Pheasant was added to the county list in 1973 on the evidence of successful breeding at Guist and Quidenham. However, with no records received in 1974, only recorded at Elsing on one date in 1975 and at Hockham also on a single date in 1977, the species has been unable to maintain a population in Norfolk.

Possible breeding only was recorded during the Norfolk Atlas survey (1980–85) from Bergh Apton and Hassingham, and these birds were considered almost certainly escapes from collections. On the strength of only a single record at Wayland Wood on 25th January 1985 and with no further sightings, the species was deleted from the county list in 1986.

Since then the only records have been of singles in 1995 at Hoe Rough on 25th May and at Pentney Gravel Pits on 15th June, and a male with an indeterminate female at Wootton Carr on 11th November 1998.]

*Peter Allard*

## Water Rail HARDLEY FLOODS. 5·3·2000.        *Rallus aquaticus*

**A scarce resident, and fairly common passage migrant and winter visitor.**

The breeding range of the Water Rail extends eastwards from Spain, France and the British Isles throughout much of the middle latitudes of the Western Palearctic with isolated pockets elsewhere. It is mainly resident throughout the west and south of its range with some of the eastern population moving south as far as the Mediterranean. It breeds extensively, if thinly, over much of Britain and Ireland, although it has almost certainly become less numerous in recent years (New Atlas).

During the 19th century the Water Rail in Norfolk was widespread, and a common resident and summer visitor 'pretty generally dispersed over the county wherever moist localities afford sufficient harbour'. Stevenson based his view that there was an increase in the spring population, on the numbers of rails appearing on the stalls of Norwich market between the middle of March and early April. Eggs and young birds were regularly obtained with the former being offered for sale on the markets along with the eggs of 'water hens, coots and grebes'. He recorded confirmed nesting in the neighbourhood of Yarmouth, Horsey Mere, Downham, Feltwell Fen, Upton, Diss and East Walton.

By 1930 Riviere still considered it a common, though local, breeding species in the county centred on the Broads and quoted an instance of six nests being found on one estate during a search for pheasants' eggs! Jim Vincent in his Hickling diaries also mentioned six nests being found at Hickling in 1934 and reported 'groaning' in nine areas on 18th May 1944. Percy (1951) considered Catfield Fen an area which perhaps contained the densest Water Rail population in the country. Nine or ten nests were found annually yet no increase in breeding numbers was noted. He concluded that the birds themselves controlled numbers, stressing the vigour of fights he had witnessed and considered that the territory claimed by each breeding pair was so considerable that that alone prevented any increase. One charming scene was the habit of carrying young described by Percy at Catfield, Emma Turner at Hickling and Anthony Buxton at Horsey.

Autumn migration was regularly recorded at the light stations around the coast during September, October and November with an atypical spring record at the Haisboro' light-ship on the night of 24th–25th March 1909. Vincent also recorded a casualty there with one being taken to him on 30th September 1925.

In the second half of the 20th century the Water Rail has remained a passage migrant and winter visitor in reasonable numbers but has become a scarce breeding species. The Norfolk Atlas disclosed confirmed breeding in only eleven of the 55 tetrads in which it was recorded. The secretive nature of the species and the difficulties of adequately surveying the marshes and swamps which comprise its preferred habitat has almost certainly resulted in under-recording. During the last 25 years or so the annual *Norfolk Bird Reports* have recorded confirmed or suspected breeding at 30 localities, but once again possible observer bias has to be taken into account, as 60% of these records have arisen from the well-known and well-watched reserves at Burnham Norton, Cley, Hickling, Horsey, Strumpshaw, Surlingham Church Marsh, Titchwell and Welney. The largest breeding concentrations reported were seven pairs at Strumpshaw in 1992 and five pairs at Titchwell in 1995. In 1997 breeding-season records came from 13 localities with breeding proved at only three.

Notwithstanding the comparatively meagre, but increasing, total of breeding season records, recent years have brought forward good coverage of the wintering population. For example, in 1996 there were records from over 40 widespread localities. A favoured autumn area is Holme with maximum counts of 23 there in 1993 and 36 in November 1995.

There is little direct evidence of the autumn migration into the county but one was in a bush in Yarmouth Cemeteries on 24th October 1979 and one was seen to fly in from the sea and land on the beach at Weybourne on 1st November 1980. Another was at Waxham Sands on 21st October 1994, while a dead bird was found at Winterton beach on 5th November 1995 and one became a window casualty at Eccles on 17th October 1996. In January 1997 one was seen in a bush at Cromer and Yarmouth Cemeteries hosted another on 9th April, where one was also present on 24th January 1998.

Dangerous times for Water Rails are the calm days of penetrating frost following heavy snowfall. Then and only then, the birds are forced to move. Over 20 were attracted to a pool at Surlingham where a spring had prevented this last feeding area from freezing over during the bitterly cold winter of 1962–63. During the same period eleven Water Rails were recovered from the tideline between Morston and Blakeney; at Wells three starving birds attacked weakened Knots and Dunlins.

Many wintering birds were disturbed from the coastal marshes following the inundation by the sea on 19th–20th February 1996. Three or more were seen attempting to feed in relatively open ground under bushes and plants on a small dry corner of the marsh at Cley after they had been flooded out from their favoured reedbeds. Others were not so lucky, with 18 tideline corpses found on the saltmarshes between Wells and Stiffkey on 21st February 1996.

Probably fewer than 100 Water Rails have been ringed in Norfolk and none has been recovered away from the site of ringing. However, in 1935 one that had been ringed on Helgoland, Germany on 4th October was found at Sustead in November. More recently, one ringed in Shropshire on 31st January 1988 was found dead at Ormesby Broad three weeks later. This was possibly an autumn immigrant to the British Isles that had commenced its journey back to the Continent.

*Don Dorling*

## Spotted Crake | *Porzana porzana*

**A very scarce passage migrant, and rare summer and winter visitor; formerly bred.**

The secretive habits of the Spotted Crake makes its breeding distribution very difficult to establish. It has recently returned as a very scarce breeder to the British Isles, with a Western Palearctic range extending from Spain and France, where it is very locally distributed, eastwards through central Europe into Russia and beyond. Some winter in the south of the region with others moving to Africa and India.

In the 19th century the Spotted Crake was a not uncommon visitor to the Broads and Fen districts of the county between March and October. Lubbock, quoted by Riviere, wrote in 1845 that they arrived 'with great regularity between the 12th and 20th of March'. By 1870 Stevenson considered 'that they were formerly more abundant in this county than they are now'. In support of this view he quoted a Mr Rising, who in earlier years had killed up to eight in a day's shoot at Horsey, but who subsequently had found them to have become comparatively rare! Eggs and young birds were regularly obtained and Riviere recorded nests and, or, clutches from Walton Fen, Hickling, near King's Lynn and Brumstead. However, by the turn of the 19th century it was becoming a rare breeder and the last known nest was 'mown out' at Hickling in 1908. Jim Vincent continued to record the species at Hickling, usually of birds being flushed from August to October, but he mentioned two spring records – one on 19th April 1925 and another when he 'listened to one calling for two hours in company with George Yeates (the photographer) on 27th April 1940. Call uttered twenty plus times then speeded up like a hen clucking. Called nightly till 2nd May.'

The majority of Spotted Crakes sent to local taxidermists were killed in October with some occasionally taken in November. The latest dates quoted by Riviere came from Arthur Patterson who saw two in Yarmouth market on 13th December 1899 and another that he picked up on the tideline at Sea Palling on 12th December 1928. Anthony Buxton writing in *Wild Bird Protection in Norfolk 1938* mentioned that at Horsey in 1938 at the end of October there was quite an invasion of Spotted Crakes. 'They were all around the mere. On 5th November I heard about a dozen, six of them all close together moving in the dead gladden. During the last hour before sunset they were seldom silent for long. I do not know what they were finding to eat, but the dykes and along the edges of the mere there were great numbers of shrimps.'

An analysis of the records appearing in the *Norfolk Bird Reports* since 1953 confirm that it is now an almost annual visitor, appearing in all but two of the last 45 years; the exceptions being 1990 and 1991. There have been nearly 140 records, two-thirds of which have been in the late summer and autumn months of August, September and October, but birds have been recorded in every month of the year. They have occurred at 34 locations with Cley being the most favoured site with nearly one-third of all records. Wisbech Sewage Farm, Holme and Titchwell have all received ten or more visits during the period under review. With such a skulking species one can speculate that there is, perhaps, an observer bias in these records from such well-watched locations.

All the records have been of single birds apart from two at Wheatfen on 24th January 1954, two at Cley on four occasions – on 14th September 1962, from 30th August to 2nd September 1973, from 28th August to 4th September 1975 and on 6th August 1983; with three there from 28th August to 19th September 1977 and again from 6th September to 4th October 1981. A second bird was also present at Titchwell on 21st–24th August 1996, while one at the same site from 21st August to 9th October 1998 was joined by a second bird on 28th–30th September.

There has been no firm evidence of breeding since the 1908 record but occasionally birds have been heard calling during spring and summer in suitable habitat, at places such as Hickling, Wheatfen, Welney and Cley with the most recent occurrence at an undisclosed site in 1994.

Two birds have been caught and ringed – at Cley on 4th September 1959 and a juvenile at Whitlingham on 2nd August 1992.

*Don Dorling*

# Little Crake                                                  *Porzana parva*

**A rare vagrant.**

Because of its secretive nature the distribution of the Little Crake is imperfectly known throughout much of its range which probably extends from Belgium and Germany eastwards to Kazakhstan, with small pockets in Spain, France and The Netherlands. In winter it occurs from the Mediterranean basin south to Kenya. It is rare vagrant to the British Isles in both spring and autumn.

The first record for the county and the second for Britain, was a bird found in a poulterer's shop in London in May 1812 amongst some birds sent 'from Norfolk'. Stevenson detailed another 11–12 examples, all from Broadland localities such as Horsey, Hickling and Heigham Sounds. Six occurred in the spring months of March, April and May, and three in autumn between August and October, with no specific dates for the remaining records. All were killed with the exception of one on 25th October 1867 which was flushed and escaped being shot because the gunner had just discharged both barrels at Snipe! It was identified before being lost to sight in marshes along the River Bure five miles from Yarmouth. Ticehurst (1932) mentioned an example which was shot 'near Yarmouth' in May 1828. This could have been the one taken at Neatishead at that time or, possibly, was another Little Crake taken south of Yarmouth which would have been considered to be a Suffolk bird in Stevenson's day. Riviere recorded the last record of the 19th century as a female taken at Hickling on 25th October 1880.

There were no further appearances during the next 79 years until a male was seen at Brinton Lake on several occasions from 15th November 1959 to 14th January 1960. On this last date it was watched and sketched by Dick Bagnall-Oakeley for ten minutes at a range of 20m. The second record for the 20th century was an immature seen on Snipe's Marsh at Cley on 13th–24th September 1969. The final sighting in the county of this rare vagrant was one seen at Selbrigg Pond, Lower Bodham on 18th–25th February 1970.

*Don Dorling*

# Baillon's Crake                                              *Porzana pusilla*

**A rare vagrant and former breeder; last recorded in 1874.**

The Baillon's Crake is a sporadic and irregular breeder from Iberia and France discontinuously eastwards through much of the Western Palearctic to Asia. There are also populations south of the equator in southern Africa and Australia. Because of its secretive nature the current range and size of population is difficult to judge with accuracy. It has undoubtedly suffered a considerable reduction in numbers during the 20th century due to serious loss of habitat. The winter range of the European population is thought to be in sub-Saharan Africa. It is an extremely rare vagrant to the British Isles.

Early writers considered that the species was very rare but less so than the Little Crake. Stevenson expressed surprise at this view as he had not known of any instance in which a Baillon's Crake had been killed in the county for 20 years prior to the completion of his second volume in 1870. Both he and Riviere repeated the records of Lubbock who stated that specimens had been shot in the first half of the 19th century on three occasions on Barton Fen, together with an adult male taken on a marsh at Dilham in April 1833. A recent discovery in the National Trust's Sheringham Hall collection was a glass shade containing a Baillon's Crake labelled 'shot Ranworth by the Revd Richard Lubbock about 1840' and acquired by Henry Stevenson in 1879. Rather surprisingly it is neither mentioned in Lubbock's *Observations on the Fauna of Norfolk* (1879), or the earlier editions of 1845 and 1848, nor was it in Stevenson's collection which was auctioned in September 1887. Another 'fine male' was killed at Burgh Castle near Yarmouth in August 1842 which was given to Mr J. H. Gurney for his collection. The final record for that period was of two shot on the same day in October 1849 by a Mr Dowell whilst Snipe shooting on Buckenham Fen in the valley of the River Thet. The last record of a bird of this species being collected in Norfolk was a female which was killed by striking telegraph wires by the Hunstanton to King's Lynn railway line on 2nd June 1874 (Stevenson 1875).

In 1866 two clutches of eggs, claimed to be of this species, were taken from Heigham Sounds. The first four eggs were collected on 9th June and sold in Yarmouth to a collector who subsequently found the nest in an area of reeds which by then had been cut. He found a second nest in the same locality with a clutch of five eggs on 7th July. Stevenson reminded his readers that although it had been taken for granted that these two nests were of Baillon's Crake, no positive evidence was forthcoming in the absence of sightings of the parents. With Little Crakes occurring in the county it was just possible that the eggs belonged to that species although it had never been proved to breed here. Mr Alfred Newton, who received one of the eggs from the first clutch, told Stevenson that he did not 'profess to know the difference (if there be any) between the eggs of the two species'.

The second breeding record was a nest containing one egg found by a marshman 'in a nest of dried sedge in a small patch of dead stuff near the edge of dyke at Sutton Broad, Norfolk. Containing this one egg only, 2nd May 1889', according to the label by T. E. Gunn in its box at the Castle Museum, Norwich (A. Irwin *in litt.*). This egg is housed with the B. B. Riviere egg collection at the Castle Museum, where it was examined in the 1920s by the Revd F. C. R. Jourdain who confirmed the identity as an egg of a Baillon's Crake.

*Don Dorling*

# Corncrake (Corn Crake)             *Crex crex*

**A rare passage vagrant and winter visitor; formerly bred.**

The breeding range of the Corncrake in Europe is rapidly declining, particularly in the west. This reduction in range is largely due to the loss of its favoured habitat resulting from the widespread introduction of improved farming practices. The wintering range is in north-east Africa as far south as Ethiopia. As a breeding bird in the British Isles the Corncrake is now virtually confined to the Scottish islands and Ireland.

Known to Sir Thomas Browne as a Norfolk bird in the 17th century, the 'Land Rail', as both Stevenson and Riviere called it, was still a regular spring and summer visitor 200 years later, breeding 'in the cornfields or amidst the rank herbage of low meadows, as well as on the ronds and marshes bordering upon the rivers and broads'. Nevertheless, even by then the population was in decline. Lubbock writing in 1845 stated that this species 'had much decreased in numbers due to the same causes which have rendered the Quail far less numerous than formerly – changes in habitat resulting in extensive drainage and cultivation'. During the autumn of 1899 the Revd Bird reported that two Corncrakes had been 'telegraphed' at Keswick and he recorded a total of 17 either shot or seen by himself from 25th August to 10th October that year. He also heard of many others.

By 1930 Riviere reported that the Corncrake had become exceedingly scarce as a breeding bird in Norfolk. No nests had been recorded since 1900 when one was found at Northrepps. Two pairs were heard at North Wootton in 1920 and a pair frequented a grass field at Ickburgh throughout June 1924. In 1928 one was heard during the summer at Welney.

It was still an autumn passage migrant at that time between August and mid-October. A number of interesting entries appear in the Hickling diaries of Jim Vincent during this period. For example, on 11th September 1913 his retriever flushed eight from a grass field in 15 minutes. On 11th August 1920 four were flushed from barley being cut at Hickling with two more, also in barley, on 17th August 1925. He also recorded a number of other sightings in September and October in the years between 1913 and 1926, as well as 'several' at Hickling on 11th September 1940. His only spring record was one calling in clover at Hemsby on 26th May 1931. The latest dates known to Riviere were 10th December 1913, 10th December 1920 and one on the Lynn Well light-vessel on 15th December 1926.

An exceptional summer record was the discovery of eight or nine breeding pairs in the vicinity of Brancaster Staithe by Guy Mountfort in 1939 (Norris 1945). The only other confirmed breeding record was in July 1965 when an adult and seven chicks were discovered at Wramplingham. In addition, birds have been heard calling in the county during the spring and summer since Riviere's day on many occasions, for example Hemsby in 1931, Hanworth in 1934, regularly in the Ormesby area up to 1947, Cley in 1956, Old Hunstanton in 1964 and 1965, Beeston Common in 1966, Ringstead in 1968, How Hill/Irstead two in 1968 and Ormesby in 1969.

An analysis of all the records since 1951 indicate that April and May have become the favoured period for this species to appear in the county with almost half the reports in these two months. The late summer and autumn months of August, September and October still produced many sightings, in line with Riviere's experience. Stragglers have turned up in both November and December with one killed by a cat at Horstead on 23rd December 1992 and the latest at Cley on 30th December 1962. Many of the records arose from the discovery of dead birds – at least four succumbed after striking wires, one was a road casualty and another was killed against a window at Gorleston on 6th September 1992. The majority of birds have appeared on or near the coast from Hunstanton in the west to Winterton and Scroby Sands in the east, with the well-watched localities of Holme, Blakeney and particularly Cley having the most records.

*Don Dorling*

## Moorhen (Common Moorhen)  *Gallinula chloropus*

MY GARDEN - CHEDGRAVE.
11-7-1999 (2)

**A very common resident and fairly common winter visitor.**

The Moorhen has an extensive breeding range throughout much of the Western Palearctic, mainly between 35°N and 60°N. It is largely a resident in the west but a migrant in the eastern part of its range. It is a common and widespread breeding bird in the British Isles, being absent only from the Scottish Highlands, central Wales and other areas 600m or more above sea-level (68–72 BTO Atlas).

The species has the dubious distinction of being one of the earliest recorded as falling victim to a firearm in the county. Stevenson quoted an extract from the L'Estrange 'Household Book' of one being 'kylled wt the gun' in 1583.

In Norfolk it is a widespread and very common species breeding throughout the county on ponds, lakes, gravel pits, the Broads and rivers. It is also a winter visitor. It occurred in all 10km squares in the New Atlas and in nearly 1,200 tetrads (82%) of the Norfolk Atlas, being by far the most common and widespread bird associated with wetlands. Sample surveys have indicated that, generally, breeding numbers have been maintained although there is some evidence of a recent decline. Few population statistics exist but in 1993 counts in north Norfolk revealed 32 pairs on the Blakeney Fresh Marshes and 48 pairs on the nearby Cley Marshes. In 1997 there was an interesting report from Flitcham of a pair raising one young Moorhen and one young Coot.

Unlike the Coot, the Moorhen does not desert its inland sites for tidal waters during periods of severe weather and as a consequence can suffer substantial declines in numbers after prolonged severe frosts. Stevenson, quoting Lubbock, mentioned 43 being together during frosty weather as an unusual gathering. In more recent times this practice does not seem to be triggered by severe conditions and Moorhens do congregate in substantial parties with records of autumn and winter flocks on or near suitable waters – 58 at Hethersett (grazing in the Park), 80 at Cantley Beet Factory and 75 at Whitlingham, being typical examples. The largest parties recorded were 109 at Holkham Park in January 1998, 117 on a Cobholm playing field in February 1979, 143 at Welney in February 1995 and 166 on the Holkham NNR in January 1996 when the WeBS count along the coastal sites in north Norfolk was 451.

There is ample evidence of autumn movements into the county. Riviere mentioned that a number were taken from the light-vessels off the coast during October and November with one bird taken on a ship 20 miles off Cromer on 28th December 1886. In recent times, before the demise of the manned light-vessel, the crews were encouraged to keep records of birds landing on their ships. The Moorhen regularly appeared in these diaries. On 7th–8th December 1953 many came aboard the Newarp lightship 16km north-east of Cromer. Another was there on 2nd November 1962, a third was reported on 12th December 1967 and one was found dead on 19th October 1968. The Inner and Outer Dowsing, Smith's Knoll, the Corton and the Haisboro' light-vessels all reported this species on dates ranging from 25th September to the end of November in various years. One found on the Haisboro' on 30th September 1962 had been ringed at Texel in The Netherlands only three days earlier.

Albino specimens were obtained on the Broads in 1903 (Patterson 1906) and at Reedham in 1952. Birds of the 'hairy' variety with the feathers which lack barbules and resemble hair, have been obtained at Ludham (Patterson 1905), Fundenhall on 17th December 1954, which is now at the Castle Museum, Norwich and Hindringham on 6th May 1961 (Seago 1967).

Over 500 Moorhens have been ringed in Norfolk but only two have been recovered more than 100km away from the site of ringing. One ringed at Dersingham on 28th December 1967 was found in Jutland, Denmark in March 1970, while one ringed at Thetford on 4th December 1996 was found on Whalsey, Shetland on 27th March 1997. Northerly movements have also been noted with the recoveries in Norfolk of birds ringed in Essex and Hertfordshire. A total of 15 foreign-ringed Moorhens has been found in the county from The Netherlands (10), Denmark (3), Germany and the Channel Islands. All but one were ringed between July and November, and most were recovered in Norfolk during the winter.

*Don Dorling*

# Allen's Gallinule                                                    *Porphyrula alleni*

**A very rare vagrant; one record in 1902.**

Allen's Gallinule is an African species found over much of tropical Africa north to Senegal and Sudan, which is subject to sporadic northwards dispersal.

The sole British record (and only accepted by the BOURC in 1974) is of a juvenile captured alive as it landed in an exhausted state on board a fishing vessel off Hopton on 1st January 1902. The winds the previous day had been very strong from the south-west. Taken into Yarmouth, it was kept alive by a local taxidermist Walter Lowne for two days on a diet of mealworms. It was then preserved, sold and passed into the collection of J. B. Nicholls, where it remained for over 25 years (Hudson 1974). It was sold at a London auction on 29th June 1929 and has not been traced since.

*Peter Allard*

# Coot (Common Coot)  *HARDLEY FLOODS. 27·9·1999.*                    *Fulica atra*

**A common resident and winter visitor.**

The breeding range of the Coot extends throughout the greater part of the Western Palearctic, except for the more northern latitudes. The western population is largely sedentary while those birds from further east move south in autumn as far as sub-Saharan Africa and south-east Asia. In the British Isles it is commonest and most widespread in the lowland areas, being absent from most of the Scottish Highlands and islands, as well as the upland areas of Wales and Ireland (New Atlas).

In Norfolk the Coot has always been a common resident on suitable waters throughout the county, from the fens in the west, through the Breckland lakes and meres to the Broads and slow moving rivers in the east. It has been able to extend its range in recent decades to include the many flooded gravel workings. Lubbock likened a Broad without its Coots to London without its sparrows and Newcastle without coal. In his day the eggs of Coots were considered a delicacy and he quoted 500–600 being taken in a season from Surlingham Broad. The present breeding range extends throughout most of the county wherever a suitable stretch of water can be found, with the thinnest distribution being in the clay- lands of central-south Norfolk. It is most abundant in the Broads, the main river valleys and the Fens and Breckland lakes and, when water levels permit, meres in the south-west. It was recorded in 387 tetrads during the fieldwork for the Norfolk Atlas with confirmed breeding in 261. The Coot is very much under-recorded as a breeding bird in the county but a summary of recently published breeding details indicated that 25 sites, on their best years, contained a total of over 450 pairs. Of this total the Breckland meres held about 25 pairs, but at the time of writing, these have become completely dry and unsuitable for Coots. The highest count of breeding pairs at any one location in the summary was 176 on the Holkham NNR in 1995 together with a further 25 pairs on Holkham Park Lake. There were 50 pairs on Bemey Marshes in 1998.

After the breeding season the Coot relaxes its strongly territorial nature and gathers in large flocks on suitable waters. Hickling Broad was long a favoured site with one marshman early in the 19th century, in answer to a question from Mr Lubbock, saying he measured them there 'by the acre'. Hickling continued to be popular with the species; Gurney estimated about 3,000 in February 1901 and 1,500 birds were counted on 18th February 1955. These winter gatherings encouraged a long tradition of holding Coot shoots on the larger Broads. Stevenson quoted references to the practice dating back to at least 1825. Records are available of the numbers shot on Hickling Broad for the period of 61 years from the winter of 1894–95 until 1955–56, the numbers for the earlier years coming from the records of the Revd M. C. H. Bird of Brumstead Rectory and those after 1911 from the Hickling gamebooks now in the possession of the Norfolk Wildlife Trust. These show that, despite the disruption to the sport caused by severe winters and two world wars, they were able to kill 55,269 Coots at an annual average of 906. The largest annual totals recorded were 2,057 in 1933–34, 2,360 in 1945–46 and 2,000 in 1946–47 when further 'hundreds perished in the ice and snow'. Riviere quoted the highest daily 'bag' as 1,175 shot on 18th February 1927 and this was exceeded with 1,213 on 10th February 1934 (George 1992). In the winters of 1938–39 and 1939–40 only small 'bags' were obtained as a result of severe habitat deterioration following the inundation of Broadland by salt water after the major sea flood of February 1938. Severe frosts stopped shoots in 1927–28, 1928–29 and 1953–54. In 1949–50 'both shoots were ruined by gales'. This annual ritual ceased at Hickling in the early 1960s.

Notwithstanding these annual culls, the Coot remained remarkably resilient as a Norfolk resident and winter visitor with about 2,000 overwintering on Hickling Broad in 1964 and 1965. However, these large gatherings on the Broads are, perhaps, a thing of the past. The decline in numbers there undoubtedly mainly resulted from the deterioration of water quality and consequent reduction of necessary plant food, rather than the cumulative effects of the annual shoots. Avian botulism in the mid-1970s may also have played a part. The mean wintering population on Hickling in the late 1970s was less than 100 birds (George 1992). As water quality improves in Broadland in general and Hickling in particular, resulting in improved aquatic plant life, wintering numbers there are increasing and it will be interesting to see if Hickling once again will regularly be host to Coots in four-figure numbers; 1,092 were counted there in November 1997 increasing to 1,270 a month later.

There is still a substantial wintering population throughout the county as a whole, with a count of the most important sites producing a total of 4,290 in January 1996, which included 400 at Hickling. Other large monthly maxima have been 1,044 at Welney in February 1993 and 1,039 in January 1995, 600 at Hardley Flood in August 1993, 724 on Holkham Lake in January 1997, 426 in Sennowe Park in October 1995, 1,022 at Colney Gravel Pits in December that year and 352 at Wroxham Bridge in January 1997. Occasionally parties will gather on tidal waters with 82 being seen off Hunstanton in January 1979 and 344 on Breydon in December 1995 where the highest recent count was 618 on 2nd December 1973. Through the years whenever the Broads have become ice-covered, large numbers of Coots have appeared on Breydon. Patterson estimated 3,000 on 24th December 1906, many falling victims to the local punt-gunners.

There is some positive evidence of the arrival of immigrants over the autumn and winter with Riviere mentioning records from the Norfolk light stations in August, November and January. More recently, birds have been recorded on the Lynn Well and Haisboro' light-vessels in October and November 1962. A first-winter female was caught and ringed on Sheringham cliff-top on 21st February 1994 and another bird on the groynes at Sheringham in November 1995 was also almost certainly a migrant; also a probable migrant was a bird in Brancaster Harbour in January 1997.

Several hundred Coot have been ringed in Norfolk, but only two have been recovered abroad. One ringed at Dersingham in February 1972 was found in The Netherlands in December 1974, while a chick ringed near Stanford in 1989 was shot in Pas-de-Calais, France the following February. Another chick from Fowlmere was recovered the following March in Northamptonshire and an adult ringed at Coltishall in January 1997 was found in Humberside one year later. Almost 40 Coot ringed in counties to the south of Norfolk, mainly at Abberton Reservoir, Essex have been reported in the county. Eight foreign-ringed Coot have been recovered in Norfolk from The Netherlands (6), Denmark and the Channel Islands. Apart from two in March, all were found in January, most as a result of having been shot. The vast majority of Dutch-ringed Coot are recovered in France.

*Don Dorling*

# Crane (Common Crane)                     *Grus grus*

**A very scarce resident in Broadland where it has attempted to breed annually, sometimes success-fully, since 1981.**

The Crane breeds from Fennoscandia and north-central Europe across the northern Palearctic to eastern Siberia. In Norway the habitat is one of desolate mountain bogs; many nests are surrounded by water and some are virtually inaccessible to man. In central and southern Sweden Cranes breed in small swampy clearings but in Denmark the birds favour undulating sand dunes with scattered marshy pools. They winter in France (from the late 1970s occupying the recently-created Champagne wetlands), Iberia, North Africa and Turkey. In Britain it is a very scarce migrant and winter visitor with most during October–November. Three notable invasions in south-east England have taken place following the departure of flocks from northern Europe in response to an abrupt fall in temperature. The birds drifted across the English Channel in easterly winds and poor visibility. The biggest and most famous occurred in 1963 when at least 500 were recorded.

Cranes
(Gary Wright)

Historically it is not absolutely certain whether the Crane bred in Norfolk before the 20th century, but the bird featured on the menu in banquets until about 1600 and Southwell (1901) was convinced that an ancient record from the Norwich Corporation of a payment for a 'young Pyper Crane' proved breeding in the county – 'there is no room for doubt that in the year 1543 the Crane bred at Hickling'. At the time of Riviere's book, the county total stood at over 30 including the first taken at Martham in February 1850 and the then most recent at Cley and Salthouse in September 1922. No less than five were shot during May 1869 at East Somerton, Martham and Winterton. The largest flock containing nine birds appeared at Blakeney on 29th August 1899. Between 1930 and May 1979 the county total increased to 62. As in earlier times, almost all observations were between April and June and during August–September. A lame individual at Breydon on 21st May 1951 visited Belton and Burgh Castle in early June before appearing at Waxham where it remained intermittently until mid-July, over Scroby Sands on 8th July and finally at Mautby until early August. Another long-stayer lingered on Welney Washes from 8th August to 27th September 1978. An adult and an immature at Holkham and Cley on 17th March 1979 and at Strumpshaw Fen on 18th March then separated with the immature visiting Geldeston on 5th–6th April and Welney on 22th–26th May; the adult put in appearances at Wortwell on 20th–21st April and at Reedham on 22nd–23rd May. One of these wanderers passed over Cley on 23rd May.

The days of Cranes remaining rarities in Norfolk ceased on 15th September 1979 when two appeared at Hickling, coming from Minsmere, Suffolk, to be joined by a third bird on 10th October. In addition, on 7th October an exhausted adult captured at Irstead was taken into care over the winter before release on 30th March 1980, but it only stayed in the area one day. The original trio remained in Broadland until 5th April 1980 when all climbed to a height of 750m to appear over Sheringham at midday before heading west. To everyone's surprise all three returned to Broadland on 22nd April, with two remaining until the year-end, apart from a three-day exploratory flight providing surprises to observers in Burton-on-Trent and Anglesey. This spring movement was probably an attempted migration back to Scandinavia with the birds refusing to undertake the hazardous North Sea crossing. It was to be repeated in subsequent years with at least some of the birds visiting the north Norfolk coast before returning to the Broads. The third bird in 1980 was joined by a fourth on 18th May but neither was subsequently seen again. The other pair which remained during the summer of 1980 spent much of the time hidden in the reedbeds.

During the spring of 1981 courtship displays were observed by the original pair; a third bird was chased off by the male in February 1981. A nesting site was selected, but high water levels in the marshes resulted in nesting activity ceasing after a few days. Further attempts resulted in a successful hatching and the lone chick was heard cheeping as it was escorted by the female. Unfortunately, a predator soon ended this first breeding attempt in June 1981. During the autumn of 1981 two new Cranes joined the residents; five were often seen. By the following spring the original pair had driven off the others and reared a young male to the flying stage. Thus in 1982 the first breeding of Cranes in this country since the 16th century had been achieved.

A similar success followed in 1983 when the same pair reared a female offspring. The previous year's young male remained with its parents until late February, but was then chased away (on several occasions it headed out to sea at a great height before returning) as were any other Cranes in the area.

During the next few years the Broadland birds usually fed as a group of up to seven. The original pair stayed close together; the others in twos or singles within the overall group. Each year, and particularly during the spring, these birds provided most if not all the reports of Cranes appearing over the Norfolk cost including a casualty on the shore at Mundesley on 7th April 1984. Others wandered inland to Strumpshaw, Barnham Broom, Great Hockham and Welney. Four were present at the now regular locality at the opening of 1985, but disappeared after the 6th January following three days of bitterly cold weather including blizzard conditions. However, four Cranes in Essex on 9th January and in Kent the next day were doubtless the Broads birds which all returned on 3rd February. The main pair attempted nesting each summer, but did not achieve success again until 1986 when a third young (a female) fledged. Springtime wanderers included three heading out to sea at Salthouse on 30th April and not returning until three hours later.

By the summer of 1986 the two young Cranes reared locally in 1982 and 1983 paired off and commenced nesting operations which were not successful. This event became a guide to the age at which Cranes will start breeding: the male at four years and the female at three years. At the beginning of 1987 six Cranes were present, but all left, perhaps heading for France, following a heavy snowfall on 12th January. Three had returned by 7th March; the other three reappeared four days later after being seen over Stodmarsh in Kent. During 1987 both pairs of residents attempted nesting, but with no success due to predation of the young. The summer of 1988 saw the young pair rearing a single fledgling thus bringing the breeding fortunes of the group to a total of four. No further success was achieved until 1997, but two new adults arrived before the close of 1989. By the beginning of 1990 there were eight Cranes on show consisting of three potential breeding pairs together with two sub-adults.

A cold spell during February 1991 resulted in all eight birds disappearing after roosting each night on ice. By the month-end six had returned at the first signs of a thaw, but the original pair was never seen again. Cranes were reported breeding in northern France that summer, possibly the Broadland pioneers? As a result of this loss only six were present during the spring of 1991 including a pair which seemed to be infertile. They were then joined by a juvenile which was soon in company with the bird reared in 1988.

Over the next few years there were a number of nesting attempts, all unsuccessful. An impressive total of 16 Cranes was present on 24th October 1995 but this high number soon reduced to nine birds. The 1996–97 winter brought additions and for a few days up to 14 birds could be observed in one place. The groups then separated into two parties of four followed by two sets of three when all headed towards night-roosts.

From late December 1996 up to twelve Cranes were on view. Six adults were present during spring 1997 including a pair which was successful in rearing two young. A total of ten birds closely observed on 6th December 1997 included two pairs each escorting two young. At least one of these family groups were Continental migrants. Yet another young bird became an addition during 1998 after its twin had been taken (almost certainly by a fox) at six weeks of age. That summer eight adults were in residence. During October 1998 up to 14 were present; three (presumably from this group) began a three-week stay at Halvergate Marshes on 14th October.

In an effort to control disturbance to the Broadland Cranes an Area of Special Protection was designated under the Wildlife and Countryside Act in 1987. However, wild predators are a constant problem. Marsh Harriers have been seen harassing the Cranes and alighting on a nest if the nest-owners are absent. A Bittern too, is capable of being a major predator in a reedbed, but the greatest threat is from foxes. The most vulnerable period for a young Crane is until it is capable of flight. During its first ten weeks it travels great distances during daily sorties with its parents between feeding ventures and night roosting at the nest-site. The greatest danger arises if two chicks have hatched with the parents taking equal turns in incubation and subsequent chaperone duties.

The most favoured areas for daytime feeding are the undisturbed open grazing marshes. Cranes move about pecking and digging for long periods seeking worms and insects and inspecting ditches for frogs. One bird in late summer was plucking a long stalk of rye grass in a hay crop before holding it down with one foot and neatly pecking each seed. Potatoes are greatly favoured, especially small new ones growing among a heap of last season's throw-outs. When escorting the young, the adults constantly pick up grubs, worms and insects before walking over to present them. A Crane family usually returns to the nest even after the young can fly. On occasion, the female will settle down first allowing the young to climb on to her back before snuggling under her wing feathers. The male roosts within a few metres preferably in shallow water and standing on a single leg. The nest site needs to be surrounded by 30cm or more of water in a marsh where it is concealed in thick reed or sedge. A lack of human disturbance is essential. The pair share nest-building, each plucking nearby material to construct a large platform well above normal water level. Incubation is shared almost equally. Each adult will fly up to one and a half kilometres away to favoured feeding places and absences may last for two hours or more.

It would be inappropriate not to place on record the great efforts of the Crane guardians ever since the unexpected arrival of the first pioneers two decades ago. The problems of predation and the activities of over-zealous birdwatchers have needed constant effort. However, among the rewards are the opportunities to listen to the wild trumpeting of these extremely shy birds at dawn and dusk and to witness dancing displays, with pirouetting and leaping into the air. Even more exciting, is the rare chance of viewing the adults proudly escorting young.

Sightings of small groups of Cranes continue to be a spring and autumn feature, but to attempt to identify them as the Broads residents or as newly-arrived migrants would be pure speculation. Such groups travel considerable distances. Four which roosted nightly at Minsmere, Suffolk, on 27th–30th April 1996 may well have been the same four birds appearing over Sheringham on both the first and last dates.

*John Buxton & Michael Seago*

# Little Bustard                                                    *Tetrax tetrax*

**A rare vagrant; only two records since 1916, both in 1968.**

The Little Bustard has two distinct breeding ranges in the Western Palearctic, both showing signs of a decline in numbers and range. The southern European population is mainly resident and is found in France, Spain, Italy and Morocco. In the east, where it is partially migratory and more prone to vagrancy, the Little Bustard is now extinct in Bulgaria, Romania and possibly Turkey; the population in the Russian steppes is also decreasing in numbers and retreating southwards. The species is a vagrant to north-western Europe, including the British Isles.

It was first recorded in Norfolk when one was taken at Mundesley in November 1820. Stevenson listed a further eleven occurrences in the next 40 or so years, five of which were 'obtained' in turnip fields; the majority appearing during the autumn and winter months. By the time of Riviere's book, the total number of records had increased to 22, with the last being killed between Acle and Yarmouth on 28th December 1916. The four of these specimens, which had been examined critically, were assigned to the eastern race *T. t. orientalis*.

No further records occurred until two birds were found, both dead, in 1968. The first, a female, collided with overhead cables at Scole on 19th December; the other, a male, was a road casualty 70km to the north-west, between North Wootton and Estuary Farm on 31st December. Both birds were examined at the Castle Museum, Norwich and again showed the characteristics of the eastern race *orientalis*. These two records bring the total number accepted for the county to 24.

In addition to the evidence from the specimens that have been examined, the reduction in the frequency of records during the 20th century, which coincides with the decline and retreat of the eastern European population, points to the conclusion that the majority of Little Bustards appearing here have come as vagrants from the east rather than the south.

*Don Dorling*

# Great Bustard                                    *Otis tarda*

**A very rare vagrant in the 20th century with four records involving six birds; formerly a Breckland resident.**

Great Bustards
(*Norman Arlott*)

The Great Bustard's range in the Western Palearctic is now fragmented with declining populations in Iberia, Germany, Austria, Poland and south-eastern Europe. The easternmost populations are migratory while those in Europe are largely resident with occasional dispersive movements. A former British breeder, it is now a rare vagrant to the British Isles.

Both Stevenson and Riviere devoted considerable space in detailing the history of the indigenous Norfolk population. Early records appeared in household and civic documents dating from as early as the fourteenth century. The population was probably never very large and Thomas Browne writing in the 17th century described the Great Bustard as 'not unfrequent in the champian [*sic*] and fieldy part of the county' – an expression interpreted by Stevenson as meaning they were not numerous at that period.

By the time more meaningful records were available there were two main flocks, or droves, of Great Bustards resident in the county, both occurring in the large open areas of Breckland. One was centred around Swaffham and Westacre with the other near Thetford. The latter adjoined the main Suffolk location in the Elveden and Icklingham area. The Westacre drove totalled 27 early in the 19th century with similar numbers in the southern party. Both droves declined rapidly thereafter with the last Norfolk breeding probably taking place in 1830. Eggs were laid at Great Massingham Heath in 1833 and as there was no evidence that a male bird was present, the clutches of three, three and one were collected. These female birds remained in the Swaffham district until at least 1838. The last Suffolk breeding record was at Thetford Warren in 1832. There were spasmodic reports of individual birds being seen in Breckland until the 1840s but whether these were lingering native birds or migrants is not certain.

Many of the final representatives of the native stock were 'collected'. The Castle Museum, Norwich has a case of seven birds, all of local origin and among the last of the native race. Their history is as follows:

1. A male found dead on Beechamwell Warren some time between 1815 and 1818 previously having been shot and wounded at Narborough
2. A female caught in a rabbit trap at Westacre in 1831
3 & 4. A male and female whose date of capture is unknown. They were purchased for the museum in 1892
5. A female kept as a pet at Eriswell in Suffolk which was presented to the museum with the Lombe collection in 1873
6. A female killed at Elveden in Suffolk about 1815
7. A female killed at Lexham in May 1838 and believed to be the last of the indigenous race

The Castle Museum also has a female in a separate case, which was shot at Horsey Warren in 1820 having been seen coming in from the sea. Riviere referred to a case containing a male, two females, a nestling and two eggs; these were destroyed by fire at Congham House in November 1939.

Further occasional migrants have occurred in the county since the demise of the native stock. One was reported over Horsey Mere on 7th January 1867, and on 24th January 1876 a fine male appeared on the

232

Hockwold Estate. In an attempt to persuade this bird to stay two females from Lord Lilford's aviary were released nearby. The first perished in bad weather and the male was seen flying towards Brandon on 23rd February 1876, the day after the release of the second female!

There have been six subsequent occurrences. A dead female was found at Stiffkey on 19th January 1891 with another female killed at Costessey on 2nd February 1894. After a gap of 69 years yet another dead female was discovered at South Creake on 28th March 1963 having been killed in collision with overhead cables. In 1979 a male was seen and photographed by John Buxton at East Somerton and Winterton on 26th February, before it moved on to Martham later that day, and two birds were seen coming in from the sea at Bacton on 2nd March. The most recent record was of two immature males which spent three days near New Buckenham from 7th to 10th February 1987 (Dorling 1988). They were part of a small invasion of birds displaced by severe weather in eastern Europe; Suffolk had parties of three and four at this time, with two seen flying inland at Kessingland on 7th February 1987, presumably the New Buckenham birds.

*Don Dorling*

HARDLEY FLOODS. (4) 4·7·2000. INCL 2 IMM'S.

## Oystercatcher (Eurasian Oystercatcher)     *Haematopus ostralegus*

**A fairly common but localised breeder and passage migrant, and very common winter visitor.**

In Europe the Oystercatcher breeds mainly along the northern and western coasts, with increasing numbers breeding inland. Those breeding along the coasts of Russia, Norway (above 64°N) and the Baltic are fully migratory, the remaining coastal breeders partially so, the degree decreasing with decreasing latitude. It breeds around much of the coast of the British Isles, and inland in north-west England north of the Ribble Valley, and throughout most of Scotland (New Atlas).

In the 1800s the Oystercatcher, or 'Sea-Pie', as it was locally known, was described by Stevenson as an abundant breeder, but increasing human predation through the 19th century reduced the breeding numbers to just a scattering of pairs along the coast. Pashley (1925) reported that Oystercatchers were completely absent from Cley and Blakeney Point between 1892 and 1905, with just a single pair returning in 1906. Since then numbers have steadily increased, such that 30 pairs were breeding annually between Wells and Salthouse by 1930 (Riviere) and Seago (1967) noted 280 pairs between Holme and Salthouse. A total of 530 pairs was reported in 1997 on coastal sites (beaches and grazing marshes) between the Wash Outer Trial Bank and Cley, including 94 at Scolt Head, 47 at Brancaster Harbour, 112 at Holkham and 200 at Blakeney Point.

Whereas in north-west England and Scotland inland breeding is widespread, in Norfolk breeding territories had remained largely restricted to coastal habitats. However, since 1940 there has been a gradual spread of breeding birds into inland locations, with pairs moving into Broadland (to within little more than 2km from Norwich Cathedral), Breckland and the Fenland levels, as well as coastal fields. During fieldwork for the Norfolk Atlas (1980–85) Oystercatchers were recorded in 217 tetrads, representing 15% of those in the county, of which the vast majority were inland. Since 1980 this spread has continued and now includes more open fields and pastures – for instance in 1997 of the 112 at Holkham, 42 pairs were on grazing marshes. In the early 1970s inland breeding records were often in single figures, but by 1996 records had increased to 69 pairs at 29 different sites, whilst in a comprehensive RSPB survey of the Broads in 1995 a total of 190 pairs was recorded; a notable increase from the 123 found in 1982. If this trend continues Oystercatchers could, one day, become as familiar an inland breeding species in Norfolk as Lapwings once were. Unusual nest-sites in recent years have included a pair which bred on the top of a post marking the main channel at Breydon and a pair at Ludham which bred successfully 2m above the ground in the crown of a pollarded willow. Breeding by one pair was suspected on the roof of the Yarmouth Asda Superstore in 1996 and was confirmed in both 1997 and 1998. Another pair also bred successfully on a flat roof in North Quay, Yarmouth (close to the town centre) in 1998.

Autumn passage commences in mid-July with small parties of Oystercatchers, which ringing has demonstrated are from Norway, flying north along the east Norfolk coast and west along the north coast, many of which eventually gather around the Wash to moult. The highest day-counts of birds flying west have been recorded at Sheringham with 174 on 31st July 1976, 210 on 6th August 1993, 290 on 25th July 1996 and 370 on 18th July 1997. While some of these birds are only transient visitors to Norfolk, many remain, with numbers steadily increasing through to the middle of winter. The mean peak winter counts on the Wash were under 20,000 in the early 1970s, rising steadily through the 1980s with the highest count, of over 45,000 birds, in January 1988. The greatest concentration in Norfolk occurs at high tide around Snettisham, with maximum counts of 16,300 in November 1988 and 15,600 in January 1990. The increases recorded around the Wash were mirrored further east where peak winter counts along the north Norfolk marshes were around 350 in the early 1980s, but are now at least 3,500. A low-tide count organised by English Nature in 1997 found 2,940 in November and 2,256 in December, with maximum site-counts all in November of 627 at Scolt Head, 994 at Wells and 472 at Blakeney Harbour.

However, during the 1990s there has been a decline in wintering Oystercatchers on the Wash, thought to be a result of depletion of cockle and mussel stocks, with the population dipping to around 30,000 by the winter of 1991–92, and 25,000–30,000 during the following November. With insufficient food stocks birds have become vulnerable to cold spells in winter. This was all too graphically demonstrated in 1992–93: an abnormal mortality rate had already been noticed during the autumn when large numbers began feeding on grassy roundabouts and on playing fields in the King's Lynn area and flocks regularly appeared up to 15km inland of the Wash. Following spells of cold weather the population fell to 12,000 in January 1993. Many hundreds of corpses were found, including both adults and juveniles (Clark 1995). Whereas normally, inland records are scarce in Norfolk in winter, there were examples of Oystercatchers continuing to wander away from the coast in a desperate search for food. Large numbers moved onto inland fields around the Wash to feed from late November onwards, with flocks reported up to 15km inland (Clark 1993). At Sheringham this was reflected in record numbers feeding on earthworms on the golf course with up to 59 in January–February and 54 in March (Shepherd 1992–94). In addition a handful of ringing recoveries from elsewhere suggested that at least some had had the energy reserves to move further afield. Peak winter counts at the Wash have seen a continuing decline since then and numbers have now fallen back to levels similar to those of the early 1970s.

Return migration gets underway in early March and passage continues into May. Smaller numbers are recorded than in autumn with maximum counts at Sheringham of 65 east on 9th March and 22 east on 8th April 1996, although a total of 94 flew west on 23rd March 1996. Eastern Norfolk sees an increase in numbers during March and April. Peak counts at Breydon have risen from about 50 in the early 1970s to a maximum count of 423 in March 1992 but have fallen back to nearer 200 since, possibly as an indirect result of the mortality suffered on the Wash. An albino Oystercatcher frequented the Wash in winter between Snettisham and Hunstanton from 1988 to 1993.

The WWRG has ringed over 30,000 Oystercatchers and recoveries show that the majority found on the Wash during the winter are from breeding grounds along the west coast of Norway, with birds arriving back in southern parts of Norway as early as mid-March. Over 600 birds ringed on the Wash have been recovered in Norway (of which just over half were ringed on the Norfolk part of the Wash), while much smaller numbers have been recovered from northern England and Scotland, the Faeroes, Iceland, Finland, Sweden, and north-western Russia during the breeding season. Ringing recoveries of Norfolk-bred Oystercatchers suxggest that some, at least, move on to estuaries further south-west in Britain and into Continental Europe or beyond – one was recovered during December in Morocco. Ringing has also demonstrated the longevity of Oystercatchers. Large-scale ringing began in the late 1960s and birds caught in these early days are still being recovered. The current longevity record stands at over 33 years, a longer lifespan than for any other species of wader in the British Isles.

*Steve Wakeham*

## Black-winged Stilt — *Himantopus himantopus*

**A rare vagrant, usually in late spring and summer; bred in 1987 and one resident in the county since 1993.**

The Black-winged Stilt breeds in the Western Palearctic from central and southern Europe across to Asia and North Africa. In western Europe it breeds regularly only in Spain, France (mainly in the Camargue) and Portugal with irregular nesting in Germany, Denmark, Belgium and The Netherlands. The birds winter mainly in Africa north of the equator. In Britain it is an irregular spring overshoot although annual since 1978. Breeding has been attempted on four occasions – in 1945 when two (possibly three) pairs nested in Nottinghamshire, in 1983 in Cambridgeshire, in 1987 in Norfolk and in 1993 in Cheshire. Autumn occurrences are distinctly rarer.

The first two Black-winged Stilts to appear in the county were obtained at Hickling and Northwold Fen in June 1822. By the time of Riviere's book the number of records had increased to 21, the most recent being two birds at Hickling on 24th May 1929. Of the dated records one had occurred in April, eight in May, four in June, one each in July and September, and three in October. No further observations were reported until 26th August 1945 when a lame bird at Breydon was almost certainly one of a pair which summered at Dunwich in Suffolk. During April and May 1965 there was an influx into the British Isles with sightings in eight counties. In Norfolk the first arrival was at Holme on 3rd May followed by another at Heigham Holmes on 11th, two at Horsey on 13th and two at Hardley Flood on 25th. In that year a number of pairs nested in inundated polders in The Netherlands.

Rush Hills, Hickling attracted single Black-winged Stilts on 17th June 1968 and on 19th–30th May 1980. The next occurrence was a female at Wisbech Sewage Farm on 29th April 1983; doubtless one of the four birds that appeared on the Nene Washes in Cambridgeshire early in April.

HoLME - 24-5-1987.

Black-winged Stilts
(Richard Millington)

Richard Millington.

A spring invasion of Black-winged Stilts took place in 1987 when an exceptional total of 38 appeared in the country. A massive anticyclone over Europe during late April produced ideal overshooting conditions. Summer migrants sweeping northwards were accompanied by a galaxy of southern wanderers. Among the many highlights was the pair of Black-winged Stilts which arrived at Holme on 17th May. The news spread rapidly among the birders visiting the north coast at this time of year. Queues soon formed and time in the observation hides was limited to a few minutes for each observer. Rain began falling solidly, but there were few complaints. Despite cloudy, cool weather the pair's ardour for one another remained undiminished and mating was observed on five occasions only a day after arrival. Yet it came as a surprise when less than a week later the gorgeous peach-flushed male stilt was observed incubating a clutch of eggs within a short distance of one of the hides. The site was an islet that had been created almost inadvertently during the winter. Newly-created wetlands often turn out to be particularly productive, but nesting stilts were a remarkable bonus! Volunteers were sought to assist with protection and three 'stilt wardens' were hired to occupy the long hours and days that the eggs would remain vulnerable to egg-collectors. Indeed, the birds were attracting sufficient revenue to pay for their protection. The watchers' log records very frequent attacks on predators. The most aggressive response was against Grey Herons, Marsh Harriers, Kestrels, Lesser Black-backed Gulls and Carrion Crows which were often pursued far beyond the pool.

The weather remained dismal throughout incubation, but the first Black-winged Stilt to be hatched in this country since 1945 peeped out from beneath a brooding parent on 15th June. Next morning all three chicks had hatched. For the 'stilt-wardens' the long hours of vigilance had passed. After surviving the miserable June weather it was a blow when the smallest chick disappeared at 14 days old; a stoat was strongly suspected of having taken it. The two survivors first became airborne by mid-July. Exploratory flights followed, the family remaining at either Holme or Titchwell until 18th August when both parents departed overnight. The juveniles remained together feeding, roosting and taking the occasional flight to Titchwell until the last day of August. However, this was not to be the last that was seen of them: two juvenile stilts arrived at Belvide Reservoir in Staffordshire the following day, a distance of 200km. Here they remained until 7th September when they departed to the south (Boyd 1988).

No Black-winged Stilts returned to Holme during 1988; they were not expected. The species occasionally breeds far north of its normal range without establishing regular colonies. A juvenile stayed briefly at Titchwell on 5th November 1990 followed by two at Rush Hills, Hickling on 16th May 1992 and a third bird visited Burgh Castle and Berney Marshes on 20th–23rd May that year. Another was found at Hardley Flood on 4th May 1993. Later that year, a further surprise – a male Black-winged Stilt was discovered among Oystercatchers at Snettisham Pits on 18th–21st August. It was almost certainly the one present in Northumberland from 31st July to 6th August. The remainder of the year was spent at Titchwell and Thornham apart from visits to the shore at Hunstanton on 26th–27th August, Scolt Head during the first half of September and on 10th October, and Holme on 18th September and on 14th–18th October. Future events have made ornithological history. The lonely resident has remained at Titchwell and is still present at the end of 1998, just making occasional brief excursions to Snettisham, Holme, Thornham and Brancaster. Such an extended stay is unique; the nearest comparison being the Black-winged Stilt overwintering in Lincolnshire in 1968–69. Is it a coincidence that the bird is so close to the site of the 1987 breeding success? This elegant wader's ability to survive the rigours of a Norfolk winter has surprised many. Roger Skeen's diary sets the scene: '23rd February 1994. A bitter east wind blowing, snow and ice covering the brackish marsh, bird crouched behind rough grass on the closest island, head tucked in, wings drooping. Asleep or frozen solid?' (Skeen 1997). And the long-stayer still bides its time.

*Michael Seago*

## Avocet (Pied Avocet) *Recurvirostra avosetta*

**A fairly common migratory breeder and passage migrant; scarce in winter.**

In the Western Palearctic Avocets breed locally in coastal areas, from southern Sweden, Denmark, Estonia, northern Germany, the Low Countries and south-east England, around western and Mediterranean Europe to the Black and Caspian Seas, as well as far inland. Birds winter in western and southern Europe and North Africa, crossing or circuiting the Sahara. In England the Avocet was formally widespread on the coast from the Humber to Sussex, but it became extinct in most of the country by 1820–40 due to land reclamation, disturbance, shooting and egg collecting. After an absence of over a century recolonisation began in the early 1940s when public access to the east coast was restricted. From 1947, following large increases in numbers on the Continent, Avocets became re-established as regular breeders in Suffolk when four pairs nested at both Havergate and Minsmere.

Stevenson described the Avocet as a vanished breeder with 70–80 pairs nesting at Horsey until 1819 and possibly for a few years later 'in the lower parts of the marshes adjoining the warren where samphire used to grow', at Winterton until 1816, on the lower Bure Marshes in the vicinity of Stracey Arms until about 1805, and at Salthouse where breeding ceased between 1822 and 1825. At Salthouse the birds had been described as nesting 'by hundreds'. The local gunners regularly filled caps, coat pockets and even stockings with Avocet eggs for puddings and pancakes. When unloading punt-guns the wildfowlers would kill 10–12 birds at a shot. Despite such enmity during those far away days a few Avocets continued visiting Salthouse each spring until the marshes were drained in 1851. Then they became rare and irregular passage migrants and were exceptional in winter. On the east coast, Breydon was renowned for visiting Avocets during the collecting era. A pair set up in a glass case by Lowne or Saunders, the two best-known Yarmouth taxidermists, found a ready purchaser. Most appearances were of ones, twos and threes although five were shot out of a flock of six at Breydon on 4th May 1887 and nine put in an appearance there on 14th–17th June 1905. A flock of 15 visiting Breydon on 21st August 1935 was exceptional.

Long after the event, it was learnt that Avocets attempted nesting at Salthouse in 1941 but the clutch was deserted and quickly added to Clifford Borrer's collection. Birdwatching steadily increased in popularity during the 1950s but sightings of Avocets remained spasmodic until the late 1960s. Usually less then six birds were involved, apart from 14 at Breydon on 11th March 1954, up to 14 at Cley on 1st–11th April 1958 and 14 there on 12th June 1958. Cley, Salthouse and Breydon attracted the majority, but Wisbech Sewage Farm, the east shore of the Wash and Hickling also featured. In contrast to 1967's single county sighting at Breydon, the following spring witnessed an influx of Avocets at Cley. One pair showed every intention of nesting, but after raising hopes for a whole week they departed. Breydon shared in the arrivals, including a flock of 26 on 15th June 1968. From then onwards, records became ever more frequent especially between March and June, and between August and October, the largest groups totalling 15 and 27 birds.

Avocets
(John Wright)

Long anticipated, Avocets finally began nesting again in Norfolk in 1977. Thirty years of expectancy were finally realised since these highly attractive birds had decided to make Suffolk their first British nursery in modern times. That year four pairs nested at Cley rearing a total of six young (Ramsay 1978). The event featured on local television enabling thousands of viewers to share in the Avocets' family life. A further pair nested at Snettisham but the nest was trampled by cattle. The Cley population increased to 26 pairs by 1981, 40 pairs in 1984, 65 pairs by 1987 and 85 pairs by 1988. At times Avocets, no longer rare wanderers, became the most numerous wader on Cley Marsh.

Further breeding colonies became established – at Salthouse in 1981, Holme and Hickling in 1982, Titchwell in 1984, Holkham in 1990, Upper Thurne floods and Berney Marshes in 1992, Welney in 1996, Heigham Holmes and Stiffkey Fen in 1997, and Buckenham and Wickhampton in 1998. The breeding season has been a disaster on occasions. One year a county total of 170 pairs reared less than 40 young due to predation by foxes, stoats and Carrion Crows. In another year at Titchwell only three young hatched from a total of 70 clutches of eggs – largely due to foxes. Cold, wet weather has also caused high mortality among newly-hatched chicks. Colour ringing indicates that Avocets usually breed for the first time when they are two or three years old. One-year immatures may return to breeding sites, but arrive later than established breeders or make only brief visits. Many remain well south of nesting areas. At times, unusually low water levels and flashes have provided opportunities to find Avocets at Gunton Park, Hardley Flood, Hockwold Fen, Holkham Lake and Wissington Beet Factory.

**Table 35. Total numbers of breeding pairs of Avocets in Norfolk 1977–97.**

| 1977 | 1978 | 1979 | 1980 | 1981 | 1982 | 1983 | 1984 | 1985 | 1986 | 1987 |
|------|------|------|------|------|------|------|------|------|------|------|
| 5 | 5 | 8 | 20 | 27 | 28 | 37 | 49 | 56 | 79 | 101 |

| 1988 | 1989 | 1990 | 1991 | 1992 | 1993 | 1994 | 1995 | 1996 | 1997 |
|------|------|------|------|------|------|------|------|------|------|
| 134 | 170 | 131 | 126 | 157 | 174 | 209 | 214 | 203 | 181 |

Although Avocets breed far inland in the central Asian steppes, those in Norfolk invariably nest within a few kilometres of the coast. Furthest inland are those at Welney Washes using purpose-made scrapes. The Avocets at Titchwell nest in an embanked brackish marsh created from saltings between 1976 and 1980. At Cley breeding takes place on islets in the brackish lagoons created and regularly improved over the years. In Broadland Avocets are attracted to shallow flood-marshes. A colony on the Wash occupies saltmarsh where nests are frequently lost due to flooding during high spring tides. Control of water levels on reserves greatly reduces such risks. Unseasonably cold weather has resulted in the failure of clutches to hatch. Foxes and stoats have been the most frequently recorded predators of eggs. Egg-collectors have robbed a few clutches, but such losses in many instances have been made good by replacements.

Avocets began regularly wintering in Britain in 1947. Initially, they were restricted to estuaries in Devon and Cornwall. A considerable increase in numbers resulted in the establishment from 1968–69 of a wintering flock on the Suffolk Alde. Wintering also soon became regular in Essex and Kent. In Norfolk small numbers became a feature at Breydon from late October 1994 and wintering was first established in 1995–96 with 72 being counted in December 1995; numbers had increased to 157 by February 1998.

Post-breeding assemblies were first recorded in 1987 when numbers at Titchwell peaked at 102 on 26th July. Since 1989 totals during July and August on the Ouse Mouth have increased almost annually from 106 in 1990 to a maximum of 600 in 1996. At times the birds move north to Snettisham. When flooded off the muds by the incoming tide they are content to swim buoyantly at sea in tightly-packed rafts. At Breydon an autumn build-up first began in 1994 with 50 birds on show followed by 158 in 1995, 170 in 1996, 192 in 1997 and 264 in 1998.

Small numbers of Avocet chicks have been ringed in Norfolk in recent years. Only two have been found outside the county – one at Cliffe, Kent in August and the other on the Tamar Estuary, Devon in November, where large numbers of Avocets are known to winter. The value of colour ringing was clearly demonstrated by an Avocet thus marked as an adult female at Schleswig-Holstein in northern Germany in May 1991 which was subsequently seen while moulting in Denmark in August before being sighted at Cley the following February. A month later, during March and April 1992, it was back at its ringing site in Germany, before returning once again to Denmark in December 1992.

*Michael Seago*

## Stone Curlew (Stone-curlew)    WEETING. 31·5·1986.    *Burhinus oedicnemus*

**A scarce summer visitor, mainly to Breckland, and very scarce passage migrant.**

The Stone Curlew is a summer visitor to central Europe north to 54°N where it breeds discontinuously from France eastwards to the Ukraine. Further east it is more widespread between the Rivers Ural and Volga. It is resident in Spain, North Africa and Egypt with the population augmented by wintering birds from further north. In England the Stone Curlew had undergone a contraction in range and in breeding numbers in the second half of the 19th century due to the spread of forestry and cultivation. Some recovery occurred in the 1920s and 1930s but further habitat loss took place during the Second World War reducing numbers. The English population reached a low of some 160 pairs in 1988 in two distinct areas – the downland of Wessex and the Breckland area of East Anglia. Due to extensive monitoring and protection organised by the RSPB, numbers increased to 215 pairs in 1998.

The Stone Curlew has had a strong association with Norfolk. In about 1674 Sir Thomas Browne sent a drawing of a bird killed near Thetford to John Ray who published a description of the bird in his book *The Ornithology of Francis Willughby* published in 1678. The exact location of the site where the bird was taken is not given so it should be admitted that this bird might have been obtained in Suffolk. A measure of how common Stone Curlews were at this time is indicated by Stevenson who expressed a 'little surprise that Sir Thomas was unable to obtain a specimen from nearer his home' which was in Norwich. As an aside, Sir Thomas was not pleased that Ray held on to his drawings for so long and wrote to his son requesting that he repossess them from a bookseller in London with whom they had been left.

There is no doubt that the Stone Curlew and its wailing, haunting calls would have been widely known by many of the population who inhabited rural areas. Hence the Stone Curlew was given a number of local names peculiar to Norfolk. The commonest in use was the 'Norfolk Plover'. This distinguished it from the Green Plover – the Lapwing. It was also known as 'Thick-Knee', 'Great Plover', 'Willie Reeve' and, very evocatively, the 'Wailing Heath Chicken'.

Even at the time that Stevenson wrote (1870), the Stone Curlew was undergoing a decline due to changing agricultural practices involving enclosures of the open heaths and through egg collecting. Up until 1850, breeding was regular on the higher ground of Costessey, Easton and Bowthorpe with birds being seen each spring at Thorpe. At this time there was heathland, though not continuous, from Rackheath, Mousehold and Thorpe on the north side of Norwich to Hempstead and Holt. At Rackheath in the 1830s, there were flocks of up to 40 and 50 seen each autumn. However, these were often noted using young plantations for shelter and food, which would, in time, have become unsuitable as the trees grew taller. The hilly country to the west of Cromer held breeding birds up to the time of Stevenson's publication and small numbers were seen between Sheringham and Salthouse in June and July. One or two pairs bred south of Beeston up to 1866 but not in the following year. Similarly, breeding ceased on Briston Common in the early 1860s prior to enclosure of the common. Birds and nests were seen at Cawston and Witchingham in 1867. Breeding took place at Woodlands, Thorpe St Andrew, within three miles of Norwich Cathedral, for 20 successive years up until at least 1866.

At this time, decreases were noted in the south of the county. On the edge of the Brecks, at Eccles, the Revd Lubbock noted only one in the four years up until 1870 whereas 20 years before he would hear them every summer evening from the rectory. One of the reasons for the decline must lie with Revd Lubbock himself, for in his *Fauna of Norfolk* he described the shooting of an adult Stone Curlew which, because it was only winged, was caught and left in a walled garden overnight. The calls at first light, of this bird, attracted a young bird to the wall of the garden. This bird though fully grown was unable to fly and was itself caught later in the day. Lubbock does not describe the fate of these birds. Certainly the species was widespread throughout Breckland with breeding noted at Swaffham, Westacre, Congham, Lexham, Cressingham and Watton. In the West Harling area a decrease had been noted. However, flocks of 20–25 were seen in autumn on fields of turnips. Both here and at Thetford, Stevenson noted a reduction of heathland and an increase of plantations. Further to the west, a flock of 150 was seen on an estate near Feltwell in the autumn of 1867 and similar flocks were noted near Swaffham and Thetford.

Stone Curlews
(*Gary Wright*)

In the decade after the publication of Stevenson an increase was noted in Norfolk especially in the west of the county (Historical Atlas). At the start of the 20th century there was a decrease in the area to the north of Norwich though pairs were noted at Honingham from 1912 until the time of Riviere's book (1930), at Taverham on at least four occasions from 1914 to 1930 and also at Drayton and Swannington up to 1929. In north Norfolk, Kelling Heath, which was a stronghold of the species, was deserted in 1901, although Pashley recorded four or five pairs in 1906. None was present from 1914 until 1925, but one pair returned in 1926 and three pairs nested in 1927. In east Norfolk single pairs bred within a short distance of the sandhills between Waxham and Winterton until 1956. Emma Turner (1924) photographed them nesting at Winterton.

While Stevenson had made no mention of the north-west of the county, Riviere noted breeding at Massingham Heath and Roydon Common, and on the heathland between Docking and Fakenham. He concluded with a warning that unless conservation steps were taken and land acquired as a reserve by a conservation body such as the Norfolk Naturalists Trust, and maintained for Stone Curlews, then the enclosure and afforestation of Breckland would drive this bird from its principal stronghold in the county. How prophetic his words were! By 1930, no less than 20,000 acres had been enclosed for this purpose with a further 2,500 acres each year. Stone Curlews would continue to breed in the young plantations until the growth of the trees reduced the amount of open ground. Some large autumn flocks were observed with over 100 on one warren in 1936 and 50 on Gooderstone Warren on 4th August 1949. Elsewhere, in Broadland a pair bred on wartime ploughed marshland at Hickling in 1943 and 1944.

The spread of myxomatosis in the 1950s caused the degeneration of heathland such that vegetation became too tall for Stone Curlews. The intensive grazing of sheep in the Stanford Training Area did keep the grass down and enable birds to continue there. Also by this time all the forestry plantations had reached an unsuitable height and amount of ground cover. A chick was found at Spixworth, one summer in the early 1950s, only 6km from the centre of Norwich. A pair was present on Kelling Heath in the summer of 1953, but there was no evidence of breeding and they did not return subsequently.

By the 1960s birds were breeding on cultivated land in several areas on the edge of Breckland (Beechamwell, Feltwell, Foulden, Marham Airfield, Roudham and West Harling) although some of these birds lost their nests to farming activities. A total of twelve pairs was present in five parishes within 8km of Holt, in the north-west between Thornham and Ringstead, and at South Creake. There were still five pairs at Ringland in 1966, while a pair bred between Weybourne and Bodham in 1969.

In the 1970s, away from the Brecks, up to three pairs bred at a disused airfield at Egmere up to 1973 with a maximum of three pairs in 1971. The total for Breckland was 61 in 1976 of which 30 were in Norfolk. The population was quoted as being between 20 and 30 pairs in the late 1970s and early 1980s although it is likely that some pairs remained undetected. The last recorded breeding in the north of the county occurred in 1980. During fieldwork for the Norfolk Atlas between 1980 and 1985 Stone Curlews were recorded in 32 tetrads with confirmed breeding in eleven. Egg collectors were noted as accelerating the decline of the species in Norfolk and all records for this period were in the western half of the county. There was an upturn in numbers at the end of the 1980s coinciding with more complete fieldwork by the RSPB Breckland Stone Curlew Project and the advent of special protection measures for pairs nesting on arable fields (McNeill 1994). By 1990, the total for the Brecks (Norfolk and Suffolk) had reached 90 pairs, while by 1997 the total had risen to 122 pairs with 114 young successfully fledged. In this latter year no less than 78% were nesting on arable land and only 22% on the more traditional heathland.

**Table 36. The total number of pairs of Stone Curlews breeding in the Norfolk Breckland and the number of fledged young where known, 1987–98.**

| Year | Pairs in Norfolk Breck | Young fledged in Norfolk when known |
|------|------------------------|-------------------------------------|
| 1987 | 39 | |
| 1988 | 34 | |
| 1989 | 33 | 29 |
| 1990 | 37 | 28 |
| 1991 | 39 | |
| 1992 | 46 | 32 |
| 1993 | 45 | |
| 1994 | 40 | 30 |
| 1995 | 48 | 46 |
| 1996 | 59 | 55 |
| 1997 | 57 | 68 |
| 1998 | 73 | 56 |

In recent years the productivity has been above 0.7 birds per pair which is the estimated requirement to maintain the population. This has been due to warm, dry summers which aid chick survival. In damper summers not only is the mortality of young directly increased by the wet weather, but it also encourages an increase in grass and crop growth thus reducing the amount of open/bare ground available. This happened in 1998, when the number of pairs in Norfolk Breckland increased by 16 but eight fewer young fledged (Hayman 1999). Unusual prey items taken have included voles, young wood mice and the chicks of both the Skylark and Ringed Plover.

In 1995 the combined total for the Norfolk and Suffolk Brecks exceeded 100 pairs. Since 1993 up to four pairs have nested in other areas of Norfolk. The continuation of this increase is reliant on the preservation of suitable habitat. Birds on heathland have a higher productivity than those on arable. A number of arable crops such as autumn-sown cereals are unsuitable as they have grown too tall and not left enough bare areas by the start of the birds breeding season. So, to some extent, a sizeable proportion of our breeding pairs, about half in any one year, could be at risk due to changes in agricultural policies and practices. The role of the farmers and landowners should be acknowledged and through their liaison with the RSPB Breckland Stone Curlew Project team chicks can be protected and made safe during any farming operations (Green 1989 & McNeill 1994).

Arrival on the breeding grounds in spring is normally in the middle of March although earlier arrivals might easily be overlooked. There have been four February records in recent years – at Stanford Training Area on 26th February 1966 and 25th February 1993, at Gooderstone on 28th February 1994 and a pair at Bodney Lodge on the exceptionally early date of 4th February 1974.

There have been about 45 records of birds away from breeding areas in the last 20 years, 30 of which have been between the end of March and mid-June. Some were clearly on passage, for instance singles seen flying in off the sea at Yarmouth on 23rd March 1996 and at Sea Palling on 15th April 1996; others were more likely to have been wandering non-breeding birds. The remainder were in July and August, with the latest in the Cley/Salthouse/Weybourne area from 21st August to 9th September 1982. Two-thirds of these records have been on the north and north-west coasts, seven on the east coast and six at inland sites not used for breeding.

In autumn there are assemblies of birds on heathland areas in the Brecks. These do not approach the flocks of over 100 that were seen in earlier times (Lubbock 1845). Often there would be numbers of birds spread over an area rather than in one large flock; Clarke (1937) stated that although he had seen up to 65 on one Breck, the largest 'flock' was of 30. In recent times post-breeding assemblies totalling up to 80 have been seen on a number of the heathlands during August and September. The main departure, with the birds migrating in flocks, is from the end of September with some birds present into October. Notable parties of late birds have included 17 on 26th October 1994 and twelve in mid-November 1995.

Stevenson referred to records in November, December and February. In recent times there have been instances of birds staying until December, but whether these actually overwinter, eventually migrate or succumb at the onset of cold weather is unknown. One recorded in December and later found dead was proved by colour ringing to be a very old bird.

For over 20 years Stone Curlews have been ringed and given unique colour combinations and it is estimated that over 60% of the Brecks population is now marked in this way. This has been invaluable in monitoring movements of breeding birds and in establishing an age profile of the Breckland birds. Based on colour ringing, the annual mortality of juveniles and first-winter birds is estimated at 50% and that for adults at 25%. The oldest known bird lived for 16 years (McNeill 1994). Foreign recoveries of these ringed birds have indicated that they travel through western France and north-east Spain to winter in southern Spain and North Africa. Sadly, most recoveries are a result of birds being shot and this slaughter could well have a profound effect on the viability of the Breckland population. Multiple sightings of one colour-ringed Stone Curlew was particularly interesting – ringed as a chick in the Brecks in May 1990, it was seen at Zeebrugge, Belgium on 13th March 1991 and was relocated in Norfolk later that month. Another ringed as a chick in May 1990 was recovered on 28th July in Essex.                    *Peter Dolton*

# Cream-coloured Courser                                   *Cursorius cursor*

**A very rare vagrant; four records.**

The Cream-coloured Courser is a species of arid grasslands and desert. It breeds from the Canary Islands eastwards across North and East Africa to Iraq and from south-west Asia to Afghanistan. Most populations are sedentary, but eastern birds in the north of their range are migratory. It is a rare vagrant to the British Isles and most have occurred between September and November.

**Cream-coloured Courser**
*(Richard Richardson)*

The first Norfolk record was one at Morston in the autumn of 1847. The second bird was at Westacre in the autumn of 1855 or 1856 in the company of Lapwings. It was shot but managed to escape and was never seen again. Stevenson, Southwell and Riviere considered these occurrences as authentic. The third was a first-autumn bird shot at Thornham beach on 3rd October 1934, now at the Castle Museum, Norwich.

On 18th October 1969 one was found in fields close to the coast road at Blakeney (which it shared for part of its stay with a Hoopoe). It obligingly remained there until the morning of 29th October. It was seen later the same day in harvested sugar beet fields at Ormesby East End. It gradually became more tame and eventually could be approached to within a couple of metres. It was last seen alive on 15th November and was found dead on 20th November (Allard 1970). The skin is at the Castle Museum, Norwich. No fewer than ten Cream-coloured Coursers were seen together in The Netherlands on 12th September 1969 and it seems likely that the Norfolk visitor was involved in the same movement.                    *Peter Allard*

# Collared Pratincole                                    *Glareola pratincola*

**A very rare vagrant; five records involving six individuals.**

The Collared Pratincole breeds from Iberia and north-west Africa eastwards across southern and central Europe to Kazakstan, Iran and Iraq; it winters in tropical Africa. It is a rare vagrant to the British Isles, most have occurred between May and July.

The first authenticated record of a Collared Pratincole in Norfolk was of a pair shot on Breydon wall on 21st May 1827 by John Bessey who sold them to Yarmouth game dealer Isaac Harvey for £1. Harvey later sold them for £7; unfortunately their present whereabouts is unknown. Further specimens were obtained at Blakeney in 1840 and Feltwell in early June 1868, both of which remain in the collection at the Castle Museum, Norwich.

Recently, and quite without precedent, what was almost certainly the same individual returned annually to Norfolk each summer from 1994 to 1998. It was first seen at Titchwell on 1st–3rd July 1994, then was present at Cley on 4th–8th and again on 10th–12th before returning to Titchwell on 14th, but was back at Cley on 15th–20th July. In 1995 it appeared first at Titchwell on 3rd–4th July, then moved to Cley on 4th–7th. It was seen flying west over Blakeney Point and Holkham Fresh Marshes on 6th, Snettisham on 13th and was back again at Cley on 22nd–23rd July. Returning for its third successive summer on 5th June 1996, it was seen flying east over Burnham Overy and Holkham Gap before arriving at Cley. It remained there until 8th, returning on 10th–11th June. Doubtless the same bird was then reported in The Netherlands before it was seen at Cley on 15th–16th, 20th–21st, 23rd–24th and at Salthouse on 25th July 1996.

A year later it first appeared at Berney Marshes on 15th–17th May 1997 before arriving in north Norfolk, halting briefly at Burnham Norton and Holkham Fresh Marshes on 26th May before finally reaching Cley later in the day. It remained in north Norfolk almost continuously until 8th June visiting Stiffkey, Burnham Norton and Titchwell; probably this same bird visited two sites in The Netherlands on 4th and 25th May. It reappeared on 5th July at Cley and later in the day at Titchwell, where it stayed until the next day. It was found in Lancashire on 7th July, returned to Holkham and then commuted between Cley and Titchwell from 14th to 24th July with brief visits to Snettisham and Thornham Point on the 19th and 21st, respectively. Amazingly, for the fifth year running it reappeared at Titchwell on 18th May 1998, having previously been seen in Kent on 11th–13th and in Northamptonshire on 15th–16th. It lingered in Norfolk, usually at Titchwell or Holme but also visiting Salthouse and Snettisham, until 8th July.

A second bird in 1997, a first-winter individual in sugar beet fields in company with Lapwings, was just south of Felbrigg village on 12th–28th October. This was, presumably, the same one seen at Corton, Suffolk on 29th September.                                                    *Peter Allard*

# Oriental Pratincole                                    *Glareola maldivarum*

**A very rare vagrant; one record.**

The Oriental Pratincole's breeding range extends from northern India to eastern China. It winters in Indonesia, New Guinea and north-west Australia. It is a very rare vagrant to the British Isles with only five records including the first in 1981.

An extremely confiding first-summer bird at Roseacre Riding Stables, Gimingham, from 14th May to 3rd June 1993 was identified by Dave Holman and David Nicholson. It was attracted to insects from freshly-spread manure heaps in the paddocks and, during its first five days at the stables, an estimated 2,000 visitors arrived to enjoy views of this long-distance migrant. It often soared after aerial prey followed by a succession of rapid twists and turns above the meadows and remained until midday on 3rd June, although it was rather elusive towards the end of its stay (Holman & Nicholson 1993). Just an hour later, a pratincole was reported flying west at Weybourne. On 4th June it was relocated at Blakeney Point before flying off west at 10:15 hrs. It was seen again at Burnham Norton on 5th–21st June, and from 13th July to 13th August. On the following day, Titchwell was favoured where it remained until 17th August, making occasional visits to Thornham saltmarsh (Gantlett *et al.* 1994).

Possibly the same bird (the third British record) appeared at Pevensey Levels, East Sussex on 29th–30th August and on Havergate Island, Suffolk on 4th and 19th September 1993. However, the BBRC could find no direct evidence to link either of these sightings with the bird in Norfolk, although it was clearly possible that only one erratically wandering individual could have been involved.                       *Peter Allard*

# Black-winged Pratincole                     *Glareola nordmanni*

**A very rare vagrant; two records.**

The Black-winged Pratincole is a central Palearctic species breeding from Romania and occasionally Turkey, across the Ukraine and south-east Russia east to Kazakstan and wintering in West and southern Africa. It is a rare vagrant to the British Isles, most have appeared in August–September.

An adult, which was only the eighth British record, remained at Cley on 3rd–5th July 1966. Over 60 birders admired this addition to the county list first found by Billy Bishop. It was sketched by Richard Richardson and the picture was subsequently published in the *Norfolk Bird Report 1966*. The second occurrence was of a bird seen at Salthouse Heath on 25th August 1974, at Cley on 27th and at Salthouse on 28th.

*Peter Allard*

# Little Ringed Plover (Little Plover)    $\underset{24\text{-}6\text{-}1986.}{CLEY.(1).}$    *Charadrius dubius*

**A scarce summer visitor and passage migrant.**

Little Ringed Plovers
*(Richard Richardson)*

The Little Ringed Plover occurs throughout the Western Palearctic except in mountainous regions; its numbers are encouraged by growth in man-made habitats, especially gravel pits. The population winters sparingly in the Persian Gulf and southern Arabia, but mainly in the northern tropics of Africa. In Britain the first recorded breeding pair was at Tring, Hertfordshire in 1938 and in 1944 two pairs bred at Tring and another in Middlesex. Since then the species has flourished and by 1972 over 400 pairs summered in Britain.

The Little Ringed Plover was added to the county list on 14th June 1943 when the writer found two at Breydon running like clockwork toys across the flats. The first two pairs nested in Norfolk in 1960 at Stowbridge and breeding has since become an annual event. The nature of occupied sites makes it easy for the birds to be overlooked (although they are noisy and conspicuous when displaying), but 41 pairs were recorded in 1993. The most popular locality has been the Bawburgh/Colney complex of gravel pits where five pairs nested in 1973. Gravel pits have become the most favoured habitat. However, nests have also been found at Welney Washes, at beet factory settling ponds, Wisbech Sewage Farm, in marshland at Titchwell, Holkham, Cley and Strumpshaw, in sugar beet fields, in Breckland in a carrot field and at Thompson Water where two pairs nested on an islet exposed by low water levels. Most unusual was the nest on a factory roof in King's Lynn in 1984, but the three young perished in heavy storms. At the present-day Bawsey Country Park, Little Ringed Plovers occupied the pools and miniature beaches until the arrival in 1973 of five pairs of Ringed Plovers; the former were rapidly usurped.

The nature of nesting sites chosen means that disturbance of one kind or another is normal rather than exceptional. The birds are disturbed by workmen, bulldozers and lorries as well as by anglers, small boys and adult egg collectors. Disturbance after the eggs are laid has provided opportunities for predation by foxes, Carrion Crows, Jays, Kestrels, Magpies and small mammals. Flooding, either deliberate or as a result of summer storms, is another cause of failure. Fortunately Little Ringed Plovers are not easily put off and usually lay again, sometimes within days. Repeat nests containing eggs have been recorded as late as 13th August at Cantley Beet Factory.

The first p-ring arrivals are generally recorded towards the end of March with the earliest arrivals at Pentney on 3rd March 1990, at Holme on 8th March 1994 and at Whitlingham Gravel Pits on 9th March

243

1995. After the breeding season finally ends, family groups head towards the coast. Wisbech Sewage Farm held special attractions and up to 27 appeared there on 5th August 1971. The maximum numbers at other well-known localities have included 17 at Surlingham Church Marsh on 17th July 1986, 19 at King's Lynn Beet Factory on 8th August 1985, 20 at Cley on 2nd August 1992 and 27 at Cantley Beet Factory on 22nd July 1989.

Most have left Norfolk by the end of September. The latest dates have been 23rd October 1966 at Cantley Beet Factory, 24th October 1970 at Wisbech Sewage Farm, 2nd November 1980 at Holme and 2nd November 1997 at Cley.

About 100 Little Ringed Plovers have been ringed in Norfolk of which three have been recovered abroad – one ringed at Great Witchingham in 1971 was recovered in France on spring passage the following March, another ringed at King's Lynn in June 1975 was controlled on autumn passage in Majorca in late August and the third ringed at Breydon in 1993 was recovered in France in mid-July 1994. There have also been controls of birds involving movements between Norfolk and London, Berkshire, Lincolnshire, Derbyshire and Staffordshire.

*Michael Seago*

## Ringed Plover    TITCHWELL· 19·9·1993.      *Charadrius hiaticula*

**A fairly common summer visitor, passage migrant and winter visitor.**

The Ringed Plover breeds along the coasts of the northern Palearctic extending from Ellesmere Island in the west to northern Russia in the east. It also breeds extensively inland in northern Europe. Two races are recognised – the nominate *C. h. hiaticula* which breeds in western Europe, Iceland and Greenland, and *C. h. tundrae* in northern Fennoscandia and Russia. The species is migratory, only the British populations being partially resident. It breeds around all the low coasts of the British Isles (New Atlas).

In the time of Stevenson the coastal breeding birds were variously known as 'stonerunner', 'Ringlestones' or 'sea-dotterel' and were plentiful between the Wash and Salthouse, the stretch of coastline still favoured today. During the 18th and first half of the 19th centuries the species had also bred regularly in east Norfolk between Horsey and Yarmouth, but by 1870 it had become extinct there as a result of the work of collectors, both of eggs and the adult birds. By the end of the 19th century a few pairs had returned to breed at Yarmouth, where four to six pairs now breed annually. During the Norfolk Atlas it was recorded in 96 tetrads, the majority being coastal squares and most of them in a continuous line from the Wash to Sheringham.

There have been three complete county surveys of nesting Ringed Plovers, and in the 1984 national survey Norfolk was found to hold 6% of the British population. During that year the main concentrations were 180 pairs at Scolt Head, 101 pairs between Burnham Overy and Morston, and 65 pairs at Blakeney Point (Bull 1985), whereas only 74 pairs were present at Scolt Head in 1993 (Rooney & Eve 1993). Since the 1993 survey numbers have continued to fall with only 190 pairs reported in the county in 1997, including 39 at Scolt Head, 30 at Holkham NNR and 50 at Blakeney Point. Foxes and stoats appear to be the greatest threat, particularly at the incubation stage.

**Table 37. Total number of pairs of breeding Ringed Plovers in Norfolk in 1973, 1984 and 1993.**

|  | 1973 | 1984 | 1993 |
|---|---|---|---|
| Coastal | 456 | 523 | 407 |
| Inland | 9 | 18 | 22 |
| **Total** | 465 | 541 | 429 |

On the coast, Ringed Plovers favour open sand and shingle beaches. Numbers nesting in vegetated sand dunes are harder to assess and may have shown local increases where beach disturbance is high. Other coastal habitats include man-made scrapes and lagoons (especially at Cley and Snettisham) and arable fields. However, in 1984, 97% of all coastal nests were located in sand, shingle and dune habitats. These areas are also popular with people for recreation and Ringed Plovers are susceptible to human disturbance, either exhibiting avoidance or greatly reduced productivity. The principle coastal sites are therefore where disturbance is less prevalent and particularly on nature reserves where special protection measures can be put in place. The principal sites, each with regularly more than 30 pairs in recent years, are Snettisham to Heacham, Gore Point to Holme, Scolt Head and Blakeney Point.

Breeding adults arrive at breeding sites in early February, both sexes arriving at the same time. Birds pair up quickly and occupy territories as soon as they arrive. The first nests appear in mid-April. Adult survival is high and a colour-ringing study at Snettisham showed that a yearly mean of 84% of adults ringed one year returned the following year. The longest-lived bird in this study was 14 years old. In 1997, 65 pairs were recorded on the Snettisham to Heacham beaches. Of these, 17 pairs returned to exactly the same territory and with the same partner. These were all pairs which had bred successfully in the previous season. Of the remaining 74% of pairs, most had only moved a few metres along the beach. Clutch size varied little, ranging from two to four eggs. Of those nests, found in 1996 and 1997, 56% hatched at least one chick. The main causes of failure were predation (22%), human trampling (10%) and desertion (8%). The length of incubation varied between territories according to temperature and adult effort (affected by disturbance), within a range of 24 to 31 days. Once the chicks had hatched it was approximately another 26 days before they fledged.

Many adults at Snettisham re-nest if they fail in their first breeding attempt and some were found to do so up to five times in a season. Pairs that had settled for the first time on a territory (usually young birds at their first nesting attempt) were much more likely to desert if the first attempt failed. Serial nesting (where one pair leaves a territory and another pair takes their place) has been recorded and occurred on five territories in 1997. Once breeding is finished (late July to early August), adults and fledged chicks leave the breeding sites fairly quickly. Flocks tend to appear at this time with adults and chicks roosting together in pre-migration flocks. The speed with which fledged chicks leave breeding sites is evidenced by two colour-ring sightings. A chick fledged at Snettisham in early July 1996 was seen in Hampshire in the first week of August and a different chick, fledging in the same year, was seen in Cambridgeshire in August and then in Brittany, France on 2nd September (Liley 1999).

Inland breeding was first noted in Breckland in 1836, where the species was known as 'stonehatch'. However, the size of the breeding population varied considerably, even during the 19th century. At Beachamwell, for instance, the greater part of the warren was broken up in the mid-1800s and by 1850 none was present where previously 'they might have been counted by hundreds' (Stevenson). Despite this, the Breckland population (including the Lark Valley in Suffolk) was estimated to be in the order of 400 pairs in the 1920s, although subsequent afforestation caused a dramatic decline and the few which remain nowadays (two pairs in 1984 and nine in 1993) have colonised arable fields and appear to be increasing slightly. Probably less than ten pairs breed on inland gravel pits and the total for all inland sites is not likely to exceed 25 pairs (Rooney & Eve 1993). The small Broads population has declined in the last 15 years. A reported great increase in coastal breeding numbers in the period 1915 to 1950 might have been in part related to the Breckland decline.

Autumn passage peaks from August to early October, with the highest recorded count of 1,000 at Snettisham in July 1987; but many sites have held more than 200 birds – notably Ouse Mouth, Holme, Scolt Head/Brancaster Harbour, Blakeney Harbour and Breydon. There are no sites in the county holding nationally important numbers (more than 290 birds) in the winter. Numbers are relatively small and scattered, with only Brancaster Harbour, Blakeney Harbour and Breydon having regular populations in excess of 50 birds in recent years. Less than ten winter regularly in the Wash, for example. A low-tide count along the north Norfolk coast between Holme and Blakeney Harbour in December 1997 found a total of 238. However, early spring returns and passage in the Wash (February–March) has increased approximately threefold in the last 25 years, with up to 400 birds present at that time of year, while 500 were present at Titchwell as early as 17th January. The wintering population, mostly from eastern North Sea coastal sites, gives way to a spring passage of returning local breeders and birds returning to Iceland and Greenland. The peak spring passage in May is bolstered by birds of the race *tundrae* returning to northern Europe, and appears to be more concentrated at fewer sites than in the autumn migration. Breydon regularly holds 300–400 birds of the *tundrae* race in May, the highest count being 457 in 1996; Snettisham and Brancaster Harbour are the other two main sites.

During the winter colour-ringed birds known to have bred or to have been reared at Snettisham have been recorded from a wide scatter of locations. The majority move south-west, one even as far County Dublin, but sightings have also come from northern England and Scotland, while a few individuals (mostly old males) winter close to the breeding grounds. A total of 16 Ringed Plovers ringed in Norfolk has been recovered abroad of which ten have been found in France, all except one between August and December. Others have been recovered in Norway, Denmark, Spain and Majorca, while two were found in March in West Africa (Senegal and Benin). A total of nine foreign-ringed Ringed Plovers has been recovered in Norfolk from Germany (4), The Netherlands (3), Denmark and Sweden.

*Durwyn Liley & Paul Fisher*

## Kentish Plover                                    *Charadrius alexandrinus*

**A very scarce passage migrant, mainly in spring, and very rare in winter; has bred unsuccessfully on two occasions.**

The Kentish Plover is a cosmopolitan species occurring in Eurasia, North Africa and parts of North and South America. In Europe it breeds mainly in coastal areas of the Continent. Birds winter in the Mediterranean area and Africa south to the equator. It bred in Britain (mainly in Kent and Sussex) regularly until 1935. Since then, breeding here has been very sporadic. The species has declined appreciably during the 20th century in north-west and much of central Europe mainly due to human disturbance. It is now only a scarce, but annual passage migrant to Britain, and very rare in winter.

The earliest record of Kentish Plover in Norfolk was of two birds obtained at Yarmouth in 1827 noted by Yarrell and mentioned by Stevenson. When pointed out as a rarity and its distinctive features made known, the Breydon gunners seem to have had no difficulty in supplying specimens to collectors. Further examples were collected in 1829, 1831, 1834 and 1836. According to Gould (1832–37), Harvey the Yarmouth bird dealer and taxidermist (who was in employment in the period 1830–55) regularly purchased specimens from the various gunners, both on the coast and on the Broads. Amongst the birds regularly sent to London by Harvey in May was a good sprinkling of Kentish Plovers. Ticehurst (1932) commented:

> [A] large proportion of the early county records were killed in the neighbourhood of Yarmouth where they are so keenly watched for, there is no reason to think they do not also visit other parts of the coast where they are far less likely to be distinguished from the more common species. The last ten days of April, the earliest 19th April and the first three weeks of May was the period when this little Plover was eagerly looked for and again in the autumn from the middle of August to the end of September. According to old records, it was twice as likely to be met with in the spring than in the autumn.

However, George Smith, a noted Yarmouth bird dealer, recorded the autumn of 1881 as particularly unusual with seven killed on Breydon alone from 18th August to 24th October. Enforcement of the close season on Breydon and elsewhere from 1880 gave protection during the spring passage at least, but a few individuals were still being obtained in August, September and October. Riviere considered it to be probably fairly regular on spring and autumn passage at the coast in small numbers, but gave very few details.

Apart from 1958, the Kentish Plover has been recorded annually since 1954, mainly in the spring, with Breydon, followed closely by Cley and Salthouse the most productive sites. Indeed, Breydon is reputed to be the best locality for Kentish Plovers in the country with over 70 sightings since 1954. Other favoured sites include Snettisham, Holme, Titchwell, Holkham, Blakeney Point and in the Broads at Hickling. Apart from several sightings at Wisbech Sewage Farm prior to 1965, the only other inland records have been from Pentney Gravel Pits where singles were noted in 1984, 1989, 1992 and 1998. An analysis of Norfolk records since 1954 revealed that the spring passage is prolonged from the second week of April to the third week of June, the peak passage being from 2nd May to 5th June. There are two March records – singles at Pentney Gravel Pits on 29th March 1989 and at Breydon on 28th March 1993. July occurrences are distinctly rare and autumn records are now very unusual: a small peak in mid-August with a few in September. The last autumn date in the period was one at Blakeney Point on 3rd October 1956. There have been four winter records – at Yarmouth in January 1834 and in February 1836, Blakeney Harbour on 30th December 1927 and Breydon on 14th–15th December 1968 with presumably the same bird again on 16th February 1969. There were marked influxes in 1976 (14 individuals), 1978 (19) and 1981 (12) including a party of five at Breydon on 8th May. Since 1984 sightings have declined and this trend has continued into the 1990s. For example, in 1997 only a single bird was recorded.

Since regular breeding ceased in Britain, sporadic nesting attempts have been made in several counties including Suffolk in 1952 and Lincolnshire in 1979. A pair was present in the Cley/Salthouse area from 19th April to 6th June 1975, being seen again on 21st June, while in the autumn an adult and a juvenile were in Blakeney Harbour on 31st August. In 1977 the Kentish Plover bred for the first time in the county when a pair was unsuccessful at Salthouse; the clutch of eggs disappeared, believed to have been taken by a collector. The following year, a pair arrived at Rush Hills, Hickling in spring. Mating was observed and two scrapes made, but they were driven off by resident Ringed Plovers. In 1983 a pair made two unsuccessful breeding attempts at Blakeney Point.

*Peter Allard*

Kentish Plovers
(Nik Borrow)

# Greater Sand Plover
*Charadrius leschenaultii*

**A very rare vagrant; three records.**

The Greater Sand Plover breeds from Turkey and Jordan eastwards to south-east Kazakstan and winters mainly in South and East Africa, Australia, New Zealand and southern Asia. It is a very rare vagrant to the British Isles, with over half of the records in July-August.

One, believed to be an immature was identified by the writer at Breydon on 17th April 1981. Added to the British list as recently as 1978, this sighting constituted the first Norfolk and fourth British record. It remained until dusk, going to roost with Ringed Plovers.

The second was a brighter individual, a first-summer or adult female which frequented Cley Marsh and Blakeney Harbour from 30th July to 22nd August 1985. It made a final high-tide appearance at Blakeney on 2nd September (Anon 1986b). Another, in similar plumage commuted likewise between Cley and Blakeney Harbour on 5th–8th August 1992. This bird was then relocated on the foreshore at East Tilbury in Essex on 10th–14th August. On the last date, it flew across the River Thames and spent several hours at Cliffe pools in Kent.

*Peter Allard*

# Caspian Plover
*Charadrius asiaticus*

**A very rare vagrant; one old record.**

The Caspian Plover breeds from central Asia eastwards to the Caspian Sea and is only recorded in substantial numbers on passage in the Middle East. Most winter in eastern and southern Africa. It is a very rare vagrant to the British Isles.

An adult male was shot by Arthur Bensley in a market garden bordering Yarmouth North Denes on 22nd May 1890. Two birds were seen, the gunman tried in vain to get both birds in line, but being unsuccessful, selected the brighter of the two and when he fired, the paler bird, presumably a female, flew off in a westerly direction and was not seen again. This was the first British record and it can be seen on display at the Castle Museum, Norwich. Since then a further three examples have appeared in Britain.

*Peter Allard*

# Dotterel (Eurasian Dotterel)
*Charadrius morinellus*

**A scarce passage migrant; very rare in winter.**

The Dotterel has an Arctic-Alpine breeding range extending from Fennoscandia and northern Russia eastwards to northern and eastern Siberia, with a few pairs on mountain tops in southern and central

Europe. A small breeding colony was established in The Netherlands from 1961–69, since when breeding has been suspected but not confirmed. In the British Isles it breeds on mountain tops in Scotland with small numbers each year in southern Scotland and northern England. It winters in North Africa from Morocco eastwards as far as Iran.

Stevenson described the Dotterel 'as by no means so numerous as in former days frequenting chiefly the warrens and fens of the western parts of the county. Here birds prefer newly sown bean and rye-lands'. He quoted historic records of one or two having been killed as near to Norwich as the verge of Mousehold Heath. He also referred to a flock of 50 at Eccles 'of which a sportsman who went in pursuit of them obtained fourteen'. Coastal fields in the vicinity of Eccles remain attractive to the Dotterel to this day.

Small numbers are recorded on passage every year, in both spring and autumn, at widely scattered localities, but coastal grazing marshes, ploughland and golf courses are favoured. Inland records are particularly unusual away from Breckland and ridge-top sites such as the ploughed fields around Ringstead Downs.

Most occur between mid-April and late May and between mid-August and mid-September, but there are records for all months. The majority are recorded in small flocks (known as 'trips') of up to about seven. In the 30 years between 1967 and 1996 an average of 13 has been recorded each spring and an average of six each autumn. This average was maintained in the autumn of 1997 but spring that year produced records on 23 dates from a total of nine sites, the last being a single bird at Holme Golf Course on 3rd June.

The largest flock on record was an exceptional 47 at Terrington Marsh on 20th August 1959, while the largest trips recorded in recent years have been 15 at Southery Fen on 26th–27th August 1992 and 17 between Docking and Ringstead on 26th August 1996. The maximum number in spring in recent years has been 18 at Ten Mile Bank on 7th May 1987, seven at Welney on 13th May 1996 and nine at Bacton on 11th May 1997 (where at least three were present daily on 5th–14th May).

There have been three winter records of birds found in flocks of Golden Plovers – at Holkham on 12th February 1983, at Cley from 9th November 1986 to 9th January 1987 and at Holkham from 26th February to 6th March 1988.

*Steve Gantlett*

## American Golden Plover *Pluvialis dominica*

**A very rare vagrant; one record.**

The American Golden Plover is a North American species breeding from southern Baffin Island to Alaska and wintering in central South America south to Argentina. It is now an annual vagrant to the British Isles with most appearing between mid-September and late October.

An adult in full breeding plumage accompanied a group of Grey Plover at Breydon on 8th–17th June 1976. It fed and roosted on the tidal flats and occasionally resorted to the adjacent fresh marshes at periods of very high water. Found and photographed by the writer it finally departed with nine Grey Plovers at midday on 17th June, heading high north-east out to sea.

Formerly considered conspecific with Pacific Golden Plover and lumped as Lesser Golden Plover, the two races were split by the BOURC in 1986.

*Peter Allard*

## Pacific Golden Plover *Pluvialis fulva*

**A very rare vagrant; five records.**

A long-distance migrant, the Pacific Golden Plover breeds in the Siberian tundra from the Yamal Peninsula eastwards, wintering chiefly in Pakistan and south-east Asia to Australia, New Zealand and Polynesia. It is a rare, but almost annual vagrant to the British Isles.

The first occurrence was a summer-plumaged adult identified by Andy Stoddart and present on pools at Holme and in Thornham Harbour with other waders on 20th–22nd July 1989. After an absence of three days it was seen briefly again in Thornham Creek on 26th July (Stoddart 1990c). The second county record was an adult in almost full summer plumage at Cley Marsh on 7th–8th August 1990. The third sighting was again at Cley, a juvenile which associated loosely with Golden Plovers frequenting the fresh marshes and those at Blakeney on 3rd–6th December 1991. Another adult in summer plumage was at Breydon on 28th May 1992 associating with Grey Plovers on the tidal flats, but was disturbed in the afternoon by a Peregrine and was not relocated. The most recent record concerned an adult at Buckenham Marshes on 5th–24th July 1998.

Formerly considered conspecific with American Golden Plover and lumped as Lesser Golden Plover, the two races were split by the BOURC in 1986.

*Peter Allard*

## [American or Pacific Golden Plover     *Pluvialis dominica/fulva*

**A very rare vagrant; two records.**

There have been two records of single adults at Wisbech Sewage Farm on 10th August 1974 and at Titchwell on 28th July 1991 which were not specifically identified but were accepted by the BBRC as either American or Pacific Golden Plovers.]

*Peter Allard*

BREYDON WATER. 100+ 20·9·1993.

## Golden Plover (European Golden Plover)     *Pluvialis apricaria*

**A very common winter visitor and passage migrant.**

Golden Plover
(*Robert Gillmor*)

The Golden Plover is a Palearctic wader, breeding in northern latitudes from Iceland to central Siberia and Greenland. Golden Plovers migrate south to winter in the British Isles, the Low Countries and the Iberian Peninsula. Smaller numbers winter around the Mediterranean and south of the Caspian Sea. The Golden Plover is an upland breeding species, inhabiting the heather moors of northern England, Wales, Scotland and Ireland (New Atlas). British breeders migrate south to winter in lowland Britain where they are joined by birds from Icelandic, Fennoscandian and Continental European breeding grounds. Icelandic birds predominantly winter in western Britain and Ireland while those in the east, including Norfolk, probably originate from northern European breeding grounds (Winter Atlas).

The species is unlikely to have ever bred in Norfolk, although Stevenson reviewed some records of individuals remaining in the county well into spring. It is as a wintering species that this bird is most familiar to birdwatchers in Norfolk, when it may form large flocks during times of passage and through the winter period. Birds begin to arrive from the end of July and rise to a peak in November. Both Stevenson and Riviere suggested that there may have been some localised declines in wintering numbers during the late 1800s and early 1900s but these trends seem to have been reversed in the latter part of the 20th century. The number of sites holding more than 1,000 birds each winter has increased from three in 1986, to 14 in 1994 and 18 in 1995, with 16 in 1997. The reason for this increase is not certain.

During the 1990s peak counts have been 7,230 at Boyland Airfield in November 1997 and 6,000 at Fakenham in December 1997, with 7,750 in December 1996, 7,200 in December 1997 and 7,700 in December 1998, all at Breydon. Other sites to have held nationally important numbers (>2,500) in 1996 or 1997 were the Wash East Bund (3,000), Ouse Mouth (3,030), Brancaster Harbour (2,700), Burnham Norton (2,500), Bressingham (2,500), Repps (3,000+) and Winfarthing (4,300). The county total in mid-winter is currently in excess of 20,000.

Habitats occupied in winter include arable land, mudflats, saltings and coastal grazing marshes. Inland flocks frequent fresh plough in September and early October before switching to winter cereals. Their continued presence through the late winter may be due in part to the abundance of sugar beet fields in the region. In late November and December large flocks of Golden Plovers may form on cleared beet fields (S. Gillings pers. obs.). Like Lapwings, Golden Plovers undertake cold-weather movements which can have one of two effects on the number of plovers in Norfolk. Cold weather to the north can cause an influx into East Anglia. Alternatively, cold weather in Norfolk causing the ground to be frozen for a prolonged period may force Norfolk's Golden Plovers to emigrate to the south and west. At such times large diurnal movements can be seen – 650 west at Holme on 19th November 1994, 600 west at Sheringham on 22nd November 1994 and 300 west at Overstrand on 5th November 1995. Return migration to breeding grounds usually takes place in April and is on a much smaller scale than the autumn migration, for instance 120 west at Holme on 8th April 1995.

Ringing on the Wash has resulted in two Norfolk-ringed Golden Plovers from the same catch at North Wootton on 13th August 1987 being controlled at Friesland, The Netherlands in February–March (only one other British-ringed Golden Plover has been recovered in that country); while one ringed at Thornham in November 1959 remains the only British-ringed Golden Plover to be recovered in Norway, at Brekken in May 1961. An earlier bird ringed at Terrington in August 1978 was found in northern France in December 1981. Four Dutch-ringed birds, all from Friesland, have been recovered in Norfolk between October and April. Two nestlings ringed in Iceland in the late 1920s were recovered in Norfolk, as was one ringed more recently in 1987 in North Yorkshire.

*Simon Gillings*

## Grey Plover | TITCHWELL. 19·9·1993.      *Pluvialis squatarola*

**A common winter visitor and passage migrant, scarce in summer; very scarce inland.**

The Grey Plover breeds in the high Arctic regions of Russia and North America, and winters on coastlines throughout much of the world including Africa, southern Asia, Australia and South America. Birds occurring in the British Isles come from breeding areas in north-west Russia. Movements are complex. Some of the birds arriving in Britain in autumn are passage migrants on their way to wintering areas on the coasts of south-western Europe and western Africa. Other birds remain for their autumn moult, after which some leave Britain for areas further south. Birds may also arrive in Britain in mid-winter from mainland Europe, in particular the Wadden Sea in The Netherlands. There is a substantial spring passage, and a small summering population of non-breeding immature birds.

In Norfolk Grey Plovers are found principally at the Wash, which is the most important estuary in the British Isles for the species. They also occur in smaller numbers at other coastal sites. They are essentially birds of the tidal mudflats, and can most readily be seen at high-tide roosts particularly around the shores of the Wash where flocks of many hundreds can be found. Numbers have increased significantly during the past 25 years from winter peak counts of 2,000–4,000 in the 1970s to 7,000–10,000 in the 1990s, with over 17,000 in the 1994–95 winter. A similar but smaller increase has also been noted at Breydon from less than 50 in the 1970s to 100–150 in the 1990s. At least on the Wash this is possibly the result of reduced shooting activity and a series of good breeding seasons (Winter Atlas). The species appears to have been reasonably common in Norfolk since records began. Stevenson referred to numbers at Breydon being not often as many as 20 or 30 at a time, but he noted that birds on spring passage were particularly noticeable in mid- to late May 1853. Patterson (1905) referred to records of hundreds being seen at Breydon in September and October 1899, when 270 were received by Durrant the Yarmouth game dealer. These numbers are not inconsistent with counts in recent years.

The average monthly counts for the Wash show a steep rise at the end of July when birds begin to arrive from Russia, although only comparatively few are recorded flying west along the north Norfolk coast. Day-counts of such birds on westerly passage at Sheringham have exceeded 100 on only three occasions – 340 on 14th August 1992, and 130 on 23rd August 1993 and 12th August 1994. In autumn, two populations are present on the Wash: (i) birds in active wing moult which remain in residence at least until October–November when wing moult is completed and (ii) passage birds not in active wing moult which pause only to build up fat reserves for the next stage of their migration further south. In early autumn flocks of many hundreds may be found at high-tide roosts, in particular at Terrington and Snettisham. Over 4,000 were recorded at Terrington in September 1995, and 5,000 at Titchwell (where birds from the Wash fly to roost on certain high tides) in October 1995. Numbers fall in November, although up to 5,800 were present at Ouse Mouth in November 1997, when birds which have completed their wing moult move elsewhere. In winter, flocks of up to 1,000 occur regularly at the principal high-tide roosts in the Wash, with 1,600 at Holme in February 1994, and over 2,000 at Terrington in February 1995. Numbers at the Wash build up rapidly from March to May as birds arrive on spring passage. In May there were counts of over 3,000 at Snettisham in the years 1990 and 1995–97, with only slightly smaller numbers in May in the intervening years. Many of the birds present in May and early June exhibit spectacular summer plumage. Only a few hundred birds remain in the Wash in the period June-August; these consist entirely of immature birds which carry out a complete wing moult during these months.

Away from the Wash, significant numbers of Grey Plover are found along the saltmarshes of the north Norfolk coast. Low-tide counts in November and December 1997 revealed up to 1,350 birds between Titchwell and Blakeney, including 333 at Scolt Head/Brancaster Harbour and 410 at Blakeney Harbour, where 800 were present in August 1987. Grey Plovers also occur in smaller, but increasing numbers, at Breydon, especially in winter with 100–150 being recorded in most years, although 248 were recorded on 1st March 1996. Spring passage in May, together with autumn passage in October has been more marked in recent years with peaks of 127 on 13th May 1980 and 147 on 19th October 1990. Smaller numbers occur at other coastal sites, including Sheringham, where 91 were counted on 21st January 1997. Inland, Grey Plovers occur in only very small numbers. In most years the occasional bird is reported from sites such as Welney, Pentney Gravel Pits and Cantley Beet Factory.

Grey Plovers exhibit an unusual pattern of wing moult. About 40% of the Grey Plovers arriving in Norfolk in autumn have begun their wing moult elsewhere and arrested their moult, arriving with typically two or three primaries fully moulted. This phenomenon is much more frequent in the Grey Plover than in any other wader species commonly occurring in the British Isles. Moreover, about a quarter of Grey Plovers are unable to complete their wing moult before the onset of winter and arrest their moult with typically one to three old primaries remaining unmoulted. Most, but not all, of these birds resume their wing moult at the end of March. The reasons for this unusual moulting behaviour are not clear, but they may be related to feeding difficulties experienced by the species in winter. The wintering areas in Britain are among the most northerly in the world for the species, and food supplies may be insufficient to enable some birds to complete their moult before the need to channel their energies into fat reserves ahead of the worst of the winter weather (Branson & Minton 1976). In severe winters the species is liable to suffer significant numbers of casualties. After particularly severe weather in February 1991, a total of 354 Grey Plover was found dead in Norfolk; apart from the Redshank this species of wader is the worst affected by severe weather.

Over 5,000 Grey Plovers have been ringed at the Wash during the past 40 years. About 90% of birds caught on more than one occasion have been retrapped within 5km of the place of ringing, indicating that individuals normally return to the same areas from year to year. One ringed at Heacham was shot at Yamal in northern Russia (70°E) in 1978, and a bird ringed at Terrington was caught at its nest near the mouth of the River Yenisey (70°E)·in 1990; these locations fall within the main breeding area of the species in north-west Russia. Another ringed at Rostock, Germany, on autumn passage in September 1982 was controlled at Snettisham in February 1985. Ten birds ringed at the Wash have been reported from Denmark in subsequent autumns, suggesting that many birds may pause in Denmark on their way from Russia to Britain.

Ringing results have indicated some movement of birds between North Sea estuaries during winter, but the full extent is not well understood and may vary from year to year depending upon weather conditions. Four examples are known of movements between the Wash and France in a single winter, including a bird ringed at Snettisham on 21st November 1968 and killed in western France ten days later. Birds ringed at the Wash have been reported from wintering areas further south. One found in Morocco in March 1964 was in active wing moult when caught at the Wash the previous September, an example of the population which leaves the Wash in late autumn after completing wing moult. Two further birds from the Wash have been found in Morocco, one in the Canary Islands and one in Ghana.  *Nicholas Branson*

## Sociable Plover (Sociable Lapwing) *Vanellus gregarius*

**A very rare vagrant; four records.**

The Sociable Plover is an eastern species breeding from south-east Russia eastwards through Kazakstan and wintering in Sudan and Ethiopia, Iraq, Israel and Pakistan. It is a very rare vagrant to the British Isles, the majority being found in the autumn.

The first Sociable Plover in the county was a very obliging bird found at Welney on 3rd–25th September 1977 by A. Hopkins. This was followed by a juvenile at Titchwell on 24th September 1988 which was also seen later that day at Holme. In 1990 another juvenile was in the Welney area with Lapwings on 15th–30th October, occasionally wandering into Cambridgeshire on several dates.

Most recently, an adult in full breeding plumage was at Cley Marsh on 21st–23rd April 1993. It had earlier been seen in Derbyshire on 17th April. This bird moved to Holkham Fresh Marshes on 24th–29th and then flew west at Burnham Norton on 30th April. It was last seen in Norfolk at North Wootton on 18th–20th May before crossing into Lincolnshire where it remained until 12th June. During its stay it was frequently in dispute with territorial Lapwings.

*Peter Allard*

## Lapwing (Northern Lapwing)   *CLEY. 21·9·1993.*   *Vanellus vanellus*

**A common, but declining, breeder and passage migrant, and very common winter visitor.**

The Lapwing is a Palearctic wader species, breeding from Iceland through Russia, mostly north of 40°N and wintering in the south-west and far south-eastern Palearctic. As a British breeding species it is widely distributed in open country habitats. Over 90% of the English and Welsh breeding population inhabits agricultural land (New Atlas). In winter British birds are joined by those from Fennoscandia and the Low Countries leading to an overwintering population in excess of one million (Winter Atlas).

Historically the Lapwing was an abundant breeding species in Norfolk. The former abundance can be illustrated by the commercial importance of its eggs. For example, during the early 1800s a single collector sent 600–700 eggs to London markets during every week of the season. The Lapwing may have undergone two periods of decline. The first probably took place during the 1800s when land enclosure, drainage and cultivation of fen, marsh and heath occurred alongside persistent egg harvesting (Stevenson, Riviere). More recently, agricultural intensification during the latter part of the 20th century has caused a second period of decline (see below). Historical information on wintering Lapwings is lacking.

Lapwings & Golden Plovers
(*Norman Arlott*)

The Lapwing is now a localised breeding species in Norfolk. The Norfolk Atlas recorded the species in 53% of tetrads, these being liberally scattered throughout the county. The elaborate aerial display and calls of the Lapwing mean that it is unlikely to have been overlooked in many localities. Breeding habitats include arable farmland, grazing marshes, meadows and heaths. Results of the nation-wide BTO Breeding Lapwing Survey in 1987 showed that in Norfolk, 20% of breeding pairs were occupying spring-sown cereal fields, 20% tilled bare ground, 15% autumn-sown cereal fields and 15% permanent grass. The presence of nearby marshy ground, to which the newly-hatched young could be taken, was also favoured by the breeding birds (Taylor 1988). Nationally, as well as locally, agricultural intensification has reduced the availability of sites containing suitable Lapwing breeding habitat and degraded the quality of those that remain. Lapwings prefer mosaics of grassland and arable land on which to rear their young. Intensification has led to the loss of rotations, particularly those involving grass leys, which the Lapwing so benefited from. Now many Lapwings breed in sub-optimal habitats where the number of young raised does not compensate for winter mortality (Peach *et al.* 1994). The joint BTO/RSPB Breeding Lapwing Survey in 1998 revealed a fall in the number of breeding pairs of 47% in only eleven years; in East Anglia the reduction was 54%.

The only large breeding populations of Lapwings in Norfolk are in the Broads, the Ouse Washes and the north Norfolk grazing marshes. Selected maximum breeding populations for sites in these areas in 1995–97 have been 693 pairs in the Broads in 1995, 147 at Welney and 240 at Holkham both in 1996. A detailed study of the breeding Lapwings at Welney in 1994 showed that spring flooding resulted in the failure of all the known nests, although the practice of regular flooding produced substantial areas of bare ground and retarded spring growth, a habitat much favoured by Lapwings and their offspring. Unusually, the majority of nests were found towards the drier field margins, rather than in the centre of fields, due to the dish-like shape of individual Washes. Second clutches were more successful but fox predation was a problem (Kemp 1995). Appropriate management can be very effective and at Holkham, where water levels were raised, numbers have increased from 81 pairs in 1986 to a population in excess of 200 pairs each year since 1992 (Bloomfield 1993). Likewise at Berney Marshes, numbers have increased from 20 pairs in 1979 to 85 pairs in 1998.

Autumn passage begins as early as late May, these records probably involving failed and non-breeders from the Continent. Numbers flying west at this time of year are far smaller nowadays than in the 1970s. The majority of birds arrive between late September and early November when they may be seen moving west and south around the coast. Compared with earlier years, day-counts now only occasionally exceed 1,000. One of the highest counts was 8,000 west at Sheringham on 9th October 1976, although on 16th October 1997, a total of 6,200 south was recorded at Hunstanton and 6,700 west at Scolt Head. More typical were maximum counts of 2,337 south on 23rd October 1996 at Hunstanton, 2,200 west at Scolt Head on 11th October 1996 and 1,400 west at Sheringham on 23rd October 1996. During this period flocks may be heard migrating at night when they are drawn to the lights of towns and cities in the region, as was noted by Stevenson.

During winter Lapwing flocks may occupy flooded marshland and meadows, cleared sugar beet fields and airfields. They normally utilise mudflats much less extensively than other wader species. Paradoxically, the site that regularly hold the largest flocks of Lapwings in the county is Breydon. The three peak counts for that site have been 41,000, 32,000 and 31,000 in 1992, 1994 and 1996 respectively. This site clearly exceeds the 20,000 individuals necessary to qualify as a site of international importance. In addition, counts of at least 3,000 in 1995–98 have included 4,000 at Ouse Mouth and 8,000 at Clippesby in January 1995, 6,460 at Terrington and 6,000 at Cley in November 1995, 3,000 at Fakenham, 5,000 at St Benet's level and 5,000 at Ludham in January 1996, 10,000–12,000 at Wash East Bund, 4,450 at Welney and 4,300 at Boyland in November 1997, 10,000 at Lynn Point in January 1998 and 3,460 at Ongar Hill in February 1998. Many other sites held between 200 and 3,000 but due to the Lapwings abundant nature in winter, many of the smaller Lapwing flocks probably go unreported, particularly those occurring inland. However, inland flock ranges can be as important as some coastal sites. During November 1997 the Winfarthing/Tibenham flock peaked at 4,500 Lapwings (S. Gillings pers. obs.).

In a mild winter Lapwings do not depart for breeding grounds until March or sometimes even April. Comparatively few are normally recorded on easterly return passage in spring. A total of 18,000 east at Sheringham on 20th March 1976 was unprecedented and has never been closely approached since. During periods of severe weather, including prolonged spells when the ground is frozen, Lapwings undertake cold-weather movements to the south and west. If conditions persist further south they may continue into France and Iberia. Upon the return of more mild conditions Lapwings may return to reoccupy the county within a matter of days. Cold weather in north-eastern England and the Low Countries probably causes influxes of birds to Norfolk.

Over 500 Lapwings have been ringed in Norfolk since 1980, the majority as chicks. A total of 19 foreign recoveries have been reported, 15 in France and two in northern Spain, areas in which British-bred Lapwings are known to winter. The other two involved a movement to Denmark of one ringed in November and another ringed at King's Lynn in August 1978 which was found near Moscow, Russia in June 1988. A total of 24 foreign-ringed Lapwings have been recovered in Norfolk, all except two from The Netherlands, ringed as chicks. Most have been found between December and February, with the earliest on 27th July from Germany and 31st July from The Netherlands, both ringed as chicks in May of the year of recovery. The foreign-ringed birds had come from The Netherlands (8), Denmark (8), Germany (4), Sweden (3) and Finland. The only other notable recovery was of a chick ringed in North Yorkshire found two years later at Acle.

*Simon Gillings*

## Knot (Red Knot)   TITCHWELL. 19·9·1993 (HUGE FLOCK.)   *Calidris canutus*

**An abundant but localised passage migrant and winter visitor, and non-breeding summer visitor in varying numbers; very scarce inland.**

The Knot is a circumpolar tundra species breeding in North America, Greenland and eastern Siberia, but only occasionally in the Western Palearctic. The population wintering in Europe south to France is from Greenland and eastern Canada, with just eight estuarine sites in the British Isles holding over half the British winter population (Winter Atlas).

Historically, the Knot was described by both Stevenson and Riviere as a spring and autumn passage migrant, and a winter visitor, in variable and often very large numbers. They also noted the presence of a few summering birds. Riviere described how 603 were killed at Stiffkey on 17th February 1901 by the two George Longs, father and son, of Blakeney and Tom Cringle of Wells, who fired their three punt guns simultaneously into one flock. Riviere also stated that no other wader was killed as often as Knot at the Norfolk light stations both in spring and autumn, and throughout the winter.

The main influx of Knot into Norfolk occurs in August, although westerly passage is noted along the north coast from mid-July to November. Autumn day-counts at Sheringham have only exceeded 1,000 on three occasions 8,500 west on 25th November 1978, and 1,500 west on 23rd and 2,300 west on 26th October 1992. At Breydon, the average date, since 1972, on which the first juveniles are recorded has been 19th August with the earliest ever juvenile on 7th August 1998.

Knot are abundant on the Wash which is of international and national importance both during passage and in winter (peak average monthly counts for the years 1992–96 were 67,407 in autumn, 186,892 in winter and 21,285 in spring). The main sites within Norfolk being Terrington, Snettisham and Holme (Gore Point particularly in the autumn), where the maximum counts in August–November 1997 were 5,598, 39,050 and 66,000 respectively. Once moult is completed in October some birds remain to winter and others disperse to estuaries around Britain and western Europe. The north Norfolk saltwater marshes also hold significant numbers, a low-tide count in November 1997 revealing 3,955. Breydon holds smaller numbers – the peak average monthly count was 695 in the winters 1992–96. Since 1950 the number of Knot wintering on this estuary has varied considerably, the largest totals usually appearing in severe weather, such as 2,000 in January 1954 and March 1956, 2,500 in December 1962 and 1,940 in January 1987.

Since the late 1960s there has been a decline in the total numbers of Knot in Britain and Ireland. Peak numbers of 400,000 in 1971–72 declined to 230,000 in 1973–74. On the Wash the winter peak count in 1970 was about 85,000. The population was at its lowest in 1976 and then started to increase. The largest counts in recent years have been in the early 1990s with approximately 186,000 in 1992. At this time a high-tide roost at Snettisham contained 100,000 birds in November, while one at Gore Point, Holme was estimated at 150,000–200,000 on 16th October 1993. However, the Wash wintering population is once again decreasing – the 1995 total was about 50% of the average for 1986–94. These recent changes in numbers may reflect the poor cockle productivity on the Wash and the recent recovery of cockles at the Wadden Sea in The Netherlands. The reduction in numbers in September and October compared to the recent massive peaks implies that the birds are remaining on the Wadden Sea at that time. During late summer and autumn Knot also roost on fields a short distance inland of the sea walls, together with many other waders. The major sites are at Terrington, Wolferton and Snettisham.

Severe weather in mid-winter has resulted in some impressive coastal movements of Knot – on 3rd February 1991, 2,500 flew west at Sheringham and Overstrand, while the passage at Paston was estimated at 1,500 per hour; also at Sheringham 1,800 flew west on 10th February 1991 and 1,100 the following day. During the same period 116 Knot were found dead on the Wash out of a total of 2,527 wader corpses (Clark & Clark 1992), while on 14th February 1994, cold weather produced counts of 650 west at Sheringham and 900 west at Mundesley. The spring passage peak occurs in April. Juveniles do not migrate to the breeding grounds in their first summer and many remain on the Wash, the average monthly count for June in 1992–96 being 1,671. Although only about 250 were present in Norfolk in June 1997, a total of 12,000 summered at Snettisham in 1961.

Knot are very scarce inland in Norfolk, a few being reported annually in parties of one to five, mostly in spring or autumn. Favoured localities in recent years have included Colney, Pentney and Cranwich Gravel Pits, Welney, Wroxham and Hickling Broads, Buckenham and Cantley Beet Factory. Up until the late 1970s Wisbech Sewage Farm was a regular haunt of Knot in autumn (Moyes 1986). Highest inland counts have been at Welney with 65 north on 23rd January 1987 and 43 in misty conditions on 19th March 1988.

Ringing studies have shown that the majority of Knot recorded on the Wash breed in Greenland and north-east Canada, while a few birds from the Siberian population also occur mainly in early autumn on migration to South and West Africa. A total of 70 Knot ringed at the Wash have been recovered in Greenland, and it is thought that birds returning to breed in the spring in Greenland and Canada use different routes according to their destination. They can stage in Iceland (where over 90 Knot ringed on the Norfolk side of the Wash have been recovered) before heading to the Greenland end of their breeding grounds or via northern Norway to Arctic Canada. Of the recoveries of Wash-ringed Knot on Ellesmere Island, Canada the remains of one was found in a Gyr Falcon's pellet.

Knot are highly mobile within the Wash at all seasons and also between western European estuaries. Many Knot using the Wash to moult in autumn are at estuaries further to the north in winter, such as Teesmouth, Mersey, Ribble or the Firth of Forth, while some move south to the Thames. From November to February there are influxes of Knot which have moulted on the Wadden Sea – thus giving the high winter numbers in Norfolk. In spring some birds move to the Irish Sea estuaries to lay down fat before migrating, while others remain on the Wash and increase their body weight by over 70% before migrating.

*Lys Muirhead*

## Sanderling  *TITCHWELL. 19·9·1993.*                    *Calidris alba*

**A common passage migrant and fairly common winter visitor, scarce in mid-summer; very scarce inland.**

Sanderling breed on the high Arctic tundra, where the summer is both short and very variable; in some years birds are unable to breed successfully because of late snow melt or high levels of predation. It is probable that Sanderling breeding in both Greenland (and possibly Arctic Canada) and Siberia occur in Norfolk. After refuelling in autumn on the Wash, birds from Greenland are believed to continue south, to wintering grounds as far as South Africa, while Sanderling from the Siberian breeding population are thought to moult on the Wash and may either overwinter there or move out along the sandy coasts of Britain.

In Norfolk Sanderling are characteristic of open, sandy shores where they scurry along the tide edge, darting in and out of the surf to feed on small marine crustaceans which are activated by the tide. The species is most numerous in the Wash and along the north Norfolk coast. The wintering population is relatively small, compared with the large-scale autumn passage. Spring passage is less pronounced, partly because of its extended duration, but also because the northward migration is predominantly along the west coast of Britain. Historically, the patterns noted by both Stevenson and Riviere were similar, with many of the spring Sanderling in summer plumage. Stevenson referred to their presence at Hunstanton and Holme, particularly using the saltmarsh at Holme during high tide. However, he believed that they were less numerous in autumn than in spring in the Yarmouth area, although the taxidermist, Edward Saunders had received specimens from the Yarmouth beaches in all months of the year, except April and July. Inland records had always been rare.

Sanderling arrive from their Arctic breeding grounds from July onwards and numbers increase rapidly, initially peaking in July–August at Snettisham which is the main roost for moulting birds. Even in the mid-19th century, the Wash and the north Norfolk coast were the stronghold in the county, with up to 500 observed there in September 1863 – identification being confirmed by taking specimens. Stevenson was uncertain whether this record was exceptional. More recently, flights of up to 2,500 have been recorded on the Wash during autumn passage (Seago 1977). Berry (1971) also referred to autumn passage peaks of up to 2,000 with the main roost being on the Snettisham foreshore. Snettisham regularly records peaks of 600–800 birds in July–August, and occasional peaks of over 1,000 have been noted on WeBS counts, with 1,565 in September 1996 and a record 2,200 in September 1998. Allowing for annual variation as a result of differential breeding success, there has been a tendency for higher peak numbers during autumn passage at Snettisham, over recent years; the average peak count in autumn during the five years 1992–96 was 1,968.

Post-moult movements away from Snettisham lead to peak numbers occurring on the north Norfolk coast in September–October, most notably at Holme, where there may be in excess of 400 Sanderling, with a record 1,273 in September 1995. Thornham and Titchwell have also recorded up to 400 at this time, but more usually peak at 100–150 in August. Several other Norfolk sites have had more irregular or smaller peaks of autumn passage birds, including 1,060 at Heacham in August 1995, 308 at Hunstanton in October 1995, 235 at Holkham Bay in August 1994 and 175 in Wells Harbour in September 1996. The aver Gravel Pits, Wissington and Cantley Beet Factories, and Hickling Broad.

Wintering birds are concentrated along the eastern side of the Wash, from Wolferton eastwards, notably at Snettisham, and along the north Norfolk coast. During 1969–75 the average winter maximum for Norfolk was 645, with up to 500 on the Wash and flocks of up to 100 on the north Norfolk coast and around Yarmouth (Prater & Davies 1978). Winter peak counts on the Wash in recent years have regularly exceeded 400 and may exceed 800, with the record being 1,022 in February 1980. Numbers present on the north Norfolk coast have increased substantially in recent winters, from up to 100 birds, prior to 1988, to nearly 700 in 1994. A low-tide count of the north Norfolk coast in December 1997 produced a total of 339 birds. From 1989 onwards, while numbers generally increased in north Norfolk, those in the Wash initially decreased, although they have recovered to some extent in the four years up to 1996. Nonetheless, the five-year average peak winter count for 1992–96 was 376 for the Wash compared with 480 for north Norfolk.

Berry (1971) noted that Sanderling roosted on the shingle beach south of Snettisham in summer and autumn, but the 50–100 wintering on the east Wash tended to roost in small groups, in daylight, between Snettisham and Heacham south beach. However, when high tide occurred in, or close to, darkness, Thornham was a regular roosting location, and was the main wader roost on the east side of the Wash in the 1960s and early 1970s. Cooper (1987) noted that Sanderling moved along the shore of the east Wash, from Snettisham towards Holme and Titchwell and back, as they fed during the flood and ebb tides. As the coastal geomorphology has changed and the RSPB Snettisham Reserve has developed, offering a safe high-tide roost, changes in wader roosting have occurred. Holme (peak of 523 in December 1994) is now preferred to Thornham by those birds which do not roost at Snettisham.

There is a regular interchange of birds between sites along the Wash and north Norfolk coasts, demonstrated by counts, ringing recaptures and resightings of colour-marked birds. These movements are partly dependent on tidal state and partly on weather conditions, with high-tide roosts moving to more sheltered locations in inclement weather. Sanderling do, however, display a high degree of site fidelity, often returning to the same wintering grounds year after year, as demonstrated by ringing recaptures of birds caught at the Wash. Some individuals have been recaptured numerous times over several years, for example one individual was caught on 13 occasions in the course of twelve years.

In east Norfolk Sanderling arrive at Breydon in early October, with up to 70 being present on the mudflats through the winter until March (Allard 1990). These relocate to Yarmouth south beach to roost at periods of high water. WeBS counts indicated that 40–60 Sanderling were on Breydon in winter (peak of 166 in February 1974), although the average winter peak count for 1992–96 was only 36. Allard (1990) also mentioned the presence of small numbers in winter on Caister, Yarmouth and Gorleston beaches, a peak of 140 having been seen in February 1987. More recently 109 were on Caister beach on 27th February 1996.

The Wash is an important spring staging post for Sanderling to put on pre-migratory fat reserves. Departure of the adults occurs mainly between late April and May, with immature birds leaving later, in May and June. Peak numbers at the Wash during spring passage are approximately 400, with the majority at Snettisham, although the average spring peak count for the Wash in 1992–96 was only 289. However, the spring record at this site was surpassed in May 1998 with a count of 1,565. Spring peaks of over 100 Sanderling are regular at several sites including Hunstanton, Burnham Overy, Holkham Bay and most notably Holme, where 603 were present in May 1993 and 620 in May 1995, and Titchwell/Thornham with 586 in May 1998. Small numbers, up to 20, are also recorded in spring at Breydon. As in autumn, few are recorded on visible migration in spring and the highest counts at Sheringham have been 46 west on 19th May 1979 and 82 west on 25th May 1991. Small numbers are noted inland in spring, generally involving only single birds but up to five at Pentney Gravel Pits in 1990, four at Wissington Beet Factory in 1991 and three at Welney in 1994. Other sites to have hosted spring Sanderling have included Wisbech

Sanderlings
(Robert Gillmor)

Sewage Farm, Lyng Easthaugh Gravel Pit, Hickling Broad and Hardley Flood. Small numbers of non-breeding birds also remain in mid-summer.

Nearly 8,000 Sanderling were ringed by the WWRG between 1959 and 1996. The longevity record for a Norfolk-ringed Sanderling is over 17 years. Overseas recoveries have come from various points along the east Atlantic flyway, southwards to South Africa, particularly in France and Morocco, and northwards to eastern Russia, representing wintering and breeding migrations. Within the British Isles, recoveries have reflected onward autumn migration from the Wash, along the east coast especially to the open coasts around the Tees estuary and to the Medway estuary in Kent, and return passage in spring to refuelling stops in the north-west, notably on the Dee estuary and Morecambe Bay.

*Rowena Langston*

# Semipalmated Sandpiper      *Calidris pusilla*

**A very rare vagrant; four records.**

The Semipalmated Sandpiper is a Nearctic species breeding across North America and wintering in Central America south to Ecuador and Brazil. Identification can be difficult and confusion with Little Stint, Red-necked Stint and Western Sandpiper is possible. It is a rare vagrant to the British Isles, most appearing between late July and early November.

The first British record was an adult commencing to moult from summer into winter plumage on Arnold's Marsh, Cley on 19th–24th July 1953. It was found by Peter Clarke who pointed out the bird to Paul Kirby and Richard Richardson. It was later filmed by Dick Bagnall-Oakeley down to 2m (Daukes 1954). This occurrence was followed by a long-staying bird at Wisbech Sewage Farm from 12th November to at least 26th December 1966. Since then there have been two further Norfolk records. Both, unusually, have been in spring – an adult in summer plumage frequented Cley Marsh on 14th–17th May 1989 and another visited the wader pools at Hickling Broad on 8th–9th May 1992.

*Peter Allard*

# Red-necked Stint      *Calidris ruficollis*

**A very rare vagrant; one record.**

The Red-necked Stint breeds in north-east Siberia, although the exact range is unknown. It winters in southern Asia and Australasia. It is a very rare vagrant to the British Isles with only four records.

An adult in partial summer plumage was seen briefly with about 20 Dunlins at Cley by Mark Golley on 29th July 1992 (Golley 1993b). What was obviously the same individual was relocated by Richard Millington on the North Scrape, Cley on 2nd August (Millington 1992). Despite mainly distant views it was seen by many observers before departing high to the west the following morning. This was only the second record for the British Isles, after the first sighting at Blacktoft Sands, Humberside in July 1986.

*Peter Allard*

### Little Stint   CLEY. 20+ 21-9-1993.                              *Calidris minuta*

**A scarce passage migrant, mainly in autumn when larger numbers are recorded in some years; rare in winter.**

The Little Stint breeds on the high Arctic, coastal mainland tundra and islands of northern Russia and Norway. The Norwegian breeding population fluctuates widely from year to year, with 200–500 breeding pairs annually. Most Western Palearctic birds probably migrate through tropical Africa to winter in South Africa. Much larger numbers occur in the British Isles in autumn than in spring, with major influxes occurring in some years. Less than 30 overwinter in Britain and Ireland, the majority along the southern coastal counties of England (Winter Atlas).

Stevenson referred to this 'elegant little sandpiper' as being 'a regular autumnal visitant to our coasts', while Fielding-Harmer (1890) recorded 35 being shot between 3rd and 30th September 1881, including six killed with a single shot. In addition, Riviere noted that it was also 'occasionally met with on the return migration in spring'. Up to 1930, the only winter records concerned three killed at Cley on 19th January 1894 (Pashley 1925) and two occurrences at Breydon on 2nd December 1909 and 12th February 1913 (Ticehurst 1932).

The Little Stint is generally considered to be a shore wader, frequenting in particular the shallow brackish pools at Cley and Titchwell, although it is also found using shallow pools on tidal mudflats, saltings and freshwater marshes. Spring passage occurs from April to mid-June, peaking in May, although only small numbers of birds are involved. The earliest records have been on 7th March 1982 at Cley, 11th March 1994 at Welney and 16th March 1974 at Wisbech Sewage Farm. In most springs the majority of sightings have been of single birds, although up to nine have been recorded occasionally in north Norfolk in May. The largest counts in spring have been ten at Cley on 10th June 1979, twelve at Cley on 16th May 1980, eleven at Pentney Gravel Pits on 11th May 1994 and ten at Hickling Broad on 17th June 1984. Both singing and displaying was noted at Cley on 4th June 1960, when six birds were present. Late June records are presumably of non-breeding birds or very early autumn arrivals.

Autumn passage occurs between early July and late October, with a peak in September. In general, records from July and August tend to be adults with the juveniles occurring later. Riviere noted that the years in which good numbers of Little Stints were reported coincided with good years for Curlew Sandpipers. This is often still the case, with particularly large numbers of Little Stints occurring in the autumns of 1954, 1957, 1960, 1976, 1978, 1996 and 1998.

Little Stints & Curlew Sandpipers
(*Norman Arlott*)

The first count of 100 was at Lynn Point on 26th–27th August 1954, with 100 at Cley/Salthouse on 27th September 1957, during an influx between 22nd and 30th September. In 1960 at least 100 were at Cley on 22nd–31st August and again in late September 1976. At Wisbech Sewage Farm 80 had assembled on 28th September 1973 and Hickling also attracted 80 on 12th September 1981. However, the largest autumn influxes occurred in 1978, 1996 and 1998. In 1978 Wisbech Sewage Farm held the highest numbers with up to 250 present in the first half of September and 100 at Cley in mid-month. Other notable counts during the same period included 58 at Hickling Broad, 23 at Cantley Beet Factory and 20 at Breydon. Wisbech Sewage Farm normally held some of the highest counts in the county during the 1960s and 1970s, but during the last few years of its existence fewer birds were recorded in autumn. Whether this was due to birds using the north-west coast, rather than the sewage farm, is unclear but there was a series of years when only small numbers of Little Stints were recorded in Norfolk after the demise of Wisbech Sewage Farm. A major influx of Little Stints was also recorded in autumn 1996, with about 800 being recorded in September and smaller numbers in October. Maximum counts between 21st and 30th September included 80 at Welney, 90 at Titchwell, 160 at Cley, 50 at Salthouse, 44 at Kelling Water Meadows, 26 at Breydon and 136 between Cantley Beet Factory and Buckenham Marshes. Two years later, the autumn of 1998 also produced good numbers of Little Stints including 115 at Titchwell on 8th September, 79 at Cley on 5th September and up to 105 at Cantley Beet Factory, 36 at Breydon and 80 at Berney Marshes.

Winter records are rare although the species has been recorded in all months. Up to at least 1930 the only known wintering records were those mentioned above. Records were more frequent during the 1960s and 1970s, particularly at Wisbech Sewage Farm where three were present on both 19th December 1964 and 14th December 1968, and one on 23rd December 1970; another lingered at Breydon until 29th December 1976. Since then, the occasional single bird has been recorded, mainly in north Norfolk, with two at Snettisham on 29th December 1984 and two at Salthouse on 7th December 1996.

Few Little Stints have been ringed in Norfolk but 24 were trapped in 1996. None of these has been recovered, but one ringed at Paarp, Tronninge, Sweden on 2nd September 1964 was found dead at Breydon on 26th September, and another ringed at Makkevika, Norway on 29th August 1990 was found dead at Cley on 24th September. The first remains the only Swedish-ringed Little Stint to have been recovered in the British Isles, although there have been several from Norway.

*Jen Keddie & Mark Smart*

## Temminck's Stint    CLEY. 23·8·1988.     *Calidris temminckii*

**A scarce passage migrant.**

Temminck's Stint is an Arctic-breeding wader with a range extending from northern Norway through Finland to the Chukotskiy Peninsula in north-east Siberia. It winters from the Mediterranean basin and northern Afrotropics across the Middle East eastwards to southern Asia and Japan. It has bred or attempted to breed sporadically in the British Isles since 1934, on each occasion in Scotland apart from one attempt in northern England in 1951. Successful breeding was first proved in 1971 and a maximum of up to ten adults were present in the summers of 1978 and 1980. Although the majority of birds migrate through mainland Europe and further east, it is an annual passage migrant in small numbers in the British Isles.

According to Stevenson, the first Temminck's Stints to be identified in Norfolk were a pair killed in the county in May 1830. Earlier writers (Shepherd & Whitear 1826 and Hunt 1829) did not include this species although it was first recognised as early as 1812. The Pagets (1834) stated that it 'probably occurs' in the Yarmouth area, and in September 1835 J. D. Hoy (Babington 1884–86) recorded two immatures killed near Yarmouth with another the following May at Breydon. In 1846 Gurney and Fisher stated that 'it was appearing occasionally, but less regularly and much less numerously than the Little Stint'. Certainly by this time the Breydon gunners were beginning to acquaint themselves with the species and the vast majority of 19th-century records in Norfolk were of birds collected there. Most were shot in May, but a few were obtained between mid-August and early October with an exceptionally late one killed at Breydon on 23rd November 1861. Riviere described it as an occasional coastal passage migrant in both spring and autumn, most often in September. He also noted that some had been obtained at Cley and Blakeney. Pashley (1925) recorded the first at Cley in August 1895.

Since 1946 it has been recorded annually in Norfolk. Seago (1967) recorded it as a passage migrant in very small numbers to shallow pools in grazing marshes, usually occurring singly, but twos and threes had been frequent. Since then observations have increased, partly due to observer awareness but also to the creation of wetlands around the county. Hickling and Cley/Salthouse are much-favoured sites together with Holme, Titchwell, Hardley Floods and Horsey. Wisbech Sewage Farm regularly attracted Temminck's Stints until its closure in December 1985. Breydon still attracts occasional passage birds, but since 1988 the adjacent Berney Marshes Reserve has become a regular site. More recently Burnham Norton, Holkham, Stiffkey Fen, Kelling Water Meadows and Buckenham have been favoured. Inland gravel workings have also been visited and have included those at Colney, Lyng Easthaugh, Pentney, Sparham and Tottenhill, while the beet factory settling ponds of the King's Lynn, Wissington and Cantley factories have proved attractive, the latter site on a number of occasions. Other inland sites have included Dickleburgh Moor, Hockwold Flood, Lakenheath Flashes and West Acre, while one spent two days by the village pond at Edgefield Green on 24th–25th April 1977. Shoreline records are unusual but have included sightings at Wolferton, Snettisham, Lynn Point, Brancaster, Blakeney Point and Bacton Gap.

In most years, certainly since 1979, spring records have outnumbered autumn records. Peak years were 1980 with at least 40 birds (32 in spring), 1987 with at least 41 (27 in spring) and 1989 with at least 43 (35 in spring). The first birds usually appear in the first week of May with a noticeable peak in mid- to late May. April records are unusual, the earliest having been at Cley on 9th April 1952, Welney on 12th April 1995 and Cley on 18th April 1974. Parties of up to four are not uncommon now, with the largest having been six at Berney on 17th May 1989 and at Hickling on 21st-22nd May 1979, on 17th May 1987 and on 3rd June 1991, eight at Cley on 17th May 1987 and ten at Hickling on 16th May 1980, with nine remaining on 18th. Displaying birds have been noted at Hardley Flood, Holme and Snettisham while a pair were displaying at Cley on 1st June 1974. Spring passage continues into early June. Mid-June records are unusual but have included one at Cley on 16th and two on 17th June 1979, and three at Hickling on 19th June 1989.

Autumn passage commences in mid-July although occasional birds are seen in late June or early July, presumably failed breeders which are returning early. The majority are seen on passage in August and September, most are singles but parties of up to four have been recorded. Some are long-stayers – one with a damaged leg remained at Cley from 8th August to 16th October 1977. October records are scarce and the latest birds have been singles at Titchwell on 30th October 1957, at Wisbech Sewage Farm from 17th October to 4th November 1978, at Hickling on 4th November 1977 and the bird shot at Breydon on 23rd November 1861.

Since 1966 a minimum of 680 have appeared in Norfolk, of which at least 459 have been in spring. Over the past 15 years, the average has been 26 records per year, making Norfolk the most likely county in the British Isles in which to see this diminutive wader.

*Peter Allard*

## White-rumped Sandpiper  *TITCHWELL 8·9·1985*   *Calidris fuscicollis*

**A rare autumn vagrant.**

White-rumped Sandpiper breeds in northern North America and winters in southern South America. It is annual autumn vagrant to the British Isles and is one of the commonest Nearctic waders to occur in Europe.

The first county record was one found at Cley by D. D. Harber and identified by A. R. Mead-Briggs and L. Salmon on 1st–2nd October 1948. The next was trapped with four Dunlins at Wisbech Sewage Farm on 13th November 1955 and remained until 17th (Minton 1956). Three more were recorded in the 1960s, since when the county total has risen to 46.

All have been found between early July and October, apart from an adult at Holme on 29th June 1989 (but almost certainly an early-returning 'autumn' bird), one at Salthouse on 2nd–5th November 1996 and one at Wisbech Sewage Farm on 13th–17th November 1955. The records fall into two distinct periods, with the majority (34) arriving in July–August and most of the rest (seven) being found in October. This corresponds with adults in the earlier period (all 13 of the birds aged as adults have been in June–August) and juveniles in the latter (the three birds aged as juveniles were singles in late September, October and November; the remaining birds were not aged, but seem likely to have fallen mostly into the same pattern). There have been no spring records.

All records have been from coastal localities and the former wader hot-spot of Wisbech Sewage Farm (where five were recorded during 1955–73), apart from an adult at Pentney Gravel Pits on 26th–30th August 1985. The most favoured localities have been Cley/Salthouse with fourteen, and Breydon with nine. Most birds have remained for a few days and have associated with flocks of Dunlins.

It is usually recorded singly, but there were two together at Cley on 1st–12th August 1980, and there was a remarkable series of up to four adults together at Breydon in July–August 1996 – one on 16th–19th July, two on 20th–27th, three on 28th–29th, four from 30th July to 3rd August, and three on 4th–5th August with one remaining until 14th.

Singles at Wisbech Sewage Farm in 1955 and 1964 were trapped and ringed.      *Steve Gantlett*

## Baird's Sandpiper  CANTLEY. 2·10·1999. BEET FACTORY.  *Calidris bairdii*

**A rare autumn vagrant; one spring record.**

Baird's Sandpiper breeds from north-east Siberia eastwards across northern North America to north-west Greenland, and winters in southern South America. It is a rare autumn vagrant to the British Isles, where it has been recorded annually since 1970.

Although Riviere gave the first county record as one shot at Hunstanton on 16th September 1903, this record has subsequently been rejected because of the specimen's uncertain history – and in particular to its connection with George Bristow, the Sussex taxidermist of 'Hastings Rarities' infamy (Seago 1993). The first acceptable record was therefore not until 1963 when one was found at Wisbech Sewage Farm by J.S. Clark, Graham Easy and Colin Kirtland. Since then the county total has risen to 11. Apart from one in May, all have been singles between 22nd July and 10th October:

> 1963: Wisbech Sewage Farm from 22nd July to 6th August
> 1966: Thornham on 18th–25th September
> 1970: Cley/Salthouse on 18th–20th September, with probably the same bird at Brancaster on 23rd–24th September
> 1971: Cley from 16th September to 10th October
> 1982: An adult at Salthouse from 22nd August to 23rd September
> 1983: Titchwell on 13th–18th May
> 1988: Lodge Marsh, Wells on 27th July
> 1992: An adult at Cantley Beet Factory on 18th–20th August
> 1993: An adult at Snettisham Reserve on 19th–22nd August, and probably the same bird at Titchwell on 25th and 27th August
> 1995: Cley on 30th July
> 1997: A juvenile at Cantley Beet Factory from 30th September to 10th October
> 1999.   ALSO AT CANTLEY BEET FACTORY!   2·10·1999.                          *Steve Gantlett*

## Pectoral Sandpiper  TITCHWELL. 8·9·1985.  *Calidris melanotos*

**An almost annual autumn vagrant; rare in spring.**

Pectoral Sandpiper
(*Richard Richardson*)

The Pectoral Sandpiper breeds in north-east Siberia and northern North America. It winters in southern South America. It has been an annual visitor to the British Isles since the 1950s, mostly in autumn.

The first Norfolk and British record was one obtained at Breydon on 17th October 1830. It was preserved by Mr J. Harvey of Yarmouth as a curious variety of Dunlin, although Mr J. D. Hoy, into whose collection it passed, felt convinced that it was an undescribed species of *Tringa*. Its correct identity was established when it was sent up to London for inspection, where Audubon, then staying in England, had an opportunity of examining it and 'he immediately confirmed the previous notion that the bird was an example of the *Tringa pectoralis* of America' (Stevenson). Of the additional three examples included by Stevenson, two were later identified as being Siberian Pectoral Sandpipers (now known as Sharp-tailed Sandpipers), including one in Stevenson's own collection (Riviere). Riviere subsequently listed seven, including the first record in 1830, all shot in autumn in the Yarmouth area between 1830 and 1897, and another believed to have been of this species seen by E. C. Arnold at Cley on 7th–17th September 1908.

No more were reported until autumn 1948 when three were seen at Cley/Salthouse, including one which was successfully photographed by Philip Wayre and Dick Bagnall-Oakeley – a unique event at the time and the first occasion the species had been photographed in Britain. Unfortunately the visitor came to an untimely end at the hands of Clifford Borrer, a local collector. Six were then recorded during the 1950s, and since then one to ten have been recorded annually in autumn, with the exception of 1984 when at least 15 were noted and 1993 when there were none in autumn but two in spring. Apart from the spring records, all have been evenly spread between early July and October, with just three in November – at Wisbech Sewage Farm from 30th October to 12th November 1955, at Cantley Beet Factory on 11th November 1994 and at Berney Marshes on 6th November 1998. There have been no records between December and March.

Most records are of singles on pools on the coastal freshwater marshes, notably at Cley where 57 have been recorded, and at suitable inland habitats such as the settling ponds at Cantley Beet Factory and Welney Washes. Two have been recorded together on a number of occasions (several times at Cley, and during the 1960s to early 1980s at Wisbech Sewage Farm), while three were at Berney Marshes on 23rd October 1998 and four were noted together at Cantley Beet Factory on 23rd–24th September 1984 (the record year when at least 15 were seen).

There have been 13 spring or early summer records of single birds:

1956: Wisbech Sewage Farm on 11th–15th June
1974: Cley on 9th–10th May
1977: Cley on 19th May
1978: Hickling on 8th–12th June
1985: Breydon on 12th–17th May
1986: Salthouse on 3rd May
Holme on 19th–21st June
1989: Holkham on 11th–16th May
1992: Cley on 3rd May, and another there on 29th–30th May
1993: Salthouse on 29th April
Holme on 13th–14th May
1998: Cley on 24th–25th May

A juvenile was trapped and ringed at Snettisham on 24th October 1976.

*Steve Gantlett*

# Sharp-tailed Sandpiper                                    *Calidris acuminata*

**A very rare vagrant; four records, last recorded in 1892.**

The Sharp-tailed Sandpiper, formerly known as the Siberian Pectoral Sandpiper, is a breeding species of the north-eastern Siberian tundra and winters in Australasia.

The only four county records of this extremely rare vagrant to the British Isles were of birds shot in Norfolk in the 19th century. The first at Yarmouth in the last week of September 1848, was originally considered to be a Pectoral Sandpiper (then called American Pectoral Sandpiper) but was recognised as an example of the Sharp-tailed Sandpiper by Thomas Southwell in 1892. The second was shot at Caister on 16th September 1865 and was also regarded as a Pectoral Sandpiper until correctly identified by Bernard Riviere in 1929.

The third was a female killed on Terrington Marsh on the most unusual date of 9th January 1868. As with the previous two birds it was also regarded as a Pectoral Sandpiper until recognised by Bernard Riviere and Harry Witherby in 1929. The last bird was obtained on Breydon on 29th August 1892 and was identified by Thomas Southwell soon afterwards. This example, a female, had earlier been seen feeding in a brackish pool close to Vauxhall Railway Station by Arthur Patterson.

The Yarmouth, Caister and Breydon examples are all in the Castle Museum, Norwich. They were examined by Dave Britton in 1979 and each aged as adult. The Terrington Marsh bird remains in the King's Lynn Museum, probably still labelled as a Siberian Pectoral Sandpiper.

*Peter Allard*

| **Curlew Sandpiper** | *TITCHWELL · 24·5·1987.* | *Calidris ferruginea* |
| | *CLEY MARSHES. 21·9·1993.* | |

**A scarce autumn passage migrant in most years, but large influxes in 1969, 1985 and 1988; very scarce in spring.**

The Curlew Sandpiper breeds in the high Arctic of Siberia. The wintering grounds range from West Africa eastwards to Australia. The species passes through the British Isles on autumn migration via the east Atlantic flyway to the West African wintering grounds. The return to the breeding grounds from West Africa is mainly via the central Mediterranean and overland across eastern Europe, so that very few occur on Atlantic and North Sea coasts in spring. Curlew Sandpipers do not occur in Britain in internationally significant numbers.

Stevenson described the status of the Curlew Sandpiper, also known as the 'Pigmy Curlew', as 'not infrequently met with' in spring and autumn, but more particularly in autumn. Riviere stated that the species was an occasional spring and more regular autumn passage migrant, but in fluctuating numbers. Exceptional numbers of birds were present in autumn in the county in 1853, 1887, 1889, 1890, 1919 and 1923 (Stevenson and Riviere), while Pashley (1925) included some additional years when the species was particularly abundant in the Cley area. Individuals in the attractive red-breasted breeding plumage were particularly noted by Stevenson and Riviere as having been shot in late spring and early autumn, although Riviere added that the large majority were in juvenile plumage. Stevenson stated that more specimens were procured at Breydon than on any other part of the Norfolk coast.

Studies have shown that male Curlew Sandpipers leave the breeding grounds immediately after mating, leaving the females to raise the young alone. Females leave the breeding grounds within a few days of the young becoming independent. The juveniles are the last to commence migration from late July to mid-August. Thus autumn passage commences with the arrival of adults, usually towards the end of July and beginning of August. Excluding birds in June, the earliest autumn arrival was on 4th July 1976. The passage of adults peaks at the beginning of August. Curlew Sandpipers are usually recorded as single birds, or in small flocks, with parties of more than 40 being exceptional. Although individual juveniles have been recorded in the second half of July, the main influx occurs at the end of August. The size of this influx can vary greatly from year to year. The passage of juveniles peaks in early September and stragglers may be found through October, with the latest records on 16th November at Titchwell (1986) and Welney (1987), and on 19th November 1976 at Breydon.

The main factor controlling the abundance of Curlew Sandpipers on autumn migration in Britain is the weather conditions at the time of migration. It has been suggested that influxes into Britain occur when unstable cyclonic conditions with easterly winds prevail over Scandinavia and the Baltic. The effect is most marked when these conditions persist throughout the time of the birds' migration. However, breeding success is also an important factor as it determines the number of juveniles on their first migration, and therefore influences the size of any potential influx. Apart from the unpredictable Arctic weather conditions, breeding success has been linked to the three-year population cycles of lemmings. Predators such as Arctic foxes switch between lemmings and waders depending on which is more abundant.

Since the time of Riviere, influxes of Curlew Sandpipers have occurred in Norfolk in 1946, 1953, 1955, 1969, 1971, 1975, 1978, 1979, 1985, 1988, 1990, 1992, 1993 and 1996, with very large numbers in 1969 and 1985. In 1969 maximum counts included 400 at Wisbech Sewage Farm on 29th–30th August, falling to 110 by mid-September, 80 at Lynn Point and 74 on Brancaster Golf Course. The county total was estimated to be in excess of 1,300 in 1985 (Anon 1986a), including more than 500 at Terrington on 14th–20th September and 200 at Wisbech Sewage Farm on 18th–20th September. Smaller, but still notable, maximum counts of 100 at Titchwell on 1st September, 75 in Blakeney Harbour on 9th, 69 at Cantley Beet Factory on 10th, 66 at Hickling Broad on 13th, 75 at Brancaster on 14th and 107 at Breydon on 18th September were also recorded in 1985. The largest count in 1988 was 250 at Ouse Mouth, followed by 200 at Titchwell. Kirby *et al.* (1989) concluded that the size of the 1969, 1985 and 1988 influxes were similar on a national scale, but in Norfolk the 1988 influx was smaller than 1969 and 1985. However, the 1988 influx occurred at unusually northern locations in Britain. Although breeding success was high, only moderate influxes occurred in 1978, 1979, 1990, 1993 and 1996, and no influxes occurred in 1972, 1973 and 1982. Low breeding success was reflected in numbers occurring in Norfolk, except in 1971 and 1992. However, unusually, in both these years the large numbers were made up of adults with few juveniles being recorded. Exceptional numbers of adults in 1971 included 94 at Breydon on 6th August and a maximum of 150, all in summer plumage, at Wisbech Sewage Farm on 7th August. In 1992 a maximum of 152 adults were at Breydon on 30th August. Very few are normally recorded on visible migration. The highest counts at Sheringham have been ten west on 26th August 1989 and 15 west on 30th August 1975, although two flocks totalling 90 flew west at Cley on 23rd August 1956 and a total of 67 flew west at Weybourne between 15th and 29th August 1988.

Spring passage typically peaks in May, although it is much lighter than autumn; single birds are most commonly recorded and flocks of more than ten are exceptional. The highest counts in recent years have been twelve at Cley in mid-May 1989, 15 at Holkham on 13th May 1990 and 15 at Breydon/Berney Marshes on 15th May 1990. The earliest record during the 20th century was a party of seven at Cley on 3rd April 1982, although an exceptionally early record was one at Haddiscoe on 19th March 1853.

Curlew Sandpipers have been recorded in Norfolk in every month except January. However, only three records of single birds have occurred outside the period April to November. The one in March mentioned above and two in 1971 at Wisbech Sewage Farm on 6th February and at Breydon on 12th December. A few individuals are seen in most winters in western Europe (BWP). Although Curlew Sandpipers may be found through the summer, there is normally a period around the middle of June, when none is present.

Curlew Sandpipers are mostly found on estuaries and coastal freshwater reserves in Norfolk. The most important sites in autumn are Titchwell, Cley and Breydon. Wisbech Sewage Farm formerly held good numbers but became less frequented after 1978, coinciding with the draining of many lagoons. The site was last occupied in 1985, the final autumn before all the lagoons were drained, when a maximum of over 200 was recorded. In years when large numbers have occurred, reports are more widespread. However, in spring only Cley, Breydon and more recently Berney are regularly visited. Apart from Wisbech Sewage Farm, inland sites are less frequented than those on the coast. The most frequently visited inland sites have been Hickling Broad and Welney in both spring and autumn. The beet factories at King's Lynn, Cantley and Wissington have been visited in autumn.

A study of birds ringed on the Wash, which were sexed by using measurements, has shown that twice as many adult males as adult females migrate through the area. Although males leave the breeding grounds earlier, no difference in the time of arrival between the sexes of adults was found. Of all the birds studied on the Wash, 80% were juveniles, with equal numbers of males and females. However, juvenile females appeared to arrive slightly earlier than juvenile males. These differences may be due to females using different migration routes and stopover sites. Alternatively, females may migrate at a faster rate, or fatten more quickly at stopover sites (Adams 1995).

More than 600 Curlew Sandpipers have been ringed in Norfolk, mostly at Wisbech Sewage Farm and Terrington, of which eleven have been recovered abroad. Of the nine birds ringed as juveniles, two were recovered in the spring in Italy 18 months after ringing, one in Tunisia in a later spring, one on the wintering grounds in Senegal and five in eastern Europe (USSR or Poland) in subsequent years in autumn. Only one bird ringed as an adult has been recovered and this was found in autumn in Sweden. Three foreign-ringed birds have been recovered in Norfolk – from Norway, Finland and Sweden. These movements fit in with the expected pattern, but also suggest that juveniles use a more easterly route on subsequent autumn migrations.

*Sue Adams*

# Purple Sandpiper                                                    *Calidris maritima*

**A scarce passage migrant and winter visitor.**

The Purple Sandpiper has a circumpolar breeding distribution, nesting around rocky shores and on the sub-Arctic tundra. In Europe it breeds in Iceland, the Faeroes and from Scandinavia eastwards to Siberia. It winters to the south of its breeding range along rocky shores which are generally clear of ice. Up to four pairs have probably bred annually in Scotland since 1978 (New Atlas). In the British Isles in winter it is concentrated in the north-east, becoming scarce south of Yorkshire (Winter Atlas).

Although Stevenson described it as occurring 'pretty regularly in autumn and winter', by 1930 Riviere found it to be only 'occasionally met with during the winter', while still being regular in autumn. Since the 1950s the number of overwintering Purple Sandpipers in Norfolk has varied from less than 30 to over 100, with the species becoming less widespread and less abundant from the early 1990s, all of which suggests that it is subject to long-term fluctuations.

The first birds of the autumn are generally recorded in August, with the main passage continuing through September. Occasional birds have been recorded in July with the earliest at Sheringham on 6th July 1955, Titchwell on 10th July 1993 and Scroby Sands on 11th–12th July 1975. Only a few are noted flying west along the north coast in autumn, with maximum day-counts of 13 at Cley on 13th September 1988, eight at Blakeney Point on 13th September 1971 and seven at Sheringham on 7th September 1990.

In winter Purple Sandpipers are invariably found along rocky shores or on the wooden beams of groynes or piers. The favoured sites in Norfolk have tended to vary over the years, although the stretch of coastline between Heacham and Hunstanton has usually held the highest concentration, at least since the 1950s. Up to the 1980s, the maximum count had never exceeded 12, but during that decade numbers gradually increased to reach a peak of 63 in February 1987, a month in which over 100 were recorded in Norfolk. Since then numbers have tended to fall back to earlier figures, although 18 overwintered in the Heacham/Hunstanton area in 1994. Also on the Wash, another favoured site, Snettisham held twelve on 3rd February 1991. Since the late 1960s Titchwell has hosted small numbers, peaking at twelve in January 1969. Elsewhere in Norfolk, the rocky shore between Sheringham and West Runton had been recognised as a good site for the species since the mid-19th century. Up to twelve were present in the 1960s and 1970s, but nowadays they are seen only infrequently.

In east Norfolk the stretch between Paston and Walcott has been increasingly favoured since the 1980s, with up to 28 in 1987, although single-figure counts only have been recorded since 1991. Further south at Yarmouth and Gorleston, a few could often be found around the wooden structures at the harbour's mouth, where in February 1987 a total of 14 was present, while 16 had been counted along the beach between Gorleston and Hopton the previous week. However, since 1991, it has become very scarce at this site and is now only seen occasionally.

While peak counts are usually achieved in February, numbers can also build up in March and April, as wintering birds are joined by migrants presumably from further south. The most impressive spring counts have been 31 on 17th March and 21 on 16th April 1986, and 24 on 3rd May 1981, all at Hunstanton, 19 at Paston in April 1996 and 14 at Scolt Head on 29th April 1967. Most Purple Sandpipers have left the county by the end of April but occasional birds have lingered well into May. There have been five June records, including one which was present intermittently at Titchwell from 18th June to 13th July 1977.

Purple Sandpipers are very rare inland and the only records have been at King's Lynn Beet Factory from 29th August to 19th September 1984 and at Salhouse Broad on 14th January 1987 during a period of severe weather; although ten have been seen at Breydon since 1950 (Allard 1990).

Less than 50 Purple Sandpipers have been ringed in Norfolk from which the only recovery was one ringed at Heacham on 16th April 1988 and found freshly dead at Hunstanton on 10th April 1995, indicating fidelity either to a wintering or passage site. Another ringed at Nidingen, Sweden on 13th April 1986 was reported at Heacham on 1st March 1987, possibly indicating the breeding area of some of Norfolk's wintering birds.

*Moss Taylor*

## Dunlin   TITCHWELL. 19-9-1993.                                   *Calidris alpina*

**A very common winter visitor and passage migrant, generally scarce inland; bred in 1938 and 1939.**

The Dunlin has a circumpolar distribution in north temperate and Arctic latitudes. In the British Isles its main breeding populations are on the Caithness and Sutherland flows, in the Northern and Western Isles, and on the uplands of the Grampians and Pennines. Three races regularly occur in Britain and it is considered to be a vulnerable species in winter due to the high concentration on a small number of large estuarine complexes.

Historically it appears that the Dunlin has always been Norfolk's commonest wader. In Stevenson's time the largest numbers occurred in July–August and again in spring, with very large numbers arriving during periods of severe weather. Indeed over 800 Dunlins were brought to a dealer in Yarmouth on 11th December 1844 and two days later another 200. Stevenson commented that 'Should the frost continue severe for any length of time or the "flats", as soon as exposed by the ebbing tide, be covered with snow, these poor birds become exceedingly pressed for food, and are then brought into our markets in a very pitiable state'. He goes on to say that 'Though, of course, far inferior to the snipe, dunlins when in condition are very good eating'. It seems clear, however, that the majority that were acquired during severe weather could not be considered to be in good condition for eating. In the late 1800s large numbers of Dunlin were also caught on the Ouse Washes in spring and autumn by fowlers.

There have been a few records of the Dunlin apparently having bred at sites like Thetford Warren. However, these have all, probably rightly, been dismissed as being birds still on passage to their breeding grounds. The only authentic records of breeding in Norfolk were of single pairs breeding on the grazing marshes at Salthouse in 1938 and 1939 (Seago 1967). The birdwatcher out in many coastal marsh sites in May may hear Dunlins singing and hope that they will stay to breed. However, birds singing at this time of year are almost always late migrants, which are bound for the northernmost latitudes and are simply waiting to migrate, knowing that their breeding grounds will be thawed out on their arrival in the first days of June.

Dunlins
(Nik Borrow)

In the last 30 years the general pattern of occurrence of the Dunlin has become clear. The Wash is by far the most important site in Norfolk, occasionally holding upwards of 60,000 birds, approximately half of them occurring on the Norfolk side of the Wash. Other important sites are the estuary at Breydon and along the north Norfolk coast, where Dunlins frequent saltmarshes, harbours, creeks and muddy channels. Average monthly counts for 1991–96 collected by the WeBS scheme show that for the Wash very low numbers are present in June when just a few non-breeding birds, mainly in their first summer, are present, with about 20,000–25,000 in July and August increasing to 30,000–35,000 between September and November. The three mid-winter months, December to February, show slightly lower numbers before an increase occurs again in March and April; departure to the breeding grounds occurs in May. In contrast, the 1991–96 WeBS counts for Breydon show low numbers in June and then a slow build-up in numbers to 1,000 in September, 2,000 in November, reaching a peak between December and February of almost 3,000 birds. Numbers then decline again in March with smaller numbers in spring. A similar pattern of occurrence to Breydon is recorded on the north Norfolk coastal marshes and creeks, with peak numbers occurring in the winter from November to February. North Norfolk sites that have held at least 1,000 Dunlins in recent years have been Scolt Head/Brancaster Harbour, Warham, Blakeney Harbour and Cley.

Despite the large numbers present on the Wash, comparatively few are recorded flying west along the north Norfolk coast in autumn. Up to 1997, the highest day-counts at Sheringham had been 1,800 on 23rd and 1,700 on 26th October 1992, although 4,440 flew west at Paston on 21st November 1987. In 1997 notable counts included 1,210 west at Scolt Head on 12th October, and 2,700 west at Sheringham and 2,360 west at Mundesley on 14th October.

The fortunes of the Dunlin wintering on the Wash might be expected to follow the national index especially as the Wash is the third most important site for the Dunlin in the British Isles (Cranswick *et al.* 1997). Numbers were very high in the early 1970s both in Britain as a whole and on the Wash. Both the national index and numbers on the Wash declined dramatically in the late 1970s and early 1980s, and then there was a dramatic improvement in the numbers on the Wash reaching a peak in 1988 before declining again. This was in marked contrast to the national index which reached an all-time low in 1987 before partially recovering during the early 1990s.

In recent years small numbers of Dunlin have overwintered inland at Welney, with numbers increasing in March and April prior to migration. In 1996 a record 423 were present in April, a year in which the species was recorded there in every month except June. Other inland sites which regularly host Dunlin are grazing marshes with up to 46 at Buckenham and 48 at Ludham; and beet factory settling pools and sewage farms, with a maximum count of 62 at Cantley Beet Factory, while under suitable conditions in September, Wisbech Sewage Farm once held a combined flock of Dunlins, Curlew Sandpipers and Little Stints numbering over 2,000 (Moyes 1984).

The complex migration patterns of the Dunlin have been largely elucidated by the work of the WWRG since its formation in 1959. By 1996 it had ringed over 116,000 Dunlins and had recorded over 1,815 movements between countries; a further 1,500 birds were recovered within the British Isles and many thousands of birds were retrapped within the Wash itself. From this wealth of information it is possible to summarise the movements of the Dunlin.

Three races occur in Norfolk, of which *C. a. arctica*, which breeds in north-east Greenland, is only a rare visitor. This is the smallest race of Dunlin and has a breeding population of probably only 5,000 pairs (Meltofte 1985). Small numbers pass through the Wash in July and August *en route* to their wintering grounds in Africa and odd stragglers return through the Wash in spring, although the vast majority migrate up the west coast of Britain. In breeding plumage *arctica* can be distinguished by their very small size and very grey appearance, even when in full summer plumage. However, identification with certainty is extremely difficult in the field.

The second race occurring in Norfolk is *C. a. schinzii*, which breeds in southern Greenland, Iceland, northern Britain and also has a small population around the Baltic. In years when there is poor breeding success a few thousand *schinzii* can arrive on the Wash as early as the last few days of June although they normally move through in July and early August. They normally stay for a period of approximately two weeks to fatten for onward migration to their wintering grounds in Africa. Very small numbers remain on the Wash through the autumn to undergo their annual moult; these may be birds from the small Baltic population. Not many Dunlins remain to winter. On return from Africa only a few come through Norfolk, the majority concentrating on the west coast estuaries, most notably in the Irish Sea.

The third, and numerically most important, population is the nominate *C. a. alpina* race that breeds in northern Fennoscandia and across the northern part of the former USSR. With over 100,000 birds ringed on the Wash, the majority of which are *alpina*, it is remarkable that there has been only one recovery of this race, of a bird definitely on its breeding grounds. That was found on the Yamal Peninsula which may be near the eastern boundary of the breeding range of birds coming to Britain. Upon leaving the breeding grounds, normally in early to mid-July, some birds stop off in the Baltic for a few days before they arrive at their autumn moulting sites, of which the Wash is the second most important in western Europe after the Wadden Sea, in The Netherlands. They remain on the Wash for the next two to three months and on completion of their moult part of the population moves on to west-coast estuaries and a few even to eastern Scotland, the English south coast, France and Spain. It is uncertain whether many of those moulting on the Wash reach the southern wintering grounds of this race in North Africa. The population on the Wash is normally reasonably stable between December and February unless there is a period of severe weather when there may be substantial influxes from the Wadden Sea or the Delta area in The Netherlands. One such influx occurred in the 1978–79 severe winter when 5,000 flew west past Sheringham on the 25th November and a further 3,500 the next day (Taylor 1987a).

When in Norfolk, Dunlins are not necessarily immune to the weather. In 1991 after a particularly severe spell large numbers of Dunlins arrived on the Wash. Over 500 were found dead on the tideline after the cold weather and the proportion of birds ringed amongst those that succumbed suggested that the new arrivals from the Continent were more vulnerable than the resident wintering birds (Clark *et al.* 1993).

In late February birds start leaving their winter quarters and return to the Wash where they remain through to May and moult their body feathers again to come into summer plumage. In mid to late-May they leave the Wash but this time do not return via the Baltic but mainly migrate directly to the breeding grounds. A few stragglers remain on the Wash throughout June, these tend to be first-year birds that have failed to come into full summer plumage.

The pattern of movement through the Wash of juvenile birds is rather different. Very small numbers of juvenile *arctica* occur in Norfolk mainly in July and August. They are often mistaken, by inexperienced birdwatchers, for Little Stints as they are halfway between the size of most juvenile Dunlin and a Little Stint. Rather larger numbers of *schinzii* move through the Wash and other sites as well and they form the vast majority of birds that turn up inland at this time of year. Even though many of the juveniles arrive on our estuaries, having never experienced this habitat before, they gain weight rapidly for onward migration to their winter quarters in Africa. The first juvenile *alpina* normally arrive in early August, with the peak arrival being in September. In its heyday, Wisbech Sewage Farm held up to 2,000 small calidrid sandpipers in autumn, most of them being juvenile Dunlins (see above). Juveniles are known to be much more mobile than adult birds but analysis of the ringing data shows that juveniles caught that have already been ringed are more likely to have come from another country than the other side of the Wash. Indeed an analysis of the retrap data showed that over 85% of juvenile Dunlins roosted in the same section of the Wash through-out their stay at the site (Rehfisch & Clark 1994). This is quite remarkable when one thinks of the complex pattern of movements that these birds undertake when they are away from the Wash.

This overall picture of Dunlin movements is put together by interpreting a large number of recoveries for which we have two points, the ringing place and the finding place. Occasionally a bird does something special: one such bird carried ring number BB30501. It was first caught as an adult on 13th April 1968 at Snettisham and retrapped there on 4th April the following year. Nothing further was heard of it until 1975 when on 21st July it was caught at Pori in Finland on the east of the Baltic, four days later it was retrapped this time at Lake Vattern in Sweden before its final capture on its wintering site on 12th February 1978 at the Severn Estuary, Weston-super-Mare, Somerset.                                                    *Nigel A. Clark*

# Broad-billed Sandpiper                                          *Limicola falcinellus*

**A rare passage migrant.**

The Broad-billed Sandpiper breeds in Fennoscandia and Siberia, with European birds migrating south-east in autumn to winter in the Arabian Gulf and the Indian subcontinent. The species was a very rare vagrant to the British Isles prior to 1972, but more recently it has become an annual spring visitor, particularly to the east coast.

The first British record was one shot at Breydon on 25th May 1836 and the second Norfolk specimen, which is displayed in the Castle Museum, Norwich was also obtained at the same locality exactly 20 years later. In common with many of the more recent records from the Breydon area, these first two were in the company of Dunlins and Ringed Plovers. Since then the county total has risen to 48, of which 23 have been in the Breydon area, the most favoured locality in the British Isles. Even more noteworthy is the fact that Peter Allard has been personally responsible for finding and identifying 19 of those in the Breydon area.

There is a clear peak in spring between mid-May and early June, with 20 of the 32 records up to the end of June, concerning birds in the Breydon area. All the records have involved single birds except at Breydon, where there were two on 17th–21st May 1985 and up to three between 18th and 23rd May 1989, a year in which a record total of eight was identified in Norfolk. There have been two records before May, both at Breydon, on 8th March 1991 (the earliest British record and the only one in March) and 23rd April 1858, the latter is also in the Castle Museum, Norwich.

Of the 15 records between July and September, only four have been at Breydon, the majority having been on the north coast with seven at Cley, one at Salthouse and two at Titchwell. However, the latest date for the county, 21st September 1977, involved one at Breydon. Juveniles are rarely seen in the British Isles and only four have been recorded in Norfolk. Inland sightings are also rare but spring birds have been present on Rush Hills, Hickling on three occasions and one was at Wisbech Sewage Farm in 1959.

*Moss Taylor*

# Stilt Sandpiper                                              *Micropalama himantopus*

**A very rare vagrant; two records.**

The Stilt Sandpiper breeds in tundra areas from north-east Alaska to northern Canada and winters mainly in central South America. It is an extremely rare vagrant to the British Isles and was not recorded until 1954. Most have occurred in late July and August.

An adult, still largely in summer plumage, remained at Wisbech Sewage Farm from 19th July to 7th August 1963, having been trapped, ringed and photographed by Clive Minton on the first date. It constituted the third British record. Remarkably, a second adult, again in summer plumage appeared at Wisbech Sewage Farm on 12th–19th August 1965. This was the fifth British record and proved as popular as the first individual two years earlier.

*Peter Allard*

## Buff-breasted Sandpiper                     *Tryngites subruficollis*

**A rare autumn vagrant; four spring records.**

Breeding in Alaska and north-west Canada, the Buff-breasted Sandpiper winters on the grasslands in northern Argentina, Uruguay and Paraguay. It is a rare, but annual, vagrant to the British Isles, mostly in autumn. It is one of the commonest Nearctic waders to occur in Europe.

Five specimens were obtained in the 19th century – at Sheringham on 29th July 1832 (now in the Castle Museum, Norwich), at Yarmouth in autumn 1840 and on 22nd September 1841, at Breydon on 20th September 1843 (now in the Castle Museum, Norwich) and at Cley on 7th September 1899.

A further 23 have since been recorded – four between 11th and 27th May, and the remainder between 10th July and 15th October. It is notable that almost half of the records have come from Cley:

    1964: Salthouse and Cley on 11th–12th May
    1965: Thornham/Holme from 26th September to 3rd October
    1970: Salthouse on 3rd–6th October
    1973: Cley on 1st–19th September
    1975: Cley on 15th–20th September
    1979: Hickling from 12th September to 1st October
    1980: Hunstanton on 5th October
           Salthouse on 5th October
    1981: Cley on 5th–6th September
    1982: Cley on 15th–18th May
    1984: Cley on 27th May
    1985: Wisbech Sewage Farm on 7th–11th September
           Cromer Golf Course on 14th September
    1986: Cley on 10th July and from 12th July to 9th August; it also visited Holme
           briefly on 10th July
    1988: Welney on 21st July
           Burnham Norton on 31st July before moving to Holkham where it remained
           until 16th August
    1990: Wolferton on 2nd–4th October
    1991: Brancaster Golf Course on 12th May.
           Snettisham on 12th August
    1993: Cley on 22nd August
    1995: Sheringham/Weybourne on 2nd–15th October
    1997: Cley from 27th July to 4th August
           Snettisham beach on 20th August

The bird at Sheringham in 1995 was trapped and ringed during its prolonged stay.

*Steve Gantlett*

Buff-breasted Sandpiper
(*Gary Wright*)

**Ruff** HARDLEY FLOODS. ♂♀ 19·4·1992.　　　　*Philomachus pugnax*

A fairly common passage migrant, scarce in winter; last bred in 1977.

Ruffs
*(Robert Gillmor)*

In the Western Palearctic the Ruff has a patchy breeding distribution extending along the North Sea coast from The Netherlands (where there has been a 90% decrease in the breeding population since the 1950s) eastwards to northern Germany and Denmark, the high Arctic regions of Fennoscandia and across Russia to the far east of Siberia. It favours hummocky marshes with shallow water margins. The winter range extends from western Europe eastwards to India; by far the largest numbers winter in West Africa where nearly a million were estimated at one roost in Senegal.

Ruffs formerly bred in many areas on the eastern side of England but numbers declined during the 18th and 19th centuries. Sporadic nesting continued until 1922 with recolonisation from 1963 in the Ouse Washes. Up to the first quarter of the 19th century Ruffs and Reeves were abundant in the Broads and Fen districts, especially Hockwold and Feltwell. Lubbock (1845) remarked that 'the Ruff has decreased much of late years, the beauty of the bird having caused it to be more than ever sought after . . . An old man who had set horse-hair snares for them during many seasons once caught six couples in a single morning.' Persistent snaring and shooting of the birds themselves and robbing nests throughout each nesting season during the next 25 years had an inevitable result. Collectors also took a toll. A case of Ruffs each 'with his show on' did not remain long in a taxidermist's window.

By 1870 when Stevenson wrote, the Ruff was extinct throughout Norfolk with the exception of birds still attempting to breed at Hickling. This situation continued until 1890 after which none was reported until 1907 when a nest (photographed by Emma Turner) was found in the traditional haunt at Rush Hills. Sadly this clutch was robbed by a collector and Redshanks' eggs substituted. Two years later during spring 1909 and following three days of easterly winds, over 200 Ruffs and Reeves collected at Rush Hills, but the majority departed early next day. Jim Vincent described the site as the 'old breeding ground in collector Booth's time and where he obtained his specimens' which are still on display in his museum in Brighton. After that, Rush Hills became overgrown with reeds, rushes and sedges, but by regular cutting Vincent had restored it to a wader ground by 1927.

The next known breeding occurrence was at Cley where Arnold Boyd found a nest with four eggs on 11th June 1922. Reeves' eggs brought from The Netherlands were put down under Redshanks at Hickling in 1925; seven young fledged. Equally unsuccessful was another attempt there in 1936 and at Cley in 1957, by releasing wing-clipped Reeves.

Ruffs may be found in a variety of habitats – shallowly flooded marshes, muddy lake margins, beet factory settling ponds and brackish lagoons. Particularly in autumn and winter newly-ploughed arable, stubble, tidal mudflats, coastal golf courses and playing fields are attractive. The extensive fields in the Docking/ Choseley area have been visited by up to 110 Ruffs feeding amongst Golden Plovers. No doubt they came from Titchwell as did a flock of 97 Ruffs found in Brancaster Harbour in December 1996. Blakeney Harbour has also attracted up to 26 Ruffs. In 1956 the old-style Wisbech Sewage Farm became the first locality in the county to receive a winter roosting group of 60 birds which fed on nearby farmland by day.

The spring passage commences early in March with the majority appearing during April and May, and late ones until early June. Prior to 1990 the maximum day-counts at favoured coastal localities had been 59 at Holkham on 22nd May 1989 and 150 at Cley on 16th April 1987 where there were 125 on 5th May 1989. Impressive counts in Broadland had included 100 at Hickling on 11th March 1983 and 116 there on 15th April 1987, 70 at Horsey on 2nd May 1982 and 50 at Berney on 8th May 1989. Other impressive spring inland counts have been 55 at Wisbech Sewage Farm on 11th April 1965. Welney has attracted some of the highest numbers in spring with 200 on 8th March 1969 and 244 on 25th April 1987.

During the past decade three large-scale spring movements have taken place. Each has been associated with easterly or north-easterly winds and have doubtless involved birds which have drifted westward as they travelled along the European coastline. During the first week of May 1990 a county total of over 950 included 313 at Holkham, 150 at Cley, 115 at Kelling Water Meadows (from where many flew off to the south-east) and 85 at Welney. A second influx was a feature of the third week of April 1992 when a total of over 530 included 98 at Holkham, 88 at Berney and 174 at Welney. Two years later on 2nd–9th May 1994 over 980 in the county included 200 at Cley, 214 at Horsey and 141 at Berney.

A great attraction following the spring arrival of an assembly of Ruffs and Reeves is the opportunity of observing their spectacular and completely silent tournaments. Each Ruff sports gorgeous ear-tufts and ruff. Colouring varies from orange, golden-yellow, fiery red and black-glossed purple. Some possess white ruffs representing non-courting young or very elderly birds belonging to a lower social class which linger at the margins of the display arena and have no chance of being selected by visiting Reeves. The tilting grounds are often on the bank of a marsh dyke. From such a vantage point the males engage in bouts of frantic running, charging and wing-flapping. Others spring from the ground, kicking one another, hitting out with opened wings and seizing one another with their bills. After skirmishing and chasing, the Ruffs suddenly squat and freeze like mechanical puppets posing before either a Reeve or a rival male with wings spread flat. Such displays were often witnessed at Cley in the late 1960s.

Following a gap of many years Ruffs returned to Britain as a breeding bird in 1963 when eggs were found on the Cambridgeshire Ouse Washes (Cottier & Lea 1969). By 1970 ten or more nests were known including three on the Norfolk section of the Washes. The following spring 21 nests were located on the complete length. There may have been up to 40, in view of the secretive nature of the Reeves when nesting. Between 1972 and 1977 up to four Reeves nested each year at Welney, but none has done so subsequently.

Small groups of Ruffs have been increasingly recorded in mid-summer. The first returning birds of the autumn appear in early July with passage peaking between August and October. The largest arrivals often coincide with influxes of Little Stints and Curlew Sandpipers. Until reclamation was completed in 1985, the most impressive autumn numbers were regularly recorded at Wisbech Sewage Farm with 200 each year from 1967 until 1978 and a peak of 240 during September 1974. Welney first came into prominence in September 1968. Since then the reserve has attracted 100–200 annually, unless there has been deep flooding, peaking at 400 during October–November 1981.

The maximum autumn counts along the north coast have been up to 150 at Titchwell, 57 at Brancaster Harbour, 80 at Holkham Fresh Marshes and 150 at Cley, in the Broads 70 at Hickling, 52 at Horsey, 68 at Ludham and 51 at Cantley, and in east Norfolk up to 51 have featured at Breydon with 75 at Berney. In the Fens, in addition to the high counts at Wisbech Sewage Farm and Welney, up to 52 have been recorded at King's Lynn Beet Factory.

Since the mid-1950s winter records have become annual. Wisbech Sewage Farm was the most favoured locality with a maximum of 80 during November–December 1957. From 1968 onwards Welney has attracted up to 280 Ruffs until late February. The highest winter counts along the north coast have been up to 100 at Titchwell in January 1997 and 80 in the Glaven water meadows in February 1994. Elsewhere maximum winter counts have been up to 50 at Hickling, 44 at Berney, 35 at Hardley Flood, 28 at Cantley and 30 at Buckenham.

About 20 Ruff ringed in Norfolk have been recovered abroad, the vast majority caught during autumn in the 1960s at Wisbech Sewage Farm. The recoveries have demonstrated the south-westerly route taken by the species in autumn through France and Iberia with single winter recoveries in Morocco and Senegal; while one colour-dyed by a team of German ringers operating in Senegal in February 1985 was seen at Hardley Flood in May. In spring a more easterly route is followed by many of the returning migrants and

271

this has resulted in five recoveries in Italy between late February and early April. There have been three breeding-season recoveries – two in Russia and one in Poland. The longest movement within the British Isles involved an autumn-ringed bird from Wisbech Sewage Farm controlled at Shotton, Flintshire in spring.

*Michael Seago*

## |Jack Snipe|                                 *Lymnocryptes minimus*

**A scarce passage migrant and winter visitor; has declined in recent years.**

The Jack Snipe is a regular but scarce passage migrant and winter visitor to the British Isles from the boreal forest bogs of northern Sweden, Finland and across northern Russia into Siberia. In Britain it is renowned for being a rather elusive species, favouring damp meadows and marshland with a mixture of both short but dense vegetation and more open areas of silty mud. Its presence is frequently undetected until it is flushed from the observer's feet, sometimes at very close quarters.

The species has always been regarded as a rather uncommon passage migrant and winter visitor in Norfolk. Evidence seems to suggest it has declined since the 19th century, although its elusiveness could lead to under-recording.

Autumn migrants usually begin to appear in September, with most passing through in October and November. Stevenson mentioned one shot at Barton Fen on 1st August 1833 while Riviere commented that a few were sometimes noted in August. Since the publication of the first *Norfolk Bird Report* in 1953, however, there have only been two such early records – at Cley on 19th August 1957 and at Wisbech Sewage Farm on 24th August 1969. Most autumn sightings of Jack Snipe are of birds flushed from coastal marshes (fresh and saltwater), and to a lesser extent dunes, stubble and arable fields. Localities with observation hides overlooking the muddy edges of marsh pools such as at Holme, Titchwell and Cley produce several records annually. Broadland and the Fens also remain attractive for the species. Large autumn counts have included 70 shot at Horsey in 1845, 43 at Wisbech Sewage Farm on 21st October 1966 and 50 there on 5th November 1966. Extracts from Jim Vincent's Hickling diaries revealed counts of 20 on 10th October 1920, 30 on 11th October 1921, 20 on 23rd November 1921 and 20 on 24th October 1933. Recent years have seen no double-figure counts at any sites in autumn, the maximum being seven at Cley on 26th September 1990 and nine at Surlingham on 13th–14th November 1986. Jack Snipe are very seldom noted actually migrating so the record of two arriving in off the sea at Sheringham on 17th September 1994 and one moving west with Starlings over Brancaster Staithe are both noteworthy.

Like Snipe and Woodcock, Jack Snipe continue to arrive throughout the winter, especially during spells of hard weather. This is illustrated by the finding of one on a gas platform 48km north-east of Yarmouth on 6th December 1995, while on 3rd February 1998, following some hard weather on the Continent, a party of six was found together at Salthouse, with an additional five at Kelling Quags (McCallum 1998d). In the winter Jack Snipe are perhaps generally scarcer than in the autumn. Traditional marshland sites both coastal and inland are inhabited annually as are fens and damp commons. The north-coast saltmarshes have also recorded a few regularly in more recent years. Information obtained from the old Hickling game books shows that Jack Snipe were shot annually there between 1911 and 1962 (with the exception of 17 years) with the largest winter bags of 29 in 1911–12, 24 in 1913–14, 34 in 1914–15, 21 in 1915–16 and 24 in 1933–34. It is also of interest to note that in all of these winters, Jack Snipe bags outnumbered those of Common Snipe. In more recent winters maxima have included ten at Breydon on 9th December 1973, five at Colney Gravel Pit in November–December 1984, five at Buckenham in January 1987 and six at Bure Park, Yarmouth in December 1996. Sightings usually increase during hard weather when birds are frequently noted feeding around ice-free pools or springs. Stevenson also spoke of the Jack Snipe seemingly being a hardier species than the Common Snipe, with the former remaining through severe spells when the latter had more often than not departed.

Spring passage is normally less pronounced than in the autumn, although a small peak is noted in March and April. The best counts from recent years are both from Wells – eleven on 12th March 1977 and nine on 20th March 1996. Jim Vincent also noted twelve at Hickling on 7th April 1924. Stragglers sometimes stay well into May with singles at Burnham Norton on 17th May 1995 and at Hardley Flood on 27th May 1962 being the latest dates. Stevenson, however, spoke of several unseasonal records – June birds were noted at East Walton and Surlingham in 1868 while one was shot at Belton Bog on 21st July

1826. He also mentioned another summering individual in the county (but did not name the locality) which remained on a fen from May until 2nd July 1825. It had undoubtedly oversummered due to its very poor condition and was so weak that when flushed it was knocked to the ground by a swipe from its finder's hat! Other summer sightings were mentioned by Vincent who noted one at Hickling from 7th June to 23rd July 1924, while others were seen on 9th June 1913 and 15th June 1925.

About 50 Jack Snipe have been ringed in Norfolk of which two have been recovered – one ringed at Wisbech Sewage Farm on 1st October 1957 was at Lozere in southern France on 21st November and another ringed at Holme on 31st October 1964 was recovered at Tunis, Tunisia on 9th December. It remains the only British-ringed Jack Snipe to be recovered in Africa. Another ringed at Greater Manchester in March 1973 was recovered at Heacham in October 1980.

*Andrew Bloomfield*

## Common Snipe CLEY MARSHES. 7-9-1985. *Gallinago gallinago*

**A fairly common, but declining breeder, and common winter visitor and passage migrant.**

The Common Snipe has an extensive world range, taking in much of the Western Palearctic and North America, with wintering occurring into South America, central Africa, the Gulf States, throughout Asia to Japan in the east and Indonesia in the south-east. It occurs throughout most of the British Isles being most abundant on upland and moorland bogs in northern Britain and Ireland with declining numbers inhabiting southern lowland river valleys, fens and coastal grazing marshes. Intensive agriculture with widespread drainage, conversion of grassland to arable fields and heavy grazing of unimproved damp meadows are all depriving the Snipe of much of its habitat (New Atlas).

Whilst many people think of the Snipe's decline in Norfolk as being a recent event, as far back as Stevenson's time numbers were diminishing. He spoke of the conversion of many thousands of acres of marsh and fen to arable land, due to drainage and cultivation. Stevenson stated that Snipe bred in good numbers in the Broads and Fens and described the lowland riverside marshes between Norwich and Yarmouth as the 'best Snipe ground in Norfolk'. Scattered pairs were also widespread throughout the county's marshes, damp commons, fens, meres and river valleys. Riviere did not mention any further decline and failed to elaborate on distribution details, stating that Snipe bred 'freely in all suitable locations'.

Seago (1967) commented that numbers were still declining but added salt- marshes to the list of breeding habitats. Apart from 15 drumming Snipe in the River Yare basin in 1979, very few details of breeding Snipe were received prior to the fieldwork for the Norfolk Atlas (1980–85) which found the species present in 325 tetrads (22%). During this period a comprehensive survey was also undertaken in 1982 and a minimum of 500 drumming Snipe was found in Norfolk, representing 23% of the English and Welsh population. The largest concentration was found in the Ouse Washes, where 173 were counted, 35% of the county total. Elsewhere poorly drained meadows and fens, particularly in river valleys, produced 58% of the total. Highest numbers were found in the Nar Valley between West Lexham and West Acre (22), in the Wissey Valley at Hilgay (ten) and Thompson Common (eight) and the upper middle reaches of the Yare (twelve at Strumpshaw and six at Postwick). A further 45 drummers were found in Broadland reed-stubble (Murfitt & Weaver 1983). As has always been the case with the county's population, numbers and breeding success regularly fluctuate depending on springtime water levels. This is particularly the case at Welney where prolonged winter and spring flooding will often lead to large areas of the Washes becoming unsuitable for nesting Snipe. Both the species' decline and fluctuating fortunes are well illustrated by the figures of drumming Snipe at Welney since 1982.

**Table 38. The total number of drumming Snipe recorded annually at Welney 1982–97.**

| 1982 | 1983 | 1984 | 1985 | 1986 | 1987 | 1988 | 1989 | 1990 | 1991 | 1992 | 1993 | 1994 | 1995 | 1996 | 1997 |
|------|------|------|------|------|------|------|------|------|------|------|------|------|------|------|------|
| 173  | 113  | 129  | 106  | 60   | 91   | 139  | 164  | 130  | 67   | 81   | 72   | 92   | 85   | 52   | 51   |

Other localities where declining numbers of Snipe have been noted include the coastal grazing marshes of the north coast. At Holkham numbers peaked at 25 drummers in 1989 following English Nature's management plan which created damper conditions, but had dropped to eleven by 1995. The whole coastal area between Snettisham and Kelling held 44 drummers in 1992, but only 19 in 1995 and 16 in 1996. In the latter year both Kelling and Snettisham failed to record any, while at Holme only one was found compared to five in 1995. A full survey of the Broads (covering all of Broadland's grazing marshes and river valleys and also the Wensum Valley to its source west of Fakenham at Raynham) in 1995 revealed a population of 95 drummers, a decline of 40% since 1988. Largest numbers were found west of Fakenham (24), Strumpshaw/Buckenham/Cantley (10 compared with 22 at Strumpshaw alone in 1989), Wroxham to Coltishall (11) and Hickling (9). The county as a whole has seen the Snipe population dwindle from 500 pairs in 1982 to 87 in 1997.

**Table 39. The total number of drumming Snipe reported annually in Norfolk 1988–97.**

| 1988 | 1989 | 1990 | 1991 | 1992 | 1993 | 1994 | 1995 | 1996 | 1997 |
|---|---|---|---|---|---|---|---|---|---|
| 216 | 242 | 194 | 111 | 141 | 135 | 147 | 204 | 88 | 87 |

Under-recording from some locations may be enhancing a depressing picture, although the evidence described above has certainly given rise to growing concern for the Snipe's future as a Norfolk breeding bird. It is especially worrying that many Snipe have disappeared from several sites where the habitat has remained unchanged, at least to our eyes.

Snipe from Europe are regular passage migrants and winter visitors to Norfolk. The greatest numbers are generally noted in the autumn months, with the passage period lasting from August to November. As with breeding numbers, a decline has been noted in recent years. On migration, Snipe frequently appear on the smallest of marshy pools, muddy edges of ponds and lakes, beet factory settling pools, ploughed and stubble fields and formerly on the old-style sewage farms, as well as in their more typical habitats. Riviere mentioned regular observations from offshore light-vessels, those in early autumn usually in the company of Knot, while October–November sightings were generally in association with Continental passerine migrants. Some of the largest autumn counts came from Wisbech Sewage Farm. Up to 100 were not infrequent, with 400 on 14th October 1961 and 300 on 28th October 1962, 17th October 1968, 20th August 1969 and 27th September 1969. Between 25th August and 16th September 1978 almost daily estimates ranged between 300 and 600, the highest total being obtained on 9th September. At this time the sewage farm was in peak condition attracting a remarkable selection of passage migrant waders. Cantley Beet Factory pools are also favoured where the highest counts have included 200 on 8th September 1968, 500 on 1st September 1974, 500 on 14th October 1984 and 200 in September 1995. Elsewhere in the county notable counts have been 240 at Titchwell in August 1983, 110 at Surlingham in September 1986, 200 at Cley on 12th August 1989, 485 at Holme on 16th August 1992, 250 at Ludham in October 1993 increasing to 500 on 31st and 700 on 2nd November, and 140 at Whitlingham Lane Gravel Pit, Norwich in October 1994.

Overhead westerly migration at coastal localities is on occasions quite pronounced. Riviere mentioned November 1859 when a cold spell triggered a massive movement. Up to 334 were shot over three days at Holkham alone. In more recent years regular migration watches at Holme have produced the following totals – 250 on 18th September 1983, 147 on 27th October 1992, 210 on 21st September 1993 and 316 on 2nd October 1994. While 297 passed over Hunstanton on 10th October 1983 and 165 flew south at Hunstanton cliffs on 16th October 1997.

During the winter, Snipe are occasionally seen in very large numbers, particularly during hard weather, when flocks often congregate around open ice-free ground where they are able to feed. It was during such conditions that many of the large 'bags' were shot in Stevenson's and Riviere's eras. Examples included 500 shot around Surlingham and Rockland in 1862–63, 168 shot over two days at Hapton in 1840, 412 at Feltwell in 1839 and 633 in 1841, 226 shot at Whitlingham Sewage Farm on 20th December 1927 (shot by only five guns and the second largest British 'day-bag' at that time). This followed an exceptionally wet November, when large numbers of Snipe appeared throughout the county. Following a sudden change of temperature, Whitlingham remained one of the only open feeding grounds free from ice and snow, thus attracting vast numbers. Riviere also mentioned one particular wildfowler who shot 158 Snipe on a single day at Horsey, 123 at Buckenham Marshes and 120 at Langley. Since those far off times, large winter concentrations in recent years have included 350 at Welney in November 1982, 140 at Burnham Norton on 27th November 1984, 275 at Chedgrave on 24th February 1984, 1,000 at Buckenham/ Cantley and 800 at Berney Marshes during mild and wet conditions in December 1987, an estimated

1,200 in the Breydon area in January 1988, 290 at Berney Marshes in December 1988, 200 at Bawburgh on 26th November 1993, 246 at Holkham in November 1993 and 250 beside the River Glaven at Cley on 23rd November 1993. As well as all the more usual habitats occupied by Snipe in the winter, increasing numbers have appeared on the north coast saltmarshes at low water. For instance maximum counts in 1997 were of 60 at Thornham, 46 at Scolt Head, 58 at Burnham Overy Harbour, 48 at Stiffkey and 181 at Blakeney Harbour. Like Woodcock, Snipe frequently suffer during hard weather. A notable example comes from Morley where a cat brought five starving Snipe back to a house on one night in January 1963.

In spring, the Snipe's return passage to its breeding grounds is usually less noticeable than in autumn. Large build-ups occasionally occur at freshwater marshes, particularly in cold, wet springs when their outward passage is temporarily held up. Maximum counts have included 1,050 at Welney in mid-March 1979 and 300 in March 1982, 300 at Cley in March 1988, 100 at Holkham in April 1988 and 183 in March 1991.

Stevenson spoke of several partially leucistic morphs seen through the years, one with an upturned Avocet-like bill and a pure white individual (shot at Walton Common in 1866). An example of the rare melanistic form of Snipe, formerly thought to be a separate species and known as 'Sabine's Snipe', was shot in a turnip field at Raynham on 17th October 1856.

Several hundred Snipe have been ringed in Norfolk, the vast majority in autumn. Recoveries have been reported, mainly in winter, from The Netherlands, France (3), Spain (3) and Portugal (2). In addition, one ringed at Wisbech Sewage Farm on 24th September 1964 was recovered in Sardinia on 12th November, while one ringed at Salthouse on 19th August 1972 was found at Vichuga, Russia on 30th August 1974. The only recovery date suggesting a bird in its breeding area was one ringed at Boughton in March 1968 and recovered on 2nd July 1970 at Partakoski, Finland. A chick ringed at Gooderstone in June 1960 was shot in Mayenne, France on 6th August, suggesting that locally-bred birds move south in autumn. Other Norfolk-ringed Snipe have been found in winter in Suffolk, Devon and Cornwall. Ten Snipe ringed abroad in autumn have been recovered in Norfolk between July and March, four from Skanor in Sweden, three from Germany and singles from The Netherlands, Finland and Poland. One ringed at Mennewitz, Germany on 22nd August 1965 and controlled at Cantley on 22nd July 1970, provided some indication of the timing of the first arrivals from the Continent in the autumn. A Snipe carrying ring number E978, ringed as a chick at Sandy, Bedfordshire on 2nd May 1912 and shot at South Walsham on 7th November 1913, provided one of the first ever Norfolk recoveries of a bird ringed under one of the British ringing schemes.

*Andrew Bloomfield*

# Great Snipe                                              *Gallinago media*

**A rare autumn vagrant; single spring and mid-winter records.**

The Great Snipe breeds in Scandinavia and from Poland eastwards to west Siberia, wintering in Africa south of the Sahara. Formerly it was a rare but almost regular autumn passage migrant to the British Isles, but numbers have fallen greatly, reflecting the drastic decline of the European breeding population.

Stevenson noted 'many' shot during the first half of the 19th century when local taxidermists readily accepted specimens. The Revd Richard Rising once shot six in a single morning in the Horsey Marshes and five were obtained in one day in a turnip field at Beeston near Cromer. Barley and wheat stubbles also proved attractive. Yarmouth gunners sought newly arrived Great Snipe in the extensive marram hills adjoining the denes. At least 53 were shot between 1856 and 1899, including eight between 14th and 27th September 1899. A further 25 were recorded (mostly shot) in the first half of the 20th century, and another 17 examples, all singles, have been recorded since 1950:

> 1952: Sidestrand on 13th October
> 1953: Salthouse Heath on 11th March
>        Brancaster Staithe on 18th October
> 1956: Bure Marshes, Stokesby on 5th November
> 1959: Corpusty Mill on 3rd–7th September
> 1962: Thetford on 1st January
> 1966: Salthouse on 27th August
>        A juvenile shot at Wiveton on 12th September, now in the Castle Museum, Norwich

1969: Wisbech Sewage Farm on 21st–24th August
1976: Hardley Flood on 25th-28th May
Blakeney Point on 28th August
A juvenile shot at Salthouse on 18th September, now in the Castle Museum, Norwich
Holkham on 26th September
1987: A juvenile on Blakeney Point on 25th–27th August
1991: A juvenile at Welney on 6th September
1994: A juvenile at Sheringham on 17th September
1998: Holkham Fresh Marsh on 12th May

*Steve Gantlett*

# [Short-billed Dowitcher                              *Limnodromus griseus*

The Short-billed Dowitcher is a Nearctic wader which breeds from south Alaska to the western side of Hudson Bay, Canada and winters on both coasts, but primarily on the Atlantic coast of south-eastern America, south to South America. There are three well-separated races with different migration routes. This and the Long-billed Dowitcher (both formerly known as Red-breasted Snipe) were generally regarded as a single species until 1950.

Two Norfolk records previously accepted as being this species have been reconsidered. One at Wisbech Sewage Farm from 28th September to 6th October 1963 was reviewed in 1980 and identified as a Long-billed Dowitcher. Another, at Cley from 5th October to 3rd November 1957 which regularly commuted to Salthouse, was filmed by Dick Bagnall-Oakeley and a photograph of the bird appeared in the *Norfolk Bird Report 1957*. This was one of four remaining accepted records of Short-billed Dowitcher in the British Isles, but it was further reviewed by the BOURC in April 1992 and found not to be acceptable; it was reclassified as dowitcher sp.]

*Peter Allard*

# Long-billed Dowitcher                              *Limnodromus scolopaceus*

**A very rare vagrant; nine records and six additional records of dowitcher sp.**

The Long-billed Dowitcher breeds in the extreme north-east of Siberia, and in northern and western Alaska, wintering in the southern USA south to Guatemala. A vagrant to Britain, it has visited annually since 1963 with most appearing from September to mid-November.

Formally known as Red-breasted Snipe, the first Long-billed Dowitcher for Norfolk, a first-winter male, was shot at Horsey on 9th October 1845 by the Revd Richard Rising of Horsey Hall. This example is still at the Castle Museum, Norwich. The second was a juvenile at Wisbech Sewage Farm from 28th September to 6th October 1963. This bird was previously considered to be a Short-billed Dowitcher, but the record was reviewed by the BOURC in 1980 and accepted as a Long-billed Dowitcher.

Since then a further seven have been identified. First-winter birds were at Snettisham on 7th–30th September 1968 and at Weybourne on 30th October 1969, the latter bird later moving to Cley where it remained until 4th November. An adult in full breeding plumage visited Titchwell on 18th–19th June 1989 and another juvenile moulting into first-winter plumage was at Lynn Point from 25th September to 16th October 1990. Another adult in breeding attire was at Pentney Gravel Pits at midday on 28th April 1994; it was present until early evening when it flew off high to the north with two Greenshanks. A first-summer bird in partial breeding plumage was located at Titchwell on 10th June 1997, remaining all day feeding in company with Redshanks and Snipe. Finally a juvenile/first-winter was at Welney from 10th October to 1st November 1998.

Dowitchers not specifically identified have been recorded in Norfolk on six occasions. The first two concerned birds shot at Yarmouth in October 1836 and early October 1841. The whereabouts of both of these specimens is unknown. The following four records were considered to relate to Long-billed Dowitchers, but specific identification was not fully proven – singles at Scolt Head on 29th–30th October 1950 and 14th October 1954, at Cley/Salthouse from 5th October to 3rd November 1957 and at Hickling Broad on 24th–26th October 1983.

*Peter Allard*

*CHEDGRAVE MANOR. 13·11·1999.*

## Woodcock (Eurasian Woodcock) | *Scolopax rusticola*

**A fairly common breeder and passage migrant, and common winter visitor.**

The Woodcock is a bird of well-wooded districts. From Ireland in the west, its range stretches across much of central Europe, Fennoscandia and Russia to the Pacific coast (New Atlas). It breeds throughout much of the British Isles, avoiding only the Fens and very high ground.

In Norfolk, the Woodcock is a resident, passage migrant and winter visitor. Due to its secretive and crepuscular habits, it remains a seldom-seen bird of mystery. Most birdwatchers encounter the species either on its autumn migration or the male on his spring-time roding display flights. Very few have had first-hand experience of it at the nest. It is undoubtedly widespread throughout the county's woodlands, but its elusiveness leads to under-recording most years in the breeding season. Stevenson spoke of many hundreds of acres of heath and woodland converted to arable land in the 60 years prior to his publication, thus depriving the Woodcock of much breeding habitat. He did, however, feel the species was increasing as a nester through the 1800s. Riviere described the Woodcock as 'locally distributed, but by no means common', noting the stronghold as the Breckland forests.

In 1957 when Dick Bagnall-Oakeley summarised all recent breeding occurrences of Norfolk Woodcock, it became quite clear that the county's population was growing. He found the favoured areas to be Breckland and the wooded areas of the north coast's hinterland, between Holkham in the west and Overstrand in the east, particularly the Holt/Sheringham area. Central Norfolk and Broadland also hosted several birds whilst east and west Norfolk (except Sandringham) had very few. By the time of the fieldwork for the Norfolk Atlas (1980–85) the situation had changed little, with the species recorded in 233 tetrads (16%), except for the addition of growing numbers in west Norfolk and in the wooded pockets between Horsford north-west to Briston. For several reasons, population figures can really only be speculative. Nests are renowned for being difficult to find, whilst male Woodcock are polygamous and their roding display flights can be lengthy and the routes variable. Nevertheless, past counts from selected sites worthy of note have included six nests at Attlebridge in 1856, six roding in the Sheringham/Weybourne area in 1949, ten to twelve within an 8km radius of Cley in 1956, five roding at Didlington in 1968, 15 roding at Holkham Park with 20 breeding females estimated to be present in the late 1980s and early 1990s, six roding at Roydon, four at Sandringham, Merton and Horsford, and five at Upton Fen in 1994, twelve roding at Wroxham and five at Buxton, Frost's Common, Marsham Heath and Swanton Novers in 1995 and twelve roding at Holkham Park in 1997. Woodcock generally commence laying in early March, thus a nest with three eggs at Hockham Fen on 2nd February 1972 is particularly noteworthy.

Woodcock numbers are boosted annually in the autumn months when immigrants arrive at coastal sites from Fennoscandia and central Europe. Many of these spend the winter in Norfolk woods, although some undoubtedly move to other parts of the British Isles. Most migrant Woodcock occur from mid-October into November and sometimes December. Riviere stated that migrants sometimes appeared at the end of September and found that the offshore light-vessels had recorded Woodcock between 24th September and 13th December. In recent years September birds have become quite unusual, with one at Wells on 24th September 1994 being the only one reported. Most migrants arrive in the hours of darkness. Full moons in late autumn were once associated with arrivals and became known by wildfowlers as 'Woodcock Moons'. Evidence, however, suggests wind direction has more influence on their arrival than a full moon, with northerly, north-easterly and sometimes north-westerly providing most of the records. Taylor (1987a) commented that up to 100 had been seen in a single day at Sheringham Hall woods during late autumn, whilst another notable count was made at Wells East Hills on 1st November 1995, when 80 were sheltering beneath pines during a northerly gale.

In the winter months, Woodcock can be abundant throughout the county. Hard weather often provokes more Continental arrivals and it is then that numbers are at their greatest. To many birdwatchers, Woodcock still remain a seldom-seen species, but information gleaned from Norfolk's shooting estates certainly illustrate the large numbers present.

The earliest gamebook held in Holkham Estate Office for the five-year period 1793–94 reveals that 544 were shot. Another Holkham gamebook for the period 1900–30 shows that 3,416 were shot. More recently the gamebook covering 1930–56 gives a 'bag' of 4,127. Stevenson noted 61 shot at Gressenhall in November 1865, and at Swanton Novers/Melton Park 155 were killed over a four-day shoot in 1865,

105 on one day in December 1872, 93 in December 1852 and 83 in November 1858. Unusual numbers appeared during the 1908–09 winter. A total of 300 were shot between 1st and 4th December 1908 on the estates at Sheringham, Swanton, Felbrigg, Hanworth, Gimingham, Stratton Strawless, Witton and Runton. Up to 334 were shot at Holkham Park in November–December 1925, while in more recent times notable counts have included 60 at Brancaster Hall on 6th January 1962, 50 at Grime's Graves on 1st November 1968, 200 at Gillingham in early January 1979, 60 at Cley on 3rd December 1988, 200–300 at Holkham Park in February 1995, 100 at Baconsthorpe and 1,000 at Holkham Park in January 1996, and 100 at South Creake and 1,500 at Holkham Park in January 1997, where 140 were shot in three days.

The continuing arrival of immigrants throughout the winter is illustrated by birds arriving in off the sea at Overstrand on 26th February 1956 and at Holme on 11th January 1989. Up to 19 also arrived at the latter locality on 10th February 1991. As well as numbers increasing during hard weather, Woodcock then become more conspicuous and often quite fearless. With prolonged frosts, they frequently leave the safety of their usual wooded haunts to feed in the daytime on grass verges, coastal grazing marshes and occasionally saltmarsh creeks. During hard weather in 1962 up to 30 were feeding on Mautby Marshes on 13th January while at the year's end during another cold snap in December, Woodcock were noted feeding in saltwater creeks at Overy Staithe, Wells and Stiffkey alongside Knot and Dunlin. Spring migration is seldom noted in Norfolk, although shooting estates where large numbers have overwintered usually notice a decrease by mid-March.

Fewer than 100 Woodcock have been ringed in Norfolk. Six autumn arrivals all ringed along the north Norfolk coast between 11th October and 2nd November have been recovered. The only foreign recovery involved one ringed at Holme in 1959 which was shot in Finistere, France on 13th December 1959, while another ringed at Holme on 14th October 1972 was shot in Staffordshire on 25th November, and one from Sheringham was shot nine days later in Leicestershire. The other three, all ringed in the Weybourne/Sheringham area were recovered during the winter in Tyne and Wear, Leicestershire and Shropshire, respectively. No less than 31 foreign-ringed Woodcock have been shot in Norfolk. The majority were ringed in autumn in The Netherlands (9), Norway (3), Denmark (2), Germany (2) and Finland, with two ringed near the Baltic coast of Russia. Three birds ringed as nestlings have been recovered in Norfolk – one from Finland and two from Sweden, one as long ago as 1932.

*Andrew Bloomfield*

## Black-tailed Godwit  BREYDON WATER. 1-12-1992.      *Limosa limosa*

**A very scarce and declining breeder, but an increasingly common passage migrant and winter visitor.**

The Black-tailed Godwit is confined to the Palearctic, with two of the three races breeding in Europe. The nominate race *L. l. limosa* is a bird of temperate grassland and moorland, wintering predominantly in freshwater habitats south of the Sahara, in Senegambia and Guinea-Bissau. The Icelandic race *L. l. islandica* nests in subarctic tundra and moorland, and winters in estuarine habitats along the Atlantic coast from Britain south to Morocco. Half of the European population of *limosa* breeds in The Netherlands, with most of the remainder extending across central Europe to Russia. During the 20th century it has bred in the British Isles not only at the Ouse and Nene Washes (see below), but also in Somerset, southern Scotland, Yorkshire and from the Humber south to Kent, while birds believed to have been of the race *islandica* have bred in Caithness, Orkney, Shetland and Ireland (New Atlas).

The Black-tailed Godwit was once a common breeding species in Norfolk. Known to Sir Thomas Browne as the 'yarwhelp' and to later Norfolk generations as the 'shrieker', it declined rapidly to extinction following the drainage of the grazing marshes and their eventual conversion to arable land, the bulk of which took place during the 18th century. Its final extinction is attributed to shooting and egg collecting, as with the Avocet and Ruff. Lubbock (1845) wrote that the Black-tailed Godwit was one of five species which 'used to swarm in our marshes' and its extinction as a regular breeding species probably occurred sometime between 1829 and 1835, although it is possible that a pair or two returned to their old haunts for the next 20 years. The last authentic record of breeding in the 19th century was a nest found at Horsey in the summer of 1829 but More (1865) expressed the belief that Norfolk was the 'only county in which there is a possibility that a pair or two may linger occasionally'. For example, Stevenson reported a Mr Gurney as remembering 30 years previously being informed that a couple of pairs still nested on Sir William

Beauchamp Proctor's marshes near Buckenham Ferry. Similarly, in the western Fens, where it was formerly widespread, it reappeared during the spring following the 'great flood' of 1852. Interestingly, in light of its eventual recolonisation, it is reported to have been a 'former abundant breeder in Holland but like the purple heron, spoonbill and little bittern has been so destroyed of late that to some degree this must account for its scarcity in Eastern England' (Stevenson).

From then until about 1917, it was known only as an occasional spring and autumn passage migrant, after which it began to be reported with increasing frequency. For example, Pashley (1925) stated that he had never handled a specimen until then, after which 'these birds have been seen or taken every year'. Recolonisation of the British Isles began with sporadic nesting in the fens of Cambridgeshire and Norfolk in the 1930s, coinciding with a marked increase in numbers nesting in The Netherlands (New Atlas). The species has bred regularly on the Ouse Washes since at least 1952 (Conder 1962, Cottier & Lea 1969). Indeed, until the mid-1970s, these washlands were the main breeding site in the British Isles, holding over 90% of the population. Since then they have been prone to spring flooding and for a while it looked as though breeding Black-tailed Godwits were in danger of disappearing once more. Between 1975 and 1993 there were only three summers without flooding and the godwit population on the complete length of the Washes (Norfolk and Cambridgeshire) slumped from 65 pairs in 1972, raising 90 young, to just six pairs in 1993. Efficient agricultural drainage, urban run-off and river engineering works are thought to be responsible for the increased frequency of summer flooding (Fowler & Buisson 1995). Numbers have still not recovered to the levels recorded in the mid-1970s. However, since then they have colonised a site on washland in Cambridgeshire, which is now the main site for the species. Nowadays up to three pairs only breed in Norfolk, and not always every year. Most of the breeding attempts have been at Welney but predators invariably take a heavy toll. Elsewhere, a pair bred successfully on the Wash at Snettisham in 1969 and 1971.

However, away from the Ouse Washes, the best-documented breeding records have come from Cley where one to two pairs attempted to breed in the most inaccessible part of the NWT Reserve in 1964. Although eggs were considered to have been laid, there was no evidence that incubation was successful. Black-tailed Godwits returned for varying periods during the subsequent three springs but without giving any indication of attempting to breed. In 1968, however, two pairs nested but unfortunately all the young were taken by stoats when only a few days old. A delightful account of this first definite breeding attempt at Cley is given by Richardson and Bishop (1969); apart from the stoats, other potential predators included the larger gulls.

The Cley reserve lies directly athwart the flyline of the larger gulls coasting westwards on their travels. Although nothing is further from the minds of these birds than godwits' eggs they have to run the gauntlet of the waspish defenders and, with the yelps of bewilderment, often swerve back and forth along their tracks in complete confusion to suffer the same punishment over and over again. Once the eggs had hatched and the young had left the nest 'the parents' alert heads and orange necks projected like watchful periscopes above the waving sea of grasses and were retracted jerkily with each repetition of their warning notes. Gulls and herons were kept on the move with redoubled urgency and it brought a glow of satisfaction to watch this delightful little tableau.

The following year, one of the males from 1968 returned to breed with a new mate, and a second pair joined them. Once again two clutches were laid but both failed at the egg stage, one again from predation and the other as a result of adverse weather. As before Richard Richardson and a team of observers kept a constant watch on the area throughout the breeding season and a detailed account of the events was published (Richardson 1970). It included an amusing observation on the way in which the godwits dealt with birds as large as geese. 'Yearling Canada geese which lounged near the nest were sent floundering ignominiously away by well-directed prods in the nether regions, [a male godwit] actually riding for a few yards on the back of one enormous outraged gander.' Unfortunately the fine weather broke on 16th May when rain began to fall and continued unremittingly for hours on end.

> [One of the male godwits] relieved his mate at noon and sat as if petrified throughout the afternoon, becoming progressively wetter as the minutes dragged by. Huddled in the nest, with white eyelids tightly shut and swallowing the raindrops as they trickled down his bill, he was the epitome of dejection. His mate became long overdue and at last he could bear it no longer, staggering to his feet, stiff-legged and saturated, before flying off to find her. She came back at once but after pecking around the nest for several minutes, refused to sit and went away.

Richard Richardson waded out to the island on which the godwits were nesting, to find that the four eggs were almost afloat, the faithful male having been attempting to brood them in an inch of water! By making some small channels to allow the water to drain away and by 'refurnishing' the nest, the eggs could be replaced on a comparatively dry platform. Within a few minutes the male was back incubating the clutch! Torrential rain the following day made further adjustments necessary, which the pair accepted, but unfortunately the eggs became addled and failed to hatch.

Despite this failure, one of the pairs returned to breed again in 1970, to be joined again by a second pair and on this occasion a total of six eggs hatched. Gradually they were lost to predators and despite one youngster surviving for three weeks, it too disappeared before fledging. Once again the events were vividly described by Richardson (1971) and on this occasion included an encounter with a Spoonbill. '[One of the male godwits] seldom missed a chance of making life a misery for some luckless creature; thus an apparition in the shape of a spoonbill which came flying along one afternoon paid the penalty for its peculiar appearance and for having a bill so obviously designed to shovel up godwit's eggs!'

As far as Icelandic Black-tailed Godwits in Norfolk are concerned their story is very different. Whereas prior to the 1970s, Black-tailed Godwits were a very scarce passage and winter species, in recent years there has been a spectacular increase in numbers both in Norfolk and elsewhere in Britain. The cause of this increase is unknown but may be related to changes in the Icelandic breeding grounds (Prater 1981).

Historically, records of Black-tailed Godwits in winter in Norfolk were scarce. Riviere (1930) noted only two winter occurrences – at Yarmouth on 10th January 1866 and on Breydon on 20th December 1920, and only occasional winter sightings were reported in the 1970s and 1980s. However, they appear to have been more common on passage in the county. Records of small numbers of Black-tailed Godwits in April, May and August exist from the 1860s (Stevenson) and the 1920s (Riviere). It is impossible to know, however, whether these birds would have been from the western European breeding population of *limosa* or from Iceland. During the 1960s parties of 60–90, presumably Icelandic birds, were recorded on the Wash during August and September (Seago 1977). Nowadays a regular spring passage is recorded in March and April, with the return passage commencing in the first half of July and generally peaking in August and September.

**Black-tailed Godwits**
*(Richard Richardson)*

The dramatic increase in the number of passage and wintering Black-tailed Godwits of the race *islandica* in Norfolk did not begin until as recently as the mid- to late 1980s. It was first noted in Norfolk at Welney in late March 1986, where up to 504 were concentrated as a result of flooding. Numbers there have steadily increased each year in spring, with 1,236 in March 1997. In some years extensive flooding on the Ouse Washes has driven the birds to the Ouse Mouth, both during the winter and in spring and up to 700 have been recorded there. Peak counts in the Wash averaged only 28 between 1970 and 1983, but since 1990 the number of Icelandic Black-tailed Godwits has increased and over 6,000 were present in autumn 1996, of which the main concentrations in Norfolk were 1,333 at Terrington and over 1,000 at Ouse Mouth. The Wash is used mainly as a moulting ground, with peak counts occurring in August and September.

An increase in the numbers of Black-tailed Godwits using Breydon was first noted in 1992 when up to 38 were seen in both May and July, increasing to 42 in August. Up to 44 overwintered and remained until March 1993. The increase was dramatic in autumn and winter 1993 with 179 in July, 209 in August and 581 in December, falling to less than 100 by the end of January 1994. Since then numbers have tended to peak at Breydon in early autumn with record counts of 881 in August 1997 and 1,103 in August 1998. The sighting of colour-ringed birds has confirmed that those at Breydon belong to the race *islandica*. Although fewer are present in winter, counts in December 1996 and 1997 peaked at 367 and 419 respectively, increasing to 503 in January 1998 with 439 remaining in February. The highest spring count has been 293 in April 1998. In north Norfolk, however, the highest counts have generally been in spring, with concentrations at Titchwell, Holkham Fresh Marshes and Cley, where a record count of 588 was made on 7th April 1998. Relatively few Black-tailed Godwits overwinter in Norfolk, although in recent years about 1,000 have remained on the Wash, in addition to those mentioned above in east Norfolk at Breydon. Apart from Welney, one of the largest parties recorded inland in Norfolk in winter were 64 at Whitlingham Gravel Pit on 4th February 1995.

Extensive colour-ringing of the Icelandic Black-tailed Godwits which moult on the Wash has shown that many subsequently winter on the estuaries of Suffolk and Essex (Gill & McNeill 1996), although several winter on the English south coast and there have sightings from The Netherlands (5), Denmark (1), Germany (1), France (2), Portugal (1) and Ireland (4). The flock which has wintered on the Humber in recent years also includes birds which have previously moulted on the Wash. Many of these Black-tailed Godwits are highly site-faithful to both passage and wintering sites. In late July 1992, out of two catches of 114 Black-tailed Godwits at Terrington, four had been ringed on 20th October 1991 at Guardbridge Saltings, Fife on the east coast of Scotland, while one of those ringed at Terrington was found freshly dead in Iceland on 25th July 1994.

*Jennifer A. Gill & Julianne Evans*

## Bar-tailed Godwit HUNSTANTON. 8-9-1985.                    *Limosa lapponica*

**A very common winter visitor and passage migrant; very scarce inland mainly in spring.**

The Bar-tailed Godwit breeds from Fennoscandia, across northern Siberia to Alaska and winters around the North Sea and the West African coasts of Mauritania and Guinea-Bissau. Birds which breed in northern Europe and Fennoscandia are believed to form the wintering population in western Europe (Prokosch 1988). In West Africa the majority of the wintering birds come from the breeding populations in the Siberian Taimyr and Yamal Peninsulas and birds which breed further east winter in Asia, Australia and New Zealand.

The Bar-tailed Godwit has always been a common shorebird in Norfolk. Stevenson described it as 'regular, and in favourable seasons abundant, on its spring and autumn passage', while 'During the winter months a few pairs still linger about our shores', and Riviere as 'in most seasons abundant'. To the local gunners of Blakeney the species was known as 'Picks' or 'Scamells'.

Bar-tailed Godwits arrive on the Wash at the beginning of July, although the main arrival takes place in August and continues through September. Comparatively few are recorded on visible migration flying west along the north Norfolk coast. Apart from a total of 1,300 at Scolt Head between 30th August and 1st September 1960, the maximum counts have been 270 on 12th July 1993, 160 on 22nd July 1995 and 170 on 9th July 1996, all at Sheringham, while at Scolt Head monthly peaks in 1997 were 84 on 5th July, 181 on 1st September and 135 on 12th October. Small numbers of non-breeding first-year birds spend the summer on the Wash and moult between the end of June and the end of August. Adult birds moult later and generally start as soon as they arrive on the Wash from the middle of July until the middle of November a period of approximately 120 days (Atkinson 1996). As the birds finish renewing their feathers in October ringing recoveries have indicated that there is some interchange of birds between other east coast estuaries in the British Isles and also the Wadden Sea. Small numbers of short-billed, heavy, non-moulting birds are seen throughout August and September and are attributed to birds breeding in western Siberia which pass through to moult and winter in West Africa. These comprised approximately 10% of the birds caught by the WWRG during this period. The situation is slightly different on the north Norfolk coast in that birds do not moult in this area but arrive in September–October presumably after they have finished moulting either on the Wash, another east coast estuary or the Wadden Sea.

Of the approximately 115,000 birds currently wintering in Europe, 45% are found in the British Isles. The Wash is the most important wintering area in Britain with an average winter peak count of 12,500 between 1992 and 1996, making it of high national (>530 birds) and international (>1000 birds) importance. The north Norfolk coast also holds internationally important numbers during autumn and winter. Bar-tailed Godwits roost in three major areas – Snettisham, Holme and Titchwell/Thornham Creek where numbers regularly reach 5,000 birds and exceptionally up to 8,000. On the highest tides in autumn and winter, large flocks can be seen at any of these sites and are presumably the result of the Wash population shifting roost sites. In recent years maximum counts at Snettisham have included 11,800 on 4th January 1987 (prior to a period of severe weather), 9,300 in February 1996 and 9,200 in February 1997, at Holme 2,600 in January 1990 and at Titchwell 5,200 on 7th October 1990. The only other concentration of note is approximately 200–400 birds that winter in the Brancaster Harbour/Scolt Head area, while smaller numbers also winter in the harbours at Burnham Overy, Wells and Blakeney although usually less than 100 are present. A large increase in the number of birds on both the Wash and on the north Norfolk coast has been noted since the late 1970s. Numbers on the Wash have increased from 3,000–4,000 birds in the early 1970s to a peak count of over 16,000 birds in 1996. Atkinson (1996) noted that the largest increase had been in February counts prior to the birds leaving the British Isles to fatten on the Wadden Sea showing that the importance of the Wash has increased for passage birds. Along the north Norfolk coast the number of birds stays fairly constant throughout the winter and from 1991 to 1996 this was between 1,000 and 1,500, while a low tide count of the entire north Norfolk coast in December 1997 produced a total of 1,853 birds.

Ringing recoveries have shown that the majority of the northern European birds move to the Wadden Sea in February and March to fatten before moving to the breeding grounds. In the Wash far fewer are seen in April and May, with generally no more than about 500 at Snettisham, although 2,000 were present in May 1997. Spring passage in north Norfolk is recorded in late April and May with unprecedented numbers recorded on 29th April 1984 with 400 at Blakeney Point and 500 at Cley, coinciding with record numbers at Breydon, as well as several inland localities (see below). In east Norfolk generally small numbers winter at Breydon and maximum counts are invariably in spring. Its appearance in good numbers was so regular at this site that during the 19th century it was traditionally stated that '12th of May was Godwit day', although wind direction is perhaps crucial. Counts of 161 on 30th April 1962 and 169 on 3rd May 1971 (virtually all of which were in 'brick red' attire) coincided with easterly winds, while exceptional numbers occurred in 1984 following strong south-easterlies with a total of 462 at Breydon on 28th April (Allard 1990). These spring birds are not European breeders but are birds from wintering areas in West Africa which move to the Wadden Sea to fatten in April and May before moving to their breeding areas in western Siberia (Prokosch 1988).

Bar-tailed Godwits are very scarce inland, although many of Norfolk's inland wetland sites have hosted the species on occasion in spring. Exceptional numbers were recorded in late April and early May 1984 with maximum counts of 50 at Welney, 19 at Pentney Gravel Pits, 18 flying north over East Tuddenham and ten at Colney Gravel Pit. Other notable spring totals have been 20 at Wisbech Sewage Farm on 20th April 1974, 36 at Welney on 21st April 1996, up to 28 at Hickling Broad from 30th April to 1st May 1988 and up to ten at Hardley Flood on 3rd–4th April 1990. Inland sightings are less frequent in autumn and have included up to 26 at Wisbech Sewage Farm in September 1973, eight at Pentney Gravel Pits on 28th August 1988 and up to 14 at Pensthorpe in November 1996.

A total of 22 Bar-tailed Godwits ringed on the Norfolk side of the Wash have been recovered abroad, including eight in their Siberian breeding grounds in Russia. Others have been recovered on passage in Denmark, Germany and The Netherlands, while a juvenile ringed at Wolferton in mid-September 1978 was found in Mauretania three months later. Four autumn-ringed birds from Revtangen, Norway and one from Poland have been recovered in the county, as well as one ringed in spring in Germany. One ringed at Thornham on 26th October 1969 which was found dead at Snettisham on 24th February 1996, over 26 years later, set a new longevity record for a British-ringed Bar-tailed Godwit.

*Phil Atkinson*

# Little Whimbrel (Little Curlew)  *Numenius minutus*

**A very rare vagrant; one record.**

The Little Whimbrel is a small species of curlew breeding in northern central Siberia, which winters in New Guinea and Australia. It is a very rare vagrant to the British Isles with just two records.

A Little Whimbrel, almost certainly an adult, was located by P. Antrobus, John Gregory, Richard Walker and E. Whittaker in rough grazing fields between Blakeney and Cley on 24th August 1985. It fed loosely with a small flock of Curlews and Whimbrels and remained until dusk. The following day it was seen again in the same area, later flying to Cley where it fed for a short time in the Eye Field before moving along the coast to Salthouse. It remained in the area between Blakeney and Salthouse until its last reported sighting on 3rd September. During its eleven-day stay it was seen by several hundred observers (Anon 1986c, Walker & Gregory 1987). This was only the second British record. A juvenile at Sker, mid-Glamorgan, which was seen from 30th August to 6th September 1982, was the only previous record and both conveniently turned up on the August Bank Holiday weekend.

*Peter Allard*

## Whimbrel — *TITCHWELL. 8·9·1985.* — *Numenius phaeopus*

**A fairly common passage migrant; very rare in winter.**

The Whimbrel has a Holarctic breeding distribution, which within Europe includes Iceland, Fennoscandia and Russia. In Scotland it nests on moorland in the Northern and Western Isles, although it is common only in parts of Shetland, where 95% of the British population breeds (New Atlas). It is a summer visitor, wintering mainly in West Africa.

During the 19th century the appearance of large numbers of Whimbrels at Breydon and Blakeney in May caused the local gunners to call it the 'May bird' (Stevenson) – a name no doubt familiar to William Betts, the Breydon Watcher, who recorded a flock of 200–300 which arrived on the mudflats near his houseboat on 1st May 1928 and which fell asleep within minutes (Allard 1990).

The main period of spring passage lasts from late April to mid-May, with very few birds recorded after early June. The earliest arrival dates have been 5th March 1995 at Cley and 8th March 1983 at Sheringham, in which year a party of eleven had arrived at Breydon by 26th March. The highest spring counts have invariably come from Breydon with a marked increase in numbers during the 1990s, presumably a reflection of the expanding European population. In the 1950s the maximum count was 72, increasing to 120 by the 1970s. During the 1990s the highest day-count has been 431 on 24th April 1992, while a total of 499 flew north-east between 7th and 9th May 1991, the same spring in which 117 were counted at Cley on 25th April. The only other occasion in recent years that over 100 have been recorded in spring away from Breydon was on 9th May 1960 with 200 at the Nene/Ouse Mouth. While most birds are recorded around the coast, small numbers are noted annually in spring at inland sites, such as Welney, and notable counts elsewhere have included 40 at Egmere on 9th May 1985 and 41 flying north-east at Strumpshaw on 1st May 1984. An albino Whimbrel was present at Breydon in spring 1998.

Occasional mid-summer Whimbrels have been reported, including up to seven at Breydon on most days in June 1976 and 15 at Sheringham on 12th June 1995. Autumn passage, which commences in early July, and occasionally in late June, is heavier along the North Sea coasts and in southern England than that in spring – the reverse of the situation in western Britain and Ireland (Winter Atlas). Peak numbers occur in August, with maximum counts being made at sites along the north Norfolk coast. A day-count of 250 at Scolt Head on 1st September 1955 remained a county record for many years, although at that time it was not unusual for up to 200 to gather at Blakeney during the autumn, where on 3rd August 1981 a high water roost contained 250 birds. Over the years some impressive westerly movements have been recorded at Holme with 300 on 21st August 1973 and another 200 two days later, while the monthly totals for July and August 1996 were 306 and 431 respectively. At the Ouse Mouth, a total of 300 flew south inland on 29th July 1988. Other notable counts have been 140 at Titchwell on 7th August 1990, 250 at Cley on 20th July 1990 and 180 west at Sheringham, in only 20 minutes, on 19th August 1977, after a heavy north-westerly squall. At Breydon, the highest autumn counts have been 200 on both 2nd August 1991 and 29th July 1992. The last birds of the autumn are generally recorded in early October, although there have been a few records up to 27th November. As in spring, parties of Whimbrel are reported inland in autumn, the highest count being 108 at Ludham on 23rd July 1993, although numbers are usually 20 or less.

Less than 30 Whimbrels winter annually in the British Isles, the majority along the south coast of England and Ireland (Winter Atlas). There have been five mid-winter occurrences in Norfolk – singles at Brancaster on 11th–12th December 1961 and at Blakeney on 5th December 1966, two at Snettisham on 2nd December 1987, a lame bird at Welney on 27th January 1988 and one at Burnham Overy from 3rd November 1993 to 25th January 1994, with presumably the same bird at Titchwell on 19th January 1994.

A Whimbrel ringed at Terrington on 21st August 1978 and recovered in Manche, France almost exactly four years later is the only recovery of one ringed in Norfolk. While one ringed at Knokke, Belgium on 27th April 1981 was recovered at Wells on 17th August 1981. Although important inland spring staging sites are known to exist in the Low Countries, this bird was ringed on the coast. A chick ringed on Unst, Shetland in 1985 was controlled at Terrington in August 1987, and an adult colour-ringed on Fetlar in June 1988 was seen at Titchwell in August 1991.

*Moss Taylor*

## Curlew (Eurasian Curlew) TiTCHWELL. 26·11·1988.    *Numenius arquata*

**A scarce and localised breeder, and common winter visitor and passage migrant.**

The Curlew, a Palearctic species, occurs in the temperate and boreal zones of Europe and Asia. The European populations winter in western Europe, in the Mediterranean region and in many parts of Africa. As a breeding species it is widespread throughout much of the British Isles, but is absent from most of south-east England and large areas of south-west England and Ireland. During the 20th century it has colonised many lowland regions, such as rough marginal grasslands and even arable fields (New Atlas).

Stevenson commented that it could be found on the coast during every month of the year but that it had never been known to breed in Norfolk. This did not occur until 1889, when a pair nested at Sandringham, and again in the following year. The next record of breeding was of a nest containing four eggs at Roydon Common in 1910, a site which was used during the next three years and again in 1920 and 1926 (Riviere). The first record of breeding in Norfolk Breckland was at Weeting in 1949 and during the following years the county breeding population increased to about 20 pairs (Seago 1967). Since then the Stanford Training Area has become the stronghold for the species in Norfolk with a maximum of 34 pairs at 22 sites in 1997. Elsewhere the Bridgham area in the Thet Valley has held up to ten pairs and one or two pairs breed annually at Roydon Common. Other sites to have hosted breeding Curlews in recent years have included East Wretham, Brettenham Heath and Wolferton Common, while a pair bred at North Creake in the early 1980s and at Fritton Warren in east Norfolk between 1955 and 1959 before it became afforested (Allard 1990). Perhaps surprisingly, it was recorded in 69 tetrads with confirmed breeding in 17, during fieldwork for the Norfolk Atlas (1980–85), although many of these records would have referred to non-breeding summering birds. An increasing number of Curlews are present in the county in mid-summer, although some will be early-returning autumn migrants. The highest counts in June 1997 were 320 at Scolt Head/Brancaster Harbour, 110 at Blakeney Harbour and 209 at Breydon.

Autumn passage commences in mid-June with peak counts of visible migration later in the month and throughout July. However, numbers at estuaries and elsewhere around the Norfolk coast continue to build-up to peaks in August or September. The highest day-counts of birds on westerly passage have all been recorded at Sheringham with 110 on 25th and 330 on 28th June 1991, 170 on 12th July 1993 and an amazing total of 590 on 9th July 1996.

Norfolk is an important moulting and wintering area for Curlews, with large numbers in the Wash, on the north Norfolk coast and at Breydon. The Wash is of international importance during the late summer moulting period and a nationally important estuary in the winter. Over half of the Wash population of Curlews can be found in the Norfolk part of the estuary, with counts by the Cambridge Bird Club in 1954 and 1962 of 8,000–10,000 birds between Wolferton and Snettisham. WeBS counts for the years 1992 to 1997 revealed that the numbers of birds on the Wash (Lincolnshire and Norfolk) are over 7,000 for the months of July, August and September, with an average peak of almost 8,000 in August. By November the average peak count is about 3,000 with a similar number in mid-winter. The two main sites in Norfolk are Terrington and Snettisham where the peak autumn counts have been 3,120 and 1,560 respectively, and in the winter 885 and 1,500. At high tide, when the mud is covered, Curlews roost for long periods, often on high saltings. On higher tides they move on to inland fields. Roosts of Curlews on the Wash can be found up to 2km inland in the summer, especially on stubble fields. In winter birds move inland from the Wash to feed on stubble and sugar beet fields, and this is not restricted to daylight hours. Some of the earlier WeBS counts may have been an underestimate. In north Norfolk, for instance, it was estimated that 40% of the 410 Curlews at Scolt Head/Brancaster Harbour in September 1996 were non-tidal feeders and would not necessarily have been picked up by WeBS. This fact was taken into account in 1997 and the peak autumn counts at Scolt Head/Brancaster Harbour, Wells Harbour and Blakeney Harbour were 1,460, 480 and 450 respectively, with 540, 252 and 257 in December.

Patterson (1905) described how 'Hundreds of Curlews frequented Breydon during the long drought in the autumn of 1899, being starved off the marshlands, the soil and ditches being so dry'. The numbers visiting Breydon and its adjacent marshlands has varied considerably since the 1950s, high counts have included 270 on 8th September 1957 and 450 on 29th August 1962. Between 1965 and 1976, an unexplained decrease was evident and a maximum of only 158 was achieved, but since 1977 numbers have increased annually. The removal of the Curlew from the national quarry list in 1981 and the establishment of large no-shooting areas on the mudflats in 1986 have certainly benefited this species at Breydon and 530 were counted on 25th November 1989. Up to 700–800 are now present throughout the year, except in April, May and June, with maximum counts of 937 on 7th September 1996 and 1,149 on 16th September 1998.

Riviere included details of a regular departure of Curlews to the north or north-west from mid-February to the end of March, as recorded at the Lynn Well light-vessel anchored at the mouth of the Wash. Nowadays, spring migration is generally reported from early March to late May, although numbers recorded are far smaller than in autumn with normally less than 30 a day. The one exception was a spectacular easterly passage at Cley on 20th April 1989 with many flocks of 20–30 birds, several of over 100 and one each of 225 and 400 having been recorded. The only other notable day-count has been 104 north at Blakeney Point on 31st May 1997.

The presence of feeding flocks of Curlews at inland sites makes it difficult to estimate the total number present in the county. In recent years flocks of 100 or more have been recorded at Ken Hill Marshes, Anmer, Massingham Heath and Knight's Hill, King's Lynn. There have been no studies of the ways that Curlews use the various habitats in Norfolk but other work in Scotland (Evans 1988) has shown that females, which have longer bills, preferentially feed on mudflats and that males are more likely than females to feed inland.

The cold weather of February 1991, which affected many wader species, did not appear to be too significant for Curlews. Of the 2,527 waders which were found dead on the tideline, only 53 were Curlews (Clark & Clark 1992). Interestingly, a wildfowler reported finding a party of several Curlews frozen where they stood after one of the coldest nights of this hard spell. Increases in Curlew numbers during the course of the winter have been attributed to movements of birds across the North Sea. Flocks have been seen arriving in all months up until December but some of the increase in counts may be due to birds leaving frozen inland fields.

Most data relating to recoveries to or from Norfolk have been generated by the WWRG, operating in Lincolnshire and Norfolk. The pattern of recoveries has indicated that most of the birds wintering in Norfolk breed in Finland, Denmark and Sweden (Bainbridge and Minton 1978). Two Norfolk-ringed birds have been recovered in Russia in May. A total of 29 foreign-ringed Curlews has been found in Norfolk, including 15 ringed in June in Finland. One of the earliest foreign-ringed Curlews found in the British Isles was a chick ringed at Ottenby, Sweden on 22nd June 1934 and found at Wells on 1st September.

*Graham Appleton*

## Spotted Redshank   CLEY MARSHES. 21·9·1993.   *Tringa erythropus*

**A fairly common passage migrant, mainly in autumn; very scarce but increasing in winter.**

The Spotted Redshank breeds in northern Fennoscandia, especially Finland, and in a narrow band along the north coast of Russia. European populations winter mainly in sub-Saharan Africa north of the equator, although some remain in western Europe. As an autumn passage migrant to the British Isles it is found both on the coast and inland, whereas in winter it is almost exclusively a coastal bird (Winter Atlas).

In discussing the species, Stevenson commented that its identification in earlier years was 'an ornithological riddle not easily solved' in view of its various plumages, and this resulted in a variety of names including 'dusky sandpiper', 'dusky snipe', 'black-headed snipe', 'spotted snipe', 'black redshank', 'Courland snipe' and 'Cambridge godwit'. It was under this last name that the first Norfolk specimen was recorded – one shot near Yarmouth on 29th October 1818. Two more obtained at Yarmouth were followed by three killed, out of a flock of 25, at Horsey on 22nd September 1828. In addition to further autumn records, Stevenson also gave details of the first seven May records, all of birds obtained in the Yarmouth area. By 1930 Riviere described it as 'A spring and autumn passage migrant, of fairly regular occurrence at the latter season, though in varying numbers'. For the winter period he was able to provide only two December records from Cley and two which were shot at Blakeney in February 1904.

Nowadays the Spotted Redshank is a fairly common autumn passage migrant to mudflats, tidal creeks and flooded marshes, but particularly to 'scrapes' on reserves, where water levels can be controlled to optimum levels for feeding waders, such as at Snettisham, Holme, Titchwell, Cley and Berney Marshes. Autumn passage commences in the first half of June with the arrival of the females, which have left the males to care for the young until fledged; peak numbers are recorded in August and September. For many years Snettisham has been the prime site in the county for attracting large numbers of Spotted Redshanks in autumn. The first sizeable flock consisted of up to 60 adults in breeding plumage throughout July 1964. Since then numbers have varied with maximum counts of 187 on 13th September 1977 and 126 on 18th July 1992, with 120 still present in mid-August. Elsewhere on the Wash, a record count of 172 was made between Lynn Point and Wolferton on 21st August 1982 (in which year the species was recorded continuously from this area between 20th March and 27th November), with 70 at Wolferton the following July. Notable counts at Holme in the 1980s peaked at 121 on 18th September 1985. Such large numbers have never been recorded at Cley, where maximum autumn counts have usually been 20–30, although 55 were present in August 1978 and on 7th July 1990, nor at Breydon where the highest autumn count was 15 on 13th September 1993.

Small numbers of Spotted Redshanks are recorded annually inland. Before its closure, up to 20 could sometimes be found at Wisbech Sewage Farm in June or July, increasing to 50–60 at high tide in August (Moyes 1984). Elsewhere the highest inland counts in autumn have been 22 at Hickling Broad on 24th August 1944, and up to ten at Cantley Beet Factory, eight at Pentney Gravel Pits, seven at Swanton Morley Gravel Pit and five at Welney. Only occasional birds are noted on visible migration, mainly in August and September, and generally involving single birds flying west along the north Norfolk coast.

Passage in spring is noted from mid-March to early May, but on a far smaller scale than in autumn, although they were rather more numerous between the mid-1970s and late 1980s than they have been in recent springs. Maximum site-counts have included 28 at Snettisham on 5th May 1988, 17 at Holkham Fresh Marshes on 2nd May 1990 and 40 at Cley on 26th April 1978. Interestingly at Welney, Breydon and Hickling Broad higher numbers have been recorded in spring than in autumn, with maximum counts of eleven at Welney on 29th April 1987, 19 at Breydon on 1st May 1990 (ten of which were earlier at Berney Marshes) and 25 at Hickling Broad the following day. Although birds recorded in June are considered to be on autumn passage, one was in song at Holkham Fresh Marshes on 24th June 1995.

At least one Spotted Redshank has been recorded in the county each winter since 1975. One or two also wintered at Cley in the earlier years, but Titchwell and Breydon are now the favoured localities. At Titchwell four were present in 1992 and 1994, up to five in 1995 and 1996, and seven in 1997, while at Breydon one or two have been noted almost annually since 1975 with up to three in 1987, four in 1996–97, six in 1997–98 and seven in November–December 1998.

There have been four foreign recoveries of Norfolk-ringed Spotted Redshanks. One ringed at Cantley Beet Factory on 24th August 1969 was recovered at Étang de la Brenne, France on 4th October and one ringed at North Wootton on 19th August 1978 was found at Bologna, Italy the following March – it remains the only recovery from that country. Up to 1996 only nine out of 372 British-ringed Spotted Redshanks have been recovered abroad. It is therefore amazing that two ringed at Terrington on 27th July 1975 (out of a single catch of 60, many of which were in winter plumage and believed to have been summering, possibly first-summer birds) should have both been found at El Jadida, Morocco on 25th March 1976 and 12th January 1983 respectively.

*Moss Taylor*

## Redshank (Common Redshank) *Tringa totanus*

HARDLEY FLOODS.
5-2-2000. (2)

**A fairly common breeder, and common winter visitor and passage migrant.**

The Redshank has an extensive Palearctic distribution, breeding mainly in the temporal and boreal zones from Iceland to eastern China. Two races breed in Europe, the nominate *T. t. totanus* from the British Isles east to Russia, and *T. t. robusta* in Iceland and the Faeroes. Three distinct populations are found in Britain either as breeding, wintering or passage birds. There is considerable variation in size between birds breeding in different parts of the range. The smallest of the race *totanus*, which breed in northern Fennoscandia, winter furthest south in West Africa; while the largest, *robusta* breeding in Iceland, winter furthest north, from southern Iceland to around the North Sea with very small numbers possibly wintering in the Vendée in France (Fournier & Spitz 1969). Intermediate-sized Redshanks of the race *totanus*, which breed in western and central Europe, including the British Isles, winter in intermediate latitudes centred on France, Iberia and the western Mediterranean. In the British Isles, however, some of the breeding birds remain in the country for the winter, inland breeders move to the coast while coastal breeders may stay within 10km of their natal area; however, many British-breeders move south and west into France and Iberia.

Redshanks breeding in the British Isles are found on inland wet grassland and coastal marsh and are concentrated in the northern half of Britain, although concentrations also occur on saltmarshes in south-east England (New Atlas). In the early to mid-1980s the population of Redshanks in Britain was estimated to be 30,600–33,600 (Reed 1985). However, breeding numbers in the country had already declined on inland sites at this time due to loss of wet grasslands following agricultural improvement (Smith 1983). Redshanks breeding on saltmarsh have been more successful, particularly in East Anglia (Cadbury *et al.* 1987). The decline in the country is graphically illustrated by the changes shown between the two BTO Breeding Atlases.

However, this reduction in numbers does not appear to be new. Stevenson noted that inland, drainage and cultivation had led to the disappearance of breeding Redshanks in many localities during the first half of the 19th century. For example, it was at one time a common breeding species in Hockwold and Feltwell Fens but disappeared following drainage. However, when thousands of acres of fen were flooded by the river bursting its banks near Southery in 1852–53, Redshanks bred there once again the following spring, along with Black Terns. In 1825 Redshanks were described as more common than any other wader in the marshes of Norfolk, but by the mid-1800s they were only thinly scattered along the coastline. The overall decline was illustrated by the cessation of sales of Redshanks' eggs on Norwich market. Whereas previously they had been collected from Salthouse, Blakeney, Warham and similar localities, there were no longer enough pairs to make commercial sale of eggs worthwhile. Stevenson commented that the decline was not due to the egg collectors, which he suggested did less harm than drainage and agricultural change. However, by 1930 Riviere described the Redshank as a common breeding bird in suitable localities along the coastline, throughout the Broads and along the river valleys far inland, and in the vicinity of the Breckland meres. It had clearly expanded its range once again, only to become less common, especially inland, during the following 45 years (Seago 1967, 1977).

During fieldwork for the Norfolk Atlas it was recorded in 167 tetrads, representing 11% of those covered and Kelly (1986) commented that it remained a 'well-represented breeding species in the major wetland complexes of the county' – these included the Fens, the Broads, and the saltmarshes and damp meadows along the north Norfolk coast, west from Kelling to the Wash. Although recent breeding data for Redshanks in Norfolk are incomplete, a total of 548 pairs was recorded in 1995, but this included only 19 pairs at Snettisham and 14 pairs at Breydon, the only counts reported from saltmarshes which is the species' most important habitat in the county. However, there have been a number of surveys of Redshanks, covering specific areas of the county in recent years, which have given a more accurate indication as to how the species is faring in Norfolk.

A survey of the Welney Washes in 1994 gave more encouraging results with 55 territorial pairs recorded of which 43 pairs were seen with chicks, a markedly better performance than Lapwing. Redshank young may be less prone to fox predation because they tend to keep in cover and often feed in the wetter areas which are more difficult for foxes to exploit (Kemp 1995). The number of breeding pairs was even higher in 1996 with 165 pairs along the Norfolk section of the Ouse Washes, including 71 pairs at Welney.

Saltmarshes are an important breeding habitat for Redshanks in Britain with about 45% of the population thought to breed in such areas. Work by the RSPB has shown that breeding densities at some saltmarsh sites have declined (Allport *et al.* 1986, Brindley *et al.* 1998). It is thought that the declines are due to changes in habitat caused by, for example, erosion and changes in grazing policy. Five sites were surveyed in Norfolk in both 1985 and 1996 and the results are shown in Table 40.

The positive results of management for breeding waders is well-illustrated by the numbers of breeding Redshanks on the Holkham Fresh Marshes, where 4,000ha of grazing marshes have been managed to increase conservation value since autumn 1986 (Harold 1994). Water levels have been kept high and the stocking rate has been low. This has resulted in an increase in the number of pairs from less than ten in 1986 to at least 50 by the early 1990s, peaking at 86 pairs in 1996. Conversely, at Breydon, whereas 30–40 breeding pairs were recorded annually on marshes adjoining the north wall of the estuary from about

1928 to 1960, numbers began to decline in about 1967 due to drainage and partial ploughing, and by 1978 there were less than ten pairs. A complete survey of the area by the RSPB in 1979 recorded 186 pairs on the marshland surrounding Breydon, but further declines had occurred by 1990 (Allard 1990). However, at the Berney Reserve, numbers have increased from 15 pairs in 1995 to 35 pairs in 1998.

**Table 40. Total numbers of pairs and density of breeding Redshanks at five saltmarsh sites in Norfolk in 1985 and 1996.**

| Site | 1985 | | | 1996 | | |
|---|---|---|---|---|---|---|
| | Pairs | Density | % with young | Pairs | Density | % with young |
| Wolferton | 38 | 74.1 | 62.2 | 16 | 32.6 | 108 |
| Thornham/ Titchwell | 19 | 29.5 | 25.3 | 26 | 40.2 | 30.8 |
| Plover Marsh | 11 | 26.6 | 30.0 | 24 | 58.1 | 20.8 |
| Stiffkey | 19 | 49.0 | 52.1 | 30 | 76.5 | 57.3 |
| Morston | 27 | 54.3 | 24.8 | 24 | 47.4 | 29.2 |
| Total | 114 | 46.7 | 38.9 | 120 | 51 | 49.2 |

Note: Density is pairs/km$^2$

Excellent data on breeding Redshanks in the Broads ESA have been provided by three surveys – in 1982, 1988 and 1996. The first took place before the Broads Grazing Marshes Conservation Scheme was set up in 1985. This was followed by the establishment of the Broads ESA in 1987 due to concerns over threats to breeding and wintering waterfowl by drainage and changes in agricultural use. The ESA scheme offers help to farmers who manage grassland for waterfowl. There are three levels of assistance depending on the value of the management for waterfowl but only nature reserves qualify for level three (Weaver & Durdin 1996). In 1982 a full survey of the Broads ESA was undertaken as part of a national survey (O'Brien & Smith 1992), in 1988 there was a partial wader survey (O'Brien & Smith 1992, O'Brien & Buckingham 1989) and an almost complete survey was carried out in 1995 (Weaver & Durdin 1996). Compared to other wet grassland sites in the country the density of breeding Redshanks in the Broads ESA is low (O'Brien & Buckingham 1989), but the 1995 survey counted over 300 pairs. This was thought to be an increase over the 1982 figure, although numbers remained stable between 1988 and 1995. The highest numbers and densities were recorded on the alluvial grazing marshes of the coastal floodplain, particularly around the lower Bure and Waveney and around Breydon.

The surveys of breeding Redshanks in the county have illustrated the problems faced by the species in a changing environment, and the importance of management, if the decline of the breeding population in Britain and in Norfolk is to be halted.

In autumn, easterly passage along the north Norfolk coast is invariably more pronounced than a westerly movement. The majority of records of day-counts have been made at Sheringham with the highest being 110 east and 55 west on 30th August 1993, 210 east and 40 west on 30th August 1994 and 225 east and 20 west on 6th September 1996. The birds moving east are often flying overland or just along the coastline, and are in parties of up to 75 or more, whereas those moving west are in small groups low over the sea. It has been assumed that those moving east are British breeding birds flying south for the winter.

WeBS counts of Redshanks over the years 1992–96 on the Wash (Norfolk and Lincolnshire), in north Norfolk and at Breydon have shown a large autumn peak at the Wash, with a maximum mean monthly count in October of 5,430. These autumn birds probably include all three populations of Redshanks although the majority are Icelandic and British breeders (see above). Many Redshanks visit the Wash in autumn to moult before moving further west for the winter. The WeBS counts, however, give no clear evidence of passage at either Breydon or on the north Norfolk coast but the overall figures may conceal turnover, as different birds use the area through the year. Allard (1990) reported spring passage on Breydon in March with peak counts of 1,500 in both 1976 and 1977, and autumn passage peaking normally at about 700 with up to 1,000 having been recorded. However, in recent years, numbers have tended to be slightly smaller averaging 850 in spring and 750 in autumn.

Peak winter counts of Redshanks on the Wash have shown considerable variation over the years, some of which may have been due to the difficulty in counting this species on a large estuary. Numbers have varied from 1,700 in 1976 to 7,500 in 1987, the year in which very large numbers of waders wintered on the Wash. The species is particularly susceptible to the effects of cold weather with large numbers dying in severe periods (Clark 1982, Cawthorne 1982, Davidson & Clark 1985, Clark & Davidson 1986, Clark *et al.* 1993). Birds on the Wash were especially badly affected in February 1991, and 1,553 Redshanks' corpses were found (Clark *et al.* 1993); many more must have been washed out to sea. The mortality in that year led to a subsequent reduction in both the numbers during the remaining part of the winter and also in the following autumn and winter. Peak winter counts have continued to vary since 1991–92 but have not approached the high numbers recorded in the 1980s. A low-tide count of all intertidal habitat from Holme to Weybourne in November 1997 revealed a total of 3,556 Redshanks, of which 70% were at Scolt Head/Brancaster Harbour, Wells Harbour, Warham and Blakeney Harbour.

Ringing recoveries and measurements of birds caught for ringing have shown that both Icelandic birds and those breeding in eastern Britain moult at the Wash in autumn before many disperse west and south, especially to France and some as far as Iberia. Only two Redshank chicks ringed in Iceland have been found in Norfolk. One was recovered in January 1982 at Terrington but the first almost 50 years earlier on 1st September 1934 at Thornham, had been ringed less than five weeks previously by Lake Myvatn.

*Jacquie Clark*

# Marsh Sandpiper                              *Tringa stagnatilis*

**A rare vagrant.**

The Marsh Sandpiper breeds in Bulgaria, Romania and discontinuously eastwards through Kazakhstan and eastern Asia. It winters in sub-Saharan Africa, south Asia and Australia. It has been an almost annual vagrant to the British Isles since 1974, with most records in May and August.

The first Norfolk record was one found at Cley by D. S. Farrow on 14th August 1979, where it remained until 19th August. Since then the county total has risen to 17 records involving 19 birds, with all occurring between 14th May and 6th September:

1979: Cley on 14th–18th August
     A different bird at Hickling on 6th September
1982: Cley on 11th–13th July
1983: A summer plumaged adult at Cley on 30th May
     A moulting adult at Holme from 29th July to 6th August
1984: An adult at Titchwell on 25th May and then at Holme on 26th–29th May
     An adult at Cley from 14th August to 4th September
1985: Wolferton on 19th–25th May
1987: A moulting adult at Cley from 19th July to 2nd August; also visited Titchwell
     on 3rd August
1988: A summer plumaged adult at Snettisham Pits on 14th–15th May
1989: An adult at Shropham on 1st June
1990: One at Lakenheath Washes on 16th May, with probably the same bird at Pentney
     Gravel Pits on 17th May
     Burnham Norton on 22nd–24th May
1992: A summer plumaged adult at Gunton Lake on 20th–22nd May
     A summer plumaged adult at Holkham Fresh Marsh on 7th–9th June
1995: Three juveniles at Cantley Beet Factory on 4th–13th August, two of which
     visited Buckenham Marshes on 6th August
1996: An adult at Hickling on 10th–12th and 17th–19th June

The only other British record of three together was at Southwold in Suffolk in May 1947.

*Steve Gantlett*

## Greenshank (Common Greenshank)

*TITCH WELL.*
*8-9-1985.*

*Tringa nebularia*

A fairly common passage migrant; very scarce in winter.

Greenshank
*(Robert Gillmor)*

In mainland Europe breeding Greenshanks are largely confined to the boreal forests of the taiga in Fennoscandia and Russia. Although some winter around the Mediterranean, the majority are trans-Saharan migrants wintering in south-west Africa. Greenshanks also breed on the blanket bogs of north-west Scotland and the central Highlands, and it is thought that those wintering in Britain and Ireland belong to this Scottish breeding population.

In Norfolk the small passage of spring Greenshanks is noted in April and May, although occasional birds have been recorded from early March. Maximum day-counts at favoured coastal localities have been 17 at Snettisham on 27th May 1989, 25 at Holkham on 18th May 1992, 15 at Cley on 14th May 1992 and 45 at Breydon on 3rd May 1990. Birds returning to Fennoscandia in spring follow a more direct route than in autumn, without large coastal concentrations (BWP), it is therefore of interest that many of the larger groups of Greenshanks in spring have been at inland localities. In recent years Welney has regularly recorded the highest number in spring with a maximum of 32 on 2nd May 1990. Other impressive inland counts have included twelve at Lakenheath Flashes on 3rd May 1990, 20 at Gunton Park on 20th May 1992, 19 at Strumpshaw on 16th May 1993, 15 at Hardley Flood on 3rd May 1990, 15 at Hickling on 24th May 1989 and 15 at Berney Marshes on 14th May 1998.

Occasional birds are recorded in mid-summer, including one which was seen and heard in full display flight over Breydon Marshes on 23rd June 1977 (Allard 1990). The first returning birds of the autumn have generally appeared by mid-July, with the passage peaking in August and early September. In contrast to the spring, the majority of birds pass through coastal sites. The largest counts have been recorded on the Wash, with 100 at North Wootton on 22nd August 1962, up to 65 at Snettisham, 58 at Terrington and a roost of 50 at Wolferton, all in August 1954. In north-west Norfolk, Holme regularly held 20–30 Greenshanks during August in the 1970s and 1980s, peaking at 39 on 1st August 1988; whereas during the 1990s, Titchwell has proved more attractive with up to 66 in August 1993. Maximum autumn counts at other sites along the north coast have been 50 at Lynn Point in 1997, 66 at Brancaster/Scolt Head in 1997 (where, in addition, 33 flew west on 28th August 1997), 50 at Burnham Norton in 1996, 49 at Holkham in 1988, 40 in Blakeney Harbour in 1985, 60 at Cley on 17th September 1989 and 45 at Breydon on 17th August 1989 (where Patterson recorded a flock of 40 in 1904). However Greenshanks are also recorded at inland sites in autumn with up to 25 previously being present annually at Wisbech Sewage Farm, 37 at Cantley Beet Factory on 19th August 1984 and up to 33 at Hickling in 1996. Many inland records, though, refer to birds seen on visible migration, their distinctive call drawing attention to their presence overhead. A party of eleven flew over Frettenham on 31st July 1993 and 14 flew south-west over Colney Gravel Pit on 21st July 1996. But migrants can occur almost anywhere, as shown by up to five feeding in a pool formed by seepage from a large manure heap near Hilborough in mid-August 1992. The majority of Greenshanks have left the county by the end of September and only the odd straggler is recorded in October and November, although three at Scolt Head on 14th November 1955 were presumably migrants.

The winter distribution of the Greenshank in the British Isles is predominantly westerly, with 75% in Ireland (Winter Atlas). Since the early 1950s one or two have been recorded in winter in Norfolk, presumably birds of the Scottish breeding population. Since the mid-1970s winter records have become almost annual with Thornham/Titchwell/Brancaster being the most favoured area, but also regularly at Cley in the early 1980s. Usually only one or two birds are involved but five were present at Titchwell on 19th December 1994, with presumably some of the same birds in Brancaster Harbour to the end of the year.

About 100 Greenshanks have been ringed in Norfolk, of which four have been recovered abroad. All were ringed in July or August, three on the Wash and one at Wisbech Sewage Farm. Three were recovered on autumn passage in a subsequent year, two in France and one in Denmark, while one was found at Settat, Morocco in late March. A Greenshank ringed at Rieselfelder, West Germany on 15th July 1984 was identified by its combination of colour rings at Cley on 17th September 1985.

*Moss Taylor*

# Greater Yellowlegs                                   *Tringa melanoleuca*

**A very rare vagrant; two records**.

The Greater Yellowlegs is a northern Nearctic wader breeding from Alaska and British Columbia eastwards across Canada to Newfoundland and wintering from the southern USA as far south as Patagonia. It is a rare vagrant to the British Isles, with May and September being the peak months for records.

A first–winter bird found by the writer frequented the 'lower drain' area at Breydon on 8th–13th September 1975. This bird was most obliging and attracted large crowds as it fed close to the north estuary wall at periods of low water. The second record was one in first–summer plumage at the western end of Breydon frequenting both the Burgh Flats and the adjacent Berney Marshes on 15th–18th May and again from 22nd–25th May 1995. It had earlier been seen in Essex on 10th May and in Suffolk on 14th May.

*Peter Allard*

# Lesser Yellowlegs                                    *Tringa flavipes*

**A very rare vagrant; ten records.**

The Lesser Yellowlegs is a northern Nearctic wader breeding from Alaska and central British Colombia eastwards to Hudson Bay and Quebec, and wintering primarily from the southern USA to southern South America. A vagrant to the British Isles, most occur from the August to October, with a scattering in spring. Most of the latter are on the east and south coasts suggesting that these were birds which had crossed the Atlantic in a previous autumn and were subsequently moving north.

The first county record was one seen at Wisbech Sewage Farm on 17th September 1966 by M. Densley, Arthur Jenkins and W. J. Lloyd. This was soon followed by another at King's Lynn Beet Factory pools on 21st September 1968. Wisbech Sewage Farm was the venue again for the third county record, with one on 11th and 26th October 1973. Further birds appeared at Snettisham Pits on 28th August 1984, Hickling Broad on 24th–27th June 1985 and Cley on 28th–29th May 1992. A more obliging individual frequented Cley on 13th–15th May 1994 allowing many observers their first opportunity to see this species in the county. One was seen on Burnham Norton Fresh Marshes on 10th–12th June and 16th–17th June 1995, and another was observed briefly at Holme in the early evening of 2nd August 1995. The most recent was one present intermittently at Welney from 12th September to 4th November 1998.

*Peter Allard*

# Solitary Sandpiper                                   *Tringa solitaria*

**A very rare vagrant; two records, last recorded in 1947.**

The Solitary Sandpiper is a Nearctic wader breeding in northern North America and wintering in Central and South America. It is a rare vagrant to the British Isles, most having appeared in September.

One was seen at Rush Hills, Hickling by Jim Vincent on 1st–2nd August 1942 and another was present at both Cley and Salthouse on 3rd–29th September 1947 (Hedley-Bell 1948).

*Peter Allard*

## Green Sandpiper    HOLME. (2) 23·6·1986.    *Tringa ochropus*

**A fairly common passage migrant and scarce winter visitor.**

The Green Sandpiper is unusual in that it is a tree-nesting wader, often using the old nest of a Wood Pigeon or a thrush. It breeds in the boreal zone between the Arctic Circle in the north and the steppe zone in the south, from Fennoscandia eastwards. It winters sparingly in western Europe, being found mainly in the Mediterranean basin and sub-Saharan Africa. During both the breeding season and in winter it tends to occur near areas of inland water, away from the coast and tidal waters. Breeding has only been proved on two occasions in the British Isles, in Westmorland in 1917 and Inverness in 1959.

Despite Gurney and Fisher's assertions (1846) that 'a few well authenticated instances of its breeding in Norfolk are on record', there are no proven nesting records within the county, although a pair spent the whole summer on a stream at Stanford Water in 1919. The Green Sandpiper remains, as in Stevenson's day, a passage migrant, more numerous in autumn than spring, and a winter visitor. In most years the species is recorded in every month. On passage, the majority are found at inland freshwater localities, such as sewage farms, beet factory ponds and gravel pits, although coastal sites with freshwater marshes are also favoured. In winter, Green Sandpipers are often found along the muddy edges of streams and ditches, or even small farm ponds.

Spring passage, in April and May, is normally light, with day-counts rarely exceeding three at any one site. Maximum counts have been ten at Cley on 10th May 1954 and 14 at Cranwick Gravel Pit on 2nd April 1994. However, this latter total may well have included some overwintering birds as ten were present at the site in mid-January and only five remained on 9th April. The Green Sandpiper is one of the earliest waders to return on autumn migration and passage commences in June, peaking in July and August. Since the early 1960s Cantley Beet Factory ponds have generally held the highest numbers in autumn, with maximum counts of 44 on 7th August 1977 (including a single party of 24), up to 32 in August 1978 (including a party of 26), 58 on 22nd August 1994, 82 on 22nd August 1997 and up to 50 in most of the other years since 1988. The extended autumn passage of Green Sandpipers is well illustrated by the monthly maxima at Cantley in 1995: 40 in July, 58 on 22nd August, 38 on 12th September and 20 on 1st–10th October. Maximum counts at other favoured localities have included 31 at Wisbech Sewage Farm on 18th August 1966, 32 at Hickling on 8th August 1976, 25 at Wissington Beet Factory on 22nd September 1988, 30 at Holme in July-August 1989, 34 at Cley on 31st July 1991 and 26 at Holkham on 4th August 1991.

The number of Green Sandpipers overwintering in Norfolk has increased from an average of seven per year between 1953 and 1983 to 22 per year since then, with maximum counts of 32 and 31 in the winters of 1989 and 1990. Generally only one to three birds are recorded at any one site but there were up to nine at Bayfield Lake in early 1989, up to ten at Great Melton fish pool in 1990 and ten at Cranwich Gravel Pit on 15th January 1995. There is considerable evidence that individual birds may return to the same wintering area for a number of successive years (Winter Atlas).

One Norfolk-ringed Green Sandpiper has been recovered – ringed at Wisbech Sewage Farm on 13th October 1963 it was found at Landes, France on 1st February 1964.

*Moss Taylor*

## Wood Sandpiper    *Tringa glareola*

**A scarce passage migrant.**

The Wood Sandpiper breeds in the northern boreal and subarctic zones from Fennoscandia to eastern Siberia, nesting in coniferous forests and further north on hillocky tundra. It winters mainly in sub-Saharan Africa, although small numbers remain along the Atlantic coast of Morocco. In Britain, the Wood Sandpiper is primarily a spring and autumn passage migrant, although a few pairs breed annually in Scotland. The first proven breeding record for Britain was in Northumberland in 1853 and the next, over 100 years later, in 1959 in Inverness. Since 1968 up to ten pairs have bred annually in Scotland (New Atlas).

As with the Green Sandpiper, there have been suggestions that the Wood Sandpiper bred in Norfolk in the 19th century. Both Stevenson and Riviere referred to the record of an immature Wood Sandpiper illustrated by Gurney and Fisher (1846), who wrote:

We are informed by Mr Scales that, several years ago, he shot two of these birds during the summer in a marsh near Beachamwell, one of which was an old female, and the other a young bird, not yet having entirely lost its down; and the latter, which we have endeavoured to represent, being evidently not sufficiently feathered to have crossed the sea, may fairly be supposed to have been hatched near the spot where it was killed.

The two specimens, originally in J. H. Gurney's collection, are now at the Castle Museum, Norwich. Unfortunately, the record is not now considered to be fully authenticated. Although it was only an occasional visitor in Stevenson's day, even then it was becoming scarcer as he explained: 'This growing rarity may perhaps be owing to the opposite shores xof Holland where, within a few years, it bred numerously'. The species ceased to breed in The Netherlands during the mid-20th century.

Wood Sandpipers are generally not seen in the spring until the last week of April and the passage often continues into early June, with a peak in mid-May. The earliest dates for the county are 2nd April 1957 at Cley and 16th April at Titchwell in 1983, Burnham Overy in 1988 and Cley in 1994. Numbers recorded in spring have varied from seven in 1983 to 25 or more. During the 1950s Cley was the favoured locality with maximum counts of 15 on 28th May 1957 and 20 on 12th May 1959. In the 1960s Wisbech Sewage Farm often held the most in spring with a maximum of twelve on 20th May 1968. Spring counts in the 1970s and early 1980s were generally low, at the time that the range of the Finnish population was contracting (European Atlas). Since then numbers have increased with 15 at Holkham on 15th May 1994, up to nine at Strumpshaw and seven at Hickling, Hardley Flood, Surlingham and Kelling Water Meadows. During the spring of 1997 a total of about 40 Wood Sandpipers was recorded in the county, almost half during an influx on 3rd–5th May, with a maximum of six at Salthouse on 17th May. Records in the second half of June are not unusual and occasional late spring migrants have been observed in display flight and in song, such as at Cley in 1958 and Winterton in 1974.

Autumn passage normally commences in early July, peaks in August and continues to mid-September or mid-October, depending on the year. The latest dates for the county have been 3rd November at Hickling (1986), at Kelling Water Meadows (1995) and Cantley Beet Factory (1998), 14th November 1952 at Cley and 20th November 1983 at Cantley Beet Factory. An unprecedented passage of Wood Sandpipers was recorded in Britain during autumn 1952, with Cley recording some of the highest counts in the country. The first arrivals at Cley were noted on 3rd July, increasing to 18 by 18th July, although most had left by early August. A second influx occurred on 6th August, when 40–50 arrived, increasing to 60 by the next day, most of which departed on the night of 13th–14th August. However, 15 were present daily until early September and the last one stayed until mid-November (Nisbet 1956). Since then, the maximum counts at Cley have been 50 on 31st July 1980 and 30 on 15th August 1959. Wisbech Sewage Farm's August counts included 35 in 1968, up to 37 in 1969 and 25 in 1977. Between 1986 and 1992, Hickling often held the highest numbers of Wood Sandpipers in autumn, peaking at 19 on 9th August 1992. An unusually high count of 23 was made at Brancaster on 11th August 1959. The trend during the 1980s and 1990s has been towards lower counts in autumn, although 1987 was an exception with over 50 passing through the county. An unusually early autumn influx was noted on 28th–30th June 1997 with maximum counts of 13 at Holkham and 15 at Salthouse. Few are recorded on visible migration and ten south at Cley on 6th September 1997 was unprecedented. Although most of the higher counts have come from coastal sites, Wood Sandpipers have also been found at various inland sites, in particular the beet factories at King's Lynn, Wissington and Cantley (where up to eleven were present in August 1980), gravel pits, sewage farms and parkland lakes, such as Gunton and Felbrigg.

*Moss Taylor*

# Terek Sandpiper                                             *Xenus cinereus*

**A very rare vagrant; ten records.**

The Terek Sandpiper breeds from Finland eastwards through northern Russia and into eastern Siberia, with a single breeding record in Norway in 1967. It winters in southern Africa, India, south-east Asia and Australia. It is a rare vagrant to the British Isles but has appeared almost annually since 1969, mostly in May and June.

The first county record was one found by the writer at Breydon on 1st June 1975. Its arrival coincided with a period of very strong northerly winds and it was seen from midday until dusk feeding in a tidal creek close to the estuary wall. It constituted the twelfth British record. Amazingly the second was soon to follow – one showed well for three days at Cley on 2nd–4th July in the same year. Another was at Breydon again on 5th July 1978 associating with Redshanks at the high-tide roost.

Terek Sandpiper
(*Norman Arlott*)

Further sightings of Terek Sandpipers were made at Cley/Salthouse on 18th–20th May 1982 and at Cley the following year on 23rd–30th May. Another graced Holkham Fresh Marshes on 18th June 1988 and following northerly winds, yet another visited Breydon on 29th–31st May 1990. Unexpectedly, one visited inland Wissington Beet Factory pools on 1st–4th June 1991. Breydon was again favoured on 15th June 1995 when one was seen at high tide and was later roosting on the Berney Reserve. This was almost certainly the same bird seen at Minsmere, Suffolk the previous day. A month later one roosted at high tide on the pits at Snettisham on 14th–15th July 1995. *Peter Allard*

## Common Sandpiper   CLEY MARSHES. 10·9·1993.   *Actitis hypoleucos*

**A fairly common passage migrant and very rare breeding summer visitor; rare in winter.**

The Common Sandpiper is a breeding summer visitor across the whole of the Palearctic region, with the exception of Iceland. The main population breeds above 55°N from northern Britain through Fennoscandia to Russia. European birds winter mainly in West Africa, although a few now overwinter within Europe. In the British Isles the species is typical of upland streams, rivers and clear lakes with stony, rather than muddy or marshy fringes, as are found in the north and west (68–72 BTO Atlas).

To the Victorians, the Common Sandpiper was known as 'summer snipe' and was referred to as such by Stevenson, although it was not recorded as breeding in Norfolk until 1897 (Riviere). Normally seen in small numbers only, a party of 30–40 along the River Bure at Wroxham in August 1847 was considered exceptional. There have been eight instances of the species breeding or summering in Norfolk as follows:

1897: A nest containing four eggs was found at Hickling on 25th May
1912: A downy young was caught by a dog along the River Bure at Coltishall
1928: A pair bred successfully at Hanworth Park
1962: A pair raised three young at Great Witchingham
1963: A nest with four eggs was found at Thompson Water
1977: A pair summered at Pentney Gravel Pits
1980: A pair raised one young at Pentney Gravel Pits
      A pair bred at Blickling

The first spring migrants usually arrive by mid-April, with the passage peaking in mid-May and being over by early June. The earliest dates (excluding birds that are known to have overwintered) have been 8th March 1997 at Stiffkey (although the very early date suggests that this may well have been a bird that had overwintered elsewhere in Britain), 18th March 1956 at Cley, 23rd March 1995 at Buckenham/Cantley Marshes and 27th March 1993 at Colney Gravel Pit. The latest spring migrants were at Breydon and Cley on 16th June 1995. Large gatherings of Common Sandpipers do not occur, as illustrated by the maximum spring counts at the following sites – 30 at Holkham Lake on 31st May 1989 and 23 at Breydon on 23rd May 1998. On 15th May 1994, several sites recorded some of their highest counts with 21 at Holkham Fresh Marsh, 20 at Holme and 17 at Breydon. A total of 15 at Gunton Park Lake on 22nd May 1992 was a good number for an inland locality.

Autumn passage commences in late June or early July and continues until the end of October or even early November, with peak numbers from mid-July through August, including a flight of 54 at Postwick on 24th August 1942. From the 1950s to the 1970s, peak counts were usually made at Wisbech Sewage Farm, with maxima of 80 on 6th August 1963 and 75 on 13th August 1969. Since then autumn maxima have included 62 (including a party of 19) at Breydon on 29th August 1987, up to 40 at Holme in August 1983, 40 at Holkham Park Lake on 27th August 1996, 36 at Colney/Bawburgh Gravel Pits on 15th July 1984, 35 at Lynn Point on 24th August 1987 and 35 at Cantley Beet Factory on 10th August 1992.

Although Common Sandpipers usually feed singly, migrating birds often keep together in fairly tight flocks. On 10th August 1956, four such groups of between three and 26 birds in each were noted flying west at Brancaster, while an excitable flock of 40 alighted in waterside trees at Hardley Flood on 21st August 1973 and 24 were present together on the River Bure at Buxton on 19th July 1966. Other records of birds on visible migration have included eight in off the sea at Waxham on 17th September 1992. As in the breeding season, migrating Common Sandpipers favour freshwater areas although occasional birds are found feeding along the tideline. The group of 13 below Hunstanton cliffs on 26th July 1985, 20 on the beach by Cromer Pier on 26th August 1989 and 13 at Sheringham on 19th July 1998 were almost certainly just resting.

Common Sandpipers wintering in the British Isles show a distinct coastal bias with about 50% of the population in south-west England and virtually no overlap with their breeding range (Winter Atlas). It is likely that those wintering in England are from the more northern latitudes, rather than British breeders. In half the years between 1953 and 1998, at least one Common Sandpiper has been recorded in Norfolk during the winter months, December to February, with a maximum of three in any one winter period. Over 15 localities have hosted wintering Common Sandpipers, both inland sites and coastal freshwater marshes, but the two areas from where almost half the records have come have been Breydon and Cley. As the species is known to show strong loyalty to favoured sites, some records almost certainly involve the same individual returning in successive winters. Such is the case with one that remained at Cley from 1st December 1987 to late March 1988 and which returned in the two subsequent winters.

Over 100 Common Sandpipers have been ringed in Norfolk, resulting in three recoveries in France while on autumn passage, between 23rd July and 15th October. *Moss Taylor*

# Spotted Sandpiper *Actitis macularia*

**A very rare vagrant; seven records.**

The Spotted Sandpiper breeds over a large area of North America from Alaska south to Texas. It winters in small numbers in the southern USA, but mainly from Central America south to Uruguay. It has become an annual vagrant to the British Isles since 1965 with most appearing in September.

The first county record was an adult in summer plumage found by Billy Bishop at Cley on 7th–8th June 1957. It was seen at close range for considerable periods and was painted by Richard Richardson (Bishop 1957). The next two records were at Wisbech Sewage Farm – a long-stayer from 9th November to 19th December 1970 and a bird in breeding plumage on 13th June, 29th July and 30th August 1971. A similarly plumaged bird was seen at Cley on 22nd–23rd May 1983. A juvenile or first-winter individual was identified at Holme on 7th October 1985 while in 1986 another bird graced Cley on 11th–14th June. The most recent record was of a juvenile moulting to first-winter plumage at Welney on 18th September 1994 which stayed in the area until 27th January 1995. *Peter Allard*

# Turnstone (Ruddy Turnstone) CLEY. 21-9-1993. *Arenaria interpres*

**A fairly common winter visitor and passage migrant; scarce inland.**

The Turnstone is one of the northernmost breeding landbirds in the world. It has a circumpolar Holarctic distribution but also breeds as far south as the Baltic and southern Norway. All populations migrate in autumn, those from Greenland and north-east Canada wintering in western Europe and north-east Africa. The species winters around the entire coastline of the British Isles, favouring rocky shores.

Both Stevenson and Riviere described it as a regular passage migrant in small numbers, with a few also being seen in winter and summer. At Blakeney it was known as the 'Tangle-picker' from its habit of turning over seaweeds and other marine substances in search of food.

Autumn passage commences in mid-July with the main arrival occurring in August. Two populations of the Turnstone pass through Norfolk. Birds from Greenland and Ellesmere Island in north-east Canada moult and winter in the county whereas birds from Finland and northern Europe use the Wash and north Norfolk coast as a staging post as they migrate to moult and winter in West Africa (Langston 1988). After a peak in August–September, the number of birds in Norfolk declines gradually throughout the winter. The majority occur on the Wash and along the north Norfolk coast with smaller numbers on the north-east coast and at Breydon. Allowing for annual fluctuations there has been no significant change in the peak number of birds on autumn passage or wintering in the county since at least the late 1960s. In the Norfolk part of the Wash, Snettisham has always held the largest numbers with maximum autumn counts of 900 in September 1981 and October 1994, while 1,000 were present on 24th December 1968. Maximum counts at sites on the north coast have included 264 at Thornham/Titchwell in January 1997, 600 at Scolt Head in February and December 1968, 240 at Brancaster Harbour in January 1989 and 1991, and 350 at Blakeney Harbour in August 1986. For a few years in the late 1980s a winter roost of Turnstones gathered on the shingle beach at the Old Hythe, Sheringham peaking at 361 in February 1989 and at about the same time up to 130 fed on the cliff-top fields at West Runton. At Brancaster Harbour there has long been an association between man and Turnstones with the birds readily landing on boats moving between the lays and the mainland and taking advantage of the mussel harvest (Brown 1993), they also roost in moored fishing boats both in daytime and overnight, when they are often joined by Rock Pipits. In the Wash 60–70 Turnstones have roosted on a Lynn Channel buoy with smaller groups occupying nearby buoys. The species is known to be very site-faithful both within and between years (Langston 1988).

In east Norfolk small numbers have been noted at Yarmouth since the 19th century but it was not until February 1968 when three wintered at Breydon, that this site was used regularly by small numbers (Allard 1990). A count of 23 in December 1973 was considered exceptional but nowadays up to 30 pass through in autumn and 20-30 have overwintered at Breydon and around the harbour's mouth, although since 1996 the numbers have declined.

Spring passage is unremarkable, usually peaking along the north Norfolk coast in May, with maximum counts in recent years of 220 at Brancaster Harbour in 1997 and 63 at Cley in 1992. There is little evidence of the northern European birds stopping off on the Wash in spring (Langston 1988). In east Norfolk peak counts at Breydon are often made in the spring with a maximum of 48 in April 1991. Only small numbers of non-breeders remain in the county throughout the summer months.

Turnstones are recorded annually inland, albeit in very small numbers. Most inland records are made in May and August when the birds are migrating. For many years spring records far outnumbered those in autumn but this has not been true since the mid-1990s. Many inland sites have been visited by Turnstones; maximum site-counts have included 30 at Wisbech Sewage Farm, eight at Welney, twelve at Hickling and 15 at Hardley Flood, while 18 were present at a car park at Eaton, Norwich on 8th–22nd January 1996 during a period of hard weather. Most records, however, refer to only one or two birds which remain for a day or two only.

It is well known that Turnstones eat a wide variety of food items and reports have included birds eating wheat, the corpse of a long-finned pilot whale, cheese and even fish and chips! In February 1991 during a period of severe weather many thousands of waders died in the Wash and along the north Norfolk coast. Large numbers of Grey Plovers, Redshanks, Dunlins and Knots died but Turnstones were relatively unaffected (Clark & Clark 1992). Of the 2,527 wader corpses picked up in Norfolk only 19 (0.75% ) were Turnstones due in some part to the bird's ability to take advantage of a new food source – the thousands of wader corpses on the tideline!

About 40 Turnstones ringed in Norfolk have been recovered abroad, including two on Ellesmere Island in Canada and three in Greenland, all during the breeding season. Six other non-breeders have been found between May and August in Iceland. Three have been recovered during the breeding season in Finland and one found on Great Ainov Island, Murmansk remains the only British-ringed Turnstone to be recovered in Russia. Onward passage of this European population has been demonstrated by autumn and winter recoveries in Morocco (2), The Gambia, Guinea Bissau, Liberia and Ghana. The most unexpected recovery concerned one found in Greece in October and it remains the only British-ringed Turnstone to be found in that part of Europe. Of the 18 foreign-ringed Turnstones recovered in the county, two were ringed as chicks, one each from southern Finland and Sweden. Birds ringed as adults or juveniles came from Ellesmere Island (Canada), Greenland, Fennoscandia (9), Germany (2) and The Netherlands (3).

*Phil Atkinson*

## Wilson's Phalarope                              *Phalaropus tricolor*

A rare vagrant.

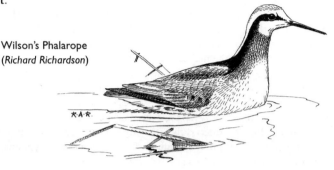

Wilson's Phalarope
(*Richard Richardson*)

Wilson's Phalarope breeds in North America, wintering in Peru and south to Argentina and Chile. First recorded in the British Isles in 1954, it has been recorded annually since 1960, except in 1993.

The species was first recorded in Norfolk in 1967, when one was found at Wisbech Sewage Farm by John Moyes and S. Greenwood on 28th September, to be joined by a second bird the following day. The two remained until 15th October during which time they were filmed and photographed by Dick Bagnall-Oakeley (Bottomley *et al.* 1967), one remaining until 2nd November. Since then 14 more individuals have been seen in the county:

1967:  One at Wisbech Sewage Farm on 28th September and two from 29th September
to 15th October, with one remaining until 2nd November
1971:  A summer plumaged female at Hickling on 17th–25th June
1973:  Cley on 21st–22nd October
1975:  A summer plumaged female at Wisbech Sewage Farm on 7th–11th June
1979:  A summer plumaged female at Cley on 17th–18th May
Two at Wisbech Sewage Farm on 29th August
Holme on 12th–20th September
1983:  A summer plumaged female at Titchwell from 25th June to 2nd July, and then
at Cley on 3rd–17th July
1985:  A moulting adult at Cley on 14th–17th August
1987:  A summer plumaged female at Cley on 9th–12th May
A winter plumaged adult at Breydon on 16th August
A winter plumaged adult at Snettisham from 28th August to 3rd September
1994:  Cantley Beet Factory on 16th–20th September

*Steve Gantlett*

## Red-necked Phalarope   CLEY. (3) 10·9·1993.   *Phalaropus lobatus*

A very scarce passage migrant.

The Red-necked Phalarope breeds throughout the Arctic with the vast majority of the European population in Fennoscandia and Iceland. Most of the latter migrate south-east through Europe to winter in the Arabian Sea. In the British Isles it declined dramatically as a breeding bird during the 19th century, possibly due to egg collecting. Less than 40 pairs now breed in Scotland, almost all in Shetland. It remains a scarce but regular spring and autumn passage migrant to the British Isles.

The first Norfolk record appears to have been one killed in winter plumage at Breydon in 1824. This was presumably the same individual that was in the collection of Stephen Miller of Gorleston; a second bird in the same collection in summer plumage was presumably also taken locally. Sheppard and Whitear (1826) did not mention this species and the Pagets (1834) noted that it was very rare in the Yarmouth area, giving details of just the two in Miller's collection. The next published record was of one shot at Scoulton Mere in August 1829. Gurney and Fisher (1846) remarked that it was 'occasionally seen'; and in the following year four were killed at or near Salthouse in September, two of which were still in summer plumage. Further autumn records followed, including one shot over the river at Trowse Eye, Norwich on 9th November 1853. The first in spring was a bird shot near Horsey Mere on 24th May 1867. Pashley (1925) was aware of eight birds in the Cley area, all between 27th August and 9th November. By the time that Riviere had compiled his county avifauna in 1930 one more Red-necked Phalarope had been recorded in May, four in June and two in July, with the majority during the autumn.

Seago (1967) described it as a passage migrant in very small numbers to tidal waters, coastal and Broadland pools, usually singly but up to three together had been reported. The favoured haunts were Cley, Salthouse and Wisbech Sewage Farm. Since 1961 the species has appeared annually in Norfolk, often in association with northerly winds. The majority have appeared on autumn passage between late June and late September. Individuals in mid-June are often early returning females. It is scarcer in spring with most between mid-May to very early June. Most spring and summer birds are in breeding plumage while a large percentage of autumn records involve juveniles.

The earliest spring record was one at Holkham on 25th April 1988 which remained until 2nd May; it remains the only April record for the county. The latest in autumn was one at Snettisham on 10th November 1971. Most records have involved single birds but occasionally two, and three together on three occasions and at Cley on 25th August 1954, at Wisbech Sewage Farm during the period 12th August to 16th September 1965 and at Cley on 9th–14th September 1993. The peak years have been 1979 and 1990, each with at least nine individuals, while an average of four per year have been noted in the county since 1968.

Cley is undoubtedly the most frequently visited site in Norfolk with at least 60 individuals recorded since 1953. Other favoured localities have included Welney, Wisbech Sewage Farm, Snettisham, Holme, Titchwell, Salthouse, Cantley Beet Factory, Hickling Broad and Berney Marshes. Although most birds are recorded at coastal sites, the species is not infrequent inland and has even been reported on village ponds, such as the one at Freethorpe on 4th September 1975. Other inland records have included singles at Langmere on 16th–20th September 1967, Thompson Water on 6th–8th September 1989, West Acre on 21st June 1992 and Little Walsingham/Egmere on 9th–11th September 1995. Occasionally passage birds remain for more than a few days – one at Cley stayed for two weeks in September 1957, as did another in October 1985. More noteworthy were singles at Salthouse on 4th–22nd October 1968, at Cantley on 2nd–20th August 1992 and at Snettisham village from 29th August to 20th September 1995. The longest-stayer, however, was one which remained at Wisbech Sewage Farm for 34 days from 8th September to 11th October 1973.

*Peter Allard*

## Grey Phalarope — *Phalaropus fulicaria*

**A very scarce autumn passage migrant and winter visitor; very rare in spring.**

The Grey Phalarope breeds throughout the Arctic tundra regions. It winters at sea, with the Western Palearctic birds primarily off western Africa. It is a scarce visitor in small numbers to British inshore waters, mostly from late September to November.

Up to 15 are recorded annually in autumn, between late August and the end of November, with most in October and November. Up to four are recorded most years in winter (December–March) but, although there are records for all months, spring and summer records are very rare. The majority of occurrences of this, normally pelagic, species are associated with strong onshore winds, when the birds are pushed inshore. Most records are of singles seen briefly on or over the sea around the coast. Very occasionally two or three are seen together and from time to time birds remain on coastal pools for a few days, such as one at Titchwell from 29th October to 5th November 1995, one at Cley on 12th–13th October 1997 and two together there on 14th–22nd October 1997. The largest day-count was eight flying west and one east off Sheringham on 29th October 1989, during a south-westerly gale.

There have been seven records of singles between April and July:

> 1963: A summer plumaged female at Blakeney on 13th July
> 1971: Cley on 22nd June
> 1975: One in winter plumage at Cley on 7th–10th May
> One in breeding plumage at Hickling Broad on 29th May
> 1983: Salthouse on 12th April
> 1984: One flying east past Holme on 7th May
> 1994: Holkham Bay on 1st–4th April

A total of 15 has been recorded inland since 1952, including only three since 1987 – singles near Wisbech Sewage Farm on 17th October 1987 and near Hockwold on 18th–20th October 1987, following the famous hurricane of that month (which also 'wrecked' a number of Sabine's Gulls inland) and two at Welney on 13th–15th October 1997, one having been present on the previous day.

One was trapped and ringed at Cley in early October 1952 and another at Weybourne on 5th November 1996.
*Steve Gantlett*

## Pomarine Skua  CLEY. ON THE SEA. 26·11·1988. *Stercorarius pomarinus*

**A scarce autumn passage migrant but fairly common in some years, very scarce in winter and spring; very rare inland.**

The Pomarine Skua has a circumpolar breeding distribution but has a very limited range in Europe, only nesting on the Russian tundra from the Kanin Peninsula, extending east to Siberia, and Arctic Canada. The number of breeding pairs is heavily dependent on the lemming population. It winters off West Africa, where some immatures remain all year (Furness 1987). It is a regular passage migrant to the inshore waters of the British Isles but numbers vary annually. Spring passage is heaviest off the Western Isles, but in autumn larger numbers are recorded along the North Sea coasts.

The first to be recorded in Norfolk was an immature taken at Northrepps in October 1822, which formed the subject of a large coloured drawing by Miss Anna Gurney (Stevenson). Thereafter it was described as an occasional autumn visitor to inshore waters, although they were frequently seen by fishermen, far out to sea, following the gulls which were attracted by the shoals of herring and sprats. Following a gale on 20th October 1884, a Yarmouth game-dealer had about 30 and Patterson (1905) described the Pomarine Skua as the commonest species of skua on the east Norfolk coast, whereas nowadays it is the second rarest (Allard 1990). In mid-October 1879 an influx of gale-driven Pomarine Skuas on to the Norfolk coast and inland was described by Stevenson as 'the great ornithological feature of the autumn', during which they were 'swarming in our harbours, bays, and estuaries . . . Mr Cole a Norwich taxidermist when at Yarmouth railway station watched several over the eastern end of Breydon . . . One shot near Rockland Broad was in company with others no doubt part of the flock seen as far up-river as Surlingham and Thorpe next Norwich.' At least 200 were killed and so the number passing must have run into many hundreds. The next heavy passage was recorded by Riviere on 14th September 1916, when 70 flew inland at Blakeney in small groups.

Between 1930 and 1952, there were only three records of Pomarine Skua in Norfolk, but they have been seen annually since. This is almost certainly due to the improvement in optical aids, identification skills, the number of observers and the dawn-to-dusk seawatches, rather than a real increase in the number of birds. Although the species has been recorded in every month of the year in Norfolk, there have been few in July. Autumn migration generally commences in late August, involving failed breeders and immatures. As the adults and young move south, numbers increase in September, peaking from October to mid-November, three or four weeks after the main passage of Arctic and Long-tailed Skuas; the adults generally precede the juvenile birds.

Migration occurs mainly over the waters of the continental shelf, the pelagic and coastal waters tending to be avoided. The appearance of Pomarine Skuas is therefore even more dependent than the other skuas on northerly winds driving the birds into inshore waters. In recent years the highest counts have been in November 1985, when a major influx took place down the eastern seaboard of the British Isles. On 2nd November, counts included 110 east at Cley and 50 at Hunstanton, and on 10th November with 200 east at Cley, 67 at Paston and 80 flying inland at Lynn Point, as is regularly recorded for Arctic Skuas. On the latter date a total of about 380 passed along the Norfolk coast and the November total was estimated to be 780 out of an autumn total of 980. In 1991 a far smaller but still notable passage occurred in mid-October when 91 flew west at Holme on 18th October and 13 flew inland along the River Ouse, while 109 flew east at Sheringham the following day. An exceptional passage of juvenile Pomarine Skuas was recorded on 23rd–25th October 1997, with birds moving west at Holme and east at Cley and Sheringham. Over the three days, at least 450 were counted with maximum day-counts both at Cley of 139 on 23rd and 173 on 24th. Also on the first date 17 came in off the sea at Titchwell and flew inland. It is during October and November that all except one of the inland sightings of Pomarine Skua have been made, with singles at Briston in 1978, at Dilham and Welney (five) in 1985, at Surlingham Church Marsh in 1987 and at Chedgrave in 1988.

A few Pomarine Skuas remain in temperate northern latitudes into mid-winter (Furness 1987) and occasional birds are recorded in December and January. The highest count has been 13 at Hunstanton on 6th December 1967, while following the exceptional influx in November 1985, up to three were seen at Hunstanton and Holme, between Blakeney Point and Sheringham (one of which often fed on carrion half-a-mile inland) and one at Breydon which fed on gull corpses on the tideline, in January 1986. However, it does appear to have been recorded more frequently in mid-winter during the last few years, perhaps as a result of seawatching being continued in every month. It is rare between February and June, although up to five present in the Yarmouth and Gorleston area, attracted by large numbers of gulls feeding on sprats, between 8th February and 19th April 1995, with one on 30th April, were the first records of overwinter-ing. Despite the annual, but small spring passage noted along the English Channel coast, the Pomarine Skua remains a rare bird in spring off Norfolk. *Moss Taylor*

## Arctic Skua    OFF CLEY. 7·9·1985.    *Stercorarius parasiticus*

**A fairly common autumn passage migrant, very scarce in winter and spring.**

The Arctic Skua has the widest circumpolar Arctic breeding distribution of the three small skuas, as well as extending further south to include northern Scotland and the Northern Isles (Furness 1987). In Europe it breeds near most coasts north of 59°N and on inland tundra in Russia, Iceland, Svalbard, Norway and Sweden. The main wintering areas lie within 50km of the South African coast. The increase in the Scottish breeding population during the 20th century is due to a reduction in persecution and probably also an increase in the population of seabirds from which they rob fish.

Stevenson recorded the Arctic Skua or 'arctic gull' as regular in autumn, being in constant attendance around the herring boats, but it was never seen in assemblies of such large numbers as the 'Pomatorhine' Skua. Adults were very rarely noted. Amongst the inland records given, was one shot in Brooke Wood, near Norwich on 13th May 1871, an extraordinary locality and date! In fact, Riviere was only able to add two more 'spring' records both at Scolt Head in April and June.

The southerly passage of Arctic Skuas in late summer and autumn is a leisurely affair through the inshore waters of the North Sea, the birds often stopping for a few days where terns are abundant, such as off Blakeney Point or Scolt Head. For instance, 30–40 were feeding offshore between Holme and Scolt Head from late July to early August 1997. The first are usually seen along the north Norfolk coast in mid-July and are failed breeders or non-breeding immatures (Furness 1987). Successful breeders and juveniles generally peak between late August and mid-September, the largest numbers appearing in coastal waters, after being blown inshore by northerly gales. The most impressive passage was recorded at Sheringham in September 1994 with 420 on 1st, 355 on 15th and 220 on 16th. The only other count in north Norfolk that has exceeded 300 was 330 at Sheringham on 4th September 1992. On each of these occasions and on the majority of days that large numbers of Arctic Skuas have been recorded passing offshore between Cley and Sheringham, the birds are flying in an easterly direction. At Holme, however, large movements invari-ably involve birds flying in a westerly direction, such as 220 west on 3rd October 1994 and 208 west on 9th September 1997. This suggests that birds moving south strike the north Norfolk coast at some point between Holme and Cley, with some turning east and others west, as they follow the coastline. This is supported by counts on 28th August 1995 of 155 west at Holme and 200 east at Sheringham.

After passing Holme, Arctic Skuas fly south at Hunstanton, following the coastline, as happened on

20th October 1970 when 152 were counted. On the following day an unprecedented total of 350 was present in the southern part of the Wash, presumably having been joined by birds that had passed south off the Lincolnshire coast. Some of the birds that are driven into the Wash in these northerly gales continue flying in a southerly direction inland following the Rivers Nene or Ouse. On 14th September 1980, 100 flew inland at the mouth of the River Nene, to be seen later the same day over Wisbech Sewage Farm; while on 7th October 1982 a total of 120 flew south at Lynn Point along the River Ouse. Not all birds, however, continue south – out of 300 at the Ouse Mouth on 21st August 1988, only about 200 flew inland and on other occasions at Terrington, some have returned to the Wash, despite heading inland for four or five miles (Seago 1967). It is known that some Arctic Skuas, probably those breeding on the Russian tundra, pass overland across Europe and central Africa to reach their winter quarters (European Atlas) and so the behaviour noted in the Wash is perhaps not that extraordinary. Before flying south overland, parties of skuas often spiral up to quite a considerable height and this behaviour has also been recorded elsewhere, especially between Cley and Sheringham.

While the highest counts of Arctic Skuas have usually been in north Norfolk or around the Wash, east Norfolk has on occasions produced some notable totals. At Winterton, 129 flew south on 11th October 1981 and at Horsey 355 flew south during a north-westerly gale in four hours on 27th August 1986. At Yarmouth, the highest count has been 47 flying south on 25th August 1982 (Allard 1990).

Although the species has been recorded in Norfolk in every month of the year, it is comparatively scarce in November and very few are noted between December and March, with the highest count of 20 off Sheringham on 6th December 1980. The northerly spring passage from March to May, involves both breeding adults, which arrive back in Shetland in mid-April, as well as immatures, which probably account for most of the May and June records. However, the Arctic Skua is an irregular and scarce spring migrant off the Norfolk coast, in some years none has been recorded, in others occasional birds have been seen from early April. As in autumn, northerly winds are associated with more sightings and a strong north-westerly gale on 20th April 1980 produced twelve at Cley and six at Holme. The spring passage in 1985 was also more marked than usual, often in association with strong northerly winds and birds were recorded from ten coastal localities, with a maximum count of eight at Paston on 28th April.

Despite Arctic Skuas being seen to fly inland, records away from the coast are rare and certainly not annual. Wisbech Sewage Farm was one of the few places where birds were recorded on several occasions and there have been other records from as far inland as Norwich, while one was seen following a tractor at Little Dunham. While on passage, Arctic Skuas have been seen to chase a variety of other birds, both large and small, in addition to the usual terns and gulls offshore. Reports have included three pursuing passerines and a Snipe over the dunes at Winterton, one chasing a Lapwing over the fields at Cley, up to 16 pursuing waders over the Titchwell freshwater marshes and three mobbing a Marsh Harrier which was flying off-shore at Snettisham.

Ringing recoveries have shown that many first-year and adult Arctic Skuas from Scottish colonies move south through the North Sea and English Channel. The only recovery affecting Norfolk was of a nestling ringed on Fair Isle in 1956, retrapped on Fair Isle as a breeder in 1960 and found dead at Winterton on 19th August 1964.                                                                                            *Moss Taylor*

# Long-tailed Skua                                           *Stercorarius longicaudus*

**A scarce autumn passage migrant, single mid-summer and mid-winter records; very rare inland.**

The breeding distribution of the Long-tailed Skua is not dissimilar to that of the Arctic Skua, being circumpolar in the high Arctic. The largest populations are present in Russia, Alaska and Canada, with smaller numbers in Greenland, Norway, Sweden and Finland. In Scotland birds have held territory in the Cairngorms and have probably nested in at least two years. The wintering area is probably mostly between Antarctica and the southern parts of Africa and South America. It is the rarest of the four skuas to British and Irish waters, though increasing numbers having been recorded in recent years. Unlike the other skuas, away from the breeding grounds it normally feeds on small organisms taken from the surface of the sea, rather than by kleptoparasitism.

Known to Stevenson as Buffon's Skua, the first reliable record was of an immature found dead at Hockham in September 1847. Strangely enough, the second record was also in the Brecks, at Methwold in

September 1854. Several more were identified during the great influx of Pomarine Skuas in October 1879 and seven were obtained during the autumn of 1895 (Riviere). Between 1930 and 1953 there had been only three records (Seago 1967) but since 1953 it has been recorded annually, except in 1955 and 1974. During the 1950s the average annual total was two, although over half of the records occurred in 1959 alone, but this had increased to an average of six between 1960 and 1989, with considerably higher numbers in most years since then.

There has been only one mid-summer record, at Scolt Head on 11th June 1962. In those years in which lemmings are scarce, some adults fail to breed and these turn up occasionally off the north Norfolk coast in July. In most years, however, the passage starts in late August and peaks in September, with only a few birds in early October and a total of only eight November records. The latest dates in autumn have been at Sheringham on 12th November 1996 and 14th November 1993, Paston on 15th November 1981 and Winterton on 22nd November 1980. With most Long-tailed Skuas passing rapidly south through the pelagic waters of the mid-North Atlantic it is not surprising that it is the rarest of the skuas off Norfolk.

Long-tailed Skuas
(*Norman Arlott*)

Prior to 1994, the record day-count for any site in Norfolk had been 25 off Cley on 30th September 1991. However, on 1st September 1994, an amazing total of 126 flew east at Sheringham, the majority juveniles. At the same site, 34 flew east on 15th September and a further 47 the following day. The autumn total at this one locality was a staggering 232. Unprecedented totals were also recorded at several other north Norfolk sites during the same period and it was suggested that the high numbers were at least partially accounted for by significant advances in skua identification and increasing observer confidence. It was felt that the species had been overlooked in the past. This certainly appears to have been the case, for the autumn total in 1995 was 126, with a maximum count of 34 east at Mundesley on 25th August and in 1996 was 90, with a maximum of 35 east at Sheringham on 30th. Long-tailed Skuas are rare off the east Norfolk coast and the few records have all involved single birds, apart from four off Horsey on 1st September 1994.

The Long-tailed Skuas seen off Norfolk are probably of Fennoscandian origin (Bell 1965), boosted as the autumn progresses by birds from further east. Sharrock (1974) also suggested that the birds are spending time in the rich feeding areas of the northern North Sea during late August and September but during northerly gales move to the calmer southern North Sea to feed, and some of them end up in the inshore coastal waters. Once the weather improves they return north to make a rapid westward departure between Iceland and the Hebrides, into the North Atlantic. This would explain the absence of records from the coasts of the English Channel, Scotland and Ireland in autumn.

Juvenile Long-tailed Skuas winter both in the pelagic waters off Namibia and Argentina, while the adults probably winter more widely to the south (Furness 1987). Despite this, there is a remarkable record of one seen by Richard Richardson at Titchwell on 3rd January 1967. There have only been two inland records since 1950 – one found dying at Wisbech Sewage Farm on 3rd October 1973 and a dead juvenile at Field Dalling on 1st October 1997. However, six (including four adults) flew inland at Ouse Mouth on 12th September 1988 and two flew high inland at Holme on 18th October 1991.

Spring migration from the wintering areas commences in April and flocks of over 1,000 pass through the middle of the North Atlantic in late May (Furness 1987). At this time small numbers are recorded off the west coasts of Ireland and Scotland but it has never been recorded in the spring off Norfolk.

*Moss Taylor*

# Great Skua

*Catharacta skua*

**A fairly common autumn passage migrant, very scarce in winter and rare in spring.**

The Great Skua is endemic to Europe and until recently bred only in Iceland, the Faeroes and north Scotland, but since 1970 new colonies have appeared further north and east, including Spitsbergen, Norway and northern Russia. More than half the population (almost 8,000 pairs) breeds on coastal moorland in the Northern Isles of Scotland. Juveniles winter off the coasts of southern France, the Iberian Peninsula and North Africa, while most Shetland adults winter between British and Iberian coastal waters with some wandering further west and south, as far as the equator (Furness 1987).

As a result of human persecution, Great Skuas had been reduced close to extinction in Scotland and the Faeroes by about 1900, which explains Stevenson's statement that the species was 'decidedly rare on our coast, appears accidentally quite independent of weather . . . but almost invariably in the autumn months'. In the 19th century it was far rarer off the coast of Norfolk than the Pomarine Skua. The slow recovery of the species during the first half of the 20th century is reflected by Riviere who described it as an occasional autumn visitor, and comparatively small numbers were still being recorded until the early 1960s. A total of 70 off Hunstanton on 23rd October 1964 was a county record at the time. However, larger numbers were clearly passing south through the North Sea, as was shown by a total of 300 which entered the Wash at Holme during a northerly gale on 15th September 1966. After leaving the breeding grounds the majority of Great Skuas migrate south over the continental shelf waters of western Europe, from 1–2km to 20–30km from the coast, thus avoiding inshore waters (Furness 1987).

Immatures leave the breeding areas in July, failed breeders and early fledglings leave in August and the majority of adults and juveniles in September. In common with the other skuas, peak numbers are associated with onshore northerly gales. Only occasional birds are recorded in July and the main autumn passage lasts from mid-August to mid-November, peaking in September and October, during which time parties of up to 35 have been noted (Seago 1967), although normally fewer than this are seen together. The highest counts have all been made off north Norfolk between Holme and Sheringham. As with the Arctic Skua, birds are generally moving west at Holme and east at Sheringham during these heavy passages and day-counts of more than 200 at any one site are unusual. However, at Sheringham, 230 flew east on 2nd September 1976 and 246 east on 15th September 1994, while on the following day the county record was surpassed when 310 moved east off Sheringham and 185 flew west at Holme. Further notable westerly movements have been recorded at Holme in 1996 with 210 on 12th September, 145 on 13th September and 231 on 5th October, and at Scolt Head in 1997 with 237 on 12th October and 281 the following day.

Observations at the mouths of the Rivers Nene and Ouse in the Wash have shown that, like Arctic and to a lesser extent Pomarine Skuas, Great Skuas also spiral up before flying south inland, often to follow the course of the rivers. This is particularly noted on days on which a heavy offshore passage of birds is recorded along the north Norfolk coast. On 27th August 1989, out of a total of 66 at the Ouse Mouth, 39 flew inland, as did 80 on 21st September 1990. At the Nene Mouth on 14th September 1980, a total of 50 Great Skuas flew inland and were subsequently recorded over Wisbech Sewage Farm, the same day that 100 Arctic Skuas followed a similar route.

As Great Skuas are regularly recorded along the Channel coast in autumn, it appears that, again like Arctic Skuas, their migration route normally takes them out of sight of the east Norfolk coast (as well as Suffolk and Essex). This is borne out by a gathering of 120, almost 100km north-east of Yarmouth on 26th August 1978. The largest numbers to have been seen off east Norfolk were 51 south at Winterton on 11th October 1981, 102 south at Horsey on 7th October 1982, 126 at Horsey on 11th September 1983 and 50 off Waxham on 10th September 1989.

Since the late 1970s a few Great Skuas have been sighted off Norfolk in mid-winter, with the highest counts being twelve at Weybourne on 29th December 1969, and at Sheringham 21 east on 31st December 1994 and 13 east on 12th December 1997. These totals, however, were dwarfed on 19th January 1998 with eleven at Brancaster, 84 at Sheringham and eleven at Eccles. Normally less than ten are recorded annually in each winter month. There have been two or three March records and only small numbers of birds have been recorded on spring passage in April and May. The heaviest movement was on 20th April 1980 with three at Holme, five at Cley and two at Sheringham. Singles have been seen on very few occasions in June and July, but there were five records at Yarmouth alone in 1997 and 1998, while a total of ten was recorded in June 1997, including five at Cley on 26th.

Apart from the 50 flying south over Wisbech Sewage Farm in 1980, the only other inland records of Great Skuas during the 20th century have been at Swanton Morley on 29th March 1973, a total of seven at Breydon, including four on 28th November 1993, one east over Felbrigg/Metton on 12th October 1997, three at Welney on 13th October 1997 and the two ringed birds at Wisbech Sewage Farm and Haddiscoe Marshes mentioned below.

Bearing in mind that only Shetland Great Skuas have been ringed with durable rings in large numbers, the 15 Norfolk recoveries of ringed nestlings from Scottish colonies confirm the origins of at least some of the birds that pass offshore. As long ago as 1939, one ringed on Shetland in July was found dead at Weybourne in October. Since then, two ringed on Foula have been recovered inland in September, at Wisbech Sewage Farm and on the Haddiscoe Marshes.

*Moss Taylor*

# [Great Black-headed Gull (Pallas's Gull)  *Larus ichthyaetus*

One old record which is no longer considered acceptable.

The Great Black-headed Gull is a central Palearctic species breeding from southern Russia east to central Asia and wintering from the extreme eastern half of the Mediterranean area, the Red Sea and Persian Gulf eastwards to Burma. The only currently accepted British record is an adult shot in Devon in 1859.

A Great Black-headed Gull was seen almost daily by Henry Cole at Cromer on 2nd–9th March 1932. It was reported and accepted by Riviere in his 'Ornithological Report for Norfolk for 1932' (Riviere 1933). From the brief description, it appears that the gull was in near-adult plumage with an incomplete black hood, a black-tipped orange bill and yellow legs, and it displayed white-tipped primaries. A review by the BOURC in 1992 of the five previously accepted British records found the Norfolk bird to be unacceptable despite the description being more convincing than those of other rejected records; it was decided that the possibility of a mistake could not be eliminated (Vinicombe & Hopkin 1993).]

*Peter Allard*

# Mediterranean Gull  *Larus melanocephalus*

A very scarce breeder; an increasing, but scarce winter visitor and passage migrant.

The Mediterranean Gull has a wide, but fragmented breeding range in the Western Palearctic extending east to the Caspian Sea area. Large numbers winter in the eastern half of the Mediterranean. It has increased westwards considerably in recent years from its main breeding range embracing the Black Sea. Breeding first occurred in western Europe in The Netherlands in 1933 and has occurred annually since 1968. Germany was first colonised in 1951 at sites on the Baltic coastline and breeding has been regular since 1963. Belgium was next, in 1964 and it bred on the Mediterranean coast of France for the first time in 1965. The species bred for the first time in the British Isles in Hampshire in 1968 and is now an annual breeder in several counties in small numbers. Many early breeding attempts involved birds hybridising with Black-headed Gulls.

The first Norfolk record was an adult male shot at Breydon on 26th December 1886. It was obtained quite accidentally when wildfowler Charles Harwood was unable to extract a cartridge from his gun and fired at the first bird which presented itself. It was later taken to George Smith, a Yarmouth bird dealer, who recognised its importance and the unfortunate gull made ornithological history. It proved to be the second British record, but the first to be recognised and may still be seen in the City of Birmingham Museum. The second county record was also at Breydon, when Arthur Patterson and Robert Chase, from Birmingham (who had in his possession the historic Mediterranean Gull shot there in 1886), saw an adult on 16th May 1909. Remarkably, the next sighting was not until 1949 when one was seen by Clifford Borrer and Peggy Meiklejohn following the plough at Wiveton in mid-March.

With the increase in observers and more awareness of the identification features of the Mediterranean Gull, sightings began to increase. Between November 1952 and February 1957 an adult, almost certainly the same individual, wintered along Sheringham seafront. Additional adults were noted at Cley in July 1953 and at Overstrand/Cromer in July 1957. The years 1958 and 1959 were blank but in 1960 with more literature available on gull identification, a first-winter bird was identified at Salthouse in September, whilst a second-winter bird patrolled the beach north of Winterton village in September and October. Since 1960 it has been recorded annually in the county in increasing numbers.

The first Yarmouth observations followed in August 1962 and again in 1964, the same year that a first-summer bird displayed to Black-headed Gulls in a colony at Cley for a week in late May. The increase continued and in 1969 at least nine individuals in varying plumages were recorded. The first multiple observations were at Weybourne in 1972 when at least five, probably seven, were present from 28th July to 15th October. A first-summer bird at Breydon on 10th July 1975 heralded a now regular late April to end of June influx of first-summer Mediterranean Gulls at this locality, often associated with a similar influx of immature Common Gulls. At least 26 birds passed through Breydon between 29th April and 25th June 1983. On 31st May 1995 a group of 14 had assembled there in one party at high tide. Elsewhere, coastal sightings up to 1974 numbered between two and seven annually; mostly singles involving adults in winter and younger birds at other times, particularly in autumn. In 1980 two observations were significant, the first Broadland sighting at Hickling on 23rd April and a sub-adult, probably a second-summer bird, displaying vigorously at Snettisham from 9th May to 27th June.

Records increased with at least 22 Mediterranean Gulls in 1981 and up to 30 in 1982 including the first in juvenile plumage (at Breydon on 14th August) and a first-winter bird inland in the Yare Valley at Buckenham. Over 50 individuals were noted in 1983 including up to four during the winter along Yarmouth seafront (Allard 1984a). There was a noticeable increase in sightings along the north Norfolk coast in 1985 and the following year saw wanderers penetrating inland including a long-staying bird in the Norwich area from 23rd January to 10th March. By the close of the decade Mediterranean Gulls were not uncommon, with the east coast dominating the scene, Yarmouth seafront and Breydon being the best places to see this attractive gull in the county. All ages were represented and it was becoming increasingly difficult to summarise records.

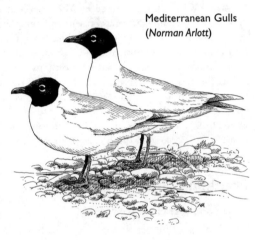

Mediterranean Gulls
(*Norman Arlott*)

Not surprisingly, Mediterranean Gulls began to breed in the county for the first time in 1992 with single pairs nesting amongst Black-headed Gulls at Titchwell and Blakeney Point. Both pairs hatched eggs, but unfortunately failed to fledge young (McNeill & Reed 1993). The following year, pairs returned to the same sites, but no eggs were laid. The first successful breeding was in 1994 with a pair at Blakeney Point which fledged one young. Three pairs at the same site in the following year all failed, but in 1996 they were more successful with two pairs raising four young. Breeding behaviour was noted at three other sites. In 1997 two pairs bred at Blakeney Point, one of which probably fledged at least one young, and three pairs bred in 1998.

Increased sightings continued unabated in the county and in May 1995 alone, at least 39 first-summer birds were present with at least 15 adults and one second-summer at various sites. That year also saw each age group recorded every month for the first time, reflecting the remarkable increase in numbers. Although the problem of exact numbers remains, some birds are very site loyal and a considerable increase along the Yarmouth seafront was noted in autumn 1998 (Allard 1999). By 12th October a record site-count of 21 Mediterranean Gulls was present, which had increased to 26 on 13th November, comprising twelve adults, three second-winter and eleven first-winter birds. Many were still present at the end of the year. The most favoured sites have continued to be Snettisham, Heacham/Hunstanton, Cley/Blakeney, Sheringham, Overstrand, Mundesley and Yarmouth/Breydon. At least eight Mediterranean x Black-headed Gull hybrids have been identified, the first at Cley in May 1984.

There are a number of ringing schemes in operation throughout the European breeding colonies, each using separate colour combinations. The ring number of one marked as a chick in Zeeland, The Netherlands on 24th June 1994 was read in the field at Overstrand on 8th November 1994 and may well have been the same colour-ringed bird seen earlier at Sheringham Golf Course on 7th–8th October; it was identified again at Overstrand on 9th October 1995. Another carrying a white ring, first seen at the entrance to Yarmouth Harbour on 29th October 1997 and which remained until March 1998, had been ringed as a chick at the same Dutch colony on 29th May 1997. It also returned to Yarmouth on 18th October 1998 to overwinter at the same site for the second successive year. Three other colour-ringed birds were also present at Yarmouth in late 1998 – two ringed as chicks at Lillo, Antwerpen, Belgium on 28th May 1998 and a German-ringed adult, the ringing details of which are awaited.

*Peter Allard*

# Laughing Gull                                            *Larus atricilla*

**A very rare vagrant; three records.**

The Laughing Gull is an abundant Nearctic gull which breeds along the eastern seaboard of North America and in the Caribbean. It winters in the USA to northern South America. It is a vagrant to the British Isles which has become more frequent in recent years.

A first-winter bird identified by Mick Fiszer at Walcott seafront on the morning of 25th December 1991 was a splendid Christmas present and completed a trio of Nearctic gulls which were all additions to the county list in 1991. A very confiding bird, it remained in the Walcott, Mundesley and Paston areas, with visits inland to Witton and Ridlington, until 8th January 1992 (Anon 1992a).

A first-summer bird appeared at Salthouse on 1st June 1995. It later flew over Cley Marsh and remained in Blakeney Harbour until dusk. This vagrant later visited both Kent and Suffolk, appearing at Lowestoft on 8th July 1995. The third record was a bird in full summer plumage seen at Titchwell on 9th–20th May 1998, during its stay it also visited Holme on 10th, 16th and 29th–31st, Burnham Norton on 18th–20th, as well as Burnham Overy Harbour on 20th, and Hunstanton where it was last seen on 3rd June (Skeen 1998). Amazingly it was joined by a Franklin's Gull, another Nearctic species, at Titchwell on 10th May.

*Peter Allard*

# Franklin's Gull                                          *Larus pipixcan*

**A very rare vagrant; three records.**

The Franklin's Gull breeds across western North America and winters mainly along the Pacific coast of Central and South America from Guatemala to Chile. It is a rare vagrant to Britain and was first recorded in February 1970.

An adult, in full breeding plumage, was found by Keith Dye at the eastern end of Breydon on 30th June 1991. It remained until mid-afternoon, occasionally flying around, before disappearing up the estuary. It was found again in the late afternoon at the western end of the estuary feeding on the Burgh Flats where it remained until dusk (Anon 1992a). This bird was considered almost certainly the same as that which had frequented Teesmouth, Cleveland, on 19th–23rd June, returning there in August. A second adult in full breeding plumage, appeared briefly on pools at Titchwell on 21st July 1992.

The third county record was a first-summer bird seen at Titchwell on 10th May 1998, where it joined a Laughing Gull. It stayed until early evening when it flew off to the west. It was subsequently located on Bain Gravel Pits at Kirby, Lincolnshire on 13th May (which locality remarkably also hosted the Laughing Gull on 23rd May) and was finally seen 500 miles north at Loch of Hillwell, Shetland on 15th May (Skeen 1998). A previously accepted record of a second-winter Franklin's Gull at West Runton on 29th October 1976 was reconsidered and withdrawn by the observers in 1982.

*Peter Allard*

# Little Gull          TITCHWELL. 24·5·1987.          *Larus minutus*
HARDLEY FLOODS. 24·7·2000.

**A fairly common passage migrant and scarce non-breeding summer visitor; bred in 1978.**

The main breeding range of the Little Gull covers Finland, the former Baltic States and northern Russia. Sporadic breeding has occurred in The Netherlands and Denmark. It winters, mainly offshore, as far south as the Mediterranean and North Africa. Breeding has been recorded in Britain on four occasions – at the Ouse Washes, Cambridgeshire in 1975, at Hickling and Fairburn Ings, Yorkshire in 1978 and at a site in central England in 1987. All were single pairs and all failed at the egg stage.

Stevenson considered that probably the earliest record for Norfolk was a pair said to have been killed on Breydon in December 1829. Little Gulls were recorded only eight times during the next 40 years, but almost annually since 1869. A remarkable influx of at least 60 birds, mainly adults, occurred in February 1870, following an easterly gale. Riviere described it as a fairly regular autumn visitor, seen less frequently in the winter and occasionally during the spring and summer. He stated that the only adults in summer plumage to have been recorded were on 27th April 1888 and 17th June 1923, on both occasions at Hickling.

The only Norfolk breeding record concerned a pair of adults that arrived at Rush Hills, Hickling during the third week of May 1978. By 1st June a nest could be detected in a rush clump. Half-a-dozen immature Little Gulls present on the shallowly flooded marsh became highly aggressive towards the nesting birds. As late as 24th June, when the clutch of three eggs was thought to be on the point of hatching, a nest changeover was observed, but a few days later only one adult remained and the nest was found to be empty (Anon 1986e). Fourteen years earlier, in 1964, hopes had been high that a pair might breed at Salthouse. They had arrived towards the end of April and had stayed well over a month in a gull colony, frequently mobbing intruders. Much courtship was recorded, including aerial chases similar to those of Black-headed Gulls and tern-like postures on the ground. Unfortunately no eggs were laid.

Little Gulls
(Norman Arlott)

Spring migration is generally light due to the majority of birds returning to breeding areas by overland routes. Main passage extends from mid-April to mid-May. An exceptional flock of 80 headed east over Santon Downham on the 29th April 1981, following prolonged north to north-easterly gales and torrential rain. Other notable spring counts have included 113 at Welney on 22nd April 1987, 42 at Lynn Point on 19th April 1991, 33 at Hunstanton on 18th March 1994 and 43 at Breydon on 29th April 1995.

Small numbers of non-breeders, usually first-summer birds, are recorded most years in mid-summer. Oversummering first occurred in 1975 when two immatures were at Wisbech Sewage Farm in June and July. Since then the most impressive gatherings have been up to twelve at Welney, 25 first-summers and four adults at Holme/Thornham, 23 at Titchwell, 24 at Cley, 15 at Kelling Water Meadows and twelve at Hickling.

Since 1976 spectacular autumn movements have become an annual event between late September and November with smaller numbers in December. Day-counts of up to 200 birds have been frequently recorded. This dispersal from breeding grounds is usually associated with strong or gale-force winds between north-west and south-east driving the birds closer inshore on their journey through the Baltic into the North Sea and on into the English Channel (Anon 1986e). The most impressive counts have been 238 at Sheringham on 30th October 1976, 274 at Winterton on 2nd October 1978, 240 at Hunstanton on 2nd November 1988, 400 at Titchwell on 28th October 1990, 318 at Snettisham on 5th October 1992, 600 at Holme on 11th October 1992, and at Sheringham 685 on 29th October 1996 and 755 east on 30th November 1997.

Little Gulls normally remain very scarce during the opening months of the year and prior to 1983 observations generally related to single birds. However, in that year, following a week of very strong north-north-east winds unprecedented numbers put in an appearance, with county totals of 147 in January and 102 in February. In 1984 strong southerlies produced 43 off Yarmouth and 23 off Paston in

January. Since then mid-winter counts have reached double figures on several occasions, the most notable being 93 at Hunstanton in January 1989, 55 at Sheringham in February 1990, 100+ at Cley in January 1995 and 43 at Winterton in February 1996. It remains uncommon in Norfolk in March.

Inland occurrences were scarce prior to 1967 but have since become almost annual, mainly during April. An increase in numbers has been noted since 1994. However, the species has remained rather infrequent inland in the autumn with the exception of 1987 when it was recorded at Ranworth, Narford Lake and Welney in mid-October.

*Keith Dye*

## Sabine's Gull                                    *Larus sabini*

**A very scarce autumn passage migrant, very rare in winter and spring; one mid-summer record.**

The Sabine's Gull breeds in Greenland, Arctic North America and north-east Siberia. It winters off the Pacific coast of South America and the Atlantic coast of South Africa. It is an annual autumn visitor to the British Isles, usually in small numbers.

Sabine's Gull
(Richard Richardson)

The first Norfolk records were in 1881 when two were obtained at Breydon, an immature male on 18th October and an immature female two days later. They came into the hands of George Smith, a Yarmouth bird dealer and the male was purchased by E. M. Connop of Rollesby Hall and is now at the City of Birmingham Museum. The female was in Stevenson's collection before being presented to the Castle Museum, Norwich where it remains on display. A severe storm accompanied by a deluge of rain had swept across the region on 14th October 1881. A further eleven were recorded by Riviere, with another twelve by the end of 1972. Since then it has been seen annually, 1997 being the single best year with at least 28 records between 19th August and 21st October, followed by 1988 with 14. Double-figure annual totals have only been achieved in five other years – 1974, 1977, 1987, 1995 and 1996.

The majority of birds have been recorded between August and October, with occasional birds in July and November. Most have been seen along the north Norfolk coast during periods of strong onshore winds. There have been four July records, two in 1980 and singles in 1987 and 1988. The majority of sightings have been on single dates only, but five have made prolonged stays. An adult that appeared at Hunstanton on 25th August 1969, two days after a strong northerly gale, remained until 21st November feeding mainly at a sewage outlet and occasionally on inland fields. On one occasion a Herring Gull was robbed of a shore crab it was about to gorge, on another a small dog retreated without dignity when swooped on by a furious Sabine's! A pellet that it was seen to eject was collected and found to contain twelve barley grains and 70 complete beetles, mainly one of the common weevils, thus showing that it did feed on its occasional excursions to inland stubble fields (Ramsay 1970). Up to two adults were at Holme and Thornham on 10th–25th September 1978, another adult remained at Sheringham on 7th–21st July 1980 feeding mainly inland but also on scraps provided by birdwatchers on the promenade and a partial summer-plumaged bird at Blakeney Point on 5th–12th September 1984.

It is very rare at other times of the year and there have been only two winter records, one shot at Blakeney on 12th January 1922 but lost in the sea and an adult at Happisburgh on 13th February 1994. Seven have been recorded in spring between 4th April and 20th May at Hunstanton, Holme, Cley, Paston, Happisburgh, Yarmouth and Breydon, and there is a single mid-summer record of a second-year bird at Holme on 22nd June 1979.

There have been four inland records, involving six birds – one at Hickling on 19th September 1935, an immature at Strumpshaw Broad on 22nd October 1985, two juveniles on the Ouse Washes at Welney on 16th October 1987 (following the hurricane that struck southern Britain on the previous night) and two adults at Dickleburgh Moor on 21st–22nd October 1987, with one remaining on 23rd.

*Keith Dye*

# Bonaparte's Gull                                       *Larus philadelphia*

**A very rare vagrant; two records.**

The Bonaparte's Gull is an abundant Nearctic species which breeds across much of North America and winters mostly from Washington and Massachusetts to northern Mexico and the West Indies, particularly on the eastern coasts. It is a rare vagrant to Britain with a westerly bias to the records, but has been almost annual since 1986.

The first county record of Bonaparte's Gull was an adult seen by Ian Wallace, moving north-west close inshore at Bacton Gap on 2nd September 1967 (Wallace 1968). The second was a first-winter bird at Cley on 26th September 1970. Both involved birds on passage and were seen by single observers. These two sightings were the first for East Anglia.

*Peter Allard*

## Black-headed Gull   CHEDGRAVE. MY GARDEN. 20·11·1999.   *Larus ridibundus*

**A very common summer visitor, and abundant winter visitor and passage migrant.**

The Black-headed Gull breeds around the coast of much of north-western Europe and a few places in the Mediterranean. The largest coastal breeding populations are in the former Baltic States, Sweden, Denmark, The Netherlands and the British Isles; it also breeds widely inland throughout Europe. One of the most 'inland' of British and Irish seabirds, the Black-headed Gull breeds colonially at sites ranging from coastal saltmarsh and sand dunes to freshwater lakes, marshes, gravel pits and upland tarns. Even those breeding on the coast may feed inland to a great extent.

Black-headed Gulls bred in reasonably large numbers in Norfolk up to the late 19th century. Stevenson referred to the ancient and celebrated gullery at Scoulton Mere where 'about 9–10,000 eggs are now taken, the numbers of birds for the last few years have been very equal'. Despite this, there were fears at the end of the 19th century that the Black-headed Gull might cease to exist as a breeding species in the county due to the combined effects of 'drainage and inclosure', as well as extensive egg collecting and persecution. It was even considered to be in danger of extinction as a British breeding bird. These fears proved to be unfounded, however, and in 1930 Riviere stated:

> Although this is an extremely abundant bird in Norfolk throughout the year it can hardly be termed a resident, for the results of ringing, and certain other evidence, make it most probable that birds which nest with us and those which are present during the winter are not the same individuals. Large numbers of Black-headed Gulls breed in the county annually, and a marked tendency to colonise fresh sites has been noticeable in recent years.

He also mentioned the Scoulton gullery which was referred to by Sir Thomas Browne in the 17th century, and stated that between the years 1860 and 1919, with the exception of 1864 when only 50 were taken, the average number of eggs collected annually from this gullery alone was 6,524. In 1918, 2,500 birds were nesting there (as calculated from a series of photographs) and it was finally abandoned in 1964.

In Breckland long-abandoned sites have included Langmere (where 50 nests in the heather in 1883) and Stanford Water. In the Broads, Horsey was also a former nesting locality extending over 300 acres 'where immense numbers bred in Thomas Browne's time' (Gurney 1920). Hoveton gullery commenced in 1854, following desertion at Rollesby, the birds nesting on ridges left by turf-cutters, but in later years reed hovers at both Hoveton Great Broad and nearby Black Horse Broad were favoured. A total of 2,000 eggs was taken in 1864 and 2,095 eggs in 1896. At the present time Hoveton Marshes is the largest Broadland gullery with up to 2,000 pairs.

Nowadays, in Norfolk, the largest breeding colonies are coastal with Broadland being the main inland breeding area. In 1985–87, 4,717 pairs were breeding in coastal colonies in the county, an increase from 1969–70 when there were 1,313 pairs compared with 1,950 in 1958. There are no comprehensive inland breeding records to compare with these figures but in 1985–87 the inland totals on record were only 5% of the coastal figures. The largest number of breeding pairs at the main coastal colonies in 1988–97 have been 1,570 at Snettisham, 600 at Titchwell, 650 at Scolt Head, 3,030 at Wells/Warham saltmarsh and 3,000+ at Blakeney Point. Inland the highest counts in the same period have been 500+ at Wissington

Beet Factory (but 60 or less since 1993), 140 at Cantley/Strumpshaw and 200-300 at Hoveton Marshes. Wolferton held 3,000 pairs in 1965, Wissington Beet Factory 400 in 1960 and Alderfen 330 in 1965 (but this has since been abandoned). During 1996 and 1997, the county total was of the order of 9,000 breeding pairs.

The arrival of Continental birds commences in early July, during which month impressive numbers have been recorded, such as 5,500 west at Sheringham on 22nd July 1980. August counts at Cley have included 3,050 on 21st, 4,340 east on 22nd and 2,590 west on 24th August 1962. Passage continues through September, October and November, during which months maximum counts have included 2,200 west at Holme on 11th November 1996, 5,000 west at Scolt Head on 11th October 1996, and 4,000 west at Sheringham on 16th October 1997. At Lynn Point 18,000 flew inland along the River Ouse at dawn on 4th October 1982.

There were few accurate roost counts prior to 1993, apart from the ten-yearly BTO Gull Roost Survey carried out in late January 1983. In that year a total of 104,369 Black-headed Gulls was counted in Norfolk with a marked increase in numbers from the Wash to east Norfolk (Taylor 1984a). The three biggest roost sites were Blakeney (32,800), Hickling Broad (40,000) and Breydon (41,000). Up to 6,000 roosted on the sea off Bacton Gas Terminal during the winter and 10,000 were at Welney in December 1984. At Breydon 27,900 were counted during a Gull Roost Survey on 2nd February 1991. Breydon has similar numbers of Black-headed Gulls roosting each autumn and winter and is certainly under-recorded as a major Black-headed Gull roost. The most important roosts since have been: in 1993 Snettisham 6,600, Lynn Point 17,500, Bob Hall Sands 7,500, Blakeney Point 8,000, and Mundesley 6,000; in 1994 Welney 6,100, Hardley Flood 5,000 and Ranworth Broad 6,000; in 1996 Wroxham Broad 10,000 and in 1997 Heacham South Beach 10,000 and Scolt Head 12,500.

Easterly emigration of Continental birds occurs between late February and the end of May with peak counts, all at Sheringham, of 3,000 on 31st March 1979, 5,000 on 13th March 1993 and 5,000 on 11th March 1995.

At least eight Black-headed x Mediterranean Gull hybrids have been recorded and a presumed Black-headed x Common Gull hybrid was seen at Sheringham on 13th May 1997 (Wright 1997b).

Over 4,000 Black-headed Gulls have been ringed in Norfolk producing in excess of 500 recoveries, of which about half have been outside the British Isles. In addition, over 300 foreign-ringed Black-headed Gulls have been found in the county, the majority of which had been ringed as nestlings in the Baltic States, Fennoscandia and The Netherlands. All these recoveries have clearly demonstrated that those wintering in Norfolk are from colonies to the east and north-east of the British Isles. They also show that eastern England is only part of a much wider wintering area, that extends eastwards and includes the Low Countries (Bruhn 1976). Many Black-headed Gulls do show wintering site fidelity, having been retrapped or had their ring number read in the field in the same area that they had been ringed in a previous winter – for example one ringed in Norwich in January 1964 was controlled by the same ringer in Norwich in January 1966 and February 1981, after 17 years (a longevity record for a British-ringed Black-headed Gull), and another ringed in a Sheringham garden in December 1981 was recorded on the promenade in January 1997, over 15 years later. Others ringed in Norfolk in winter have been found wintering outside the county in subsequent years. Many have been reported on passage through Denmark, both to and from their Baltic breeding sites, including one which was ringed in Norwich in January 1987 and the ring number read by Kjeld Pedersen in Copenhagen in no less than seven of the years to 1996, both in spring and autumn. Seven winter-ringed Black-headed Gulls from Norfolk have been recovered in Russia, the most easterly of which reached Arkhangelsk, at the south-eastern corner of the White Sea, a distance of 2,456km. The only Russian-ringed bird found in the county was one ringed as a nestling at Vitebsk and seen at Yarmouth the following February. Autumn arrivals from as far afield as eastern Europe appear as early as mid-July, for instance a Polish-ringed nestling was found dead at Brancaster on 16th July. The speed of passage of a presumed immigrant was shown by one ringed near Ipswich on 4th October 1997 which was found dead at Hickling Broad the following day, a distance of 80km.

Ringing has also demonstrated that most, if not all, young Black-headed Gulls from the Norfolk colonies move out of the county in autumn, most in a general westerly direction reaching the Midlands, Wales and south-west England. Two ringed at Cantley in June 1986 even reached as far as Eire in subsequent winters. Although there have been no recoveries in recent years of Norfolk-ringed nestlings in Iberia, one from 1957 and two from 1966 were found in Spain, while a nestling ringed on Scolt Head on 13th June 1925 was found freshly dead near Lisbon, Portugal on 18th October 1928, and remains the only recovery from Norfolk in that country!                                                                                        *Keith Dye*

## Slender-billed Gull                                                    *Larus genei*

**A very rare vagrant; one record involving two individuals.**

A southern Palearctic species, the Slender-billed Gull breeds in the Western Palearctic mainly in widely scattered colonies in the Mediterranean, Black and Caspian Seas, and from western Siberia east to Pakistan. The Mediterranean population is mainly resident whilst the migratory Russian population winters in the Persian Gulf. It is a very rare vagrant to the British Isles with only three accepted records prior to the pair in Norfolk.

   A pair of adults in full breeding plumage frequented Cley Marsh on 12th May 1987 having been discovered by Martin Gilbert in the afternoon. They remained in the area, with visits to Blakeney Harbour at low tide, until dusk on 15th May. Throughout the period, the larger male remained very protective towards the female, frequently positioning himself between her and other gulls, and often chasing them away. They were seen to copulate on numerous occasions (Varney 1988).                              *Peter Allard*

## Ring-billed Gull                                                      *Larus delawarensis*

**A very rare vagrant; eight records, all since 1991.**

The Ring-billed Gull breeds across North America from the prairies and lakes of Canada south to California, wintering south to Central America and even northern South America. The first British record was at Blackpill, West Glamorgan, as recently as 1973. The species was dropped from the list considered by the BBRC at the end of 1987, by which time 501 had been identified in the British Isles. It therefore seems rather surprising that the first Norfolk record did not occur until 1991, when Neil Bostock found one standing on the ice at Pentney Gravel Pits on 5th February (Anon 1992a), since when there have been a further seven records in the space of six years:

   1991:  A first-winter at Pentney Gravel Pits for ten minutes only on 5th February
          A second-winter took up residence at the University of East Anglia and the
          Earlham area of Norwich, also visiting Colney Gravel Pits and Norwich
          Waterworks, from 15th October to 7th April 1992
   1992:  A first-winter at King's Lynn Docks on 16th February
          A second-summer at Cley on 1st May
          A first-summer, later moulting into second-winter plumage, in the Breydon
          and Yarmouth areas from 3rd July to 29th March 1993 and again from 18th
          April to 1st May 1993
          A first-winter at Walcott on 21st December
   1994:  A first-winter at Nunnery Lakes, Thetford on 15th November
   1996:  A first-winter at Breydon on 25th November

Their increasing presence in the British Isles is doubtless related to an increase in numbers in Canada and the USA during recent years. Many have become permanent residents on this side of the Atlantic, migrating north and south along the European coastline. Some are very site-loyal in Britain returning in consecutive years. The two long-stayers in Norfolk, however, did not conform to this pattern.                         *Keith Dye*

## Common Gull (Mew Gull)   MY GARDEN. 24-12-1999.          *Larus canus*

**A very common winter visitor and passage migrant; a very scarce breeder.**

The Common Gull breeds in north-west Europe and across Russia to Alaska and north-west Canada. Its largest breeding populations are in Norway and Sweden where most colonies are on or near the coast. In other countries, including Britain and Ireland, the majority of birds nest inland. The British stronghold is in Scotland and the west of Ireland, with few breeding in England and Wales (New Atlas).

Both Stevenson and Riviere commented that the Common Gull was abundant on passage and during the winter months, with small numbers present around the coast in summer. Apart from an increase in oversummering birds, the species status has changed little since then.

The Common Gull first bred successfully in Norfolk in 1966, when two young were fledged at Blakeney Point, following an unsuccessful attempt in 1965. A pair again raised two young there the following year and at Cley a male defended a territory in a Black-headed Gull colony, even 'feeding' an imaginary female for eleven days. After that, nesting occurred annually at Blakeney Point until 1979, but since then the only certain breeding successes have been in 1985, 1989, 1991, 1994, 1995 and 1997, again mainly on Blakeney Point. No more than nine pairs have bred in a single year, raising no more than ten young annually.

Autumn passage commences in early July and peaks September–November. Early movements have included 2,200 west at Sheringham on 22nd July 1980 and 400 west on 9th August 1993, with 640 west at Scolt Head on 19th July 1997. The largest movements later in the autumn have been 3,000 west on 2nd and 800 west on 3rd November 1995 at Holme and 600 west on 14th and 950 west on 16th October 1997 at Sheringham. On 14th October 1997 a total of 5,000 was recorded at Cley.

Winter movements have been few and 3,000 west at Sheringham on 2nd January 1995, 800 west at Holme on 27th January 1996 and 700 east at Weybourne on 31st January 1996 have been the only notable counts. Some impressive winter roost counts have been recorded though, with site maxima including Breydon 3,100 in 1991, Snettisham 5,716 and Thornham 5,200 in 1993, Welney 6,000 and Marham 6,600 in 1994, Overstrand 5,000 and Attlebridge 4,000 in 1996, Heacham 4,000 and Scolt Head 7,500 in 1997, and Lynn Point 3,750 and Titchwell 6,000 in 1998. The ten-yearly BTO Gull Roost Survey carried out in late January 1983 recorded a total of 22,148 Common Gulls in Norfolk (Taylor 1984a).

Spring passage generally peaks in March and April with maximum counts of 600 east at Sheringham on 6th April 1975, 420 west at Sheringham on 18th April 1993, 500+ north at Yarmouth on 1st April 1995, 640 at Mundesley on 2nd April 1995, 400 east at Sheringham on 10th March and 300 east at Holme on 17th March 1996.

An albino was at Wells on 19th October 1968, a partial albino first-winter bird was at Wroxham Broad on 3rd March 1996, a hybrid Common x Mediterranean Gull was seen at Cley on 7th December 1995 and a presumed Common x Black-headed Gull hybrid was at Sheringham on 13th May 1997.

About 400 Common Gulls have been ringed in Norfolk of which 25 have been recovered abroad; in addition 45 foreign-ringed birds have been found in the county. Recoveries from both sources indicate that those which winter in Norfolk mainly originate from the breeding colonies in Fennoscandia, with smaller numbers from breeding sites in Germany and The Netherlands. One ringed at Ketteringham in February 1976 and recovered at Karelia on 27th April 1981 is the only recovery in Russia, although a nestling ringed at Murmansk was found 15 years later at Grimston. Further evidence of the species' longevity was shown by two Norfolk-ringed Common Gulls found abroad freshly dead also 15 years later. One whose ring number was read at Terrington on 19th August 1997 was known to have bred at Matsalu Nature Reserve, Estonia each year since 1987. Winter site fidelity was also demonstrated by one retrapped in the same Norwich garden in 1985 in which it had been ringed five winters earlier; while a cold-weather movement during the severe conditions in early 1985 was well-illustrated by one ringed on Helgoland, Germany on 13th January which was found dead at Brancaster ten days later. The longest movement within Britain involved one found dead at Sea Palling which had been ringed at Exmouth, Devon.

*Keith Dye*

## Lesser Black-backed Gull   HICKLING BROAD. 25·6·1986.   *Larus fuscus*

**A fairly common, but very localised, summer visitor and common passage migrant; a fairly common, but localised, winter visitor only in recent years.**

The Lesser Black-backed Gull breeds only in northern and western Europe, from Iceland to the White Sea and south to the Iberian Peninsula. The nominate Baltic race *L. f. fuscus* breeds around the Baltic Sea, in northern Fennoscandia and the far north-west of Russia, *L. f. intermedius* is present in southern Scandinavia and *L. f. graellsii* in the rest of the range, including the British Isles. Since the early 20th century the species has shown a marked increase in both numbers and distribution, except for *fuscus*, which has declined dramatically since the mid-1960s (Buckingham 1998 and Jonsson 1998). Both *graellsii* and *intermedius* migrate south after the breeding season, wintering as far south as the Iberian peninsula and north-west Africa, but *fuscus* migrates south-east, overland, to tropical East Africa. In recent years, however, increasing numbers of adults and second-year birds are overwintering in the North Sea or along the Biscay coast. In the British Isles the species breeds around much of the coast, albeit at well-scattered colonies in eastern England, as well as at inland sites. Although breeding Herring Gulls are often present in the same colonies, mixed pairings are very rare (68–72 BTO Atlas).

The Lesser Black-backed Gull was not recognised as a separate species from the Great Black-backed Gull until the early 19th century and early writers were thus able to provide very few records of its occurrence in Norfolk. Riviere described it as a 'regular but by no means common spring and autumn passage migrant to the Norfolk coast'. He had no personal records of the species between November and January, and noted that it did not take part in the regular daily movements of the larger gulls to and from the herring grounds during the fishing season.

Lesser Black-backed Gulls of the race *graellsii* first bred successfully in Norfolk at Blakeney Point in 1978, raising one chick. Since then it has bred there almost annually, peaking at eight pairs in 1982, 1983, 1985 and 1987. On the Wells/Warham saltmarsh a small colony has built up since 1984, with a maximum of 40 pairs in 1995. However, the largest Norfolk colony by far has become established on the Wash Outer Trial Bank, where 100 pairs were present in 1991, increasing to an amazing 860 pairs by 1995 and 900 in 1997. Unfortunately, no details concerning the success at this colony is available. In 1995 five pairs nested on factory roofs at Yarmouth and several young were fledged; they were discouraged from breeding the following year, but tried again in 1998. This was the first ever nesting on buildings in Norfolk, a habit which was first noted in the British Isles in the 1940s. Single pairs have also nested, but with mixed success, at Hickling (1980), Titchwell (1980 and 1982), Scolt Head (1983) and Snettisham (1992).

Spring passage along the Norfolk coast generally commences in late February or early March, peaking in April and May. Immature birds do not appear in any numbers until May. Maximum counts have generally been made at Sheringham, where there were 140 west on 23rd May 1991 and 90 west on 28th April 1996. Impressive mid-summer gatherings have been a feature of recent years with up to 300 at Lyng Easthaugh in 1990, 800 at Titchwell in 1993, 450 at Rush Hills, Hickling in 1994, 604 at Breydon and 200 at Cley both in 1995, 900 at Keswick in July 1997, and 949 at Lynn Point and 1,338 at Eau Brink in July 1998.

With a bird such as the Lesser Black-backed Gull it is never easy to decide when autumn passage commences, but increasing numbers begin to move west off the north Norfolk coast from mid-July with the passage continuing until mid-October. Maximum counts, both at Sheringham, have been 135 west on 14th August 1993 and 130 west on 18th September 1994, while 300 were following a fishing boat off Holme on 2nd September 1993. Observations at Sheringham have indicated that very few birds of the race *graellsii* are recorded after mid-September, with those racially identified in late autumn considered to be *intermedius* (Young-Powell 1995–96). In addition, 90 *intermedius* flew west at Sheringham on 5th August 1996, on which date 30 were also present close inshore. During the 1990s there have been some notable inland gatherings of Lesser Black-backed Gulls in autumn – 2,000 at Hickling Broad on 7th September 1992, 500 at Colney Gravel Pit in 1993, 580 at Winfarthing in 1994, 600 at Horsey/West Somerton in 1996, 650 at Boyland Common and 600 at East Harling both in 1997, and 1,500 at Saddlebow in 1998. A total of 279 flying north-east over Norwich to roost, presumably in Broadland, on 19th September 1991 must have been an impressive sight.

Formerly, all Lesser Black-backed Gulls left Britain in autumn, to winter further south, but nowadays large numbers overwinter, mainly in the southern half of England (Winter Atlas). Despite this, only small numbers are normally found in Norfolk in winter, for instance in January and February 1996 highest counts were eleven at Breydon, 14 at Attlebridge and 33 at Rockland Broad. Occasionally larger numbers have been reported such as 100 west at Cley on 4th January 1960, 106 at Filby Broad on 11th December 1982 and an exceptional 580 at East Harling Heath in December 1997.

There has been much debate in recent years, over the racial identity of Lesser Black-backed Gulls passing through the county in spring and autumn. Of 200 Lesser Black-backed Gulls at the Smith's Knoll light-vessel on 20th August 1953, the majority were considered to be *fuscus*, as were 91 adults at Rollesby on 16th September 1976, but these were surely *intermedius*. Nowadays, *fuscus* is believed to be a very rare visitor to Norfolk or not to occur at all. Most of the darker Lesser Black-backed Gulls are now considered to be *intermedius*, and we await the first fully confirmed record of *fuscus*. (One other race *L. f. heuglini*, from Russia, may have occurred in the county. The first example was claimed by M. F. M. Meiklejohn at Blakeney Point on 4th January 1960 and the second, found by the same observer and also seen by Richard Richardson, was present at Cley on 14th–20th December 1965. However, this race is not on the British list and these records remain unproven.)

Nine foreign-ringed Lesser Black-backed Gull nestlings have been found in Norfolk in recent years, none from the range of *fuscus* – six from southern Norway, two from The Netherlands and one from Sweden. In addition, nestlings from colonies at Lancaster and South Walney, Cumbria have been recovered in the county, while colour-ringed birds from Suffolk occur regularly. Most have been found between July and September. *Moss Taylor*

## Herring Gull HUNSTANTON. 23-6-1986. *Larus argentatus*

**A fairly common, but localised, resident and common passage migrant and winter visitor.**

The Herring Gull has a Holarctic distribution, breeding mainly in the mid- to high latitudes on marine coasts. Colonies in both coastal and inland towns are increasingly becoming established. The species is generally resident, except for the northern population which migrates south-west in autumn to winter around the Baltic and in the southern North Sea. During the 20th century there has been a marked increase in numbers in north-west Europe due to increased protection and the species' opportunistic adaptation to new sources of food, available all the year round. The nominate race *L. a. argentatus* breeds in Fennoscandia and the Baltic, and winters from the breeding grounds southwards to France. The race *L. a. argenteus* which breeds around almost the entire coast of Britain and Ireland, except between southern Yorkshire and the Thames estuary, is also resident in Iceland, Faeroes and along the western seaboard of the Continent. A yellow-legged form '*omissus*' breeds in Finland and Estonia, and is thought to be a colour variant of *argentatus* (the leg colour perhaps being diet-related).

Stevenson stated 'adult [Herring Gulls] are decidedly scarce at all seasons', while even as recently as 1930, Riviered commented: 'Immature Herring-Gulls are not uncommon about the coast-line through-out the summer, and even an occasional adult may be met with at this season.' A great influx, however, occurred annually in the autumn, coinciding with the arrival of the herring shoals, numbers decreasing considerably in December with the finish of the local herring fishing. Riviere (1921) over a period of twelve years studied the movements of the vast army of Herring Gulls and Great Black-backed Gulls between the North Sea fishing grounds and three main assembly places on the coast: Breydon estuary, the shore and marshes between Horsey and Winterton, and the sands between Wells and Blakeney Harbours. At its peak the Yarmouth-based fishing fleet totalled 1,000 drifters, declining to 110 vessels by 1957.

The species first bred in Norfolk, at Blakeney Point, in 1972, when one pair raised three young. Since then breeding has occurred there almost annually, but with varying success. The highest number of breeding pairs has been 120 in 1997. In 1984 two pairs were behaving as if breeding on the Wells/Warham saltmarsh, since when a colony has become well established, peaking at 130 pairs in 1996. As at Blakeney Point, breeding success has been very variable, with high tides destroying many of the nests in some years. Since 1991 a large mixed colony with Lesser Black-backed Gulls has become established on the Wash Outer Trial Bank, where 574 pairs were estimated in 1996 and 900 pairs in 1997. Elsewhere in Norfolk, single pairs have bred at Scolt Head in 1984 and 1997, at Titchwell and Strumpshaw in 1996 and four to five pairs at Brancaster Harbour in 1997, while at Cantley Beet Factory in 1981 a pair attempted to nest on an artificial cliff at the edge of a rubbish tip but the nest was later found empty. Nesting on buildings was first recorded in Britain in the 1920s, principally in the south coast resorts (68–72 BTO Atlas), but it was not until 1995 that it first occurred in Norfolk, when six pairs bred on factory roofs at Yarmouth, raising several young. Unfortunately they were discouraged from doing so the following year but nested successfully again in 1998.

Away from the breeding colonies surprising numbers of Herring Gulls may be present during the summer months, for instance 1,400 at Snettisham on 22nd June 1997 and 450 at Scolt Head on 6th July 1997. From mid-July onwards they become more widespread as a result of post-breeding dispersal. Numbers build up during the autumn with the highest count recorded in Norfolk of 16,000 between Snettisham and Heacham on 31st October 1971, compared with the peak 1996 WeBS total for the Wash of 5,000 in September. In 1994 up to 2,100 were present at Hunstanton and Gore Point in October–November. Mid-winter counts in recent years have included 3,500 at Thornham in 1995 and 3,000 at the rubbish tip at Aldeby in 1996, a habitat which is commonly used for foraging by the species, especially in winter. Some impressive movements have been recorded during winter gales – at Sheringham 5,500 east on 1st January 1979, 1,100 west (including 300 *argentatus*, see below) on 24th and 1,180 west (350 *argentatus*) on 28th December 1991, and 1,050 east on 10th December 1995, at Mundesley 1,280 east on 16th December 1995 and at Holme 1,500 west on 27th January 1996 and 2,300 east on 19th February 1996. At Welney 180 north-east on 5th January 1997 was highly unusual for this site.

Although most Herring Gulls roost on the coast, Riviere mentioned a large winter roost on Hoveton Great Broad, while Mickle Mere in the Brecks held up to 1,000 during the mid-1950s and up to 700 roost regularly at Breydon. While numbers in the county begin to fall during February, 3,500 were still present at Holme on 10th March 1996 and some impressive counts of birds on passage, presumably returning to breeding grounds, have been made in March and early April – the maximum being 2,000 west at Sheringham on 28th March 1992 and 1,000 north at Yarmouth on 1st April 1995. It is of interest that only 150 out of 700 flying west at Sheringham on 6th March 1993 were considered to be *argentatus*.

The number of Herring Gulls wintering inland in England and Wales has increased dramatically during the 20th century. Although suspected for a number of years, the first definite evidence that the majority of overwintering Herring Gulls, at least in London, belonged to the northern, nominate race *argentatus* was obtained in 1975 from an analysis of body measurements, timing of primary moult and recoveries of birds trapped for ringing on the London reservoirs (Stanley *et al.* 1981). Increased observer awareness, aided more recently by identification papers such as that by Golley (1993a), describing the field characteristics of all plumages of argentatus, has meant that the race has been increasingly recognised amongst the parties of Herring Gulls, both on passage along the Norfolk coast and those wintering in the county. Occasional birds are also identified during the summer months, the largest number being ten at Cley on 27th June 1994. The first few winter visitors begin to arrive during late August and early September; however, the main arrival is not until late October and November, with numbers peaking in January (Golley 1993a). The heaviest recorded passages of *argentatus*, all at Sheringham, have been 300 west on 24th and 350 west on 28th December 1991, 500 west on 22nd February 1993 and 400 east on 24th December 1995. Other notable concentrations have been 100 at Cley on 20th December 1996 and 50 at Breydon the following day. The first British record of a Herring Gull with yellow legs, and the only one up to 1930, was one shot by John Thomas at Breydon on 4th November 1886 and the specimen is now in the City of Birmingham Museum. It was subsequently identified as belonging to the form '*omissus*'. The only other record of '*omissus*' was one identified at Cley on 5th November 1991, with three present the following day. A first-winter showing characteristics of the North American race *L. a. smithsonianus* was seen at Cley on 31st December 1997.

One of the earliest recoveries of a foreign-ringed bird in Norfolk concerned a Herring Gull ringed as a nestling at Bergen, The Netherlands on 22nd July 1928 which was shot at Blakeney on 5th September. The origins of Herring Gulls wintering in Norfolk have been further demonstrated by other recoveries of birds from The Netherlands (5), Norway (2), Denmark and Germany, most of which were ringed as nestlings. A nestling ringed at the Kandalakshskiy Nature Reserve, Murmansk, Russia on 13th June 1992 and found dead at Scratby on 20th November provided the most easterly origin for one in the county. One found on the Smith's Knoll light-vessel in October 1955 had been ringed in a colony at Vardo, Norway, in the northernmost part of the breeding range. Other ringed Herring Gulls have come from the Scottish colonies on the Isle of May (4), Bass Rock and Nigg, while one ringed at Ord of Caithness on 3rd July 1966 was recovered at Blackborough End on 16th September 1979. Further evidence of the Scottish connection came with three recoveries in the Grampian Region, Highland Region and Tayside of birds ringed at Wolferton. Gulls are long-lived birds as was demonstrated by a Herring Gull ringed at Norwich in December 1968 and recovered on the Varanger Fjord, Norway in July 1988. The fjord lies at over 70°N and is part of the Arctic Ocean. The bird was over four years old when ringed and thus its total life span was in excess of 23 years. The longevity record for a British-ringed Herring Gull is over 27 years. The first evidence of fidelity to a wintering area in Norfolk was provided by a recovery at Eaton in December 1986 of a bird ringed 5km to the south-west at Ketteringham in January 1977, while another Ketteringham-ringed bird was found in a subsequent winter at Stiffkey.

*Moss Taylor*

## Yellow-legged Gull     HARDLEY FLOODS. 18-9-1999.     *Larus cachinnans*

**A scarce, but increasingly frequent visitor.**

The relationships between the various populations of Yellow-legged Gull, Herring Gull, Lesser Black-backed Gull and the other large gulls are exceedingly complex and uncertainties will remain into the foreseeable future. However, for the purposes of this book, the authors have followed the opinion of many, if not all of the taxonomic authorities, and have given the Yellow-legged Gull full specific status. The European race *L .c. michahellis*, breeds around the Mediterranean, on the Atlantic coast of the Iberian Peninsula through to France and scattered pairs nest inland in Austria and Switzerland, while the nominate race *L. c. cachinnans* breeds from the Black Sea to eastern Kazakhstan. Although adult *michahellis* are generally resident in the Mediterranean, immatures apparently tend to move into central Europe in autumn and since the early 1980s the species has been pressing north along the Channel coast of France, with increasing numbers being reported in south-east England.

The first Norfolk records were not until 1961, with singles at Scolt Head on 23rd August and at Blakeney on 4th November. Following one at Yarmouth on 15th August 1964, one or two were recorded annually from 1973 to 1976 and the species has been noted annually, in increasing numbers, since 1983. Initially birds were almost invariably reported between spring and autumn but since 1995 records have covered all months of the year. However, there has still been a clear mid- to late summer peak, involving birds of the race *michahellis*, with a county total of 20 in June and 23 in July 1997. Records are mainly from coastal localities, especially Cley and Breydon, but Colney Gravel Pit, Hickling Broad and Edgefield Tip have also been favoured. The largest parties to have been seen in Norfolk are up to five at Blakeney Point, Hickling, Yarmouth and Tunstead, six flying west at Cley on 5th March 1995, eight at Breydon on 21st July 1995, and in 1998 six at Aldeby on 11th January, eight at Edgefield on 18th April, nine at Eau Brink on 26th July and 13 at Saddlebow on 12th September. An adult at Kelling Water Meadows on 22nd April 1997 was displaying to an *argentatus* Herring Gull. The first records of the race *cachinnans* were at Cley in 1997 – a second-winter on 18th November and an adult on 17th December. In 1998 further singles were seen at Cley and at the rubbish tips at Aldeby, Blackborough End and Edgefield.

*Moss Taylor*

## Iceland Gull     *Larus glaucoides*

**A very scarce winter visitor and passage migrant; one mid-summer record.**

The nominate race of the Iceland Gull *L. g. glaucoides*, which visits the British Isles in winter, breeds in Greenland. There are two distinct populations – one in the west which largely remains in Greenland through-out the year and the other in the east which is believed to winter in Iceland, from where the visitors to the British Isles originate. The Iceland Gull shows a more marked western distribution in Britain and Ireland in winter, compared with the Glaucous Gull; it is also less frequently found inland (Winter Atlas).

Stevenson described the Iceland Gull as 'An exceedingly rare bird on the Norfolk coast; it seems probable that most of the specimens said to have been met with were small and pale-coloured examples of the glaucous gull, a much more common species.' In fact he was able to give only a single definite record – an immature female shot at Caister on 14th November 1874, received by George Smith the Yarmouth dealer who sold it to a Dr Crawford of Beccles. Up to 1930, Riviere gave details of a further 14, although this did not include a male shot at Breydon on the very early date of 22nd September 1880, which was only the third record for Norfolk. Despite the specimen being in the Connop Collection at Rollesby Hall (and now at the City of Birmingham Museum) where it was examined and catalogued by Thomas Southwell in 1898, it was not mentioned by either Arthur Patterson or Riviere (Allard 1990).

The county total currently stands at about 170 records, the species having been recorded annually since 1952, except for 1959, 1960 and 1969. There has been a slight increase in the number of annual records since 1983, probably a result of an increase in the number of observers, rather than a real increase in the number of birds. Individuals can also be very wide-ranging within the county and it is not always easy to be certain exactly how many birds are involved. The highest yearly total was ten in 1996, with nine in 1989 and 1997, and eight in 1984 and 1995.

The earliest autumn record involved the bird mentioned earlier at Breydon on 22nd September 1880, but more recently one was at Holme on 24th September 1963, followed by one at Cley on 1st October 1996. There have been seven other October records. The main arrival, however, takes place in November, undoubtedly involving some birds which are passing along the Norfolk coast to winter further south. A second influx is often noted in January with some of the birds remaining for several weeks. The longest-staying individuals having been at Yarmouth from 1st January to 19th March 1989 and at Sheringham from 3rd January to 22nd May 1993, during which time it roosted regularly on Blakeney Point and was also seen at Mundesley, Paston and Winterton on 9th–10th January. Peak numbers have been recorded in Norfolk in March, as Iceland Gulls return north to their breeding areas. A few have been noted in April and a total of seven in May, the latest at Holme on 29th May 1979 and 29th May 1988, and at Whitlingham Lane Gravel Pit on 28th–30th May 1997. There has been a single June record – one at Sheringham on 2nd June 1956.

The majority of sightings have been along the north Norfolk coast, with the stretch between Cley and Cromer being particularly favoured. Excluding Holme, very few have been recorded in the Wash, with most having been seen at Hunstanton or Heacham. As Iceland Gulls are attracted to fish quays and sewage outfalls, it is not surprising that in east Norfolk the Yarmouth area has hosted several, with the birds wandering as far north as Winterton. The large majority of records have involved single birds, but on occasions long-staying individuals have been joined temporarily by a second.

Inland, Iceland Gulls occasionally have been attracted to the Broads, gravel pits and refuse tips. Wroxham Broad has hosted the species on two occasions; the only other site to have held one more than once was Strumpshaw Refuse Tip, where four different individuals were identified between 10th January and 25th February 1984.

*Moss Taylor*

## Glaucous Gull CLEY. 8-10-1986. (BOY GEORGE) *Larus hyperboreus*

**A scarce passage migrant and winter visitor, very rare in mid-summer.**

The Glaucous Gull breeds from the high Arctic to subarctic coasts, which in the Western Palearctic includes northern Iceland, Spitsbergen, Novaya Zemlya and northern Russia. The Icelandic population, which increased by over 50% in the period 1970–90, is mainly resident, while other European populations winter as far north as weather conditions allow. As a winter visitor to Britain and Ireland, the species shows a marked northerly bias, with many occurring in Shetland and Orkney, and comparatively few in southern England (Winter Atlas).

Stevenson described the Glaucous Gull as a not infrequent autumn and winter visitor in immature plumage, but adults were rare. At Blakeney, it was known as the 'cream-coloured gull' and was renowned for being much tamer than the other gulls and therefore more easily 'procured'. The famous gales of 18th–19th January 1881 resulted in an unprecedented influx of Glaucous Gulls, after which 40–50 were offered for sale at Yarmouth. Riviere stated that the species occurred most frequently in hard weather or after north-east gales, but could provide no authentic records between the end of February and the second week of October. Since then the majority of sightings have continued to be between October and March, although it has been recorded in the county in all months, including occasional birds in mid-summer.

The first birds of the autumn are generally recorded in late September or early October, but in those years in which regularly-returning adults have overwintered at the same locality, they have often been seen by the end of August. Usually seen singly, larger numbers have invariably been associated with northerly gales in late October and November. The highest day-counts have been 15 near the Watch House at Blakeney Point, in the company of Great Black-backed Gulls, on 19th November 1952, up to seven west at Cley and Sheringham on 17th and six west on 21st November 1977, and seven past Cley between 27th October and 2nd November 1974. During an influx on 19th–21st October 1991 from one to three were recorded at twelve sites around the coast from Yarmouth to Holme. Peak numbers in the county were recorded between the late 1970s and mid-1980s, during which time a maximum of nine were present on many dates along the coast between Heacham and Holme in early 1984, and up to five in the same area in the winters of 1983 and 1986. Elsewhere, the highest mid-winter count concerned five first-winter birds west at Sheringham on 2nd January 1980, while at the same locality, a total of 16 birds were involved in movements of large gulls between January and April 1979. While fewer were recorded in Norfolk between 1987 and the early 1990s, numbers each winter are now once again increasing.

Glaucous Gulls show a tendency for individuals to return to the same wintering site over a number of years – the most famous in Norfolk was one which first appeared at Cley as a first-winter bird in autumn 1963 and returned annually to winter along the coast between Blakeney Point and Weybourne until it was last seen in spring 1979. During the 16 years it became a familiar bird to most visiting birdwatchers, being known variously as 'Weybourne Willie' and latterly as 'George'. No regular replacement occupied the vacant winter territory until 1982–83, when an adult first appeared which subsequently returned each winter and it was last seen in spring 1990. It, too, regularly patrolled between Blakeney Point and Sheringham and was given the name 'Son of George', which was inevitably shortened to 'Boy George' (Gantlett 1986).

8-10-1986.
CLEY.

The last Glaucous Gulls in the spring are generally seen in early April but occasional birds stay into May. There have been a few records in both June and July, often at Breydon including one from 6th June to mid-August 1968. In the same year a sub-adult was present between Cley and Weybourne throughout the year.

In recent years a few Glaucous Gulls have been recorded annually inland, either scavenging at rubbish tips or on inland stretches of water, such as the Broads, the upper reaches of the Wensum Valley and Aldeby Refuse Tip in the Waveney Valley. The Cobholm Refuse Tip, along the south wall of Breydon, proved an attraction to the species until it was closed in 1974, with a maximum of up to four birds in early 1971 (Allard 1973).

A large proportion of the Icelandic breeding population consists of Glaucous x Herring Gull hybrids and it is the likely origin of hybrids that have appeared in Norfolk in recent years. The majority have been first-winter birds and since the first was identified at Wereham Refuse Tip in March 1987, about ten have been reported. One hybrid which arrived in first-winter plumage on the north coast on 1st July 1989 remained between Blakeney Point and Cromer until 20th April 1990, and during its stay caused great confusion, frequently being mistaken for a pure-bred Glaucous Gull.

*Moss Taylor*

## Great Black-backed Gull   GREAT YARMOUTH. 4·7·1993.    *Larus marinus*

**A common passage migrant and winter visitor, and fairly common non-breeding summer visitor.**

The Great Black-backed Gull breeds mainly on the maritime coasts of the North Atlantic and Baltic Sea, with a few breeding on inland lakes and moors. The largest populations are in Norway, Iceland, Britain and Ireland. Large increases in numbers have taken place in many areas since the 1970s. In the British Isles it is the most maritime and least common of the five breeding species of *Larus* gulls. It nests around most of the northern and western coasts, but is absent from the east and south coasts of Britain between the Firth of Forth and Chichester Harbour (New Atlas).

Great Black-backed Gull
*(Gary Wright)*

Although the species has never bred in Norfolk (despite the erroneous record of one apparently nesting on Blakeney Point during the 68–72 BTO Atlas), it has always been present in the county throughout the year (Stevenson and Riviere). During the late 19th and early 20th centuries the presence of large numbers of Great Black-backed Gulls coincided with the herring-fishing season, between late August and early December. At this time, thousands of Great Black-backed and smaller numbers of Herring Gulls daily followed the herring drifters to the herring-grounds in the North Sea, to return to their resting places later in the day at Breydon, on the foreshore or marshes between Winterton and Horsey, or on the five-mile stretch of sands between Blakeney and Wells Harbour. On occasions the day-long movements were on a mammoth scale. Riviere (1921) described an astonishing total of 72,000 large gulls, 80% of which were adult Great Black-backs, moving north-west off Palling on 13th October 1913. This passage coincided with the season's record herring catches made by Yarmouth boats at the time. Despite the disastrous decline in the herring fishing, large numbers of Great Black-backed Gulls have continued to arrive in Norfolk in autumn and to overwinter in the county, both around the coast and inland.

The first birds of the autumn have begun to pass west along the north Norfolk coast by early July, with the main arrival in August and September. Although the highest daily count of birds on passage in early autumn has been only 120 west at Sheringham on 31st August 1996, by this time many hundreds and on occasions over a thousand have been present in east Norfolk. A gathering of 5,000 adult Great Black-backed Gulls on Scroby Sands on 25th August 1971 must have made an impressive sight, while in more recent years Breydon has held up to 1,200 in late August, numbers building up to 1,400 in December 1996.

In the mid-1950s up to 550 Great Black-backed Gulls also roosted on Winterton beach in autumn. The Wash WeBS count in September 1995 was 1,150 but numbers in autumn in north Norfolk are generally smaller with maximum counts of 275 at Thornham in September 1993, 450 at Scolt/Brancaster on 2nd September 1996 and up to 800 at Stiffkey in October–November from 1956 to 1960. A recent trend is for the species to roost on the numerous unmanned satellite gas platforms off the Norfolk coast, causing a considerable mess and a great hazard to the helicopter crews.

Away from Breydon and the Wash, the largest mid-winter counts have often been at inland sites. In the 1950s roosts of up to 400 at Mickle Mere and 100 at Fowlmere in the Brecks were regular, with the birds feeding on the heaths over a large area, returning each evening to the meres to roost. In recent years the Wensum Valley has held large numbers with 675 in January 1994, and a roost at Attlebridge peaking at 640 in February 1996. Up to 185 have been recorded at Colney Gravel Pits and in the Broads, Wroxham has attracted up to 210. At Welney, a few wintering individuals have specialised in catching sick or injured ducks, which they obtain by flying through flocks of waterfowl to disturb them and then quickly selecting any that have been knocked to the ground or into the water. Some impressive coastal, hard-weather winter movements, often in association with Herring Gulls, have been recorded in north Norfolk – at Sheringham 3,500 east on 1st January 1979, 1,200 west on 15th November 1993 and 1,200 west on 2nd January 1995, on which date 1,000 flew west at Burnham Overy.

Spring passage is mainly from March to mid-May, but numbers are generally small and the largest counts have all been at Sheringham – 330 west on 20th March 1980, 140 east on 14th May 1994 and 120 east on 10th and 17th March 1996. Small numbers of non-breeders remain in the county during the summer months, during which time they are particularly attracted by the terns' eggs and young on Scolt Head and Blakeney Point, while up to 350 immatures have spent the summer months on Breydon in recent years.

Almost complete albinos have been recorded at Breydon in September 1900, October 1905, each winter from November 1960 to February 1969 and in September 1994.

The majority of the foreign-ringed Great Black-backed Gulls found in Norfolk have been ringed as nestlings in Norway, with another from Murmansk, in the far north of Russia; while an adult ringed on the Kharlov Islands, Murmansk in June 1982 was found dead at Breydon in November. Ringed nestlings from Fair Isle and Orkney (3) have been found in the county. Only two Norfolk-ringed Great Black-backed Gulls have been recovered abroad, both from Coltishall on 25th November 1977 and found in Norway in 1983 and long-dead in Sweden in 1990.

*Moss Taylor*

# Ross's Gull                                   *Rhodostethia rosea*

**A very rare vagrant; one record.**

The Ross's Gull of the high Arctic breeds only in the valleys and deltas of a few large north-flowing rivers in the extreme north-east of Siberia. Pairs have bred occasionally in arctic Canada and exceptionally in Greenland and Spitsbergen. Soon after breeding, adults and young disperse northwards to the shores of the Arctic Ocean and most then head west, some reaching the edge of the pack ice through the Kara Sea until they arrive at Franz Joseph Land and Spitsbergen, the northern limits of the Norwegian Sea. It is a rare vagrant to the British Isles, with the majority of records relating to adult birds.

Following days of strong north-easterly winds, an adult in immaculate pink breeding plumage was found by Eddie Myers on Arnold's Marsh, Cley on 9th May 1984 causing much excitement. The next day it appeared at Blakeney Point, returning to Cley on 11th–12th May. It fed by both periodically dipping to seize food and swimming against the current whilst rapidly picking at the surface of the water in the manner of a phalarope (Myers 1985). Its final appearance was at Titchwell on 13th–14th May 1984.

*Peter Allard*

# Kittiwake (Black-legged Kittiwake)                    *Rissa tridactyla*

**A very common passage migrant and rare breeder.**

The Kittiwake breeds at all latitudes from the Iberian peninsula, the Gulf of St Lawrence and the southern Kuril Islands in the south, to north-east and north-west Greenland and the islands of the Arctic Ocean. The British population, numbering about half a million pairs, breeds around almost the entire coastline, although more sparsely distributed in the south and west than in the north and north-east. There are no breeding colonies between south Yorkshire and Kent with the exception of one at Lowestoft in Suffolk. Outside the breeding season indications are that British birds disperse into the North Atlantic, the Bay of Biscay and even as far west as Newfoundland and Nova Scotia.

Stevenson stated: 'This elegant species is described by the Messrs Paget as rather rare at Yarmouth, and recent observations both in that neighbourhood and on other parts of the coast, have convinced me that at no season can it be termed common.' Riviere commented: 'The Kittiwake is essentially an oceanic species, appearing inshore only under stress of exceptionally severe weather, and for this reason it comes comparatively seldom under observation', and that 'unusually large numbers were found dead along the coast in the latter half of February 1890, just previous to the severe weather, accompanied by easterly winds and heavy snowstorms, which prevailed from 28th February to 3rd March'.

Kittiwakes
(Gary Wright)

Successful breeding has never occurred in Norfolk. Unsuccessful breeding attempts occurred at Scolt Head in 1946, with two pairs at Blakeney Point in 1958, five pairs at Scolt Head in 1968–71, at Trimingham in 1970–74, up to 15 pairs on the gas rig Amoco 49/27B positioned 70km off Yarmouth in 1979 (these attempted to breed but the nests were destroyed for safety reasons) and two pairs nest-building at Hunstanton in 1994.

Spring passage is light, the only counts of note since 1975 being 2,100 at Sheringham on 2nd March 1990, 1,350 at Holme on 17th March 1994 and 1,400 at Sheringham on 5th May 1997. Between the mid-1940s and the mid-1960s, large mid-summer gatherings of Kittiwakes occurred with some regularity. Peak counts included 3,000 at Blakeney Point in July 1965, 10,000 at Scolt Head in 1967 and 5,100 at Scroby Sands in 1972. Numbers have now reduced dramatically. Since 1976 Scroby Sands has been covered by all but the lowest of high tides and no concentrations are now recorded there. The only recent mid-summer count of note was 500 roosting at Scolt Head on 22nd July 1993.

Autumn passage occurs from September to December and peaks in October and November. A remarkable flock of Kittiwakes estimated to be seven miles long was feeding down the centre of the Wash on 24th December 1961. An immense eastward passage took place off Cley on 21st November 1965 with birds passing all day at a rate of 3,000 per hour. Storm-driven movements can be quite spectacular with 6,000 off Wolferton and 20,000 in the south Wash on 21st October 1970, and 6,000 off the Ouse Mouth on 17th November 1975. More recently 5,000–10,000 at Brancaster on 22nd November 1977, 20,000 east at Sheringham on 22nd November 1989, 3,500 per hour at Paston on 19th November 1991, 5,000 at Overstrand on 16th November 1995 and 3,500 east at Sheringham on 12th November 1996 were all notable. A heavy easterly passage was noted at several north coast sites on 24th October 1997 with 5,270 at Cley, 6,800 at Sheringham and 9,600 at Mundesley. Winter counts are generally unexceptional, the highest counts since 1976 have all been at Sheringham with 3,000 on 12th January 1984 and 3rd January

1986, 6,500 east on 13th February 1996 and 4,000 on 19th January 1998.

Inland occurrences are very scarce with double-figure counts unusual. Stevenson referred to an adult being shot near the railway bridge at Thorpe next Norwich during the first week in June (exact year uncertain but probably 1861). However, an amazing 132 were at Tottenhill Gravel Pits on 24th March 1986 in strong westerly winds and 200 were roosting on the River Ouse north of King's Lynn on 3rd May 1987 during strong north-easterly winds. During a north-westerly gale with sleet on 29th February 1988, 1,300 were at Lynn Point, of which over 1,000 spiralled up and flew inland, while 60 headed inland over Choseley on 21st February 1993.

A Kittiwake x Common Gull hybrid was at Hopton-on-Sea on 25th December 1995. Ten nestlings ringed in Northumberland, nine from the Farne Islands and one from North Shields, have been recovered in Norfolk, and two each from Scottish and Welsh colonies, while one ringed in the North Sea, off Belgium in October 1977 was found at Terrington in February 1983.

*Keith Dye*

# Ivory Gull                                    *Pagophila eburnea*

**A very rare vagrant; one record.**

The Ivory Gull rarely strays south of the Arctic seas, breeding in scattered colonies on coasts and islands in north-west Canada, Greenland, Spitsbergen, Franz Josef Land, Novaya Zemlya and northern Siberia. It winters near the edge of the pack ice. It is a rare vagrant to the British Isles, with the majority of records being in Scotland, especially around Shetland, and mainly involving immature birds.

A first-winter bird found by Margaret Clarke remained in the Brancaster/Burnham Overy and Holkham area on 5th–9th January 1978, being last seen near Gun Hill before heading east. It fed frequently on an almost totally buried seal on the beach, as well as on other tideline corpses and allowed a close approach by those observers fortunate enough to see it (Clarke 1979).

*Peter Allard*

# Gull-billed Tern                              *Sterna nilotica*

**A rare vagrant.**

The Gull-billed Tern has a cosmopolitan but very discontinuous distribution, breeding in the Neotropical, Nearctic, Australian, Oriental, Afrotropical and Palearctic regions. The European population is mainly in the Mediterranean and Black Sea regions, with over 50% in Spain. Most European colonies have been decreasing since the early 1900s, due to a variety of causes, including loss of foraging habitats (e.g. wetlands, fields and ditches), destruction and disturbance of colony sites, and drought and pesticides in the winter quarters. Gull-billed Terns winter in the tropics, with those from Western Europe wintering in West Africa. To Britain, the Gull-billed Tern has always been a rare visitor, with only a few records most years and it is likely to become even rarer as the European population falls. A pair bred unsuccessfully at Abberton Reservoir, Essex in 1950, having summered the previous year.

The first Norfolk record concerned an adult male shot at Breydon on 14th April 1849, which is now in the collection at Bury St Edmund's Museum. Three further Gull-billed Terns, including two shot on 1st September 1849 and on display in the Castle Museum, Norwich, were also collected at Breydon during the same year. By the end of the 19th century the county total stood at ten, all except one of which had been obtained at or near Breydon. Stevenson considered that the birds recorded during the spring of the mid-1800s were on passage to their breeding colonies in the Frisian Islands. Almost 30 years were to pass before the species was once again seen in the county. On 17th May 1925, no less than five were recorded – one at Langmere and four seen by Arthur Patterson while he rowed up the main channel at, where else, but Breydon. This remains the largest party to have been recorded in Norfolk and, probably, the British Isles. Since then three or four have been recorded in each decade, except for seven in the 1960s and ten during the 1970s, bringing the county total to 48.

Apart from the first Norfolk record in April 1849, the earliest spring date is 8th May, with a pair at or near Breydon in 1878 and one at Salthouse in 1947. From then until early September the records are fairly evenly spread throughout the summer months. The latest the species has been recorded were two at Cley on 28th September 1974, one at Thornham and Holme on 14th October 1974 and one at Blakeney on 25th–26th October 1967. The vast majority of records refer to single birds, seen on only one date.

Whereas Breydon accounted for almost all the records up to the 1930s, only one has been seen there since, on 6th June 1977. Almost half the Gull-billed Terns recorded in Norfolk since 1932 have been between Weybourne and Blakeney Point. Apart from those mentioned earlier, the only other inland records have been a total of four at Hickling Broad between 1937 and 1947, and a second bird at Langmere on 9th May 1947.

Although a Gull-billed Tern was present between Weybourne and Blakeney from 27th August to 3rd September 1972, the most famous long-staying individual was at Titchwell on 7th–27th July 1980. This bird remained in the tern colony during its unusually lengthy stay, during which time both Little and Common Terns were very aggressive towards it, whenever it approached their nests or chicks. Despite this it regularly seized Little Tern chicks, which on being dropped scampered off apparently none the worse for the experience. There was no evidence that any were killed although it was seen to eat terns' eggs. On one occasion it even seized a sitting adult Little Tern by the bill, flying off with it dangling below! By mid-July it had changed its diet and began feeding on fish discarded by Little Tern chicks. Towards the end of its stay it became more elusive, often heading off towards Scolt Head where at least twelve Ringed Plover chicks were taken. The majority of Little and Common Terns had fledged and had left Titchwell by late July, and the Gull-billed Tern was last recorded on 27th July (Wells 1981).

*Moss Taylor*

## Caspian Tern                                                        *Sterna caspia*

**A rare vagrant, mainly in mid-summer.**

The Caspian Tern has a cosmopolitan, but highly scattered breeding distribution across every continent except South America and Antarctica. In Europe there are three separate migratory populations, the nearest to Britain being in the Baltic. Although there was initially a marked increase in numbers during the 20th century, in recent years the Baltic population has decreased, although the stronghold remains in Finland. The Baltic birds winter mainly in Mali, West Africa.

The first British record was of an immature shot at Breydon on 4th October 1825. In a striking parallel with the Gull-billed Tern, of the first 14 Norfolk records up to 1918, all but one were in the Yarmouth area. Stevenson described the curious history attached to the fourth Norfolk record: on 16th April 1839 someone went into a Yarmouth gunsmith's to buy a gun, and chose one which suited him, but before completing his purchase he asked the gunsmith to allow him to try it, and, the latter consenting, he took it just outside the town and shot the first bird which passed over him, which proved to be this Caspian tern! The specimen may still be seen in the Castle Museum, Norwich. Another of these early Breydon records concerned one on 10th August 1910 which alighted on a punt, 15 yards away from Arthur Patterson and George Jary who were both aboard the Watcher's moored houseboat.

The next Norfolk record was not until 1959 when two were seen at Hickling Broad on 17th–26th June and one on several dates from 10th September to 2nd October, one of several that have made prolonged, if intermittent, stays at this site. Since then five were recorded in both the 1960s and 1970s, nine in the 1980s and so far ten during the 1990s. Presumably the increase in observer coverage balances the decline in numbers in the Baltic. The county total is currently at least 45.

The 1839 record described above is one of only two in April, the other being at Breydon on 29th April 1988 which was seen earlier in the day at Lowestoft, Suffolk and an adult male also at Breydon on 2nd May 1862, is the only one in the first half of May. The majority of sightings have been between mid-May and August with a peak in July. The latest dates have involved the one at Hickling Broad on 2nd October 1959 and the first British record at Breydon on 4th October 1825. The favoured haunts of Caspian Terns in Norfolk have been Breydon, Hickling Broad and Cley. The longest-staying bird was one seen intermittently at Hickling Broad and Breydon from 23rd May to 7th July 1987. Other birds have wandered more widely during their stay in Norfolk, making it difficult to decide how many individuals are involved. For example, in 1991 a bird ringed on its left leg was seen at Breydon, Cantley Beet Factory, Hickling and Filby Broads between 6th July and 1st August, with a second bird, ringed on its right leg, in mid-July; the pair roosted together at Breydon on 15th July (Allard 1992). It was presumed that one of the same birds was also photographed at Minsmere, Suffolk on 28th July. One also wandered between Breydon and Hickling Broad in July 1993, while the same bird was also seen at Bacton on 28th July and flying past Blakeney Point and Brancaster, and Spurn, Humberside the following day. There have been three other records of two birds together – at Hickling on 3rd–8th August 1973, at Breydon on 4th–7th July 1987 and at Hickling on 18th June 1988. Single Caspian Terns were attracted to the Scolt Head ternery on 29th June 1970 and 28th–30th May 1971.

*Moss Taylor*

## Lesser Crested Tern                          *Sterna bengalensis*

**A very rare vagrant; four sightings involving at least two different individuals.**

The Lesser Crested Tern breeds in North Africa, particularly on the Mediterranean coast of Libya. Other populations breed in the Red Sea, Gulf of Aden and Persian Gulf. In recent years, there have been several instances of pure or mixed breeding pairs (with Sandwich Terns) in southern France, Italy and Spain, as well as on the Farne Islands, Northumberland. The North African breeders winter in West Africa, particularly in Senegal and The Gambia. It is a rare vagrant to the British Isles, first recorded in Wales in 1982.

An adult Lesser Crested Tern was found by Steve Gantlett associating with Sandwich Terns on Blakeney Point on 9th August 1983. It remained there, being seen almost daily, until 17th September and was watched by many hundreds of birders during this period. The same individual was also recorded at Morston on 21st August, at Scolt Head on 27th August and at Holme on 29th August. This was only the second record for the British Isles (Gantlett 1987). An adult, believed to be this same bird, roosted on Arnold's Marsh, Cley on 26th August 1988 and was later seen at Titchwell on 3rd September. What was almost certainly the same bird, a female, appeared on the Farne Islands, Northumberland annually from 1984 to 1997, either to breed or summer with Sandwich Terns. This individual, nicknamed 'Elsie', reared four hybrid young during this period but failed to return in 1998.

What is accepted as a different adult, and the fifth British record, associated with Sandwich Terns at Scolt Head on 8th–21st July 1993 and was also seen in Thornham Harbour on 11th July. This bird was assumed to be a male as it was seen stealing a sand eel from a male Sandwich Tern which it then presented to a presumed female Sandwich Tern. A Lesser Crested Tern which flew east past Sheringham on 22nd August 1993 was considered to have been the Farne Islands female.

*Peter Allard*

TITCHWELL. RSPB. 19-9-1993.

## Sandwich Tern    GREAT YARMOUTH. 22-6-1991.      *Sterna sandvicensis*

**A common summer visitor and passage migrant; very rare in winter.**

The nominate race of Sandwich Tern *S. s. sandvicensis* breeds along the Atlantic coasts of Europe, around the North Sea, in the Baltic, the western Mediterranean, Sea of Azov and the Black and Caspian Seas. In autumn the western European population migrates south along the west coast of Africa to winter between Mauritania and the Cape of Good Hope. There are often large fluctuations in the local numbers of breeding pairs, but overall there has probably been an increase in the European population during the 20th century. The species has a scattered distribution around the coast of Britain and Ireland, mainly in densely-packed colonies, many of which are on nature reserves (New Atlas).

Stevenson's opening sentence is perhaps surprising: 'This species has occurred much more frequently on the Norfolk coast than the Caspian tern, although perhaps not so frequently as might have been anticipated.' In fact, the first fully authenticated record was not until one was taken at Yarmouth in September 1827 with only a further 24 examples up to 1881, most of which were in autumn. Pashley, the Cley taxidermist, did not handle one until August 1891 and he also commented that the species was unknown to any of the local gunners before that date; but the species was seen and taken almost annually thereafter, being very plentiful in some years (Pashley 1925). It was suspected of nesting on Blakeney Point in 1893, 1895 and 1897, but it was not until 1920 that the first authentic evidence was forthcoming, when Clifford Borrer reported finding a nest (Gurney 1921). By 1922 nine nests were located on Blakeney Point, but the main colony had become established on an island on Salthouse Broad where 99 nests were present. Numbers increased dramatically the following year with at least 100 breeding pairs on Blakeney Point, 303 at

Salthouse Broad, 180 on Cley Marsh (the only year that the species has ever nested at this site) and 59 pairs at Scolt Head. The colony on Salthouse Broad increased each year with 923 nests in 1935 and an estimated 1,000 nests between 1937 and 1941. In 1943, the colony settled on Cley beach in the middle of a minefield and 20 pairs nested on Salthouse Broad in 1944, since when the site has been deserted for nesting purposes (Seago 1967).

The Sandwich Tern colonies at both Blakeney Point and Scolt Head have been carefully monitored since their establishment in the 1920s. It has become apparent that in some years Blakeney Point has been favoured and in others Scolt Head, while the overall trend in the combined population at the two sites has been one of increasing numbers since the early 1960s to reach a peak in 1979 of 5,600 breeding pairs (McNeill 1993a). The Blakeney Point colony held 1,500 pairs in 1929, only nine years after the species first bred there. However, between 1930 and 1944 breeding was spasmodic with no more than 50 pairs annually. A total of 1,000 pairs nested in 1945, and up to 194 pairs between 1946 and 1956. In 1957, 600 pairs bred increasing to 800 pairs the following year, both with high breeding success. Despite this, the colony was deserted the following year, the birds probably moving to a newly-established site at Warham, where 400–600 pairs nested during the next two summers. No further successful nesting took place at Blakeney Point until 1966 when 105 pairs bred and then not again until 1976, since when, Sandwich Terns have bred there annually with between 1,000 and 4,000 pairs.

**Sandwich Terns**
*(Richard Richardson)*

R·A·R

Since Scolt Head was first colonised in 1923, the species has bred annually at this site, except for 1990 when fox predation was at its peak (see below). Up to 150 pairs bred up to 1941, increasing dramatically to 1,042 pairs in 1942 following the desertion of the Salthouse Broad site. During the next 20 years numbers varied from 1,900 pairs in 1946 to just two pairs in 1960. Peak numbers were reached in the 1970s and 1980s, with a maximum of 4,800 breeding pairs in 1972. In general, the more pairs there are at Scolt Head, the fewer are at Blakeney Point.

Elsewhere in Norfolk, the Warham colony moved to Stiffkey Binks in 1963, with 250 pairs, and was used intermittently until 1977. It became the main locality for Norfolk's breeding Sandwich Terns in 1973 with 3,500 pairs, when Scolt Head held 800 pairs and there were none at all at Blakeney Point. About half the breeding population moved back to Scolt Head the next year, with the entire north Norfolk breeding population at Scolt in 1975.

In east Norfolk, the nesting of Sandwich Terns at Scroby Sands was first confirmed in 1947 and continued until 1965 with a peak of 450 pairs in 1952. In most years breeding success was disappointing and in only four years were many young fledged. Strong winds combined with high tides often resulted in the sandbank being completely covered at the crucial period. The subsequent lowering of the sandbank made it unsuitable for nesting terns although two pairs bred in 1972, 60 pairs in 1975 and an estimated 200 pairs in 1976. Nowadays, Scroby Sands are usually covered at each high tide.

The presence of breeding Black-headed Gulls within a Sandwich Tern colony appears to be one of the factors governing breeding success. In the early part of the season, when both species are incubating or brooding young, it is the Black-headed Gulls which rise off their nests to challenge potential avian predators, such as Herring or Lesser Black-backed Gulls. The terns benefit by losing fewer eggs or young at this time because they very rarely leave them exposed. Later in the season, Black-headed Gulls regain the advantage through kleptoparasitism, robbing the Sandwich Terns as they return from their fishing trips and feeding their own young with the prey items, usually sand eels (McNeill 1993a). However, also at this period, the Black-headed Gull chicks are dispersed over a wider area, consequently the aggression of the adult Black-headed Gulls is less concentrated against the larger gull predators and the Sandwich Tern chicks are more vulnerable (Gilbert 1996).

Potentially, the most devastating predators at a Sandwich Tern colony are foxes. At Scolt Head, where foxes first appeared in 1988, they were responsible for the loss of about 1,200 chicks and 60 adult birds from a breeding population of 2,775 pairs. The following year 1,052 nests were counted on 3rd July but most were soon deserted and no young were reared due to the activities of foxes. None nested in 1990, due to fox disturbance at night and the next year, despite 320 nests being located, the breeding season was once again a complete failure. By intensive control of foxes, involving night-sight shooting, snares and electric fences coupled with hunting on the mainland (over 90 were killed in the area adjacent to Scolt in a single year) Sandwich Terns once again bred successfully at Scolt Head in 1992. Unfortunately though, adverse weather in early July caused extensive damage to the colony with high tides and flying foam, followed by a violent thunderstorm and strong northerly winds, which resulted in the deaths of all chicks under ten-days old. Thus the breeding success of Sandwich Terns in Norfolk is very variable from year to year.

The adults are known to travel considerable distances when feeding young. Favoured fishing areas include Seal Sand in the centre of the Wash and the vicinity of the Race Bank, 12km north of Blakeney Point. Those passing Sheringham and Cromer are thought to fish near Happisburgh Sands ten kilometres offshore. Despite the clamour at a colony, Sandwich Tern chicks are known to be able to identify the calls of their approaching parents.

The Sandwich Tern is one of the earliest migrants to return in spring. In 1930 Riviere stated that the first arrivals were normally seen in the second half of April with the earliest ever on 8th April 1923. Between 1953 and 1980, the first Sandwich Tern was usually recorded in the last ten days of March, while since then the first sightings have generally been in the second or third week of March. Even allowing for the increase in the number of observers, it does appear that Sandwich Terns have been arriving back earlier in recent years. The earliest record was one at Hunstanton on 24th February 1981, although a freshly-dead·Sandwich Tern, ringed on the Farne Islands, Northumberland two years earlier, was found at Happisburgh on 13th February 1974. More recently the first returning birds were noted on 7th March 1996 and 2nd March 1997. While many of the breeding birds have arrived back at the Norfolk colonies by the end of April, the spring passage generally peaks in May, presumably involving birds from the colonies further north. An arrival of 400–500 adults at Scolt Head on 18th June 1957, which left the next day were probably birds which had been disturbed from another colony outside the county. During the 1950s and 1960s Arnold's Marsh at Cley often acted as a spring assembly point with up to 500 Sandwich Terns in late April and early May. Nowadays, away from the breeding colonies, Breydon usually holds the largest numbers with a maximum of 351 on 2nd May 1996, although the North Scrape at Cley held 173 on 10th May 1996. Highest counts of birds on offshore passage have all been made at Sheringham with 300 west per hour, during a south-west gale, on 27th May 1972, 500 west on 23rd May 1978, 440 east on 22nd April 1995, 650+ west on 29th May 1996 and a gathering of 340 offshore on 3rd May 1997 during a heavy passage of terns.

Towards the end of the breeding season some very impressive totals have been recorded in Norfolk. The highest count was 18,500 at Scolt Head on 16th–18th July 1969, comprising 8,000 breeding adults, 2,500 fledglings and 8,000 non-breeders, presumably displaced birds from a failed colony. By late July Sandwich Terns, both adults and accompanying juveniles, are feeding offshore along the north Norfolk coast. Away from the breeding sites the highest count at this time has been 500 off Sheringham on 24th July 1996, while at the same site 1,500 flew east during a northerly gale on 28th July 1976. In east Norfolk the largest gatherings have been at Breydon, with 800 on 24th July 1980 and 750 on 31st July 1979. Throughout August and the first half of September the passage of Sandwich Terns continues around the Norfolk coast. At Lynn Point migrants have been noted flying high inland along the River Ouse, including 63 on 28th August and 109 on 14th September 1981. At Hunstanton 800 were feeding off Sunk Sand on 1st September 1993, while the highest count at Holme was 1,100 on 10th August 1995 and at Mundesley 512 flew east on 1st September 1994. The latest sightings each year are generally in the first half of November, although birds have been recorded in December in five years since 1963. This includes one at Sheringham up to 12th with four on 16th December 1997, and the latest at Cley on 17th December 1988.

Sightings of Sandwich Terns at inland localities appear to have become more frequent since the 1970s, with annual records since 1987. However, as long ago as the mid-1950s parties of up to six had been noted at Hickling Broad. In recent years the more notable groups have been 25 at Surlingham Church Marsh on 3rd September 1986, twelve at Flitcham on 10th September 1990, seven at Hickling Broad on 16th April 1991 and six flying east over Norwich on 15th September 1994, a day on which large numbers of seabirds were recorded around the Norfolk coast in a northerly gale.

The vast majority of first-summer Sandwich Terns remain in their African winter quarters, but five have been recorded in Norfolk – the first at Breydon on 20th–21st June 1993 was joined by a second bird the following day, one in the Cley/Blakeney Point area on 6th–23rd June 1994, and at Breydon on 1st–2nd July 1994 and 15th–16th June 1997.

One of the first foreign-ringed birds ever to be found in Norfolk was a Sandwich Tern at Yarmouth on 29th August 1917 which had been ringed as a nestling at Kerkwerve, The Netherlands on 29th June 1912; while one of the first foreign recoveries of a Norfolk-ringed bird was also a Sandwich Tern from Scolt Head, ringed in 1925 and recovered two years later in Portugal. Two others ringed at Blakeney Point in 1928 which were found in Angola in January 1929 became the first African recoveries from the county. Since these early days many thousands of Sandwich Tern nestlings have been ringed in Norfolk. These have produced almost 200 foreign recoveries, mainly from ringing at the north coast colonies particularly Salthouse in the 1930, and Scolt Head in the 1930s and from the late 1950s to the mid-1960s. The majority of early autumn recoveries have come from France and Iberia, although one bird in its first autumn was controlled as far south as the Ivory Coast by 24th September, the same date that a four-year old adult was caught in Senegal. During the winter months recoveries have come from virtually all the coastal countries south from Senegal in West Africa to Cape Town in South Africa, but with the majority in Senegal (23), Ghana (47) and Angola (35). Many recoveries have demonstrated that first-year birds remain in their winter quarters throughout the year, but a third-year adult found freshly-dead at Cape Town, South Africa on 24th April was unusually far south for a bird of that age in late April. The early rings were far less durable than those in use today, but despite this a nestling ringed at Salthouse in 1931 was found at Coruna, Spain in September 1944. An even longer-lived bird providing an interesting multiple recovery was ringed as an adult at Terrington in September 1975, controlled at Teesmouth, Cleveland in July 1986 and was eventually found dead at De Panne, Belgium in June 1992, in at least its 18th year (the longevity record for a British-ringed Sandwich Tern is over 30 years!) and was the first British-ringed Sandwich Tern to be recovered in that country. There have been many recoveries of birds on passage in Norfolk which had been ringed on the Farne Islands, Northumberland, but despite 3,000 chicks a year being colour-ringed on the Isle of Griend on the Wadden Sea, one seen at Breydon in July 1995 was the first Dutch colour-ringed bird to be seen in the British Isles.

*Moss Taylor*

## Roseate Tern                                                          *Sterna dougallii*

**A very scarce summer visitor and passage migrant; bred annually between 1923 and 1948, nested unsuccessfully 1996–98.**

In Europe the Roseate Tern's preferred breeding habitat is small islands in sheltered bays and lagoons. About half the European population nests on the Azores, with other large colonies at Rockabill and Lady's Island Lake in Ireland, and in Brittany. Numbers have fluctuated widely during the last 200 years, with a marked decline during the 19th century, to be followed by a marked increase in the 20th century due to special protection for the species. However, during the 1970s and 1980s numbers once again fell due to loss of breeding habitat and high mortality in the wintering areas. This has since been reversed by specific conservation measures. In autumn Roseate Terns migrate along the north-west African coast to winter around the Gulf of Guinea. The species is one of the rarest breeding seabirds in Britain and Ireland, nesting at scattered locations around the coast, always in the company of other species of terns (New Atlas).

The first fully authenticated record for Norfolk was of an adult male shot at Hunstanton by George Hunt on 12th July 1880, which remains in the Castle Museum, Norwich. However, Stevenson also mentioned one at Breydon on 26th May 1871, which was luckier, when it 'flapped slowly past [Mr Booth's] punt on Breydon mudflats, but with both barrels being empty at the time, the bird was out of shot before another cartridge could be inserted'! It was thought that a pair present at the Wells Common Tern colony in June 1897 was likely to have bred (Bloomfield 1993). Between 1923 and1948, up to three pairs bred almost annually at either Scolt Head or Blakeney Point, since when ones and twos have visited the terneries intermittently.

A few were recorded annually between mid- to late May and early September, from at least 1952 until 1973, mainly at Scolt Head and Cley. During this period they were frequently seen at the Scolt Head ternery, where two pairs were displaying on 7th July 1959, three oversummered in 1964, up to four were present in July 1965 and three remained during the breeding season of 1975, but there was no attempt at nesting. A pair was also present at Stiffkey Binks throughout the summer of 1966. Thereafter, until the early 1990s, the Roseate Tern became an even scarcer bird in Norfolk with few records annually and occasional blank years. However, 1986 was an exception, with ten records including four at Horsey on 7th June and one displaying with a Common Tern at Scolt Head on 15th June. From 1993 there was an upsurge in the number of records, with many sightings in that year between Blakeney Harbour and Sheringham. But it was not until 1994 that two non-breeding pairs remained at Blakeney Point for most of the summer, with one pair the following year, when there were also up to three birds around the Common Tern platforms at Breydon between 17th July and 5th August. In 1996 the first nesting attempt since 1948 was recorded near Wells, eggs being laid but unfortunately the nest was washed out in early August. A second pair was also present there but did not attempt to nest. In the same year a pair was displaying on an offshore reef at Eccles/Sea Palling from 16th June to 3rd July. Further breeding attempts were also made in north Norfolk in 1997 and 1998, but no young were fledged from either site due to predation with one pair and flooding with the other (J. Reed *in litt.*). Also during 1998 up to three Roseate Terns frequented the Little Tern colony on the north beach at Yarmouth from 7th July to 8th August. They fed mostly by kleptoparasitism, by stealing fishes brought back by the adult Little Terns which were meant for their chicks.

The Roseate Tern is the latest tern to arrive in Britain and the first Norfolk sightings are generally not until mid-May. Occasional birds have been recorded in early May and the earliest have been two at Hunstanton on 26th April 1981 and one at Cley on 29th April 1973. There have been few records after mid-September, the latest being singles at Cley on 24th September 1995 and 28th September 1971, and an extremely late bird in the Blakeney Point/Cley/Salthouse area on 14th and 21st October 1984. Apart from breeding season records, most sightings concern single birds and there have been very few records

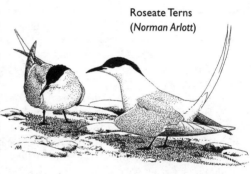

**Roseate Terns**
*(Norman Arlott)*

of birds on passage. Exceptions have included five at Cley on 15th September 1968, four flying north-west at Happisburgh on 5th May 1975 and four with a flock of mixed terns at Blakeney Point and Cley on 3rd–4th September 1988. Apart from the years in which Roseate Terns have bred in Norfolk, there have been only five records of juveniles on the Norfolk coast. The only sighting of a first-summer (or possibly second-summer) bird was at Breydon on 2nd–6th July 1992.

A nestling ringed at the large colony at Rockabill, Dublin, Eire on 13th July 1991 was found dead at Weybourne on 7th July 1995.

*Moss Taylor*

**Common Tern** \ HARDLEY FLOODS. 17·5·1991.                    ***Sterna hirundo***

**A fairly common summer visitor and passage migrant; very rare in winter.**

The Common Tern is the most widespread of the *Sterna* terns, occurring widely from the Arctic fringe south through the boreal and temperate zones, extending east from the British Isles. The species nests colonially on marine and freshwater shores and islands, often in association with Arctic Terns and Black-headed Gulls. The northern European birds winter offshore in sub-equatorial Africa, further south than those from southern Europe. Common Terns are widely distributed around the coasts of Britain and Ireland but, as with Little Terns, the coasts of south-west England and Wales are sparsely populated. There are also many inland colonies in central and eastern England, Scotland and Ireland (New Atlas).

A marked decline in the number of Common Terns occurred in Britain during the 19th century as a result of egging and shooting, and this was noted in Stevenson. By 1890 none bred at Winterton, Salthouse or Holme, nor in Broadland, all former breeding sites. The species did, however, continue to breed at other coastal sites, although the exact localities were not given by Stevenson, for obvious reasons. Their cause was helped by the establishment of a 'close time', during which it was illegal to collect their eggs and in addition the Earl of Leicester totally forbade his tenants from taking the eggs of 'the two terns and the ring dotterel' which bred on his estate.

By 1890 a 'flourishing colony' had become established at Wells (Riviere), which contained 400–500 pairs by 1908. Scolt Head was presented to the National Trust and a 'watcher' appointed in 1922, at which time only 17 pairs were nesting, but the colony rapidly increased due to the protection afforded and by 1925 the number of nests was estimated at 700–1,000. Peak numbers were reached in 1938 with 2,470 pairs. Between 1945 and 1958 the total varied between 900 and 1,400 pairs (Seago 1967). Apart from 900 pairs in 1961, the total declined to between 400–600 pairs from 1959 to 1976, since when it has fallen even further. During the 1990s the colony has not exceeded 150 pairs, except in 1997 when 168 pairs were present but not a single young bird successfully fledged. This was due to adverse weather affecting the first clutches, while later attempts were all predated (similar problems also caused a total failure at Blakeney Point in 1997). While the threat of human predators has fallen, avian predators have taken their toll over the years in the form of Kestrels, Short-eared Owls and the large gulls. Between 1988 and 1992, foxes were a major problem on Scolt Head, reducing the colony to only 14 nests in 1990, and combined with cold, wet weather and flood tides resulted in few young surviving. In fact, no young fledged in 1990 or 1991.

Blakeney Point was first known as a breeding locality for Common Terns as long ago as 1830, with the largest numbers between 1935 and 1940, and again from 1950 to 1952, when well over 2,000 pairs nested. Between 850 and 1,800 pairs bred annually up to 1979, but since then, as at Scolt Head, numbers have fallen with 200–300 pairs since the mid-1980s. The main limiting factor on Common Tern breeding success and therefore presumably on subsequent colony size has been found to be the level of predation. At Blakeney Point, Kestrels, Short-eared Owls, Herring Gulls and even Black-headed Gulls, and stoats have all been implicated (McNeill 1993b).

On the Wash, Common Terns formerly bred at Wolferton where there were over 200 nests in 1914, but the erection of bungalows close to the foreshore resulted in considerable disturbance (Riviere) and the site was eventually abandoned. Nowadays a thriving colony is present at Snettisham, which peaked at 160 pairs in 1980, since when 60–130 pairs have bred annually. Breeding was first reported on the Wash Outer Trial Bank in 1989, peaking at 150 pairs in 1990. Elsewhere in north Norfolk, breeding has occurred sporadically at Titchwell with 120–135 pairs in 1981–83, but up to only six pairs in the 1990s. Common Terns have bred for many years at Stiffkey Binks with a maximum of 150 pairs in the late 1960s and early 1970s. Variable numbers have bred intermittently at Cley and Salthouse over the years – up to 500 pairs bred annually on Salthouse Broad in the 1920s, while up to 200 nested on Cley Marsh in 1923 and 1924 (Riviere). In 1956, although 50 pairs nested on Arnold's Marsh, Cley only one chick was reared and 31 pairs bred at Cley in 1969; more recently five pairs bred at Cley in 1994.

In east Norfolk the mining of Yarmouth beach complete with barbed wire entanglements during the Second World War enabled a large colony to become established there, but with the easing of access restrictions after the war the birds were disturbed and relocated to Scroby Sands. In 1947 Robin Harrison found the number of breeding pairs impossible to assess, but the following year 368 nests were counted, although high tides and storms meant that no young fledged (Allard 1990). Between 1949 and 1965, and from 1971 to 1976, from 50 to 360 pairs bred annually with varying success. Elsewhere in east Norfolk, a pair bred on Winterton beach in 1967.

In April 1977 a small raft was converted for use as a floating breeding platform for Common Terns and was anchored at the eastern end of Breydon. In its first year it attracted 17 pairs (Allard 1987). Since then six substantial fixed platforms, each with raised sides and divided into sections by partitions, have been constructed at Breydon, resulting in the most successful inland breeding colony in the county. The numbers of breeding pairs has steadily increased, exceeding 100 for the first time in 1990 and peaking at 188 nests in 1997. The breeding success on the Breydon platforms has been better than at any other site in Norfolk and 2,140 young have successfully fledged since 1977, a remarkable achievement. Over the years, the average number of chicks fledged per pair has exceeded one, the best year being 1994 when 164 pairs raised 236 young.

In Broadland, where Common Terns bred until abandoning the area during the 19th century, Ranworth was colonised in 1949, the birds initially nesting on partially sunken old wherries and since 1961 on specially constructed rafts. The number of breeding pairs peaked at 57 in 1973, gradually falling since then to an average of about 20 pairs now. Ormesby Broad was the next to be colonised in 1952, with up to ten pairs until 1986, but not subsequently. Up to 16 pairs have bred intermittently at Hickling since 1953 and up to 39 pairs at Hardley Flood from 1961 to 1990. At Hoveton Broad, where breeding first took place in 1973, up to 26 pairs have bred regularly on a raft, a nest-site also used at Barton Broad by up to 21 pairs and at Martham Broad by up to 16 pairs. Many of the smaller areas of water within Broadland have also hosted a few pairs of breeding Common Terns in recent years and as at Breydon, have often proved to be far safer places for the birds to nest, away from the threat of avian and mammalian predators, as well as the vagaries of the North Sea.

Gravel pits along the Wensum Valley were first used as breeding sites by Common Terns in 1969, since when up to nine pairs have nested at Lyng Easthaugh. Similar localities have been used in many other parts of Norfolk but not always with the same success. At Ditchingham Gravel Pit, a tern raft occupied in 1991 and 1992 was destroyed by fishermen during the 1992–93 winter, as it was being used by roosting Cormorants. In addition to the Broads and gravel pits, inland breeding has also been recorded at Wisbech Sewage Farm and the beet factories at Wissington and Cantley. The total number of pairs of Common Terns breeding in Norfolk has fallen from about 2,000 annually in the 1960s and up to the late 1970s, to an average of about 750 since.

The first Common Terns of the spring are generally seen in the first half of April with the main passage in late April and early May. Occasional birds have been recorded in March with the earliest at Wroxham Broad on 24th March 1993, at Cley on 27th March 1977 and three at Wroxham Broad on 29th March 1994. The largest numbers recorded on spring passage have been 200 south at Waxham on 2nd May 1990 and 220 south at Winterton later the same day, 480 east at Sheringham the following day, 300 at Lynn Point on both 25th April 1994 and 3rd May 1996, 150 west at Holme on 21st May 1996 and 610 east at Sheringham on 3rd May 1997.

Late summer assemblies of Common Terns were formerly an annual event at Scolt Head, where counts of about 5,000 were made in late July 1955 and 1956. By 1960, the maximum count had fallen to 3,000, with up to 2,500 at Holme by the end of August. In recent years the highest counts have been 320 at Holme on 1st August 1996, 500 at Scolt Head on 2nd August and 600 on 2nd September 1997, and at least 500 at Breydon on 16th August 1997. The highest offshore counts of birds on autumn passage have mostly been on days with strong northerly winds. The most impressive movement was on 30th August 1992 when a total of 1,150 flew west at Sheringham and 325 south at Winterton. Other notable counts have included 510 west at Sheringham on 23rd August 1992 and 613 west at Holme on 9th August 1993. There is a rapid departure of birds in September with only a few recorded in October. The last Common Tern of the autumn is generally seen between late October and mid-November, with the latest at Cley on 26th November 1984, although single 'Comic' terns on 29th November 1963 and 21st November 1977, would almost certainly have been this species rather than the Arctic Tern.

There have been six winter records of Common Terns – one found freshly dead at Wroxham Broad on 3rd February 1967, one recorded as a 'Comic' tern off Sheringham on 30th December 1978, one which remained at Ellingham throughout the year in 1980, another 'Comic' tern at Heacham on 31st December 1984 and singles at Wells on 6th December 1992 and off Weybourne on 17th–18th February 1995.

First-year Common Terns normally remain in their winter quarters during their first year, but since 1986 between one and five have been seen annually at Breydon in June and early July, with second-summer birds being identified in most years. Elsewhere singles were at Cley and Overstrand in June 1997.

Over 2,000 Common Tern nestlings have been ringed at Norfolk colonies in recent years, the vast majority at Breydon. A total of 63 foreign recoveries has been notified, including twelve in autumn and one in spring as the birds have passed along the coasts of France and Iberia. Over 40 have been reported along the African coast with winter recoveries extending south from Morocco to West Africa, as far east as Nigeria. Most recoveries have been reported from Senegal (9) and Ghana (10). A recovery in Morocco on 10th October was fairly typical of the time taken for birds to reach this far south by then, but a nestling ringed at Breydon on 23rd June 1990, which had reached St Louis, Senegal on 11th September was unusually far south for the time of year. There have been several recoveries of first-year birds in Senegal and

Liberia in June. Three birds have shown easterly movements from Norfolk colonies the month after ring-ing, having been recovered in The Netherlands, Denmark and Germany in mid-August. Two nestlings ringed at the Welsh colony at Shotton have been found at Norfolk colonies in subsequent summers, including one ten years after ringing. Further evidence to suggest breeding away from the natal colony was provided by a nestling from Rye Meads, Hertfordshire found four years later at Hardley Flood in June. Finally some indication of the origin of autumn passage birds was provided by one found at Yarmouth in September which had been ringed earlier that summer on Coquet Island, Northumberland. However, not all autumn movements are in a southerly direction for there have been several controls of Breydon-ringed nestlings in the autumn of the year of ringing at Teesmouth, Cleveland.

*Moss Taylor*

## Arctic Tern                 *Sterna paradisaea*

**A scarce summer visitor and passage migrant.**

As its name implies, the Arctic Tern is a truly Arctic breeding bird, having a circumpolar distribution extending into the boreal zone. In Europe it breeds in Iceland, the British Isles, Fennoscandia, The Neth-erlands, northern Germany and the former Baltic States. It winters in the Antarctic and it has the longest known avian migration route. In Britain it is widely distributed throughout the Northern and Western Isles, along the west coast of Scotland and patchily south to Anglesey, also along the British east coast south to Northumberland and around the coast of Ireland. There are a few small colonies in East Anglia and on the English south coast (New Atlas). Between 1980 and 1990, the Orkney and Shetland populations fell by about 50% due to a lack of sand eels, on which the species depends.

Stevenson stated that the Arctic Tern was mainly noted inland in spring, passing north in small parties, whereas in autumn, when it was more common, it was invariably found along the coast. A statement which still applies today. The main change compared with the 19th century, however, is the status of the species today as a breeding summer visitor, albeit in small numbers. The first proof of breeding in Norfolk was obtained on Blakeney Point in 1922, with ten pairs recorded the following year. Since then the species has bred there almost annually, with up to a maximum of six pairs to 1990. In the following year 15 pairs nested and a record 22 pairs in 1992, since when about 20 pairs have bred annually, but with varying degrees of success. Like Common and Little Terns, they nest in more widely dispersed colonies and do not obtain the benefits from nesting in close proximity to Black-headed Gulls, as do the Sandwich Terns (Gilbert 1996). In fact throughout their entire breeding range, 10% of Arctic Terns nest solitarily (Euro-pean Atlas).

Although Arctic Terns have bred at Scolt Head for many years, only one or two pairs have nested almost annually there since the 1950s. Up to two pairs also nested near Wells in 1958 and 1959, while one or two pairs have bred intermittently at Stiffkey Binks since 1966, with three pairs in 1996, although no young fledged. Elsewhere, single pairs bred at Brancaster in 1990 and 1993, and at Cley/Salthouse in 1993.

The first spring migrants are generally seen from mid-April onwards, passage peaking in late April or May. The earliest records have been on 1st April 1994 at Wroxham Broad and on 4th April 1989 at Weybourne. Arctic Terns migrate on a broad front, and as noted by Stevenson many spring records come from inland localities. At Welney a total of 104 moved north between 22nd April and 7th May 1991, while the highest day-counts, prior to 1998 (see below), had been 30 flying north-east on 20th April 1986 and 24 on 15th April 1992. Other notable inland counts have included 31 at Holt on 2nd May 1987, a party of 30 flying north over Norwich on 23rd April 1990 and 24 at Wissington Beet Factory on 6th May 1991. Similar numbers have been recorded at coastal sites on a number of occasions in spring, with up to 30 at Lynn Point, 31 at Salthouse, 34 at Sheringham and 54 at Yarmouth, while at Breydon 42 Arctic Terns flew east on 30th May 1995. Most movements have occurred in sunny or windy conditions, the day after strong northerly winds and rain. One of the largest 'wrecks' took place on 26th–27th April 1981, when a great many Arctic Terns were recorded feeding over and sheltering in coastal fields after a northerly gale. The highest counts were up to 200 at Paston, 147 at Salthouse, 100 on Arnold's Marsh, Cley and 54 at Wells. However, the largest numbers ever to be recorded in Norfolk were noted in early May 1998, during a period of strong northerly winds. At Welney a total of 1,046 flew north following the River Ouse on 1st–

4th May, with a peak of 586 on 2nd. At the mouth of the River Ouse, at Lynn Point, 504 were recorded continuing north on 1st–3rd May, in flocks of up to 40 birds. Double-figure counts during the same period were also made at many sites throughout the county including Breydon, Cley, Colney Gravel Pits, Filby Broad, Holkham Fresh Marsh, Rockland Broad, Whitlingham Lane Gravel Pit and Wroxham Broad. Apart from known breeding birds, Arctic Terns have occasionally been noted in mid-summer, such as 24 flying west at Paston on 7th June 1986 and 30 feeding in the pit at Blakeney on 27th June 1993.

Autumn passage continues from August to October, but unlike the spring, inland records are very unusual. However, the largest numbers are again invariably associated with adverse weather conditions. In early August 1983 an unprecedented passage was noted during north-west to north-east winds, during which period 73 flew west at Cley on 1st August and 415 flew west at Paston on 6th August. Heavy rain can also result in a heavier passage than usual, such as occurred on 25th August 1987 with 85 at Paston and 350 west at Holkham in only two hours. Normally though, day-counts in excess of about 20 are unusual. The last Arctic Terns of the autumn are generally noted in late October or early November with the latest records on 15th November 1989 at Salthouse, two on 16th November 1996 at Blakeney Point, on 18th November 1985 at Langley Marshes, on 20th November 1994 at Cley and on 22nd November 1997 at Waxham.

Arctic Terns first breed at 3–4 years of age and are not common in British waters in their first two summers. The first Norfolk record of a first-summer bird was at Winterton on 8th June 1976 with another at Cley on 30th June 1986. Birds of this age have been more frequently reported in the 1990s with about nine at Breydon, four at Cley and one at Hickling. In addition, a second-summer bird was at Breydon on 13th–16th June 1995. In 1987 a mixed pair of Arctic and Common Terns bred at Scolt Head but although two eggs hatched, the young disappeared.

Four ringed Arctic Terns have been recovered in the county – a nestling ringed at Bergo, Finland on 15th July 1967 was found exhausted at Winterton on 4th May 1980 and another nestling ringed at Isefjord, Denmark on 4th July 1981 was found dead on Blakeney Point on 12th August. While two nestlings from the Farne Islands, Northumberland were found dead on Norfolk beaches, one of which was 12 years old.

*Moss Taylor*

# Sooty Tern *Sterna fuscata*

**A very rare vagrant; two records.**

The Sooty Tern breeds abundantly on tropical islands in all oceans from the Caribbean and mid-Atlantic, to the Indian and Pacific Oceans, and on islands in the Red Sea. It ranges widely outside the breeding season. It is a rare summer vagrant to the British Isles, the most recent in 1989.

The first Norfolk record was one seen by John Sladen Wing in Blakeney Harbour on 11th September 1935 which he later described in *British Birds*:

> Returning from Blakeney Point to Blakeney by boat on 11th September 1935 a tern about as big as a Sandwich Tern flew in front of the boat. My wife and I noticed the white forehead and black band through the lores and eyes. The underparts were white. The upperparts, bill and wing were black. We have since identified it at the British Museum as an adult Sooty Tern. (Sladen Wing 1936)

A Sooty Tern had also been identified earlier that summer at Dungeness on 29th June.

The second individual was better documented. It was an adult which commuted between Scolt Head and Blakeney Point terneries on 14th–19th June 1966, appearing again on Scolt Head on 11th July. It had been seen earlier on the Scrape at Minsmere, Suffolk on 11th June. Whilst at Scolt Head, it was filmed when displaying to a Common Tern by Dick Bagnall-Oakeley. On 21st June a Sooty Tern also appeared on the Farne Islands, Northumberland.

*Peter Allard*

# Little Tern  SCROBY SANDS. 4·7·1993.                    *Sterna albifrons*

**A fairly common summer visitor.**

The Little Tern has a scattered breeding distribution throughout the middle and lower middle latitudes of the Western Palearctic, with the largest numbers in Italy, Spain and the British Isles. It nests colonially, on marine and lakeside shores, and on islands along inland rivers, often far from the sea. Most of the European population winters off West Africa, between Guinea and Cameroon. The species has a patchy distribution around the British and Irish coasts, being noticeably absent or scarce in the south-west. The coast south from Lincolnshire to Hampshire holds over half the British and Irish population, although numbers have always fluctuated widely, probably reaching a peak during the 1920s and 1930s (New Atlas).

Stevenson is understandably vague about the exact location of Little Tern colonies, in view of the threat from collectors, while Riviere described the species as more widely scattered along the coastline than the Common Tern. In the late 1930s the main breeding stronghold was Scolt Head where just over 200 pairs bred in 1937, with smaller numbers at Blakeney Point and on other less disturbed beaches from Holme to Salthouse, and between Horsey and Winterton. A much-disturbed colony at Caister moved to Scroby Sands in the late 1940s (Seago 1967). The number of breeding pairs in Norfolk has steadily increased from about 200 in the 1950s to over 600 by the late 1990s, as a direct result of the conservation measures outlined below.

In Norfolk, Little Terns breed on open sand and shingle beaches, clear of any vegetation and often within a few metres of the high tide mark. They avoid those beaches that are backed by cliffs. The nests are therefore vulnerable to being covered by sand in strong winds or washed out on particularly high tides, as well as being exposed to heavy summer rains. Norfolk's beaches have become increasingly popular with holidaymakers, whose presence, often inadvertently, can cause serious and repeated disturbance to nesting Little Terns. Although the species typically nests in small, scattered groups, which may provide some protection from predators, the presence of a large, obvious breeding colony makes it particularly susceptible to the attention of both avian and mammalian predators. Species known to have predated the eggs or young of Little Terns in Norfolk include foxes, stoats, hedgehogs, cats, dogs, Kestrels, Oystercatchers, Herring Gulls, Lesser Black-backed Gulls, Magpies and man. Thus both eggs and young are at great risk throughout the breeding season and breeding success varies considerably from year to year, and from colony to colony. In 1992, for instance, 249 pairs at Yarmouth fledged 176 young, whereas on the Holkham Reserve only ten young were raised by 123 pairs. The most effective conservation measures have been found to be the fencing-off of colonies, wardening and predator control, with most recently, the provision of small plastic camouflaged shelters under which the young could hide. It has been estimated that a productivity rate of 0.6 fledged young per pair per year is enough to maintain a population, which is almost certainly being achieved on average in Norfolk.

Where known, the history of the main Norfolk colonies is as follows, commencing with the Wash. Little Terns first bred on the Wash Outer Trial Bank in 1989 with seven pairs in 1992, but none since. Riviere described a long-established colony with Common Terns at Wolferton, but by 1930 numbers were steadily falling as an increasing number of bungalows were erected on the beach. Nearby, at Snettisham, up to 25 pairs bred in the mid-1950s but very few since and the last breeding pair was apparently in 1969. A few pairs formerly bred at Heacham but the site was abandoned in 1957. Up to 30 pairs of Little Terns have bred at Holme and/or Thornham since at least the late 1970s, while at nearby Titchwell breeding was first noted in 1964, the colony peaking at 67 pairs in 1981, although far fewer birds are present nowadays.

The present colony of about 20 pairs at Brancaster has been in existence for over 70 years, with 42 nests being counted as long ago as 1928. The colony, however, is not free from disturbance, as a result of which, in 1983, it relocated for the season to Scolt Head later in the summer. The acquisition of land by conservation bodies has had an enormous effect on the success of breeding terns. Following the transfer of ownership of Scolt Head to the National Trust in 1922, with the subsequent control of visitors, an increasing number of Little Terns bred at this site, with over 100 pairs by 1927. Ten years later the total had passed 200, with 184 pairs in 1947. Thereafter numbers began to fall, as more bred at Blakeney Point, and the colony has varied from 30 to 70 breeding pairs in the last 40 years. The extermination of foxes in 1993 enabled 37 pairs to raise 45 young, which was the most since 1987. The area now covered by the Holkham

NNR includes several long-established Little Tern colonies between Gun Hill and Stiffkey Binks. The largest single colony having been one of 100 pairs at Stiffkey in 1965 (Bloomfield 1993), where there was none in 1982 due to disturbance by motor-cycles. Nowadays the area in total has held between 50 and 125 breeding pairs, but as elsewhere with varying degrees of success.

Riviere described the Little Tern as having bred at Blakeney Point since 'time immemorial' and, as at Scolt Head, numbers increased significantly after it had achieved 'reserve' status. By 1912, about 100 pairs were present at Blakeney Point, although this had fallen to between 20 and 60 pairs in the 1930s, as Scolt Head became the favoured site. By 1949, however, both Bob Chestney and Ted Eales, the respective wardens at each site, claimed to have 127 nests! Thereafter the number of breeding pairs has varied at Blakeney with as few as 54 in 1954, but generally with 100–200 in most years and a maximum of 215 in 1996. In recent years the Little Terns have bred in two distinct areas, one at Halfway House, where in 1993, 62 nests were predated by a pair of Kestrels resulting in total failure and the other in a mixed colony with Common Terns on Far Point. In 1993 this second colony contained 75 pairs and the main predators were Oystercatchers – which were seen to kill both Little and Common Tern chicks by pecking them on the head – and the larger gulls. Short-eared Owls were also seen to take adult Little Terns (McNeill 1993b). Here fencing, wardening and restricted access, as well as the control of mammalian predators have all had beneficial effects on the breeding success of Little Terns. A few pairs also formerly nested on the south side of Blakeney Harbour, but have not done so since 1964. Nearby, Riviere recorded a 'good colony' on the beach at Salthouse since at least 1920 and in the 1950s up to twelve pairs nested between Cley and Salthouse, but not in recent years.

In east Norfolk a few pairs of Little Terns bred in the Waxham/Sea Palling area in the mid-1970s, with a maximum of eleven pairs in 1976. While a colony had been known at Horsey since 1919, where 20–40 pairs were recorded by Riviere. Following a severe storm in February 1938 when the sea broke through at the mouth of the Old Hundred Stream, up to 30 pairs nested on shingle swept inland of the breach in 1938 and 1939. By 1967, the colony had spread along the beach towards Winterton and had grown to 90 pairs by 1972, the second largest in the county. As a direct result of increasing human pressure, numbers fell dramatically and by the early 1980s single-figure counts only were made and breeding no longer occurs there annually. Similarly the colony between Winterton and Hemsby, which held 20 pairs in 1985, had been deserted for the same reason by 1990. Inland, Little Terns bred at Rush Hills on Hickling Broad in the 19th century (Lubbock 1845), as they did between 1969 and 1983, peaking at 41 pairs in 1978, from which only 30 young fledged out of a total of 85 chicks.

At Caister, Riviere recorded that a few pairs attempted to breed from time to time in the early 20th century but the nests were invariably robbed. By the early 1950s, Little Terns were once more trying to nest at Caister south beach, but were much disturbed. Since 1955 up to eight pairs have nested but with little success. None attempted to breed in 1998. The first authenticated breeding at Yarmouth was after the north beach had been mined during the Second World War and by 1945 a large colony had become established there. Unfortunately with the opening of the beach to the public in 1946, the site was abandoned. Between 1950 and 1983, Little Terns bred intermittently at this site with a maximum of only nine pairs. However, during 1983 and 1984, part of the north beach was fenced-off while a sewer pipe was laid, allowing the terns to nest successfully in an enclosed area. In 1986 the RSPB became involved in wardening the site and 55 pairs raised 95 young, despite considerable problems with holidaymakers, dogs and Kestrels (Bubb 1987). As a result of improvements in both fencing and wardening, largely undertaken initially by members of the Yarmouth RSPB group, the colony had grown to 140 pairs raising 244 young in 1988 (Anon 1989). By the following year, the number of pairs had increased to 180 and it had become the largest Little Tern colony in the British Isles (Allard 1990). Since then numbers have increased even further with 277 pairs in 1991 and 255 in 1995.

However, it has not always been easy for either the birds or the wardens at Yarmouth. In 1993, for instance, the colony attracted cats throughout the season, which were thought to be responsible for the remains of five adult Little Terns found within the colony and just four cats were believed to have accounted for 90 young which disappeared by night. Hedgehogs were live-trapped in and around the colony, and despite the supplementary feeding of Kestrels with dead mice (Durdin 1993), a total of 85 Little Tern chicks was seen to be taken by them. The 200 wooden shelters, first used in 1992, were again scattered throughout the colony. Set at an angle against the north-easterly wind they were regularly used by chicks as soon as they were mobile. Torrential rain on a single day resulted in the deaths of 14 chicks. Despite all these precautions, 147 chicks were taken by Kestrels in 1995 and it was thought likely that an additional 124 were taken during unwardened periods. The following breeding season was even more disastrous with a total failure due to a combination of high tides, and serious fox and Kestrel predation, the latter being able to land on the beach and simply extract the chicks from the shelters. As a result, the wooden shelters were replaced in 1997 by 200 shelters consisting of lengths of six-inch plastic piping. The lower circumference was buried in the sand at a level which prevented ground predation by the Kestrels and the upper circumference was camouflaged with the aid of glue and sand. These were quickly taken to by the Little Tern chicks and along with 24-hour wardening, resulted in 138 young fledging from the 191 breeding pairs (Thomas & Atkins 1998). In 1998 the results were even more impressive with 222 pairs raising 338 young.

Offshore from Yarmouth, Little Terns had become established on Scroby Sands by 1945 and this sandbank held up to 27 breeding pairs between 1948 and 1951, with up to 15 pairs between 1955 and 1963. In recent years Scroby Sands have remained below the high water mark for most of the time, although 15 pairs did return in 1976. Two pairs nested at Breydon for the first time in 1973, raising one young, and one to two pairs were present again in 1977.

The first Little Terns of the spring are generally reported offshore in mid-April, although breeding does not commence until towards the end of May. The earliest records have been two at Yarmouth on 24th March 1988 and singles on 7th April 1985 at Titchwell and on 9th April 1957 at Blakeney. Spring passage is unremarkable and the most notable movements have been at Sheringham with 55 east on 7th May 1988, 215 east on 3rd May 1997 and 75 west on 7th, and at Paston with 40 west on 1st June 1980 and 60 west on 29th. A spring roost at Hickling Broad, which peaked at 126 on 11th–16th May 1979, presumably also involved birds from other colonies.

Post-breeding gatherings occasionally involve impressive numbers of Little Terns. The Ouse Mouth at Lynn Point not infrequently attracts large numbers in late July with maximum counts of 280 on 21st July 1996 and 220 on 12th July 1989. Up to 275 were at Scolt Head in late July and early August 1997, while in east Norfolk up to 400 collected on the north beach at Yarmouth at this time and 174 were at Breydon on 24th July 1995. Little Terns depart soon after the end of the breeding season and are very scarce after the end of August. Occasional birds are noted in September with the last one of the year generally being reported in early October. There have been two November records – one on 1st November 1995 at Terrington Marsh and a very late individual at Blakeney Point on 13th November 1988.

Little Terns do not breed until their second spring, and first-summer birds have only been recorded in Norfolk on two occasions. The first was at Cley from 29th May to mid-July 1966 and the next at Breydon from 15th June to 2nd July 1993, during which time it visited the Yarmouth colony on 25th June. The Little Tern is a not infrequent visitor to the coastal Broads with a recent maximum of 18 at Hickling on 30th July 1996. A few are also seen further inland in most years, with highest counts of 18 at Wisbech Sewage Farm on 19th July 1975, nine at Cantley Beet Factory on 3rd August 1991 and four at both Colney Gravel Pits and Rockland Broad in early May 1995.

Over 1,000 Little Terns have been ringed in Norfolk, six of which have been recovered abroad. A juvenile ringed at Snettisham in July 1972 was found as a breeding adult on the East Frisian Islands, Germany in 1977 and 1978, while a nestling ringed at Waxham in 1976 was found dead in the same general area in May 1993, in its 17th year, creating a new longevity record for a British-ringed Little Tern. Further evidence of the species' tendency to move away from the natal colony was provided by nestlings from Thornham which were controlled three years later in The Netherlands and after seven years at Venezia, Italy. While one from Yarmouth was recovered inland at Queyras, Haute Alps, France in July, mid-way between the breeding areas on the Mediterranean coast and the upper River Loire. The only recovery in the wintering area involved a Yarmouth nestling which was found four months later at El Mhaijrat, Mauretania on 29th November 1994. It was the first recovery of a Little Tern in that country.

*Moss Taylor*

# Whiskered Tern                                    *Chlidonias hybridus*

**A rare vagrant, mainly in mid-summer.**

The Whiskered Tern has a scattered breeding distribution throughout southern and eastern Europe, as well as in Asia, Africa and Australia. In Europe it breeds predominantly in the steppe and Mediterranean regions, in colonies rarely containing more than 50 breeding pairs, on areas of freshwater with floating vegetation. Currently the largest breeding numbers are in the Ukraine, Romania and Spain. Western Palearctic breeders winter mainly in Africa, although an increasing number are overwintering in the Mediterranean region. To Britain, the Whiskered Tern has always been a rare visitor, not always appearing annually, even in recent years.

The species was added to the Norfolk list on 17th June 1847, when an adult female was shot by Mr J. Sayer at Hickling Broad. According to Stevenson 'it contained ova in an advanced stage, the largest being apparently almost ready to receive the shell'. The specimen is now in the Castle Museum, Norwich. Since then a further 18 have been recorded in Norfolk:

Whiskered Terns
*(Norman Arlott)*

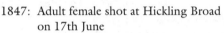

- 1847: Adult female shot at Hickling Broad on 17th June
- 1890: One obtained at Dersingham in early October
- 1906: Hickling Broad on 16th June
- 1912: Hickling Broad in May
- 1913: Hickling Broad in June
- 1918: Hickling Broad in June
- 1933: Hickling Broad on 7th July
- 1939: Hickling Broad on 4th–5th June
- 1942: An adult male at Hickling Broad on 3rd May  
  Rush Hills, Hickling on 30th June
- 1943: An adult at Hickling Broad on 11th July
- 1947: Salthouse on 24th May
- 1987: Yarmouth on 27th June, Titchwell on 28th June and Pentney Gravel Pits from 30th June to 1st July – presumed to be the same bird
- 1988: A juvenile at Welney on 17th and 21st–23rd October
- 1989: Welney on 12th-13th May
- 1994: Two at Rockland Broad on 15th May and presumed the same at Cley on 22nd May
- 1995: Breydon on 15th June
- 1997: One flew east at Cley on 20th June

Until 1943, ten of the first eleven county records were from Hickling, but none since. Juvenile Whiskered Terns are extremely rare in Britain and the one at Welney in late October 1988 is the latest date ever in the British Isles. The records of two at Rockland Broad and Cley in 1994 probably relate to pairs of birds, as pair bonding persists from year to year (BWP).

*Moss Taylor*

## Black Tern   *HARDLEY FLOODS. 1-9-2000.*        *Chlidonias niger*

**A fairly common passage migrant and occasional birds have oversummered; bred in 1969 and 1975, having formerly been a common breeding summer visitor to the Broads and Fens.**

In the Western Palearctic the Black Tern has a patchy breeding distribution in the middle latitudes from western Europe eastwards towards Asiatic Russia. It favours eutrophic natural freshwater marshes with stagnant shallow pools, rich in floating aquatic vegetation. The European population winters mainly along the West African coast. August roost counts suggest that the entire northern and eastern European population probably remains at the Ijsselmeer in The Netherlands for two to three weeks, partly to moult, prior to departing on their autumn migration (European Atlas). The breeding population in western Europe and the Mediterranean has fallen by more than 50% since the 1970s.

Black Terns formerly bred in large numbers in central and south-east England, notably in the Fens and Broadland. Numbers fell dramatically in the early part of the 19th century and the species last nested in that century in England at Sutton in 1858. Since then there has been only the very occasional attempt to breed in the British Isles, most notably in 1975, with unsuccessful nests in County Fermanagh and Nottingham, and a pair which raised one young at Welney.

The decline of the Black Tern as a Norfolk breeding bird is well documented by Stevenson. He quoted a letter from Sir Thomas Browne, dated 29th December 1668, in which he stated '[the Black Tern is] common about broad waters and plashes not farre from the sea'. A wet alder carr at Upton held 'hundreds upon hundreds of nests', where the Black Tern was known as the 'blue darr', but following the Upton Drainage Act of 1799, the colony soon disappeared. The species also nested in the marshes between Winterton and Horsey, but it ceased to breed in the Broads in the 1830s. 'Immense numbers' also bred in the Fens, where it was known as the 'stern' or over the border in Lincolnshire as the 'carr-swallow'. Stevenson blamed the dramatic demise of the Black Tern on agricultural improvements, especially wetland drainage, but there is little doubt that its extinction as a Norfolk breeding bird was due to the attentions of egg collectors. The few pairs that attempted to breed at Hockwold and Feltwell Fens in the early 1850s, following severe flooding, thus lost their clutches. The last pair to nest in Norfolk (and in England) during the 19th century, did so in 1858 when a pair returned to breed at Sutton Broad, laying two eggs, both of which were taken, and the birds shot. Both specimens and their eggs formed part of Stevenson's collection until auctioned in 1887 for five and a half guineas. The historic case remained in the Castle Museum, Norwich until at least 1967. Over 100 years were to pass before Black Terns attempted to breed once again in the county. Following the wet spring of 1969, four pairs nested at Welney, but no young survived due to the flood waters rapidly drying, leaving the young helpless to any predators. However, in 1975, one pair bred successfully at Welney raising one young. In addition, two summered at Wisbech Sewage Farm in 1964 and three at Hoveton Great Broad in 1979.

Following the last breeding attempt in his day, Stevenson described the Black Tern 'as a mere passenger in spring and autumn, of pretty constant appearance indeed, and sometimes in not inconsiderable numbers', a description which still applies today. The number of Black Terns recorded annually has varied from less than 100 to over 1,000, in spring alone. Since 1953 the first birds on spring passage have appeared between 9th April and 13th May, with the majority of first sightings during the last ten days of April. The earliest dates have been 9th April 1989 at Holme, 11th April 1979 at Cley and Welney, and 11th April 1989 at Rollesby. Spring passage often continues into early June with peak numbers during May. Prior to 1990, maximum counts at Cley had been an unprecedented 1,000 east on 5th–6th May 1970, 372 on 12th May 1960 and 250 on 14th May 1980, at Rockland Broad 160 on 1st May 1958 and 120 on 24th May 1959, at Hickling Broad 200 on 13th May 1960 and 250 on 14th May 1980, at Wisbech Sewage Farm 180 on 23rd–24th May 1959 and at Welney 100 on 7th–8th May 1981. However, these numbers were mostly surpassed in early May 1990, at which time large numbers were reported throughout much of England. In Norfolk large groups passed north through inland waters, flying east along the north coast before moving south along the east Norfolk shore. On 2nd May, inland counts included 160 at Horsey Mere, 100 at Hickling Broad, 95 at Pentney Gravel Pits and 60 at Lyng Easthaugh/Swanton Morley Gravel Pits. In the Wash 150 were at Snettisham. At least 1,000 were counted flying east over Holkham Marshes, at Cley and at Sheringham, while 400 passed south-east at Waxham and Winterton. Smaller numbers were recorded on the following day but there were still 450 at Cley and 200 at Sheringham. Such large passages of Black Terns in May are invariably associated with east or north-east winds and are presumably birds displaced westwards as they pass north along the western European seaboard.

The arrival of the first birds on autumn passage is very variable, some years being in early July and in other years not until well into August. Passage is generally lighter than in spring with peak numbers in late August or early September. In recent years high counts at Lynn Point have generally been in early August, with 124 flying south upriver, in a strong south-west wind, on 2nd August 1986 and 110 present at high tide on 5th August 1994, the day after 75 had flown west at Holme. At the same site in 1954 a build-up in numbers from the end of August peaked at 220 on September 9th, with many birds flying inland at each high tide. On 31st August 1958 a total of 148 Black Terns flew west at Scolt Head, presumably also making their way to the mouth of the River Ouse, while 160 in two flocks entered the Wash at Hunstanton on 26th September 1965 and were later seen heading south-west at Lynn Point. The largest autumn passage, however, recorded at Cley and Sheringham, occurred on 11th September 1992 and involved birds flying east, with counts of 350 at Cley and 710 at Sheringham. In east Norfolk Breydon attracted 87 on 30th August 1992 and a total of 161 moved through Breydon on 13th September 1993, after strong overnight south-east winds and rain. A few Black Terns continue to be recorded in October, although 62 flying west at Holme on 2nd October 1994 was unusual. Most birds have left by mid-month, although occasional stragglers remain into November. The latest birds have been singles at Titchwell on 8th November 1982 and 11th November 1983, with presumably the same at Holme on 12th November 1983, and one at Snettisham on 10th–14th November 1968.

*Moss Taylor*

## White-winged Black Tern (White-winged Tern)   *Chlidonias leucopterus*

A rare vagrant, in both spring and autumn.

White-winged Black Terns
(Norman Arlott)

The White-winged Black Tern breeds in eastern Europe, extending eastwards discontinuously to China. In the west of its range, as a result of wetland drainage, numbers have declined in the Ukraine and Hungary, and it ceased to breed in Germany and Austria in the 1960s. European populations winter in sub-Saharan Africa. The species is an annual spring and autumn migrant to the British Isles, often associating with flocks of Black Terns. A record 49 were noted in 1992 but strangely enough not one was identified in Norfolk that year.

Stevenson recorded the first for Norfolk on 17th May 1853, when one was killed from a small flock of Black Terns at Horsey Mere, by Mr Rising's keeper. The next was shot at Hickling Broad on 27th June 1867, and Stevenson continued: 'On the 26th May 1871, after a very tempestuous night, Mr Booth killed four of these birds, two males and two females, out of a flock of five, at one discharge of his big gun, soon after daylight, on Breydon; the odd bird was saved by not alighting with the others.' The specimens may still be seen in the Booth Museum in Brighton. The same collector killed a further five, out of a flock of seven, at Hickling Broad on 28th May 1873. Thomas Southwell who completed Volume 3 of Stevenson's *Birds of Norfolk* after the author's death, concluded the section on White-winged Black Tern with 'it would really seem as though there had been attempts to establish itself in this county – attempts which might have succeeded but for the cruel reception they have always met with. Their wanton destruction therefore under such circumstances cannot be too strongly denounced by all true ornithologists.' A truly enlightened view for someone writing as early as 1890. It appears, however, that he was not alone, for Jary, the Breydon Watcher, recorded a flock of eight on 22nd April 1901.

Up to 1911, all the records of White-winged Black Tern were in Broadland, the majority at Hickling

Broad or Breydon in spring. Since then the favoured localities have been the stretch of coastline between Morston and Salthouse, and the west of the county, including the Fens, with more records in autumn. The county total stands at about 90, with clear peaks in May–June and August to early September. Apart from one at Breydon on 13th April 1888, which is perhaps not fully authenticated (Allard 1990), the earliest date for the county was the flock of eight seen at Breydon on 22nd April 1901, with the latest in spring on 27th June. There have been just four July records – adults at Cley on 14th July 1976, 27th July 1981, 13th July 1982 and 30th–31st July 1998 (subsequently seen at Titchwell from 31st July to 1st August). Most autumn sightings have been in August with few after early September. A total of 17 juveniles has been seen in the county with the earliest on 10th August 1975 at Winterton.

Most of the seven late autumn records have involved birds which have remained from a few days to two or three weeks, the longest-staying being an immature at Wisbech Sewage Farm from 21st September to 7th October 1958 and a juvenile in the Titchwell/Holme area from 20th October to 3rd November 1980. The latest was an elusive adult between Sheringham and Cley on 4th–11th November 1994, which was presumably the same bird seen at Cantley Beet Factory on 19th–23rd November. Britain's latest-ever White-winged Black Tern was recorded the same autumn in Shropshire from 6th November to 1st December. The majority of records in the last 50 years have involved single birds, with a maximum of three at Blakeney Harbour on 25th May 1950 and one to three at Brancaster/Titchwell on 4th–11th May 1970.

*Moss Taylor*

## Guillemot (Common Guillemot) · AT SEA, OFF TITCHWELL. 8·10·1986. · *Uria aalge*

**A common passage migrant, and fairly common winter visitor and non-breeding summer visitor; rare inland.**

The Guillemot is the most widespread of all the auks, with a circumpolar breeding distribution around the northern boreal and low-Arctic coasts of the Atlantic and Pacific Oceans. The population in the British Isles is almost at the southern limit of its range, although it does extend to islands off Portugal. It breeds on rocky cliffs and stacks around the coast of Britain and Ireland. The nearest colony to Norfolk is on Flamborough Head, Yorkshire. Most populations disperse southwards in autumn, to winter offshore. Many more auks have been seen in the southern North Sea in recent years, suggesting a change in winter distribution which matches a southern shift of sprats (Camphuysen 1989). The British breeding population also doubled between 1969–70 and 1985–87 (New Atlas).

Stevenson could find no proof that the species had ever bred in Norfolk, although he quoted an extract from Miss Anna Gurney's notebook in which she stated that a Guillemot's egg was found on Cromer beach on 12th June 1839 and another the following day. These were presumed to have been eggs dropped at sea, as others had been found in the shrimpers' trawl-nets off Lowestoft and King's Lynn.

Guillemots are recorded off the Norfolk coast throughout the year, although generally in large numbers only in October and November. Adults and young vacate the colonies in late July and early August, and at about this time family groups including half-grown flightless young appear off Norfolk, presumably from the Yorkshire colonies. In 1994 the first family parties were noted far earlier than usual, 17km off Brancaster on 29th June. The highest October count of Guillemots was 2,000 flying east at Sheringham on 5th October 1984. However, the difficulty in separating flying Guillemots from Razorbills at the range at which most of the offshore passage occurs is being increasingly recognised. As a result, most of the large-scale movements of auks are now recorded in the *Norfolk Bird Report* as Guillemot/Razorbill. Such was the case on 4th October 1992 when a record total of 6,100 passed Sheringham and between then and 21st October, at least 12,000 moved offshore. During October 1997 over 16,000 Guillemots and Razorbills flew east at Sheringham. The highest daily counts of Guillemot/Razorbill in November were 3,250 on 2nd November 1995 and 3,130 the following day. The highest mid-winter counts have been at Sheringham with 360 east on 10th December 1990 and 1,200 east on 4th January 1997.

Adults normally return to their colonies in February and March. However, on 20th February 1994 immediately following a major auk 'wreck' (see below) exceptional numbers were recorded off the Norfolk coast. Birds were moving east along the north Norfolk coast and south at Waxham, during relatively calm conditions, probably as a result of food shortages further north. Birds were passing all day with large numbers reported from most of the regular seawatching points between Blakeney Point and Waxham.

Highest counts were 5,300 at Sheringham and 4,800 at Mundesley, with an estimated all-day total of 10,000 at Overstrand. By March and April smaller numbers are noted offshore, but daily movements of up to 400 Guillemot/Razorbill have been recorded at Holme and Sheringham, while 1,030 passed Holme on 13th June 1993 and 900 (considered mainly to have been Guillemots) flew east at Sheringham on 6th May 1997. During the 19th century fishermen believed that both Guillemots and Razorbills came down from the Yorkshire colonies, a distance of over a hundred miles, to fish in Yarmouth Roads and return daily apparently laden with food (Stevenson). However, it seems much more likely that these were in fact non-breeding birds; Guillemots do not breed until four to five years old.

Major auk 'wrecks' have been recorded since the mid-1800s. Stevenson described one on 11th May 1851 (Riviere gave the year as 1856), after protracted storms. Very large numbers of corpses, mainly Guillemots, were found along the Norfolk coast – for example they stretched for six miles from Cromer and 240 'seabirds' were found in just two miles. The largest 'wreck' in recent years occurred in February 1983 (Durdin 1984), but as it affected particularly Razorbills it is described in detail under that species. Another auk 'wreck' occurred in February 1994, but unlike that in 1983 the worst area affected was the north of Scotland (Durdin 1994). Nationally at least 50,000 auks perished, of which only 208 were found in Norfolk, but on this occasion 59% were Guillemots, and Razorbills constituted only 3% of the total. As before, severe weather rather than oiling was responsible. Oiling, however, is the cause of death for many of the auks found on Norfolk beaches, and it is not a recent phenomenon. In 1930 Riviere wrote: 'In recent years dead or dying (Guillemots), whose plumage has become clogged with oil, are also only too frequently met with.'

Guillemots are rare inland. Apart from one in September, all the records have fallen between November and March. The majority have been in the Fens, of which seven have been at Welney. Others have been found at Diss, near Aylsham and at Strumpshaw.

The recovery of ringed birds provides valuable information as to the natal colonies of those Guillemots unfortunate enough to be found dead or dying on Norfolk's beaches. Over 80 ringed nestlings have been found in the county – 66 from Scottish colonies, six from northern England (including the Calf of Man) and four from Ireland (including Great Saltee). Foreign-ringed birds have come from Helgoland, Germany (three of which had been ringed between 8th and 10th July 1966) and one from southern Norway. An adult ringed at Den Helder, The Netherlands on 30th March 1989 was found freshly dead at Yarmouth nine days later, while another Dutch-ringed bird from Noordwijk was found dead at Salthouse on 25th December 1990, also nine days after ringing. Presumably neither was in prime condition when caught and ringed.

*Moss Taylor*

## Razorbill  OFF CLEY, & TITCHWELL.  8·10·1986.  *Alca torda*

**A fairly common passage migrant and winter visitor, and a scarce non-breeding summer visitor; very rare inland.**

The Razorbill is endemic to the North Atlantic and associated seas. Those breeding in Iceland represent 50% of the world population, with the majority of the remainder of the European population nesting in Britain, Ireland and Norway. In the British Isles it breeds on rocky islets and stacks, and the more remote cliffs. It is absent between Flamborough Head and the Isle of Wight. It is partially migratory, with most birds from the northern colonies moving south for the winter. First-year birds from the Scottish colonies pass through the North Sea and Straits of Dover to winter in the Bay of Biscay, the western Mediterranean and off the coast of Morocco.

Generally, the Razorbill is less numerous off the Norfolk coast than is the Guillemot, although in the mid-1950s the reverse was true and hundreds were noted passing along the north Norfolk coast during a north-westerly gale on 26th and 28th September 1955. Flightless young accompanied by their parents are occasionally seen in mid-July, presumably from the breeding colony at Flamborough Head in Yorkshire, although one, about two-thirds grown, was off Weybourne being fed by a single parent as early as 7th July 1998. Only small numbers of Razorbills are present in late summer and early autumn. The main passage occurs in October and November with the highest recorded counts being 2,000+ east on 5th October 1984 at both Blakeney Point and Sheringham and 3,000 off Sheringham on both 13th and 21st October

1997. The maximum in November was 567 flying past Sheringham on 30th November 1975. As explained above, flying Guillemots and Razorbills in winter plumage are not easy to separate at long range. Some of the totals in the Guillemot text, included as Guillemot/Razorbill may have been birds of this species. On 2nd October 1997 a very impressive movement of auks was recorded off north Norfolk, and counts included 11,750 east and 1,250 west at Scolt Head, and 5,100 east at Sheringham. All the observers at the main seawatching sites considered that the majority of the birds were Razorbills.

Razorbill corpses are not infrequently found on the tideline, often the victims of oil pollution. The largest auk 'wreck' in Norfolk in recent years occurred in February 1983 (Durdin 1984). It affected the entire British east coast, with the greatest numbers of corpses being found in Norfolk, Lincolnshire and Humberside. The final national total was 34,000 of which 31,500 were auks. In Norfolk 6,450 bodies were located on the beaches, of which 92% were auks. Normally Guillemots outnumber Razorbills after oil spills or on routine Beached Bird Surveys. On this occasion, however, 53% (2,927) of the auks were Razorbills compared with Guillemots at 35%. Only 8.5% of the auks were oiled and autopsies indicated that the majority of the birds had died from emaciation. The weather in the North Sea had been appalling for about a week after 5th February, with 100mph winds and waves up to 12m high. This had prevented the birds from feeding and as Razorbills tend to winter further out to sea than Guillemots, they were more severely affected.

The few Razorbills that have been found inland in Norfolk have all been between January and April, with the majority in February. Most have been in the Fens, but singles have turned up at Colney Gravel Pit and Strumpshaw.

During the auk 'wreck' of February 1983 five ringed Razorbills were found on the beach between Weybourne and Sheringham, three from Shetland and two from Highland region. One had been ringed on Handa in 1968 as an adult, in at least its fourth year and was therefore in at least its 18th year when found. An additional 27 ringed Razorbills from Scottish colonies and one from Wales have been found in Norfolk. However, the most distant recovery involved an adult ringed at Storhofdi, Iceland on 15th July 1977 and found dead at Happisburgh on 7th December 1983.

*Moss Taylor*

## Black Guillemot                                           *Cepphus grylle*

**A very scarce passage migrant and winter visitor; very rare in mid-summer.**

The Black Guillemot has a Holarctic breeding distribution along the Arctic and North Atlantic coasts, being most numerous within the Arctic Circle. It is at the southern limit of its breeding range in Britain and Ireland, where it occurs around the rocky coasts of north and north-west Scotland, on the Northern and Western Isles, the Isle of Man, Anglesey and around most of the Irish coast (New Atlas). It is the most sedentary of the British auks, adults often remaining within 15km of the breeding colony throughout the year. It is widely known by its Shetland name of Tystie, which is similar to most Scandinavian names for the species.

Stevenson believed that the first Norfolk record was of an immature shot by a Mr Loads at Blakeney on 16th November 1850. Up to 1930, there had still been only 20–30 county records, all between September and April (Riviere). Today it remains a very scarce bird off the Norfolk coast (particularly in the east), but with records every year since 1954, except for 1964, 1970 and 1994. Up to eight have been seen annually, at an average of three per year. The majority have been recorded in autumn along the north Norfolk coast between Holme and Sheringham with a clear peak between September and November. The earliest have been singles at Winterton on 16th July 1960 and at Cley on 18th July 1987. Most of the remaining records have involved birds present during the winter months, with a few in March and April. There have been three May records – at Cley on 4th–9th May 1982, one in summer plumage at Weybourne on 7th May 1988 and one in Brancaster Harbour on 15th May 1957. The sole June record concerned a bird close inshore at Cley on 13th June 1958.

The vast majority of records have involved single birds, but off Cley three were seen on 29th October 1955 and two on 29th October 1959, two were in Wells Harbour on 21st–30th November 1971 and two flew past Sheringham on 17th October 1973 and on 6th October 1981. Occasional birds have made prolonged stays, including one at Cley/Salthouse from 25th August to 17th November 1981 and one between Cley and Sheringham from 19th September to 19th November 1995. At Wells Harbour the same individual may have accounted for records each winter between December 1974 and January 1977 (Bloomfield 1993).

The early record at Winterton on 16th July 1960 concerned an exhausted bird, which died two days later. It had been ringed as a nestling at the lighthouse on Tistlarna Island off the west coast of Sweden on 22nd June 1960, less than a month previously. It was the first foreign-ringed Black Guillemot to be recovered in the British Isles and there has only been one other since, also from Sweden.

*Moss Taylor*

# Little Auk                                                                    *Alle alle*

**An annual autumn passage migrant and winter visitor in varying numbers; very scarce inland.**

The Little Auk is probably the most abundant Atlantic auk. It breeds in large colonies in the high Arctic, extending further north than any of the other Atlantic auks. It normally overwinters in the pelagic waters of the low Arctic, often remaining near the edge of the pack ice, where the greatest abundance of oceanic zooplankton is to be found (del Hoyo *et al.* 1996). However, it is also distributed widely throughout the northern North Sea during the winter, moving back north in March. Despite this, it is rarely visible from the coast, except when strong winds drive it onshore (Winter Atlas).

To Norfolk, it has been an annual autumn and winter visitor to coastal waters since at least Stevenson's time, but in very variable numbers. In some years they are extremely scarce, as in 1976 when only four were recorded and in 1979 and 1994 with just seven. In other years large numbers of apparently healthy birds pass close inshore and this may be associated with a 'wreck', in which weakened birds are found dead or dying, both on the coast and often many miles inland. Since the first recorded 'wreck' in Norfolk in October 1841, about 14 have occurred. The events of January 1895 were outstanding. It was a month of arctic weather with a succession of northerly and north-easterly gales. Wrecked Little Auks became widespread. A total of 248 was stuffed by taxidermists in Snettisham, King's Lynn, Cley, Holt, Northrepps, Norwich and Yarmouth. Casualties were reported as far inland as Quidenham and Thetford. The peak day was 23rd January (when Eccles Church on the shore was swept away). One bird was picked up outside Norwich Hospital and another in Chapelfield Gardens in the city. Yet another which alighted on the stable roof of Hunstanton Hall was snowballed into the moat.

The first birds of the autumn are generally recorded offshore during the second half of October and in those years in which good numbers are seen, the peak passage occurs from then until the end of November. The earliest record was one photographed inland on the River Yare at Bramerton on 29th August 1970 and the earliest coastal sighting was at Cley on 6th September 1973. Up to the mid-1970s, the heaviest passage had been recorded in association with north to north-westerly gales on 28th–31st October 1974, with a maximum count of 130 west at Sheringham. As with many of the large westerly movements of Little Auks, birds were frequently caught up with flocks of Starlings and small waders, and the passage was noted from Yarmouth in the south around the coast as far as Cley. On 29th October 1983, even larger numbers were recorded – from first light to midday 850 flew north at Horsey Gap, many in small groups of three to seven, the largest party consisting of 17 birds and many in the company of Dunlin and Knot, while others passed inland with Starlings; over 600 were counted at Paston, moving at a rate of about 100 per hour, and 155 flew west at Cley in two hours. As in 1974, comparatively few were recorded off north-west Norfolk. Weather maps revealed very strong north to north-west winds in the Norwegian Sea on 27th–28th October, at the time that immense numbers of Little Auks would have been travelling from the High Arctic south-westwards into the Atlantic, well north of the British Isles. But the storm swept them into the North Sea instead of the Atlantic (Allard 1984b).

The record day-count of Little Auks at a single site was 1,800 east at Sheringham on 10th December 1990, during a north-easterly gale, although about 2,000 were estimated to have passed the Norfolk coast on 2nd November 1995. In that year an extraordinary passage of Little Auks was noted off north Norfolk in calm, sunny conditions on 29th October, with counts of 250 at Cley, 190 at Sheringham and 120 at Mundesley. By 2nd November the wind had freshened from the north and spectacular numbers of Little Auks were recorded with 625 at Holme, 1,200 at Cley, 1,375 at Sheringham, 570 at Overstrand, 1,688 east at Mundesley and 302 north at Yarmouth. The first exhausted birds were being found by 3rd and the first corpses were on the tideline the following day. Many were blown inland where they were discovered dead or moribund in gardens and on roads, one even being found as far inland as Diss Mere. A further significant movement was recorded from 13th to 18th November with a maximum count of 420 east at Sheringham on 13th. Many exhausted Little Auks remained in the lower reaches of the North Sea until the following February, while at Snettisham pits the species was present continuously from 30th October 1995 to 16th February 1996 (Taylor 1997a).

Far fewer have been recorded in the early part of the year with maximum counts of 44 west at Overstrand on 6th and 40 west at Cley on 9th January 1991. In fact, of the records between December and April, tideline corpses predominate. A few are recorded inland in most years, with 17 reported in 1995. In recent years four have been recorded in April, with the latest, an oiled bird at Cley on 11th–12th April 1977 and an apparently healthy bird off Sheringham on 13th April 1982. Stevenson, however, included details of one in full summer plumage shot whilst it was skimming low over the waves at Wells on 25th May 1857, which is in the collection at the Castle Museum, Norwich. He also gave two July records – an adult obtained at Downham in July 1846 and one in summer plumage on the sea, five miles from the entrance to King's Lynn Harbour on 15th July 1872.

*Moss Taylor*

## Puffin (Atlantic Puffin) — *Fratercula arctica*

**A scarce passage migrant; very scarce in winter, rare in summer and very rare inland.**

As a breeding species, the Puffin is restricted to the colder more northern parts of the North Atlantic and adjoining areas of the Arctic Ocean. It nests on maritime coasts from Greenland in the north to Brittany in the south, with the largest population in Iceland. After the breeding season it disperses widely at very low densities over vast areas of ocean. In the British Isles it breeds on isolated islands and steep, inaccessible mainland cliffs. The largest numbers are in north and west Scotland, with smaller colonies on islands off the coast of England, Wales and Ireland. The nearest breeding birds to Norfolk are at Bempton cliffs, Yorkshire.

To Norfolk, the Puffin has always been only an occasional visitor in small numbers, mainly in association with northerly gales. Although it has been noted in every month of the year, the majority of records have been between September and November, with surprisingly few during the winter months. An unprecedented passage occurred between 27th August and 22nd November 1989, during which period Puffins were recorded flying along the north Norfolk coast, mainly in an easterly direction, on at least 30 dates. Although most records involved one to two birds, 18 flew past Sheringham on 8th September and 10 flew past Blakeney Point on 8th October. Since then the number of Puffins noted annually in autumn has increased, possibly due to a better understanding of the identification features of flying Puffins coupled with improved optical equipment. Most birds continue to be recorded in autumn with maximum counts generally noted off Sheringham, where 30 on 4th October 1992, 31 east on 14th September 1994 (when 22 east at Cley), 50 east on 19th September 1995 and 31 east on 13th September 1998 (when 41 east at Cley). Elsewhere, notable counts have been 19 at Paston on 5th October 1992, and 21 west and four east at Scolt Head on 2nd October 1997.

In the early part of the year the highest count has been eleven east at Sheringham on 20th February 1996. Compared with Guillemots and Razorbills very few Puffins are found as tideline corpses, reflecting their comparative scarcity offshore. However, during the major auk 'wreck' in February 1983, a total of 388 Puffin corpses was found around the Norfolk coastline, which included 51 between Mundesley and Bacton, and 72 between Sea Palling and Winterton (Durdin 1984). Over the years, a few have been noted in May and June along the north Norfolk coast, some in full breeding plumage and occasional birds in July and August. However, in June 1997, over 20 were recorded off the north coast with a maximum of eight east at Sheringham on both 26th and 27th, and 30 flew past Cley on 11th June 1998. Puffins are very rare inland, amongst the records have been singles in the Fens at Eau Brink on 9th and Welney on 11th February 1992.

Puffins from colonies along the east coasts of the British Isles remain in the North Sea throughout the winter, which is borne out by the recoveries of ringed birds found dead on Norfolk beaches. A total of 28 British-ringed birds has been found in Norfolk, the majority in February, 17 from Scottish colonies and eleven from northern England. One from Craigleith, Scotland was ringed as a nestling in 1980 and was found at Weybourne in its 17th year in February 1996; the longevity record for a British-ringed Puffin is nearly 30 years. The only foreign-ringed Puffin was found at Sheringham on 25th February 1962 – it had been ringed in Nordland, Norway but the inscription was almost completely worn away and all that could be said was that it had been ringed sometime between 1952 and 1957.

*Moss Taylor*

# Pallas's Sandgrouse *Syrrhaptes paradoxus*

**A rare irruptive vagrant; last recorded in 1908.**

Pallas's Sandgrouse has occasionally bred in the Western Palearctic, including the British Isles, following westerly irruptions from their main breeding areas in the vast temperate steppe regions across much of Asia. Nowadays it is an extremely rare vagrant to the British Isles with the most recent records of singles in 1975 and 1990 both being found on Scottish islands in May.

The first record for Norfolk, and possibly Britain and Ireland, was a bird taken at Walpole St Peter in July 1859. It remains on display in the King's Lynn Museum. Four years later there was a major immigration into the county which was fully documented by Stevenson. The first report was of a female found dead on Yarmouth beach on 23rd May, followed by a small flock of eight which appeared at Waxham on 4th June; four of these, a male and three females were shot. In the next few days others were taken at Yarmouth and Breydon with 18 obtained out of a flock of more than 40 which appeared on Horsey beach on 10th–11th June 1863. The birds were mainly recorded on the dunes and fields around the coast from Blakeney, Morston and Holme, in addition to the locations mentioned above, as well as two inland sites at Croxton and Methwold. During this irruption between May and November, 60 birds were killed in the county, equally divided between the sexes. Norfolk also was represented in the smaller irruption into the British Isles in 1876 with a party of 15–20 birds being seen at Winterton.

Pallas's Sandrouse
(Norman Arlott)

The largest recorded invasion took place in 1888 when arrivals were seen at east coast sites from 13th May including 15 at Cley on 30th. The principal concentration settled on a Mr Wood's farm at Morston where between 160 and 180 remained until the third week of October. Their favoured feeding places included a large area of clover and also bare knolls in an adjacent turnip field. From time to time all headed for the nearby saltmarshes. Elsewhere a flock of 200 appeared at Bacton on 29th May 1888; the following day 80–100 left the locality heading out to sea. Other impressive totals during the summer included 40 on the saltings at Wells and 40–50 at Snettisham. Inland, 25 passed over Mousehold Heath on the outskirts of Norwich on 24th May followed by 10 briefly at Hethersett on 25th June. Breckland attracted some numbers with 70–100 at Didlington during June–July and 100 in flight over Sturston Warren (now part of the military Stanford Training Area) on 14th September and 60 at Swaffham until 1st October (Gurney 1888). There were 30 still at Holkham on 13th October and in the five months since the first arrivals in May, Southwell estimated that there had been a total of between 1,100 and 1,200 birds recorded in the county of which 186 were shot. Pashley, the Cley taxidermist, had 33 of these through his hands.

Breeding was attempted in some parts of the British Isles with an unsubstantiated record of a female being shot off a nest containing three eggs at South Pickenham. Unfortunately the eggs, which were almost ready to hatch, were broken in attempts to 'blow' them and destroyed before they could be authenticated. Some birds remained over winter with the last two being seen at Cley on 17th February 1889. No more were reported until October when a flock was seen in the Hunstanton area, with eleven at Docking and 20 'in the next parish' on 4th December 1889 (Stevenson).

Mounted specimens obtained during the two main invasions may still be seen at Felbrigg Hall, Holkham Hall, Sheringham Hall, the Tolhouse Museum, Yarmouth and the Castle Museum, Norwich.
A further small invasion took place in the following year when three birds were seen to come in from the sea at Holkham on 22nd April 1890. The next arrivals of these distant wanderers occurred on 11th June 1906 when 20 were seen flying over Winterton and ten at Somerton on 17th June. The county's final records were of a flock at Blakeney at the end of May 1908 and two birds at Brancaster on 28th June 1908.

*Don Dorling*

## Rock Dove (Rock Pigeon)    *Columba livia*

**A very rare vagrant; one record in 1925.**

The long history of domestication of the Rock Dove, together with the subsequent escape of birds to the wild, have led to a large feral population throughout much of the Western Palearctic. This obscures the status of the truly wild birds, which in the British Isles are now limited to isolated populations in the extreme north and north-west of Scotland and in western Ireland.

The only county record of an absolutely typical pure Rock Dove was picked up dead at Ludham on 9th December 1925 during several days of north-easterly gales and blizzards. There was a wound to the breast. Although there is some concern regarding this record, Riviere considered it to be fully authentic.

The Feral Pigeon is an increasingly abundant town resident in the county, preferring to nest in churches and old buildings. Recent bird surveys have largely neglected Feral Pigeons and more information is required as to their distribution. However, during the Norfolk Atlas it was recorded in 240 (16%) of the tetrads with clear concentrations in virtually all the towns in the county. The largest population was present in and around the City of Norwich (Kelly 1986). During the 1994–96 BBS it was recorded in 14 to 16% of the 1km squares covered in Norfolk, and had almost doubled to 28% in 1997. It remains to be seen whether this is an indication of a genuine increase, but there is no doubt that the population is still being reinforced by escaped birds as pigeon-fancying becomes increasingly popular.

*Peter Allard*

## Stock Dove (Stock Pigeon)    *MY GARDEN –*    *Columba oenas*
CHEDGRAVE. 12·3·2000.

**A very common resident and scarce passage migrant.**

The Stock Dove breeds across the middle latitudes of the Western Palearctic, but is absent from the mountainous areas of the Alps and the Pyrenees. The populations from Germany eastwards are summer visitors, wintering in Iberia, France and around the northern Mediterranean basin, whereas those in the west and south of its range are resident. It was not distinguished as a separate species from the Rock Dove until the latter part of the 18th century and so its distribution in Britain was uncertain. The only breeding records known to Yarrell (1837–43) were in Norfolk and Suffolk. At present, it breeds across England and Wales apart from the western extremities. There was an extension of range and numbers from the early part of the 19th century until the 1950s when seed dressings, coupled with an expansion of arable farming, caused a decrease that continued until the middle of the following decade.

Stevenson stated that Stock Doves were plentiful, but not as numerous as Wood Pigeons and that they occurred in the north-east and south-west of the county since these areas provided sufficient suitable nesting sites. It nests in holes in trees, in disused buildings or, particularly in the Brecks, in old rabbit holes. Stanford Training Area has all three and as a consequence it has a high population. A flock of 72 noted on 5th June 1998 at The Arms would be expected to be young from first broods. In days gone by, warreners would fix sticks across the entrance of a rabbit burrow containing a nest. This would allow the adults to continue to feed the young who were trapped in the hole. They would then be sold in the market for 1/ 6d to 2/- for a couple (Stevenson). It was also noted as numerous in the sandhills that were around Hunstanton. Stock Doves were believed to leave breeding areas in the north-east of the county from

September to return in January or later if the winter was severe. Stevenson doubted the statement by a Mr Salmon that it was as a migratory visitor around Thetford with all the birds departing by the end of October. Stevenson believed that wintering birds were possibly mixed in with flocks of Wood Pigeons and hence were overlooked. However, Bloomfield and McCallum (1999) also believe that, although the species is a widespread breeding summer visitor in the area of north Norfolk from Burnham Norton east to Blakeney and southwards in a square to Swaffham, it is an exceptionally scarce winter resident in this same area.

There were records from every 10km square for the Norfolk Atlas with the species being noted in 50% of the tetrads. It was still commoner in the south-west, in both the Brecks and the Fens, as well as north-east from Norwich towards Cromer. This mirrored its distribution 80 years earlier. It was noticeably scarcer in the Broads and some central areas of the county. During the 1994–97 BBS it was found in 46–55% of the 1km squares surveyed in Norfolk. One of the highest concentrations of breeding pairs is at Holkham Park where a minimum of 50 pairs have bred in the last few years. A pair on Blakeney Point nested in the Old Lifeboat station and raised four broods in both 1994 and 1995.

The Stock Dove has been recorded as a passage migrant in spring with day counts of up to 20 passing in March and April at coastal sites. In 1995, much larger numbers were seen from 14th February onwards, with peak counts of 138 west at Holme on 10th March followed by 85 the next day when 150 moved east and 28 west at Sheringham; on 23rd March, an unprecedented 330 flew west at Holme and 90 west at Sheringham. A late movement of 26 east was recorded at Sheringham on 14th May 1997.

In autumn small groups pass along the coast from July onwards which could be locally-bred birds dispersing. The highest counts, which are in November, are likely to be immigrants from the Continent. The largest counts have been on 2nd November 1994 when 153 flew south at Hunstanton and 70 south at Winterton. No other day-counts have exceeded 50 birds.

The largest flocks in recent years have been 270 at Welney on 3rd February 1991, 140 at Wissington on 2nd April 1991, 120 at Flitcham in December 1996, 200 at Gooderstone in January–February 1997, 120 at Frettenham and Ringstead both in February 1997, and 200 at Brograve Level in October 1997. The largest flock ever recorded in the county was one of 600 on the south side of Breydon on 17th January 1980.

About 300 Stock Doves have been ringed in Norfolk from which the longest movement concerned one ringed near Watton in August 1993 and recovered near Kings Lynn one year later, a distance of 33km. Five other recoveries involved movements of 14–30km. However, evidence of immigration from Fennoscandia was provided by one ringed at Tyrvanto, Finland in July 1954 and found at Ormesby the following March. There have only been two other foreign-ringed Stock Doves recovered in the British Isles, from Belgium and The Netherlands.

*Peter Dolton*

*MY GARDEN - CHEDGRAVE. 26-7-1999.*

## Wood Pigeon (Common Wood Pigeon)     *Columba pàlumbus*

**An abundant resident, and common passage migrant and winter visitor in varying numbers.**

In the Western Palearctic the Wood Pigeon is mainly migratory in northern and eastern Europe and western Siberia. Elsewhere in Europe it is partially migratory with the extent of movement declining progressively towards the south and west until becoming largely resident from Britain and Ireland to Morocco and through the Mediterranean basin to the Near East. The migratory population of Fennoscandia and eastern Europe heads south-west from mid-September to early November. Wood Pigeons are reluctant to cross wide seas, preferring to follow coastlines and winter in south-west France and Iberia. The autumn occurrence of Continental birds in (mainly eastern) Britain is almost certainly due to drift movement during overcast conditions above the North Sea. In Britain and Ireland it breeds almost everywhere except on the higher hills and mountains and is increasingly found in the centres of towns and cities. The highest concentrations appear in major farming areas, feeding on a wide range of natural foods (including weed seeds, acorns, beechmast and a variety of berries). The acreage of oilseed rape is a major factor in limiting the population size (New Atlas).

Stevenson considered that the enormous increase in Wood Pigeon numbers of late years was due largely to the extension of fir plantations in the county. He also mentioned a 'most fearful hailstorm' during the autumn of 1843 which caused 'frightful havoc' to cereals between Attleborough and Postwick in a swath from two to three miles in width. Crops were levelled to the ground and the grain scattered to a depth of nearly three inches. Not surprisingly 'immense flocks of Wood Pigeons and hundreds of Stock Doves descended as though summoned by invitation'. As many as 30 to 40 were killed at a time without apparently diminishing their numbers. Riviere described a similar picture of abundance adding that 'Wood Pigeons have not infrequently been observed coming in from the sea . . . in November, December and January . . . and been recorded at light-stations both by day and night in October and December'.

During fieldwork for the Norfolk Atlas it was found in 96% of the tetrads covered, being the third most widespread species. In the 1994–97 BBS it was the only species to have been found each year in every 1km square covered in Norfolk, thus illustrating just how widespread it is in the county. The Wood Pigeon has a long breeding season, eggs having been found in each month of the year. In addition to woods including the densest Breckland plantations, the birds readily nest in spinneys, hedges and in isolated trees. Within towns nest-sites include trees and shrubs in gardens. At Yarmouth it has nested on buildings and a pair bred in a busy aircraft hangar at Caister Heliport in 1997.

Until very recently spring movements had seldom been recorded apart from 20, two of which were killed, flying west at Lynn Well light-vessel on 11th April 1910, about 100 heading out to sea at Yarmouth on 13th May 1917, a total of 1,100 west at Sheringham on 22nd May 1976, 72 east at Winterton on 4th April 1976 and 4,000 west at Holme on 27th April 1977. Since 1993, however, spring passage has been recorded annually with birds usually heading west along the north Norfolk coast between early March and early June. The highest count has been 1,100 at Holme on 23rd March 1995.

In the autumn Patterson (1905) reported thousands arriving from the north-east on 22nd–23rd December 1893; Yarmouth market stalls rapidly reflected the influx. A further arrival there of similar numbers from the east took place on 12th December 1898. It was not until 1959 that another large-scale influx was reported. Between 19th November and 5th December remarkable totals were noted. At Yarmouth, during several days, flight after flight of up to 500 arrived from the north-east. An estimate of over 25,000 passed over the town during a 15-day period. Cley, too, shared in this invasion and phenomenal numbers arrived during three different days. One flock on 24th November was described as being '150 yards in width and extending half a mile'. At Scolt Head flocks of up to 300 headed both east and west. At night three light-vessels offshore reported Wood Pigeons dazzled by the lanterns, several of which became casualties. Since that heady period subsequent movements at Yarmouth have included several hundreds on 18th and 25th November 1960, followed by 400–500 on the 26th and 350 there on 22nd November 1970. As in spring, since 1993, autumn movements have become an annual event including 6,500 moving west at Lynn Point on 19th December 1993 and a total of 6,922 passing south at Hunstanton between 29th September and 15th November 1997, including 2,105 in two and a half hours on 10th November.

During severe winters tens of thousands of Wood Pigeons have been shot or have died of starvation. In 1963 numbers were killed by traffic when seeking exposed road surfaces in an apparent quest for grit. Yet others died at night whilst at roost, even becoming frozen to the branches as if they were asleep. Pheasant feed-rides enabled some to survive.

About 500 Wood Pigeons have been ringed in Norfolk but not a single recovery has been reported from abroad, although two foreign-ringed birds have been found in the county. One ringed at Helgoland, Germany on 30th August 1962 was shot on the nest at Burnham Market five years later and another ringed in Belgium in November 1966 was shot at Kirby Cane in August 1971. There have been only four recoveries over 100km away from the site of ringing – in Essex, Sussex and Hampshire, with the most distant by far involving one ringed at Sheringham in September 1993 which was shot at Duns, Border Region, Scotland in October 1995, a distance of 387km. The longest movements of birds ringed outside Norfolk and recovered in the county have involved an adult from Northamptonshire and one ringed as a nestling from Buckinghamshire.

*Michael Seago*

MY GARDEN, CHEDGRAVE. 8-7-1999.

## Collared Dove (Eurasian Collared Dove) — *Streptopelia decaocto*

**A very common resident and scarce passage migrant.**

The Collared Dove has achieved a spectacular and well documented rate of colonisation in Europe since about 1930. At the end of the 19th century it had but a slender foothold in Europe, being restricted to

Turkey and the Balkans. Progressing initially via the Danube, Collared Doves began breeding in Hungary in 1932, the Czech Republic and Slovakia in 1938, Austria in 1943, Germany in 1945, Italy in 1947 and The Netherlands in 1949. Breeding commenced in Denmark in 1950, Sweden in 1951, Switzerland and France in 1952, and in both Belgium and Norway in 1955 – the year in which the colonisation of Britain commenced. The species had exceeded 1,600km of north-west expansion from the Balkans to the North Sea in less than two decades (Hudson 1965).

The initial colonisation of Norfolk, and thus of Britain, was recorded by Richardson, Seago and Church (1957). The article contained a colour plate of adult and young Collared Doves specially painted for *British Birds* by Richard Richardson. The writer of this species text found three Collared Doves on 3rd July 1956 at Overstrand in a large walled garden containing extensive lawns, shrubberies, evergreen oaks, pines, Spanish chestnuts, and also a poultry run. That summer the known pair raised three broods and five young fledged. Nearby at Cromer two pairs nested and three young flew from the nests. The following year details came to light of a pair of Collared Doves which had bred in 1955 at Cromer and reared two young.

Within a decade of discovery, Collared Doves had outnumbered the familiar Turtle Dove in many areas and had become so widespread and locally numerous as to be taken for granted by British birdwatchers; a measure of the remarkable rate of expansion across an entire continent (Hudson 1965).

During the early years, five centres of abundance developed in Norfolk. The original Overstrand/Cromer area contained a feeding concentration of 150 at East Runton by February 1966. Yarmouth and Gorleston were first occupied in 1960, the colonists soon spreading to neighbouring villages; a wintering group of 95 discovered an abundance of food at a local maltings. The same year breeding began at Hunstanton where an autumn gathering of 83 appeared on cliff-top allotments. The first inland breeding commenced in 1961 at Little Cressingham in the Brecks. In 1962 nesting was recorded in King's Lynn and a flock of 110 was at West Lynn in 1964. Collared Doves had spread to over 80 towns and villages in the county by late 1966, including Brandon, Dereham, Downham Market, Swaffham and Wells. Breeding in Norwich was first recorded in 1967 and by December 1973 over 200 were roosting at Carrow Works.

By 1975 roosting concentrations regularly featured in the *Norfolk Bird Report* – 270 at Blakeney, 250 at Downham Market, 100 at Wells and 140 at Yarmouth. Numbers continued to increase until 1982 when national CBC data showed that the population had peaked (Marchant *et al.* 1990). During fieldwork for the Norfolk Atlas (1980–85) it was recorded in 47% of the tetrads and during the 1994–97 BBS it was found in 38–55% of the 1km squares covered in Norfolk. Gas rigs off the Norfolk coast have continued to receive visits by parties of up to twelve Collared Doves. The most recent coastal movements have included 67 heading north at Hunstanton on 29th October 1995, 103 west at Holme on 27th April 1996 and 141 passing Hunstanton on 11th October 1996, out of an autumn total of 477. A considerable number of ringing recoveries confirm that after colonisation of this country there has been a succession of new arrivals from the Continent. Birds ringed in Belgium, Germany and The Netherlands have all been recovered here.

Will the Atlantic act as a permanent barrier to onward flights? Continental Collared Doves heading irresistibly west over the North Sea cannot know that this country exists until they make landfall. Doubtless many have flown westward from Atlantic coasts and perished at sea. This explains the colonisation of Iceland and also why Collared Doves reach isolated St Kilda so frequently. There have been sightings of birds heading westward from the Outer Hebrides and from western Ireland. The Collared Dove, a grain eater and easy to care for, raises the thought that it might obtain ship-assisted passage to the New World, but this will never be known with certainty. Over 50 Collared Doves released in the Bahamas in 1974 have subsequently colonised Florida.

Recording the Collared Dove's spread was greatly facilitated by its marked preference for human habitation. It is more at home in parks, gardens and churchyards of towns and villages than in open farmland. Large private gardens containing ornamental conifers are especially favoured. Not surprisingly, the Thetford Forest plantations are avoided. In winter large flocks appear at grain silos and where grain is spilled, especially at docks. Collared Doves may be found nesting at any time between March and October. Unusual nest-sites for the flimsy platforms of twigs and roots have included pylons, telegraph poles, ledges of buildings and roof guttering. A nest was also constructed from short lengths of copper wire.

The largest flock recorded in the county totalled 350 birds attracted to waste corn at Holme during March 1983. They formed part of a large-scale westerly movement on 5th–7th March which included 1,000 passing through during two days. In the same year 300 assembled at King's Lynn Docks in November. More recently the highest counts have been at Downham Market and The Nunnery, Thetford where up to 200 have been noted during January 1995 and October 1996 respectively. Local declines in breeding numbers may be due to increased levels of protection given to grain stores and to the activities of Sparrowhawks and grey squirrels. An additional factor is the decline in numbers of garden poultry-runs.

About 550 Collared Doves have been ringed in Norfolk but only one has been recovered any distance away from the site of ringing – ringed at Hunstanton on 17th December 1967 it was killed by a cat at Ballinlough, County Cork, Eire on 6th November 1969 – an indication of the westerly expansion of the species during the 1960s. Another ringed at Broadstairs, Kent on 28th January 1967 was found at Gorleston four months later, and one ringed in Essex in December 1971 was recovered in Norfolk in January 1976.

*Michael Seago*

MARSH BY MY GARDEN, CHEDGRAVE. (2) 22-6-2000.

## Turtle Dove (European Turtle Dove)          *Streptopelia turtur*

**A common but declining summer visitor and fairly common passage migrant; very rare in winter.**

The Turtle Dove is a breeding summer visitor across the upper and lower middle latitudes of the Western Palearctic. It winters in Africa from Senegal and Guinea to the Sudan and Ethiopia and as far south as northern Ghana. There are numerous records from oases indicating the Sahara is crossed on a broad front. In the British Isles there has been a marked decline since the mid-1980s due to drought in the winter quarters, large-scale shooting on migration and modern farming methods on the breeding grounds. The birds feed mainly on weed seeds, nowadays much reduced in quantity.

Early writers described the Turtle Dove as a rare bird, but by 1866 Stevenson was able to describe it as breeding very numerously. Riviere considered it abundant and well distributed. In Norfolk Turtle Doves favour open country with overgrown hedges and thickets, also developing conifer plantations, open woodland and large gardens. The species was found in 81% of the tetrads covered during fieldwork for the Norfolk Atlas. During the 1994–97 BBS it was found in 43–54% of the 1km squares covered in Norfolk.

The first spring arrivals usually appear in the second half of April, with passage continuing through May and into mid-June. The earliest ever were singles at King's Lynn on 21st March 1990 and at Paston on 28th March 1981. During May a movement heading west along the north Norfolk coast and then following the Wash shore past Hunstanton and Snettisham was often on an impressive scale. Daily counts of over 500 were not unusual, often associated with warm settled conditions. Maximum counts have included 1,000 passing Titchwell in a single day in late May 1972, 700 at Cley on 19th May 1982, 1,300 at Snettisham on 24th May 1985 and 950 there on 16th May 1986. In east Norfolk a peak northerly movement of 569 passed Winterton in three hours on 1st June 1975. Late spring passage has included 90 at Brancaster on 6th June 1979 and 80 at Holme on 15th June 1980. Flights began declining in numbers from 1992 onwards as ever fewer birds survived to run the gauntlet of the Mediterranean shooters. Since then, no day-total has exceeded 160 birds. In 1998 the highest day-count was 50 south at Snettisham on 9th May.

The first observation of a late summer concentration was 154 on cables at Great Plumstead on 3rd September 1943 (Seago 1953). During the 1960s summer flocks of up to 300 were regularly reported and duck farms became highly attractive. The most recent three-figure flocks were 500 at Snettisham in late August 1976, 680 increasing to 820 at Foulden on 23rd–27th June 1977 and 230 at Gayton on 1st–5th September 1985. Since then the highest counts have been 60 at Attlebridge on 9th July 1994 and 50 at Warham Green on 6th August 1995.

The last birds are usually seen in early October, but since 1963 there have been stragglers during November in eight different years with the latest on 23rd November 1977 at Yarmouth and 26th November 1966 at Cley. Late-staying or overwintering birds, usually associating with Collared Doves, have included singles at Wells until 2nd January 1969, at Yarmouth/Gorleston until 16th December 1976, at Buckenham on 5th December 1981, at Tattersett on 26th February 1988 and at Norwich on 24th January 1990.

Very few Turtle Doves are ringed nowadays in Norfolk but in earlier years when they were more plentiful, birds were regularly caught or ringed as nestlings, particularly in west Norfolk. No less than five from Gooderstone were recovered abroad, out of a total of 13 foreign recoveries from Norfolk. All were killed while on migration, through France (8), Spain (4) and Portugal, to their African winter quarters;

four in April–May and the rest in September–October. The most rapid movement concerned a late bird ringed at Salthouse on 1st October 1953 and shot in France at Quimper, Finistère three days later. The only recent recovery was one ringed near Wells on 13th August 1993 and recovered at Villar del Rey in southern Spain, one month later.

*Michael Seago*

# Rufous Turtle Dove (Oriental Turtle Dove)      *Streptopelia orientalis*

**A very rare vagrant; one record in 1946.**

The Oriental Turtle Dove breeds from the Ural Mountains eastwards to China and Japan, wintering in India and south-east Asia. There are several races, but only two that are highly migratory *S. o. meoma* which breeds in the Himalayas and *S. o. orientalis* breeding in Siberia, China and Japan. It is an extremely rare vagrant to the British Isles with only five records.

A female, moulting from juvenile to first-winter plumage, killed during a Pheasant shoot at Castle Rising on 29th January 1946 proved to be of the race *orientalis*. Although badly damaged it was identified by Ted Ellis at the Castle Museum, Norwich, where it remains today (Riviere 1946). It was only the second British record.

*Peter Allard*

# Ring-necked Parakeet (Rose-ringed Parakeet)      *Psittacula krameri*

**A very scarce introduced visitor.**

The Ring-necked Parakeet is widely distributed throughout much of the Afrotropical and Oriental regions. In Europe it occurs patchily in The Netherlands, Belgium and Germany, as well as in England, which supports the largest naturalised European population. Those in Europe are assumed to have originated from escaped or released birds. It first appeared in the wild in England in 1969 and by the time that it was admitted to Category C of the British and Irish list in 1977, the feral population was estimated at 500–1,000 birds, mostly in Kent and the Thames Valley. On 19th August 1998 no less than 1,507 were counted leaving a roost at Esher in Surrey.

As long ago as 1855 J. H. Gurney confirmed nesting in the wild at Northrepps and on five occasions young were successfully fledged. The only other breeding record in Norfolk concerned a pair which bred in the King's Lynn area just prior to 1974. However, it was not until 1975 that the species featured for the first time in the *Norfolk Bird Report* with sightings from five localities in the east, three in the north and one in the Broads. There do not appear to have been any attempts at breeding in recent years and the Ring-necked Parakeet was apparently not recorded during fieldwork for the Norfolk Atlas in the years 1980–85. Indeed most records have related to birds seen in flight either during spring or autumn passage, or in the winter months, when they visit garden bird-tables; the species' success has been related to its ready acceptance of artificial feeding in winter. Of the twelve records at a coastal site at Sheringham between 1975 and 1990, the majority were of adults flying west in the spring or autumn, including one with a migrating flock of Redwings and Fieldfares. In the early years the majority of sightings were made at coastal localities, but perhaps that was more a reflection of the distribution of observers rather than birds. The number of records appeared to peak in the late 1980s and early 1990s, when more were being found inland, particularly in the Broads. Numbers, however, have remained small with rarely more than a dozen reported per year. Most records concern single birds and occasionally two, but five were at Holme on 9th August 1996. There were only two accepted records in 1997 – singles at Burnham Norton on 21st July and at Norwich on 3rd November. Numerous sightings of one on the north and east coasts from 21st October to the end of November 1998 may possibly have involved just one bird.

The number of escaped Alexandrine and Plum-headed Parakeets is increasing and it is no longer safe to assume that a free-flying green parakeet in Norfolk is a Ring-necked. Perhaps this is one reason why fewer are now being reported in the county.

*Moss Taylor*

# Great Spotted Cuckoo                    *Clamator glandarius*

**A very rare vagrant; five records.**

The Great Spotted Cuckoo breeds from Iberia and southern France, discontinuously eastwards to Iran and southwards to South Africa. It winters in Africa primarily south of the Sahara, but small numbers winter as far north as western Morocco. It is a rare vagrant to the British Isles, most have been recorded between March and June.

The first Norfolk, and only the second British, record was of a young male shot by Edmund 'a gunner' on the denes between Yarmouth and Caister on 18th October 1896. The bird had been feeding on the larvae of the buff-tip moth. Formally in the Connop collection at Rollesby Hall, this specimen was donated in 1954 to the City of Birmingham Museum where it is currently on display.

The second occurrence was a near-adult, watched on cables at the edge of Hickling Broad by Jim Vincent on 29th July 1941. This was the third British record. A freshly dead immature picked up in the North Dunes at Winterton, on 6th August 1958 is at the Castle Museum, Norwich. The fourth occurrence was of an immature, at Cley East Bank on 21st October 1977 which later moved to Salthouse. Another immature was seen by a lone observer flying west over Cley Marsh on 7th July 1992. At midday it was relocated on Blakeney Point where it remained until dusk. Early next day the bird flew off towards Stiffkey, returning briefly to Blakeney Point on 11th July.

*Peter Allard*

# Cuckoo (Common Cuckoo)    HARDLEY FLOODS. 17·5·1991.    *Cuculus canorus*

**A fairly common, but declining, summer visitor.**

The Cuckoo's extensive breeding range covers Europe and most of Asia, from the Arctic tree limit south to north-west Africa and east across Russia and China to Japan. It winters in sub-Saharan Africa. Although its distribution has remained unchanged, numbers have probably declined in many areas since 1965, possibly due to loss of habitat through agricultural intensification. Its range and abundance are influenced by its two main requirements – nests of potential host species and a diet of hairy caterpillars. It is found throughout the British Isles and although many observers in Norfolk have commented on a decline in numbers in recent years, there is conflicting evidence of a national decline (Marchant *et al.* 1990).

Both Stevenson and Riviere described the Cuckoo as an abundant summer visitor. Stevenson also noted that the Pied Wagtail was the favourite host species and that parasitised Reed Warbler's nests were 'distinctly scarce', despite the abundance of the species in the county. This is in contrast to nowadays, when Reed Warblers, Meadow Pipits and Dunnocks are the most common foster parents. The Cuckoo was recorded in all of the 10km squares in Norfolk for both the BTO Breeding Atlases and the Norfolk Atlas, when it was present in 75% of the tetrads. Its absence was apparent from localities where hedgerows and marginal habitats had been removed, but was otherwise found in open country, parkland, woodland, heaths, wetlands and coastal dunes. During the 1994–97 BBS it was recorded in 54–67% of the 1km squares in Norfolk, with no obvious trend.

Carefully recorded observations concerning the arrival dates of the first Cuckoos of spring have produced some interesting results. The average arrival date for the period 1751–85 was 25th April and for 1891–1925 was 23rd April, a difference of only two days (Margary 1926), while in the 1950s it was 13th April and in the 1990s the 10th April. For a species with such a familiar call, this change is unlikely to be related simply to increased observer coverage. Irrespective of the dates of the first records, the main arrival is generally not until the last ten days of April or early May, with most birds being found inland rather than on the coast. The earliest records were both in 1903 at Horsey on 21st March and at Yarmouth on 29th March. The only other records before April were on 29th March 1965 at both Blakeney and Surlingham. Early April records have included birds at Narborough on 4th April 1993 and Paston on 6th April 1990. Birds clearly on spring passage are noted along the north Norfolk coast in May, generally moving in a westerly direction. Ten at Holme on 5th May 1995 were noteworthy, while at the same locality four arrived in off the sea on 18th May 1996 and on the following day four flew west at both Holme and Sheringham.

Post-fledging dispersal begins in July and by early August the juveniles start their southward migration, the adults having departed a few weeks earlier. An interesting observation concerned a juvenile which flew in off the sea at Winterton on 3rd September 1997. Very few Cuckoos are recorded in Norfolk after mid-September and there have been only eight records after the end of the month. Seven have been recorded in early October (three of which were in 1998), the latest on 9th October 1994 at Foulden, while an exceptionally late bird was at Haddiscoe on 14th–17th November 1960.

Examples of the rufous colour-morph, the so-called 'hepatic phase' females are occasionally seen in Norfolk, with recent records at Gooderstone and Sparham in 1991, Hickling in 1992 and Cantley Beet Factory in 1994. A 70% albino juvenile Cuckoo was at West Acre in August 1990.

Less than 100 Cuckoos have been ringed in Norfolk, of which six have been recovered. A nestling ringed at Kelling on 29th June 1931 was found at Evres-en-Argonne, in north-eastern France on 21st September, almost certainly the first foreign recovery of a Cuckoo from the British Isles. Over 40 years were to pass before the second recovery from Norfolk – a juvenile ringed at Holme on 13th August 1972 which was found dead six weeks later near Rome, Italy, once again illustrating the south-easterly route taken by British Cuckoos in autumn. Another ringed at Holme on 15th May 1977 was found dead at Finningham, Suffolk at the end of the month, an interesting example of a bird moving south in spring. Finally, adults show a marked fidelity to the breeding areas used in previous summers, as was indicated by a male ringed at Waxham on 9th June 1992 and found dead at Martham, only 7km away, on 10th May 1996, and another male ringed at Burgh Castle on 9th June 1996 which was found dead there in May 1997. Perhaps juveniles also show a similar tendency – one ringed at Holme in July 1984 was found dead there in May 1987.

*Moss Taylor*

## Barn Owl — *Tyto alba*

LANGLEY. 6·1·2000. OPPOSITE "WHERRY." P.H.

**A fairly common resident; the Continental race *guttata* is a rare vagrant.**

The Barn Owl is a widely distributed species and is found on every continent except Antarctica. The population in the British Isles, represented by the nominate race *T. a. alba*, is at the northern limit of the species' range. Throughout the 20th century it has suffered a dramatic decline in numbers across the Western Palearctic (Tucker & Heath 1994) and North America. Between the two BTO Breeding Atlases the number of 10km squares in which it was recorded fell by 43% and by the time of the New Atlas it was absent from large areas of central England, where it had previously been recorded.

Within Norfolk a decline was first noted by Stevenson in 1866, his concerns being echoed by both Lubbock (1879) and Riviere. The species appears to have suffered less from persecution than other raptors, possibly because of its reputation as a 'mouser'. The process of agricultural intensification appears to be the main cause of the decline, resulting in the loss of both hunting habitat and traditional nest sites. The county population just prior to the Second World War has been estimated at 442 breeding pairs (Shawyer 1987), based on data gathered by Blaker (1933). The Hawk and Owl Trust survey of 1982–85 recorded 191 pairs, a decline of 56% (slightly less than the national average, but still alarming). During fieldwork for the Norfolk Atlas, which was carried out at about the same time, the species was recorded in 340 tetrads, covering all but four of the 10km squares in the county.

Norfolk remains a stronghold for this species with pairs still widely distributed across the county. It appears to breed at the highest densities along the coastal marshes of north Norfolk, in the Brecks and throughout the Broads. In the two former regions, the widespread provision of nest boxes has enabled the species to exploit areas of ideal hunting habitat, notably rough grassland, Breckland and coastal grazing marsh (Johnson 1991). The highest natural densities are to be found on traditional country estates with lightly-grazed parkland and an abundance of mature trees containing suitable cavities.

Comparison of *Norfolk Bird Reports* with other data sources shows the species to be substantially under-recorded within Norfolk and the true breeding population is likely to be in the range of 150–300 pairs. Many pairs go unreported, partly because nest sites are difficult to locate, but also because many landowners are understandably protective about their nesting pairs. Examination of nest sites notified during the Hawk and Owl Trust survey has shown that many sites have been lost over the last 15 years, although owls still occur locally in most parts of the county. Provision of nest boxes, coupled with targeted habitat management has increased opportunities for the species in those parts of the county where such schemes operate, although there is a need for more work outside these areas. It is hoped to increase annual monitoring of nesting pairs within the county through the joint BTO/Hawk and Owl Trust monitoring programme (Toms 1996). Nesting sites are becoming more limited due to the conversion of old barns into dwellings. Formerly many such buildings contained an 'owl window'. In addition, Egyptian Geese also favour nesting in hollow trees; their breeding season may well be in advance of the Barn Owl's, often commencing early in the New Year.

Just over a third of the fledged nestlings will die during their first winter (36% of the Norfolk birds), the majority of them succumbing to the hardships of winter or through collision with motor vehicles. Fast, open roads (particularly those passing through the Broads) with rough grassland verges bring about the demise of a significant number of owls each year (Johnson 1990). It has been suggested that as many as one in three youngsters will die on the road within the first year of life. The impact of roads on local Barn Owl populations can be reduced by planting screening hedges and by keeping the roadside verges short and unfavourable for the small mammals that are the main source of prey for Barn Owls (Toms 1997).

The diet of Barn Owls within the county shows pronounced regional and seasonal variation (Buckley & Goldsmith 1972, 1975). Small mammals dominate the diet throughout the year, but small passerines are also taken, usually from roost sites, during the winter months. Within the Broads, Brecks and parkland areas, the field vole is the preferred prey species, with common shrew and wood mouse of secondary importance. In the more intensive areas of north-west Norfolk, wood mice become the primary prey species, possibly increasing the risk of pesticide poisoning to the owls.

Dark-breasted Barn Owls *T. a. gutatta* are occasionally recorded in the county, usually in early winter or early spring. These are vagrants from Europe and have been most commonly recorded along the eastern fringe of the county. Young of the dark-breasted race show more pronounced movements than our own race. Since the 1970s, single dark-breasted individuals have been recorded in 1975, 1976, 1978, 1979, 1985 and 1991, with two in 1990, 1994 and 1997, and four in 1995.

A total of 83 Barn Owl pulli ringed in Norfolk was subsequently recovered between 1978 and 1995. This represented about 15% of the Barn Owls ringed in the county during the same period. On average, these birds moved 23km away from their natal sites over a period of 381 days. One ringed in 1979 and recovered in 1986 had moved only 22 km from its ringing site. Generally Barn Owls do not disperse far from their natal sites and there is no clear direction favoured during these short-distance movements. However, Norfolk-ringed Barn Owl pulli have been recovered outside the county, the most distant being two to North Yorkshire and one to Hampshire, with others in Humberside (2), Essex (2) and Suffolk. The majority have been found during the winter months. In addition, nestlings ringed in Lincolnshire (3), Essex (2) and Northamptonshire have been found in Norfolk. The only bird ringed as an adult to have moved any distance was one ringed near Boston, Lincolnshire on 17th June 1996 and recovered at Bowthorpe in November.

*Mike Toms*

## Scops Owl (Eurasian Scops Owl)                     *Otus scops*

**A very rare vagrant; eight records.**

The Eurasian Scops Owl is mainly a summer visitor to southern Europe. It breeds from Iberia eastwards to Russia and winters in the African savannahs between the Sahara and the rain forests. Prior to 1910 it was a rare but relatively regular visitor to the British Isles. However, since then it has become extremely rare with far fewer records.

The first authenticated record for Norfolk was one picked up alive, slightly injured, at the foot of the Cromer lighthouse on the morning of 27th November 1861. Previously in the Henry Stevenson collection, this individual is now at the Castle Museum, Norwich. Thirty years later, two males were shot in 1891, the first at Walsingham Abbey on 21st May and the second at Martham on 1st June. The following year, a female was shot on the late date of 18th November at Holt. On 6th April 1902 one was seen at close quarters at Sidestrand, another on 15th June 1912 was shot at Heacham and on 6th October 1922, one was seen well by Robert Pinchen, the warden at Blakeney Point. The final record is of a female found exhausted by the roadside at Horsey on 27th August 1954. It died the following day and is now in the Castle Museum, Norwich.

*Peter Allard*

# Snowy Owl                                    *Nyctea scandiaca*

**A rare vagrant.**

The Snowy Owl has a circumpolar distribution, breeding in Iceland, the mountains of northern Fennoscandia, Lapland and Arctic Russia, as well as on the Arctic islands of Canada and north-west Greenland. The breeding range can fluctuate greatly depending on the supply of mammalian prey, particularly lemmings. When food is scarce, dispersive irruptions take place with birds being forced to move much further south than normal. A rare vagrant to much of Britain, it is more regular in mainland Scotland and the Northern Isles where breeding was recorded on Fetlar between 1967 and 1975 (Evans 1994).

The first record of a Snowy Owl in Norfolk was one shot at Felbrigg in April 1814. Another was obtained in a similar way at Gunton in January 1820. A specimen in the Castle Museum, Norwich, from Carlton Rode was probably obtained about 1830. In the spring of 1847 one was killed at Beeston and another was seen at Hedenham Wood, near Brooke in January or February of that year, which was later killed in Suffolk (Stevenson, Riviere).

Since then the following have been recorded, bringing the county total to 14:

- 1849: Swannington, one seen in autumn
- 1850: One shot at Beeston on 22nd January
  An immature male shot at St Faith's in late February
- 1871: An immature female shot at Southrepps on 4th December
- 1876: One shot at Burnham Overy on 2nd or 3rd November
- 1905: On trapped at Cockley Cley in early April
- 1922: Waxham on 1st May, the same appearing at Horsey and Winterton sandhills for a week in early May and last seen at Sutton on 13th May
- 1938: Gunton on 27th October
- 1991: A second-winter bird on Blakeney Point on 23rd March had been seen in Lincolnshire on 18th March. After being watched for three hours, it moved to the Warham area. It was seen at Burnham Overy on 24th and finally at Norton Creek, Scolt Head on 25th March. Later it was seen flying north at Easington, Humberside on 30th March and was possibly the same bird recorded at several sites in Orkney during April (Stoddart & Eldridge 1992).

*Peter Allard*

---

**Little Owl**  LANGLEY. 2-4-2000.                    *Athene noctua*

**A fairly common but localised introduced resident.**

The Little Owl breeds throughout central and southern Europe being absent only from the mountainous areas of the Alps and to a lesser extent the Pyrenees. It is a resident across all of its range. Decreases have been noted in many countries since the 1930s. In Britain it occurs over much of lowland England with small numbers in southern Scotland. The New Atlas recorded a drop in numbers in East Anglia, Lincolnshire and the East Midlands, partly offset by increases in the Welsh borders and northern England.

The Little Owl is not a native species to Britain. Introductions commenced in 1843 though it is thought that birds released in Kent in the 1870s and in Northamptonshire in the 1880s gave rise to the successful colonisation of England. Records in Norfolk predating these could have referred to immigrants from the Continent, possibly The Netherlands.

Hunt, in *British Ornithology*, published in 1815–22, referred to a nest being taken 'at no great distance from Norwich' but the record was not included in his 'List of Norfolk Birds' of 1829. Stevenson recorded one killed at Blofield in 1824 noted by Mr Lombe, and Paget gave two instances of specimens having been taken in Yarmouth prior to 1834 and commented that they were 'well authenticated'. An example that could refer to an immigrant from the Continent came on to a fishing smack ten miles off Yarmouth in February 1862. In 1876, Lord Kimberley released six birds on his estate in Norfolk and records followed at Haveringland in May 1877 and at Harleston in April 1886. No further records were noted by Riviere until 1905 when one was killed at Kelling in November. Records became far more frequent from 1910 onwards – a pair bred near King's Lynn in two consecutive years and in the period 1913–16, 43 were taken and analysed by T. E. Gunn who found the remains of no gamebirds in the stomach contents. That the spread was accelerating can be shown by the numbers taken on two estates, totalling 5,000 acres, with ten in 1919, 28 in 1920 and 71 in 1921. By 1930, it was common and noted as breeding freely throughout the county.

It is a wonder why this species was introduced onto estates where gamebirds were reared for shooting. However, further research carried out by Dr W. E. Collinge, who looked at the stomach contents of 194 adults and 18 nestlings, found that only 0.05% of prey items were young gamebirds, confirming the earlier findings of T. E. Gunn. Large numbers of click beetles, wireworms and other insects are taken to the benefit of the agriculturist.

A decline was noted in Norfolk and across England from the 1950s onwards due to a combination of hard winters, pesticides (especially from 1955) and the enlargement of field units with the removal of hedges and trees, causing the loss of suitable nest sites.

The Norfolk Atlas recorded Little Owls in 225 tetrads (15%), covering all but six of the 10km squares in the county, although at low density in a central swathe from the Suffolk border to the north coast. It was most frequently located in the extreme south-east where the stiff boulder-clay soils retain the suitable mixture of woodland and pasture, in the Stanford Training Area and the Fen border to the west, where there are suitable nest-sites, hunting perches and open ground over which to hunt.

There has been an increase in the past two decades aided by provision of nest boxes in several areas. The success of these may be judged from an increase of eleven pairs on a 200ha farm at Caistor St Edmund in 1993, to 25 by 1997. Accurate assessments of the current population are difficult owing to the species' unobtrusiveness and because many of the areas where it is found are not watched systematically. Along the north Norfolk coast, there has been an upturn in the number of records since 1993, where it had been in decline since the start of the 1990s. Although it was found in up to only 5% of the 1km squares covered in Norfolk during the 1994–97 BBS, it was recorded at almost 100 sites in the county in both 1996 and 1997.

Less than a hundred Little Owls have been ringed in Norfolk and only two have been recovered more than 10km away from the site of ringing – a nestling from West Tofts was found near Thetford and one ringed at Kelling in June 1934 was found dead at Congham, near King's Lynn the following June, a distance of 43km.

*Peter Dolton*

## Tawny Owl | CHEDGRAVE: BY MY GARDEN. 6-8-2000.     *Strix aluco*

**A common resident.**

The Tawny Owl is the most common breeding owl across its Western Palearctic range. It is absent from northern Fennoscandia and, rather interestingly, from Ireland, the Isle of Wight and the Isle of Man. European populations have remained stable in recent decades and some populations have shown a slight increase.

The story of the Tawny Owl in Norfolk is similar to that of the species elsewhere in England and Wales. During the 1800s, constant persecution by gamekeepers had a tremendous impact on the population. Stevenson noted that the species was extremely scarce within the county. With a reduction in keepering and more tolerant attitudes towards the species, the Norfolk population increased dramatically during the period 1900–30. Riviere described the Tawny Owl as a fairly abundant resident generally distributed throughout the wooded districts of the county. Although the cessation of persecution is often cited as the reason for the observed increase, it should also be noted that the Tawny Owl population in Europe showed an expansion in range over the same period. This may have contributed to the increase in the Norfolk breeding population.

The Tawny Owl is now the most common breeding owl in Norfolk and pairs breed in most parts of the county. The species is only limited by the availability of suitable woodland habitat where it usually nests in hollow trees. During fieldwork for the Norfolk Atlas it was found in 40% of the tetrads surveyed, being absent mainly from the Fens and more open areas of the Broads. Occasionally it will nest in the old nests of other species, and it has been recorded nesting on the ground; notably in Whiteslea Wood, Hickling in 1943 where it was photographed by Eric Hosking and in Dead Man's Wood, Sheringham in 1982 (Taylor 1987a). In wooded parts of the county, pairs may breed at a density of 10–15 pairs per 10km$^2$ (Percival

1990), although a survey in 1997 revealed 15 pairs in Holkham Park alone.

Tawny Owls are adaptable and are increasingly reported breeding in urban and suburban areas, exploiting roosting House Sparrows and Starlings as the primary prey source. This was demonstrated by Kelly (1990) with records from town parks, cemeteries and large gardens. Owls nesting in farm woodlands will also utilise open farmland and field margins when hunting, thus allowing them to breed in plantations that may be substantially smaller than expected to hold a breeding pair (Hardy 1992).

Despite the widespread distribution of the species in Norfolk and its vocal territorial nature, the Tawny Owl is heavily under-recorded with few records submitted annually to the county bird recorder. Established pairs defend a territory throughout the year and are most vocal during the winter months prior to the onset of breeding. If food is scarce during this period, females are unable to lay down sufficient body reserves to allow gonad development and laying does not occur (Hirons 1982). It is difficult to pinpoint nest-sites during the early part of the season without intensive fieldwork. For this reason the number of territorial 'calling' pairs is often used as a measure of breeding numbers (Redpath 1994). Tawny Owl chicks develop quickly and will often leave the nest prematurely before they can fly. Such chicks are adept at climbing and even if they fall to the ground they will quickly climb back up into the tree. The chicks are dependent upon the adults for food for the first three months after fledging and during this period they are more readily located. After this the young will disperse a small distance seeking out territories of their own.

Individuals of the 'grey' phase have been occasionally recorded in the county. One was shot at Topcroft in 1919 (Riviere), one was found at Hardingham in 1979 and more recently one was found dead in Sheringham in 1993. These morphs are probably eastern European birds.

About 200 Tawny Owls have been ringed in Norfolk. One ringed at Rackheath in July 1970 was recovered in Norwich in July 1989 having travelled only 6km. This recovery illustrates the sedentary nature of the species. Despite living for 19 years it was still four years short of the longevity record for a British-ringed Tawny Owl. The only other noteworthy recovery involved one ringed at Salthouse Heath in May 1956 and controlled at Great Witchingham two years later.

*Mike Toms*

## Long-eared Owl | *Asio otus*

**A scarce resident, passage migrant and winter visitor.**

The Long-eared Owl has a circumpolar Holarctic distribution, breeding right across Europe. As with the Short-eared Owl, breeding numbers often fluctuate with the availability of small mammal prey and this, coupled with the fact that the species is easily overlooked, make it difficult to estimate population size. Within the British Isles the species has shown a steady decline since about 1900, attributed to the increase in Tawny Owl numbers (Historical Atlas). At the present time it has a scattered distribution throughout Britain and Ireland, being particularly scarce in central and south-west England, Wales and western Scotland (New Atlas).

Long-eared Owl numbers in Norfolk increased during the 1800s, probably due to the increasing establishment of conifer plantations and Stevenson described it as 'a numerous resident'. Persecution of Tawny Owls would have also benefited the species by reducing competition. Tawny Owls dominate Long-eared Owls and the two species seem unable to coexist. During an intensive west Norfolk survey Kemp (1981) never found Tawny Owls and Long-eared Owls breeding closer than 0.5km apart.

The decline of the Long-eared Owl in Norfolk stems from the early 1900s and coincides with the increase in the county's Tawny Owl population. Since then, the Long-eared Owl has gone from being fairly abundant in most districts, to being a locally-distributed resident breeding in isolated conifer plantations. The species nests in old Crow or Heron nests, or in squirrel drays, usually in mature conifers near to open areas of rough grassland or farmland. However, there are several records of birds nesting on the ground at sites in the Broads, having been documented by Gurney (1881–1912) and Turner (1915) and which are supported by photographs. In fact at Hickling, Jim Vincent's diaries make frequent reference to ground nests and he once 'showed J. H. Gurney four such nests in a single day'.

Less than a dozen breeding sites are now reported annually, although the survey work of Kemp during the early 1980s illustrated just how under-recorded this species is (Kemp 1981, 1982). During fieldwork for the Norfolk Atlas it was recorded in 75 (5%) of the tetrads with concentrations in Thetford Forest and the Brecks, and in an area to the east of King's Lynn. Other breeding pairs were reported along the Cromer to Holt Ridge and from areas within the Broads. Most pairs appear to be site faithful and often occupy the same plantation or patch of woodland in successive years. Long-eared Owls are prone to disturbance and avoid nesting near to human habitation; there is evidence that they also avoid nesting near busy roads or railways (Kemp 1982).

Breeding Long-eared Owls are difficult to detect without extensive survey work. Breeding begins early in the year and the triple hoot can be heard from January through into March. The hunger call (a drawn-out squeak) of developing chicks is easier to identify and locate, being most evident through late May to the end of July. Adults will forage at some distance from the nest and pairs in areas of good habitat may occur at a spacing of 2.0km. The owlets are able to move away from the nest quite quickly because of the rapid development of their wing feathers (Glue 1977b). The current county breeding population is likely to be in the range of 75–150 pairs.

Passage birds appear from October and are regularly recorded arriving at the coast in small numbers. In 1927 a total of 14 singles was recorded at the East Dudgeon light-vessel during November and December. During October and early November 1975 a total of 60 arrived on the coast, in addition to observations at the Inner Dowsing light-vessel and on gas production platforms north-east of Yarmouth. Again in 1994 there was a marked arrival of birds, with about 35 individuals appearing between 20th and 24th October. These birds joining the resident population come from the mainly migratory populations in Scandinavia which respond to the availability of small mammal prey and as a consequence of which the numbers arriving in Britain vary from year to year. Occasional birds are also reported on passage in April and May, including one seen to arrive in off the sea at Wells on 18th May 1997.

In recent winters the number of birds arriving here has been quite low. Recent work has demonstrated a clear sex bias in the arriving migrants, with significantly more females reaching Britain than males (Wyllie *et al.* 1996). The males appear to migrate only a short distance, preferring to remain close to their breeding areas, while the females move farther to avoid winter food shortages. Winter roosts are often located at traditional sites and may be used for many years provided they are not subject to continual disturbance. A wide variety of habitats may be used; conifer belts and dense thickets of hawthorn – with perhaps elder and other shrubs – are particularly favoured (Kemp 1992). Although there has been a decline in the presence of large communal roosts in recent years, up to 15 roosted at New Buckenham Common during February and March 1987 and 19 were at a Fenland locality in January 1990. Smaller roosts on private land are likely to go unrecorded and it is becoming more difficult to determine the wintering population within the county. An analysis of pellets collected over a ten-year period at four Long-eared Owl roosts showed that Norfolk Long-eared Owls catch significantly more wood mice than elsewhere in mainland Britain, with field voles and bank voles making up a large part of the remaining prey items (Kemp 1992).

A nestling ringed in Germany in June 1974 was controlled at Happisburgh on 24th October 1975, while an adult ringed on Helgoland, Germany in April 1989 was found at Beighton in March 1992. The third Swedish-ringed Long-eared Owl to be recovered in Britain was one ringed as a nestling and found the following February at Wroxham. Another nestling ringed at Woodwalton Fen, Cambridgeshire was recovered at Reedham the following January, and one from Holbeach, Lincolnshire was found further south around the Wash at Terrington three years later.

*Mike Toms*

## Short-eared Owl BY CHEDGRAVE CARR. 19·4·1992. *Asio flammeus*

**A rare breeder, and scarce passage migrant and winter visitor.**

The Short-eared Owl has a circumpolar distribution, breeding in northern Europe and North America. The species is migratory, although less so in southern and central Europe where it sometimes breeds. Populations fluctuate widely between years and large influxes are occasionally reported as birds respond to changing prey abundance. Such fluctuations make it difficult to detect underlying population trends. However, the species is listed as 'vulnerable' (Tucker & Heath 1994) and is thought to be under threat from the drainage of wetlands and marshes in central and eastern Europe. In the British Isles it is most abundant as a breeding species in the upland areas from north Staffordshire northwards, with scattered populations in Wales and the south-east counties (New Atlas).

The species has always been a scarce breeder within Norfolk and breeding populations have come and gone over time. A small number of pairs bred in the county up until the 1850s, typically in the Fens and the Broads. Riviere noted that breeding was not recorded again until 1878 after which a handful of pairs bred annually for several years. In the 1920s breeding took place regularly on Scolt Head and in 1924 five nests were found in one area of Broadland. During 1933, an exceptional 18 pairs were found at Hickling and Horsey, following a plague of short-tailed field voles which were piled high around each nest, the numbers taken being far in excess of the birds' needs. A further two pairs were recorded in Breckland. From the 1930s regular breeding was also recorded along the north Norfolk coast and in the Brecks. Colonisation of the Wash took place during the 1960s and is now the only area in which nesting attempts are made in most years.

Short-eared Owls
(Nik Borrow)

Short-eared Owls require large areas of open ground, free from disturbance and an abundance of small mammal prey. Birds can be located displaying and holding territory, but isolated pairs can be easily over-looked. Confirmation of breeding is difficult to achieve with the female sitting very tight during the egg stage. During the first week or so after hatching delivery of food to the nest usually takes place after dusk. Provisioning may occur during daylight hours as the chicks grow bigger. It is at this stage that nests are easiest to locate as adult males will hover and 'bark' at intruders (Glue 1993). Of the 33 records in the Norfolk Atlas, six were of confirmed breeding, five were of probable breeding and the remaining 22 of possible breeding. This highlights the difficulties in confirming breeding. No doubt, more pairs breed than are reported, but the breeding population within the county is unlikely to be more than a few pairs. For instance, two to three pairs bred in 1995, but none in 1994 nor 1996, while a breeding attempt was made in the Wash in 1997.

With such a small breeding population, it is passage birds that are usually recorded. The numbers arriving in Norfolk on passage vary from year to year, substantial numbers having been noted on occasions. In recent decades large-scale arrivals of Short-eared Owls have been recorded within the Halvergate Triangle on five occasions, commencing with the 1961–62 winter when up to 18 occupied a daytime roost throughout February. Spectacular numbers were on show in 1964–65 between November and late January. At least 80 were counted on several occasions departing from two roosts. The majority of the owls became the last occupants of a marshman's cottage alongside Halvergate Fleet close to High's Hill. Despite an impressive wingspan the tenants readily gained entry through broken dormers. The second roost was in an abandoned garden at Berney. The next large-scale arrival was in 1969–70 when a total of 47 Short-eared Owls assembled in three roosts with an additional seven at Limpenhoe and six at Hardley. During the following winter a total of 60 again occupied three roosts in January 1971. Halvergate Triangle provided its most memorable display on Christmas Eve 1972 when 116 were found roosting along the Fleet wall. This remarkable total provided the unique sight of over 80 in the air at the same time. Food was abundant, the owls remaining for several weeks. The scantiest cover was favoured where grasses had been burnt with only odd thistles and reed surviving (Allard 1990, 1998). Another roost site at Sommerfield near Docking held 22–35 individuals each winter between 1966 and 1969 (Bagnall-Oakeley 1969). Pellets from this roost site were analysed and found to contain mainly the remains of the brown rat, which was abundant in this arable area. This contrasted with pellets collected from roosts at Hardley, Haddiscoe and the Halvergate Marshes, in which the field vole comprised 70% of the prey items (Buckley 1974). Far fewer have been recorded in recent years, for instance Short-eared Owls were reported from only 30 localities in early 1997, the majority coastal, with maximum counts of eight at Snettisham and five at Warham Greens, while five were in the Chedgrave area at the end of the year. However, up to 22 were seen in the Halvergate Fleet/Berney and lower Bure Levels in November-December 1998.

Autumn arrivals are generally recorded from mid-September onwards, peaking in October and with occasional birds coming in off the sea as late as December. An unusually early one was present in Yarmouth Cemeteries on 27th August 1997. Their arrival often coincides with that of Woodcock, hence the old local name of 'Woodcock Owl' (Stevenson). Usually only one or two are recorded on a single day at any one site but six arrived in off the sea at Sheringham on both 28th October 1974 and 4th October 1992. National ringing recoveries have demonstrated that the majority of these autumn arrivals have come from Scandinavia, although other individuals had been ringed in The Netherlands and Belgium (Glue 1977a). A small coastal passage is noted in March and most wintering birds have departed by mid-April, although some individuals remain through to the beginning of summer.

Nine Norfolk-ringed nestlings have been recovered. Three from the same brood ringed at Morston in June 1957 were recovered at Wells in July, at Sleaford, Lincolnshire in November and at Andilly, France in December, respectively. A Cley-ringed nestling was also recovered in France in December, while a nestling from Hickling in 1933 was found the following October near Gozo, Malta. This remains the only recovery of the species in that country. Another Hickling nestling, also from 1933, was recovered in Gwent, Wales in September. The earliest recovery, however, was one ringed in the Broads in 1928 and found at Roughton the following month. A nestling ringed at Bergsatern, Sweden in July 1973 was found dead at Cley in October and a nestling ringed at Goole, Yorkshire in June 1975 was shot at Terrington in October. The October arrivals in Norfolk clearly involve British, as well as Scandinavian, birds.

*Mike Toms*

# Tengmalm's Owl                                   *Aegolius funereus*

**A very rare vagrant; five records, the last in 1903.**

Tengmalm's Owl is a northern Holarctic species breeding from northern Fennoscandia to eastern Siberia and from Belgium and Germany east to central Asia and western China. It also breeds in North America.

Although largely sedentary and strictly nocturnal, Tengmalm's Owl is prone to occasional eruptive movements in late autumn and winter. Most British records are considered to relate to the nominate race *A. f. funereus* which breeds across Europe east to central Russia. It was formerly a much more frequent visitor to Britain, certainly prior to 1918, including a small irruption in 1901.

The first county record was one caught at Beechamwell, near Swaffham on 27th June 1849. An adult female was shot at Burlingham on 6th April 1857 and is now in the collection at the Castle Museum, Norwich. One was taken alive at Cromer lighthouse on 30th October 1881. This is also in the Castle Museum, Norwich. One obtained at Thornham on 30th October 1901 was part of an irruption, when two others were picked up alive at Southwold, Suffolk. The final record, a female taken by B. Harrison at Rainthorpe Hall, Norwich, in July 1903 and preserved by T. E. Gunn, was only discovered in 1996 in the National Trust collection at Sheringham Hall. It has since been accepted by the BBRC.

*Peter Allard*

SALTHOUSE HEATH.

# Nightjar (European Nightjar)  24·6·1986.  *Caprimulgus europaeus*

**A fairly common but localised summer visitor and rare passage migrant.**

The Nightjar occurs as a breeding summer visitor over most of Continental Europe, being absent mainly from the highlands and tundra of northern Fennoscandia and Russia, the Alps, and Iceland and Svalbard, as well as areas of intensive farming. All populations are migratory wintering in sub-Saharan Africa. A reduction in the range and numbers has been recorded throughout much of Europe since the 1950s. In the British Isles, this decline was first noted in the early 1900s, becoming more pronounced since 1950 and believed to be linked to habitat change, as much former prime habitat became covered by commercial even-aged woodland (European Atlas). By the time fieldwork for the New Atlas was carried out (1988–91), the main concentrations for the species were confined to southern and south-eastern England, and East Anglia.

Nightjar *(Gary Wright)*

Although the enclosure of commons and waste lands had 'banished' Nightjars from many of their former haunts in the 19th century, Stevenson still described the species as

> . . . common enough on the wild heathery districts in the western and south-western parts of the county, as well as in the vicinity of the coast, at Beeston and Hempstead, and on the Sandringham and other adjoining estates, in the neighbourhood of Lynn. In the vicinity of Norwich they may be seen as well as heard during the light summer nights on Mousehold Heath, also in the fern-growing lanes about Cossey, Bowthorpe, and Earlham.

Riviere stated that they were still fairly common in the 1920s, being most abundant in the Brecks.

The crepuscular and nocturnal habits of the Nightjar mean that reasonably accurate estimates of the county population have only been obtained during the national BTO surveys of the species carried out in 1981 and 1992. However, the decline in the species was shown by the number of 10km squares in which it was recorded during fieldwork for the 68–72 BTO Atlas, the Norfolk Atlas (1980–85) and the New Atlas (1988–91). The respective figures were 28, 20 and 16. As has been the case for the last 200 years, the stronghold for the species remains in west Norfolk, especially Breckland, where pairs occupy both heathland and Forestry Commission clearfell areas and young forestry plantations. A total of 145 churring males was located in west Norfolk during the 1981 survey, the majority in the Sandringham area and the Brecks. This had increased by almost 30% by the time of the 1992 survey, with a county total of 223; the Norfolk part of Thetford Forest alone holding 177 males. The increase appeared to be directly related to the increased amount of clearfell and young forestry plantation available. The latter apparently holding the greatest attraction with over 55% of the national population nesting at that time in young plantations. Elsewhere in west Norfolk, Roydon Common has been a traditional breeding site for many years where appropriate habitat management by the Norfolk Wildlife Trust attracted a record number of 23 churring males in 1997. A report on the habitat and breeding requirements of Nightjars at Dersingham Fen and Leziate was published by Berry (1979).

Stevenson mentioned breeding Nightjars in north Norfolk at Beeston and Hempstead, and the Cromer to Holt Ridge continues to hold a small population. The stronghold was formerly at Kelling Heath, where up to 24 pairs bred but, as a result of ceaseless military activity, this had been reduced to just two males in 1957. Small numbers continue to breed at both Kelling and Salthouse Heaths, and occasionally elsewhere in the area. In central Norfolk, a few pairs continued to breed on the outskirts of Norwich in the 1950s, but had become confined to the Horsford/Felthorpe area by the 1970s. In east Norfolk, up to three pairs of Nightjars have bred at Winterton since 1976 and in the Fritton/Herringfleet and Belton areas sporadic breeding has occurred since 1978; while Lound Waterworks occasionally hosts a pair.

The first Nightjars of the spring are generally recorded back at their breeding sites during the first half of May. The earliest dated records have been at Roydon Common on 28th April 1988 and at Martham on 2nd May 1998, with several records on 3rd May over the years. However, in the 1970s Nightjars were heard churring in the last week of April at Dersingham Fen (Berry 1979). The species is rarely recorded on spring passage but migrants have been noted at north Norfolk coastal sites between 7th May and 8th June, mainly at Scolt Head, Holkham and Cley. A male was seen to arrive in off the sea at Cley on 8th June 1957, while one arrived at the Dudgeon light-vessel (35km north of Sheringham) at 11:00 hrs on 19th June 1985 and remained on board for eight hours.

As a result of their comparatively late arrival in spring, small recently-fledged young are not infrequently found at breeding sites well into August, with the last records in mid-September. As in spring, Nightjars are rarely reported on autumn migration, but have been recorded at coastal sites from Snettisham to Weybourne, the majority between mid-August and mid-September. The latest dates for the county have been 2nd October 1985 at Cley, 5th October 1998 at Blakeney Point, 14th October 1882 at Northrepps and 13th November 1984 at Holme.

Less than 100 Nightjars have been ringed in Norfolk, including both chicks and free-flying birds, and three have been recovered. A young bird ringed near Thetford on 19th August 1996 was found dead at Charente in central France one month later. A chick ringed at Thetford Forest on 28th June 1988 was controlled at Lakenheath Warren, Suffolk on 2nd August, and another Thetford Forest chick ringed in 1993 was breeding at Wangford Woods, Suffolk two years later, 24km away from its natal area. Interestingly, a female ringed at Wangford Warren in June 1988 was breeding at West Tofts Heath the following year, a distance of 12km from the site of ringing.

*Moss Taylor*

## Swift (Common Swift) *NESTING IN MY ROOF. 8·7·1999.*          ***Apus apus***

**A common summer visitor and passage migrant.**

The Swift breeds throughout Europe, except for the far north (Iceland, northern Fennoscandia and the tundra zones of European Russia) and the Mediterranean islands. It winters mainly in Zaire and Tanzania south to Zimbabwe and Mozambique. It is common in most of the British Isles apart from the most northerly part of mainland Scotland and the Scottish Isles.

The Norfolk Atlas showed a widespread distribution in the county with records in 75% of the tetrads, while during the 1994–97 BBS it was found in 53–64% of the 1km squares covered in the county. The largest colonies are to be found in the City of Norwich and in towns and villages where there is an abundance of older buildings providing suitable cavities under eaves for nesting. Smaller numbers may be found in farm buildings and in country houses. However, nest-sites are diminishing due to changes in building regulations and better maintenance. Norwich City Council is thought to be the first local authority to have installed custom-made nest boxes for Swifts in the roof space of its properties. Of 19,500 homes in its area, a third were built before the Second World War and are in need of refurbishment. With a budget for 1997–98 of £8,000 it is hoped to provide two boxes in each of 200 homes. The policy will continue indefinitely and sponsorship is being encouraged. The Council was first alerted to the needs of the birds by the tenants themselves.

Stevenson described Swifts 'breeding regularly in the dark crevices of the chalk cliffs at Hunstanton . . despite being frequently shot at from the beach'. One or two pairs continued to occupy this traditional site during most years between 1966 and 1973 with an increase to three or four pairs in 1976 but only a single pair in 1981, when young remained in the nest until the remarkably late date of 1st October.

The first Swifts are usually seen in the second half of April. An average date of 3rd May has been noted over a period of 39 years in east Norfolk (P. Allard pers. obs.). The earliest ever were in 1985 with two or three at Cley and one at Wells on 3rd April which were followed by singles at Cley and Sheringham on 5th and at Paston and Winterton on 6th. The main arrival takes place in May followed, usually during the second half of the month, by large numbers of passage migrants invariably heading west along the north coast before following the shore of the Wash. These movements may continue well into June. They have included, for example, 2,000 at Titchwell on 3rd May 1982, thousands passing Wolferton on 23rd June 1982, 4,000 at Sheringham on 13th May 1992, hundreds passing Cley on 30th May 1993 and 2,100 over a three-hour period at Mundesley on 23rd May 1994.

During late spring large assemblies may appear over flooded gravel pits, flood-marshes, lakes and Broads during windy, cold or wet weather when the birds are forced to feed at low levels. Several hundreds were feeding low over Fowl Mere in the Brecks on 6th June 1953. At times the birds appeared to collide in mid-air and when the movement ceased in the early evening four were recovered having struck overhanging branches of trees edging the mere.

Later in the summer, but before the start of obvious return passage, substantial movements of Swifts occur which have included 5,000 west at Sheringham on 7th July 1981, 5,000 east at Sheringham on 6th July 1991, 1,200 west at Paston in four hours on 3rd July 1993, 3,700 west at Sheringham on 4th July 1995 and 2,150 west at Sheringham on 9th July 1996. Such movements have not been fully explained. Early departure of non-breeders may be involved, or the flights may be the result of long-distance feeding movements or may be ahead of advancing weather fronts to avoid rainfall, as was the case on 21st June 1998 at Titchwell where about 1,800 flew north between 18:30 and 18:50 hrs, only to return south after the storm had passed. Riviere was aware of the complicated patterns with 'spring and autumn passage migrations practically merging into each other'. A day of large-scale movement is spectacular. One such occasion featured 5,000 Swifts per hour moving east at Paston on 2nd August 1986 ahead of torrential rain the next day. Others involved 7,000 heading south at Horsey during two hours on 9th August 1996 and 5,000 south at Snettisham on 27th July 1998. On 3rd September 1997 an exceptional 2,000 birds passed over Cromer Golf Course.

Swifts are known to spend the night on the wing, drifting in all directions and rising so high that they become mere crescentic specks in the darkening sky. Hanging in the heavens they balance on warm air currents content to play away the darkness under the summer stars. However, on the evening of 26th July 1953 over 200 settled to roost on the floodlit stonework of Cromer Parish Church. Autumn departures continue until mid-August by which time almost all have left the county. In fact by the second week of the month the main arrival has reached the northern Afrotropics. Suddenly Norfolk skies become silent, the communal screaming display flights around the rooftops again become a memory.

Small numbers of Swifts are reported each year in September. Between 1953 and 1997 there were October occurrences in 25 years including a total of almost 50 records, mainly at coastal sites, during October 1976. There were also 37 November sightings of which singles at Cromer on 16th November 1984 and at Holme on 25th November 1992 followed the next day by two at Overstrand and East Runton were the latest. Warm southerly winds during November 1984 resulted in deposits of Saharan dust being widely recorded in Britain. These unusual conditions resulted in Swifts appearing at eight localities between West Runton and Snettisham on 10th–12th November with one at Cromer on 16th. The event coincided with a remarkable influx of four Pallid Swifts in England and Wales. An exceptionally late Swift was reported at Yarmouth on 18th and 20th December 1951. Partial albinos are occasionally recorded and can sometimes cause confusion. One at Breydon in May 1985 had both a white belly and a white rump.

Over 2,000 Swifts have been ringed in Norfolk but only two have produced foreign recoveries. A nestling from Cley in 1952 was recovered five years later in September in France and an adult ringed at Earlham in June 1982 was found in Natal, South Africa on 9th February 1985 and remains the only British-ringed Swift to be recovered in that country. Only one other Norfolk-ringed Swift has been recovered more than 100km from the site of ringing – ringed at Pensthorpe in June 1995 it was found near Leicester the following May. Birds ringed outside the county have come from Essex, Hertfordshire (2), Greater London, Lincolnshire and Cheshire (2). Site fidelity is demonstrated by an adult ringed at Earlham in July 1968 and controlled there in July 1980, while another ringed at Earlham in July 1980 was recovered at Eaton in May 1993, in at least its 14th year, compared with the longevity record for a British-ringed Swift of 16 years.

*Michael Seago*

# Pallid Swift                                        *Apus pallidus*

**A very rare vagrant; two records.**

The Pallid Swift breeds from north-west Africa and Iberia east through the Mediterranean to Iran, and winters mainly in northern tropical Africa. It is a very rare vagrant to the British Isles, with twelve records all between May and November.

This extremely difficult bird to identify has been recorded in the county twice. The first-found by Peter Colston, flew over Burnham Overy Fresh Marshes heading inland with other Swifts on the morning of 25th July 1993. Part of a weather-movement of Swifts moving ahead of an approaching storm, it was seen by four observers and constituted only the eighth British record (Colston 1995).

A second was identified in a weather-movement of Swifts at Mundesley cliffs on 28th August 1997. The lone observer saw the bird at close range, but it soon departed prior to the arrival of a storm and was never seen again.

*Peter Allard*

## Pacific Swift                                                    *Apus pacificus*

**A very rare vagrant; one record with an additional offshore sighting.**

The Pacific Swift is an Oriental species breeding in central and eastern Asia, and wintering in south-east Asia to Australia.

A Pacific Swift, the first for Britain, was identified by Steve Gantlett at Cley on 30th May 1993 following a heavy arrival of Swifts. It was initially found by Alan Brown who alerted other observers as it fed over Cley Marsh in mid-morning where it remained feeding until late afternoon when it disappeared inland. The bird gave excellent views to over 600 admirers as it performed between the roadside pools and the North Scrape (Gantlett 1993, 1994). Several photographers obtained flight views showing the white rump and deeply forked tail.

An offshore record involved an exhausted individual captured on 19th June 1981 on the helideck of the Shell BT gas production platform on the Lemon Bank, 40km east-north-east of Happisburgh. It was flown by helicopter to the heliport at Beccles, Suffolk where it was released. It remained until dark and was seen briefly the following morning several kilometres to the south at Shadingfield, Suffolk. These two occurrences are the only British and European records of Pacific Swift.

A swift displaying a clear white rump at Thornham on 9th November 1994 was either this species or White-rumped Swift *A. caffer*.

*Peter Allard*

## Alpine Swift                                                    *Apus melba*

**A rare vagrant.**

The Alpine Swift breeds throughout southern Europe and north-west Africa, east into Kazakhstan and western Pakistan. The winter is spent in the northern African tropics, but its range is little known due partly to the difficulty of distinguishing it from endemic African races. It is an annual vagrant to the British Isles with up to ten birds appearing annually.

Stevenson included the first Norfolk record when one, now in the Castle Museum, Norwich, was shot near the castle at Old Buckenham in the latter part of September 1831. Another bird was seen near Norwich in June 1871. Riviere added a third specimen – one which was obtained over Breydon wall on 4th September 1872. It is also on display in the Castle Museum, Norwich Three further sight records followed – at Cobholm Marshes on 13th September 1887, at Cromer on 29th September 1890 and another there on 25th–31st July 1909.

A further 21 years were to pass before the next Alpine Swift was found in Norfolk, at Hunstanton on 25th September 1930. The county total currently stands at 35 records, all involving lone individuals. Early arrivals tend to travel alone, but later birds are often detected amongst flocks of Common Swifts. The earliest was at Brancaster Staithe on 19th March 1988 while the latest were at Hunstanton on 25th September 1930 and at Cley on 3rd October 1965. As might be expected the majority of occurrences are of birds seen only briefly. However, in 1981, one appeared at Cley and Sheringham on 29th–30th May. In 1985 one first seen at Cley on 3rd April subsequently appeared at Holme, Sheringham and Cromer, remaining until 8th. It was timed to fly at an average speed of 50mph. The same bird, distinguished by a missing primary from its right wing, was observed on 10th April at Colne Point, Essex. In 1994 an Alpine Swift put in appearances at Beeston Regis on 27th–29th April, Cley and Wiveton on 28th and Titchwell on 30th before heading south.

A high proportion of observations have been along the north Norfolk coast between Hunstanton and Mundesley. Cley has been specially favoured with a total of twelve birds. In east Norfolk there are records from Bacton, Horsey, Hickling Broad, Breydon and Gorleston.

*Michael Seago*

CHEDGRAVE COMMON -

## Kingfisher (Common Kingfisher) R.CHET 29·6·1998.     *Alcedo atthis*

**A scarce resident and very scarce passage migrant.**

The world range of the Kingfisher encompasses more ground than any other member of its family. From Britain and Ireland in the west, it is found throughout most of central and southern Europe, North Africa across Asia to Japan and south-east to New Guinea and the Solomon Islands. It frequents most lowland water courses, favouring slow-moving freshwater rivers and streams as far north as central Scotland. The British population has declined since the mid-1970s, with hard winter weather bringing high mortality. Additional factors such as river pollution, wetland drainage, the removal of riverside vegetation and grading of river banks have all been detrimental to the species (New Atlas).

With numerous rivers, streams, broads, freshwater marshes, lakes, Breckland meres and in more recent years, flooded gravel pits, Norfolk has always had plenty of fine Kingfisher habitat. Stevenson spoke of its county-wide distribution but feared for the Kingfisher's future due to its popularity amongst taxidermists and a growing craze of decorating lady's hats with their bright feathers. His concern for the widespread slaughter led him to predict the Kingfisher becoming a great rarity. Fortunately, by the time of Riviere's avifauna, the Wild Bird Protection Act had been passed and he judged the species to be commoner than it had ever been. Seago (1967) also noted its widespread distribution. During fieldwork for the Norfolk Atlas, the Kingfisher was recorded in 158 tetrads, which represented just 11% of those covered (Kelly 1986).

Kingfishers are recorded annually in the breeding season, although positive proof of nesting is infrequently obtained. Under-recording is no doubt a factor although periodic fluctuations are frequent amongst Kingfishers, particularly following severe winters. This was well illustrated in the early 1960s when prolonged frosts in the winter of 1962–63 resulted in the virtual absence of breeding birds in the following summers. Only single nests were found in 1963 and 1964. A succession of mild winters (as in the early 1990s), however, soon enabled the population to become re-established. The Kingfisher's ability to produce two or three broods in a good year also helps with building up the population. In 1994, Kingfishers were noted at 32 localities during the breeding season with up to 20 actual pairs seen. However, although the species was reported from 79 sites in 1997, breeding was confirmed at only eight with a further seven pairs present elsewhere during the summer.

All the county's rivers have traditionally been favoured by Kingfishers, particularly the Wensum and the Yare, as have Broadland and Breckland. The Fens, in contrast, have always had fewer records. Most sites in Norfolk usually hold only single pairs but three pairs were noted at Downham Market and Sparham in 1975 and at Fritton in 1976. Nest-sites reported have frequently been in river banks, whilst the root systems of upturned trees are equally favoured. In 1966 a pair nested at Taverham in a dry gravel pit quite some distance from the nearest water. Another pair excavated their nest in the midst of a colony of Sand Martins in the upper Yare Valley. More unusual was the pair which bred successfully in 1984 on Mousehold Heath, Norwich. The nest was tunnelled into a miniature sandy cliff face. Obtaining food took the parents over busy Barrack Street and through an intervening wood – a distance of over 400m.

During the autumn and winter months, Kingfishers are often observed on the coast, especially the sheltered harbours and saltmarsh creeks of the north and west. Hard weather brings the species into even more prominence as it searches out any ice-free water from which to feed. Presumably Kingfishers were more numerous in earlier years, judging by counts of 18 near Yarmouth in September 1878, seven together at Stiffkey in December 1898 and eleven at Cley in January 1953. Sights such as these have seldom been reported in recent years. Taxidermist records also point to its former abundance and concentrations during hard weather. Up to 50 were shot around Yarmouth in autumn 1833, while 80 were in one Yarmouth shop alone in 1884, 30–40 were collected around Norwich in January 1864 during severe frosts and 33 were sent to a Yarmouth taxidermist over a short period in the winter of 1878. All this seems hard to imagine these days. Like many birds faced by cold and starving conditions, Kingfishers have been known to exploit man's handiwork. In January 1963 up to five regularly visited Norton Sub-course, where they fed on the offal discarded from filleted fish. Garden fish ponds are also occasionally visited. In 1973 one was attracted to a Sheringham garden pond where it caught up to 52 five-centimetre goldfish within an 18-hour period, which it took through an eight-inch square hole in a pond covering. Another surprise garden visit was made at Toftwood, where one landed briefly on a linen line on 27th September 1985.

Kingfishers from the Continent have long been thought of as being autumn visitors. There have been several records through the years of birds arriving from the sea at sites such as Snettisham, Scolt Head, Blakeney Point, Sheringham, Cromer, Overstrand and Bacton. Riviere drew attention to five sightings on offshore light-vessels between 1844 and 1925. All were in the period from 16th September to 12th October. Another struck the Inner Dowsing light-vessel on 17th September 1931 where one also appeared on 27th September 1957.

No foreign-ringed birds have been recovered in Norfolk although movements between Norfolk and other English counties have been noted on eight occasions, including five birds to Suffolk. One ringed at Salthouse in November 1972 was found in Huntingdonshire the following April, while perhaps of more interest was one ringed at Abberton, Essex in August 1972 and found as a decaying skeleton in a gutter below a window in Anglia Square, Norwich in October 1973. One ringed at Gillingham in August 1977 was found at Mildenhall, Suffolk in November 1978, a nestling ringed at Colney on 1st June 1976 was recovered at Marlesford, Suffolk on 10th August, and a first-autumn bird ringed at Cantley in August 1985 was in Northamptonshire the following April. Yet another intriguing recovery was made when one ringed at Scolt Head in August 1971 was found in the remains of an owl's pellet at the same locality in April 1974, while another ringed at Gillingham in July 1982 was found at Lynn Point the following January.

*Andrew Bloomfield*

## Bee-eater (European Bee-eater)         *Merops apiaster*

**A rare vagrant.**

Typically a summer visitor to warm, open countryside, nesting in sand pits and river banks, the Bee-eater's range extends from south-western, central and eastern Europe into Asia and north-west Africa. During the non-breeding season it migrates south to spend the winter in central and southern Africa. Here it joins another population which breeds in the far south of the African continent. It is an annual vagrant to the British Isles in varying numbers, generally appearing during the spring and early summer in fine, sunny weather with south or south-easterly winds, when migrants overshoot their usual destinations.

Most British Bee-eater records are of single high-flying migrants (sometimes so high that only their distinctive calls can be heard) whilst occasionally flocks appear. Indeed the first British record was of one killed at Mattishall in June 1794 from a group of 20, with some apparently lingering there until October. Since then at least 31 have been recorded in Norfolk. Bee-eaters occasionally have nested in the British Isles but never in Norfolk, although a pair did remain in a small sandpit at Blakeney from 21st to 26th April 1960, thus raising high hopes. Stevenson also possessed a pair in his collection which were shot by a wherryman as they hawked insects over the River Yare at Coldham Hall near Brundall on 3rd June 1854. Despite much

Bee-eater
*(Norman Arlott)*

searching in suitable habitat nearby, he was unable to find any evidence of a nest hole. These historic specimens remain on display in the National Trust's Sheringham Hall. Riviere mentioned three others which were shot in the 1800s (two at Yarmouth and one at Gillingham which is now in the Castle Museum, Norwich) while another was seen at Billingford on 19th May 1880. The next was not until 12th June 1939 when a male met a similar fate to most of its predecessors and was shot at Gooderstone. It also remains in the collection at the Castle Museum, Norwich.

In 1958 one appeared on 17th September at Morston and since then Bee-eaters have appeared in Norfolk in 13 different years. The earliest date was 21st April 1960 when one of the previously mentioned Blakeney birds arrived at Cley. Six have since been seen in May, nine in June (including three together over Holme on June 29th 1986), one in July, four in August, four in September and a particularly late bird at Surlingham on 21st–22nd October 1966. Very few seem to have lingered, although two were seen on three dates between 8th August and 2nd September 1973 at Caister and Winterton. Other coastal sites at which Bee-eaters have been recorded are Wolferton, Snettisham, Hunstanton, Titchwell, Burnham Norton,

Burnham Overy Dunes, Holkham Meals, Holkham Park, Salthouse, Paston, Sea Palling and Waxham. Of particular interest was a juvenile on 4th September 1988 seen at nine localities, initially at Waxham heading west along the coast, before finally appearing inland at West Winch. Also worthy of note is the one fortunate observer who has twice noted a Bee-eater inland over East Harling on 17th June 1992 and 10th May 1994.

*Andrew Bloomfield*

## Roller (European Roller)      *Coracius garrulus*

**A rare vagrant.**

The Roller is a summer visitor to much of southern and eastern Europe, wintering in southern and western Africa. It is a rare but annual vagrant to the British Isles.

Due to their great rarity and exotic beauty, many Rollers met the same fate as most of the early Bee-eaters – shot by collectors. Stevenson mentioned 13 examples, dating back to 1664, when the first British example was obtained at Crostwick on 14th May. Most of the other early records were unfortunately undated, although one at Bircham in 1847 was shot in September, while one shot at Waxham in February 1824 is one of only two British winter records. Another interesting occurrence Stevenson mentioned was that of a Roller's wing found on the tideline of Brancaster beach. Riviere mentioned a further nine individuals, including a male caught on a fishing boat just off Yarmouth Harbour entrance on 25th May 1865, which is currently in the collection at the Castle Museum, Norwich, along with others from North Walsham and Little Melton. An immature male, killed at Bradwell on 9th October 1883 is preserved at Yarmouth Tolhouse Museum.

Since Riviere's time the Roller has become somewhat more erratic in its appearances with only another eleven noted between 1938 and 1991, bringing the county total to 32. The Waxham record in February remains unprecedented, with the next earliest date being 28th April 1938, when one was found at Hickling. From the dated records, both May and September are the peak months with six each, while four have been noted in both June and October, two in July and one in August. The latest, an immature shot at Barton, was obtained on 23rd October 1894. Most of the county's Rollers have been very short-stayers. Apart from singles at West Caister, which remained for a week in May 1970, at Wells East Hills on 8th–16th August 1973 and at West Tofts on 11th–12th June 1983, all have been recorded on only a single date.

The species has been recorded at the following localities – Acle, Antingham, Barton, Bircham, Blofield, Bradwell, Brancaster, Burgh Castle, Cawston, Cromer, Crostwick, East Wretham, Earsham, Felthorpe, Garboldisham, Gayton, Gresham, Hickling, Hilborough, Holkham Park, Holkham Meals, Horsey, Little Melton, North Walsham, Rushford, Southery, Stracey Arms, Upton, Waxham, Weeting, Wells, West Caister, West Tofts, Yarmouth and Yelverton.

*Andrew Bloomfield*

## Hoopoe      *Upupa epops*

**A very scarce passage migrant.**

The breeding range of the Hoopoe covers most of central and southern Europe extending to Africa, the Middle East and Asia. It is a scarce passage migrant to the British Isles, appearing annually in both spring and autumn, particularly in southern and eastern England.

In Norfolk, the Hoopoe has always appeared annually in small numbers. Even as far back as Sir Thomas Browne's writings in the 17th century, it was described as 'a gallant marked bird, which I've often seen, and it is not hard to shoot them'. All of Norfolk's county avifaunas have said words to that effect, although opinions on the season in which it was most frequently observed have varied between authors. Gurney and Fisher in 1846 described the Hoopoe as more regular in the autumn, whilst Stevenson said autumn sightings were the 'exception'. He included 38 between 1850 and 1865 of which only four were in autumn, and earlier Dawson Turner, a well-known Yarmouth naturalist, once had 15 brought to him after a great gale in May about 1840, all having been obtained locally. As is to be expected from that era, many, to quote Stevenson's words, were 'lost to the greed of the collector'. Riviere commented that autumn occurrences slightly outnumbered those of spring although its appearances were 'less often and in smaller numbers' than in Stevenson's time. He knew of 42 records between 1867 and 1928. Of these a long-stayer remained in a Mundesley garden from 28th August to 18th September 1924. He also gave two offshore records from the Happisburgh light-vessel on 8th April 1884 and in early March 1912.

By the time of Seago's revised edition of his *Birds of Norfolk* (1977), a further 160 Hoopoes had been recorded between 1930 and 1976. Since then about 120 more have been reported. Indeed, since the *Norfolk Bird Report 1953*, the Hoopoe has been recorded annually. Numbers have varied from singles in 1962, 1964, 1967 and 1980 to twelve in 1966 and 1978, 17 in 1971 and 30 in 1968, of which 24 were in spring. The highest autumn total was nine in 1966. Hoopoes have now been recorded in every month of the year in Norfolk. Arrival dates vary from year to year but April–May and September–October have proved to be the peak months in each of the two passage periods. Of the twelve recorded in March, the earliest have been on 12th March at Wheatfen and Aylsham in 1959 and at Winterton in 1978. Seven have been noted in June, presumably late over-shooting spring migrants, while mid-summer sightings have been very rare with only five in July and three in August.

The latest migrants have been at Ridlington on 18th November 1961 and at Holkham on 23rd November 1975, although a few wintering birds have also been seen in the county. On 7th December 1955 one was found at Beechamwell, while one remained in the Thorpe Marriott/Taverham area from 15th November 1989 to 2nd January 1990. Another winter bird was found at Forncett on 2nd January 1993, but became ill and died two days later when it was caught at Shipdham. One which arrived at Horsford in November 1993 also remained in the Taverham area from 23rd December 1993 to 21st April 1994.

Hoopoes are birds of open country, appearing at coastal dunes, golf courses, cliff-tops, scrubby commons, heaths, parkland and very occasionally in gardens. Coastal sites have, as expected, hosted the majority of Norfolk's Hoopoes, including sightings of birds arriving in off the sea at Cley, Kelling and Yarmouth, although well over 50 inland localities have attracted the species. The majority have been in Breckland, Broadland and the Norwich area, while a few have been recorded in the Fens and west Norfolk. Most Hoopoes seen in the county have been brief-staying singles, although two together have been noted at Cley, Cromer, Frettenham, Great Hockham, Heydon, Holkham, Horsford, Hunstanton, Norwich, Wheatfen, Winterton and Yarmouth. These were all short-stayers and none has shown any evidence of prospecting. One which was at Cromer from 23rd September to 2nd October 1998 was incredibly tame and frequently perched on buildings; it showed certain characteristics suggesting that it may possibly have been one of the eastern races. There have been two instances of Hoopoes associating with other rare visitors to the county – one shared a sugar beet field with a Cream-coloured Courser near Blakeney on 23rd October 1969, but was chased away by the courser when it approached too closely and another was feeding near a Broad-billed Sandpiper at Breydon on 18th May 1985.

*Andrew Bloomfield*

## Wryneck (Eurasian Wryneck)                                    *Jynx torquilla*

**A scarce passage migrant, mainly in the autumn; last bred in 1955.**

The Wryneck is a summer migrant which breeds throughout Europe and North Africa and is found as far east as China and northern Japan. During the 20th century it has undergone a pronounced decline in western Europe and in Britain it is now virtually extinct as a breeding bird. Throughout its range it favours both deciduous and mixed woodland, woodland clearings and urban wooded enclaves. During its non-breeding season it migrates south, with the European population wintering throughout Africa (New Atlas). In Britain Wrynecks were once found throughout most of central and south-eastern England, northwards to the Lake District and County Durham and westwards to Wales and Devon. First signs of a decline were noted in the mid-1800s. By the 1950s, the English population was only 150–400 pairs, dropping dramatically to 40–80 pairs in 1966 and none by 1974. Small numbers began to colonise Scotland in the 1950s and 1960s although this tentative foothold has never increased from a handful of breeding pairs. Indeed, into the 1980s nesting attempts were not even annual and it seems clear that the days of the Wryneck as a British breeding bird are certainly numbered. Loss of habitat, cooler summers and an increase in pesticides damaging the Wryneck's food source (primarily ants) have been suggested as causes of the population crash, although nothing for certain has been proven (New Atlas).

Although Stevenson and Riviere both described the Wryneck as a breeder throughout Norfolk, very

Wryneck
(Bryan Bland)

few references to sites or numbers were mentioned. Riviere did, however, draw attention to a decline in many parts of the county, although a few were still to be found in south-west Norfolk. Some of the most comprehensive and interesting information on breeding Wrynecks came from the diaries of an egg-collecting parson, Frank Norgate, who died in 1919. From these it appears that Wrynecks were far from uncommon. In the late 1800s he found nests at Barnham, Bramerton, Elsing, Fritton, Hardwick, Heydon, Hickling, Hockering, Santon Downham, Sparham, Weeting and Weston Longville. Nest-sites were primarily dead trees (alder, apple, birch, elm, oak, pine, poplar and willow were all listed) but also included holes in fence and gate posts, water-pump housing and old Green Woodpecker and Tree Sparrow nest holes. The largest single clutch he took was eleven (from Weeting) whilst he removed a remarkable total of 42 eggs from a nest at Sparham within two months, both in 1872 and 1873. After the end of the 19th century Wrynecks were still to be found nesting at Aylsham in 1900, Fleggburgh until 1907, Lakenham (in a broken street lamp) in 1910, Drayton until 1913, Wymondham until 1914, Ellingham Hall until 1919, Thetford until 1927, Thursford until the late 1940s and Cringleford in 1942, with the last confirmed Norfolk breeding at Great Massingham in 1955. In the period from 1955 to 1971 a further nine inland sites hosted either territorial or mid-summer birds. Pairs were seen at Two Mile Bottom and St Helen's Well in 1962 and Boughton in 1964. In more recent years the only mid-summer sightings have been at Anmer on 18th June 1979, North Walsham on 13th–26th July 1981 and Ashwicken on 18th June 1992.

Nowadays the Wryneck is a scarce but annual passage migrant. Most sightings are from coastal sites such as dunes, woods and open scrubland although inland sightings are virtually annual. Of all the regular Scandinavian 'drift' migrants, Wrynecks appear inland far more regularly than any other species. They are rather conspicuous, showing a preference for feeding on garden lawns. During the spring Wrynecks could be described as a rarity with usually less than double figures being seen in the county. Most are noted in late April and throughout May, although the earliest and latest dates in recent years have been 1st April 1991 at Cley and 18th June 1998 at Happisburgh. (Frank Norgate's diaries, mentioned earlier, included some very early arrivals on 27th March 1867, 19th March 1872, 5th April 1892, 29th March 1893 and 31st March 1894, all except the latter being at Sparham. Thus the species was truly the 'harbinger of spring', as it was formerly known.) The best year for spring Wryneck sightings was 1978 when a total of 26 was seen between 29th April and 23rd May, including five at Scolt Head on 5th–6th May.

The Wryneck is more usually associated with the autumn migration period. As a typical Scandinavian 'drift' migrant, its appearance can almost be guaranteed between mid-August and the end of September, providing winds prevail from the east or north-east. Extreme dates are 1st August and an exceptionally late record of one found dead at Sheringham on 22nd November 1969. One of the largest arrivals of Wrynecks occurred during a huge 'fall' of Scandinavian migrants in September 1965. Heavy rain and north-east winds grounded up to 130 during the month (with most between 4th and 6th September). Several birds were obviously very weak, making prolonged stays, whilst up to four were found dead in Sheringham. High concentrations included 17 at Holme, 18 between Overy Dunes and Wells, 27 between Blakeney Point and Cley, and 19 at Sheringham. As many as 18 penetrated to inland sites. The autumn of 1976 provided 62 records (including ten on Blakeney Point) while between 19th and 21st August 1977 concentrations of ten at Holkham, 14 at Blakeney Point, 13 at Sheringham and eleven at Winterton were noted. Similar conditions to those in 1965 occurred on 25th–26th August 1987 and ensured another large-scale arrival with peaks of 14 at Holme, 11 at Holkham, 25 at Wells East Hills (where one was noted feeding on the saltmarsh alongside some Little Stints) and 21 between Blakeney Point and Cley. About 35 Wrynecks have been ringed in Norfolk, over half at Holme Bird Observatory.

*Andrew Bloomfield*

## Green Woodpecker CHEDGRAVE - MY GARDEN. 26·7·1999. (JUV.) *Picus viridis*

**A fairly common resident.**

The Green Woodpecker occurs in fairly open, deciduous and mixed woodland broken up by large tracts of grass and heathland throughout most of Europe, extending north to Norway and Sweden and east into Russia, Turkey and Iran. In Britain Green Woodpeckers are most abundant in the well-wooded areas of southern England and Wales, although their range has spread during the 20th century north to the Lake District and into central and eastern Scotland. Population fluctuations have been noted more frequently than with the Great Spotted Woodpecker. Severe weather with prolonged spells of frosts make ground feeding on ants (favoured by Green Woodpeckers) difficult, causing past population declines. Farming practices such as extensive ploughing of their open parkland habitat, the demise of sheep farming in many areas and periodic rabbit population crashes (caused by myxomatosis) have all had an impact on reducing suitable Green Woodpecker habitat and feeding grounds (New Atlas).

Both Stevenson and Riviere stated that the Green Woodpecker was 'a not uncommon resident' in Norfolk, although both failed to elaborate much on distribution details. Stevenson did, however, mention its popularity amongst collectors and taxidermists (many a gamekeeper's cottage was graced with a stuffed Green Woodpecker) and drew attention to the severe winter of 1860–61 when one Norwich taxidermist had 20 or 30 brought to him. Seago (1967) described the Green Woodpecker as being a numerous breeder particularly in the Brecks and in open parkland. Results found during fieldwork for the Norfolk Atlas showed that Green Woodpeckers, whilst still remaining fairly widespread (having been recorded in 23% of the tetrads visited), had declined noticeably, with some areas in the west (Fenland) and the south of the county failing to record any. Breckland continued to be the species stronghold, whilst other areas such as the well-wooded regions north-west from the Brecks to Hunstanton and Sheringham south to Norwich were also favoured. Allard (1990) stated that despite a recent decline, a few pairs still nested around Yarmouth. During the 1994–97 BBS the species was recorded in 26–33% of the 1km squares visited in Norfolk, suggesting little change during those years. As a result of increased reporting, the species was recorded at 82 localities in 1997 of which 51 were during the breeding season. The majority of sightings were in the north and east of the county, including Broadland, although it was almost certainly under-recorded in Breckland. The largest concentration was Holkham Park where six pairs bred. Whilst most Green Woodpeckers in Norfolk are found in open parkland with large stands of trees, on heaths and in mixed woods, gardens are also visited. During the autumn and winter months it is not unusual to encounter a Green Woodpecker at coastal sites such as dune systems, sea walls and at the edge of saltmarshes, although singles flying over Hunstanton cliffs on 18th October and 11th November were unusual records.

Despite over 130 Green Woodpeckers having been ringed in Norfolk, only one has been recovered at any distance from the site of ringing – a juvenile ringed at Weybourne in July 1997 was found 19km away at Cawston in September. However, a juvenile ringed at Minsmere, Suffolk on 27th July 1960 was found near Norwich on 20th February 1961, a movement of 49km and highly unusual for the species.

*Andrew Bloomfield*

## Great Spotted Woodpecker CHEDGRAVE - MY GARDEN. 14·9·1999. (♀) *Dendrocopos major*

**A fairly common resident and very scarce autumn passage migrant.**

The Great Spotted Woodpecker is found throughout most of Europe's deciduous and coniferous woodlands, except in Ireland and the northern extremities of Fennoscandia. Its range extends into northern Africa, Turkey and across Russia to Japan and south-eastern China. In Britain the Great Spotted Woodpecker is the most widespread and common member of its family, being absent only from the Fens, the uplands and offshore islands of Scotland (New Atlas).

Great Spotted Woodpeckers remain the most frequently encountered and widely distributed of Norfolk's woodpeckers. Stevenson, however, described them as 'by no means numerous and somewhat local in distribution'. He believed that the scarcity was due mainly (like the Green Woodpecker) to their popularity amongst collectors and taxidermists. Nevertheless he described them as being well distributed amongst the woodlands surrounding Norwich. By the 1920s Riviere noted the Great Spotted Woodpecker as being 'fairly common throughout the wooded parts of the county' and 'abundant in the pinewood districts in the south-west of the County'.

The Norfolk Atlas showed that every 10km square except two in Fenland held Great Spotted Woodpeckers and they were recorded in 37% of the tetrads visited. Indeed, Kelly (1986) came to the conclusion that in the previous 20 years they had increased in numbers due to the abundance of food provided by dead or dying elms since the onset of Dutch elm disease. It also became apparent that an increasing number of sightings were coming from mature, well-timbered hedgerows and gardens. The ever-increasing habit of Great Spotted Woodpeckers visiting peanut feeders in gardens (both rurally and in towns throughout the county) is also no doubt an aid to survival and accounts for the presence of this attractive species, both in the winter months and breeding season. The spread to many localities during the 1980s and 1990s has been reflected in the 1994–97 BBS, which has shown an increase in the number of 1km squares in which it was found in Norfolk from 21% to 33% over the four years. Concentrations of breeding pairs reported in 1996 and 1997 included 19 at Holkham Park, eight at Overstrand and six at both Ludham and Raynham Park/South Raynham.

As a passage migrant, Great Spotted Woodpeckers of the northern race *D. m. major* are noted irregularly in the autumn months, usually between mid-September and November at coastal sites. The first proven Norfolk specimen was shot at Yarmouth in November 1881, although Riviere drew attention to unusually large numbers of Great Spotted Woodpeckers present between November 1861 and February 1862, when up to 20 or 30 were shot, with 15 from the King's Lynn district alone. Similar numbers arrived in Shetland at the same time. Since then, other years in which notable numbers were recorded were 1898 (when many arrived in October, including one caught offshore from Yarmouth on a fishing boat), 1901, 1929, 1962 (when seven offshore light-vessels noted up to nine birds in October) and 1968. At such times birds have occasionally been found exhausted on beaches. One at Yarmouth in September 1968 died after striking a window at Yarmouth Harbour front. During more recent years, coastal sightings have been almost annual, not infrequently involving immigrants arriving from offshore. Between 18th September and 29th October 1997 a total of 21 coastal migrants was recorded at eight localities, including four flying overhead at Overstrand on 18th September and at Hunstanton on 16th October, and three at Holme on 22nd October. One of the most intriguing records concerned a bird which arrived from over the sea at a great height at Wells East Hills on 16th October 1996, landed in the nearest pine tree, where it was instantly attacked by a Sparrowhawk as a result of which it promptly flew straight back out to sea again!

Other interesting observations of Great Spotted Woodpeckers in Norfolk have included December drumming from both Holkham Park and Merton, drumming at 23:00 hrs in March 1988 at Holkham Park and a male in Raynham Park displaying reddish-brown back colouring and primary barring in March 1996. In the 1960s Dick Bagnall-Oakeley (1972) noted two males regularly excavating holes during the autumn months at Brinton in dead birch trunks, which were subsequently used for roosting throughout the following winter. For ten minutes on 30th July 1997 one was hunting insects high over Caister Cemetery in the company of Swifts.

About 400 Great Spotted Woodpeckers have been ringed in Norfolk but there have been no notable recoveries. A juvenile ringed at Sandwich Bay, Kent on 3rd August 1991 was controlled at Ickburgh in January and June the following year, and again in 1994, 1995 and 1997.

*Andrew Bloomfield*

## Lesser Spotted Woodpecker CHEDGRAVE. 24·4·2000 (3) *Dendrocopos minor*
BY MY GARDEN - NOT IN IT.

**A scarce and declining resident.**

The Lesser Spotted Woodpecker is a resident of deciduous and mixed woodlands ranging from western Europe and Fennoscandia east into Russia and Asia. Due to its small size and rather elusive behaviour it is the least observed of its family in Britain. Although it tends to feed in the canopy of trees and nest in the smaller branches (rather than the main trunk as with Great Spotted Woodpecker), its distinctive call and drumming should lead to its discovery during the early stages of the breeding season. However, both BTO Breeding Atlases showed the Lesser Spotted Woodpecker to be the least numerous member of the family. It is found locally throughout England and Wales as far north as Lancashire, Cumbria and Northumberland, being most abundant in south-eastern England. Its population increased greatly in the 1970s and 1980s, with Dutch elm disease providing both an abundant supply of invertebrate food and nesting sites. The subsequent removal of dead wood from many areas has led to a population decline with numbers returning to earlier levels (New Atlas).

Stevenson, Riviere and Seago (1977) all commented on the Lesser Spotted Woodpecker being Norfolk's scarcest woodpecker, although Stevenson did admit to it being 'easily overlooked'. Periodic reviews in the *Norfolk Bird Report* have shown that 83 sites held the species in 1959, while in the period from 1960 to 1968, up to 81 localities were occupied. Records were widely distributed across the county with the least in west Norfolk. Mature deciduous woodland, orchards, Broadland carrs and well-wooded gardens were favoured. When the Norfolk Atlas was published in 1986, the Norfolk countryside still hosted many dead or dying elm trees and the Lesser Spotted Woodpecker population was probably more numerous than ever before. Kelly (1986) described it as being 'a not uncommon resident in many parts of the county' and it was recorded in 265 tetrads for the Norfolk Atlas, representing 18% of those visited. This figure was supported by a total of 228 widely-scattered sites, as given in the *Norfolk Bird Reports* from 1977 to 1986. Even mature hedgerows and urban gardens attracted breeding birds.

Lesser Spotted Woodpecker
(Norman Arlott)

Following the great storm of 1987 and the subsequent widespread removal of many dead elms, the onset of the 1990s brought a widespread decline in the Norfolk population. Many sites throughout the county lost them completely. During the 1994–97 BBS it was found in only 2–4% of the 1km squares covered in Norfolk. The species has been reported at less than 50 localities in each year from 1995 to 1997, and at Holkham Park where nine breeding pairs were present in both 1995 and 1996, only four pairs were located in 1997. However, the species was noted feeding on peanuts at both Houghton St Giles and Thorpeland (near Fakenham) in 1997, a habit seldom noted in the county and it will be interesting to see whether this spreads and produces the same advantages as it appears to have done for Great Spotted Woodpeckers.

In the northern extremities of its European range Lesser Spotted Woodpeckers are prone to make occasional southern irruptions. There are, however, very few proven records in Britain of migrants. Patterson (1905) mentioned one picked up on Yarmouth beach which could conceivably have been a migrant. In more recent years another possible migrant was noted flying south along Snettisham Beach on 18th September 1993 and at Cromer Golf Course one was flying west with a Great Spotted Woodpecker on 7th October 1996. Only about 35 Lesser Spotted Woodpeckers have been ringed in Norfolk and, not surprisingly, there have been no recoveries.

*Andrew Bloomfield*

# Calandra Lark                                    *Melanocorypha calandra*

**A very rare vagrant; one record.**

A southern Palearctic species of the wide open steppes, plains and agricultural areas, the Calandra Lark breeds from Iberia and Morocco eastwards through the Mediterranean to northern Afghanistan and Russian Turkestan. It is mainly sedentary throughout its western range but partially migratory in the east. It is an extremely rare vagrant to the British Isles.

One was found on Scolt Head by Jonathan Brown on 19th May 1997. It was seen soon afterwards by Neil Lawton and Michael Rooney briefly on the ground and in flight on at least five occasions, and was heard to call frequently. Pursued and chivvied regularly by resident Skylarks, it was last seen at midday heading out over the saltmarsh in thick sea fog and was not seen again (Brown *et al.* 1997, 1998). It was the seventh British record. It is interesting to note that a Calandra Lark was present near Castletown, Isle of Man on 17th–18th May and this could conceivably have been the same one reorienting through Norfolk.

*Peter Allard*

# White-winged Lark                              *Melanocorypha leucoptera*

**A rare vagrant; one record.**

The White-winged Lark is a central Palearctic species which within Europe breeds only in Russia. It is a short-distance migrant moving south-west in autumn with some birds reaching Romania. It has decreased in numbers in recent years and is a very rare vagrant to Britain with only two acceptable records.

A White-winged Lark, probably a first-winter male, was found by John Lines frequenting rough grass alongside King's Lynn Beet Factory with a flock of ten Skylarks on 22nd October 1981. It was also seen there next day by John Moyes and remained with the Skylarks until 24th October (Lines 1987). The general pallor of the bird, the stout bill and the strikingly white wing pattern caused instant reaction when first seen. The record was submitted in 1982 and given full acceptance in 1986.

Following a review of all British White-winged Lark records by the BOURC in 1993, there is only one other acceptable record – a female captured with Snow Buntings near Brighton, East Sussex on 22nd November 1869.

*Peter Allard*

# Short-toed Lark (Greater Short-toed Lark) *Calandrella brachydactyla*

**A rare vagrant, mainly in autumn.**

The Short-toed Lark has an extensive range throughout the Southern Palearctic, from Portugal and Morocco to central China, breeding in arid grasslands of the steppe and semi-desert zones. The Iberian Peninsula holds 85% of the European population. Birds from the western part of the range winter in North Africa and along the southern edge of the Sahara. The species is an annual vagrant to Britain, mainly in May, involving overshooting southern birds and in September–October, when birds from the eastern populations are thought to predominate (Dymond *et al.* 1989).

The species was added to the Norfolk list on 7th November 1889, when a male was shot near the south wall of Breydon, although at the time the land was on the Suffolk side of the county boundary, which has since changed. The specimen passed into the Connop collection and was donated to the City of Birmingham Museum in 1954, where it remains today (Allard 1990). A further 70 years passed before the next Short-toed Lark was found in Norfolk, at Cley on 14th October 1959 and the third was at Salthouse on 8th September 1968. Since then the county total has risen to 27, the species becoming increasingly frequent in the 1990s. The highest annual totals have been three in 1979, 1994 and 1996, and four in 1997.

Eight have been recorded in spring, at Sheringham from 24th April to 3rd May and another on 30th May 1996, at Blakeney Point on 7th–10th May 1990, on 4th May 1992, on 31st May 1997 and on 13th May 1998, at Wells on 26th May 1984 and at Breydon on 17th May 1997. The earliest in autumn was on 8th September 1968 at Salthouse and the latest on 16th November 1975 at Holme, with the majority between 10th and 29th October. Four have remained for over a week, the longest-stayers being at Holme from 27th October to 16th November 1975 and at Overstrand from 30th September to 12th October

1997. All the autumn records since 1959 have been on the north coast between Holme and Sidestrand, with no less than ten on the cliff-top fields at Sheringham, where an adult and first-winter bird on 15th October 1978 provided the only multiple record.

*Moss Taylor*

## Woodlark (Wood Lark)                                 *Lullula arborea*

**A fairly common but localised breeder and scarce passage migrant.**

The Woodlark has a patchy distribution throughout south and central Europe, being absent from Norway, northern Sweden and Finland. Three-quarters of the European population are found in Spain and Portugal. The northern populations move south in winter.

Woodlark
(Richard Millington)

In Britain its range is now confined to England south of a line from the Humber to the Severn Estuary with discrete populations in Devon, the New Forest, the Hampshire/Surrey border, Lincolnshire, the Suffolk coastal sandlings and Breckland. In the 19th century the range extended further north to the south Pennines and throughout Wales (Historical Atlas). The population reached a low point in the 1880s but numbers began to increase again in the 1920s, reaching a peak by the 1950s (Sitters 1986). In the second half of the 20th century there was a considerable contraction in range between the two BTO Atlas surveys but little change in the overall size of the population. During 1968–72 the population was estimated to range between 200–450 pairs, followed by a drop to 160–180 pairs in 1975. However, the surveys during 1988–91 produced a figure of about 350 pairs with up to 93 of these occurring in Breckland (New Atlas).

Stevenson, in the 19th century, found that the Woodlark was 'by no means numerous in Norfolk' and was confined almost entirely to the western parts of the county where its habitat preference of extremely short turf could be found in Breckland. Apparently, it had enjoyed a wider distribution in the county before much open heath and common land was enclosed. For example, Mr Hunt writing in 1829 said 'It was common at Hethersett previous to the enclosure of the common lands,' which occurred in this area about 1800 (Stevenson). The Pagets (1834) described it as 'not uncommon' in the Yarmouth area but Patterson (1905) stated that it occurred there in 'small parties, mostly observed here in severe weather, seven shot in the snow by a gardener on 20th December 1890'. During the winter of 1887–88 a total of twelve was caught in nets on Yarmouth Denes (Allard 1990).

By the time Riviere was preparing his book he considered it to be a very rare breeding bird in Norfolk until the early 1920s. It then followed the national trend and he was able to record a 'marked increase in its numbers and a very considerable extension to its range'. A small colony nesting near Weeting in 1923 had spread further north and by 1925 Woodlarks had appeared at Castle Rising in the west and in the opposite direction four nests were found at Drayton near Norwich. A year later numbers had increased further in the Brecks and at Castle Rising with nesting again recorded at Drayton and Taverham. About this time Clarke in *Breckland Wilds* (1937) refers to 'bents of the heathland shelter the abundant nests of Meadow Pipit, Woodlark and Skylark'. Subsequently, the range extended further along heath-covered land bordering the River Wensum to include the parishes of Honingham, Ringland and Horsford. Birds continued to appear on the edges of the traditional range and in May 1949, A. W. P. Robertson heard one in full song at Dersingham Warren and another singing at Holkham Dunes in April 1951 (Robertson 1954). A 'few pairs' were nesting on Salthouse Heath in 1953. In east Norfolk it was certainly breeding at Belton Common in 1953, but probably ceased nesting there in about 1956 (Allard 1990).

After the mid-1950s there was a rapid decrease in numbers and a contraction of range. This coincided with an increase in the agricultural use of parts of Breckland coupled with the absence of intense grazing by rabbits following the outbreak of myxomatosis in 1953. Seago (1967) reported that only a few pairs were left in the Horsford/Felthorpe area with breeding ceasing on Salthouse Heath after 1956 and Wolferton in 1962. However, one was heard singing at Pretty Corner, Sheringham on 4th May 1964. In 1965 a few sites in Breckland were still occupied, particularly in the Stanford Training Area but by 1973 Woodlarks were recorded in only four Breck localities in the county. This appears to have been the nadir of the fortunes of this attractive species. A total of eleven pairs was reported there in the following year plus one singing on Sheringham Golf Course in late June to mid-July 1974, nine pairs in the Brecks in both 1975 and 1976 and eleven again in 1977. By 1983 the *Norfolk Bird Report* was able to record them as 'locally common in the Brecks, especially in recently-stocked conifer plantations' with another pair near Kelling Heath.

The conifers planted in the 1920s and 1930s have been felled and harvested as they reach maturity. The replanted parts of the forest produce suitable habitats for Woodlarks for up to six years. After that time, the trees have reached two metres in height and the ground cover will have established itself such that the area becomes unsuitable for Woodlarks (Hoblyn in Sitters 1986). In this habitat the birds are at their most dense in the second year with 3.2 pairs per 100ha tailing off to 0.5 pairs in the 5th–6th years. The current forecasts of future felling predict a reduction in new planting for a time after the year 2000 thus decreasing the amount of suitable habitat for Woodlarks. One short-term solution to overcome this temporary reduction in habitat is to retain suitable conditions by ploughing between the rows of young trees so that the vegetation remains low with areas of open ground (Bowden 1990).

The total number of singing males recorded in the Norfolk Breckland each year since 1984 is shown in Table 41.

**Table 41. Total number of singing Woodlarks in Norfolk Breckland 1984–98. The figures in parenthesis show the number of singing males included in the total figures which were present on open heathland rather than in forestry plantations.**

| 1984 | 23 | 1991 | 53 | (4) |
|---|---|---|---|---|
| 1985 | 15 | 1992 | 69 | (8) |
| 1986 | 26 | 1993 | 82 | (12) |
| 1987 | 23 | 1994 | 108 | (23) |
| 1988 | 20 | 1995 | 134 | (20) |
| 1989 | 39 | 1996 | 167 | (35) |
| 1990 | 48 | 1997 | 232 | (43) |
| | | 1998 | 309 | (77) |

A thirteen-times growth in the population since 1984 is remarkable and the spread back to Breckland heaths at an even greater rate during the last seven years is very encouraging. Single records in both 1990 and 1991 from the Stanford Training Area were followed by breeding being proved at Cockhat Corner there, in 1992. Of the 77 birds outside Thetford Forest in 1998, a total of 55 was on Ministry of Defence land confirming the view that the largest remaining tract of typical open Breck habitat is in the Stanford Training Area. Of the other 22 songsters, three were on Thetford Golf Course, two on arable, one on urban wasteland and the remainder on lands controlled by conservation bodies, including six at Weeting Heath. In 1998 Suffolk Breckland held another 240 singing males, 51 of which were outside Thetford Forest. The Norfolk total in 1997 represented 16% of the British population. The equivalent figure for 1998 was not available at the time of writing.

By 1988 singing birds were recorded again away from Breckland with one over Sandringham Warren on 2nd March and another at Burnham Overy Dunes on 20th March. In 1993 singing was heard at Sandringham, North Walsham and Hempstead Woods with up to four present on Salthouse Heath between 12th March and 12th June but without any evidence of breeding. In the following year, from five to seven were singing at four sites away from the Brecks with breeding proved at one location. By 1996 the total had risen to ten sites with fledging confirmed at two and eleven singing males were heard in north Norfolk in 1997. In east Norfolk, on the extreme borders with Suffolk, one singing bird was at Hopton in 1997 and there were four in song in the Lound Waterworks/Herringfleet area in 1998. The first birds are to be heard singing over their breeding territories in Breckland on mild sunny days from early February and, given these favourable conditions, even in the last days of January. In 1998, possibly due to the very mild weather, the majority of territories were occupied by the middle of February, with the 'earliest ever' egg reported to the BTO Nest Record Scheme on 1st March 1998 (Glue & Bowman 1998).

The birds disperse during the autumn but some are usually present throughout most of October but the Breckland haunts are generally deserted by Woodlarks during the winter; a situation confirmed by the Winter Atlas. Before moving away, post-breeding flocks gather with 50 being seen at Croxton Heath on 1st September 1997 and 27 at Weeting in October. However, in recent years there appears to have been a tendency for some birds to linger later into the autumn. In 1993 between eight and 18 stayed on barley stubble at Feltwell from 9th November until 31st December. In the next autumn, mild weather encouraged birds to remain in Breckland until 22nd November with the latest-ever singing on 18th November. Feltwell stubbles proved attractive again in 1995 with at least 37 remaining until the year-end on farmland including periods on autumn-drilled rye and weedy remnants of sugar beet tops. However, only five remained feeding on set-aside in this area at the end of 1997.

The Woodlark also occurs regularly along the coast as a passage migrant, usually in ones or twos but occasionally in larger parties such as the nine at Thornham on 9th–11th October 1965, seven at Holme on 10th February 1991 and six at Muckleborough on 7th March 1992. An analysis of all the records of migrants appearing in the *Norfolk Bird Reports* from 1953 show that appearances are roughly equal in spring and autumn with the peaks occurring in March and October with April and November also producing many records. Migrants have also been recorded in January, February, May, August, September and December. Records have come from 26 coastal sites stretching from Snettisham, Heacham and Hunstanton in the west to Waxham and Winterton in the east, with the larger numbers of sightings from such well-watched localities as Holme, Overy Dunes, Holkham, Cley and Winterton. There have also been a few inland records such as Holt in March 1962, Eaton in March 1977, Binham in February 1983 and Roydon Common in February 1991. As the majority of local breeding birds have returned to their territories by March it has to be assumed that many of these spring coastal migrants are Continental birds.

The Woodlarks' winter quarters have not been positively identified. A programme of colour-ringing which commenced in 1986 has started to give clues to the whereabouts of these local larks during their absence from the breeding grounds. In the Brecks as a whole, 180 nestlings were ringed from 77 nests in 1997, with another 169 from 69 nests in 1998, bringing the grand total of birds marked in this way by the end of 1998 to 1,207, of which 785 were from Norfolk. The majority of subsequent sightings have been within the Breckland area although one from 1997 was seen six months later at Dungeness, Kent and another nearer home at Roydon Common. A bird ringed at Santon Downham in May 1997 was seen at Holme in February 1998. One ringed in 1993 was seen in the Isles of Scilly in late October that year and another in The Netherlands on 9th October 1996, the sole British Woodlark known to have moved out of the country. A bird ringed just across the county boundary at Elveden, Suffolk on 1st June 1995 was reported at Dawlish, Devon in the following February and was seen again at Elveden in May, while a nestling ringed at Thetford in 1994 was seen at Sheringham on 23rd March 1996. Other birds have been seen in Lincolnshire – one ringed at Lynford in 1993 was breeding in that county in 1994 and three birds marked at Santon Downham in 1992 and 1994 were found in Lincolnshire in March, April and May 1995.

*Don Dorling*

*NEAR HARDLEY FLOODS. (2) 2-4-2000.*

| **Skylark (Sky Lark)** | *TITCHWELL. RSPB. 8-9-1985.* | *Alauda arvensis* |

**A very common resident, and common passage migrant and winter visitor.**

The Skylark breeds extensively across the upper and lower middle latitudes of the Western Palearctic. It is one of the most widely distributed species in Britain and Ireland occurring in all areas of open countryside. The principal habitat is lowland farmland, but it does breed on upland moorland.

It has been described historically as an abundant breeding species in Norfolk and as such its breeding habitats have been little discussed, while its movements appear to have been of greater interest. Riviere commented that the Skylark took part in migration in almost every month of the year, with the exception of the period May to August. An 'extraordinary' number of birds were involved in the daily and nightly movements to and from the Continent. Late autumn and early spring were the main periods for passage, although severe weather would often cause winter movements. Both Riviere and Stevenson noted the importance of winter stubbles for birds arriving on the Norfolk coast, when huge flocks were regularly encountered on stubble fields during autumn migration.

Skylarks prefer to nest in open arable countryside, making Norfolk one of the most important areas for the species in the British Isles. The Norfolk Atlas identified the Skylark as the second most widespread species in the county, being found in 97% of the tetrads surveyed. It was only absent from the inner parts of Norwich and the larger blocks of coniferous forest, although in the latter habitat it was frequently found in large clearfell areas. National surveys have shown that the Skylark has undergone a population decline of about 50% over the last 25 years. However, in Norfolk where Skylarks have always been numerous, it has been difficult to detect this trend and during the 1994–97 BBS it was found in 96–100% of the 1km squares surveyed in the county. At Flitcham the number of breeding territories has remained fairly constant at between 23 and 28 during the five years 1993–97 and similar results have been obtained on arable and set-aside in the Wensum Valley/Sparham area. In 1997 localised concentrations of breeding pairs included 69 at Scolt Head and 40 at Blakeney Point, while a 12ha field of permanent set-aside at Burnham Market held 200 pairs of breeding Skylarks, possibly the highest concentration in the British Isles.

Historically spring passage started in early February and continued into April, with the peak in mid-March. There was usually a two-way passage of birds, with Continental breeders heading north-east across the North Sea and British breeders, which had wintered further south, heading north-west. Large numbers of birds were involved in this spring passage. However, in recent years there has been little evidence of this, probably due to a series of mild winters. The Skylark is one of a number of species to undergo hard-weather movements, when birds will come and go *en masse* to avoid cold weather, as shown by counts in 1979 at Sheringham of 2,300 west on 24th January, 3,000 west on 3rd February and 1,200 west on 4th February. The recent mild winter weather and early springs has probably resulted in less birds moving, and those that do move, returning as a steady trickle throughout winter and spring. The largest spring migration flock noted in recent years was 116 flying east at Mundesley in February 1992, while at Sheringham in 1990 there were influxes of 140 on 11th February and 150 on 26th February, during spells of mild weather.

Compared with spring, the autumn migration of Skylarks is much more noticeable, as many more birds appear to be involved and the passage is condensed into a much smaller time period. However, autumn migration is complex. Some birds migrate to Norfolk from the Continent, others are on passage from the Continent and continue south and others may be moving from Scotland to southern England. This is made even more complicated by the constant coming and going of birds in response to cold weather. Autumn migration commences during the latter half of September and continues into early or mid-November. Peak numbers have been recorded during the second half of October with 3,500 west on 27th October 1978, 2,000 east on 23rd October 1979 and 1,800 west on 15th October 1993, all at Sheringham, while on the last date 3,250 flew west at Holme, and 2,160 south at Hunstanton on 16th October 1997.

The wintering status of the Skylark in Norfolk is very much dependent on the severity of the weather. Generally the British breeding population is supplemented by immigrants from the Continent. Inland the Norfolk breeding population amalgamates into small flocks which are scattered across the countryside. On the coast the breeding population is joined by the immigrants and much larger flocks are formed. The size of both the inland and coastal flocks then fluctuate with the weather. One of the largest inland flocks recorded in recent years was of 250 at Wramplingham in November 1997, whereas on the coast flocks of between 500 and 1,000 have been recorded, with a total of 1,500 at Holme in February 1994 and up to 600 at Weybourne in November 1997. The importance of saltmarsh as a habitat for wintering Skylarks was well demonstrated when an intertidal survey between Holme and Weybourne found totals of 5,500 in November and 5,409 in December 1997, which included up to 744 at Thornham, 1,034 at Scolt Head, 738 at Wells, 707 at Warham, 671 at Stiffkey and 1,151 at Blakeney Harbour.

A pale grey Skylark at Sheringham on 25th–26th September 1979, which arrived and departed on the same date as a Short-toed Lark, was considered to have been one of the eastern races, as was another at Sheringham on 5th October 1998 which showed the characteristics of *A. a. dulcivox*.

Despite their abundance, comparatively few Skylarks have been ringed in Norfolk (only about 700 in total) and only one has been recovered away from the site of ringing – ringed at Cley on 31st August 1951 it was found near Bordeaux in south-western France in March 1953. It remains one of only four British-ringed Skylarks to have been recovered in that country.

*Stephen J. Browne*

## Shore Lark (Horned Lark)        *Eremophila alpestris*

A scarce winter visitor and passage migrant; very rare in summer and very rare inland.

Shore Larks
(*Richard Richardson*)

The Shore Lark is a widely distributed Holarctic species with several races occurring in the Western Palearctic. The northern race *E. a. flava* occurs at high latitudes and breeds in subarctic or Arctic lowland tundra westwards from the Kolyma river and in the Fennoscandian mountains. In autumn, most of the Fennoscandian population migrates in a south-easterly direction to winter in north-east and central Europe, with comparatively few along the coasts of the southern North Sea. In Britain, the majority of the birds are distributed along the east coast, with the main concentration from the Humber to the Thames estuaries (Winter Atlas). A dramatic decline in the Fennoscandian population, which commenced in the early 1950s, has been reflected in a marked reduction in the number of Shore Larks wintering in the British Isles since the 1980s. During the previous decade the species had bred in Scotland on two occasions.

The first British record of a Shore Lark concerned one shot at Sheringham in March 1830 and the second Norfolk record also came from the same locality, while the third was obtained at Yarmouth in November 1850. By 1866 the county total had still only risen to ten, although by the 1880s their numbers had greatly increased. In October 1882, George Smith, a Yarmouth dealer, received 50 birds in four days, 19 of which had been obtained from a single flock (Patterson 1905) and by the late 1890s Pashley, the Cley taxidermist, had them brought to him 'in dozens' (Pashley 1925). During severe weather in January 1947 the count at Cley reached 100.

The first birds of the autumn are generally seen in late September or the first half of October, with passage continuing through November. In recent years, the earliest arrivals have been on 15th August 1998 at Blakeney Point, and on 17th September 1969 and 19th September 1970, both at Weybourne, while Riviere was aware of one on 11th September 1893 taken at Yarmouth. In many years, peak numbers are present in the county during late autumn, as birds arrive and then presumably either continue south or disperse around the coast of East Anglia, while some remain to overwinter in Norfolk. In 1966, for example, 40–50 had arrived at Cley by mid-October to peak at 100 by the end of the month, after which numbers decreased, although 40 were still present at Salthouse at the end of the year. It is not unusual in autumn for small parties of Shore Larks to be recorded flying west or even arriving from the north, but 41 west at Weybourne on 18th October 1970 was unprecedented, while at West Runton during the influx of 1998, 26 flew west on 19th October, 14 west on 20th and two parties of 11 and 14 west on 24th. Occasionally the same group of birds can be recognised as it moves along the north coast over a period of days, such as in 1991 when three were at Waxham on 29th–30th September 1991, at Cley on 2nd October and at Holme on 6th October, and a party of five at Salthouse on 14th November 1991 before being found again at Holkham Bay two days later.

Some of the highest numbers ever recorded in the county, at least in recent times, occurred during the winters of the early 1970s. Between Holme and Weybourne 190 were present in November 1971, while in the following year the count in November was 228 (including a record count for Cley of 110), reaching a peak of 245 in January 1973, which included 70 at Scolt Head and 80 at Cley. Even as late as May, 35 were still present in north Norfolk. Up to 75 were at Scolt Head in January 1974, but thereafter numbers began to decline annually. By the autumn of 1988, only five were recorded on passage and none at all overwintered in 1988–89. During the peak years the favoured localities for wintering Shore Larks included Holkham Beach, Blakeney Point and Salthouse, as well as the localities mentioned above.

Since 1992, overwintering Shore Larks have once again become more numerous with highest counts often being made at Titchwell, peaking at 32 in 1992, 38 in 1993 and 63 in early December 1996, which may well have been the same party recorded at Gibraltar Point, Lincolnshire later in the month. Elsewhere up to 23 were present at Scolt Head/Brancaster Harbour in early 1997, Holkham Bay hosted up to 30 in November 1994 and up to 22 were at Cley/Salthouse in November 1996. The species has never been numerous in east Norfolk during the 20th century and 22 at Winterton on 2nd November 1986 was exceptional.

However, all these totals were exceeded during an unprecedented influx in autumn 1998, which affected many parts of the British east coast with some birds even reaching western England and Wales. Following occasional birds in September, and one even as early as August, Shore Larks arrived daily throughout October with highest counts on the east Norfolk coast, which included 67 at Happisburgh on 11th, 70 at Eccles on 12th, 40 at Horsey on 12th–13th, 100 at Paston on 17th, 20 at Breydon on 18th and 100 at Waxham on 27th. During the second half of November many of these east coast flocks began to move around to the north coast, with numbers at Holkham increasing almost daily – 80 on 15th November, 94 on 16th, 210 on 22nd–23rd and an amazing 240 on 24th. This last count was more than double the previous county record for a single flock and was probably the largest ever recorded in the British Isles. Other notable counts in north Norfolk at this time included 40 at Holme, 80 at Titchwell, 55 at Scolt Head, 88 at Wells East Hills and 75 at Blakeney Point (Lawton 1999).

Birds feed on the exposed saltmarsh at low tide, mainly on the seeds of *Salicornia* and retreat at high tide to the shingle area among the dunes. The flocks are very mobile and may forage along several kilometres of suitable coastline, but often have one or more preferred areas where food is abundant (Winter Atlas). As a result it can be very difficult to be certain how many birds are present along the Norfolk coast at any one time. Therefore a co-ordinated count was organised by the Norfolk Bird Club for 5th December 1998, during which the entire Norfolk coastline was covered. This resulted in a total of 591 Shore Larks being found in the county with the majority on the north coast between Gore Point and Salthouse. All the birds were feeding on developing saltmarsh or along the beach strandline, except for those on arable at Titchwell and Warham, or on winter stubble at Eccles and Waxham (Lawton 1999).

Spring passage is evident from mid-March to mid-May, although the number of birds involved is small. The latest dates have involved birds at Cley on 24th May 1973 and at Blakeney Point on 22nd May 1993 and 27th May 1996, while Pashley received one shot at Salthouse on 29th May 1907 (Pashley 1925). A male was in song at Winterton on 19th April 1987. A party of four in long grass on the north side of Breydon during a strong south-east wind and driving rain on 16th June 1956 was a highly unusual record (Roberts 1956).

In earlier decades when Shore Larks were more abundant on passage or in winter, inland observations on farmland were much commoner. Nowadays, the species is almost invariably restricted to the coast and the only inland records since 1960 have been up to eight feeding on arable fields a mile inland at Cley in January 1963, one at Hulver Hill, Litcham on 2nd April 1991, one at Boyland Airfield on 14th 15th October 1997, two which paused briefly on waste ground at Fakenham on 7th March 1998 before continuing to fly south and one at Cantley Beet Factory on 10th October 1998.

A Shore Lark ringed at Cley in 1959 was only the second to have been ringed in the British Isles. Up to the end of 1996 the grand total that had been ringed in Britain was still only 102, therefore a single catch of 44 at Holkham in late December 1998 was all the more notable.

*Moss Taylor*

| Sand Martin | HARDLEY FLOODS. 19·4·1992. | *Riparia riparia* |

**A common summer visitor and passage migrant; very rare in winter.**

The Sand Martin is very widely distributed in the Palearctic and Nearctic regions. In Europe, it breeds mainly in the lowlands from the Mediterranean region through steppe, temperate and boreal zones to 70°N in the subarctic. It winters in sub-Saharan Africa, those from western Europe in the Sahel region immediately south of the Sahara. Numbers are subject to wide fluctuations, due both to the transitory nature of most breeding sites and drought in the wintering areas.

In the British Isles, Sand Martins have a widespread but patchy distribution, being absent from large areas of southern and eastern England, where chalk and limestone predominate, and from the Scottish Highlands and Islands (68–72 BTO Atlas). As a direct result of the Sahelian drought during the 1968–69 winter, the number of Sand Martins returning to breed in Europe the following summer fell dramatically and a similar situation developed after the winter of 1983–84 (European Atlas). In 1984, the British Sand Martin population fell to about 16% of the peak recorded during the mid-1960s. Recovery was slow, as was shown by the New Atlas (1988–91) in which Sand Martins were breeding in only 50% of the 10km squares in which the species had been recorded in 1968–72. In Norfolk, the Sand Martin was recorded in all except two of the 10km squares for the 1968–72 BTO Atlas, whereas during the fieldwork for the Norfolk Atlas in 1980–85, it was absent from almost a third of the 10km squares and was recorded in only 15% of the tetrads in the county.

Sand Martins are gregarious at all seasons and breed in colonies varying in size from a few pairs to many hundreds. Nest burrows are excavated most commonly in vertical sand or gravel faces. Although some nest along river banks, the majority nowadays are at man-made sites, such as gravel pits, the birds preferring recently excavated sand quarries to those that are derelict (Bruhn 1966). Stevenson reported nesting at Cromer and Hunstanton cliffs, and an 'immense' colony in chalk pits at Horstead. Another colony was present in a high gravelly bank behind Brundall Station, which accounted for large numbers of feeding birds at Surlingham and Rockland Broads. Stevenson saw '1,000s' on the wires at Brundall on 23rd July 1864, the numbers no doubt swelled by juveniles from other colonies.

In the mid-1960s, the largest colonies, each containing 1,500 pairs, were at gravel pits at Sparham and Horstead, with 1,200 at Aldeby and 1,000 at Strumpshaw, although by 1971 few colonies exceeded 300 pairs (Bruhn 1972). Since the mid-1990s, the largest reported gravel pit colonies have been 100 at Whitlingham in 1994, with 152 at Lyng-Easthaugh, 80 at Crimplesham and 78 at Cranwich in 1996, and 200–220 at Middleton and 100 at Sparham in 1997. The sandy cliffs of north Norfolk have held variable numbers of Sand Martins for many years, with 300– 400 pairs between Overstrand and Weybourne in 1957. An annual survey of the number of apparently occupied burrows between Sheringham and Weybourne has been carried out since 1976. From an initial peak of 269 in 1981, the number of pairs crashed to only six in 1984, following drought in the Sahel, but the remarkable powers of recovery are demonstrated by a record count of 594 burrows in 1989. Since then further fluctuations have occurred with only 75 in 1994 but back up to 388 by 1996.

Over the years, many unusual and often transient sites have been used by nesting Sand Martins. These have included five to six pairs which nested below ground-level in a silage pit at Gooderstone, nests in pipes along the River Wensum in Norwich, the Little Ouse at Thetford and just below the cliff-top at Hunstanton, in road banks following road widening schemes at Wells and West Barsham, over 50 nests in an archaeological excavation in the Brecks, a colony in the railway embankment at Wolferton and burrows in marram dunes above concrete sea defences at Horsey.

Sand Martins are usually the first of the hirundines to be seen in spring, with the return passage commencing in the second or third week of March and continuing through until mid-May. The earliest records have been at How Hill on 6th March 1996, at Cley on 7th March 1992 and at Titchwell on 8th March 1989 (during the following four days Sand Martins were reported from seven other localities). Spring passage is not especially marked, birds simply tending to appear back at their colonies during April. Nevertheless, the highest numbers recorded in spring have been 1,000 west at Sheringham on 26th April 1977 and 1,050 west at Holme on 15th April 1996.

During late summer, juveniles from the early broods begin to disperse and to form communal roosts in reedbeds. During the 1960s, when the population was at its peak, spectacular numbers of birds began to roost at Wiggenhall, having deserted an earlier roost on the Ouse Washes. In July 1965 a total of 15,000 was present, peaking at an estimated 75,000 in early August, with 40,000 still present in the second half of the month. Concentrated ringing at this site over a period of two years demonstrated that birds gathering there had arrived from a wide area to the north. Of nearly 12,000 Sand Martins handled at this site, 27 had been ringed in Scotland and over 100 came from English counties north of a line from the Wash to the Mersea (Bruhn 1966). At the same time 15,000 were roosting at Cantley Beet Factory, and Seago (1967) described Broadland roosts as containing 'thousands' of birds. Since the 'crash' following the Sahel drought, such numbers have not been repeated and maximum roost counts in recent years have been 2,000 at Welney in 1986 (where the highest count in 1993 was only 60), 3,000 at Strumpshaw in mid-July 1987,

1,000 at King's Lynn Beet Factory in August 1991 and 2,000 at Cantley Beet Factory in mid-September 1992. An unusual record was of 500 apparently roosting in a field of ripe barley at Sheringham on 26th July 1995.

Autumn passage commences in early to mid-July and continues through to late September. Numbers are swelled by the presence of juveniles and maximum day-counts are therefore higher than in spring. The highest counts in recent years have been 10,800 flying south in three hours at Winterton on 19th August 1989, 4,500 east at Paston on 19th July 1992, 2,000 west at Weybourne on 17th and 19th July 1995, with 3,000 west on 20th and 5,000 west at Holme on 24th August 1996. The last birds of the autumn are usually seen in the second half of October, but occasional ones linger into early November. There have been five December records, involving six birds, the latest at Cley on 2nd December 1967, at Cromer on 4th December 1994 and at Happisburgh on 25th December 1960.

Four albino Sand Martins have been recorded in Norfolk – at Cley on 13th July 1982, Colney Gravel Pit on 27th June 1987, Surlingham on 7th July 1987 and Hemsby on 17th August 1993. In addition, four leucistic birds have been seen – at Cley on 1st August 1976, Sheringham/Weybourne on 5th August 1978, Cley on 25th July and Kelling Quags on 30th July 1992, and Welney on 4th–5th September 1993.

Over 20,000 Sand Martins have been ringed in Norfolk, the majority during the years of the BTO Sand Martin Enquiry 1962–68. As a direct result, vast numbers of recoveries, mainly controls made by other ringers, were reported, both within Britain and abroad. Norfolk-ringed Sand Martins have been reported from Denmark, France (23), The Netherlands (2), Belgium (5), Guernsey, Spain (7), Morocco (5), Algeria (2), Tunisia and Senegal (8), indicating the route taken by migrants to their winter quarters in West Africa. One of the recoveries in Morocco was a result of the ring being given by a local tribesman to a Belgian tourist, who returned it to the BTO! The early departure of some Sand Martins is shown by one ringed at Sparham on 4th July 1970 which was controlled in France on 21st July. Seven of the controls in Senegal were made between February and April, and one on 28th November, although it is known that Sand Martins reach the Sahel by October or early November. Over 20 foreign-ringed Sand Martins have been found in Norfolk, of which nine have come from France. One ringed at Gozo, Malta on 10th April 1971 and controlled at Boughton 17 days later, had averaged 128km per day and is one of only three Maltese-ringed Sand Martins to have been recovered in Britain. Only three Swiss-ringed Sand Martins have ever been found in Britain, of which two were ringed in spring 1975 and both were recovered in Norfolk on 12th July 1975, an amazing coincidence. After leaving Norfolk in autumn, most Sand Martins fly south, travelling together from given breeding areas, using 'traditional' routes and roosting communally in reedbeds on the south coast (Mead & Harrison 1979). Many Norfolk-ringed birds have been controlled at such roosts in Sussex, prior to their departure for the Biscay coast of France. However, two July-ringed birds moved west and were controlled two to three weeks later in South Wales, while an adult ringed in Surrey on 4th July 1987 was controlled at Cantley on 19th August, a highly atypical north-east movement for an adult in autumn. A juvenile ringed near King's Lynn in August 1965 was controlled in Denmark the following July, one of only four British-ringed Sand Martins to have been recovered in that country. Further details of the results of Sand Martin ringing in the county are included in the chapter on the history of ringing in Norfolk.

*Moss Taylor*

## Swallow (Barn Swallow) WILLOW FARM, LANGLEY. C.100. 4-9-2000. *Hirundo rustica*

**A very common summer visitor and passage migrant; rare in winter.**

The Swallow is a Holarctic breeding species, occurring throughout Europe, except in Iceland, where it breeds sporadically, and in the mountainous regions of northern Norway. It winters in Africa south of the Sahara, with the northern and eastern European populations (including those from the British Isles) leap-frogging those from southern Europe to winter in South Africa. In Britain and Ireland, the Swallow is a common and widespread breeding bird, being absent only from parts of the Scottish Highlands and Islands (New Atlas).

Since records began, the species has bred throughout Norfolk, although in common with many other parts of Europe, there has been a decline in numbers since the 1970s. Being totally dependent on a constant supply of insects taken in flight, the Swallow has been adversely affected by a reduction in available prey items as a result of the increased use of pesticides. But numbers have probably been affected even more by the periods of drought in their wintering quarters in South Africa (Marchant *et al.* 1990). Although there are few data to support a recent decline in Norfolk, the number of 1km squares in which the species was found during the BBS fell from 83% to 73% between 1994 and 1995, but in the following two years remained at 77–78%. However, the number of pairs in the Stanford Training Area fell to 75 in 1996, from a previous count of about 100 pairs annually, and the number of nesting pairs in a Breydon/Berney area survey had fallen from 69 in 1964 to only nine in 1998.

Swallows
(Norman Arlott)

Swallows are typical of lowland farms and, as a largely agricultural county, Norfolk supports a large breeding population. It was found in 95% of the tetrads for the Norfolk Atlas, being the most widespread summer visitor and the sixth most widespread breeding species. It is semi-colonial, nesting in a large variety of buildings, nowadays generally unoccupied by people, to which permanent access is available. Favoured sites include barns, outhouses and garages, as well as under bridges and in disused drainage mills on the marshes. Coastal pill boxes have been used by nesting Swallows for many years and at military establishments such as the Stanford Training Area and Weybourne Camp, birds have nested below ground in bunkers and gun emplacements. Other unusual sites have included the wreck of an old Yarmouth steam drifter alongside the south wall of Breydon (Allard 1990) and two pairs which bred under the swing-bridge at Heigham Holmes; while a nest under a low railway bridge between the Berney Arms and Reedham was used for up to ten consecutive years, at the end of which time it was about 45cm high. In 1955 a colour-ringed male Swallow mated with two females, one of which was colour-ringed, and both nested at the same time, within four yards of each other in an outbuilding of Richard Richardson's house at Cley. The male ignored one brood from the time it hatched and the nestlings died when half-grown. The successful female disappeared after her brood had fledged, and the male and the 'neglected' mate then co-operated in rearing a second brood (Richardson 1956).

The first Swallows of the spring are generally noted during the last week of March with the earliest arrivals at Titchwell on 10th March 1997, Thornham on 11th March 1989 and Holme on 12th March 1991, although one was reported in Norfolk during the fieldwork for the Winter Atlas (1981–84) on 21st February. Spring passage continues through to early June, usually peaking in early to mid-May. The highest counts have included 12,000 at Cley on 21st May 1991, 600–800 per hour flying south at Horsey and Winterton throughout the day on 14th May 1992, '1,000s' west at Cley on 4th June 1992, at least 2,500 per hour west at Blakeney Point on 8th May 1994, 3,750 west at Holme on 21st May 1996 and 6,500 west at Scolt Head on 13th May 1997.

In late summer and early autumn, both Swallows and Sand Martins, along with Pied Wagtails and Starlings, form communal roosts in reedbeds. Over the years, many reedbed sites in Norfolk have hosted such roosts, numbers varying considerably not only annually but also from night to night, as birds undertake the first part of their autumn migration. The maximum counts at some of the better-known roosts have included 5,000–7,000 at Hickling in September 1953, 6,000–10,000 at King's Lynn Beet Factory in September 1966, at Holme 10,000 in September 1982 and 7,500 in September 1994, 4,000 at Stoke Ferry in 1990, up to 3,000 at Saddlebow in 1991, at least 2,000 at Cantley in August 1992 and 5,000 at Martham in August 1996. However, the largest roost reported in Norfolk was at Titchwell in the latter half of September 1980, where possibly up to 100,000 were estimated to be present.

Autumn passage commences in late July and peaks in late August or early September. Maximum counts have included 4,500 flying west at Sheringham on 30th August 1977, 1,500 west at Holme on 25th August 1994, 2,000 east at Mundesley on 9th September 1994, 2,500 south at Snettisham on 9th–11th September 1995 and an amazing day-total of 12,000 west at Sheringham on 12th September 1995. Although most Swallows have left Norfolk by early October, a few are always reported during the second half of November and in eleven of the years since 1953, one or more have been present in December. The latest dates have been 24th December 1977 and 25th–26th December 1953 both at Thornham, 26th December 1971 at Wells and presumably the same bird at Brancaster and Hunstanton on 27th December. It is of interest that all of the earliest and latest dates mentioned above have been from west Norfolk.

Over 20 albino Swallows have been reported in Norfolk since 1953, of which four were in 1954 and five in 1955, all at well-scattered localities. They do appear to have been recorded less frequently in recent years, although three juveniles were present around Ludham Bridge from 24th August to 3rd September 1995. Another normally-plumaged pair reared a brood of albino nestlings at Marlingford Hall in 1980 and 1981. There have been two records of leucistic Swallows – at Cley on 13th September 1953 and at Twyford on 4th October 1975. Two apparent Swallow x House Martin hybrids have been reported – at Blakeney Point on 10th September 1991 and at Cley on 1st May 1993.

Over 15,000 Swallows have been ringed in Norfolk resulting in 35 foreign recoveries, while eight foreign-ringed birds have been found in the county. Many more have been recovered in other parts of the British Isles, allowing their migration routes to be mapped. Of particular value are those recoveries made later during the same migration season. Examples are one ringed in Belgium on 14th May 1963 found at Swardeston six days later and another ringed at Windhoek, Namibia on 5th March 1984 found dead at Long Stratton on 25th May; or later the same year such as the one ringed on spring passage at Happisburgh on 10th May 1979 and recovered at Selby, North Yorkshire on 7th July. Swallows controlled in Norfolk that had been ringed earlier the same autumn have come from Lincolnshire, Humberside, Yorkshire (4) and Durham, while one of two Scottish birds had been ringed near John O'Groats. Swallows ringed in Norfolk, have been controlled later the same autumn at Dungeness, Kent and at Icklesham, Sussex, one of which had been ringed only four days earlier. Same-season recoveries occasionally produce movements in apparently the wrong direction, as demonstrated by two ringed on passage at Happisburgh in May, one of which was found in Hampshire three weeks later and the other ringed on 11th May 1987 was recovered at Flines les Rachas, France on 5th June, a distance of 290km to the south-east; a movement which may have been precipitated by the miserable spring weather that year. Another recovery directly related to adverse weather concerned one ringed at Happisburgh on 13th May 1974, which was one of many hundreds of thousands of hirundines stranded to the north of the Alps in bitterly cold weather in early October and which were air-lifted over the Alps (Spencer & Hudson 1976). Unfortunately it was found dying at Zurich Airport and it is not known exactly where in Switzerland it was picked up. It was the first British-ringed Swallow to be recovered in Switzerland, while another ringed on 19th May 1976 at Happisburgh and found at Pop Gruevo, Bulgaria on 31st August 1976 remains the only British recovery from that country. Other surprising recoveries have included an autumn-ringed bird from Thornham to Norway the following spring and a nestling ringed at Holme in 1980 recovered at Castel Porziano, Italy on 3rd May 1982.

Norfolk-ringed Swallows on spring or autumn passage have been recovered in Norway, Germany, The Netherlands, Guernsey, France (4), Spain, Morocco and Algeria, while twelve have been found, mostly controlled, in the winter months in South Africa, in both the Transvaal and Cape Province. The only other recovery south of the Equator was one controlled at Kapanga, Zaire as early as 15th October. Another was reported from the Ivory Coast in February, while one was trapped for food, at a huge but hitherto unknown roost at Boje Ebok, Nigeria on 6th April 1995.

Ringing has often confirmed site fidelity for returning adults in subsequent summers – a breeding male returned to Cley for five successive years (Seago 1967). Young birds often return to the same general area in which they were reared – a juvenile ringed at Earlham in August 1969, was controlled at Skinnerspruit, South Africa on the early date of 2nd November and was killed by a cat at Mulbarton (6km from Earlham) the following June. However, this is not always the case as shown by a nestling ringed at Spurn Point, Yorkshire in July 1971 and found dead below its nest at Cromer the following June.

*Moss Taylor*

## Red-rumped Swallow — *Hirundo daurica*

**A rare spring and autumn vagrant.**

The Red-rumped Swallow breeds in the lower middle latitudes of the Western Palearctic, with the Iberian and Balkan Peninsulas holding almost the entire European population. It is a summer visitor, presumed to winter in the savannah zone of the African tropics. From the 1920s, the species spread northwards in

Iberia and from the 1950s in the Balkans. Up to 1958, there were only seven British records, but it has become annual since 1964.

The first Norfolk record occurred on 6th March 1952, when a bird subsequently identified by Billy Bishop and Joe Johnson was seen at Cley. It remained in the Cley/Blakeney area until 25th March, during which time its favourite haunt was Blakeney Quay (Meiklejohn & Richardson 1953). It was the first of many rarities to be filmed in colour by Dick Bagnall-Oakeley. Such was the rarity of the species in Britain (there had been only four or five previous records) that one on Lundy Island, Devon on 27th March and on Great Saltee, County Wexford on 10th April were considered to have been possibly the same bird.

A further 16 years were to pass before the next was seen in the county, at Mundesley on 18th April 1968. The county total had increased to only six by 1980, but since 1987 a further 19 have been recorded. Although it typically occurs in Britain as a spring overshoot, almost half the Norfolk records have been in autumn, as a result of three birds together in November in both 1987 and 1994.

The earliest spring record remains the one at Cley on 6th March 1952 and the latest in spring was also at Cley on 11th June 1977. The majority of the 13 spring records are between mid-April and mid-May. Apart from singles at Winterton and Mundesley, all the Red-rumped Swallows at this time of year have been seen along the north Norfolk coast between Holme and Cromer, including seven at Cley. In April 1987, one was photographed roosting in the porch at Cley Church (Myers & Jarvis 1988).

A total of twelve Red-rumped Swallows has been reported in autumn, the earliest on 7th October 1992 at Sheringham and the latest on 15th November 1994 at Winterton and 17th November 1997 at Breydon. Nine of the autumn birds have been in the first three weeks of November, a surprisingly late period for a summer migrant. In 1987, three were seen at Winterton on 12th November (Myers & Jarvis 1988), the day after one had been found at Happisburgh. During late October and early November of that year, an unprecedented total of over 50 was recorded in Britain, during a period of southerly winds. Warm south-easterly winds in late autumn 1994 again resulted in a party of three Red-rumped Swallows appearing at Titchwell on 6th November. They remained in the area between Burnham Norton and Holme until 11th November, roosting each evening in a reedbed between Titchwell and Brancaster.

An indication of how wide-ranging individual birds can be, is shown by a juvenile in November 1994, which was present at Winterton on 1st–8th, Cley on 12th–14th, Sheringham on 14th and back at Winterton on 15th. One Red-rumped Swallow has been ringed in Norfolk, at Holme on 3rd June 1979.

*Moss Taylor*

| **House Martin** | *Delichon urbica* |

*A very common summer visitor and passage migrant; rare in winter.*

The House Martin breeds in almost the entire Palearctic region, extending from the British Isles in the west to Japan and China in the east. In Europe, it is absent only from the Faeroes, Iceland and Svalbard. It winters in sub-Saharan Africa. It is common throughout most of Britain and Ireland, but is very local on exposed and coastal areas in the west and north (New Atlas). Its distribution in Europe has remained unchanged since the 1960s, although there has been some indication of a decline during 1970–90 in Fennoscandia, Germany and the Low Countries. In Britain, there has probably been a slow, long-term decline in numbers (Marchant *et al.* 1990).

House Martins were nesting on man-made structures early in the 19th century (European Atlas) and Stevenson made an amusing and interesting comment on the additional use of telegraph wires by hirundines:

> Whether or not our British *Hirundines* believe that the telegraph wires were erected for their special accommodation, undoubtedly one of the strangest points in their modern history is the manner in which they avail themselves of these novel resting places. Indeed, when beholding, as I have often done in autumn, each wire lined with their little bodies . . . one wonders, almost, how they managed without them, since no other perch seems half so suitable for their tiny feet . . .

Although House Martins breed throughout Norfolk, having been recorded in 85% of the tetrads for the Norfolk Atlas, including those covering the centre of Norwich, the larger colonies have generally been found in more rural areas. All colonies are subject to large annual fluctuations, but it does appear that former large and successful colonies are much reduced in size. In 1930 Dr Sydney Long organised a competition to discover the largest number of House Martin and Swallow nests on a single building in Norfolk. The two highest counts of House Martin nests were 106 on Newfound Farmhouse at Cringleford and 89 on Grape Farmhouse at Beighton. At Itteringham Mill over 100 breeding pairs in the 1940s had fallen to only seven by 1967. Other well-known colonies in the 1950s and 1960s included occupied nest counts of up to 68 at Oxburgh Hall, 50 at Guist Clock Tower and 100–150 at Middle Level Drain Pumping Station, Wiggenhall. At Cley the Watcher's Cottage held 58 nests in 1950 and 1951 but only 14 in 1998, and in 1951 a total of 93 nests was counted on three council houses at West Somerton, but there was not one in 1997. In the 1970s, counts included 76 on a bungalow at West Rudham, 56 at Home Farm, Didlington, 52 on a disused house at Gunthorpe and 42 on the gantry at Wells Quay. On the old railway gatehouse at Rudham Grange 110 occupied nests were present in 1974, where previously 199 pairs had nested; although a well-recorded colony at Saddlebow Bridge increased from 130 nests in 1974 to 150 in 1982. During the mid-1990s, the largest colonies reported were 58 at Aylmerton Lodge and 60 at Manor House Farm, Geldeston. There is also a decline in the numbers breeding in the larger towns in Norfolk, for instance none nowadays nest in Yarmouth town centre (Allard 1990). Despite this decline, between 1994 and 1997 the percentage of 1km squares in which House Martins were recorded in Norfolk during the BBS has risen from 29% to 43%.

Cliff-nesting by House Martins, which is now virtually confined to southern Europe, was recorded in the 19th century by Stevenson at Hunstanton and continued intermittently into the second half of the 20th century. As recently as 1966 a total of eleven pairs bred at this site but there have been no reports since 1967. An interesting development in Belgium and northern France is the increasing number of birds breeding inside cattle sheds and barns since the mid-1970s (European Atlas).

The habit of House Sparrows usurping House Martin's nests was known to both Stevenson and Patterson (1905), some recent authors even blaming the decline in urban House Martins on this behaviour. However, their presence is occasionally beneficial, as was demonstrated by a House Sparrow at Wiveton in September 1953, whose nestlings had been drowned in a water-butt and which subsequently regularly fed a brood of young House Martins with the apparent approval of their parents. It is surprising to read that in both 1951 and 1952 two pairs of House Martins at Whiteslea Lodge, Hickling lost their nests to an increasing colony of Tree Sparrows.

The first House Martins of the spring have generally been reported by the second half of March, with the main passage occurring between mid-April and the end of May. Birds tend to have returned to their colonies in Norfolk by early May. Nowadays, House Martins would appear to be returning to Norfolk about three weeks earlier than was the case up to the first half of the 20th century. Stevenson gave the average date of the first arrival as 20th April, while the earliest date ever up to 1930 was one at Mundesley on 27th March 1903. Since then, the earliest date has moved back to 8th March 1977 at Winterton, with others on 9th March 1985 at Wells and 10th March 1975 at California. The highest numbers recorded on spring passage have been 1,500 at Cley on 21st May 1991, associated with a heavy passage of Swallows, 2,500 west at Holme on 21st May 1996 and 500–600 per hour west at Paston and Sheringham on 29th May 1993. On some evenings in May, up to 500 House Martins are over Holkham Lake, presumably mainly birds on passage (Bloomfield 1993).

House Martins, like Swallows, have a protracted autumn passage, extending from August until November, with some birds not leaving until winter has begun. Peak counts have generally been between September and early October. Heavy autumn passages are a spectacular sight when extensive loose flocks of noisy House Martins pass along the coast over a period of several hours. The earliest such movement recorded was of 15,000 west at Overstrand during the morning of 13th September 1905 (Riviere). On 3rd October 1984 a total of 5,000 flew west at Sheringham in just three loose flocks in less than an hour, while at the same site 25,000 flew west during the day on 12th September 1995. At Mundesley, a total of 17,000 passed in just over two hours on 9th September 1994, while a county record of 33,500 flew east on 4th October 1995. During the preceding three days, a total of 8,500 had flown west at nearby Overstrand and 5,070 had flown south at Hunstanton on 3rd October.

Nestling House Martins have a very protracted fledging period, remaining in the nest for up to 30 days after hatching. Second broods are often still being fed in the nest in October and at East Tuddenham in 1976 a brood did not leave the nest until 1st November. It is therefore not surprising that small numbers of House Martins are recorded annually in November. Since 1953, the majority of last dates have fallen between mid-November and early December. In some years, surprising numbers hang on into early winter, such as 67 at Weybourne on 19th November 1966 and 83 at Winterton on 12th November 1977. The latest dates at the end of the year have been at Blakeney on 14th December 1965 and 17th December 1962, at Cromer on 18th December 1984 (a year in which at least nine were present in Norfolk in December, including six at Hunstanton) and at Gorleston on 22nd December 1848 (Ticehurst 1932). Two flying over a frozen pool surrounded by snow-covered ground at Thwaite Common on 1st January 1971 must have been an unforgettable sight, while the latest (or was it the earliest?) record was one recorded in Norfolk on 10th–20th February during one of the years in which the fieldwork for the Winter Atlas was carried out in 1981–84.

A total of eight albino House Martins has been recorded in Norfolk since 1976, all except one in August or September and apart from one at East Wretham, all have been between Titchwell and Paston. Leucistic birds have been seen at Cley on 19th September 1981 and at Waxham on 1st September 1985. Two apparent Swallow x House Martin hybrids have been reported – at Blakeney Point on 10th September 1991 and at Cley on 1st May 1993.

Over 3,000 House Martins have been ringed in Norfolk since 1983 but very few of these have been recovered. The majority of recoveries and controls relate to birds ringed before that time. One ringed at Downham Market on 5th September 1974 was recovered at Zarauz, Spain on 29th October 1974, but only five other British-ringed House Martins have been found in that country, while two ringed in Norfolk have been found in southern France. One ringed at Wiesbaden, Germany on 13th May 1962 and recovered at Hilborough on 20th June 1963 remains the only German-ringed House Martin to be found in Britain. One ringed on Zeeland, The Netherlands on 26th May 1972 and found dead at Starston in October, is one of only three Dutch-ringed House Martins to be recovered in Britain. One ringed on spring passage at Happisburgh on 18th May 1975 was controlled in Lancashire two weeks later, while one ringed in Greater Manchester on 8th August 1981 was controlled at Happisburgh on 3rd October. An adult ringed at Topsham, Devon on 23rd June 1972 and found dead at Neatishead on 19th June 1973, demonstrates how breeding birds can change colonies, several hundred miles apart in successive years. One ringed at Happisburgh in August 1980 and found dead at Overstrand in September 1987 is one of the oldest House Martins from the BTO ringing scheme.

*Moss Taylor*

# Richard's Pipit                                   *Anthus novaeseelandiae*

A scarce autumn passage migrant, very rare in winter and spring.

Richard's Pipit breeds from western Siberia to Mongolia, wintering in the Indian subcontinent and south-east Asia. It does not breed within the Western Palearctic and prior to the mid-1960s was a rare vagrant to the British Isles. Since 1966 it has become an annual visitor, with marked influxes in certain years, such as 1968. The species is a long-distance migrant and its appearance in Britain is as a result of reversed migration. Although it did not previously winter in the Western Palearctic, a regular wintering range has probably been established in southern Spain and possibly also in the Sahel region of West Africa.

The first three records for Norfolk, on 22nd November 1841, in April 1842 and on 23rd April 1843 were all taken on the Yarmouth North Denes, while the next three were all collected on the Yarmouth or Breydon Marshes between 26th and 29th December 1866. These last three were all shot by a Sergeant Barnes, who had also obtained two of the first three birds (Stevenson). By 1966 the county total had risen to 31, of which only three had occurred in spring (Seago 1977). Since 1964, the species has been recorded in Norfolk in every year, except 1975, the annual totals ranging from one to almost a hundred (in 1994) with an average of 17 per year.

The first birds of the autumn are normally seen from mid-September, with the earliest on 5th September, at Blakeney Point in 1964 and at Burnham Overy in 1993. Passage often continues until mid-November, with peak numbers through October. Usually recorded singly, but there were seven at Weybourne on 4th October 1988, six at Holme on 7th October 1967 and at Holkham on 17th–19th October 1968, five at Weybourne and five to eight at Winterton/Horsey Gap on 14th October 1967 and four at Sheringham on 19th September 1992. An unprecedented influx of Richard's Pipits took place in 1994, when at least

95 were found in Norfolk, eclipsing the previous county record of 53 in 1968. All but one occurred at coastal localities, the majority being in the north of the county. For many years, the cliff-top fields between Sheringham and Weybourne have been one of the most reliable sites at which to find the species in autumn. The distinctive call allows the species to be reliably identified in flight and accounts for a total of six being recorded flying south at Hunstanton cliffs during October 1995. Apart from five in the Breydon area, there have been only five other inland records – two at Potter Heigham on 14th October 1987 and singles at Gillingham Marshes from 30th March to 1st April 1989, Wymondham on 10th October 1994 and Honing Common on 28th–29th November 1996.

Most Richard's Pipits have left the county by mid-November, but occasional birds linger such as one at Salthouse from mid-October to 16th December 1967. A total of about ten has been recorded in mid-winter, all except one between Snettisham and Kelling Quags, four of which have made prolonged stays – singles at Holme from 14th January to 15th February 1978, at Cley from 21st December 1979 to 15th January 1980, at Snettisham from 1st January to 13th March 1990 and at Overy Dunes from 29th December 1994 to 23rd March 1995.

Richard's Pipits are rarely recorded in spring, although the second and third records for the county in 1842 and 1843 were obtained in April. The next spring sighting was not until one at Cromer on 1st May 1950, since when one was present at Winterton from 30th March to 17th April 1980 and the next two both in 1989, at Gillingham Marshes from 30th March to 1st April and at Blakeney Point on 30th April. It was perhaps not surprising that after the exceptional autumn influx in 1994, five were found in spring 1995 – three at Holme and singles at Snettisham and Sheringham between 20th March and 3rd May. Another was in the Sheringham/Weybourne area on 25th–26th April 1997, and in 1998 singles were at Waxham on 14th–20th March, Weybourne on 27th April and Sheringham on 8th May, which is the latest spring date for the county.

*Moss Taylor*

# Blyth's Pipit
*Anthus godlewskii*

**A very rare vagrant; one record.**

The Blyth's Pipit breeds eastwards from Tibet, through Mongolia to northern China, and winters mainly in India and Sri Lanka. It is a very rare late autumn vagrant to the Britain.

A first-winter bird found by Tim Wright was present in cliff-top fields between Sheringham and Weybourne on 16th–18th October 1996 (Wright 1997a, Golley *et al.* 1997). This was the first Blyth's Pipit to be accepted in the British Isles which had not been trapped, photographed or found dead. With an increasing awareness of the field identification features, further records may be expected.

*Peter Allard*

# Tawny Pipit
*Anthus campestris*

**A very scarce spring and autumn passage migrant.**

The Tawny Pipit breeds in the lower middle and middle latitudes of the Western Palearctic. In Western and central Europe it has a patchy distribution. Since the mid-1960s it has declined in Western Europe due to habitat change, many of its favoured dry, open areas having been taken over by intensive agriculture, afforestation or shrub encroachment. The nominate race which breeds in the Western Palearctic, winters mainly in the Sahel region of Africa and Saudi Arabia. Small numbers are recorded each spring in the British Isles, with a more marked passage in autumn, particularly along the south coast.

The species has been recorded annually in Norfolk since 1984, with the exception of 1995. Almost 90 have been seen in the county, of which just under half have occurred in spring, in contrast to the national picture. Riviere described the first two Norfolk records, a female netted on Yarmouth North Denes on 9th October 1897 and one shot at Blakeney on 15th September 1910. The next was not until one at Cley on 6th–7th September 1949.

The earliest spring record was one at Holme on 19th March 1977, which remained for three weeks until 10th April. Apart from one at Weybourne on 12th April 1980, the remainder have been recorded from 20th April, with the majority between late April and early June. The latest spring record was one at

Cley on 24th–25th June 1987, assuming that one at the same locality on 2nd July 1973 was an early autumn migrant. The only other July record concerned one found at Snettisham on 18th July 1989 which also made an unusually prolonged stay, remaining in the area until 24th September.

Two at Blakeney Point on 23rd August 1955 were more typical of the time that the first autumn birds have been recorded, the majority being seen between late August and late October. The latest records for the county have been at West Runton on 26th–31st October 1976 and at Winterton on 3rd November 1973. Although most records concern singles and on five occasions two birds, three were together at Winterton on 21st April 1968, one remaining until 5th May and four were found at Sheringham on 24th September 1977, including three in a single party.

Just over half the records have involved birds present on the north coast between Blakeney Point and West Runton, with over ten at both Cley and on Blakeney Point. In east Norfolk, the sandy habitat at Winterton has also attracted an impressive total of twelve Tawny Pipits. There have been two inland records – at Wisbech Sewage Farm on 25th September 1970 and Brundall on 29th August 1985. One Tawny Pipit has been ringed in the county, at Holme in autumn 1965.

*Moss Taylor*

## Olive-backed Pipit                                  *Anthus hodgsoni*

A rare autumn vagrant.

The race of Olive-backed Pipit *A. h. yunnanensis* which is a vagrant to the British Isles breeds in coniferous forests from the Ural Mountains, across Siberia to the Pacific. It winters in India, south-east Asia and the Philippines. Up to 1979, it was an extremely rare vagrant to Britain, since when there has been a marked increase in the number of records, peaking at 46 in 1990.

The first in Norfolk was found by Steve Joyner and Norman Williams in The Dell at Wells on 10th October 1975 and was only the sixth British record. Since then the county total has risen to 14, all singles between 21st September and 7th November, with the majority in October:

      1975: Wells on 10th October
      1976: Holkham from 31st October to 4th November
      1981: Holkham on 25th October
      1987: Blakeney Point on 2nd October
             Sheringham on 7th November
      1988: Stiffkey on 13th October
      1990: Blakeney Point on 18th October
      1992: Singles at Holkham on 4th–10th October and on 15th October
             Stiffkey on 7th–12th October
             Yarmouth Cemeteries on 13th October
      1993: Holkham from 24th October to 2nd November
      1996: Wells on 21st–22nd September
             Holkham on 22nd–23rd September

*Moss Taylor*

## Tree Pipit   SALTHOUSE HEATH. 24-6-1986.                *Anthus trivialis*

A scarce summer visitor and fairly common passage migrant.

The Tree Pipit breeds in the middle and upper middle latitudes of the Western Palearctic, and in Fennoscandia through the subarctic to the borders of the Arctic. It winters in sub-Saharan Africa, south of the Sahel. It is a widely distributed breeding summer visitor to Britain having spread northwards in Scotland during the last 100 years. It is most abundant in upland regions, being relatively scarce in central and eastern England. Between the early 1970s and late 1980s there was a striking decline in abundance, especially in central and southern England (New Atlas).

Stevenson described it as being generally distributed and 'may be heard from the trees in our hedge-rows, most frequently from the upper branches of a lofty elm', indicating that it was far commoner during the 19th century. Even in Riviere's day, it was nesting not uncommonly in suitable localities throughout the county. But by the late 1960s, it was a summer visitor in only small numbers to heaths, commons and small conifer plantations (Seago 1977).

The Tree Pipit requires both tall bushes or trees for song posts and sparsely vegetated areas in which to feed (New Atlas). In Norfolk, these requirements are met in open deciduous woodland, well-wooded heathland and young conifer plantations. During the early 1980s the highest concentration of breeding pairs was in Breckland, with smaller numbers east of King's Lynn and in the hinterland of Sheringham (Kelly 1986). In east Norfolk, the Winterton area was first colonised in 1978 and three to four singing males were located annually, but none has been present since 1993. The Norfolk Atlas also showed that the species was located in only 87 (6%) of the tetrads surveyed, although the number of 10km squares holding Tree Pipits was about 25, a similar number to that found during both the BTO Breeding Atlases. The number of 1km squares surveyed in Norfolk for the 1994–97 BBS, in which Tree Pipits have been recorded, has remained constant at 5–7%. Tracing the apparent decline in the number of breeding Tree Pipits in Norfolk is not easy, as sites holding breeding pairs have only been regularly reported in the last few years. In 1994, a total of 31 pairs was recorded, including eleven at Dersingham Heath, while 53 singing males were located in 1995, the majority in the Brecks and along the Cromer to Holt Ridge, the favoured localities for many years. Of 33 pairs reported in 1997, East Wretham held eleven and Kelling Heath six.

The first Tree Pipits of the spring are invariably recorded in early April, although there have been four March records, the earliest at Merton on 26th March 1997 and at Holme on 28th March 1992. Spring passage, as noted along the Norfolk coast, continues until late May. Peak counts have been at Sheringham with 50 west on 26th April 1977 and 40 west on 8th May 1979, and 42 west at Holme on 2nd May 1995.

Autumn passage, which is less pronounced than in spring, occurs from mid-August, peaking during September. During the drift migration of early September 1958, up to 25 were counted at Cley, since when day-counts in excess of 20 have been made on only three dates, all at Sheringham in the mid-1990s, including a 'fall' of 28 on 8th September 1995. Late birds are regularly recorded into October, with two in November – at Holme on 1st November 1987 and at Cromer from 29th October to 3rd November 1991.

Less than 100 Tree Pipits have been ringed in Norfolk, mainly birds on passage, and none has been recovered. However, one ringed in northern Italy at Torascia-Cadegliano, Varese on 26th September 1976 was found dead on the road at Sheringham on 14th May 1977. This was the first foreign-ringed Tree Pipit to be found in Britain (two others since have come from Belgium and Norway) and was all the more extraordinary as most of the British-ringed Tree Pipit recoveries have been from near the Atlantic seaboard of Portugal.

*Moss Taylor*

## Meadow Pipit BLAKENEY POINT. 9·10·1986. *Anthus pratensis*

**A common migratory breeder, very common passage migrant and fairly common winter visitor.**

The Meadow Pipit breeds throughout the middle and upper latitudes of the Western Palearctic. In Britain and Ireland it is a very widely distributed bird of open country (breeding in every British and Irish county) from sea level to mountain tops, up to 1,000m (New Atlas).

Stevenson described it as one of the most common resident species in Norfolk being most abundant on the marshes in Broadland, and flocking in sharp weather in winter to feed in stockyards, while in autumn immense flocks from the north passed south. Riviere also commented that autumn passage was heavier than in the spring.

Today the Meadow Pipit has a fragmented breeding distribution in Norfolk, despite being common in a wide range of habitats. The familiar parachute display flight of breeding males can be seen over rough grassland, particularly on cliff-top fields and coastal golf links, the drier coastal and inland marshes, sand dunes, on heaths and commons, on the edges of arable land, in young forestry plantations and even on waste ground in some Norwich suburbs (Kelly 1986). Meadow Pipits were recorded in just over a quarter of the tetrads covered for the Norfolk Atlas, with a tendency to be concentrated along a narrow coastal strip (especially in north and east Norfolk) and inland around North and South Creake, in the Fens, at Thetford Warren and along the Waveney Valley. In common with other parts of eastern England, the heavier clays are generally avoided.

From Stevenson's comments it would appear that there has been a reduction in both the abundance and distribution of Meadow Pipits during the 20th century. The most recent decline is at least in part related to the conversion of grassland to arable and loss of marginal land to cultivation and afforestation. But the fall in the numbers of breeding pairs, noted at a national level in the mid-1980s, may have resulted from the severe 1984–85 winter in southern Europe, where most British breeding Meadow Pipits winter (see below), accentuated by the cool, wet British summers of 1986–88 (New Atlas). However, over 100 breeding pairs were counted at Welney each year from 1995 to 1997, and in the latter year 65 breeding pairs were present at Scolt Head and 60 at Blakeney Point. During the 1994–97 BBS Meadow Pipits were recorded in 11–22% of the 1km squares covered in Norfolk, with no apparent trend over the four years.

From late February, Meadow Pipits which have overwintered south of the British Isles begin to pass around the Norfolk coast, the largest numbers being recorded flying west in north Norfolk. The passage generally peaks between late March and mid-April, and continues until mid-May. In recent years, some very impressive day-totals have resulted from dawn to dusk counts of birds flying west, in particular at Sheringham and Holme. Day-counts of over 1,000 were recorded at one or both of these sites in spring 1989, 1992–95 and 1997, with maximum counts of 1,900 at Sheringham and 2,400 at Holme on 20th March 1993, followed by 2,600 and 2,500 respectively the next day, 4,400 at Holme on 6th April 1995 and a county record of 7,000 west at Sheringham on 1st April 1997. On occasions, loose flocks have become grounded during the spring, including over 200 at Holkham, Cley, Sea Palling and Waxham in April 1994, up to 300 on Caister Golf Course held up by strong northerly winds (Allard 1990) and 350 at Holkham and 300 at Burnham Norton on 11th–12th April 1996.

Although there is a vast southward emigration of Meadow Pipits from Britain in the autumn (Winter Atlas), the passage in Norfolk is generally far less evident than that in spring. This is in contradiction to the findings in Stevenson's and Riviere's day. Autumn passage is mainly in September and October, although until recently maximum counts rarely have exceeded 200 (see below). However, at Sheringham 300 flew in from the north during a westerly gale on 1st October 1977, up to 220 were recorded flying south at several localities between Happisburgh and Yarmouth on 28th–29th September 1992, 520 flew west at Holme on 8th October 1994 and in the same autumn there were counts of 300 at Wells East Hills and 250 at Hickling, while 300 were present at Sheringham on 16th October 1997. The cliff-top fields at Sheringham have also attracted loose flocks of Meadow Pipits in autumn, including 300 on 18th September 1995. At Hunstanton, where daily counts of autumn migrants have been carried out since 1995, large numbers of Meadow Pipits have been recorded passing south between September and November. The autumn total in 1996 was nearly 3,000 including several day-counts of over 300. Elsewhere in west Norfolk, 500 flew south at Snettisham in just one hour on 22nd October 1995 and 1,000 flew west at Scolt Head on 11th October 1996.

National ringing recoveries have demonstrated that the vast majority of British breeding birds winter in south-west Iberia, but the origin of most of our wintering birds is unknown (Winter Atlas) and those overwintering in Norfolk are probably from breeding areas to the north of the British Isles. Smaller numbers of Meadow Pipits are found in the county during the winter months, in particular they appear to be scarce along the north coast, although about 75 were located in November and December 1997 between Holme and Weybourne during a low tide intertidal survey. The largest mid-winter count in recent years has been 75 at Cantley Beet Factory in December 1994.

Over 1,200 Meadow Pipits have been ringed in Norfolk, of which six nestlings have been recovered abroad – three in France in October, two in Portugal in October–November and one in Spain in February, while two adults ringed in autumn were found in winter in Portugal. Another autumn-ringed bird from Spurn Point, Humberside was recovered at Terrington. No Fennoscandian-ringed Meadow Pipits had been found in Britain, until one ringed at Hodne on the south-west tip of Norway on 6th September 1992 was found dead at Happisburgh about ten days later (another from the west coast of Norway was also found on a North Sea gas platform off Yorkshire at the end of September). Since then there have been two further recoveries from the southern coast of Norway – another ringed at Hodne on 5th September 1993 was found freshly dead at Waxham twelve days later and one ringed at Monstermyr on 13th October 1995 was controlled at Weybourne on 4th November 1995. Finally, a nestling which was colour-ringed at Cley in 1950, nested in the same area at Weybourne for the next three years.

*Moss Taylor*

# Red-throated Pipit

*Anthus cervinus*

**A rare spring vagrant, very rare in autumn.**

In the Western Palearctic, Red-throated Pipits breed in the Arctic and subarctic tundra of Fennoscandia and Russia. They winter mainly in sub-Saharan Africa, although some are found in scattered sites around the Mediterranean and in the Middle East. The species is an annual vagrant to Britain, both in spring and autumn.

The first for Norfolk was found by Martin Woodcock on a small pool by the East Bank at Cley on 8th June 1954. Since then, about 51 have been recorded in the county with all but 14 in May. The peak years have been 1992 with twelve and 1995 with eight.

Birds on spring passage have been noted between late April and early June, with over half the records during the period 13th–19th May. The earliest date was one at Waxham on 28th April 1997. All records have involved single birds apart from two at Scolt Head on 16th May 1959, two at Blakeney Point on 16th May 1988, three at Happisburgh on 15th–17th May 1992, three at Blakeney Point on 25th and 28th May 1992 and two at Blakeney Point on 23rd–26th May 1995. The longest-staying individual was a male at Scolt Head on 15th–21st May 1959, most birds remaining for only a day or two.

There have been only eleven autumn records, one at Blakeney Point on 28th August 1976, four in September, five in early October and the latest at Brancaster on 6th November 1994. Over half the birds have been located between Blakeney Point and Sheringham. Two have been found inland, at East Winch on 2nd October 1984 and at Welney on 21st May 1992.

*Moss Taylor*

## Rock Pipit    BREYDON WATER. 1-12-1992.

*Anthus petrosus*

**A common but localised winter visitor and passage migrant.**

Two subspecies of Rock Pipit breed in the Western Palearctic *A. p. petrosus* in Britain, Ireland and north-west France, and *A. p. littoralis* in Fennoscandia and the former Baltic states (Knox 1988). It breeds on the rocky coastline around Britain, being absent only from Lancashire, and on the east coast from the Humber south to Essex (68–72 BTO Atlas). Along ice-free shores the species is mainly sedentary but the more northerly populations of *littoralis* move south in autumn.

Stevenson described it as a rare bird in Norfolk with only a few appearing on migration. However, this was certainly due to the species being under-recorded, as Riviere included 400 at Blakeney Point on 21st–22nd October 1884, while 50 were netted on Yarmouth Denes by bird-catchers during the 'season' of 1887. One carrying food in its bill at Blakeney Point on 8th August 1880 is the only suggestion of possible breeding in the county (Riviere).

The first birds of the autumn are generally recorded in mid-September, although there have been three sightings during the first week of the month and four in August – at Blakeney Point on 1st August 1994, and at Breydon on 3rd August 1997 and on 8th August in both 1982 and 1997. Autumn passage, almost exclusively along the coast, continues until mid-November, peaking during the second half of October. The majority of records involve no more than two or three birds together, unlike Meadow Pipits which migrate in flocks of 10–20 birds or more. Day-counts at individual sites normally number less than 50 birds and generally involve a westerly movement along the north Norfolk coast and southerly at the Wash. The highest day-count was 350 trickling west in small parties at Sheringham on 8th October 1990, the majority considered to be *littoralis* (see below), while at the same site a total of 500 flew west during October 1996. At Hunstanton cliffs, a total of 490 was counted flying south between 23rd September and 13th November 1995, including 73 on 26th October and 60 on 28th October. Other high counts have included 50 west at Holme on 24th September and 16th October 1993, 70 west at Overstrand on 14th October and 150 west at Sheringham on 16th October 1997, while numbers on the saltmarshes begin to build up at this time of year with 125 at Scolt Head/Brancaster Harbour and 160 at Blakeney Harbour in October 1997.

In winter, Rock Pipits are found mainly along the tidal areas in the saltmarshes and harbours from the Wash to Cley, and at Breydon; areas where it is not easy accurately to count the number of birds present. McCallum (1997b) estimated that a couple of hundred are present between Wells Harbour and Cocklestrand Drove, Warham in mid-winter and in 1968, up to 110 were counted along the east shore of the Wash. In

January 1994, counts included 60 at Snettisham and 57 at Thornham, with 80 at Wells on 4th February 1995. However, these figures are a gross underestimate of the actual number of overwintering Rock Pipits in north Norfolk (see below). The wintering Breydon population is estimated as averaging about 35 (P. Allard pers. obs.); a figure which was supported by a full survey of Breydon on 20th November 1997 when a total of 37 was found.

Spring passage, which is far less marked than autumn, is most obvious from mid-March to early April and invariably concerns spring-plumaged birds of the race *littoralis* (see below), although ten west at Sheringham on 28th March 1976 may well have been *petrosus*. Rock Pipits are not normally recorded in Norfolk after mid-April, although there have been six May records, interestingly all except one from the Yarmouth area – singles at Breydon from 27th April to 4th May 1998, Yarmouth on 9th May 1986, Paston on 11th May 1989 and at Breydon on 17th May 1984, 24th May 1976 (a bird of the British race *petrosus*) and the latest on 31st May 1980. In addition there are three July records, all from the Yarmouth/Breydon area – one of the British race *petrosus* in song on a factory wall at Yarmouth South Denes on 3rd July 1989 (the observer assumed that it had wintered in the south of England, had been delayed for some reason on its return passage and was briefly holding territory as it finally returned northward), one along the tideline at Yarmouth on 5th July 1997 and two at Burgh Castle on 19th July 1956.

Occasional Rock Pipits are found inland, the majority on passage in October. The most favoured localities have been Welney, Cantley Beet Factory and Colney/Bawburgh Gravel Pits. Other inland sites to have hosted the species are the River Yare at Reedham and at Buckenham, the lakes at Gunton and Holkham, the River Ouse and Beet Factory at King's Lynn, Ringstead and Wisbech Sewage Farm.

The British race *petrosus* is undoubtedly an occasional and possibly annual visitor to Norfolk, for instance, a small number have been seen at Wells Harbour (McCallum 1997b). However, both Taylor (1997b) and McCallum (1997b) considered that the vast majority of Rock Pipits, both on passage and overwintering, belong to the race *littoralis*. In autumn, the westerly passage along the north Norfolk coast suggests an easterly or north-easterly origin and the heaviest movement often coincides with arrivals of Scandinavian migrants, such as Chaffinch and Brambling. This is supported by a Rock Pipit colour-ringed as a nestling at Malon Island, Halland, Sweden on 3rd June 1991, where it remained until 23rd August and which was seen at Lynn Point on 6th February 1992, before returning to Malon on 26th March 1992. (An adult male also ringed on Malon Island was seen at Benacre in Suffolk the following winter and it too was subsequently seen again on Malon in mid-summer!) Further evidence was provided by one ringed as a nestling at Nidingen, Sweden in 1996 which was found freshly dead at Terrington in January 1997. Unfortunately the origin of another colour-ringed Rock Pipit at Breydon in two successive winters in the early 1970s could not be ascertained, but it was probably from Scandinavia. Unlike British Rock Pipits, the Scandinavian race *littoralis* undergoes a partial late-winter body moult which results in a distinctive spring plumage. The majority of spring records refers to these birds and even includes some as early as mid-February. The highest counts have been at Lynn Point with 26 on 23rd February 1992, 19 on 14th February 1993 and 22 on 10th March 1996, at Burnham Norton with twelve on 5th March 1997 and at Cley with ten on 17th March 1991, 11th March 1995 and 2nd March 1997.

During November and December 1997 low tide counts of all intertidal habitat between Holme and Weybourne were carried out by a small group of observers under the auspices of English Nature. This confirmed suspicions that the number of overwintering birds has been grossly under-counted in the past. In November a total of 3,200 Rock Pipits was found, all on saltmarshes, including 268 at Thornham, 875 at Scolt Head/Brancaster Harbour, 327 at Burnham Overy Harbour, 367 at Wells, 336 at Warham, 428 at Stiffkey and 693 at Blakeney Harbour. Numbers at each site were lower in December probably due to some passage birds moving on, but still 2,010 were found. All were considered to have been of the Scandinavian race *littoralis*, as in The Netherlands, where large numbers of this race winter, feeding exclusively on small molluscs on saltmarshes. It seems likely that Norfolk birds have similar habits. Further confirmation of the race involved was obtained by McCallum (1998d) who carefully examined 40 of the 200 still present at Wells and Warham in March 1998. Without exception, they all showed strong characteristics of the race *littoralis* in early summer plumage.

Only a few Rock Pipits have been ringed in Norfolk, but if good numbers can be trapped and ringed in the future, final confirmation of their origin could be obtained from subsequent ringing recoveries.

*Moss Taylor*

# Water Pipit                                   *Anthus spinoletta*

**A scarce winter visitor and passage migrant.**

In the Western Palearctic, Water Pipits breed in the middle and lower middle latitudes at considerable elevations, typically on wet meadows or moorland with small pools, often above the tree line. In winter, they descend to the lowlands, with some migrating to the Channel and Atlantic coasts of Western Europe and around the Mediterranean, where they occupy both coastal and inland freshwater sites. Those wintering in Britain are thought to come from the mountains of central and southern Europe.

Riviere detailed the first record for Norfolk – one shot by M. A. Catling at Cley on 25th January 1905, followed by a second at Hickling on 20th March 1911. It is of interest that these localities remain two of the sites from where Water Pipits have been most frequently recorded in recent years.

Up to 1942, it had been recorded regularly at Hickling in spring, but even as late as 1966 it remained a very scarce bird elsewhere in Norfolk, being seen annually only at Cley from 1959 to 1964 (Seago 1967). In an attempt to establish the winter status of the species in Britain, the BTO organised a survey during the winters of 1966–67 and 1967–68, one result of which was to make observers more aware of the field characters of Water Pipits. The survey also showed that the species was being recorded increasingly as a winter visitor to the British Isles (Johnson 1970). Certainly in Norfolk, an increasing number of records were being published in the early 1970s with up to seven birds at Cantley Beet Factory from early January to 21st March 1972. This has remained an important overwintering site for Water Pipits, the highest count being 25 on 3rd February 1991. Hickling regularly hosted Water Pipits from 1971 to 1986, usually no more than five birds, but 14 on 29th January 1984 were attracted to a newly-cut reedbed. Other regular wintering sites in Broadland have been Strumpshaw (since a newly restored Broad was excavated in 1980), with up to nine in March 1991, and Surlingham Church Marsh. More recently, maximum counts at other Broadland sites have included twelve at How Hill and 22 at Buckenham, while an unusually high count of 27 at Wood Street near Catfield were feeding on harvested onion and sugar beet fields near to a flooded grazing meadow. There is evidence from elsewhere that Water Pipits exhibit site fidelity in consecutive winters (Johnson 1970).

On the coast only single birds were present at Cley until 1989, when at least 13 were present during the late autumn. Since then, good numbers have been recorded each winter on the flooded meadows, peaking at 40 in January 1993. At Burnham Norton, up to eleven were present in March 1995, while in the west of the county Wissington Beet Factory has attracted up to nine winter Water Pipits annually since 1991. The species is also being increasingly identified at many other scattered localities, albeit in small numbers. The Water Pipit was first treated by the BOURC as a separate species in 1986, prior to which Rock and Water Pipits were generally regarded as one polytypic species of Holarctic distribution (Knox 1988). Some of the recent interest in finding the species in winter may have been related to this decision!

The first birds of the autumn are generally recorded in early to mid-October, with the passage continuing through to late November. There have been five September records, involving seven birds, the earliest at Hickling on 17th September 1936 and Titchwell on 23rd September 1993. Numbers in the county often appear to increase during March and some sites have recorded their highest counts at this time of year, such as 23 at How Hill on 15th March 1994 and 33 at Cley on 23rd March 1994. However, this may be related to the development of their more distinctive spring plumage and tendency to flock in late winter, thus making the increase more apparent than real (Johnson 1970). Many birds remain into April, by which time they have often attained their attractive spring plumage but most have departed by mid-month. Occasional stragglers remain into late April, with three at Cley on 8th May 1990 and the latest spring sighting at Hickling on 22nd May 1986. One at Surlingham on 15th June 1993 is the only midsummer record.

*Moss Taylor*

## Yellow Wagtail   HUNSTANTON. 23·6·1986.                *Motacilla flava*

**A fairly common but declining summer visitor and passage migrant; very rare in winter.**

The Yellow Wagtail breeds across most of Europe in the form of at least eight races, covering all latitudes. It winters in subtropical and tropical zones, with those from western Europe moving to sub-Saharan Africa. In Britain, where *M. f. flavissima* is the race concerned, it has been in decline as a breeding species since the 1930s and is currently undergoing a south-easterly contraction of its range, having formerly bred as far north as Aberdeen and west to Cornwall. It no longer breeds regularly in Ireland. Yellow Wagtails are notorious for intergradation between races. Norfolk lies on the edge of the breeding range of both *flavissima* and the nominate Blue-headed Wagtail *M. f. flava*, thus intergrades between these races occur.

In Norfolk, Seago (1977) recorded the Yellow Wagtail as a decreasing summer visitor to grazing marshlands, water meadows and Breckland heaths. It would appear that the last named habitat is no longer utilised within the county and both the former are under constant threat. Drainage of great tracts of marshland for arable use in the east and west of the county and the pressure of constant grazing by wild-fowl and late-season livestock grazing on coastal marshes is apparently producing too short a sward at the time when migrant Yellow Wagtails are arriving in search of breeding territories.

Riviere mentioned that the decline of this species was noted by Emma Turner (1924) as being directly related to the advent of the motor-car, the favoured Broadland hay-meadows being allowed to become over-grown with rank vegetation as the hay crop was no longer needed as fodder for London bus and cab horses.

During fieldwork for the Norfolk Atlas (1980–85) it was recorded in 19% of the tetrads visited with fewer 10km squares occupied compared with the 68–72 BTO Atlas. It appeared to be most widespread on Broadland, Fenland and coastal levels, and grazing marshes (Kelly 1986). More recently, during the 1994–97 BBS the number of 1km squares visited in which it was recorded in Norfolk has varied from 9% to 23%, but with no definite trend. The current county breeding population may be as few as 200–300 pairs. Agricultural practices and apparent climatic changes offer little hope of an immediate return to former strengths. Indications of continued decline come from Holkham where 22 pairs bred in 1990, but only twelve pairs in 1996. Interestingly a reversal of this trend has occurred at Welney where numbers declined slightly from 32 pairs in 1990 to 27 pairs in 1994, but then underwent a 90% increase with 46 pairs in 1995, 51 in 1996 and 57 in 1997. This increase was apparently as a result of a lack of spring flooding in the latter years, producing ideal breeding conditions.

The earliest spring migrants have been at West Acre on 11th March 1990, at Sheringham on 13th March 1977 and at Welney on 16th March 1992. Passage usually commences in late March, peaking between late April and early May. Numbers can be impressive at coastal sites during settled conditions often associated with southerly winds. The marshes extending from Blakeney to Salthouse (particularly Cley Eye field) are at times most favoured although the dunes and fields between Happisburgh and Horsey, the cliff-top fields from Weybourne to Cromer, and the marshes at Snettisham and Holme have all received sizeable arrivals. The largest 'falls' have involved 170 west in three hours at Cromer Golf Course on 24th April 1983, 400 at Cley on 24th April 1986, 250 at Snettisham, 320 at Cley Eye and 190 at Hunstanton cliff-top and bowling green between 21st and 27th April 1987, 300 at Holme on 26th April 1992, 150 at Ludham on 30th August 1992, 200 at Cley on 21st April 1993, 170 at Snettisham on 24th April 1994 when 200 at Waxham, 450 at Holme on 2nd May 1995 and 300 on 27th April 1996, and 160 west at Scolt Head on 30th April 1997.

Post-breeding communal roosting by Yellow Wagtails is well recorded, with reedbeds usually being the favoured site. Between 1979 and 1982 up to 500 roosted annually at Stow Bridge and over 800 assembled at Burgh Castle in both 1990 and 1992. More recently a peak of 290 was attained at Welney on 25th August 1995. Most have departed by early October, but late ones have appeared until the month-end. Since 1953 there have been 13 November records and the latest at Snettisham on 6th December 1970, at Wisbech Sewage Farm on 6th December 1981 and at Narborough on 23rd December 1982.

Northward moving flocks of spring migrants often contain more than one race of Yellow Wagtail and five races including *flavissima* have been recorded in Norfolk (Williamson 1997c). The nominate Blue-headed Wagtail *flava* breeds in southern Fennoscandia and western Europe (except Britain) and Iberia. It is a scarce spring and rare autumn migrant to Norfolk, averaging 30 records annually. During May 1979 a total of almost 50 appeared including six at Sheringham, eight at Happisburgh and twelve at Winterton, while in spring 1997 about 60 were reported with maximum day-counts of six at Overstrand and five at Waxham. Single pairs bred on Kelling Heath in 1931 and 1932, Hickling in 1940 and Salthouse in 1958. A number of mixed pairs with *flavissima* have occurred.

The Grey-headed Wagtail *M. f. thunbergi* breeds in northern Fennoscandia, northern Russia and north-western Siberia. It is a very scarce spring migrant in Norfolk first obtained at Sheringham in May 1842 (the specimen is still in the Castle Museum, Norwich). Currently it averages ten records annually, usually arriving in mid- to late May. An exceptionally large arrival took place in 1992 when 50–60 were recorded, including over 25 at Happisburgh on 15th May.

The Ashy-headed Wagtail *M. f. cinereocapilla* breeds in Italy and southern France. It is a rare spring overshoot to Norfolk, single males having been recorded at Cley on 16th May 1955, 21st April 1964, 18th May 1970 and 7th–9th May 1977, at Hardley Flood on 19th May 1978, at Winterton on 19th May 1979, at Cley on 4th May 1981, at Horsey on 26th April 1983 with another on 30th April when one at Cley, at West Runton on 30th April 1989, at Holme on 21st May 1991, at Cley on 24th April 1994 and at Blakeney Point on 21st May 1994.

The Spanish Wagtail *M. f. iberiae* breeds in Iberia, the Balearic Islands and north-west Africa. It is a very rare spring overshoot with only two accepted records of birds showing the characteristics of this race, at Happisburgh on 8th May 1994 and at Salthouse on 23rd May 1997.

The Black-headed Wagtail *M. f. feldegg* breeds in south-east Europe, Asia Minor, the Caucasus and the Near East to the Caspian Sea. Seago (1977) included a number of occurrences which have subsequently been rejected by the BBRC. A male at Cley from 23rd July to 11th August 1983 showed the characteristics of *feldegg* but unfortunately the record has not yet been submitted to the BBRC. Another at Cley Eye on 14th May 1993 considered by many observers to be an example of *feldegg* may have been a particularly dark-headed *thunbergi*.

Examples of Sykes's Wagtail *M. f. beema* breeding in north Kazakhstan and south-west Siberia have been claimed on a number of occasions both as breeders and migrants. Williamson (1997c) considered it likely that most, if not all, of the records relate to hybrids between other races of Yellow Wagtail. This would account for sightings at Burnham Norton and Welney during 1989–94. Yellow Wagtails resembling *beema* did in fact breed at Hickling as long ago as 1894. The adults were obtained and are on display in the Castle Museum, Norwich. There are no accepted records of *beema* in Norfolk, indeed it is the race least likely to put in an appearance.

About 500 Yellow Wagtails have been ringed in Norfolk and only three have been recovered abroad – a nestling ringed at Salthouse in 1952 was recovered in France on 25th August, another nestling from Cley in 1958 was found near Lisbon, Portugal the following September and a first-autumn bird ringed at Stowbridge in 1981 was recovered on spring passage at Mahbes, Spanish West Africa on 18th March 1986. One ringed at Cap Breton, France on 2nd October 1976 was controlled at Tottenhill the following June. There have also been movements between Norfolk, Kent, Buckinghamshire and Berkshire.

*John R. Williamson*

**Grey-headed Wagtails & Red-throated Pipit**
*(Gary Wright)*

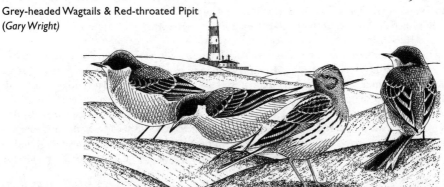

# Citrine Wagtail

*Motacilla citreola*

**A very rare vagrant; three records.**

The Citrine Wagtail is a central Palearctic species, breeding primarily from central Asia eastwards to Amurland and wintering in India and south-east Asia. In recent years it has become an annual vagrant to the British Isles.

The first Norfolk sighting was of a first-winter bird found by Tim Inskipp at Welney on 16th–17th November 1980. Following submission of details, the record was finally accepted in May 1997 and became the first for the county. The second record was of a very confiding juvenile at Blakeney Fresh Marsh pools on 26th–29th September 1986. The third was at Kelling Water Meadows, in juvenile to first-winter plumage, on 17th September 1995.

*Peter Allard*

## Grey Wagtail    *Motacilla cinerea*

LODDON STAITHE. R·CHET. JUV. 21·5·2000.
CHEDGRAVE GARR. R·CHET. 25·10·1999.

**A scarce resident, passage migrant and winter visitor.**

In the Western Palearctic, the Grey Wagtail breeds across north-west Africa and Europe, mainly in temperate lower and middle-lower latitudes with slight overlaps into boreal and Mediterranean zones. In winter, it is found throughout the European breeding range, and as far south into Africa as Malawi and east into India and south-east Asia. It is widely distributed in mainland Britain and Ireland, although it is scarce or absent from much of the lowland eastern and central counties of England (New Atlas). There is a shift in the distribution of the British population in winter with birds moving to more low-lying areas. Grey Wagtails are susceptible to extended periods of severe winter weather, thus numbers of breeding and wintering birds tend to fluctuate periodically.

Riviere recorded a failed breeding attempt at Ellingham Mill in 1921 followed by the first successful county breeding record of what, in Britain, is primarily an upland bird requiring fast-flowing streams, at Taverham Mill in 1923.

Seago (1967) noted the Grey Wagtail as a decreasing summer visitor, yet Kelly (1986) indicated the Norfolk breeding population to be possibly at its highest level ever, being recorded in 58 (4%) of tetrads surveyed for the Norfolk Atlas. However, the number of breeding pairs reported annually since 1986 has been as low as three and up to a maximum of only 20. The crumbling brick-work of old bridges, water mills and weirs, and narrow streams and culverts are all favoured sites, although breeding has also been recorded at Cantley Beet Factory. The Rivers Wensum, Yare, Waveney, Nar, Bure and Wissey have provided the majority of favoured breeding locations within the county.

Both spring and autumn passage through the county is often protracted and light. Spring passage usually commences in March and extends well into May. In autumn, return passage is mainly coastal, usually exceeds 100 birds in total, and may commence as early as late June, continuing into early November. Passage becomes more concentrated during September and October, when double-figure day-counts have been recorded at the sites with more extensive coverage, such as 20 west at Sheringham on 18th September 1993 and twelve the following day. During the autumn of 1997, a total of 19 flew south at Hunstanton cliffs, including six on 16th October. Generally, in both spring and autumn, it is unusual for more than two or three birds to appear together at any one site.

Wintering numbers within the county are generally fairly low, usually less than 40. At this time, sewage treatment plants, farmyards (especially slurry pits and manure heaps), watercress beds, pools and lakes are favoured, although anywhere where invertebrate prey is available may be utilised, including urban flat-roofed buildings providing shallow pools. In severe weather, bird-table scraps may be taken.

Just over 50 Grey Wagtails have been ringed in Norfolk. One ringed as a nestling near Brussels, Belgium on 6th May 1952 was recovered at Long Stratton on 13th March 1953, and was the first foreign-ringed Grey Wagtail to be recovered in the British Isles. Another ringed in Surrey in July was found in Norfolk the following January, while a nestling from Buckenham was recovered at Bury St Edmunds one year later.

*John R. Williamson*

## Pied Wagtail    *Motacilla alba*

MY GARDEN, CHEDGRAVE. 22·11·1999.

**A common resident and passage migrant.**

In the Western Palearctic, the nominate race of White Wagtail *M. a. alba* breeds throughout Continental Europe, Iceland, The Faeroes, Asia Minor and Levant. The British race, known as Pied Wagtail *M. a. yarrellii*, breeds throughout Britain and Ireland and locally on adjacent coasts in north-western Continental Europe. Most migratory (northern) populations winter in the Mediterranean area, tropics and subtropics of Africa, peninsular India and south-east Asia. Most southerly populations tend to be non-migratory. The

British race is considered to be mainly resident, with a few birds wintering in France and western Iberia. Although there have been recent increases in Ireland, decreases have occurred in areas of southern and eastern England, due primarily to changes in agricultural practice.

Although Stevenson described the Pied Wagtail as being resident throughout the year, he qualified this statement with 'the majority of our home-bred birds leave us for a time in mid-winter'. Riviere also stated that the species was common and generally distributed throughout the summer, but that many left in autumn and winter, to return in spring. Seago (1967) described it as being a widespread resident, but less common in winter. Kelly (1986) recorded the Pied Wagtail in 53% of the tetrads surveyed for the Norfolk Atlas, noting a desertion of not inconsiderable tracts of agricultural land which has assumed a 'prairie-like' appearance, both in the Fens and Broadland. However, the Pied Wagtail is highly adaptable, and is often closely linked with human habitation. Any area with open spaces and low vegetation which holds invertebrate prey will be readily utilised. Airfields, school playing fields, parks, car parks, roads and industrial estates are all examples of how human development has created suitable habitat. During the 1994–97 BBS it was found in 55–68% of the 1km squares covered in Norfolk, demonstrating just how widespread it remains in the county.

A spring passage of *yarrellii* occurs along the north Norfolk coast, mainly in March, with at times some impressive numbers recorded. At Sheringham, a total of 34 west on 10th March 1989 was a record day-count at the time. However, since then, possibly due to counts being made for at least four hours from dawn, much higher numbers have been recorded flying west – 150 on 11th March 1990, 335 on 18th–20th March 1992 (including 135 on 18th) and 120 west on 21st March 1993. Smaller numbers are recorded on autumn passage and at Sheringham, the highest count has been 60 west on 14th November 1996.

Post-breeding (autumn) and winter communal roosts are a feature of Pied Wagtail behaviour and a number have been well recorded over recent years. Heat sources from buildings and industrial plants are often utilised and a roost at Bacton Gas Terminal, in use since 1980, regularly holds 350–700 birds. A roost at the Rhone-Poulenc factory in Norwich held 400 birds in 1993 and was in use for several years. Reedbeds are another favoured site with 690 roosting at Whitlingham Marsh in October 1988 and 430 at Scarning Fen in 1983–84. Other large roosts have included 400 at Coltishall in 1976, 490 at Attleborough in 1994 and 300 at Thetford Industrial Estate in early 1997. Roosts in trees are also recorded, notably up to 650 in three plane trees in Brigg Street, Norwich, in December 1997, just a few metres above the heads of late-night Christmas shoppers, which still held 515 birds on 7th January 1998. It was in use again in December 1998 when the maximum count was 575, after the satellite roosts had been abandoned.

Although the Continental race *alba* is strongly migratory throughout its range, Stevenson could find no evidence of it having occurred in Norfolk. Riviere recorded two males which were obtained at Yarmouth on 20th April 1888 and a third killed there on 1st May of the same year – the first authenticated county examples. Riviere also mentioned that subsequently *alba* had become a not infrequent passage migrant in spring and autumn.

Passage of *alba* is currently most pronounced in spring, between mid-March and mid-May, with a peak in April; but numbers in Norfolk are generally small, involving single-figure counts at coastal sites. However, larger numbers have been recorded in several years recently with 20–30 at Cley on 18th–20th April 1987, 26 at Cley on 21st April 1988, 15 at Weybourne on 27th March 1989 and at Winterton on 24th March 1994. Arrivals often coincide with that of the Yellow Wagtail. The dune systems and adjacent fields between Winterton and Waxham, and the coastal marshes between Salthouse and Cley are often favoured.

The first county breeding record of a pure pair of *alba* occurred as recently as 1997 (Millington 1997b, 1998a) when two broods were raised at Cley, the nest in the roof of a cottage on the north side of the village. A mixed pairing of *yarrellii* x *alba* was recorded at Cley by Richard Richardson in 1966 and a male *alba* was seen feeding young at Burnham Norton in 1990, although no female was seen on that occasion. Whilst *alba* breeds regularly in Shetland and occasionally elsewhere in Scotland, and has recently colonised the Channel Islands, English records are apparently scarce.

Over 2,000 Pied Wagtails have been ringed in Norfolk since the 1960s and yet not a single bird has been recovered abroad, suggesting that at least nowadays there is minimal emigration of Norfolk birds in autumn. However, one ringed as a nestling at Kelling in July 1929 was reported near Soustons, Landes, France on 13th October, supporting earlier claims that many left the county in autumn and winter. The only long-distance recoveries in recent years have concerned two nestlings ringed at Langford and recovered in Sussex and Somerset, and an adult ringed at Earlham on 27th October 1988 which was recovered in Cromarty, Scotland on 1st May 1989. Others ringed in Suffolk, Essex (2), Hampshire and Durham have been reported in Norfolk.

*John R. Williamson*

## Waxwing (Bohemian Waxwing) *Bombycilla garrulus*

ROCKLAND.
5-12-1999.

An irruptive winter visitor, fairly common in some years.

Waxwings
(Bryan Bland)

The Waxwing breeds in the vast tracts of taiga forest stretching across northern Europe from Fennoscandia east through Siberia and into western North America. In winter, they are noted for their erratic wandering, their journeys dictated by the available food supply.

The chief winter food is the berries of the rowan (or mountain ash), an abundant tree in northern Europe where it is found both wild and lining the avenues in towns. The rowan crop varies widely from year to year; warm conditions when rowans are in flower produce a heavy crop of berries. In a poor year the fruits are rapidly exhausted. Warm spring weather in the northern forests is also conducive to a high survival rate among nestling Waxwings. The subsequent heavy berry crop provides ample food during the following winter and the Waxwing population builds up rapidly. Since, however, a poor berry crop often follows a heavy one it is in the autumn following a heavy crop that food is in the greatest demand. Waxwings must then migrate from the taiga or starve. During the 1965–66 large-scale invasion, remarkable distances were achieved by these always immaculate berry-seekers. Iceland, Portugal, Spain, southern Italy, Greece and Turkey were all penetrated. If they fail to find food, the population crashes bringing invasions to an end for several winters.

Observers in this country, in the far westward fringe of even the extended winter range, only occasionally see what is in fact an annual event. During their visits, Waxwings are readily approachable, often frequenting small gardens close to busy streets, and are indifferent to passing traffic. Some even become casualties when flying too low after gorging themselves on berries.

Stevenson considered that 'among our occasional winter visitants none is so eccentric as the Waxwing . . . [at times] creating a perfect sensation by its numbers'. He described a large-scale arrival during 1866–67 followed by a lengthy obituary list: 144 specimens were received by the county's taxidermists; of this total Stevenson handled over half and Thomas Gunn set-up 41 birds. Among Gunn's finest work is a case containing ten Waxwings at the National Trust's Felbrigg Hall.

Riviere listed invasions in 1872–73, 1892–93, 1903–04, 1913–14, 1920–21 and 1921–22, with the largest arrivals featuring over 100 birds. Further influxes were recorded during 1931–32, 1932–33, 1936–37 and 1941–42. From 1946 Waxwings were recorded every winter during the following 50 years with the exception of 1980–81 and 1983–84. The more impressive numbers arriving during this period are shown in Table 42.

**Table 42. Total numbers of Waxwings recorded in Norfolk in selected winters from 1946–47 to 1995–96.**

| 1946–47 | 100 | 1971–72 | 280 |
|---------|-------|---------|-------|
| 1956–57 | 140 | 1972–73 | 100 |
| 1957–58 | 316 | 1974–75 | 356 |
| 1958–59 | 213 | 1988–89 | 315 |
| 1959–60 | 304 | 1989–90 | 100 |
| 1963–64 | 275 | 1990–91 | 370 |
| 1965–66 | 1,400 | 1991–92 | 300 |
| 1970–71 | 860 | 1995–96 | 1,200 |

ROYDON, SURREY. 3-2-1966.)

The four successive large-scale irruptions to Britain and Ireland, commencing with that in the winter of 1956–57, constituted an unprecedented series since records began (Cornwallis 1961). The two most spectacular immigrations into the county were those in 1965–66 (Cornwallis & Townsend 1968) and 1995–96, both surpassing all previous records in both numbers and distances reached by the furthest stragglers. Both events are dealt with in detail below:

**1965–66**: A feature of this movement was its extreme earliness; birds began arriving at Hunstanton and Wiveton on 14th October. The size of the invasion was not fully realised until a few days later when a flock of 230 reached Holkham. On 20th October over 200 headed south at Holme followed shortly afterwards by 300 on Roydon Common, with similar numbers at both Wiveton and Beeston, and 100 in the Horning/ Ranworth area. Dispersal of the largest flocks began early in November at which time flights of between 50 and 100 appeared along the county's east coast. Yet others put in appearances at many inland localities including the Brecks. This pattern continued during December when the larger groups totalled 50 at Burgh Castle and 40 in Norwich. Ever-wandering parties remained until late March with stragglers at Hellesdon until 12th and at Taverham until 14th April.

**1995–96**: The vanguard of a mid-winter invasion arrived at Holme on 7th December although by the year-end no party exceeded 23 birds. Little were observers to guess at future events. During January growing numbers were reported throughout Norfolk as a high pressure area intensified over the nearby Continent drawing a bitterly cold easterly airstream of Siberian origin. The first three-figure Waxwing flocks were attained by 4th February including 100 at both Snettisham and Cromer with 138 in the Mile Cross district of Norwich. The Norwich arrivals soon moved to the Sweet Briar Industrial Estate where up to 285 remained from 4th to 13th February. This gathering attracted much attention, seeking food in an area of 6km$^2$, swooping into roadside hedges, tree-lined avenues and gardens. Periodically all rested in large groups in trees, on rooftops, television aerials, telegraph-poles and wires. The birds regularly divided into smaller groups heading in different directions before re-grouping.

Between the second half of February and late March, large flocks, often up to 200 together, put in brief appearances at many localities both in the City of Norwich and well beyond the circular ring road, including Taverham, New Costessey, Eaton, Spixworth, Sprowston and Thorpe. Food became ever less abundant, the Waxwings regularly feeding on the ground attacking fallen apples. A wide range of berries was also taken – rose-hips, *Pyracantha*, ornamental cherries, and crab apples, guelder rose, rowan, *Cotoneaster* and hawthorn. With the arrival of warmer days birds began flycatching from treetops and overhead wires. The majority of the Waxwings in Norwich roosted in Earlham Cemetery, flocks returning to feeding locations soon after dawn.

Elsewhere in the county during this time the numerous observations included up to 100 Waxwings at Snettisham, 75 at King's Lynn, 70 at North Walsham, 70 at Hoveton and 50 at Diss. During April each flock disappeared. The Bowthorpe district of Norwich was favoured with 130 until 16th and at Mile Cross eleven lingered until 27th April. Not surprisingly, optically-clad birdwatchers viewing such tame and brightly coloured birds in public places led to some intriguing questions and comments from passers-by.

Extreme dates for Waxwings have included 11th May 1957 at Holt, 12th May 1967 at Freethorpe, 13th May 1996 at Holkham and 21st September 1967 at Wolferton.

About 50 Waxwings have been ringed in Norfolk and three have been recovered abroad. Two ringed at Heacham on 3rd November 1974 were found at Kumla, Sweden on 6th December 1975 and at Kirov,

Russia on 27th October 1977, a locality 700km east of Moscow. The third ringed at Blakeney on 12th November 1965 was found in France, near Lake Geneva on 25th March 1966. All three recoveries are the only ones involving British-ringed Waxwings to those countries.

*Michael Seago*

## Dipper (White-throated Dipper)        *Cinclus cinclus*

**A rare winter visitor and passage migrant; very rare in summer.**

The Dipper is extensively distributed in the western half of the Western Palearctic, wherever there are swift-running streams and rivers in mountainous or hilly regions. Most populations are resident but undertake local post-breeding dispersal movements, often involving altitudinal change. However, birds of the nominate race *C. c. cinclus*, known as Black-bellied Dipper, breeding in Fennoscandia, are subject to medium or long-distance partial migration and a few from Norway and Sweden winter each year in eastern England. The British race of Dipper *C. c. gularis* is sedentary and breeds mainly in the uplands of northern and western Britain, but also on lowland streams, especially where there are stretches of fast flowing water.

Stevenson described the Dipper as an 'accidental visitant' to Norfolk, mainly from November to March and usually in severe weather. Three on the River Yare at Earlham in about November 1855 still remain the most recorded on a single stretch of river. At about the same time, Stevenson recorded one shot in Norwich between Foundry Bridge and Pull's Ferry. The specimen ended its days in his collection after 'sporting over a river turbid and discoloured from neighbouring factories with the noise of traffic on every side'.

By 1930, the county total had risen to 35, since when about 100 more have been recorded. Since 1950, the species has been noted in all except 15 of the years but it is unusual for more than three birds to be found in a single year. However, seven were located in the winter of 1950–51 and six in 1969, including two at Bintree and another two at Hunworth, one of which was in song in January and February. Dippers were recorded annually between 1972 and 1977, with up to six to seven birds in most years. Since then, it does appear to have become a less frequent visitor to the county.

In Norfolk, most Dippers are found near watermills or weirs, mirroring the aquatic conditions found in their breeding areas. The earliest autumn arrival was a bird of the British or Continental race at Bawburgh in mid-August 1983, which made an unprecedented stay of over a year. During this time it roosted on the rafters of a garage and became increasingly tame, frequently singing from a porch roof or telegraph wires. Unfortunately, it was found dead on the garage floor on 24th October 1984. It had become such a part of village life that it had an obituary in the Parish Magazine! (Hobbs 1985). Apart from this bird and three recorded by Riviere in September, the earliest date has been 1st October 1983 at Hardley Flood. The remaining records have all been after 18th October, with most sightings between December and February.

The interconnecting river systems in central and eastern Norfolk make it extremely difficult to decide exactly how many birds are involved during the course of a winter. However, some individuals are known to have made prolonged stays at single sites. One which arrived at Taverham Mill on 24th November 1950 remained until 24th March 1951 and another stayed at Aylsham Mill from 29th October 1953 to 30th March 1954, and was joined briefly by a second bird. One seen at Holkham Lake on 22nd October 1990 was almost certainly the same bird found at Overy Mill five days later, where it remained, commuting along the River Burn to Mill Farm at Burnham Overy, until 23rd March 1991. Other long-stayers have been recorded at Ormesby Waterworks, Honingham and Gressenhall. Most overwintering Dippers have left by the end of March, although one remained at Honingham until 11th April. The majority of April records probably refer to spring migrants prior to their departure to Scandinavia or the Continent, such as those at Snipe's Marsh, Cley on 7th April 1984, Letheringsett Mill on 13th April 1966 and two on 11th–14th April 1986, and one at Ickburgh on 28th–30th April 1993. Apart from the bird which took up residence at Bawburgh in 1983–84, there have been two mid-summer records – a bird of the British race at Earlham Park, Norwich on 15th June 1989 and a bird of one of the Continental races at Corpusty Mill on 8th July 1984.

The vast majority of Dippers recorded in Norfolk have belonged to the nominate Scandinavian race, the Black-bellied Dipper. About ten have shown some chestnut on the underparts and were identified as belonging either to the British race *gularis* or the central and western European race *C. c. aquaticus*. However, some individuals are not readily separable, as there is considerable variation in the presence and extent of chestnut on the underparts of birds from both Scandinavia and the Continent (BWP). It may therefore be better to describe these birds as showing some of the characteristics of the other races.

Six have been ringed in Norfolk, most of which were also colour-ringed and although birds do appear at the same locality in the following winter, there has been no evidence from ringing that birds return to the same site in subsequent years. Indeed, the bird ringed at Burnham Market on 16th February 1991, which had been in the area since the previous October, was controlled at Belstead, Suffolk on 14th November 1991.

*Moss Taylor*

## Wren (Winter Wren) *MY GARDEN, CHEDGRAVE. 1-8-1999.* *Troglodytes troglodytes*

**An abundant resident and scarce autumn passage migrant.**

The Wren is a Holarctic species which breeds throughout most of the Western Palearctic. Except for the north-eastern and eastern populations which are totally migratory, wintering in the south of the range, it is a sedentary or partially migratory species. In Britain and Ireland it is one of the most widespread and abundant species (New Atlas), despite being susceptible to severe weather, as occurred in the winters of 1947 and early 1963.

From Riviere's comment that the Wren was ubiquitous and common throughout the year in all districts, it can be assumed that there has been no real change in its status since at least 1930. It was found in 93% of the tetrads covered for the Norfolk Atlas and during the 1994–97 BBS it was recorded in 87–90% of the 1km squares visited in Norfolk. Although primarily a woodland bird, it is found throughout the county wherever low scrub is present, being absent only from the Halvergate Levels, parts of the Fens and the coastal saltmarshes; although in 1953 it was noted nesting in *Suaeda* bushes in the Blakeney area, especially when tide wrack was evident.

As long ago as January 1926, the species was recorded using the nests of House Martins as communal winter roost-sites. Although Riviere does not give the exact locality, he stated that at least 30 were seen going to roost during an exceptionally cold night, and the following morning twelve were picked up dead under the nests. Since then there have been many similar reports, including up to 49 Wrens roosting in House Martin nests at Hoveton and up to 20 at Brinton Hall, both in 1970, and up to 30 at Stoke Holy Cross and 28 occupying just two House Martin nests at Brundall in 1986. Other records of communal roosting have included 15–20 Wrens in a heated outhouse at Surlingham in January 1968, up to 20 in cavities in the walls of Ted Ellis's house at Wheatfen in 1970 and six in an old Magpie's nest at Lessingham in November 1992. Communal roosting, however, does not always have the desired beneficial effect – 19 were discovered frozen to death in a hollow apple tree at Filby on 24th January 1987. The record number of Wrens to use a single nest box was 61, as noted by Winifred Flower at High Kelling in February 1969. It took the birds about 20 minutes to emerge from the box each morning (Flower 1969).

Riviere stated that there was some evidence of migratory movements on the coast in autumn, based on records of Wrens amongst the *Suaeda* bushes on Cley beach and that a few had probably been correctly identified on the offshore light-vessels, although most of the claimed records of 'wrens' would have referred to Goldcrests. At several ringing sites on the north Norfolk coast an October peak is recorded in many years, suggesting a degree of partial migration, rather than simply post-fledging dispersal, while an increase in numbers on Scolt Head on 27th–28th September 1998 was considered to have been a result of newly-arrived migrants.

About 10,000 Wrens have been ringed in Norfolk and only three have been recovered over 100km from the site of ringing, which indicates just how sedentary is the species. A young bird ringed at Wortwell on 22nd August 1990 was found at Bath, Avon on 26th November, one ringed at Fowlmere in November 1992 was recovered in Shropshire the following October, and one ringed at Garboldisham in October 1993 was found at Louth, Lincolnshire in April 1995. In addition, four Wrens ringed in other counties have been found in Norfolk. The longest movement involved one ringed at Adwick-le-Street, Yorkshire on 1st November 1971 and recovered at Shotesham on 2nd June 1973, while one ringed at Gibraltar Point, Lincolnshire in April 1958 was found at Buxton the following April. One ringed at Gotham, Lincolnshire in April 1981 was controlled at Sheringham in October and the only movement in a northerly direction involved a bird ringed at Abberton, Essex in January 1959 recovered at East Harling in May.

*Moss Taylor*

MY GARDEN, CHEDGRAVE.

## Dunnock (Hedge Accentor)    8·7·1999.    *Prunella modularis*

**An abundant resident and fairly common passage migrant, mainly in autumn.**

The Dunnock is widely distributed as a breeding species in the upper and middle latitudes of the Western Palearctic, mainly in the temperate zone. In much of Europe it is typically a woodland species, but in Britain and Ireland a shift away from montane and coniferous habitat is almost complete, having commenced about 200 years ago. It is now a pioneer species commonly invading a variety of scrub-grown situations. It has adapted to coppiced woodland with vigorous ground vegetation and widely-spaced tall standard trees and then to field hedgerows, farms, railway embankments and cuttings, churchyards, parks, gardens and vacant urban land as well as semi-natural bushy and scrubby areas. As a result, it occurs throughout Britain and Ireland, except for Shetland and the central Highlands of Scotland (68–72 BTO Atlas). In Europe since 1850 the breeding range has expanded, particularly to the north, whereas a slow population decline in the British Isles and Denmark has been noted since the mid-1970s (Marchant *et al.* 1990).

Stevenson described the Dunnock as one of the most familiar species in Norfolk, along with House Sparrow and Robin. While this may not be true nowadays, it still has a widespread breeding distribution in the county. During fieldwork for the Norfolk Atlas, it was recorded in the seventh highest number of tetrads, being found in 95% of those surveyed. It was only absent from areas lacking cover in which to nest, which included coastal locations, especially saltmarshes, and open areas of the Fens and Broadland, most obviously Halvergate Levels (Kelly 1986). More recently, it was found in 79–86% of the 1km squares covered in Norfolk during the 1994–97 BBS.

British Dunnocks are mainly sedentary, so the winter distribution is similar to that during the breeding season. The species is generally solitary in winter but can have overlapping ranges and may aggregate temporarily at rich food sources (Winter Atlas). However, the Fennoscandian population migrates south for the winter, reaching as far as the Mediterranean region. Autumn passage of Dunnocks occurs through-out September and October and early records from the light-vessels indicated that birds of Continental origin were clearly involved. Nowadays, small numbers of migrant Dunnocks are regularly recorded, mainly along the north coast, often peaking in the second half of September. The arrival of such birds is most easily recorded in areas of isolated cover, such as exists at Holme, where maximum counts of 50 were made on 17th September 1993 (the day before a Norwegian-ringed Dunnock was controlled) and on 18th September 1995, and 150–200 on 22nd September 1997. Elsewhere, maximum counts have included 30–40 in Dead Man's Wood, Sheringham on 29th September 1979, 27th–28th September and 29th October 1997, and 50+ at Scolt Head on 27th September 1997. In autumn, small groups of Dunnocks may be seen flitting around the tops of bushes and low trees along the coast, calling repeatedly, before flying off to-gether, often in a westerly direction. However, at Mundesley, twelve were recorded flying east on 15th October 1994 and six flew high south at Hunstanton cliffs on 11th October 1996, where the autumn total in 1997 was 21 flying south. There is little evidence of passage in the spring although 60 were reported at Wells on 5th April 1958 in association with increased numbers of Blackbirds, Robins and Goldcrests.

Some of these autumn Dunnocks are undoubtedly of the nominate race *P. m. modularis*. Riviere pro-vided details of the first record – one shot at Blakeney Point on 17th October 1919, while the second was also obtained at the same locality on 25th September 1931. Since then, further Dunnocks trapped for ringing on the north Norfolk coast in autumn have shown the characteristics, including the wing formula, of the race *modularis*, most notably during the 'fall' of Scandinavian migrants in early October 1998. At Weybourne ten such birds were trapped from 1st to 7th October 1998, including one carrying a Swedish ring; while another ringed in Norway was controlled at Holme during the same period.

Over 10,000 Dunnocks have been ringed in Norfolk, but only two have been recovered outside the county – one ringed at Holme in June 1966 was found at Beccles, Suffolk in July 1972 and another ringed as a juvenile at Gillingham on 23rd August 1980 was controlled at Dungeness, Kent on 30th September 1980, a most unusual movement for a British-bred Dunnock. Four autumn-ringed birds from Gibraltar Point, Lincolnshire have been controlled in Norfolk, two each at Holme and Sheringham, and another ringed at Flean Dyke, Cambridgeshire was found dead at Holme the following spring. Five recoveries indicate movements by Continental birds – one ringed on Helgoland, Germany on 10th October 1960 was controlled at Holme one month later, the first foreign-ringed Dunnock to be recovered in Britain; another ringed at Giljastolen, Norway on 4th September 1993 was controlled at Holme two weeks later,

400

and one ringed on Fair Isle on 17th September 1984 was found freshly dead at West Runton the following February. One ringed at Skane on the southern tip of Sweden on 17th September 1998 was controlled at Weybourne two weeks later, the first Swedish-ringed Dunnock to be recovered in the British Isles; details are awaited of another ringed in Norway and controlled at Holme, also in early October 1998. Finally, one ringed at Thorpe End in December 1971 was found freshly dead in Norwich in February 1980 in its tenth year, which may be compared with the longevity record for a British-ringed Dunnock of just over eleven years.

*B. D. Harding*

## Alpine Accentor                                    *Prunella collaris*

**A very rare vagrant; one record.**

The Alpine Accentor is a montane species with a patchy breeding distribution from the mountains of north-west Africa and Iberia, through central and south-eastern Europe to Asia. It is a partial migrant making regular altitudinal movements according to season and is a rare vagrant to the British Isles.

One was found and identified by Kevin Shepherd on the cliff-face between Sheringham and Weybourne (near Spalla Gap) on 30th April 1978. It was trapped and photographed the following day and became only the second Alpine Accentor to be ringed in the British Isles (the first had been ringed at Portland, Dorset only three weeks earlier). It remained until 4th May when it departed high to the south-east.

A previous record of one seen under Gorleston South Pier on 21st September 1894 by Arthur Patterson is no longer acceptable. The record was poorly documented with few details (Patterson 1905).

*Peter Allard*

## Robin (European Robin)          MY GARDEN, CHEDGRAVE.          *Erithacus rubecula*
                                   8-7-1999.

**An abundant resident and common passage migrant, mostly in autumn.**

The Robin breeds in the upper and middle latitudes of the Western Palearctic, with its range extending over most of Europe. The majority of the Fennoscandian, central and eastern European populations are migratory and winter in western Europe and around the Mediterranean. It is a common breeding bird throughout Britain and Ireland, except for Shetland (New Atlas).

It has always been a familiar bird in Norfolk, largely due to its habit of breeding in close proximity to man. During the fieldwork for the Norfolk Atlas it was found in 93% of the tetrads in the county, while it was recorded in 79–83% of the 1km squares covered during the 1994–97 BBS, possibly suggesting a decline in abundance. It requires light or medium cover, often favouring moist habitats and it is particularly abundant in woodland, scrub, gardens, parkland and along farmland hedges.

Although the British race *E. r. melophilus* is largely sedentary, the nominate Continental race *E. r. rubecula* is a common passage migrant in Norfolk, but the number of birds involved appears to have declined in recent years. The first Norfolk record of the race *rubecula* was one obtained by Harry Witherby at Holkham in September 1905, although it was not recognised as such until 1910. Riviere also noted a regular autumn arrival of Robins on the coast, often in considerable numbers. While arrivals are largely related to weather conditions, in particular easterly gales, autumn passage is generally recorded from the second half of September through to early November. In early October 1951, an unprecedented 'invasion' of Robins was recorded along the British east coast from Shetland to Kent. This spectacular fall or 'rush', as it was known in those days, was described in *Wild Bird Protection in Norfolk 1951*, (the predecessor to the annual *Norfolk Bird Report* which first appeared in 1953).

> During the night of September 30th/October 1st, a steady easterly wind prevailed, accompanied however by considerable low cloud, which conditions continued during the day of October 1st but, with the exception of a few chaffinches and redstarts, nothing of particular interest occurred during the morning of that day. About 1 p.m., however, the ruins of the camp at the end of the Beach Road at Cley and the bushes and buildings between the road and the Observatory were suddenly swarming with robins; it was estimated that there were at least 200 in the camp buildings alone, in addition to vastly larger numbers in the

grass, the bushes and buildings in the neighbourhood of the Observatory . . . In the course of the afternoon many Robins were observed coming in from the sea in a very exhausted condition and could have been picked up by hand . . . Between 3 p.m. and 5 p.m. on the same day the bushes suddenly became alive with goldcrests and song thrushes . . . (Daukes 1952).

Notable 'falls' also occurred in 1955 with 500 at Blakeney Point on 23rd November and on 4th October 1973 with 80 at Holme, 200 at Wells and Blakeney Point, and hundreds at Cley. Some of the largest numbers recorded in recent years, however, were noted on 25th September 1976, during heavy rain and an easterly gale, with at least 1,000 in the Sheringham area, including 400 at Dead Man's Wood and 400 at Yarmouth Cemeteries. Although the 'falls' are usually only recorded around the coast, an influx of Robins on 18th–20th September 1995 was also noted at Welney. One of the largest 'falls' of Robins ever to have occurred in Norfolk was recorded in early October 1998. The first indication of unusual numbers were 140 on Scolt Head on 27th September, which heralded daily 'falls' around the entire Norfolk coast on 1st–6th October. Maximum counts included 650 on 1st and 1,000+ on 3rd at Scolt Head, an amazing 3,000 at Holkham Meals (between Wells car park and Lady Anne's Drive) on 1st, 510 at Wells on 1st, 375 on 1st and 500 on 3rd at Blakeney Point, 400 at Sheringham on 1st and 450 on 6th at Yarmouth Cemeteries. A full account of this remarkable 'fall' will appear in an article in the *Norfolk Bird Report 1998*.

A small, but annual, spring passage is recorded at coastal sites from mid-March to early May. Birds showing characteristics of the race *rubecula*, caught for ringing, have been noted in mid-May with one as late as 22nd May 1996 at Weybourne. The highest counts in spring, of birds on passage, have been 30 at Sheringham on 1st May 1978 and 40 at Holme on 8th April 1996.

Over 12,000 Robins have been ringed since 1980 and several thousands in earlier years. These have included large numbers trapped on autumn migration at coastal ringing sites, with about 2,000 ringed in early October 1998 alone. Out of the total of 23 which has been recovered abroad, 18 were ringed in autumn (the majority in October) and the rest in April–May. The autumn-ringed birds, clearly of northern European origin, have been recovered later the same autumn in France (2) and Spain (3) and Algeria, in the winter months in The Netherlands, Spain (2), Morocco and Algeria, and in the following spring in The Netherlands, Germany (2) and Menorca. Others have been recovered the same autumn or winter in Cambridgeshire, Essex and Kent. Birds ringed on return migration in spring have been found in Germany (2), Belgium, Portugal and Spain. Other notable movements of autumn-ringed birds have involved recoveries in Poland in a subsequent autumn, on Fair Isle in the following spring and at Bodø in northern Norway, in mid-June. While those ringed abroad in autumn and found in Norfolk, have also confirmed their Scandinavian origin, with two each from Norway, Denmark and Sweden, as well as four from The Netherlands. In addition, one ringed on North Ronaldsay, Orkney on 29th September 1969 was found dead at East Runton on 2nd November. Locally-bred birds are generally sedentary but three juveniles ringed in June–July have been recovered as far away as Essex, Sussex and Cheshire.

*Moss Taylor*

# Thrush Nightingale                                   *Luscinia luscinia*

**A very rare vagrant; six records.**

The Thrush Nightingale is a central Palearctic species with a breeding range extending from southern Norway and Denmark, eastwards through central Europe to Siberia. It winters mostly in East Africa, south of the Equator.

The first county record was one trapped at Holme by Peter Clarke on 14th May 1977. This bird was not seen in the field before or after capture. The second was ten years later, a singing male, in dense privet at Holkham Meals on 24th May 1987. Typically, it mostly remained hidden from a frustrated audience of birdwatchers. A year later, a male at Blakeney Point on 15th–18th May 1988 responded instantly to a tape, which simplified identification. The species was recorded for the third consecutive year when another singing male appeared at Walsey Hills, Cley on 20th–22nd May 1989. There have been two subsequent records, both in the autumn of 1992 – a first-winter bird in Burnham Overy Dunes on 18th September and an extremely confiding individual on Gramborough Hill, Salthouse on 26th September.

*Peter Allard*

## Nightingale (Common Nightingale)     *Luscinia megarhynchos*

**A scarce summer visitor and very scarce passage migrant.**

The Nightingale breeds in the middle and lower-middle latitudes of the Western Palearctic, being widely distributed throughout the Mediterranean and temperate zones. A marked decline occurred in central Europe between 1830 and 1920, although its original status has subsequently been restored. The species migrates south-west in autumn, to winter in sub-Saharan Africa. In the British Isles it is confined as a breeding bird to England, breeding south-east of a line from the Humber to the Severn, being most abundant in Suffolk, Kent and Sussex (New Atlas). A continuing decline in numbers and a contraction of its range has been taking place in England since about 1910 (Marchant *et al.* 1990).

Stevenson described the Nightingale as being very local and 'not visiting us in large numbers', although in certain localities it was much more numerous than in former years. He continued:

> The immediate vicinity of Norwich is particularly rich in their 'favourite haunts' and for some weeks on their first arrival they may be heard, both day and night, on the Ipswich, Newmarket and Unthank roads. [The Nightingale] is by no means a shy bird, at least on its first arrival, but sings fearlessly throughout the day in the most exposed situations.

This appears to indicate a change in behaviour, as well as distribution, compared with today. By the 1920s, with the exception of Thorpe, all of the breeding localities mentioned by Stevenson in the vicinity of Norwich had been deserted, and by then the stronghold was in Breckland; it was also fairly abundant within an area a mile or two inland from the coast between Cromer and Cley (Riviere). This situation still holds true today. The most recent record of a Nightingale in the centre of Norwich concerned one found dead on 26th May 1959, which was probably the one heard singing earlier in the month near Chapelfield Gardens.

In Norfolk, Nightingales favour areas of dense vegetation in open woodland and around overgrown gravel pits, blackthorn thickets on heaths and commons, and young conifer plantations; coppiced woodland not being used to the same extent as it is in other parts of south-east England. As elsewhere, numbers have continued to decline since the 1950s. A survey by Peter Clarke in 1953 of the Sheringham, Kelling, Weybourne, Salthouse and Cley parishes located 50 singing birds, and a similar number was found in 1958, up to 5km inland, between West Runton and Blakeney. Although the breeding population on Salthouse Heath has remained fairly constant with up to ten pairs, very few others are now found in north Norfolk. A full county breeding survey, undertaken as part of the national BTO Nightingale Survey in 1980, located 345 singing males, with the greatest density in west Norfolk, to the west and south-west of Swaffham, and in central Norfolk around the western approaches to Norwich. The highest counts were of 25 at Foulden Common, 16 at Narborough Broadmoor and 10 at Muckleburgh Hill, Weybourne. Although its range within the county remained well scattered, it was recorded in only 15% of the tetrads covered during fieldwork for the Norfolk Atlas. During the 1990s, the main concentrations have included up to 22 in the Stanford Training Area and twelve at Pentney Gravel Pits with a maximum of about only 80 singing males reported in the county in 1994. The decline in the Brecks is believed to be due to the ever increasing numbers of muntjac in the area (P. Dolton *in litt.*). The national BTO Nightingale Survey planned for 1999 should help to elucidate the current status of the species in the county.

The first Nightingales of the spring are almost invariably heard singing in the third week of April and most territories have become occupied by early May. The earliest records have been on 10th April with birds in song at Cley in 1960, at Salthouse Heath in 1961 and 1998, and three in the Brecks in 1993. Until the 1980s, very few Nightingales had been recorded on spring migration at the coast, but as the number of observers and ringers has increased, so has the number of records of spring migrants, and one or two are now found annually. The main period of passage runs from the third week of April to mid-May, but apart from two at Holme on 24th April 1987, all records have involved single birds.

The first record of an autumn migrant involved one taken in the bushes on Cley beach during a heavy fall of Wheatears, Redstarts and Pied Flycatchers on 30th September 1899. It was taken to Pashley, the well-known Cley taxidermist, who commented that '[it was] the first I have had from the bushes' (Pashley 1925). In 1957, three were recorded in autumn – at Ditchingham on 6th–15th September, at Belaugh where one entered a house on the night of 21st September and at Blakeney Point on 24th September. But apart from these occurrences, the species remained a very rare autumn migrant until the mid-1970s since when it has been recorded almost annually. Single birds on passage have been seen between 4th August and 24th September, with the exception of singles at Welney on 20th July 1986 after a period of heavy rain, at Holme on 20th July 1997, at Wells on 10th–11th October 1992 and an exceptionally late bird at Blakeney Point on 17th–18th November 1984.

Four Norfolk-ringed Nightingales have been recovered – of two nestlings ringed from the same brood at Weybourne on 10th June 1951 one was controlled at Salthouse on 12th August and the other was shot in the Algarve at Portimao, Portugal on 25th September 1952. A juvenile ringed at South Lopham Fen on 20th July 1993 was controlled near Elsingham, Suffolk on 15th May 1994, and one ringed near Didlington on 26th July 1997 was controlled at Landguard Point, Suffolk a month later. Three ringed outside the county have been found in Norfolk, by coincidence all in the April after ringing – an adult ringed at Peakirk, Cambridgeshire in June 1961 was found near Attleborough, another adult ringed at Dartford, Kent on 12th August 1983 was recovered at Walcott and one ringed at Portland Bill, Dorset on 22nd August 1993 was controlled at Garboldisham.

*Moss Taylor*

| **Bluethroat** | HoLME. N.O.A. 24·5·1987. | *Luscinia svecica* |

A very scarce passage migrant, nowadays mainly in spring.

Bluethroat
(Bryan Bland)

The Bluethroat breeds from the Arctic and boreal upper latitudes to temperate and steppe middle latitudes and montane regions of the Western Palearctic. It bred in Scotland in 1968, 1985 and 1995. The Red-spotted Bluethroat, the nominate northern race *L. s. svecica*, breeds in Fennoscandia east across northern Russia. The White-spotted Bluethroat of the race *L. s. cyanecula* is principally a central European breeding bird. Western Palearctic populations have an extensive wintering area extending from the Mediterranean basin south to the northern Afrotropics and east to the Indian subcontinent.

The 'Blue-throated Warbler', as it was known by Stevenson, was added to the county list when a male was picked up dead on the beach at Yarmouth on 21st September 1841. An exceptionally large 'immigration' was noted in September 1884, with 80 seen between Blakeney Point and Cley by Dr Power. Since then, Riviere noted that it had become a fairly regular autumn and occasional spring passage migrant. Pashley (1925) included one on 20th November 1900 at Cley, which remains the latest date for the county. Seago (1967) stated that the species was a scarce autumn drift migrant with occasional records in the spring. More recent publications have noted the surprising changes in the pattern of Bluethroat passage, which are most likely to be climatic. Blocking anticyclones in spring, bringing Fennoscandian migrants, are apparently occurring more frequently, such as in 1970, 1985 and 1987. During these three years a total of 90 springtime Bluethroats was reported in Norfolk. The autumn decline has been well documented with, for instance, only one record between 1979 and 26th October 1985 even though there had been increased observer coverage and awareness. A likely factor behind this autumnal pattern is a lack of easterlies during the main southerly passage of Scandinavian Bluethroats in late August and early September.

All the spring records relate to the Scandinavian Red-spotted race *svecica* apart from six White-spotted Bluethroats *cyanecula* – males at Sheringham on 30th April 1906 (on display in the Castle Museum, Norwich), at Salthouse on 7th–8th April 1930, at Brinton on 18th April 1954, at Waxham on 17th April 1988, at Cley on 28th March 1998 and one in song at Hickling Broad on 21st and 23rd May 1998. Single Bluethroats at Sheringham on 20th April 1994 and at Snettisham on 17th April 1996 were probably of the White-spotted race, due to the dates of occurrence, but as both were females racial identity could not be established. The earliest spring date for *svecica* is 6th May with the passage continuing into early June, apart from singles on 16th, 25th and 26th June and on 5th–13th July. The peak passage period is between 11th and 26th May. The *Norfolk Bird Report 1970* commented that it had been an unusual spring with ten Bluethroats being recorded from 9th to 18th May. From that year on, spring records became more notice-able with 1985 and 1987 being exceptional. In 1985, an extraordinary and unprecedented arrival of 54 birds occurred, the majority being males, several of which were heard singing. The passage started on 8th May and birds were present until 22nd. Passage peaked on 14th May when a total of 32 was known to be present in the county, including 14 on Blakeney Point and eleven at Holme. Another excellent, but smaller, passage occurred in late May 1987 with over half the records involving females. Birds were present from 22nd to 27th May with a total of 18 birds on 23rd and 17 on 24th, as before the majority were at Blakeney Point and Holme. Since then numbers have varied, from years with only single spring records to others with good daily counts, such as nine on 10th May 1993 and ten on 21st May 1994. On the unlikely date of 1st July 1992 a male Red-spotted Bluethroat appeared at Holme where it remained until 13th August, during which time it underwent a complete moult. Another, a female, was present at Salthouse on 22nd–23rd July 1997 and was one of only two records that year, both at the same locality.

Autumn passage usually commences in the third week of August and continues to the third week of October. Most records are along the north Norfolk coast notably in the Cley/Blakeney Point area but also at Holme, Scolt Head and Thornham. There are a few records from the east coast and in autumn 1968, the last year light-vessel crews off the Norfolk coast kept bird diaries, a casualty recovered on the Dudgeon was identified as a Bluethroat at the British Museum. One was observed inland at the University of East Anglia on 12th October 1977. Most autumn records have involved one to three birds, although seven were present in the Cley/Blakeney area on 10th–18th September 1956 and eight in the same area on 20th September 1960. In 1969 a record total for the month of September involved at least 30 birds. For the second consecutive year there were more records in spring than autumn in 1975 and by 1979 it had become an increasingly rare passage migrant especially in the autumn. Surprisingly, fewer than 20 Bluethroats have been ringed in Norfolk, of which only three have been trapped since 1983.

*B. D. Harding*

# Red-flanked Bluetail                                            *Tarsiger cyanurus*

**A very rare vagrant; one record.**

The breeding range of the Red-flanked Bluetail extends from northern Russia eastwards through Siberia to Japan, and the species winters in south-east Asia from India to Taiwan. A few pairs now breed annually in Finland following a westward expansion since the early 1950s. Single pairs bred in Estonia in 1980 and in Sweden in 1996, with other males holding territory. The northern populations are long-distance mi-grants.

This is a charismatic species that regular observers working coastal sites in Norfolk dream of finding. The dream came true for the writer on 18th October 1994 in Yarmouth Cemeteries where a female or first-winter male became a long-awaited first for Norfolk. The bird remained until 20th and provided excellent views during its three-day stay (Allard 1994, 1995). This record constituted the 14th British sighting and was followed by another in Suffolk six days later.

*Peter Allard*

## Black Redstart BREYDON WATER. 20·9·1993. *Phoenicurus ochruros*

**A very scarce breeder and scarce passage migrant; rare in winter.**

Black Redstart
(*Norman Arlott*)

In the Western Palearctic the Black Redstart breeds throughout Europe from England, southern Sweden, the Baltic shores and southern Russia to the Mediterranean and Black Seas. Other races occur in eastern Europe and Asia. In winter, it is primarily found in western and southern Europe, North Africa and southern Asia. England was colonised in the 20th century, the first nests being found in Sussex in 1923 and from 1926 it nested in London. Breeding has been regular since 1939, initially on bombed sites in London and Dover and then elsewhere. It bred in Suffolk at Ipswich for the first time in 1938 and Lowestoft was colonised in 1943.

Until 1848 the Black Redstart had not been recognised in the county but on 31st October of that year an adult female was shot on Yarmouth Denes. Two others were obtained in a similar way in November the following year. Stevenson mentioned no others, although by the end of the 19th century a number had been obtained on the coast, mostly in late autumn.

In 1950 Black Redstarts nested in the county for the first time with two pairs in Yarmouth in bombed buildings and a third pair at Gorleston in an air-raid shelter. At the latter site, five old nests suggested breeding had taken place here in at least two previous years. The first nest found at Yarmouth on 4th May was in a hole on a wall in Row 49, just west of the Market Place. Two young eventually left the nest on 29th May having been ringed. One or two nests were found at Yarmouth in most years between 1951 and 1963, mainly in bombed areas or, increasingly, in industrial sites. In 1964 a survey by the writer found eight singing males in Yarmouth and Gorleston; successful breeding took place at two sites and two other pairs probably bred. Nesting continued in the town and there were ten singing males in both 1969 and 1970. Four pairs bred successfully in 1969, a fifth failed at the egg stage and two other pairs may have nested. In 1970 five pairs reared young.

Nationally 1973 was good for Black Redstarts and the writer again organised a Yarmouth survey. By mid-June, a remarkable total of 18 singing males was located, twelve of which were first-summer birds. Breeding was confirmed for 17 pairs and a total of at least 50 young fledged. Birds were present at one site until 28th October. Since 1975, singing males and breeding pairs at Yarmouth have varied in number, with ten singing in 1976 and 16 in 1985 (including two at Gorleston). Since 1990 the average number has declined to between two and four. This decline has been mirrored elsewhere in the country. All recent breeding records have been concentrated in the South Denes industrial areas and the demolition of Yarmouth Power Station (a regular breeding site) in 1997 was a considerable setback.

At Norwich, singing males were first noted in 1953, a pair was present in 1956 and breeding proved in 1959. The following year two pairs bred. Between 1957 and 1997, singing males were present most years, except between 1964 and 1971, with three singing again by 1975. Breeding was proven on nine occasions. At Cromer singing males were first noted in 1951 with the first breeding there in 1958 and on five subsequent occasions, the last being in 1986. Breeding has also been recorded at Hellesdon Mill (1972), Sheringham (1973) and Wissington Beet Factory (1974 and 1988). Weybourne Camp was occupied between 1977 and 1980, breeding being proved in 1978 and 1980. A pair bred at Bacton in 1978. King's Lynn was colonised in 1983 and breeding occurred for four years with from one to two singing males in 1992–94. Additionally, a pair bred at King's Lynn Beet Factory in both 1987 and 1988. An expansion of the population in the mid-1980s (notably 1985) saw further breeding recorded at Thetford (1985–88), Hunstanton (1985 and 1986), Heacham (1986), Cantley Beet Factory (1985–87), Salthouse (1986) and North Walsham (1987). Further pairs may have bred at both Caister and West Runton in 1985. The only new site in recent years was Snetterton in 1995.

Breeding sites have been varied and have included beet storage silos, old garages, power stations, derelict buildings, railway stations, seafront hotels and timber yards. The first Norwich nest was found in the broken grating of a house almost in the city centre and another pair later reared young at a height of 30m in a partly completed office block in St Stephen's Street. A nest at Cromer was in a ruined building on the seafront. Yarmouth nest-sites have included the top of a transformer close to the bandstand at the Marina and on a ledge of a locum at a maltings. Male Black Redstarts regularly use tall buildings as song posts. In Yarmouth the highest was on the top of the boiler house at the former power station, 45m in height; another sang regularly from the top of the 34m high Town Hall weather vane. In the centre of Norwich lofty song-posts included a Surrey Street flagpole and the jib of a nearby giant crane, both over 40m high.

In the 20th century the Black Redstart has become a regular early spring and late autumn passage migrant in small numbers. It is often one of the first spring migrants to be seen, appearing in mid-March. Spring passage is usually more marked; in 1993, about 100 were reported along the coast between 12th March and 29th May, whilst the total was 118 in 1994. Double figures at any one locality are unusual but occasionally occur, for example, twelve at Blakeney Point on 18th April 1989, 16 at Sheringham on 27th March 1959 and a remarkable 23 at Winterton on 13th April 1996. Autumn passage is less and usually peaks in late October or occasionally early November. About 90 were estimated along the coast in autumn 1994. Peak counts have included ten at Blakeney Point on 19th October 1987 and ten at Yarmouth on the same date the following year. Inland passage records are not unusual; three were together at Colney Gravel Pits on 3rd April 1986.

Both Riviere and Seago did not differentiate between passage birds and winter visitors and noted both in small numbers. Since 1953 an analysis of winter records (the December–February period) reveals that between 1953 and 1971 only six winter sightings were recorded, but since 1972 single birds, or occasionally two, have been reported at several sites in most years. Coastal areas, especially Heacham/Hunstanton and Sheringham/Cromer, are particularly favoured. One at Holme on 8th February 1997 may have been an early migrant a month earlier than the main arrivals. Inland winter sightings are very unusual, but birds have been recorded at Norwich on three occasions, and once at Martham, South Creake, Mundford and Cantley Beet Factory.

A male showing the characteristics of the Iberian/Moroccan race *P. o. aterrimus* was present at Burnham Overy Dunes on 6th June 1992.

About 100 Black Redstarts have been ringed in Norfolk but there have been no recoveries.

*Peter Allard*

## Redstart (Common Redstart)        *Phoenicurus phoenicurus*

**A scarce and localised summer visitor, and fairly common passage migrant.**

The Redstart breeds widely across Europe, except for Ireland, the southern part of the Iberian Peninsula and Greece. The wintering area is sub-Saharan Africa. A recent decline, noted in several areas in north-west Europe, was originally attributed to drought in the Sahel region but it is more likely that a combination of factors was responsible including habitat changes, increased interspecific competition and human activities. In the British Isles, the main centres of population are in Wales, the northern Pennines and the Lake District with lower densities in the wooded areas of Scotland. A decline was noted in the last 20 years of the 19th century. This was possibly due to removal of dead trees which were used for nest sites. Since the Redstart does not excavate its own nest hole, but has to utilise those already present, it can be particularly susceptible to this change. There is a sporadic distribution across East Anglia and the Midlands with a considerable decrease noted between the two BTO Breeding Atlases.

Stevenson described it as a common summer visitor but without any particular reference to numbers or distribution. He noted it as arriving in early April and occasionally from the middle of March. He found birds breeding in the walled gardens of both town and country areas. Gurney and Fisher (1846) wrote of it as being abundant and later Gurney (1881–1912) described the parish of Keswick as being 'as usual full of Redstarts' in the summer of 1892. So it can be assumed to have been abundant and widespread at that time.

In the early part of the 20th century there were annual variations in breeding numbers but the general trend was one of decline. There was a considerable influx in the spring of 1903 with many more staying to breed than in any of the previous 20 years. However, Riviere described it as becoming exceedingly scarce between 1910 and 1930. By 1916 it had disappeared from east Norfolk, and to the north-east of Norwich the only breeding records were from Thorpe in 1918, Keswick in 1923 and perhaps again in 1927, at Taverham in at least 1927 and possibly in the years before. In north Norfolk one pair bred at Kelling in 1923 and four pairs in 1928. In the west of the county, there were three pairs at Middleton in 1916 and up to ten pairs around South Wootton. Throughout this time, pairs were scattered across the south-west of the county with Castle Acre being the stronghold.

More recently in the 1960s the main concentration was in the oak woods of the Stanford Training Area. Breeding was also noted in the north in an area bounded by Glandford, Felbrigg and Holt, as well as in the wooded estates of Melton Constable, Swanton Novers and Felthorpe. There was a concentration in west Norfolk between Leziate and Dersingham.

Throughout the 1970s there was a contraction in both range and numbers, especially in west Norfolk. The total of males singing and holding territory in the county did not exceed 20 birds in any one year. The only sites that held birds in successive seasons were Felbrigg, where eleven singing males were present in 1978 (following a spring characterised by persistent easterly winds) and at other localities along the Cromer to Holt Ridge, and also Weeting where up to six pairs bred. By the time of the Norfolk Atlas (1980–85), the population was concentrated in the Brecks and there were only three instances of confirmed breeding elsewhere in the county – at Sandringham, Gunthorpe and Felthorpe.

There have been signs of an improvement in the last ten years; the numbers recorded in the Stanford Training Area have increased with 25–30 pairs in 1992, about 55 singing males in 1994 and 75 in both 1996 and 1997. As there were other suitable areas that could not be visited in 1996 the total could have been nearer 85–90 birds. Some of this increase is due to more thorough surveying, so the actual growth of the breeding population cannot be accurately assessed. Birds are found in oak woods and stands, in hedge lines with hawthorn predominant and also in pines. Other Breckland localities are Brettenham, East Wretham Heath and Thetford Warren. Occasional pairs are found in Thetford Forest either in mature stands of mixed trees that have not been felled but left for environmental areas or in recently cut down compartments with nests in the lines of stumps and roots that are dragged up into lines prior to replanting.

The most recent breeding records in west Norfolk have been single pairs at Roydon Common in 1990 and at Sandringham in 1991. In the north, singing males are recorded almost annually from Sheringham Park where one pair bred successfully in 1997 and two pairs in 1998. Other localities to have hosted singing birds in at least one summer since 1990, but not regularly, have been West Acre, Narborough, Swanton Novers, Briston, Kelling and Blickling.

The first spring arrivals are usually in mid-April. There have been two March records at Paston on 27th March 1993 and Itteringham on 30th March 1993. Passage continues to the end of May, or even early June. Numbers are invariably small with maximum counts of 20 at Holme on 15th May 1985 and 25 at Blakeney Point on 11th May 1993. Autumn passage normally commences in mid-August and continues until early October. A few stragglers are occasionally recorded in late October and the latest dates have been 3rd November 1993 at Wells, 6th November 1984 at Blakeney Point, and 11th November 1983 and 18th November 1977 both at Holme.

The Redstart is a classic 'fall' migrant and given the ideal conditions which are associated with an anticyclone centred over Scandinavia and a low pressure system with its weather fronts moving north into the southern North Sea, large numbers can appear along the Norfolk coast. Such conditions have occurred on a number of occasions. In 1965 the onset of heavy rain during the morning of 3rd September produced a 'fall' centred on the north Suffolk coast but an estimated 2,000 were in the parks, gardens and cemeteries of Yarmouth and Gorleston, where many became road casualties. On the following day, a conservative estimate of 1,000–1,500 was made at Winterton North Dunes. Elsewhere around the coast over 100 arrived at Holme in 30 minutes, and there were 200 on Blakeney Point, 500 in the Cley area and hundreds at Horsey. An influx of Scandinavian migrants on 16th–17th September 1968 involved hundreds perhaps thousands of Redstarts in the Cley area. Amongst the many that must have moved inland were eight at Norwich Water Works on 18th. Three did not make it to the coast and were taken by a Great Grey Shrike on the Inner Dowsing light-vessel. Between 13th and 17th September 1993, maximum counts included 200 at Holme, 100 at Wells East Hills, 600 between Stiffkey and Overy Dunes, 130 at Blakeney Point and 100 at Sheringham.

Finally, September 1995 produced the biggest 'fall' since 1965 and certainly the best documented one with counts from all around the Norfolk coastline The main arrival was at midday on 18th September. The highest counts were 550 at Holme, 230 at Thornham, 500 between Burnham Overy and Holkham, 300 each at Wells and Wells East Hills, 400 at Blakeney Point, 700 at Sheringham, 200 at Mundesley and 100 at Yarmouth. The overall number reaching the coast of Norfolk must have been in excess of 5,000.

Birds showing the characteristics of the eastern race *P. p. samamiscus*, with white wing patches, have appeared in the county on five occasions – an adult male in summer plumage at Heacham on 26th October 1975, a first-winter male at Holkham Meals on 12th September 1989, one at Sheringham Cemetery on 24th October 1994, at Mundesley on 13th September 1995 and at Yarmouth Cemeteries on 6th October 1998.

Over 1,000 Redstarts have been ringed in Norfolk, seven of which have been recovered abroad. Two ringed in spring and two in autumn have been found in autumn in Spain (2) and Portugal (2), one of which was part of the 'fall' of 1995 – ringed at Weybourne on 19th September it was found dead near Madrid six days later, indicating the speed with which these drift migrants moved south. One ringed at Titchwell in September 1974 was recovered at Bremerhaven, Germany the following May, while one ringed at Sheringham in autumn 1981 was found at Casablanca, Morocco in April 1983. The only 'fall' migrant to be recovered back in its natal area was one ringed at Holme on 25th September 1965 and found in summer 1972 at Bonskaret, Sweden (the only British-ringed Redstart to be recovered in Sweden). Three foreign-ringed Redstarts have been found dead in Norfolk – one ringed in The Netherlands on 14th September 1988 at Colby eight days later, one ringed in Denmark on 1st September 1991 at Caister four weeks later and one ringed on Helgoland, Germany on 1st September 1992 at Crostwight the following May. In addition, one ringed at Revtangen, Norway on 10th September 1968 was found on the Lady Edwina supply-vessel at sea off Yarmouth four days later. An even quicker recovery involved one ringed at Beechamwell on 11th October 1987 which was found dead at Petts Wood, Greater London the following day. Finally, one ringed at Weybourne in May 1990 was recovered at Chippenham, Wiltshire in April 1994.

*Peter Dolton*

# Whinchat                                                                *Saxicola rubetra*

**A fairly common passage migrant and formerly a very scarce summer visitor which last bred in 1992; very rare in winter.**

The Whinchat breeds in the boreal and temperate areas of the Western Palearctic. It is absent or has a scattered distribution in Mediterranean countries. It is a trans-Saharan migrant but with occasional winter records from south-west Europe. In Britain, it is widespread in upland areas utilising open grassland, bracken, gorse, heather and mixed low vegetation. In lowland Britain it has undergone a long-term and widespread decline since the 1930s. This is due to areas of marginal land such as railway embankments, roadside verges and areas of rough cultivation diminishing. Between the two BTO Breeding Atlases, Whinchats almost totally disappeared as a breeding species from the English Midlands, the Thames Valley and the coastal fringes of Kent and Suffolk. During the same period, the upland population remained unaffected and could possibly have increased (68–72 BTO Atlas, New Atlas).

In the 19th century the Whinchat was common throughout the county, breeding on the heaths and sand hills. It also occupied damper areas with pairs breeding at Surlingham Marsh. In 1864, there were at least 14 nests on the gorse of Mousehold Heath. It was described as common on the North Denes of Yarmouth prior to 1834. The Pagets (1834) noted that it preferred the more sheltered gorse clumps nearer to the cultivated land but had ceased to breed there by the end of the 19th century. Its association in the county with gorse gave rise to its local name of 'Furr Chuck'. By 1930, the Whinchat was already becoming restricted to the heaths and warrens of the south-west of the county. At this time, the young conifer plantations of Thetford Forest would have brought about an increase in the available habitat though this would have been short-lived as the trees grew towards maturity.

At the time of the 68–72 BTO Atlas, Whinchats were found in the Fens, in the extreme south-west of the county and the Ouse Washes, as well as in the Brecks. Birds were also present in six 10km squares between Swaffham and Dersingham and four along the north coast from Holme to Sheringham. The only occupied square in the east of the county – although there was no proof of breeding – centred on Yarmouth. During the 1970s Whinchats deserted the Fens and the Ouse Washes. In this period, the soil from the banks of land drains was removed to raise the banks of the tidal rivers. This removed the scrub layer of vegetation and replaced it with grass, hence the habitat became unsuitable.

Whinchat
(Norman Arlott)

Throughout the 1970s there were breeding records of up to seven pairs on the Stanford Training Area and the adjacent heathlands of Bridgham and Brettenham. In 1972, seven pairs were noted between Stanford and Sturston but there were no records from these areas in 1973 and 1974. Away from the Brecks, a pair bred at Beeston Common in 1973 and at Winterton in 1978. In 1980, pairs were present at nine separate sites including Leziate and Gooderstone but these numbers were not to be repeated and there was a gradual decrease throughout the decade. It could be that coverage of some of these sites might not have been complete each year but this would not have altered the overall trend.

Isolated pairs continued to be found away from the Brecks – a pair summered at Happisburgh in 1990 and a pair bred at Horsey in 1991 and 1992. This constituted the last confirmed breeding in the county. Birds summered in the Stanford Training Area in 1993 at Smoker's Hole and Tottington but there was no evidence of breeding. Since then the only records from there were of migrants on single dates in spring. The reason for the demise of this species at this locality in recent years is unclear as the habitat has not undergone any reduction or change. There is still a population just across the county border in Suffolk that has not declined to such an extent.

In recent times, a singing male was present in May 1994 at Kelling Water Meadows. Intriguingly a juvenile was present there in July but it was not known whether these two records were related. Likewise in 1995 the only July record was of an adult and a juvenile at Breydon, again without any other evidence indicating that breeding had occurred locally. There were no mid-summer records in 1996–98 and this species would appear to have been lost as a breeding bird in Norfolk.

As a migrant, the first birds are seen in the last ten days of April. Between 1990 and 1998, the first arrival has been between 20th and 23rd April in eight of the nine years. The earliest ever have been on 2nd April 1975 near Brandon and 12th April 1958 at Blakeney. Spring passage continues through to the first week of June at localities around the coast. A few are recorded inland especially in the Broads and at Welney. Numbers are invariably in single figures with the only totals above ten being 32 at Holkham on 22nd May 1991, twelve at Holkham on 13th May 1992, 15 at Blakeney Point on 11th May and 15 at Holme on 13th May both in 1993, and 14 at Holme on 8th May 1998.

Autumn passage starts in early August with the largest numbers being seen in September. The highest autumn counts in recent years have been at Blakeney Point with 60 on 12th September 1989 and 50 on 17th–19th September 1992, and 60 at Sheringham on 13th–14th September 1993. Notable maxima elsewhere have included 35 at Holme, 30 at Scolt Head, 35 at Mundesley and 34 in the Sea Palling to Horsey area. Birds are present into October with the last stragglers generally recorded in November. The latest records have been on 28th November 1983 at Rackheath and on 29th November 1982 at Holkham, with an exceptional record of one at Fakenham on 16th December 1994. The only other winter record concerned a male at Hethersett in January 1864 (Stevenson).

Larger numbers are recorded in autumn than in spring, with up to 50 at a single locality when 'falls' of migrants have occurred. It was estimated that about 500 were seen in the county in autumn 1994. The highest counts have been 60 at Blakeney Point on 18th September 1992 and at Sheringham on 13th September 1993. Small numbers are recorded inland at a variety of sites.

Over 200 Whinchats have been ringed in Norfolk but only one has been recovered – a spring migrant ringed at Weybourne on 18th May 1995 was found dead at Echt, The Netherlands on 16th May 1996, the first British-ringed Whinchat to be recovered in the Low Countries.

*Peter Dolton*

# Stonechat

## *Saxicola torquata*

**A very scarce breeder, and scarce passage migrant and winter visitor.**

The Stonechat breeds across western, central and southern Europe. It is absent from Fennoscandia (except for parts of Norway) and the Baltic States. Birds are resident in the Iberian Peninsula, France, Italy and Greece but are summer visitors to Germany and further eastwards. The two eastern races *S. t. maura* and *S. t. stejnegeri*, known as Siberian Stonechat, breed from north-eastern Russia eastwards. In the British Isles, the breeding distribution of the Stonechat is biased towards the west where it occupies both upland and coastal areas. Parslow (1973) suggested that hard winters in the 1940s together with habitat loss through land-use changes had caused the range to contract. The New Atlas showed a further retreat from the east coast with few breeding between Norfolk and Aberdeenshire. There has also been a decline in numbers in its traditional stronghold areas in the west. Its wintering distribution mirrors the breeding range closely though birds move away from upland areas.

Stevenson recorded it as a spring visitor to Norfolk and a frequent breeding bird in the 'wild open districts that were covered in furze', as well as grassy cliff-tops mixed in with gorse. A small number of birds were noted in winter. As Stevenson did not give any particular localities, it could be assumed that Stonechats were widespread in the county. The Pagets (1834) quoted Stonechats as being common on the North Denes, Yarmouth. Patterson (1905) stated that some breeding birds would linger on until late in the year and would stay if the winter was mild. Nesting was noted on common land between Scratby and Winterton until 1938. Riviere's statement of the distribution is very similar to that given by Stevenson. As a passage migrant, he noted it was commoner in autumn than spring. Clarke (1937) noted that it bred in the gorse clumps of Barnham Common. A decline from the late 1930s meant that by 1940 there were few breeding sites occupied other than in the Brecks. There the hard winters of the 1940s and habitat loss, as heaths were ploughed and forestry plantations grew up, caused the demise of the Breckland population. None was seen there in the breeding season from 1946 until 1961.

Seago (1967) noted that it bred again in the county from 1958 onwards but never more than five pairs. During the 1960s breeding numbers varied from one pair in 1963 (at Brettenham Heath) to ten pairs in 1967. From 1966 onwards the coastal belt from Waxham to Hemsby has held a breeding population of up to ten pairs and a few pairs have bred elsewhere within the county. In addition to those sites already mentioned Stonechats also bred in the 1960s and 1970s at Wolferton on the Wash, at Bridgham Heath, East Wretham, Frog Hall and Grimes Graves in the Brecks, at Holme, Blakeney/Morston, Salthouse and Kelling Heaths, Weybourne and Sheringham in the north, at Horsford Heath in central Norfolk and at Caister Golf Course and Breydon in the east. The Norfolk Atlas (1980–85) showed confirmed breeding in only three areas – Breckland, Salthouse and Kelling Heaths, and the east coast. Since then there has been a contraction of the range with very few pairs now breeding away from the east coast. In 1996 four pairs bred at Winterton and single pairs inland at Smokers Hole (Stanford Training Area) and Hickling, with two pairs present at Horsey in April and May. The following year five pairs bred in east Norfolk and one pair at Kelling Heath, with a pair on territory at Heacham north beach from May to August but no young were seen. In 1998, a pair raised three broods at Santon Downham, single pairs bred on Salthouse and Kelling Heaths, and four pairs bred in east Norfolk.

Autumn passage is mainly recorded at coastal localities in September and October. Numbers are smaller than for other chats and the species is not numerous in falls of migrants. The largest group noted was of ten at Happisburgh on 27th October 1978. The species was most abundant in the autumn of 1993 when 70 were reported, including an arrival of 15 birds scattered around the county on 30th September.

There is a small wintering population largely in coastal areas but with some in the Broads and Brecks. The number present in any winter rarely exceeds 30. Wintering birds depart by mid-April. Spring passage occurs from late February peaking in March, involving for instance a total of 20 birds in 1992 and 40 the following year. However, an unprecedented influx occurred in 1994 with a total of perhaps 200 birds involved. The first wave was on 27th February with 75 between Holme and Sheringham including eight at Holme, twelve at Wells, 23 at Cley and nine at Sheringham. New arrivals continued to be reported until 20th March with twelve at Stiffkey on 6th March, and on the following day 14 at Holme and from seven to nine at Titchwell/Brancaster, Burnham Norton, Burnham Overy and Cley, with 16 at Holme on 20th March. Throughout this period very few were reported on the east Norfolk coast or inland, although exceptional numbers were also recorded in Suffolk and Lincolnshire, as well as in north-east and north-west England (Rooney 1994b).

The Siberian Stonechat is a rare, but annual, vagrant to the British Isles mostly in autumn. The first was recorded in 1913. All the Norfolk records relate to the races *maura* or *stejnegeri*, with the majority almost certainly being the former, which breeds over much of northern Asia. The first county record was a male identified by Richard Richardson at Cley on 6th May 1972. It showed strong characteristics of the race *stejnegeri* and was only the sixth British record of a Siberian Stonechat and the first in spring. The second was an immature at Snettisham on 4th November 1974. Since then it has been noted almost annually with a current county total of 40 records, of which seven have been in spring. All these spring records have related to males and have occurred between 4th May and 9th June. With the exception of one at Mundesley in 1998, all have been found between Holme and Cromer. Of the 33 autumn occurrences, most arrivals have appeared between late September and mid-October, the earliest being one at Cromer on 4th September 1994. The highest annual total has been eleven in 1991, which included a multiple arrival of five at Blakeney Point on 29th September, three of which remained the following day. Almost all of the records are from the north coast between Holme and Sheringham, including the high total of twelve at Blakeney Point. Elsewhere, singles have been recorded at Happisburgh, Paston, Winterton and Breydon. Winter records are distinctly unusual. One, an immature first seen at Winterton Dunes on 9th November 1985, remained until 5th February 1986 disappearing only at the onset of deep snow. One at Stiffkey on 4th–16th October 1990 showed some characteristics of the race *S. t. variegata* which breeds in the Caspian Sea region. A Stonechat shot at Cley on 2nd September 1904 was long-accepted as the first British record of Siberian Stonechat. However, the specimen, held at the Castle Museum, Norwich, was re-examined in the mid-1970s when it was decided that it was probably an old male of one of the two western European races, and it was subsequently removed from the British List in 1977.

Less than 100 Stonechats have been ringed in the county and only one distant recovery has been reported – a first-autumn bird ringed at Happisburgh in October 1974 was controlled in Yorkshire in February 1976.

*Peter Dolton*

## Isabelline Wheatear                                   *Oenanthe isabellina*

**A very rare vagrant; one record.**

The Isabelline Wheatear is a steppe species breeding from southern Russia, southern Greece and the Middle East, eastwards to Mongolia and Tibet; it winters in the Sahel zone of East Africa, in Arabia, Pakistan and the southern parts of its breeding range.

An extreme vagrant to the British Isles, one found by the writer spent the whole day at Winterton North Dunes on 28th May 1977, favouring a recently burnt area of sandy heather and gorse. Its arrival coincided with a very warm spell with south-easterly winds. There had been only one previous British record – shot in Cumbria in 1887. Recently, however, an upsurge in occurrences has taken place and although over ten have been seen in the British Isles, the Norfolk record remains the only spring sighting.

*Peter Allard*

## Wheatear (Northern Wheatear)   TITCH WELL. 19-9-1993.   *Oenanthe oenanthe*

**A very scarce and decreasing breeding summer visitor and common passage migrant; very rare in winter.**

The nominate race of the Wheatear *O. o. oenanthe* breeds across much of Europe and central and northern Asia. The race known as the Greenland Wheatear *O. o. leucorhoa* breeds in Greenland, Iceland and northeast Canada and appears in Britain and Ireland as a passage migrant. All populations winter in sub-Saharan Africa. In the British Isles it is found commonly in the north and west. The prime Wheatear areas are the uplands above 300m. Breeding at lower altitudes used to be more widespread across southern and central England. However, in every English county south of Yorkshire and Lancashire there has been a decline which began in about 1900. The principal cause for this was the loss of suitable habitat – heaths lost to afforestation, downland being ploughed up for agriculture and urban spread. Myxomatosis in the 1950s reduced rabbit numbers resulting in the vegetation of downs and commons becoming too tall to be suitable. On one Suffolk heath, 40 pairs bred in 1954 prior to the outbreak of myxomatosis but none after 1957 (Pearson 1963). There is little evidence of long-term changes in the upland areas of Britain.

Stevenson knew the Wheatear as a common visitor to the open parts of the county 'its heaths, common lands, sandy hills by the sea coast and in the vicinity of gravel pits'. He mentioned it as being numerous along 'the extensive line of marram hills in the vicinity of Hunstanton'. Yarrell (1837–43) described Wheatears as being common on the warrens and that they were taken in nets from nests in deserted rabbit burrows. Sir Thomas Browne (1835–36) wrote that they made a good dish. In Norfolk, the Wheatear has also been known as the 'White Rump' and, showing its association with rabbits, the 'Coney Chuck'.

In the days of Riviere, the Wheatear was still described as abundant as a breeding species on the Brecks and warrens, with a few pairs on other inland heaths and the coast in the north-east of the county. The planting of Thetford Forest from the 1930s onwards reduced the available habitat. This was then followed in the 1950s by a reduction in rabbit numbers. So the population decreased and the number of occupied sites across the county was reduced. In the 1960s, the Stanford Training Area was the most important centre in The Brecks, while a few pairs were hanging on in coastal warrens in the north and north-west of the county.

By the time of the Norfolk Atlas (1980–85) breeding was only regular at Weeting and in the Stanford Training Area. The scattered distribution of proven breeding from other parts of the county was considered to be due to opportunistic late spring migrants that had found suitable habitat. Disused airfields were used at Salhouse and Sculthorpe, while other sites included Kelling Heath in 1977 and Weybourne in 1983 and 1984.

Wheatear
(*Gary Wright*)

In more recent years the numbers of birds breeding in the county has continued to fall. The stronghold at Weeting held over 30 pairs throughout the 1970s and 36 pairs in 1983. This decreased to 24 pairs in 1984, then to 20 in 1986 and the species was lost as a breeding bird at Weeting sometime prior to 1993. The cause of the decline cannot have been due to habitat loss or change, as this reserve has been specifically managed to produce the short-cropped grassland favoured by Wheatears.

In the same period the number of pairs on the Stanford Training Area has decreased substantially. There was poor breeding success in 1987 and 1988. In 1991 about 10,000 rabbits were culled to ensure more grass for grazing sheep. A total of 27 pairs was noted in 1992 at eight separate sites. One of these, Sturston Carr, held seven pairs in 1993 but none was present the following year. It cannot have been a coincidence that a large proportion of the rabbits in nearby warrens had been removed at this time to ensure a supply of grass for the sheep. Two pairs reappeared here in 1995 but have not done so since. An escaped ferret x polecat hybrid was observed taking six young rabbits from a burrow in 20 minutes in May 1997 and a group of six or seven were seen together on another piece of Breck. Their presence puts more pressure on the rabbit numbers. In 1996, only one brood of fledged Wheatears was seen on the entire

Stanford Training Area, while in 1997 the species was recorded at 15 sites but only two broods were seen. During the same period, the numbers breeding on the Suffolk Brecks have also decreased. Away from Breckland, recent breeding records have come from Cley and Burnham Overy in 1990, Bacton in 1991, Brancaster, Cley and Overstrand in 1993 and possibly at Paston in 1996. There would appear to be a bleak future for the Wheatear as a breeding species in Norfolk.

The Wheatear is one of the first spring migrants to arrive. In 1997 the first birds were exceptionally early with one on 2nd March at East Ruston, others at Bacton and Happisburgh (two) the following day and two at Horsey on 4th March. Otherwise the earliest arrivals have been on 5th March 1990 at Horsey and 5th March 1995 at Winterton, while in several years they have been on 6th March. In most years the first birds have been recorded by mid-March with records from many localities by the end of the month. Spring passage continues through to the end of May, with influxes of birds occurring during periods of fine weather particularly in April. The highest counts have been 75 on a burnt area of Salthouse Heath on 5th May 1982, 113 between Heacham and Hunstanton on 13th April 1984, 100 at Hunstanton and 70 at Holme on 3rd–6th April 1985, and 70 at Blakeney Point on 13th May 1985. In 1992, larger numbers than usual were recorded at many localities from 24th to 28th April with 70 at Holme, 65 at Holkham, 50 at Blakeney Point, 70 at Salthouse and 65 at Sheringham. The spring of 1997 was also characterised by a widespread arrival at the end of April, including more inland records of migrants than usual, the maximum counts being 110 at Sheringham on 25th April and 70 at Cromer Golf Course on 28th April.

For many years, birds of the Greenland race *leucorhoa* were considered to pass through Norfolk in small numbers in late April and May. However, ringing studies in north-west Norfolk since 1990, based on measurements, have shown that while birds on passage in March are exclusively *oenanthe*, those ringed in April have been equally divided between the two races. Birds of the race *leucorhoa* appear from mid-month, the earliest being on 4th April, while in May *leucorhoa* outnumbers *oenanthe* (Middleton 1996). Similar findings have been made in a smaller-scale ringing study at Weybourne. Up until 1998 maximum counts of birds considered to be *leucorhoa* in the field had included eight at Winterton on 2nd May 1992, ten at Burnham Overy Dunes on 28th May 1996 and eleven at Hopton Point (Stanford Training Area) on 26th April 1996. In the light of the above findings these figures were clearly on the low side and on 22nd April 1998 a large influx of *leucorhoa* was noted in the county including 50 at Snettisham, 100 at Holme, 50 at Cromer Golf Course and 140 at Sidestrand, as well as smaller numbers at many other north and east coast localities.

Return passage commences as early as the last week of June. These early records have often referred to Wheatears with loose-textured, rather 'fluffy' feathering characteristic of recently-fledged birds and which have been assumed to have been reared by undetected pairs within the county. However, it is now believed that these juveniles, recorded especially along the north Norfolk coast, are birds from elsewhere in the British Isles or even the Continent. Generally only small numbers are noted on autumn passage except for those involved in 'falls' in late August or September. In the 'fall' of 1965 'many hundreds and perhaps many more' were in the Yarmouth area with Wheatears being 'conspicuous in every open space in the town', while hundreds were present at Winterton North Dunes. In more recent years the highest numbers have been 160 at Hunstanton, 150 at Holme, 200 at Blakeney Point and 280 at Sheringham between 13th and 15th September 1993, and 200 at Holme, 130 at Holkham, 200 at Blakeney Point and 550 at Sheringham on 18th–19th September 1995. Small numbers of Wheatears are present in October and the last of the autumn is usually recorded in the first half of November. Occasional birds have lingered, with the latest on 24th November 1979 at Snettisham, 25th November 1984 at Old Hunstanton and 4th December 1963 at Blakeney. There have been three mid-winter records – one seen by Emma Turner on 27th February 1926 (Riviere), and singles at Twyford on 3rd January 1910 and at Cley on 23rd January 1954.

Over 1,000 Wheatears have been ringed in Norfolk but only three have been recovered outside the county. A nestling ringed at Wretham in 1992 was controlled at Cavenham Heath, Suffolk on 11th March 1994 and an adult male ringed at Holme on 31st March 1997 was taken by a raptor, possibly a Merlin, on its breeding grounds at Glen Dye, Grampian Region, Scotland on 16th July. All the effort put into trapping Wheatears by the North-west Norfolk Ringing Group was additionally rewarded when one ringed at Snettisham on 28th April 1997 was found at Khouribga, Morocco one year later, a country in which over 75 British-ringed Wheatears have been recovered. Two nestlings ringed elsewhere in the British Isles have been recovered in Norfolk in April – from Sedburgh, Cumbria and Canna, Highland Region; while a juvenile ringed on North Ronaldsay, Orkney on 28th June 1989 was controlled at Holme on 21st April 1990. All three birds would have been of the race *oenanthe* and fit in with the pattern of spring migration discussed above.

*Peter Dolton*

## | Pied Wheatear |                                           *Oenanthe pleschanka*

**A very rare vagrant; seven records.**

The Pied Wheatear breeds from the Black Sea eastwards across the mid-latitudes of Asia to Mongolia and China. It winters in East Africa and the south-western part of the Arabian Peninsula. Prior to 1968, it was an extremely rare vagrant to the British Isles with only four records. It has become more regular since 1976, and apart from 1995, it has been recorded annually since 1985.

The species typically occurs in Britain in October or November, and it is therefore surprising that the first Norfolk record was in the spring at Winterton on 28th May 1978. Even more amazing was the fact that it was found by the same observer, Peter Allard, who had identified Norfolk's first Isabelline Wheatear, at the same locality exactly one year earlier! All subsequent sightings in Norfolk have been in the autumn and the county total currently stands at seven:

1978: A first-summer male, frequently in song, at Winterton North Dunes on 28th May
1983: A female in the Sheringham/Weybourne area from 30th October to 4th November
1985: A first-winter male at Sheringham on 21st–23rd November
1988: A female at Blakeney Point on 16th October
1989: A first-winter male at Winterton North Dunes on 13th–14th September, an exceptionally early date and the earliest ever autumn bird in the British Isles
1990: A first-winter male at Holme on 19th–21st October
1997: A first-winter female at Sheringham on 20th October

*Moss Taylor*

## | Black-eared Wheatear |                                     *Oenanthe hispanica*

**A very rare vagrant; four records.**

There are two distinct races of the Black-eared Wheatear – *O. h. hispanica* which breeds from north-west Africa, Iberia, southern France, Italy and north-west Yugoslavia and *O. h. melanoleuca* breeding from southernmost Italy, Yugoslavia and the Balkans eastwards to Iran and the Middle East. This species is a rare vagrant to the British Isles in spring and autumn, with most records involving the western race *hispanica*.

The first county record of Black-eared Wheatear, an adult of the race *hispanica,* was found by Peter Thompson at Salthouse on 30th August 1965. It remained until 14th September. The second and third occurrences were both in the spring of 1975 when adult males appeared at Cley on 13th May and at Holme on 2nd–21st June. The fourth was a first-winter male which showed well at Warham and Stiffkey from 24th October to 1st November 1993, the latest dates on which one has been recorded in the British Isles.

*Peter Allard*

## Desert Wheatear                                               *Oenanthe deserti*

**A very rare vagrant; eight records.**

The Desert Wheatear breeds in the deserts from North Africa east through Arabia to central Asia, and winters in Saharan Africa, Arabia and parts of the Indian subcontinent. Three distinct races are recognised.

A male of the western race *O. d. homochroa* was obtained between Cley and Blakeney Point on 31st October 1907. This individual is at the City of Birmingham Museum, formerly being in the Connop collection at Rollesby Hall. Another male, a very confiding first-winter bird frequented the shingle ridge

Desert Wheatear
*(Graham Easy)*

at Cley on 14th–17th October 1978. One appeared briefly at Horsey Gap on 29th October 1993 and was almost certainly a first-winter male. A first-winter female, first seen at Old Hunstanton on 16th November 1993, was found on Heacham beach on 19th November where it remained until 7th December. A superb male which appeared at Weybourne on 5th November 1994 was relocated at Salthouse and Cley the next day. Two were recorded in 1996 – a male at Wells East Hills on 11th November and a first-winter male at Salthouse on 14th–18th November, which made a brief visit to Weybourne Camp in the early morning of 15th November. The eighth, a female, frequented the beach just south of the Snettisham beach car park on 7th–12th December 1997.

*Peter Allard*

## Rock Thrush (Rufous-tailed Rock Thrush)     *Monticola saxatilis*

**A very rare vagrant; three records.**

The Rock Thrush is a Palearctic species breeding in the montane areas of north-west Africa and Iberia, eastwards through southern Europe north to Switzerland, Poland and southern Russia to Mongolia. It is a highly migratory species wintering in Africa south to Kenya.

An extremely rare vagrant to the British Isles, the first Norfolk record was of a male found by Mr and Mrs A. Kneen at Salthouse Heath on 9th May 1969. A more obliging male for those who managed to see it, was at Horsey Gap on 30th April 1989. Another male appeared at Holme/Hunstanton Golf Course on 22nd May 1994; fortunately it stayed for three days allowing excellent views to all who visited the area. On the evening of its first day, it survived an attack by a Sparrowhawk. Only slightly injured, it was kept overnight and released next morning.

*Peter Allard*

## White's Thrush     *Zoothera dauma*

**A very rare vagrant; one record in 1871.**

White's Thrush is a highly distinctive species breeding from central and northern Siberia east to Japan, and wintering in south-east Asia. It is a rare, mainly autumn and winter vagrant, to the British Isles.

A male was shot by a Mr Borrett at Hickling on 10th October 1871, it constituted the fifth record for the British Isles. The mounted specimen is at the Castle Museum, Norwich.

*Peter Allard*

## Siberian Thrush     *Zoothera sibirica*

**A very rare vagrant; two records.**

The Siberian Thrush breeds from central Siberia east to Japan, wintering in India, south-east Asia and Indonesia. It is a very rare vagrant to the British Isles.

A male seen briefly by Peter Wilkinson in Yarmouth Cemeteries on 25th December 1977 was only the second British record (Wilkinson 1979). A first-winter male at Gun Hill, Burnham Overy on 18th September 1994 was the fifth British record and also the earliest. This individual was a breathtaking sight for all who managed to arrive before dusk (Cowan *et al.* 1994).

*Peter Allard*

## Ring Ouzel

*Turdus torquatus*

A fairly common passage migrant; rare in mid-summer and in winter.

Ring Ouzels
(Gary Wright)

GW

The world distribution of the Ring Ouzel is virtually confined to the Western Palearctic. Two races occur in Europe – the nominate *T. t. torquatus* which breeds in Scandinavia, Britain and Ireland, and *T. t. alpestris* in the alpine areas of southern and central Europe. The northern race *torquatus* winters in southern Europe and north-west Africa, while *alpestris* often remains in the southern part of its breeding range. In Britain it is an upland and montane species, being extensively distributed in the Pennines, Lake District, and parts of Scotland and Wales, but with only fragmented populations in other suitable areas (New Atlas). A marked population decline was apparent between the two BTO Breeding Atlases.

Although Stevenson believed that the Ring Ouzel had bred in Norfolk on a number of occasions, naming Horsey and Holkham as two of the sites, later authors believed that the observers were mistaken and that there have been no authentic breeding records for the county (Riviere and Seago 1967). It is as a passage migrant, more numerous in spring, that the species is known in Norfolk. Favoured localities include coastal golf courses, scrub, heathland, dunes and meadows.

The first birds of the spring are often recorded in the last week of March with passage continuing through April and into late May. The simultaneous arrival of birds at various coastal localities is often noted and peak numbers are usually found in late April or early May. Riviere gave four February records, although these may well have involved overwintering birds. Excluding all those seen in February, the earliest spring records have been on 5th March 1989 at Wereham, three on 11th March 1982 at Wolferton/Snettisham and on 12th March 1977 at Burnham Overy. Small parties of 5–6 Ring Ouzels are not unusual in spring and the largest site counts have been 27 at Winterton on 30th April 1974, 17 at Caister Golf Course on 30th April 1980, 20 at Holme and 16 at Holkham Park on 16th April 1988 (when at least 35 were estimated to be present in north Norfolk), 20 at Waxham on 27th April 1990, and 21 at Snettisham, 17 at Cromer Golf Course and 11 at Sea Palling on 22nd April 1998, while 21 flew south-west over Hunstanton on 10th April 1993. Although spring passage is often a fairly leisurely affair with birds remaining at the same locality for up to a week, during which time occasional males may be heard singing, 1984 was exceptional with many birds being present for several weeks presumably as a result of having been held up by the prevailing cold north-east winds. The majority have passed through by the end of May but occasional stragglers are seen in early or even mid to late June. In 1995 one was noted at Burnham Overy Dunes on 9th–10th June, 7th July and 13th August, while two males were at Winterton on 2nd July 1967.

Far fewer Ring Ouzels are recorded in autumn, as was noted by Stevenson in the 19th century. Autumn passage occurs between mid-September and mid-November, with very occasional birds in early September and an exceptionally early male at Cley on 11th August 1958. In autumn the largest falls of Ring Ouzels have often been associated with major influxes of other thrushes, suggesting that autumn immigrants are of Scandinavian origin, whereas the majority of those on spring passage are probably of British stock. Unlike spring, the area around the pines at Holkham Meals often attracts some of the highest counts in the county with 24 on 18th–19th October 1990, when there were also 20 at both Stiffkey Greens and Blakeney Point. In addition there were 20 at Holkham on 16th October 1966 and 17th October 1980. Elsewhere maximum site counts have included 11 at Hunstanton Golf Course in 1973, 21 at Blakeney Point on 29th September 1993, 14 at Cley in 1973 and 12 at Yarmouth on 14th–16th September 1967.

Although Riviere had seen one as late as 14th December, until the winter of 1995–96, there had only been two December records since 1950 – at Blakeney Point on 1st December 1958 and at Burnham Norton on 2nd December 1994. However, in late December 1995, a small number arrived in the county along with a huge influx of Fieldfares, some of which remained into the New Year. Birds were recorded at Holkham Park and Wells intermittently from 19th December 1995 to 25th January 1996, with two at Wells on 1st–8th January, and singles at Salthouse on 23rd December, Trowse on 24th December, West Runton intermittently from 31st December to 11th February, Langham from 30th January to 1st February, Thornham from 30th January to 8th February 1996 and Sheringham on 21st–26th January. The only other mid-winter record in recent years concerned one at Hickling from 10th February to 9th March 1991.

During the 1990s increasing numbers of Ring Ouzels have been found inland in spring, at a maximum of 16 localities in 1997. The highest counts inland have been eight at Corpusty on 7th May 1990, seven at Potter Heigham on 21st April 1979 and five at Ringstead Downs, Bale, Felbrigg, North Walsham and Edingthorpe. The species is rare inland in autumn.

Three Ring Ouzels ringed at Holme have been recovered abroad. Of two ringed in autumn 1968, one was found the following autumn in Ain, France on 24th November 1969 and the other at Fosso della Moletta, Italy on 25th March 1969, suggesting a more easterly route in spring. It was only the second British-ringed Ring Ouzel to be recovered in Italy, since when there has been only one more. The third bird from Holme was ringed in April 1970 and recovered at Valcivieres, France on 6th October 1970.

*Moss Taylor*

## Blackbird (Common Blackbird) *Turdus merula*

*MY GARDEN, CHEDGRAVE.*
*8·7·1999.*

**An abundant resident, and very common passage migrant and winter visitor.**

The Blackbird breeds throughout Europe, except for the northernmost part of Fennoscandia and the Kola Peninsula. Since the mid-1850s it has colonised most European cities, having originally occupied just mixed and deciduous woodland. It is the most adaptable of the thrushes and is found throughout the British Isles, except for areas of bare moorland and mountains in Scotland (New Atlas).

Both Stevenson and Riviere described it as an abundant resident. During the period of the Norfolk Atlas, it was the most widespread breeding bird, having been recorded in 98% of the tetrads, with breeding proven in 94%, more tetrads than for any other species. Only five inland tetrads failed to produce a relevant Blackbird record. Three were in the Halvergate Levels area and may well have related to genuine absence from this particularly open landscape; the other two tetrads were in the Brecks, where suitable habitat was present, and the species may simply have been overlooked. During the 1994–97 BBS, the species was found in 93–98% of the 1km squares surveyed. The breeding habitat of the Blackbird is exceptionally diverse, including dense woodland, varied types of farmland, heathland, scrub and gardens, in fact anywhere providing adequate cover for nest sites. The species occasionally nests out of season – a pair at Acle had young in the nest on 2nd December 1953, a pair nested in a Christmas tree at Norwich Station in late December 1984 but failed to produce any young, while a pair that nested in a Christmas tree on the steps of Norwich City Hall in early January 1998 attracted widespread media coverage. The clutch consisted of a minimum of two eggs and two young were first seen on 16th January. Unfortunately three days later they were both catapulted out of the nest in a gust of wind and subsequently died (Durdin 1998).

Norfolk's population of breeding Blackbirds is largely resident but in the autumn large numbers of immigrants arrive on the Norfolk coast from the Low Countries, Scandinavia and Germany. Riviere noted that a high proportion of these migrants were first-winter males. Since 1958, recoveries of ringed Blackbirds have indicated that birds are also now arriving from Finland, the former Baltic States and the adjacent parts of Russia. This may have been due to the colonisation of Finland from Sweden and their subsequent spread eastwards or a reflection of increasing urbanisation (and hence the likelihood of ringing) of Blackbirds in north-eastern Europe (Spencer 1975).

Autumn migration appears to come in waves, sometimes commencing as early as late September and continuing through to early December. Peak numbers are usually recorded from mid-October to mid-November, and on occasions some spectacular movements have been witnessed. An enormous immigration was noted at Cley on 6th December 1953 and the following year extremely large numbers were present around the Wash, where over Snettisham beach at sunset, at least 2,000 Blackbirds flying west-south-west in large straggling flocks were counted in eight minutes. In 1961 there was a most spectacular arrival on 5th November, which included 3,000 at Holme, many 1,000s at Cley, flights of up to 50 arriving almost continuously from the east at Corpusty for over three hours, 270 on cliff-top fields at Mundesley, 300 in a meadow at Surlingham and several 100s in floodlit trees at Cantley Beet Factory. In the Yarmouth area numerous parties were observed flying in off the sea and by the afternoon the whole district was alive with Blackbirds. Over 25 years were to pass before another large-scale immigration was recorded – on that occasion the peak count involved 5,000 west at Holme on 2nd November 1987. Other large influxes involving day-counts of several 1,000s at various localities along the north Norfolk coast to the Wash were recorded in the first half of November in 1991, 1992, 1994, 1996 and 1998.

It is likely that the majority of these immigrants pass through the county although winter numbers are augmented by birds from elsewhere. Although there is little evidence of hard-weather movements involving Blackbirds, unlike other members of the thrush family, occasional influxes are noted in mid-winter, such as on 28th January 1995, when there was a noticeable increase in numbers around the coast. Spring passage is on a much smaller scale than in autumn and is recorded from mid-March to mid-April. The heaviest passage in recent years was noted in April 1996 with 100s at Paston on 7th–14th, 60 at Holme on 8th, 70 at Holkham and 120 at Sheringham on 9th, and 55 at Happisburgh on 10th.

As in Stevenson's time leucistic and varying degrees of albinistic Blackbirds are not infrequently reported; in fact more abnormally-plumaged Blackbirds are probably seen in Norfolk than any other species, with the exception of Pheasants.

Over 30,000 Blackbirds have been ringed in Norfolk. In excess of 1,500 recoveries (including over 225 from abroad) have resulted which have demonstrated that those which pass through the county on autumn migration, some of which winter in Norfolk, are mainly from breeding areas in Fennoscandia and Germany. Further evidence of their place of origin comes from the large number of foreign-ringed Blackbirds found in the county, including some which had been ringed as nestlings, for example at Flekkefjord, Norway and at Paikuse, Estonia. Others had been ringed while on passage to and from Norfolk in Germany, Finland, Denmark and The Netherlands. Several have been found within a day or two of ringing, including a Dutch-ringed bird controlled the next day at Sheringham and another found dead at Yarmouth. However, the route by which the immigrants reach Norfolk is not always direct – one ringed on the Isle of May, Scotland on 7th October 1965, was controlled at Stiffkey in December and again in February 1966, before being found in Norway in September 1968. Some of the birds passing through Norfolk are making for wintering areas further west as shown by two ringed in the county in October and controlled off Wales at Skokholm and Bardsey within two weeks. Others ringed in Norfolk in October have moved west in response to hard weather and have been recovered in Wales and Eire. Norfolk-bred Blackbirds are generally sedentary but a juvenile ringed at Hethersett on 14th July 1968 was recovered in France in December. One of the oldest was a second-year Blackbird ringed in Finland in 1969 and recovered at Loddon in 1983.

*B. D. Harding*

# Black-throated Thrush (Dark-throated Thrush)     *Turdus ruficollis*

**A very rare vagrant; five records.**

The Black-throated Thrush is an eastern thrush, breeding in central Asia and wintering in Iran eastwards to northern India and Burma. There are two distinct subspecies *T. r. ruficollis* which has a rufous-red chin, throat and breast and *T. r. atrogularis* which has a blackish chin, throat and breast. A rare vagrant to Britain, virtually all records relate to *atrogularis* which has a more western distribution. The five Norfolk records are all of this race.

The first county record of Black-throated Thrush (and only the fifth for the British Isles) was found at Holkham on 21st October 1975 by Winifred Flower and D. G. Wright. It remained until 24th October during a magical month for arrivals of Asiatic vagrants. Aged as a first-winter male, it was remarkably tolerant of admirers who surrounded its favourite bramble patch. A second bird, another male, was found soon afterwards at Coltishall on 21st February 1976. A most obliging bird, it frequented meadows close to a public footpath, attracting a procession of observers during its long stay until 3rd April (Dormer 1977). A third individual, a first-winter female, was trapped at Sheringham on 31st October 1993 and was seen later in the day at nearby Sheringham Park. An elusive first-winter female was at Holkham Park on 13th–16th March and 4th April 1996, and another female was at Snettisham on 25th-28th April 1998.

*Peter Allard*

**Fieldfare** MY GARDEN, CHEDGRAVE. 3-12-1999. *Turdus pilaris*

A very common winter visitor and passage migrant; rare in mid-summer.

Fieldfare
(Gary Wright)

The Fieldfare breeds in the middle and higher latitudes of the Western Palearctic, extending from the Channel and North Sea coasts, across central Europe and into Russia. It is typical of farmland and other cultivated landscapes, and mixed woodland. It is both a solitary and colonial breeder, and is one of the most abundant breeding birds of northern Europe. In autumn it migrates south and west, adults generally migrating further than first-year birds. The species has colonised and spread in Britain with breeding first proved on Orkney in 1967, then annually in Shetland in 1968-70. Since then breeding has occurred in mainland Scotland and south to Staffordshire, with one pair successfully fledging young in Kent in 1991 (New Atlas). Up to 13 pairs possibly bred in the British Isles in 1989-91, but only five in 1994 (Ogilvie *et al.* 1996).

In Norfolk occasional birds linger into early summer but breeding has never been proved in the county. Single pair(s) summered at Winterton/East Somerton in 1975-77 and four were present at Winterton up to 21st June 1978. A pair was observed displaying at Cranworth one summer during the early 1980s and single birds have summered at scattered localities throughout the county, including some which were known to be injured.

As with the Redwing, we have become familiar with the Fieldfare as a passage migrant and winter visitor when it inhabits farmland, fresh marshes, tall hedgerows and orchards. Since the late 1960s the first Fieldfares of the autumn have tended to be recorded earlier in Norfolk than in previous years, with ones and twos appearing by the second half of August. Occasionally the first are noted in July, such as three at Cley on 10th July 1964, while at least 140 had been reported at various sites throughout the county by the end of August 1968. The main arrival, however, at least since Stevenson's day, has been from mid-October. In Scandinavia, the area of origin of our wintering population, studies have shown that the time of departure of the Fieldfare population depends on the abundance, and hence the time of depletion, of the rowan fruit crop (Tyrvainen 1975). Some of the most impressive passages have been recorded over Hunstanton with 35,000 on 5th November 1961 and 15,000 on 28th October 1978. On 22nd October 1996 a major influx of Fieldfares was heralded with 5,500 south at Snettisham; the main movement took place on 30th October with 30,000 south in three hours at Snettisham, 10,000 south at Hunstanton and 15,000 west at Paston. Another wave of migrants followed on 8th November with 36,700 at Hunstanton and reports of 1,000s moving west along the north coast from Holme to Sheringham. The passage continued for several days, again with maximum counts at Hunstanton, including 13,000 in two hours on 9th November and 8,000 on 14th November. The autumn total at Hunstanton cliffs in 1996 almost reached a staggering 72,000.

The highly modifiable, nomadic and migratory behaviour of the Fieldfare results in mid-winter arrivals in severe weather (Winter Atlas), such as the massive influx which occurred at the end of December 1995 with 7,000 at Anmer-Flitcham, 4,800 at Holme, 1,200 at Ringstead, 1,000 at Kerdiston and Syderstone, 850 at Bridgham and Welney, 750 at Martham, 600 at Lenwade, 500 at Great Massingham, and 400 at Lynn Point, Stanhoe and Hickling. Previously, an exceptional large-scale coastal movement had occurred on 30th January 1993 with 3,500 south at Snettisham, 3,000 west at Titchwell and 600 west at Holkham and Sheringham. Once in their winter quarters the movements of Fieldfares are variable from year to year, evidently depending on the availability of wild fruit crops and of other food. Occasionally, very large flocks can be seen during the winter months – 3,000–5,000 roosting in a wood at Cranworth in November 1960, 4,000 on Breydon Marshes in February 1973, four flocks totalling 4,500 at North Lopham in March 1994, 3,000-3,500 at Thornham, Quarles/Creake and Felbrigg in January 1996, following the massive influx the previous month, and 3,400 at Potter Heigham marshes in December 1997. However, on occasions Fieldfares are unable to escape the harsh weather. During the 1962–63 winter ten weeks of severe frost and biting easterly winds reduced Fieldfares at Cley to a pitiable condition. They had to content themselves with pecking frozen carrots in the fields. So feeble did they become that many, clustering around a water-hole in the ice of a marsh dyke, were blown in by the bitter wind and drowned.

Combined flocks of Fieldfares and Redwings often remain into the early spring prior to their nocturnal departure for Scandinavia. In recent years, Felbrigg Park has held good numbers of Fieldfares well into April. The spring of 1996 was characterised by exceptional numbers being present in Norfolk up to mid-April, when a mass exodus was noted over the east coast on 15th–16th April. Prior to their departure, flocks included 1,240 at Felbrigg on 7th April, 2,000 at Cockley Cley on 8th April, and 2,000 on the Berney Marshes with 1,000s around the Breydon area and at other suitable sites as far north as Horsey on 8th–16th April. Although most Fieldfares have left Norfolk by the end of April, 150 were still present on Salthouse Heath on 1st May 1995, and in most years the last birds of the spring are generally recorded in the second half of May or even early June.

Occasional albinistic Fieldfares have been reported, including one mentioned by Stevenson at Hickling in 1848, one entirely white apart from a black tail bar at Lower East Carlton in January 1975 and others at Colney Gravel Pit and Merton. A cinnamon-coloured leucistic bird was reported by Stevenson at Swardeston in 1858, with others seen at Attlebridge in January 1980 and Waxham in October 1994.

Due to their extreme wariness, less than 1,000 Fieldfares have been ringed in Norfolk. Despite this, 34 have been recovered abroad equally distributed between the breeding areas in Fennoscandia and wintering or passage sites on the Continent. The majority of breeding season recoveries and the few foreign-ringed birds marked as nestlings or breeding adults, all fall within a comparatively narrow band across Norway, Sweden and Finland (Taylor 1982), which comprises only a part of their much wider European breeding range. However, one ringed at Snettisham in October 1967 was recovered in June 1971, much further north than usual, at Tromso, Norway, a locality within the Arctic Circle. Multiple recoveries are of particular interest and one ringed at Burnham Market in February 1991 was controlled in Sweden in June 1992 and finally found dead in Denmark in February 1993. Fieldfares tend to winter further south in subsequent winters, as shown by ten recoveries in France and one in Spain, including one found in the Camargue in at least its ninth year and one of the oldest British-ringed Fieldfares. Of three recoveries in Italy, two were reported in December 1966, a year in which Fieldfares ringed in the British Isles were found further afield than previously. One ringed at Saddlebow in January 1979 was found freshly dead in Poland the following January, providing dramatic evidence of a bird which was spending successive winters in areas 1,400km apart.

*B. D. Harding*

## Song Thrush   MY GARDEN, CHEDGRAVE. 22·11·1999.   *Turdus philomelos*

**A common resident and passage migrant.**

The Song Thrush breeds throughout much of Europe, from Ireland to Lake Baikal, and from northern Spain to northernmost Fennoscandia. It is present in all of the British Isles, except for most of Shetland and the bare moorland and mountains of northern Scotland, breeding in almost any habitat with trees or bushes (New Atlas). At the beginning of the 20th century Song Thrushes were more abundant than Blackbirds but recent data from the BTO show that this is not the case today. Between 1975 and 1986 the British population was declining at an average rate of 7% per year (Baillie 1990) and the decline between 1969 and 1994 reached 54%.

Stevenson started his species account with 'The Song Thrush or Mavis, as it is more commonly called in this county, is plentiful enough...' and Riviere stated that it was '... exceedingly common throughout the county, save in the winter months'. During the early 1980s, when the fieldwork for the Norfolk Atlas was carried out, it was recorded in 96% of the tetrads with breeding proved in 84%, making it the fourth most widespread species in the county. It was present along woodland margins and hedgerows, on bushy commons and heathlands, and in gardens and cemeteries, but was absent from saltings, open fen, parts of Halvergate Levels, dense coniferous plantations and open heathland in the Brecks. Since then, many observers have noted a decline in the county and the number of 1km squares in which it was found during the BBS in Norfolk fell from 71% in 1994 to 54% in 1997. However, at least in certain parts of the county, a recovery appears to be taking place during the late 1990s. Song Thrushes are one of the first species to nest in the spring, but compared with Blackbirds breed less frequently in December. However, a pair had young in the nest in early December 1953.

The autumn arrival of Song Thrushes from the Continent was recorded as early as the 17th century (Browne 1835–1836) and Stevenson added that 'These [Continental birds], together with the majority of our native birds, again proceed southwards on the approach of winter, till in severe weather, a few pairs only remain'. The first confirmed specimen in Norfolk of a bird of the nominate Continental race *T. p. philomelos* was shot at Holkham in late September 1905 (Riviere).

Autumn passage is recorded from mid-September to early November, with variable numbers noted annually, mainly at coastal localities. High counts have included 150 at Holme on 11th November 1994, 250 at Holkham Meals on 18th October 1990, 200 at Blakeney Point on 28th September 1993, 100 at Weybourne on 20th October 1987, 250 at Waxham on 28th September 1992 and 100 at Winterton in September 1996. However, these numbers were surpassed by a major 'fall' along the north coast on 1st October 1998 with counts of grounded migrants including 500 at Scolt Head (and a further 1,000 flying over), 3,000 at Holkham Meals and 700 at Blakeney Point. Peak counts are often made in the area of Dead Man's Wood, Sheringham, where annual records have been kept for 25 years – up to 400 were present in mid-October 1990 and 240 on 28th September 1992; but these totals were eclipsed by an exceptional passage of thrushes on 3rd November 1994, with birds arriving from the north throughout the day and not departing until dusk or after dark. The final total included 1,200 Song Thrushes. An unusual fall of at least 100 birds of the British race *T. p. clarkei* was recorded at Sheringham on 23rd September 1977 after prolonged south-westerly winds. A smaller spring passage occurs from March to early May, with maximum daily site counts of 20-30.

Recoveries from more than 5,000 Song Thrushes ringed in Norfolk have shown that some locally-bred birds move south and west in autumn, with some even reaching the Continent in winter. A nestling ringed at Kelling in April 1932 was recovered in Belgium five months later and two other Norfolk-ringed nestlings were found in France; while a juvenile ringed in June was recovered during the winter in Portugal. However, not all Norfolk-bred birds move in that direction as shown by one ringed at Gillingham which was reported at Bradford, Yorkshire in November. A highly unusual movement involved an adult ringed at Wolferton on 4th June 1967 which was recovered at Bayern, Germany on 8th June 1969. Most of the Song Thrushes which pass through the county in the autumn are destined for wintering areas in southern Europe and ringed birds have been recovered mostly in France, Spain and Portugal, with one even reaching as far south as Kabylie, Algeria in February 1990. However, two autumn immigrants ringed on the north Norfolk coast have been recovered to the west, in Dyfed, Wales in January and in Tipperary, Eire in February. Few of these passage birds have been reported in their possible breeding areas, although two, amazingly ringed on the same day 7th October 1978, at Waxham were recovered at Otepaa, Estonia on 30th August 1979 and at Kostroma, USSR on 15th December 1980, respectively; while one ringed at East Ruston on 16th October 1977 was found at Kalinin, USSR on 8th May 1978. Both the Russian localities were within 300km of Moscow. The only foreign-ringed bird from its possible natal area was a juvenile ringed at Nummi, Finland in July 1993 and controlled at Wells in September. A hard-weather movement was demonstrated by one ringed at Utrecht, The Netherlands on 20th December 1995 and found dead at Sprowston 12 days later.

*B. D. Harding*

## Redwing   BLAKENEY POINT. 9·10·1986.     *Turdus iliacus*

**A very common winter visitor and passage migrant; very rare in summer.**

The Redwing has an extensive Palearctic breeding distribution, extending from Iceland to eastern Siberia mainly in the boreal taiga, but also in the subarctic and alpine zones. It reaches as far south as the British Isles, southern Sweden, Germany and Poland. It migrates south in autumn to more temperate latitudes and is highly nomadic in winter, in response to weather conditions and the availability of food. Redwings first bred in the British Isles in Sutherland in 1925, but then in only 17 of the next 41 years, although it has bred annually since 1967 (68–72 BTO Atlas). The majority of pairs are around and to the north of the Great Glen, where their essential requirements of scrub with easy access to damp patches for feeding are met, although a few scattered pairs have bred in England, notably five pairs in Kent in 1975–91 (New Atlas). The British population is probably less than 100 pairs (Marchant *et al.* 1990).

In Norfolk they will often linger well into the spring when singing is often heard but mid-summer records are very rare and breeding has never been proved. A pair summered at Winterton/East Somerton in both 1976 and 1977, where the male was heard singing on a number of occasions in the first year. Other mid-summer records have been of singles at Holme on 5th June 1963, at Horsey on 18th July 1964, one at Corpusty on 13th June 1968 which was found dead the next day and birds in song at Carbrooke and Grimston during fieldwork for the Norfolk Atlas. More recently one was at Horsey Gap on 13th June 1998.

It is as a passage migrant and winter visitor that we have become familiar with this species when it inhabits fresh marshes, farmland, thickets and areas of open grassland such as school playing fields. It also visits gardens in harsh weather. The Redwings that visit Britain and Ireland in large numbers are predominantly from the Fennoscandian and Icelandic breeding populations. Ringing recoveries have suggested that the Icelandic birds winter mainly in Scotland and Ireland. While the main autumn arrival is from mid-October, the first few Redwings are generally recorded in the second half of September and occasionally even earlier. The earliest records have been on 8th August 1971 at Roydon Common, on 23rd August 1975 at Felmingham, on 25th August 1968 at Cley and on 25th August 1973 at Winterton. The most impressive autumn arrivals have been on 1st November 1995 with 7,500 west at Holme and 6,000 south at Hunstanton, although these numbers were totally eclipsed by a count of 60,000 which flew south at Snettisham in three hours on 29th October 1996. Other notable counts have included several 1,000s arriving with Song Thrushes at Blakeney Point on 16th October 1988, 2,000 at Holkham Meals on 18th October 1990, 1,200 in off the sea at dawn at Mundesley on 16th October 1994, 1,850 east at Holme on 18th October 1994 and 4,000 west at Sheringham on 3rd November 1994.

Hard weather on the Continent can result in further mid-winter arrivals, and if the severe conditions also effect Norfolk, the Redwings move through the county fairly rapidly, those remaining often succumbing to the cold weather. Such an event occurred towards the end of 1981 with 2,600 moving west at Paston on 13th December. By the end of the month many had been found dead in the county, although one enterprising bird survived by being adopted by a greengrocer at Wells who fed it on grapes and cranberries. The following month many 100s were found dead at Scolt Head. The largest recorded hard-weather arrival in recent years occurred following north-east winds and severe frosts in late December 1995. On 1st January 1996, 1,000s were reported at Cley, although they soon dispersed and 1,500 were present in the Wensum Valley on 5th January. Smaller numbers were reported from many localities.

Comparatively few are seen in February, but numbers once more build up in spring with maximum counts usually in late March or early April, as flocks gather prior to their departure to Fennoscandia, such as 600 at Holkham Park on 21st March 1993 and 1,150 at the same site on 17th March 1996. In April 1996 counts in excess of 1,000 were made at Burnham Norton, Felbrigg (3,000), Repps (1,550), Berney (2,400) and Breydon Marshes, most of which had left by 16th April. Flocks such as these are frequently in sub-song, whilst perched in the taller trees. Peak counts of visible migration were also made in this period with 11,500 west and 600 east at Sheringham on 9th April and 1,100 west at Holme on 10th April. Similar spectacular spring movements of Redwings had been noted in previous years at Sheringham with 1,400 west on 30th March 1980 and 4,500 west on 20th April 1993, on which date an amazing 15,000 flew west at Titchwell in just over three hours. All these heavy movements have occurred on westerly winds and presumably have involved birds which have wintered south of the British Isles, but which of the two races is involved and where the birds are heading for is uncertain (Shepherd 1993). In most years the majority of Redwings have left Norfolk by mid-April, although the odd straggler is often reported up to late May. In 1958 flocks of up to 200 were still present at several localities up to 20th April and 25 were in the Stanford Training Area on 25th April 1994.

An albino Redwing at King's Lynn in 1863 was mentioned in Stevenson and leucistic birds have been reported from Holkham, Hoe Common and the Belton/Burgh Castle area. On 26th March 1994 a highly aberrant Redwing was found amongst a flock of 80 at Holkham Park – it had cold grey upperparts, black crown and ear-coverts contrasting with a vivid white supercilium and white throat, and virtually no red on the flanks (Bloomfield 1994).

Over 2,000 Redwings have been ringed in Norfolk, resulting in 25 foreign recoveries, most of which had been ringed on passage in October and November. Of these 11 have been in France and nine in Iberia, 16 of which have been between November and January. Although there have been several instances of Redwings returning to the same general area in Norfolk in subsequent winters (unlike Fieldfares), some of the recoveries demonstrate the different wintering areas that may be used from year to year. The most outstanding of these were two ringed in autumn in west Norfolk and which were recovered in Italy, one almost exactly a year later and the other in February. One ringed at Leziate on 25th January 1969 was found at Hetlvik, Norway on 22nd October 1969, and is the only recovery of a Norfolk-ringed Redwing in the species' Fennoscandian breeding area, but it may well have been already on passage when recovered. Details of three foreign-ringed birds have been reported – one mentioned by Riviere which had been ringed on Helgoland, Germany on 14th April 1924 was reported by Dr Sydney Long in Norwich on 3rd February 1927, one ringed as a nestling near Lake Engure, Latvia in June 1960 was recovered at Acle the following February and one ringed at Kroonspolders, The Netherlands was controlled at Banningham five days later. Other recoveries made within a few weeks of ringing have all involved movements in an easterly or south-easterly direction into Norfolk. They have included an autumn migrant ringed on Fair Isle in October 1964 found at Trunch two months later, one ringed in Yorkshire in January 1968 recovered in Norfolk six days later and one ringed at Swanwick, Derbyshire on 12th March 1993 controlled at Garboldisham three weeks later.

*B. D. Harding*

## Mistle Thrush   MY GARDEN, CHEDGRAVE. 8·8·1999.   *Turdus viscivorus*

**A common resident and scarce passage migrant.**

The Mistle Thrush breeds throughout much of the Western Palearctic though not in the most northerly or the most southerly latitudes. Those breeding in Fennoscandia and eastern Europe are wholly migratory and winter mainly in France and Spain, while some from southern and central Europe disperse and winter around the Mediterranean. In Britain the Mistle Thrush is widespread with only upland areas of Scotland and the Northern Isles not occupied. There has been an explosive spread since 1800 when birds were rare north of a line from the Gower peninsula to the Wash (New Atlas). This increase has been attributed to the utilisation of young conifer plantations and to an increasing use of town parks and large gardens.

Stevenson noted a great increase in the years leading up to 1890. He referred to large flocks over grassland and pasture but considered that confusion with the Fieldfare was possible, thus the actual status is unclear. Riviere believed that the increase was sustained into the early decades of the 20th century and recorded a number of obvious migrants including one on East Dudgeon lightship on 4th March 1927.

In Norfolk the Mistle Thrush is recorded as a breeding species across the county where there are areas of scattered woodland, parks and large gardens. It is absent from the Broadland levels and marshes, from large areas of mature coniferous plantation, from open farmland, especially if cultivated intensively as in the Fens and, perhaps surprisingly, in a central swathe of the county between Dereham and Fakenham. The species was recorded in 65% of the tetrads surveyed for the Norfolk Atlas. This is markedly lower than for Blackbird and Song Thrush despite the adults being very conspicuous when carrying food. This could have been due to its being an early breeder and the mobility and flocking of young birds. During the 1994–97 BBS it was found in 45–64% of the 1km squares covered in Norfolk, with a year-on-year increase almost annually.

Flocks in excess of 30, largely of young birds, are noted from breeding areas across the county from mid-summer onwards. Larger groups have been recorded on clearfell areas in Thetford Forest, sheep pasture on the Stanford Training Area and pasture areas on the edge of the Fens. The highest counts have been 150 at Stanford on 12th August 1983, 100 at Hockwold on 21st July 1883, 100 at Santon Downham in August 1986 and 100 at Sugar Fen in summer 1995.

Passage birds are seen annually in small numbers from coastal localities. The earliest record being one in off the sea at Yarmouth on 7th July 1987. Most records occur with movements of the other larger thrushes. Largest day-counts have been 24 west at Sheringham on 16th October 1994, 25 south at

Snettisham on 22nd October 1995, 21 west at Holme on 3rd October 1997 and a flock of 54 in off the sea at Overstrand on 29th October 1997. However, these are dwarfed by an account by Ticehurst (1932) of 100s arriving at Yarmouth on 20th October 1883 (but could these have been misidentified Fieldfares?). A total of 109 was recorded at Hunstanton cliffs in autumn 1996, the majority moving south, as were a total of 74 in autumn 1997.

In winter adult Mistle Thrushes will defend fruit-bearing trees and shrubs rather than feeding in flocks. The young will move so as to find their own food supply though the distance travelled will vary from a few kilometres to several hundred (Winter Atlas). In Norfolk small numbers are noted across the county with the highest concentrations in Breckland – the maximum flock size rarely exceeding ten.

Over 400 Mistle Thrushes have been ringed in Norfolk, from which there has been one foreign recovery – a bird ringed at Hilborough in June 1980 was found in France on Christmas Day the following year. The only other recoveries of note have been of one ringed at Littlebourne, Kent on 15th November 1959 found at Wortwell on 3rd June 1962 and an adult ringed at Gibraltar Point, Lincolnshire on 31st July 1984, recovered on the other side of the Wash at Hunstanton the following May.

*Peter Dolton*

## Cetti's Warbler     CHEDGRAVE CARR. 30·4·2000.     *Cettia cetti*

**A scarce resident; first colonised Broadland in 1974.**

Cetti's Warbler is the only Western Palearctic member of an essentially east Asian genus, the bush warblers. It breeds in the lower middle and middle latitudes of the Western Palearctic, having spread north from the Mediterranean region to the lowlands bordering the Bay of Biscay, English Channel and North Sea from the 1920s. Breeding was first suspected in Britain in 1972 at Stodmarsh, Kent. By 1977 over 150 males were present along various lowland river valleys from East Anglia, through Kent and along the south coast to Cornwall. The number had increased to over 300 by 1984 and peaked at 345 in 1990, in both years following mild winters (New Atlas).

The first Norfolk record involved one which was found dead in Norwich City Centre on 28th June 1973. As the bird carried a ring on its leg, it was fortuitously handed in to the Castle Museum, Norwich where it was duly placed in a freezer for later examination and identification. Several weeks passed before it was removed and found to be not only a Cetti's Warbler, but one carrying a Belgian ring. It had been ringed as a first-year bird at Hensies, Hainaut, Belgium on 23rd August 1970, at the locality where the species was first known to breed in that country. The specimen remains in the Castle Museum. This was the first foreign-ringed Cetti's Warbler to be found in Britain.

Breeding was first proved in Norfolk, by Barry Jarvis, the following year, 1974, when five singing males were present in Broadland, along the River Yare. By 1975 the Yare population had increased to 12 singing birds with one also along the River Bure, and in 1976 a total of 22 males was located in the Yare Valley with males also in song at Hardley Flood, Burgh Castle and near Beccles. In 1981 there was a noticeable increase in the number of birds being reported from other parts of Broadland. During the next five years, the Yare Valley, in particular Strumpshaw Fen (where a peak of 15 males held territory in 1983) and Rockland Broad, remained the species' stronghold with smaller numbers colonising the Rivers Bure, Waveney, Chet, Ant and Thurne. The highest county population has been 63 singing males in 1984.

Cetti's Warblers breed in low, tangled vegetation in wet or damp situations, in reedbeds, scrub or Broadland carrs. As they are resident throughout the year, depending on insect prey even during the winter months, they are vulnerable to severe weather, in particular long periods of sub-zero temperatures and prolonged snow cover (Winter Atlas). Such conditions occurred in January 1987, as a result the Norfolk population fell from 43 males in 1986 to 26 in 1987 and to a record low of 16 in 1988. Since then, numbers have returned to earlier levels although the species is mainly confined to the Yare and Bure Valleys, and along the River Ant. In 1992, 19 singing males were present along the Yare between Surlingham and Cantley, while by 1995 the Yare Valley held 35 out of a county total of at least 51. Male Cetti's Warblers are polygynous, spending much of their time patrolling and singing in large territories, contributing very little to parental care (Bibby 1982). Nests are not easy to locate and thus the annual totals are based on the number of singing males.

In 1996, the RSPB and English Nature organised the first national survey of Cetti's Warblers, with plans to repeat it every ten years. A total of 41–48 singing males was located in Broadland, which constituted 8% of the national population. The main sites were Surlingham/Rockland Broads (15–17 singing males) and Strumpshaw Fen (nine), all in the Yare Valley. Elsewhere, 2–3 singing males were located along the River Ant, 4–7 along the Bure, four in the Thurne Valley, two on the Norfolk side of the Waveney and two at other sites in Broadland (Wotton 1996). However, additional birds were located in the Broads, by other observers which were not included in the above survey figures, bringing the county total in 1996 to at least 56 singing males.

Away from Broadland and the central river valleys of Norfolk, the Cetti's Warbler is a rare visitor. The majority have been found in north Norfolk with three records each at Holme and Weybourne, and two at Cley, mostly in late autumn and probably as a result of post-breeding dispersal from Broadland, rather than immigration from the Continent. Singing males have been recorded at Titchwell on a number of occasions since 1982, including one which was present from 7th February to 13th June 1994, while in 1984, a male was in song by a small pond at Edgefield Green from 1st June to 21st July. The species almost certainly bred at a north Norfolk locality in 1989. There have been five records in the west of the county – singles singing at Stanford Water in January 1981 and at Lower Stow Bedon Bridge on the Breck borders in 1985, and at Welney on 8th October 1986, on 5th–20th April 1996 and from 16th December 1996 to 1st January 1997.

A total of 20 Cetti's Warblers has been ringed in Norfolk. Apart from the Belgian-ringed bird mentioned earlier, one ringed at Alder Carr, Gillingham on 22nd April 1978 was controlled at Oulton Broad, Suffolk on 28th October 1978.

*Moss Taylor*

## Fan-tailed Warbler (Zitting Cisticola)     *Cisticola juncidis*

**A very rare vagrant; one record.**

The Fan-tailed Warbler is a fairly abundant species frequenting the grasslands and marsh edges of Iberia, North Africa and most countries bordering the Mediterranean. Since 1971, it has spread north from Spain along the Atlantic and Channel coastline of France and even into Belgium and The Netherlands, although numbers have dwindled since 1984. It is a very rare vagrant to the British Isles.

One was observed by Nick Dymond at Cley in full song-flight on the morning of 24th August 1976 and constituted the first British record. After a short period of observation, it ceased singing and flew purposefully west. What was presumably the same bird, was relocated on 29th August at Holme where it remained in an area of small hawthorns, sedge and reeds close to the car park until 5th September 1976.

*Peter Allard*

## Pallas's Grasshopper Warbler     *Locustella certhiola*

**A very rare vagrant; one record.**

Pallas's Grasshopper Warbler is a skulking species which breeds from western Siberia and Turkestan east to Kamchatka and Japan, and winters from India and south-east China south to the Philippines. It is a very rare autumn vagrant to the British Isles, with the majority of records from Shetland.

One was seen extremely well by Graham Smith after being flushed along the West Bank at Cley on 13th September 1976 (Smith 1980). It proved to be only the third British record.

*Peter Allard*

## Lanceolated Warbler     *Locustella lanceolata*

**A very rare vagrant; two records.**

The Lanceolated Warbler breeds from central Russia eastwards across Siberia to Kamchatka and south to North Korea and Japan. It winters primarily in south-east Asia to the Greater Sunda Islands. It is a rare autumn vagrant to the British Isles with the vast majority of records from Shetland.

A first-winter bird trapped by Dave Riley, Kevin Shepherd and Steve Votier at Dead Man's Wood, Sheringham on 29th September 1993 was later released in the nearby cliff-top vegetation where it remained for the rest of the day (Riley *et al.* 1993, Shepherd & Votier 1994b). This was only the fifth record away from Shetland and completed a remarkable trio of new warblers to the county in 1993. One year later, observers searching for a reported Ortolan Bunting in cliff-top fields at Mundesley, identified Norfolk's second individual on 21st September 1994. However, like the Sheringham bird, it was not present the following morning (Heath 1994).

*Peter Allard*

## Grasshopper Warbler (Common Grasshopper Warbler) *Locustella naevia*

**A fairly common summer visitor and very scarce passage migrant.**

The Grasshopper Warbler is a breeding summer visitor to the middle, mainly temperate, latitudes of the Western Palearctic. The winter quarters are not well-known but are probably mainly in West Africa, south of the Sahara. In Britain, it has a wide but scattered lowland distribution, the numbers of breeding pairs fluctuating annually, related to local habitat changes (68–72 BTO Atlas), but the steep decline since 1970 has been partly due to the reclamation of marginal land for agriculture. The Sahelian drought in West Africa may also have had a detrimental effect, although Grasshopper Warbler numbers remained high in 1969–70 when typical Sahel species, such as the Whitethroat, declined (Marchant *et al.*1990). The field-work for the New Atlas (1988-91) demonstrated a 38% reduction in the number of 10km squares in which the species was found in the British Isles compared with the 68–72 BTO Atlas.

An earlier decline in Norfolk, during the mid-19th century, was clearly described by Stevenson. In 1838, Macgillivray found '... [the Grasshopper Warbler] is nowhere, perhaps, more abundant than in the neighbourhood of Norwich ...I once heard two crying in the gardens attached to the Bishop's Palace, at Norwich... On Costessey common, a few miles from Norwich, I have never met with it, although it is abundant in all the neighbouring hedges, so much so that on a fine evening, I have at one time listened to at least a dozen, and have heard their cries even until the goatsucker and the bat flitting about, on noiseless wings, announced the close of day'. By 1866, Stevenson found them to be far less plentiful with their stronghold then in Broadland. He also mentioned that the species was formerly abundant in the Fens, but drainage and cultivation had reduced them to a few pairs.

Grasshopper Warblers breed in areas of thick, low, tangled vegetation either in damp situations such as Broadland marshes and alder carrs, or dry sites such as heathlands, commons and young conifer planta-tions; the latter habitats being favoured in the west of the county (Kelly 1986). The national decline in the species has been mirrored in Norfolk, as shown by the percentage of 10km squares in which the species was found during the three breeding bird surveys, 77% (68–72 BTO Atlas), 70% (Norfolk Atlas) and 55% (New Atlas). Although the loss of some wetland habitats has been partly compensated for by the planting of conifer plantations, these too are deserted once the trees are much taller than two metres (BWP). The continuing loss of marginal scrub land and the grubbing up of thick hedgerows has also reduced the number of possible breeding sites in Norfolk. During the fieldwork for the Norfolk Atlas, Grasshopper Warblers were found in 125 of the tetrads surveyed with the highest concentrations in Broadland and west Norfolk (Kelly 1986). More recently the percentage of 1km squares covered in Norfolk for the BBS, in which Grasshopper Warblers were recorded, has fallen steadily from 10% to 2% over the four years 1994-97.

The Halvergate Marshes area has been colonised since 1992 with up to three reeling birds, and it is of interest that the re-colonisation of Beeston Common was noted at the same time. During the summer of 1994, a total of 87 singing males was reported in the county, of which 45 were in Broadland and the highest counts were seven at Hickling Broad/Heigham Sounds, Whitlingham and Dersingham Reserve, and six in the Stanford Training Area. The following year, the number of reeling birds in north Norfolk had increased from ten to 23 with eight at Holkham and six at Titchwell. In 1996 a total of 89 singing males was reported including 13 in the Heigham Sounds/Hickling Broad area, ten at Strumpshaw/Cantley/Buckenham and nine at Holkham. By 1997 the number of reeling birds during the summer exceeded 100 of which 23 were in the Hickling/Heigham Sounds area, the highest concentration noted in the county in recent years, while two pairs bred at Scolt Head.

The first birds of the spring generally appear in Norfolk by mid-April, with singing males widespread by the end of the month. The earliest sightings have been at Sidestrand on 7th April 1994, Holme on 8th April 1987 and Horsey Gap on 8th April 1993. In recent years, a few birds have been found annually on autumn passage, mainly at the better-watched coastal sites along the north Norfolk coast, such as Blakeney

Point. The majority have been seen between mid-August and early October. There are three records after mid-October - at Sheringham on 18th October 1994, Happisburgh on 19th October 1977 and the latest at Weybourne on 4th November 1967.

A Grasshopper Warbler of the eastern race *L. n. straminea* was trapped and ringed at Sheringham Bird Observatory on 20th September 1998; there have been very few previous records of this race in the British Isles (Millington 1998c).

About 160 Grasshopper Warblers have been ringed in Norfolk since 1980, of which 125 have been trapped since 1990. There have been no recoveries or local controls.

*Moss Taylor*

# River Warbler                                       *Locustella fluviatilis*

**A very rare vagrant; two records.**

The River Warbler breeds from Poland eastwards to western Siberia and winters in East Africa. It is a rare vagrant to Britain; at least half the records relate to birds in spring and mid-summer.

A singing male was found by Paul Pratley in a rye field adjacent to hawthorn and elder hedgerows at Roydon Common on 29th May 1981; it remained until 6th June. This was the first mainland record for Britain and the first ever singing individual (Pratley 1982, 1984). A second singing bird was found at Boughton Fen on 8th July 1989 and remained until 21st July.

*Peter Allard*

# Savi's Warbler CLEY MARSHES. 24·5·1987.    *Locustella luscinioides*

**A very scarce summer visitor, almost annual since 1967; formerly bred regularly until the mid-19th century.**

Savi's Warbler breeds in the lowlands across the middle and lower middle latitudes of the Western Palearctic; it has a scattered distribution in western Europe but is more widespread in the east and in Russia. Its winter distribution is uncertain but is probably in a narrow band across sub-Saharan Africa, with those from western Europe wintering in West Africa. Formerly small numbers bred in the wetlands of the Fens and the Broads but the species became extinct as a breeding bird in England in the mid-19th century, probably as a result of drainage and land reclamation. Since the 1940s, there has been a moderate range expansion in north-west Europe as a result of which Britain has become recolonised.

The first British specimen was taken at Limpenhoe in Norfolk in May 1819 and was examined by Temminck who thought that it was a variety of Reed Warbler (Stevenson), as the species had not yet been described at that time. Following the recognition of a specimen collected in the Cambridgeshire Fens in 1840, the Norfolk bird was finally correctly identified as a Savi's Warbler (Historical Atlas). Between 1819 and 1856, a total of six specimens was obtained in Norfolk (four of which are in the Castle Museum, Norwich), including a pair which were shot at South Walsham in 1840 (Riviere) and one shot at Surlingham on 7th June 1856, which was the last record of one found in breeding habitat in Britain during the 19th century (Historical Atlas).

In 1954, a male was in song during the summer at Wicken Fen, Cambridgeshire but breeding was not proved again in England until 1960 at Stodmarsh, Kent. The first Norfolk record in the 20th century was a male in song at Cley from 28th May to 10th June 1967. Since then, at least one singing bird has been recorded in the county annually, except in 1970, 1972, 1994 and 1997. The majority of records have come from Broadland with Hickling, Horsey and Martham Broads, and Strumpshaw, Upton and Catfield Fens being the most favoured localities, although eight other Broadland sites have hosted singing Savi's Warblers. On the north coast the species has been recorded during the breeding season in eight years at Cley and in 1992 at Holkham. The preferred habitat is extensive stands of *Phragmites* in wet reedbeds, with a thick ground cover of sedges or rushes, and scattered bushes (New Atlas), requirements met at most of the sites mentioned above. The number of singing males in Norfolk has fluctuated each year, but normally represented between 25% and 60% of the British population. From the mid-1970s, birds began to be recorded at several localities each year, with an average of six singing males annually between 1976 and 1992. The summer of 1980 was exceptional with 18 in song, including eight at Hickling and four at

Martham Broad. Even as recently as 1991, ten were in song in the county. Unfortunately, in common with a recent decline on the near Continent, Savi's Warbler is maintaining a very tenous hold as a Norfolk breeding bird. A single bird in song at Catfield in mid-June 1993 was the sole record that year and the only ones since were heard at Hickling on 22nd April 1995, at Surlingham Church Marsh from 24th July to 1st August 1996 and again at Hickling from 18th–30th April 1998.

In spring, the first Savi's Warbler was normally heard in the second or third week of April, very often at Hickling Broad, where the earliest county record occurred on 11th April 1980. Birds have rarely been reported in late summer and the only autumn record concerned one at Holkham on 13th October 1976.

*Moss Taylor*

# Aquatic Warbler                              *Acrocephalus paludicola*

**A rare autumn vagrant; one spring record.**

The Aquatic Warbler breeds in the mid-latitudes of the Western Palearctic, east from eastern Europe, where the distribution is patchy and has declined recently due to wetland drainage, through to Russia. The winter range is poorly known, but almost certainly includes sub-Saharan West Africa. On autumn migration, the species passes through England in small numbers, the majority being recorded from areas of *Phragmites* along the south coast. It has always been a rare passage migrant to Norfolk.

The first ten Norfolk records, between 8th September 1896 and 11th September 1925, all involved birds shot at Cley or Blakeney. All except one occurred between 4th and 21st September (Stevenson and Riviere).

Since then the county total has risen to 36. During the 1970s a total of 11 was recorded, the highest number in a single decade. Only three have been found since, despite the increase in observers, a reflection of the marked decline in the breeding population in eastern Europe.

The earliest autumn record was one trapped at Blakeney Point on 6th August 1954. All but five have occurred between the second week of August and the third week of September, with a small peak in early September. There have been two October records, one shot at Blakeney Golf Course on 23rd October 1912 and one at Cley on 11th October 1994.

In recent years, the majority have been found in the *Suaeda* bushes along Blakeney Point during easterly winds (Gantlett 1995a), although one was actually seen flying in from the sea and landing on Blakeney Point on 13th August 1985. There have been only six records away from Cley or Blakeney - three at Holme (20th August 1958, 17th September 1961 and 5th September 1965), two at Waxham (26th August 1972 and 27th September 1977) and one at Burnham Overy dunes (17th September 1994).

There is a single spring record of one at Cley on 12th May 1938. British records at this time of year are exceptional. Two autumn birds have been ringed in Norfolk.

*Moss Taylor*

| Sedge Warbler |   HARDLEY FLOODS.   *Acrocephalus schoenobaenus*
                    20·6·1991.

**A common summer visitor and fairly common passage migrant.**

In contrast to other *Acrocephalus* warblers, the breeding range of the Sedge Warbler extends from the high Arctic, south to the mid-latitudes of the Western Palearctic, but only marginally to the Mediterranean zone. It winters extensively in Africa, south of the Sahara. It is widely distributed as a breeding summer visitor to the British Isles, being absent only from the higher areas (68–72 BTO Atlas). In common with the Whitethroat, the numbers of Sedge Warblers began to decline in 1969 and by 1974 had fallen dramatically due to the Sahelian drought. Following a partial recovery in the late 1970s, numbers fell once again to an all-time low in 1985, but have now returned to their former level (Marchant *et al.* 1990).

Stevenson stated that it was more numerous in Norfolk than the Reed Warbler; but even in the 19th century annual fluctuations in the numbers of Sedge Warblers had been noted and in some years he estimated they were less abundant than Reed Warblers.

Nowadays the species can be found breeding in areas of low, dense and luxuriant vegetation along the main river systems and their tributaries, along marshland dykes, around the drier margins of reedbeds, especially in Broadland and along the north Norfolk coast, near ponds and gravel pits, and in the peat Fens. Drier areas, such as young conifer plantations are particularly favoured in Breckland (Kelly 1986).

The species was recorded in all the 10km squares in Norfolk for the 68–72 BTO Atlas and in all except two for the Norfolk Atlas and the New Atlas. It was found in 34% of all the Norfolk tetrads surveyed for the Norfolk Atlas and its distribution was similar to the Reed Bunting (Kelly 1986). It is only during the 1990s that counts of singing males have been carried out at some of the county's reserves. The maximum site-counts have been 82 at Cley in 1990, 86 at Welney in 1996, 33 at Brancaster Fresh Marshes in 1997, 35 at Holme in 1995 and 28 at Blakeney Freshes in 1993.

Small numbers of Sedge Warblers are recorded on spring migration, the first singing males generally being found in early April with the main influx after mid-month. The earliest dates have been 21st March 1994 at Martham Broad, 28th March 1989 at Holme and Titchwell, and 29th March 1981 at Cley. Autumn passage, involving more birds than in spring, occurs from early August to mid-September, most having left by the end of the month. The latest dates have been 3rd October at Winterton (1976) and Warham (1998), 5th October 1989 at Holme, 8th October 1995 at Titchwell and 14th October 1998 at Strumpshaw. A pure albino was recorded at Wells on 14th August 1977.

Since 1980, about 5,500 Sedge Warblers have been ringed in Norfolk, of which a record 864 were trapped in 1995, the year in which both the BTO's Common Birds Census and Constant Effort Site indices were at significantly higher levels than for many years (Marchant & Wilson 1996). There have been 15 foreign recoveries of Norfolk-ringed Sedge Warblers, and three French-ringed birds and one from the Channel Islands have been found in the county.

From late July, Norfolk's Sedge Warblers begin to leave the breeding areas, dispersing to the pre-migratory feeding grounds in the wetlands along the south coast. Several recoveries have demonstrated this, including one ringed at Weybourne on 25th July 1981 which was controlled at Dungeness, Kent eight days later and another ringed at Haddiscoe on 5th September 1997 controlled at Icklesham, Sussex three days later. The movement of birds through Norfolk, from further north, is shown by one ringed at Bolton, Greater Manchester on 10th August 1984 and controlled at Hardley Flood nine days later. However, not all movements fit into this pattern – two first-autumn birds ringed at Icklesham, Sussex in late July-August were controlled at Pensthorpe and Holme, respectively, each three days after being ringed.

Two autumn-ringed birds from sites along the French Atlantic coast and one each from central France and Jersey have been found in subsequent years in the county. Norfolk-ringed Sedge Warblers have been recovered in August-September in Belgium (3), France (9) and Portugal, while one ringed at Hardingham on 21st July 1981 was controlled on Helgoland, Germany on 10th May 1982. The only recovery outside Europe, concerned one ringed at Holme on 5th August 1971 and reported from Douar Drarine, Safi, Morocco on 24th November 1973.

*Moss Taylor*

# Paddyfield Warbler                     *Acrocephalus agricola*

**A very rare vagrant; two records.**

The Paddyfield Warbler breeds from Romania, Bulgaria and southern Russia eastwards through central Asia to Mongolia. It has bred recently in Turkey. It winters mainly in India and south-east Asia. It is rare vagrant to the British Isles, the majority being found in autumn.

A first-winter bird was found and subsequently trapped by Kevin Shepherd and Steve Votier in a hedgerow between Weybourne and Sheringham on 24th September 1993. It remained until dusk but could not be found the following day (Golley 1993d, Shepherd & Votier 1994a). This was the second of a trio of new warblers for Norfolk during 1993. Three years later another was identified at Wells East Hills on 23rd September 1996. Like the first, this bird had departed by the following day (McCallum 1997a).

*Peter Allard*

# Blyth's Reed Warbler                     *Acrocephalus dumetorum*

**A very rare vagrant; one record.**

Blyth's Reed Warbler is a central Palearctic species breeding from Sweden, Finland and the Baltic States eastwards across Russia, Siberia, on to Mongolia and Afghanistan, and wintering in India and south-east Asia. It is a rare vagrant to the British Isles, mainly in the autumn.

A first-winter bird, found by Mark Golley and Richard Millington, was at Warham Green on 25th–27th September 1996. This confiding individual remained for three days in an overgrown pit and proved a great attraction (Golley *et al.* 1997, Golley & Millington 1997). Great credit must go to the finders of this, the first to be identified in the field in the British Isles. An offshore record previously claimed for Norfolk was of a bird found dead at the Dudgeon light-vessel on the night of 20th–21st October 1912, which at the time was positioned 19 miles north of Wells, too far offshore for a valid county record.

*Peter Allard*

# Marsh Warbler                                    *Acrocephalus palustris*

**A very scarce passage migrant; annual since 1990.**

The Marsh Warbler is a widespread, breeding summer visitor to the middle latitudes of the Western Palearctic, but rare in England and northern France. It winters in south-east Africa. Although it still breeds in England, there has been a marked decline in numbers since about 1950. At the time of the 68-72 BTO Atlas, 50-80 pairs bred annually in scattered localities in southern and western England, with 75% in Worcestershire. By the late 1980s, less than 12 pairs were breeding each year, centred on a newly-established population in south-east England (New Atlas).

The first fully accepted Norfolk record concerned a male shot at Blakeney Point on 10th October 1923, which is now in the Castle Museum, Norwich (Seago 1967). Almost exactly 60 years were to pass before the next was found in the county – trapped at Sheringham on 13th September 1983. Then in 1985, singing Marsh Warblers were identified in early June at both Cley and Holme. Since then, the species has been recorded in every year, except 1986 and 1989, and the county total has reached 36.

Marsh Warblers arrive in the northern and western limits of their breeding range in late May or early June. All the spring records in Norfolk fall between 18th May and 29th June, with a peak during the first three weeks of June. Every spring record has involved a bird in song, with many of the recent ones remaining for several days. Apart from singles at Elsing on 12th June 1987 and at Winterton on 27th May 1994, all single date records have been made at sites along the north Norfolk coast between Holme and Sheringham, suggesting these are passage migrants. However, some birds have made longer stays including singles at Cley on 4th-18th June 1985, Hempstead on 10th-19th June 1990, Surlingham on 5th–16th June 1991, Titchwell on 9th–17th June 1993 and Hempstead on 15th–29th June 1997. The spring and early summer of 1998 was exceptional with one at Ludham Marshes on 18th–29th May, one at Whitlingham Marsh on 3rd–15th June, which was joined by a second bird on 15th–19th June, one at Sheringham on 5th–10th June and one at Sea Palling on 7th–19th June where a probable female was also present and nest building was recorded. Although both sexes sing, the full, amazingly imitative song is given only exceptionally by female Marsh Warblers (BWP) and all the Norfolk records of singing birds almost certainly refer to males.

It has never been proved conclusively that Marsh Warblers have bred in Norfolk, but mention should be made of one other possible instance given by Riviere. During one or two summers prior to 1903, an ex-keeper at Hickling Broad heard the song of a bird which was unfamiliar to him in an osier carr, where in June 1903 he found a nest containing four eggs. Although not typical of either Marsh or Reed Warbler eggs, the Rev F. C. R. Jourdain thought that they were most likely to be Marsh Warbler's. The clutch is in the Castle Museum, Norwich. Male Marsh Warblers which pair quickly stop singing, whereas those that remain unpaired sing for several weeks (Kelsey 1989), so it may well be that the occasional pair has bred in Norfolk, even in recent years.

There is only one mid-summer record, an adult trapped at Weybourne on 12th July 1996. On measurements, it was probably a female and it was not heard singing. It had a high fat score, indicating that it was on active migration. The pristine condition of the flight and tail feathers indicated that it had not bred, suggesting that it was probably a late spring bird rather than one on early autumn migration.

There have been six autumn records, five of which have involved birds examined in the hand – the one obtained at Blakeney Point on 10th October 1923, singles trapped at Sheringham on 13th September 1983 and Weybourne on 28th August 1988, one seen at Cromer on 17th–25th September 1988, and singles trapped at Sheringham on 11th October 1995 (the latest date for the county) and Winterton on 26th September 1998. Five have been ringed in Norfolk, all except one in the Sheringham/Weybourne area.

*Moss Taylor*

HARDLEY FLOODS. 20·6·1991·

## Reed Warbler (Eurasian Reed Warbler) | *Acrocephalus scirpaceus*

**A common summer visitor and fairly common passage migrant.**

The Reed Warbler breeds extensively in the middle latitudes of the Western Palearctic, but because of its close association with mature stands of *Phragmites*, its distribution is patchy. It winters in sub-Saharan Africa, south at least as far as Zambia. In Britain, the Reed Warbler is a summer visitor to the lowlands of mainly eastern and southern England, although in recent years it has extended its range to the north and west, and small numbers now nest in Ireland (New Atlas). Unlike the Sedge Warbler, its numbers have not been affected by the Sahelian drought as its winter quarters lie further south (Marchant *et al.* 1990).

As in the time of Stevenson and Riviere, the species' stronghold is in the extensive reedbeds in Broadland, where it breeds in loose colonies. The Norfolk Atlas also showed concentrations in the larger reedbeds on the Ouse Washes and along the north Norfolk coast. Pairs also nest in narrow stands of *Phragmites* along drainage ditches and dykes, in isolated patches of reeds by small ponds, as well as in willowherb or even crops near to water. There were only a few 10km squares in which Reed Warblers were not found during the fieldwork for the BTO Breeding Atlases and the Norfolk Atlas, and in the latter survey it was recorded in 23% of the tetrads. It is only during the 1990s, that attempts have been made to estimate the number of singing males at selected reserves. The maximum site counts have been, Welney 99, Holme 65, Brancaster Fresh Marshes 43, Blakeney Freshes 65 and Cley 96. While in east Norfolk, a survey in 1998 found 39 singing males around the Breydon and Berney Marshes.

The first spring arrivals tend to be a couple of weeks later than Sedge Warblers, not appearing until the latter half of April, with the main arrival in early May. The earliest dates have been 13th April at Blakeney Freshes in 1993 and at Rockland Broad in 1997, 14th April 1995 at Burnham Norton and 15th April 1984 at Heacham. Ringing has demonstrated that in some years, breeding birds continue to arrive in Norfolk reedbeds in late May and that passage continues through early June (see below). On autumn passage, which commences in late July, Reed Warblers can be found in almost any scrubby habitat, particularly coastal, although ringing again has shown that the majority move through reedbeds. Adult Reed Warblers leave first and by early September most of the young have also left Norfolk. Passage birds, however, continue to be recorded until mid-October. Occasional birds linger into November and the latest have been on 11th November 1994 at Weybourne, 12th November 1983 at Blakeney Point and 13th November 1982 at Titchwell.

Over 10,500 Reed Warblers have been ringed in Norfolk since 1980. A total of 32 has been recovered abroad, 14 foreign-ringed birds have been found in the county (including seven from Belgium) and there have been many recoveries to or from other English counties.

Ringing has demonstrated that the autumn migration takes place in a series of short journeys through western Europe. Many Norfolk-ringed birds have been recovered later in the same autumn in southern England, the majority controlled in reedbeds along the Sussex coast at sites known to be used by the species as pre-migratory fattening areas. For example, two ringed at Titchwell on 29th July 1975 were controlled at Bexhill on 30th August and 1st September, respectively and were clearly following a similar route. However, there have been four recoveries in Belgium later the same autumn, suggesting that some reach the Continent by crossing the North Sea, rather than over the English Channel.

An idea of the timing of migration after they have left Britain is shown by two recoveries in the Channel Islands (on 8th and 11th August), four in France (22nd August–7th September), five in Portugal (8th September–13th October), three in Spain (6th–25th September) and three in Morocco (16th September–14th October). There have also been four controls at Parc National du Djoudj in Senegal, between 28th March and 19th April, while one ringed there on 18th April 1993 was breeding at Lopham Fen in 1993 and 1995. Others ringed at Wetteren, Belgium in May 1995 were controlled sixteen days later at Keswick and at Pensthorpe in July, indicating the route taken by at least some of our spring arrivals. The only other recovery involving Africa, concerned one ringed at Ilha das Areias in Guinea Bissau on 2nd February 1987 and found dead at Cley on 21st July 1988. This was only the second British recovery of a Reed Warbler from this West African country, the first had been ringed on the same date, at the same site and was found in Glamorgan in 1987.

The most unexpected movement was one ringed at Haademeeste, Parnu in Estonia on 27th July 1987 and controlled one month later at Sheringham. This was the first British recovery of a Reed Warbler ringed in eastern Europe and it was trapped during a large 'fall' of Continental migrants, during which period seven Greenish Warblers were found in Norfolk. Another passage bird ringed at Sheringham on 28th August 1990 was controlled at Mortagne, France on 26th May 1991, the late date suggesting that it was from a more northerly breeding population. Only one Reed Warbler ringed in June has been recovered later the same summer outside Norfolk, but it does demonstrate the prolonged period of passage that occurs in spring. It was ringed at Gillingham on 15th June 1980 and controlled two days later at Hornsea Mere, Humberside.

Ringing has shown that both adult and juvenile Reed Warblers return to the same reedbeds in subsequent summers and there have been many instances of birds being retrapped over several years. The records for longevity in Norfolk include an adult male ringed at Earlham in 1978, retrapped at the same site in 1987 (during its life, it must have flown over 160,000km on migration alone), one ringed at Lagoa de Santo Andre, Portugal on 5th September 1989, controlled as a breeding male at Wey-bourne in both 1995 and 1996, and one ringed at Holme in 1974, controlled at Old Hunstanton in 1980.

*Moss Taylor*

## Great Reed Warbler                               *Acrocephalus arundinaceus*

**A rare vagrant.**

The Great Reed Warbler breeds in the middle latitudes of the Western Palearctic, its range having expanded in northern and eastern Europe, while it has decreased in other areas in recent years. It winters extensively in sub-Saharan Africa. It has never bred in Britain, where it remains a rare visitor, mainly in the spring.

Riviere included three records, involving four birds, up to 1912. Both the 1886 and 1906 records were made by the Rev M. C. Bird. Interestingly, they were all later in the summer than the more recent records made since 1969. The county total stands at 16, of which ten have occurred since 1984, some of which have made prolonged stays:

> 1886: A pair on the River Bure on 8th July.
> 1906: Horning on 1st August.
> 1912: Near Horning on 21st July.
> 1969: A male in song at Cantley on 18th–30th June.
> 1978: A male in song at King's Lynn Beet Factory from 23rd May to 10th June.
> 1984: Titchwell on 20th May.
> 1985: A male in song at Holkham on 15th–21st June.
> 1988: A male in song at Cley on 5th–24th June.
> 1993: A male in song at Titchwell on 11th–17th June.
> 1994: A male in song at Cley from 11th May to 27th June.
>       A male in song at Rockland Broad on 22nd May.
> 1995: One ringed at Weybourne on 31st May remained until 4th June.
> 1996: One ringed at Sheringham on 21st May.
> 1998: Two at Berney Marshes on 26th May.

All the recent records have occurred between 11th May and 30th June. Nationally, the majority of Great Reed Warblers are found between late May and early June, in southern and south-eastern England.

*Moss Taylor*

## Booted Warbler                                       *Hippolais caligata*

**A very rare vagrant; three records.**

The Booted Warbler is an eastern warbler breeding from north-west Russia across southern Siberia to Mongolia and southern Iran. It winters in India. An autumn vagrant to Britain, it has become an almost annual visitor since 1975.

The first for Norfolk was one found by Giles Dunmore and Steve Joyner at Titchwell on 18th–21st

September 1982. It frequented the *Suaeda* and sparse vegetation along the footpath to the main hide (Joyner 1984). The second individual was in coastal fields at Cromer on 4th–5th September 1994. Discovered by observers looking for a Siberian Stonechat, it proved very confiding flitting from weed to weed almost alongside the main coast road. In addition to the Booted Warbler and Siberian Stonechat, a Wryneck was also found in the same field! A third bird frequented Hopton cliffs alongside Gorleston Golf Course on 3rd–4th September 1996, which proved to be equally obliging.

*Peter Allard*

## Icterine Warbler · *Hippolais icterina*

**A very scarce passage migrant.**

The Icterine Warbler breeds in the middle and upper latitudes of the Western Palearctic, reaching as far as the low Arctic in northern Norway. It winters extensively in Africa, south of the equator. To Britain, it is a regular spring and autumn passage migrant with the first successful breeding in Britain recorded in Scotland in 1992 (Ogilvie *et al*. 1995).

The first Norfolk record was given by Southwell in his Appendix to Stevenson's third volume and concerned one shot by F. D. Power at Blakeney on 11th September 1884, one week after the same collector had obtained Norfolk's first Barred Warbler also at Blakeney. By 1930, the county total had risen to 11, all the records falling between 4th and 26th September, except for one in a wood at South Wootton on 30th April and 1st May 1929 (Riviere).

Since 1964 the species has been recorded annually in Norfolk, the majority in autumn, but annually in spring or early summer since 1987. This recent upsurge in spring records is probably related to an increase in the number of breeding pairs in Sweden and probably also in Finland and The Netherlands (Cottridge & Vinicombe 1996). A total of 43 Icterine Warblers have been seen between 11th April and 10th July. Most have been found from mid-May to early June with a distinct peak in the last ten days of May. Many have been records of males in song, usually for a single day, but longer staying individuals have included one at Wells on 4th–11th June 1990 and another at Fordham, near Hilgay from 29th June to 10th July 1991. All records have involved single birds apart from two at Titchwell on 23rd May 1984, three at Blakeney Point on 27th–28th May and two on 30th May 1992, and two at Blakeney Point on 27th May 1993.

Icterine Warblers have been recorded annually in autumn since 1964, the number varying from just a few each year to maximum autumn totals of 57 in 1977, at least 40 in 1968 and 28 in 1984; the occurrence of the species being largely dependent on easterly winds. Over 430 have been recorded in Norfolk in autumn, between 4th August (at Holme in 1968 and Wells in 1974) and 15th October (at Yarmouth in 1972, Holkham in 1980 and Happisburgh in 1990), with the latest record on 16th October 1990 at Yarmouth.

The majority of birds are found between the second week of August and the third week of September, with a peak in late August. Usually recorded singly, seven were present at Wells/Holkham, including four together, on 10th–11th August 1968 and eight a week later; eight were also counted on Blakeney Point on 7th and 19th August 1977. Most birds are recorded along the north Norfolk coast and there have been two inland – at North Walsham on 10th August 1977 and at Keswick on 17th September 1994. Of the 29 Icterine Warblers which have been ringed in Norfolk, 16 have been trapped since 1972.

*Moss Taylor*

## Melodious Warbler · *Hippolais polyglotta*

**A very rare vagrant; two records.**

The Melodious Warbler breeds in north-west Africa, Iberia, France and Italy, and has recently spread into Germany and Belgium. It has also bred recently in The Netherlands with summer records in Denmark. The species is a scarce, but annual, spring and autumn visitor to the British Isles, mainly to the southern counties.

Two adults were trapped and photographed by Richard Richardson in 1957, at Cley on 7th June and 5th September, respectively. They constitute the only records for Norfolk. However, with the increasing breeding range of the species on the Continent and records in both Suffolk and Essex in recent years, it is likely to appear in Norfolk again in the future.

*Peter Allard*

# Dartford Warbler

*Sylvia undata*

**A rare vagrant.**

The Dartford Warbler breeds in the lower middle and middle latitudes of the Western Palearctic. Although many are resident on their breeding grounds, it is a partially migratory species with some reaching north-west Africa in winter. In Britain, it is confined as a breeding bird to the lowland heaths of southern England, but it did breed annually in Suffolk until 1916 (Payn 1962), and again from 1996.

Stevenson included two Norfolk records in the 19th century, one obtained at Yarmouth sometime before 1846 and another, a young male, caught by a dog in a furze bush on Yarmouth North Denes on 25th February 1859. In addition, Riviere mentioned two which were shot in the county in June 1828 and which were included by Hunt (1829). There have been ten records in the 20th century:

1905: One shot on the sea wall at Wells on 14th December.
1928: Sheringham Golf Course on 9th January.
1986: A female at Blakeney Point on 17th–19th May.
1990: Waxham on 17th March.
    Cromer Golf Course on 2nd–6th April (a different bird).
1994: A male at Weybourne on 26th April.
    A male at Winterton on 30th April.
    Winterton from 27th October to 8th November.
1996: A male in song at Winterton on 5th–7th May and at Caister on 13th–14th May.
1997: A singing male was present at an inland site from 21st March to 3rd July. With the continued increase in the British breeding population, there is a possibility that this species may attempt to breed in the county in the future and hence the locality has not been included.

It is interesting to note that all the dated records up to 1928 were in winter, whereas all except one of the more recent ones have occurred in spring from mid-March to mid-May. A marked increase in the number of breeding pairs in southern England in the 1990s (1,600–1,670 pairs in 1994), is undoubtedly related to the recent spate of records. Most have been located in areas of scrub, often where gorse is present.

*Moss Taylor*

# Subalpine Warbler

*Sylvia cantillans*

**A rare spring vagrant; one autumn record.**

The Subalpine Warbler breeds in the Mediterranean region, from Tunisia to Morocco in the south and from Portugal to western Turkey in the north. It winters in Africa, mainly along a narrow band just south of the Sahara. Although only 12 had been recorded in Britain prior to 1958, the species has since become an annual vagrant and the British total now stands at over 370.

The first for Norfolk was found by Peter Hayman at Cley on 11th June 1951. The bird had entered the trap behind the Cley Bird Observatory, which at that time was situated on the shingle bank, but unfortunately the trap was under repair and the bird escaped. Although it was the ninth British record of a Subalpine Warbler, it was the first in England. The next two in Norfolk were both trapped on Blakeney Point in 1955 and 1960, and the fourth county record was not until 10th April 1974, when one was found inland at Lower Bodham.

Since then, the county total has risen to 20, of which four were noted in 1994 and five the following year. All except one have been found in the spring, between 10th April and 11th June, with a distinct peak in the last two weeks of May, during which period eleven have been found. The single autumn record involved one on Blakeney Point on 29th–30th September 1955. Most have remained for only a single day but birds have remained on Blakeney Point for up to four days. All except three have been identified as male, suggesting that females are probably being overlooked. The favoured locality has certainly been Blakeney Point, where nine have been found and all but one have been sighted between Holkham and Sidestrand. The only one away from the north of the county was found inland at Rollesby. A total of four has been ringed in Norfolk.

*Moss Taylor*

## | Sardinian Warbler |                                    *Sylvia melanocephala*

**A very rare vagrant; seven records.**

The Sardinian Warbler breeds from Iberia and North Africa eastwards across the Mediterranean basin to Afghanistan, wintering mainly south to the Sahara. A large proportion of the Mediterranean population is sedentary. It is a rare spring and autumn vagrant to the British Isles.

The first county record was a male trapped at Waxham by Ted Williams on 28th April 1973. It was still present next day, but at times was difficult to locate. The second was also a male, a long staying, but also often very elusive individual at Weybourne from 1st September to 5th October 1980.

Since then, a singing male frequented Muckleburgh Hill, Weybourne on 27th April 1991, with a female trapped, remarkably again at Weybourne, on 14th May 1992 and released at dawn next day on Muckleburgh Hill where it remained until the evening. In 1994, an immature male was located in Burnham Overy Dunes on 21st April followed by a first-year male at Holme on 15th–16th May. The following year, an adult singing male remained in the same bush at Holme on 18th–19th May 1995, only two days later than the 1994 occurrence.

*Peter Allard*

## | Rüppell's Warbler |                                    *Sylvia rueppelli*

**A very rare vagrant; one record.**

The Rüppell's Warbler breeds from southern Greece, Crete and the Aegean Islands south to Rhodes and Turkey, and eastwards to the Lebanon, wintering in north-east Africa. It is a very rare vagrant to the British Isles with only five records up to the end of 1997.

A female was found by Gary Hibberd in dense blackthorn scrub at Holme Dunes on 31st August 1992. It was last seen on 4th September before departing during overnight clear skies and light winds (Hibberd 1993a). This was only the fourth British record and the first for the mainland. Fortunately it stayed in one sheltered area and proved a very popular bird.

*Peter Allard*

## Desert Warbler                                    *Sylvia nana*

**A very rare vagrant; one record.**

The Desert Warbler breeds in north-west Africa and from the Caspian Sea to southern Iran eastwards to Mongolia. The African population is largely sedentary whilst the eastern race is highly migratory and winters from north-east Africa eastwards to the deserts of north-east India. It is a rare vagrant to the British Isles.

One found by Mark Golley frequented The Hood at Blakeney Point from the evening of 27th May to 1st June 1993. One of the surprises of the spring, it was often in full song and was even observed nest-building (Golley 1993c, 1994). Most occurrences in Europe relate to the central Asian race *S. n. nana*. This was the tenth record for Britain and the first in spring.

*Peter Allard*

## Barred Warbler                                    *Sylvia nisoria*

**A very scarce autumn passage migrant; one spring record.**

Barred Warblers breed in the upper middle latitudes of the Western and central Palearctic, extending eastwards from north-west Italy to central Asia, and from southern Finland in the north to Greece and Turkey in the south. They winter in East Africa, mainly in Kenya. To Britain, they are annual autumn migrants, although numbers vary each year in relationship to the occurrence and timing of anticyclonic conditions. Their arrival has been variously linked to reversed migration and/or post-breeding dispersal, as first-autumn birds are invariably involved (Cottridge & Vinicombe 1996).

The first Norfolk record was of a bird shot by F.D.Power at Blakeney on 4th September 1884, during the same autumn visit which produced Norfolk's first Icterine Warbler. F.D.Power also claimed the county's second record when he obtained another near the same spot at Blakeney on 10th September 1888

(Stevenson). By the time that Riviere produced his county avifauna, the total had risen to 18, all of which had been recorded between 27th August and 27th September, with the majority during the first week of September. Amongst them was an adult female shot on 27th September 1897.

The county total now stands at over 570 with but a single spring record – at Caister on 13th–14th May 1985. Recorded each year since 1952, the annual total has varied from one (as recently as 1978) to at least 38 in 1994, 35 in 1995 and 34 in 1996, with 28 in 1977. The first Barred Warblers of the autumn are not usually seen until after mid-August, with the earliest dates being at Holkham dunes on 2nd August 1960 and at Blakeney Point on 8th August 1968 and two on 8th August 1977. An earlier record on 29th July 1975 at Sheringham, published in the *Norfolk Bird Report 1975*, has subsequently been withdrawn by the observer. The majority of birds are recorded in the last two weeks of August and the first three weeks of September, with a peak in late August and early September. Occasional birds are found in October, including one which lingered at Cley from 22nd October to 5th November 1970, mirrored by another at Eccles from at least 17th October to 4th November 1996. There have been two other November records - one at Blakeney on 2nd November 1963 and an exceptionally late bird which was ringed at Happisburgh on 13th November 1976.

It is not unusual for Barred Warblers to remain in the same area, or even the same clump of bushes, for several days in the autumn. In addition to the two described above, other long-staying individuals have been at Holme from 27th August to 17th September 1983 and at Salthouse from 24th August to 4th September 1986 and on 1st–12th September 1995. While most records involve single birds, six were present at Holme on 3rd September 1994, five at Blakeney Point on 21st August 1971 and four at Holkham Meals on 3rd–4th September 1981. There has been only a single record of a Barred Warbler away from the coast – one at East Winch on 15th September 1985.

A total of 52 Barred Warblers has been ringed in Norfolk, including eight in 1996 and six in 1995. There is a single recovery involving one ringed at Sheringham Bird Observatory on 5th September 1995 and controlled 22 days later at Weybourne Camp, just over 2km to the west.

*Moss Taylor*

## Lesser Whitethroat

SEA PALLING. 1·5·2000.
SNETTISHAM. 23·6·1986.

*Sylvia curruca*

**A common summer visitor and passage migrant; two mid-winter records.**

The Lesser Whitethroat is a breeding summer visitor to the middle and upper middle latitudes of the Western Palearctic, being absent from the Iberian Peninsula, much of southern France and Italy. It winters in north-east Africa, chiefly in Sudan and Chad. It breeds throughout most of southern, eastern and central England, becoming increasingly scarce further north and west.

Stevenson described it as generally distributed but decidedly local, adding '... my own personal acquaintance with it in this county is very slight', which suggests that it was far less numerous than it is today. By the time that Riviere wrote his county avifauna it was '... a not uncommon summer visitor, less numerous and more local in its distribution than [the Whitethroat]'; a description of its status which still holds true today.

Lesser Whitethroats, unlike Whitethroats, favour tall, dense hedgerows, thorn thickets and tall scrub, such as is present along overgrown railway embankments, nesting higher off the ground than other *Sylvia* warblers. During the fieldwork for the Norfolk Atlas, it was found in only 20% of the tetrads but was thought to have been under-recorded. Its distribution was somewhat patchy, being sparse in the open landscapes of Broadland and the Fens, and it was surprisingly absent in the Aylsham/North Walsham area in both the Norfolk Atlas and the New Atlas. A decline in numbers during the 1990s is suggested by the number of 1km squares in which it was recorded in Norfolk for the 1994–97 BBS, falling from 29% in 1994 and 1995, to 25% in 1996 and only 11% in 1997. The highest reported breeding concentration in recent years was eight singing males at Holme in 1997.

The first Lesser Whitethroats are normally seen in Norfolk during the third week of April with passage peaking in mid-May. The earliest arrival date for the county is 10th April 1961 and the highest spring counts have been 20 at Blakeney Point on 20th May 1988 and 15 at Holme on 19th May 1996. Autumn passage takes place during August and September, but as in the spring, only small numbers of birds are generally involved. Counts of 20 or more are unusual and the highest was 40 at Blakeney Point during the 'fall' of 13th–16th September 1993. The last birds are normally recorded in the last week of October, but since 1987 there have been seven sightings in November, the latest at Holme on 20th November 1988. Birds showing the characteristics of the eastern race *S. c. blythi* have been recorded in Norfolk on about 16 occasions, the majority between mid-September and mid-October, with up to three at Sheringham on 22nd–26th September 1996.

There have been two instances of Lesser Whitethroats wintering in Norfolk. One, possibly of the eastern race *blythi*, fed on suet, bones and scraps at a bird table at Welney from 11th December 1984 to 14th January 1985 and another was present at Hardley Street from 20th December 1994 to mid-March 1995.

About 1,400 Lesser Whitethroats have been ringed in Norfolk since 1980, compared with over 5,000 Whitethroats, which is probably a reasonable indication of the comparative abundance of the two species within the county. Only three Norfolk-ringed Lesser Whitethroats have been recovered abroad and one Belgian-ringed bird has been found here. The three spring recoveries of Lesser Whitethroats provide conflicting evidence of the route taken at this time of year. One ringed at Sandwich Bay, Kent on 1st May 1990 was controlled at Sheringham two days later, another ringed at Wanze in Belgium on 25th May 1981 was controlled at Salthouse one month later and the third ringed at Spurn Point, Yorkshire on 30th April 1966 was found at Attleborough two weeks later, an unusual southerly movement in spring.

In autumn, more typical movements were shown by two ringed in Norfolk and found in Suffolk the following month, by one ringed near Wakefield, West Yorkshire recovered at Kirby Cane three weeks later and by another from Gibraltar Point, Lincolnshire found at Great Ormesby two weeks later. European populations of the Lesser Whitethroat breeding west of about 30°E, which include those in Britain, take a heading between east-south-east and south-south-east to arrive at their winter quarters via the eastern Mediterranean (BWP). The recovery of one ringed at Holme on 9th May 1970 and found near Alexandria, Egypt on 4th November 1970 and another ringed at Weybourne on 4th July 1995 and controlled at Focagne, Belgium on 2nd September 1995 thus fit the expected pattern. The third foreign recovery was of a male ringed at Lessingham in May 1988 found in The Netherlands the following July. Finally, one ringed at Kettlestone on 21st May 1983 and retrapped there on 22nd August 1988 sets the longevity record for a British-ringed Lesser Whitethroat.

*Moss Taylor*

## Whitethroat (Common Whitethroat)    *Sylvia communis*

TITCHWELL.
23·6·1986.

**A very common summer visitor and common passage migrant; one mid-winter record.**

The Whitethroat is a breeding summer visitor to the middle latitudes of the Western Palearctic, occurring extensively in Europe. It occurs throughout England and Wales, apart from the highest ground in the more mountainous areas, and it also breeds on the lower ground in southern and eastern Scotland (New Atlas). British Whitethroats winter mainly south from the southern edge of the Sahara and across northern tropical Africa.

In common with many of the authors of the first county avifaunas, Stevenson described the White-throat as one of our most common summer visitors and goes on to say '... our hedgerows and bushes fast budding into leaf are alive with its simple song, and its trim little figure is seen flitting from spray to spray, or rising into the air, hovering and singing in the pure enjoyment of the renewal of spring'.

Whitethroats are one of the most typical breeding birds of scrub, favouring areas with patchy, low, tangled vegetation. Thus they are commonly found in Norfolk on heathland and commons, as well as along hedgerows, on golf courses, along woodland edges and in clearings. Many of the nests are built in brambles or nettles, accounting for the old rural name of 'nettle creeper' (Stevenson).

Until the late 1960s, the Whitethroat remained as abundant as in Stevenson's and Riviere's day but the well-documented crash in numbers in 1969, dramatically affected the situation. In winter Whitethroats remain in the northern semi-arid Sahel zone, rather than moving further south after a few weeks, unlike the other small, insectivorous migrants (BWP). Severe droughts in this region of West Africa drastically reduced the numbers of Whitethroats able to survive the 1968–69 winter and successfully undertake their spring migration. As a direct result, the breeding population of Whitethroats in 1969 fell to about a quarter of the previous year's figure (Winstanley *et al.* 1974). Since then, numbers have gradually recovered, although two more declines in 1984 and 1991, due to similar problems in the winter quarters, once again reduced their abundance.

The species was recorded in 54% of the tetrads for the Norfolk Atlas. The fieldwork for this was carried out during 1980–85 at a time when the population was low and this may well account for the very patchy, if widespread, distribution. More recently Whitethroats were recorded in 75–86% of the 1km squares covered in Norfolk for the BBS in 1994–97. The highest concentrations in the last few years have been 25–30 in the Choseley/Thornham/Titchwell area, 30 at Weybourne Camp and Muckleburgh Hill, and 20–30 in the area covered by Sheringham Bird Observatory all in 1996, while maximum counts in 1997 were 24 at Welney, 18 at Boyland Wood and 21 on Salthouse Heath.

In spring, the first Whitethroats generally arrive in Norfolk during mid-April, the earliest date being 8th April 1956. Influxes of apparent passage migrants along the coast have been noted in late April and early May, but the majority of spring Whitethroats are recorded singing at their breeding sites. The maximum spring counts have been 80 at Sheringham on 6th–7th May 1995, 50 at Holkham Meals on 1st May 1996 and 40 at Waxham on 7th May 1994.

Autumn migration, at least in part associated with post-fledging dispersal, commences in late July and peaks in late August, with far smaller numbers evident through September. Autumn arrivals of Continental migrants may involve Whitethroats, as in the 'fall' in mid-September 1993, when up to 45 were present at Sheringham. Very few are seen in October and the last is generally recorded in mid to late October. There have been only two records later than this – at Marham Fen on 16th November 1968 and at Horsey on 10th November 1987. A record of one in a Scratby garden on 19th–28th February 1992, during which time it was caught and ringed, is unprecedented.

Over 5,000 Whitethroats have been ringed in Norfolk since 1980. In general, the annual county ringing total has been steadily increasing since the late 1980s, with a peak of 1,200 ringed in 1995, compared with an average of only 325 during the previous five years. Part of this increase is undoubtedly due to the improving fortunes of the species in its winter quarters. Only four Norfolk-ringed Whitethroats have been recovered abroad and two foreign-ringed birds have been found in the county.

Some indication of the route taken by spring arrivals is shown by a Whitethroat ringed at Dungeness, Kent on 4th May 1957 and found at Spixworth eight days later, while another ringed at Landguard Point, Suffolk on 4th May 1984 was at Briningham in early July. Onward movement through Norfolk is demonstrated by one ringed at Sheringham on 12th May 1979 and controlled at Saltfleetby, Lincolnshire on 1st June. One ringed on the East Frisian Islands, Germany on 29th April 1952 and found at Salthouse on 27th June may well have taken a more westerly route across the North Sea. An indication of how late some Whitethroats pass through Iberia in spring, is shown by an autumn-ringed bird from Sheringham found freshly dead at Alcazar, in Central Spain on 15th May.

A Whitethroat ringed at Fjell on the south-western coast of Norway on 24th August 1996 and controlled at Holme four weeks later was only the second recovery in the British Isles of a Scandinavian-ringed Whitethroat and the first from Norway. Two recoveries provide some indication of the route taken after birds have left Norfolk – one ringed at Didlington on 20th August 1995 was controlled at Beachy Head, Sussex on 17th September and the other ringed at Snettisham on 2nd August was controlled at Icklesham, Sussex on 22nd August. Two recoveries have involved birds passing through the south-western tip of the Algarve in Portugal in autumn – one ringed at Cley on 29th April 1959 was found at Lagos in September and the other ringed at Cape St Vincent, Portugal on 1st October 1961 was found at Saxthorpe on 14th July 1962. A nestling ringed at Mundford in 1967 was recovered in northern Portugal in September and another ringed on autumn passage was found freshly dead in November along the Atlantic coast of Portugal. Finally, there have been many instances of ringed Whitethroats, both juveniles and adults, returning to the same general area in subsequent summers to breed.

*Moss Taylor*

| **Garden Warbler** | CHEDGRAVE. 4-7-1993. | ***Sylvia borin*** |

**A common summer visitor and passage migrant.**

The Garden Warbler is a breeding summer visitor to the middle and upper middle latitudes of the Western Palearctic, wintering extensively from West Africa to East Africa, south to South Africa. It is generally distributed throughout England, Wales and southern Scotland with localised populations in Ireland.

Both Stevenson and Riviere described it as less abundant and more locally distributed than the Blackcap, suggesting that its status has not changed since at least the mid-19th century.

Garden Warblers breed in areas of open deciduous woodland with a dense scrub layer, often with a tangle of brambles. Compared with Blackcaps they are more often found away from mature trees, nesting in thickets of blackthorn and hawthorn, in clumps of rhododendrons and in young conifer plantations. They have a rather patchy distribution in Norfolk, having been found in only 25% of the tetrads during fieldwork for the Norfolk Atlas, but they were well represented in Breckland and in the belt of well-wooded country interspersed with heathland towards Hunstanton. They were not reported from areas of apparently suitable woodland in the south of the county, but this may have been related to the similarity between the songs of the Garden Warbler and Blackcap. Although there was a decline in numbers in the early and mid-1970s, related to the drought in the Sahel region, the Garden Warbler was less severely affected as it simply passes through this part of Africa en route to its winter quarters. During the four years 1994–97 it has a shown a slight but annual increase in the number of 1km squares in which it has been recorded in Norfolk for the BBS, from 21% to 30%. The highest concentration reported in recent years was of 11 singing males at East Wretham in 1997.

The first Garden Warblers of the spring are generally heard singing in the last week of April, about a month later than the earliest Blackcaps. Spring passage peaks in mid-May although only small numbers are involved and the highest site count is just ten at Blakeney Point. The passage, however, can be prolonged as shown by one at Scolt Head on 5th June 1997 and four at Blakeney Point on 11th June 1988. There have only been two records of Garden Warblers arriving in Norfolk before mid-April, on both occasions at Holme, on 3rd April 1988 and two on 10th April 1993.

A more noticeable autumn passage commences in August, with maximum numbers occurring between late August and mid-September, usually in association with east or north-east winds. The famous 'fall' of drift migrants on 3rd–4th September 1965 resulted in record numbers of Garden Warblers at many sites around the Norfolk coast, including an estimated 500 between Blakeney Point and Salthouse. More usual counts have been 35 at Holme, 50 at Holkham Meals, 45 at Wells East Hills and 80 at Blakeney Point all on 26th August 1987. Similar 'falls' were also recorded between Holme and Sheringham in September in 1993 and 1994, almost certainly involving birds displaced from northern Europe. The unprecedented 'fall' of Redstarts on 18th September 1995, included some Garden Warblers with counts of 60 at Holme, 35 at Wells East Hills and 40 at Blakeney Point. However, they may have arrived from further east than usual as two Garden Warblers ringed at Holkham at this time showed the characteristics of the Siberian race *S. b. woodwardi*. Passage continues into October with the last birds generally being recorded late in the month. However, since 1984, single Garden Warblers in November have become almost annual, in addition to three at Wells on 1st–5th November 1993 and up to six at Sheringham on 9th–15th November 1995. The latest was at Norwich on 28th November 1992.

Over 3,000 Garden Warblers have been ringed in Norfolk since 1980, of which 2,000 were ringed between 1993 and 1998. Three birds ringed abroad in August have been controlled in the county in early September – two from Belgium at Holme and Waxham respectively, and one from Norway at Weybourne. In addition, a June-ringed bird from Helgoland, Germany was controlled two years later at Gillingham. Three foreign recoveries have resulted from Norfolk ringing in autumn – one ringed at Holme on 21st August 1977 was controlled one month later at Helgoland, another ringed at Sheringham in 1985 was found dead in Morocco in January 1988, presumably having perished several weeks earlier while on passage to West Africa, while the third was ringed at Banningham and was recovered in Algeria the following April. Two other birds from Holme have also provided interesting recoveries – one ringed on 9th October 1974 was found dead near Manchester in November and the other ringed on 12th August 1975 was found in Cornwall in spring 1980. The more expected route taken by Garden Warblers after leaving Norfolk was shown by controls at Fagbury, Suffolk and Icklesham, Sussex later the same autumn.

*Moss Taylor*

**Blackcap** CHEDGRAVE . MY GARDEN. (♂) 22-4-2000.     *Sylvia atricapilla*

**A common summer visitor and passage migrant; scarce in winter.**

The Blackcap breeds throughout much of the middle latitudes of the Western Palearctic. Northern and eastern populations are wholly migratory, southern birds partially so and the species winters within and south of the breeding range, south to sub-Saharan Africa. In Britain, the Blackcap is widely distributed throughout England, Wales and southern Scotland, only being absent from higher ground and The Fens, having spread northwards in the last 50 years (New Atlas).

Historically, Blackcaps have always been widespread and common breeding summer visitors to Norfolk, although Stevenson and Riviere were only able to give a single winter record on 22nd December 1852.

The Blackcap breeds in mature deciduous and mixed woodland throughout the county, including Broadland carrs, sallow thickets around worked out gravel pits and Fenland poplars, also in large gardens with mature trees from which the males can sing. It is generally absent or sparse in The Fens and intensively farmed areas (Kelly 1986). It is more widespread than the Garden Warbler, having been recorded in every 10km square in Norfolk during the fieldwork for the New Atlas and in 45% of the tetrads covered for the Norfolk Atlas. During the 1994–97 BBS it was found in 55–66% of the 1km squares covered in Norfolk.

The first spring migrants, generally males, are recorded in late March or early April; the birds ability to feed on berries, such as ivy, enabling them to survive any cold spells in early spring (68–72 BTO Atlas). Females tend to arrive about a week or more later and the species is normally widespread by the end of April. Spring passage around the coast is on a small scale, although a widespread arrival on 23rd April 1994 included 35 at Holme. A few passage birds are noted until mid-May.

From late July onwards, the post-fledging dispersal of young Blackcaps takes them away from their natal areas, as shown by a total of 100 juveniles ringed in early autumn 1993 at a site in the Stanford Training Area; while the adults remain to undergo a complete moult before migrating. Autumn passage is generally recorded from late August, the majority of British birds having left the country by early October. The autumn departure of one individual was delightfully described by Richard Richardson in the *Norfolk Bird Report 1955* 'A male hand-reared from the age of 6 days, became excessively tame. It first bathed at 10 days, first uttered sub-song at 14 days, slept inside my cupped hand and later on bed-rail or among flowers in vase. It would forage for aphids among the broad beans and come when called. Despite this confiding behaviour it began to show restlessness during the night early in October and on the 5th departed with scarcely a backward glance'.

While small numbers of Blackcaps are a regular feature of late autumn along the Norfolk coast, larger numbers only occur with a north-east to south-east airstream (Taylor 1981), usually in the first half of October. The highest counts have been 60 at Holkham Meals on 12th and 17th October 1980, 80 at Holkham Meals and 60 at Blakeney Point on 6th October 1982, 35 at Blakeney Point on 29th September 1991 and 30 at Overstrand on 4th October 1994. A total of 15 in a single tree in Yarmouth Cemeteries on 13th October 1988 was also noteworthy. This late autumn passage, noted in the last 20 years, would appear to be a recent trend. During the 1950s, Blackcaps were rarely recorded in Norfolk in October, as shown by the following entry in the *Norfolk Bird Report 1959* '[The Blackcap] was more than usually in evidence during October along the North coast', referring to up to four at Cley, two at Holme and one at Scolt Head!

The most notable change in recent years, however, has been the dramatic increase in the number overwintering in Norfolk. During the winter of 1966–67 at least ten Blackcaps were present in the county, the first occasion that more than one or two had overwintered. In December 1992, no less than 53 were included in the *Norfolk Bird Report*, so the actual figure overwintering in Norfolk must have been far higher. Since then, Blackcaps have become regular visitors to gardens during the winter months, albeit in small numbers. Although the majority of records refer to single birds, up to eight have been seen at the same locality. Some remain faithful to the same area for several weeks, others are present for just one or two days. Suburban gardens appear to be the favoured localities, especially in the Norwich area, but this may simply be a reflection of the distribution of observers. During the early winter, natural foods, particularly berries, form a high proportion of the diet and the presence of large stands of sea buckthorn at Holme probably explains the frequency with which numbers of wintering Blackcaps are recorded there.

From late December, the birds begin to exploit the available food sources in gardens, taking bread, cheese, fat, birdseed and peanuts. Thus enabling them to maintain their optimum weight even during severe weather. Indeed, colder spells often result in an increase in winter records from gardens (Winter Atlas). Although wintering Blackcaps are far more widespread and numerous in southern and western England, they were recorded in nearly one third of the 10km squares in Norfolk during the Winter Atlas fieldwork.

Berthold *et al.* (1990) have shown that migration in Blackcaps is strongly influenced by genetic factors and that they can rapidly respond by natural selection to changes in the environment. The increased availability of artificial foods in gardens in recent years has enabled Blackcaps to successfully overwinter in Britain and Ireland in ever increasing numbers (Berthold & Terrill 1988). The Blackcaps wintering in Norfolk, however, are not local breeding birds or their offspring but are visitors from the central European populations, which have shown an increase in recent years.

Over 12,000 Blackcaps have been ringed in Norfolk since 1960, the vast majority in late summer and autumn. Further evidence of the increasing abundance of Blackcaps in recent years is provided by the ringing totals for each decade – 1960s – 500, 1970s – 1,500, 1980s – 2,200 and 1990s (up to 1998) – over 8,000. Although ringing activity has certainly increased in recent years, this does not account for the dramatic rise in numbers.

There have been many instances of ringed Blackcaps returning to the same breeding area in subsequent years. To date, about 90 Blackcaps ringed in Norfolk have been recovered away from the site of ringing, including 29 from abroad – Germany, The Netherlands, Belgium (4), France (3), Spain (6), Morocco (5), Algeria (four, including two to the same locality in successive years), Corsica, Italy, Lebanon, Syria and Guinea. In addition, 11 foreign-ringed Blackcaps have been found in the county.

Spring recoveries of Blackcaps, of probable British stock, ringed in Norfolk the previous year, indicate that migrants leave northern France and Belgium to make the short sea-crossing to south-east England, before moving north into Norfolk. Similarly in autumn, birds arrive via Belgium, from where five ringed in August-September have been controlled later the same autumn in Norfolk.

The Blackcap is one of the species which shows a clear cut migratory divide, with those breeding in Scandinavia and to the east of 12°E migrating in a south-easterly direction towards Cyprus and the Levant, while those from western Europe, including Britain, are south-west oriented heading to southern France and Iberia. However, autumn arrivals on the Norfolk coast can include birds from both populations, as shown by one ringed at Stiffkey on 17th September 1968 found in Lebanon on 6th May 1969 and another ringed at Holme on 16th October 1970 and found just 44 days later in southern Italy on 29th November 1970. More difficult to explain was one ringed at Holme on 7th May 1996 which was recovered in Syria in March 1997.

British Blackcaps winter in southern Iberia and North Africa, and from Norfolk there have been ten recoveries within this area in mid-winter. Another ringed at Happisburgh on 12th October 1982 and found in Corsica on 31st January 1983 was unusually far to the east and may well have been a bird from the eastern population. One ringed at Walton Common on 24th July 1982 and found at Belongo, Guinea on 2nd March 1985 was only the fifth British-ringed Blackcap to be recovered south of the Sahara.

There have been two recoveries involving overwintering birds – a female ringed at Bexhill-on-Sea, Sussex on 12th February 1987 and retrapped at West Walton on 17th January 1988 and a male ringed in a Sheringham garden on 16th November 1994 found dead at Ouddorp, The Netherlands on 28th January 1995. These movements indicate that wintering Blackcaps are not necessarily site faithful in subsequent years and even wander widely during the course of a single winter.

*Moss Taylor*

# Greenish Warbler        *Phylloscopus trochiloides*

**A rare autumn vagrant; two spring records.**

In the Western Palearctic, the western race of Greenish Warbler *P. t. viridanus* breeds in the lowlands of the upper middle latitudes. It winters in the Indian subcontinent. Until the late 1950s the Greenish Warbler was a rare vagrant to the British Isles but since then it has become an almost annual visitor in small numbers.

After the first Norfolk record on Blakeney Point on 6th September 1951 – a bird found by Peter Browne and Arnold Hichon – a further 16 years were to pass before the next two occurred, both in 1967: one trapped at Holme on 12th September and one seen at Holkham on 17th–24th September.

The county total currently stands at 50, of which three have been in spring, all between 30th May and 1st June. All three spring records have involved males in song – two in 1992 at Blakeney Point on 30th May and at Waxham the following day, and one at North Lopham Fen on 1st June 1998.

Of the remaining records, most have arrived after easterly or south-easterly winds in early autumn, with the majority between 25th August and 3rd September. The earliest was at Horsey on 10th August 1983 and only two have been found after the end of September – the Two-barred Greenish Warbler *P. t. plumbeitarsus* described below at Wells on 15th–16th October 1996 and one of the race *viridanus* trapped at Holme on 9th November 1968, an extremely late date for the species.

Two-thirds of Norfolk's Greenish Warblers have been found either at Blakeney Point or Holkham Meals. There have also been four sightings at Waxham, including two on 26th August 1987. On only three other occasions have multiple occurrences been recorded – two at Blakeney Point on both 13th August 1977 and 27th–28th August 1987, and two at Holkham Meals on 3rd September 1995. Bloomfield (1997a) has drawn attention to the ease with which the number of vagrant warblers at Holkham Meals can be overestimated. In September 1995, he followed a typically mobile, mixed flock of tits, containing both a Greenish and an Icterine Warbler, a distance of 2km in about 15 minutes. Greenish Warblers have been found at several other sites along the north Norfolk coast between Hunstanton Golf Course and Overstrand, and from Paston south to Yarmouth.

Greenish Warblers tend to arrive in Britain in invasion years, alternating with years when the species is absent or very scarce (BWP). In Norfolk, the highest annual totals have been five in 1972, seven in 1987 and nine in 1995. It appeared annually in the county between 1990 and 1996.

The only Norfolk record of a Two-barred Greenish Warbler *plumbeitarsus*, which breeds from eastern Siberia to China and winters in south-east Asia, was one found by John Kemp in The Dell at Wells on 15th October 1996, where it remained for two days (Golley *et al.* 1997, Kemp 1997a). At the time, it was only the second British record of this east Asian race, which was formerly considered to be a separate species. Four Greenish Warblers have been ringed in Norfolk, all at Holme between 1967 and 1976.

*Moss Taylor*

# Arctic Warbler                    *Phylloscopus borealis*

**A rare autumn vagrant; one mid-summer record.**

The breeding range of the Arctic Warbler lies entirely within the subarctic region, extending from northern Norway, in the Western Palearctic, east across Siberia to western Alaska and south to Japan. It winters in southern south-east Asia. To the British Isles, it remains a rare vagrant with no increase in the number of records in recent years.

Riviere included the first British record of 'Eversmann's Warbler', as it was then known – one shot by E. C. Arnold on Blakeney Point on 4th September 1922, which is now in the Castle Museum, Norwich. The county total currently stands at 13:

> 1922: One shot at Blakeney Point on 4th September
> 1951: Blakeney Point on 21st September
> 1968: Blakeney Point on 24th–31st August
> Wells on 7th September
> 1975: One ringed at Titchwell on 5th July
> 1976: Holme on 14th–19th October
> 1977: Wells on 18th–23rd September
> 1978: Blakeney Point on 8th September
> 1984: Holme on 10th September
> 1988: Yarmouth Cemeteries on 1st–2nd October
> 1993: Blakeney Point on 1st–2nd September
> 1994: Wells on 2nd September
> 1998: Eccles on 29th September

Autumn arrival dates fall between 24th August and 14th October, with a peak in the first ten days of September. The bird trapped in July at Titchwell was the earliest British record by a month. Since then others have been ringed on Fair Isle on 3rd July 1982 and 27th June 1995. As Arctic Warblers do not leave their winter quarters until April or early May, these mid-summer records are probably overshooting spring migrants rather than early autumn birds.

*Moss Taylor*

## Pallas's Warbler (Pallas's Leaf Warbler)     *Phylloscopus proregulus*

A very scarce autumn vagrant.

Pallas's Warblers
(Bryan Bland)

Pallas's Warbler breeds in southern Siberia, east from the Altai Mountains to Manchuria and winters in south-east Asia. Since the 1960s, it has become a regular autumn vagrant to north-west Europe, almost certainly as a result of reversed migration, assisted by anticyclonic conditions.

The first British record was of a bird shot by Edward Ramm at Cley on 31st October 1896. This historic specimen formed part of the outstanding Connop collection housed in Rollesby Hall until 1912. It was later acquired by Birmingham City Museum, where it still remains. Members of the Cambridge Bird Club on a field expedition to Holme on 17th November 1957 found and subsequently trapped the next for Norfolk, which was still only the third in the British Isles. The next two Norfolk records were also birds at Holme in 1963 and 1968. Strangely enough, the next occurrence in Norfolk on 30th October 1971 was well inland, in the garden of a Norwich ringer, although much to his disappointment the bird was not trapped.

The Norfolk total has subsequently risen to 159, and since 1980 small numbers have appeared annually, except in 1983 and 1990. Excluding 1996, the vast majority have arrived between the second week of October and the first week of November, with a peak from mid- to late October, about two weeks later than that for Yellow-browed Warbler. The earliest record was at Holkham Meals on 7th October 1982, a year in which record numbers were found in both the British Isles and Norfolk, with a county total of over 20. Of these, 14 were seen at Holkham Meals with record day-counts of nine on 10th and 15th October 1982. However, this arrival was eclipsed in 1996, the first wave between 22nd and 31st October totalling seven birds, while in the second wave from 11th to 23rd November at least 22 were found, making a total for the autumn of 29. The following year the autumn total was 22, the second highest annual total.

The simultaneous arrival of birds is often noted at widely-scattered localities on the Norfolk coast. This was particularly obvious between 13th and 15th November 1996, when a total of 16 birds was located at twelve sites, the majority between Cromer and Caister. It is interesting to speculate how many more actually made landfall on those days. Fraser (1997) suggested that about half the rare passerines arriving on the east coast of Britain are missed, and Sharrock and Fraser (1997) estimated that it is nearer two-thirds.

Only five Pallas's Warblers have been recorded in the last ten days of November – singles at Waxham on 21st November 1986, Wells on 21st November 1998 and Sheringham on 23rd November 1996, and two at Holkham on 24th November 1987, one remaining until 29th November.

As indicated earlier, Holkham Meals is the most favoured locality in the county with 45 records of Pallas's Warbler. Other sites where the species has been recorded on a number of occasions, often as a result of birds being trapped for ringing, are Holme (12), Sheringham/Weybourne (10), Waxham (8) and Winterton (10, of which 7 were in 1996). In addition to the Norwich record mentioned earlier, two others have been found inland, both in 1994 – one at Strumpshaw Fen on 3rd November and the other at Colby on 9th November, which was a surprise find in a mist net in a ringer's garden. A total of 22 Pallas's Warblers has been ringed in Norfolk, including five at Winterton in 1996.

*Moss Taylor*

## Yellow-browed Warbler | HOLKHAM NNR. 7·10·1986. *Phylloscopus inornatus*

**A scarce autumn migrant.**

The Yellow-browed Warbler is the commonest Siberian vagrant to occur in western Europe, breeding from the Ural Mountains east across Siberia and wintering in southern Asia. There has been a steady increase in the number of records in the British Isles since the late 1960s, although the annual totals fluctuate from year to year.

Riviere described the circumstances of the first Norfolk record: '[It] was killed [at Cley] on 1st October 1894 by a working man, who appears to have fired at it merely for the purpose of discharging his muzzle-loader.' This constituted only the fourth British record. He goes on to give seven further autumn records, the last in 1918. The sole spring record claimed by Jim Vincent near Hickling Broad on 4th May 1928 is no longer fully acceptable (Seago 1977).

A further 43 years were to pass before the next Yellow-browed Warbler was seen in Norfolk. This bird was found in the *Suaeda* bushes at The Hood on Blakeney Point on 21st September 1962. Attempts by Richard Richardson to trap it, to confirm the identification in the hand, were thwarted, as it twice flew through a mist net – the finer mesh nets were not available at that time (Taylor 1987c). Amazingly, since then, the species has become an annual autumn passage migrant along the Norfolk coast.

The county total now stands at over 610, although up to 1983 double figures were only achieved in two of the years, with ten in 1968 (including single specimens obtained on the Inner Dowsing light-vessel on 6th October and the Smith's Knoll light-vessel on 12th October, both of which were identified at the British Museum) and 18 in 1975. Between 1984 and 1998, an average of 33 Yellow-browed Warblers were recorded annually in Norfolk, with a maximum of 69 in 1988, in which year a record total of 771 was found in the British Isles. The reasons for the dramatic increase in recent years are not fully understood. It may be related to a change in the post-fledging dispersal behaviour of juveniles, (all the trapped birds have been in their first-autumn), associated with high population levels or range expansion. The more frequent easterly winds in late autumn may also be partly responsible, although Yellow-browed Warblers arrive in Norfolk in a variety of weather conditions from clear skies with light sea breezes to gale force winds anywhere between north-west and south-east (Bloomfield 1993).

Yellow-browed Warblers leave their breeding grounds in August and September. During both the 1960s and 1970s the average date of the first autumn record in Norfolk was 28th September, in the 1980s it was 22nd September and during the 1990s (up to 1998) it was 20th September. A typical pattern is for a wave of birds to arrive during the day, often in calm anticyclonic conditions, at several sites around the coast. Within a few days most have moved on, sometimes to be replaced by other fresh arrivals (Stoddart 1990a). The majority of birds are recorded in the last ten days of September through to the end of October. The earliest autumn arrivals were on 13th September 1993 at Wells, on 14th September 1990 at Sheringham and on 15th September 1968 at Holme. Occasional birds are recorded in November, the latest being one that remained at Holkham Meals from 3rd November to 1st December 1968. There has been one other December record – at Brundall on 6th December 1991.

On passage, Yellow-browed Warblers favour sallows and sycamore, and over half of all the Norfolk records (280+) are from Holkham Meals. One even set up a territory and sang for several days in the Dell at Wells in the autumn of 1986. In recent years, the species has been found at most of the regularly watched sites around the Norfolk coast.

While most records refer to single birds, multiple occurrences are not unusual and the highest counts at a single locality have both been at Holkham Meals with 15 on 12th October 1975 and 18 on 12th

October 1988. The first inland record was at Strumpshaw on 21st October 1984, since when there have been a further eleven – at Pensthorpe on 24th September 1988, East Winch Common on 14th October 1988, Brundall on 6th December 1991, Docking on 13th October 1992, North Walsham on 19th October 1992, The Nunnery, Thetford on 17th–18th September 1993, Stalham Green on 22nd September 1994, UEA, Norwich on 29th September 1994, Hempstead on both 16th–18th November 1996 and 16th October 1997, and East Ruston on 11th October 1998. A total of 35 Yellow-browed Warblers has been ringed in Norfolk, of which eight were trapped in 1988 and seven in 1994.

*Moss Taylor*

# Hume's Warbler (Hume's Leaf Warbler)     *Phylloscopus humei*

**A very rare vagrant; five records.**

Hume's Warbler breeds in south-central Asia from the Sayan and Altai Mountains south to the north-west Himalayas, and winters mainly in the Indian subcontinent from Pakistan to Bangladesh. Until 1997 it was considered to be a race of the Yellow-browed Warbler. It is a rare late autumn (mostly November) vagrant to Britain and was first identified here in 1966. Its migration pattern differs markedly from that of its Siberian cousin, the Yellow-browed Warbler, but closely mirrors that of Pallas's Warbler though with a greater propensity to overwinter.

The first county record was one found by Richard Richardson frequenting a small wood by Snipe's Marsh at Cley from 3rd December 1967 to 7th January 1968. It was initially identified as a Yellow-browed Warbler but in 1998, following advances in warbler identification, especially the importance of vocalisation, the record was reviewed and recognised as the second British record of a Hume's Warbler. Another was found in tall oaks at Winterton on 1st December 1989 where it remained until 8th December (Stoddart 1990b).

The third county record was one at the west end of Holkham Meals from 25th October to 1st November 1991. Another was present in Yarmouth Cemeteries from 2nd January to 28th April 1995, which had possibly been present since 15th December 1994. It also visited adjacent gardens, but was mostly loyal to Holm oaks in the cemeteries and gave observers the chance to familiarise themselves with the characteristics and vocalisations of the species. A further individual appeared at Holme on 22nd October 1997.

*Peter Allard*

# Radde's Warbler     *Phylloscopus schwarzi*

**A rare autumn vagrant.**

The Radde's Warbler breeds in Siberia and northern Korea wintering in Burma and Vietnam. It was extremely rare in the British Isles until the mid-1970s, since when small numbers have been recorded almost annually.

One was on Blakeney Point on 3rd–5th October 1961. It was trapped by Barry Spence on the first date and as it could not be identified with certainty was kept overnight in Richard Richardson's outdoor aviary until confirmation of its identity was made by Ken Williamson who travelled overnight from Scotland! (Richardson *et al.* 1962). It remains the only one to have been ringed in the county. It was also only the second British record. Since then, a further 22 have been recorded in autumn, representing 14% of those found in Britain.

Radde's Warblers depart from their breeding grounds late August to mid-September and autumn vagrancy occurs as a result of reverse migration or westward displacement in anticyclonic conditions (BWP). Virtually all of the Norfolk records have been in association with easterly or north-easterly winds. Apart from one at Waxham on 26th September 1976 and singles on 2nd and 3rd October, the majority of the sightings have occurred between 9th and 26th October, with one on 29th October and the latest at Holkham on 1st–6th November 1982. All records have involved single birds and the highest annual totals have been four in 1988 and five in 1991.

A total of twelve has been recorded at Holkham Meals, which represent the most for any mainland site in Britain (Bloomfield 1993). In addition to two each at Holme and Blakeney Point, singles have also been seen at Brancaster, Warham, Stiffkey and Kelling Water Meadows, while on the east Norfolk coast there are records from Happisburgh, Waxham and Yarmouth Cemeteries.

*Moss Taylor*

# Dusky Warbler                                  *Phylloscopus fuscatus*

**A rare autumn vagrant; one spring record.**

The Dusky Warbler breeds throughout much of Siberia and south to the eastern Himalayas, wintering from northern India and Nepal east to southern China and south-east Asia. Since 1978 it has been an annual autumn visitor to the British Isles in small numbers.

The first Norfolk record, and only the eighth for the British Isles, was found by the writer and Michael Bowtell, and identified later by Enid Allsopp and Howard Medhurst at Holkham Meals on 26th October 1968, a second bird being found there three days later. Since then the total has increased to 33 autumn records and one in spring (representing about 15% of the British records).

Dusky Warblers leave their breeding grounds in western Siberia in August and September, on average slightly later than Radde's Warblers and, like that species, the majority in Norfolk have occurred following easterly or north-easterly winds. An exceptionally early bird was trapped at Weybourne on 23rd September 1996 and remained in the area for six days. Otherwise Dusky Warblers have been recorded between 3rd October and 21st November, with 70% from mid-October to early November. Most records have involved single birds, but two were present at Holkham Meals on 29th October and 2nd November 1968, and also on 13th–21st November 1996. The highest annual totals have been five in 1990 and 1994.

The majority of Dusky Warblers in Norfolk have been found along the north coast with 13 at Holkham Meals, four at Holme and Blakeney Point, two at Sheringham, Happisburgh and Waxham, and singles at Stiffkey, between Blakeney and Morston, at Wiveton, Weybourne, Mundesley and Yarmouth Cemeteries.

The single spring record, only the third for the British Isles, involved a male in song at Holkham Meals on 21st–23rd May 1985, the bird almost certainly having been present since 12th May (Bloomfield 1993). A total of six has been ringed in the county.

*Moss Taylor*

# Western Bonelli's Warbler                          *Phylloscopus bonelli*

**A very rare vagrant; six records and four additional records of Western/Eastern Bonelli's Warbler.**

Bonelli's Warbler has only recently been split into two species: Western and Eastern Bonelli's Warblers. In the Western Palearctic, the breeding range of Western Bonelli's Warbler includes part of north-west Africa, and from Iberia and France east to Italy. It winters in a narrow belt in West Africa, immediately south of the Sahara. In Europe, the population has slowly increased in numbers and range in the 20th century, reaching north-east France, then Belgium (in the late 1960s) and The Netherlands (in the mid-1970s), and this may partly explain the increase in British records from the early 1970s. The Western Bonelli's Warbler is replaced by the Eastern Bonelli's Warbler *P. orientalis* in south-east Europe, Turkey and the Levant.

As a result of Eastern Bonelli's Warbler being awarded specific status in 1997, the BBRC have reviewed all the available evidence in the files relating to the previously published records of Bonelli's Warbler. Six of the Norfolk records have been accepted as proven Western Bonelli's Warblers, while the other four have been classified as Western/Eastern Bonelli's Warblers.

The first Western Bonelli's Warbler for Norfolk was one found by Peter Clarke at Holme on 7th August 1970, which remained until 13th. The second record was one in Yarmouth Cemeteries and the neighbouring gardens from 30th August to 3rd September 1974. It was unusual in that it arrived with a large 'fall' of Scandinavian night migrants. The next three records involved birds at Holkham on 5th September 1976, the first spring record for the county at Holme on 9th April 1988 and again at Holkham on 10th–17th September 1989. The only one to have been ringed in the county was a first-winter bird trapped at Dead Man's Wood, Sheringham on 3rd September 1994. Although it was retrapped on 6th September, it was not seen in the field during the intervening period despite intensive searching.

Four other records are now classified as Western/Eastern Bonelli's Warblers – singles at Holkham on 22nd August 1971, 14th September 1976 and 12th–13th September 1982, and at Blakeney Point on 14th May 1988.

*Moss Taylor*

## Wood Warbler

*Phylloscopus sibilatrix*

**A very scarce summer visitor and passage migrant; last bred in 1995.**

The Wood Warbler is a breeding summer visitor to the middle and upper middle latitudes of the Western Palearctic, preferring hilly terrain to flat plains, it winters in equatorial Africa. In the British Isles, it is a characteristic species of sessile oak woods with a predominantly southern, western and northern breeding distribution (New Atlas).

Both Stevenson and Riviere described the Wood Warbler as locally distributed with a fondness for beech trees but gave only four records of coastal passage migrants. Unfortunately, this attractive summer visitor has declined steadily as a breeding species since the mid-1950s. This is demonstrated by a well-documented series of records from Blickling, where it bred from at least 1917, with four singing males in 1953, to the mid-1960s but not since, at Snettisham with four pairs in 1935 but none since 1956 and at South Wootton with ten pairs in 1927 and still eight singing males in 1944 but none after 1957 (Seago 1977).

The species was recorded in 16 of the 10km squares in Norfolk, during the fieldwork for the 68–72 BTO Atlas, but breeding was proved in only three of the squares for the New Atlas. However, in the Norfolk Atlas it was recorded in 62 tetrads, involving no less than 31 of the 10km squares. The fieldwork for this latter survey was carried out between 1980 and 1985, during a decade when there was a transient upsurge in the number of singing Wood Warblers in Norfolk, a trend which was reversed after 1990. During the early 1990s the few pairs of Wood Warblers which continued to breed in Norfolk were mainly confined to the beech woods or mixed deciduous woodland along the Cromer to Holt Ridge with occasional pairs in the woods around Norwich, which provide a well-developed canopy and a sparse ground layer. Only a single breeding pair was reported in 1995, at Dersingham, and none in 1996. In 1998 one was in song from 30th May to 6th June at Fritton Warren but there was no evidence to suggest breeding.

Spring passage occurs mainly from the last week of April to late May, with occasional birds on the coast in early June, the latest being in Holme village on 7th–8th June 1993, while one at Sea Palling on 5th July 1997 may have been an early autumn migrant. Although up to four were in Yarmouth Cemeteries on 12th–18th May 1993, most spring migrants are recorded singly. The earliest dates the species has been recorded in Norfolk are 10th April 1983 at High Kelling, 11th April 1985 at Strumpshaw and 11th April 1991 at Sandringham Warren. It is interesting that all three sites are inland and this illustrates one of the problems in attempting to assess breeding numbers, as Wood Warblers often sing while on spring passage.

Autumn passage peaks between mid-August and mid-September. Only occasional birds are seen in October, although there were three in 1988 – at Holme on 12th–14th, at Waxham on 13th and at Sheringham on 15th–29th, the latest date for the county. As in Riviere's time, the Wood Warbler remained an infrequent passage migrant until the mid-1980s. Since then more have been recorded in spring, with a record total of 24 in 1993. The number of autumn migrants has generally remained unchanged at about five annually, although there were 19 in 1994 and 17 in 1995.

Wood Warblers, unlike Willow Warblers, depart in a south-easterly direction on autumn passage, crossing the central Mediterranean via Italy, from where there have been eight recoveries of British-ringed birds. Some, possibly all, British breeding birds take a more westerly route through France in spring. It is of interest that only 30 Wood Warblers have been ringed in Norfolk, compared with 35 Yellow-browed Warblers.

*Moss Taylor*

MY GARDEN-CHEDGRAVE.

## Chiffchaff (Common Chiffchaff) 25-9-1999.

*Phylloscopus collybita*

**A common summer visitor and passage migrant; scarce in winter.**

In the Western Palearctic, the Chiffchaff breeds in the upper and middle latitudes, extending south to the Mediterranean countries, but not as far north as the Willow Warbler. The western populations winter within and south of the breeding areas, in the Mediterranean region, North Africa and in a narrow belt in West Africa. It is a widespread breeding bird in lowland Britain, being absent from much of the uplands of Snowdonia, the Pennines, border hills and the Scottish highlands and islands. It is also not found in the treeless Fens. While some overwinter in Britain, the majority move south to the areas outlined above.

Riviere described the Chiffchaff as 'one of the earliest summer visitors, nowhere abundant, somewhat local but not uncommon', a statement which holds true today. In Norfolk, the Chiffchaff is a widespread breeding summer visitor to mature, deciduous and mixed woodland with not too dense a canopy, but well developed undergrowth for nesting. During the fieldwork for the Norfolk Atlas it was found in just over half the tetrads covered and was absent from the Fens (apart from the Ouse Washes), open areas of Broadland and intensively farmed tracts of country. In the New Atlas it is shown as being present in all the 10km squares in Norfolk, being most abundant in the wooded areas in the north of the county, where it probably outnumbers the Willow Warbler. During the 1994–97 BBS it was found in 39–43% of the 1km squares covered in Norfolk, indicating no change in its breeding status during the four years.

Because of the presence of wintering birds, it is not always easy to define when the first spring migrants arrive, but it is usually in the first half of March. Spring passage is generally unremarkable and continues into early May, with 48 at Holkham Meals on 9th April 1996 being noteworthy. In autumn, passage birds are noted from late August until early November. Prior to 1998 the maximum count had been 70 in The Dell at Wells on 14th September 1993, at the same time as a large 'fall' of Willow Warblers and other Continental drift migrants. However, unprecedented numbers were present during the 'falls' on 1st–7th October 1998 with maximum counts of 150 each in The Dell area at Wells, at Stiffkey, at Sheringham and at Paston, 70 at Wells East Hills and 65 at Warham Green.

In addition to the nominate race *P. c. collybita*, which breeds in the British Isles and much of central, southern and western Europe, two others are very scarce autumn passage migrants and occasionally overwinter – *P. c. abietinus* from Scandinavia and north-eastern Europe, and *P. c. tristis* from Siberia. Both races tend to occur later in the autumn with the majority recorded from October to mid-November and a maximum count of 20 at Holkham Meals on 15th October 1982. Stoddart (1995a and 1995b) highlighted the problems associated with the identification of *tristis*, particularly in the field, and fewer records may be acceptable in the future. There have been only two spring records of birds showing the characteristics of the eastern races, both in 1993 - *abietinus* at Paston on 24th April and *tristis* at Blakeney Point on 11th May.

While the majority of Chiffchaffs winter south of the British Isles, wintering birds have been recorded in Norfolk since the start of the 20th century. Riviere gave two examples on 21st January 1909 and 15th February 1914. Since the 1980s, numbers have increased steadily, from one to three winter records in most years in the 1960s and 1970s, to a record 24 (including ten at Cley) in the first winter period and 38 in the second winter period of 1995. Six were present at Holkham Meals throughout January and February 1998. Occasional birds of both the eastern races have been recorded during the winter months.

About 6,000 Chiffchaffs have been ringed in Norfolk since 1980, resulting in five foreign recoveries, one each in Belgium, Germany, Portugal, Spain and Senegal, in addition to an earlier recovery from France. One Belgian-ringed Chiffchaff has been found in the county. The timing and direction of autumn movements is demonstrated by September recoveries in Bedfordshire, Kent and Sussex (2) of Chiffchaffs ringed in Norfolk earlier that summer or autumn, and another controlled in Belgium in October. Possible wintering areas are shown by birds recovered in northern France in January, and in the Algarve, Portugal and in southern Spain in November, while a juvenile ringed near Fakenham on 27th July 1995 was controlled at Djoudj, Senegal on 5th December.

One ringed at Happisburgh on 12th May 1980 and controlled at Trischell, Germany nine days later is a good example of reorientation of a spring arrival. One ringed at Uppelo, Antwerpen, Belgium on 5th July 1983 and controlled at Sheringham on 2nd May 1984 was presumably still on passage and was the first British recovery of a Belgian-ringed Chiffchaff. Another passage bird controlled at Sheringham on 2nd April 1992 had been ringed on Pitsea Marshes, Essex on 31st December 1991. Finally, one ringed at Sheringham on 12th November 1988 was controlled at the same site on 3rd December 1988, 18th March 1989, 2nd June 1989 (as a breeding bird) and 13th September 1989, possibly the first proven instance of a wintering bird remaining to breed at the same locality the following summer.

*Moss Taylor*

## Willow Warbler | *MY GARDEN - CHEDGRAVE. 14·8·2000.* ***Phylloscopus trochilus***

**A very common summer visitor and common passage migrant.**

The Willow Warbler is a breeding summer visitor to the middle and upper latitudes of the Western Palearctic, extending widely into the Arctic but only marginally into the Mediterranean region. It winters extensively in sub-Saharan Africa, from southern Senegal east to Ethiopia and south to South Africa. In Britain it is the commonest and most widely distributed summer migrant, breeding throughout the British Isles, except in the Fens and Shetlands (68–72 BTO Atlas). The race breeding in north-west Europe (including Britain), *P. t. trochilus*, winters in West Africa.

Historically it has always been a widespread and very common breeding bird in Norfolk, favouring young woodland and the more open areas of mature woodland, lacking a closed canopy. It nests in almost any type of scrub with more mature trees, especially on commons and heathland with scattered birches, in young conifer plantations, thorn and sallow thickets of the Ouse Washes and in Broadland carrs (Kelly 1986). During the fieldwork for both the BTO Breeding Atlases it was found in all except one of the 10km squares in Norfolk (in the Fens) and in 77% of the tetrads covered during the Norfolk Atlas. During the 1994–97 BBS it was recorded in 55–59% of the 1km squares covered in Norfolk. The highest breeding concentration in recent years has been 36 singing males at East Wretham Heath in 1997.

Riviere noted that it was a regular passage migrant through Norwich gardens in April, while on the coast it was more frequent in the first half of May. In recent years, the first birds of the spring have generally been males singing in suitable breeding habitats in the last week of March. The earliest records have been at Salthouse on 11th March 1989 and at Thompson Water on 20th March 1957. Spring passage peaks between mid-April and mid-May, with many of the males in song while clearly still on migration. Peak numbers are usually recorded along the north Norfolk coast with the highest counts both at Holme with 75 on 23rd April 1994 and 60 on 1st May 1995. Birds of the northern European race *P. t. acredula* are scarce passage migrants in the spring, generally not appearing until the last week of April or early May.

In autumn, passage generally peaks in the second half of August with influxes of Continental birds often appearing in mid-September, in association with easterly winds. In recent years, the largest 'falls' have occurred on 14th September 1993 with 200 in The Dell area at Wells and 100 each at Holme, Holkham/Overy Dunes and Blakeney Point, and on 18th September 1995 when these numbers were eclipsed with 700 at Sheringham, 600 at Holkham, 400 at Wells East Hills, 300 at Mundesley/Paston, 200 each at Holme and Blakeney Point, and 130 at Yarmouth Cemeteries.

In most years, the majority of Willow Warblers have left by late September, with the last being re-corded in early to mid-October. Since 1980, there have been eleven November records with the latest at Holkham on 11th November 1992, Yarmouth on 11th–15th November 1992 and Burnham Deepdale on 11th–13th November 1996. As in the spring, birds showing characteristics of the northern race *acredula* are occasionally recorded in autumn from mid-August. However, during an influx of Willow Warblers in mid-September 1989, when there were counts of 30–40 at several coastal sites, many of the birds were considered to be of this race.

Since 1980, about 8,000 Willow Warblers have been ringed in Norfolk, resulting in only two foreign recoveries (albeit one in Senegal, which was only the sixth recovery of a British-ringed Willow Warbler south of The Sahara), illustrating the very low recovery rate of many of our summer visitors.

The destination of some of our spring migrants is demonstrated by one ringed at Cley on 6th May 1955 recovered in Clackmannanshire, Scotland on 11th June and two birds ringed at Sheringham, one on 4th April 1985 and found freshly dead in Lancashire on 7th May 1985 and another on 3rd May 1990, controlled in Derbyshire on 30th June 1990. A fourth, probably a bird of the northern race, was ringed at Didlington on 27th May 1994 and controlled on North Ronaldsay, Orkney on 3rd June 1994. One ringed at Weybourne on 25th May 1984 was recovered in Londonderry, Northern Ireland on 7th May 1988, while another ringed at Weybourne on 23rd April 1994 was controlled at the Calf of Man on 22nd April 1995. Both these illustrate the very different routes that may be taken by spring migrants in subsequent years. An unusual recovery involved one ringed at Christianso, Bornholme, Denmark on 5th June 1977 and found at Terrington on 2nd July 1977.

The origin of some of our autumn arrivals is shown by one ringed at Blavland, Denmark on 25th August 1987 and controlled at Sheringham one week later, and another ringed in southern Norway on 4th

August 1984 and found dead at Bacton ten days later; another ringed in southern Norway in early August was found at Holkham five years later in May. Other foreign-ringed birds have come from Belgium and one ringed on the Balearic Islands in April 1995 was controlled near Wells in September.

In autumn, Willow Warblers head south to south-west, as shown by a recovery of one ringed at Boughton on 3rd July 1969 and controlled in Sussex in mid-August, and another ringed at Loinnbuie, Highland on 12th August 1994 and controlled at Holme two weeks later. On leaving England they pass through south-west France and Iberia, from where one ringed at Stibbard on 10th June 1962 was recovered at Cantanhede, Beira Litoral, Portugal on 4th September 1962. One ringed at Waxham on 1st October 1985 was recovered in the West African winter quarters at Richard Toll, Senegal on 14th December 1985. There has been one other recovery of note, a bird ringed at Hoboken, Antwerpen, Belgium on 8th August 1977 and found the following June at Yarmouth.

*Moss Taylor*

## Goldcrest   MY GARDEN - CHEDGRAVE (3) 11·7·1999.                     *Regulus regulus*

**A very common resident and common passage migrant, mainly in autumn.**

The Goldcrest, the smallest European passerine, is typically associated with boreal and temperate forest, especially spruce and fir. It breeds across most of northern and central Europe, except for Iceland, and extends east into Asia. Its winter range extends southwards to southern Europe and the Mediterranean region. It is one of the most widespread breeding species in the British Isles, being absent or scarce only from the treeless areas in the Northern Isles, the Outer Hebrides and the Fens (New Atlas).

Stevenson believed that the Goldcrest had probably become far more plentiful since the mid-19th century due to the extensively-adopted system of planting larch, spruce and other firs. He was also aware of the autumn immigration from northern Europe which coincided with the arrival of the heaviest catches of herring, from which the Goldcrest obtained its local name of 'herring-spink', as it frequently landed on drifters in the North Sea.

As a breeding bird, the Goldcrest is found throughout the county, wherever there are areas of coniferous trees, including small isolated plantations. The highest concentrations are found in the Breckland conifer forests. Larger gardens and churchyards possessing isolated mature conifers often also hold pairs of breeding Goldcrests. Occasional pairs are found in oakwoods and one was even found nesting in a hedgerow oak during the Norfolk Atlas, in which the species was recorded in 40% of the tetrads visited. The treeless areas of the Fens and parts of the Broads hold few if any pairs. Goldcrests were recorded in 18–28% of the 1km squares covered in Norfolk during the 1994–97 BBS. In winter, the species typically associates with flocks of tits, moving noisily through the woodland. Also at this time of year it visits parks and gardens more readily, even frequenting bird tables on occasions. By how much the winter population in Norfolk is swelled by visitors from northern and central Europe is uncertain. Because of its small size, the Goldcrest is particularly susceptible during periods of severe winter weather and following such conditions the population crashes. This was the case, as noted by Riviere, after the exceptionally hard winter of 1916–17 and more recently in 1947 and 1962–63. However, it is able to recover within a couple of years, as a result of being double-brooded and having clutches of nine or more eggs.

The number of Goldcrests arriving from Fennoscandia and the Continent in autumn is very variable, the highest numbers being associated with north-easterly gales. Although occasional migrants have been recorded as early as the end of August, passage normally commences in mid to late September and continues until early November. Peak numbers are invariably recorded in October with the birds often arriving in distinct waves, as in 1993. On 28th September, an influx occurred with 200 at Wells and 100 at Sheringham, a second in mid-October with 150 at Holme, 'several' hundreds at Holkham, 400 at Sheringham, 250 at Paston and 100 at Waxham, and a third influx on 23rd–24th October with 200 at Wells, 500 at Sheringham and 200 at Happisburgh. The largest 'falls', however, were recorded in 1975, with 500 at Happisburgh on 10th October, 500 at Sheringham on 11th October and 1,000 at Yarmouth Cemeteries on 13th October; in 1990 with 600 at Holme and 1,200 at Sheringham on 21st October; and in 1992 with thousands at Holkham Meals on 3rd October and 400 at Holme on 4th October. Such impressive numbers arriving on the Norfolk coast were well known to Stevenson, as was described by a Captain Longe of Yarmouth who was walking to Hemsby along the Caister Road in the early morning of 2nd November 1862:

451

[My] attention was attracted to a small bush overhanging the marsh dyke, which borders the pathway, by the continuous twittering of a small bird. On looking closely, I found the bush, small as it was, literally covered with golden-crested wrens. There was hardly an inch of twig that had not a bird upon it, and even from my rough attempt at calculation at that time, I feel sure there were at least between two and three hundred. . . . The wind had been easterly, with much fog.

Richard Richardson described a delightful scene at Cley on 21st September 1949 following an immigration of Goldcrests: 'The birds were so hungry that one engaged a large dragonfly in the air being actually towed along by the insect before releasing it undamaged'.

The spring exodus is on a much smaller scale and presumably involves those few Goldcrests which have overwintered in Norfolk and the adjoining counties. Passage birds are noted in March and April, with normally fewer than 20 at any one site. The highest count has been 25 at Sheringham on 27th–31st March 1989, on 17th March 1990 and on 16th March 1996, and at Holme on 27th March 1994.

About 7,500 Goldcrests have been ringed in Norfolk, the vast majority consisting of birds on autumn passage. These have produced six foreign recoveries and eleven foreign-ringed birds have been found in the county, all of which were ringed in autumn, thus there is no direct evidence indicating the natal area of our immigrants. Of the six foreign recoveries, one was ringed at Bacton on 1st October 1983 and controlled at De Panne, Belgium ten days later, and another at Winterton on 18th October 1997 was controlled at Grembergen, Belgium one week later; both suggesting an attempt at reorientation. One ringed at Holme in October 1966 was found in Denmark one year later; two October-ringed birds from Titchwell and Happisburgh were controlled the following spring in The Netherlands and at Akeroya, Norway respectively, the latter being the first Norwegian recovery of a British-ringed Goldcrest, and one ringed at Holkham on 28th March 1967 was recovered at Lake Bukowo, Poland on 2nd October. The eleven foreign-ringed controls have come from Belgium, The Netherlands (2), Sark, Sweden (3), Norway (2), Poland and Russia. Many of them were recovered or controlled later the same autumn, several within two weeks of ringing – the quickest movement being one ringed at Falsterbo on the southern coast of Sweden on 8th October 1975 which was controlled at Titchwell three days later. The longest movement concerned one ringed at Maychino, Karelia, Russia on 10th September 1993 and controlled at Sheringham on 30th September, a distance of 2,103km in 20 days. It is one of only two Russian-ringed Goldcrests to have been found in the British Isles. Other recoveries and controls within England have indicated an onward movement to the south and west in autumn, and to the north and east in spring. However, not all the movements affecting Norfolk fit into this pattern – one ringed at Waxham on 20th April 1984 was controlled on Bardsey Island, Wales four days later and one ringed on the Calf of Man on 20th September 1987 was recovered at North Burlingham on 24th October. The longest movement within the British Isles involved one ringed at St Andrews, Fife on 1st October 1990 which was found dead at Thetford in mid-November.

*Moss Taylor*

## Firecrest                                    *Regulus ignicapillus*

**A very rare breeder, scarce passage migrant and very scarce winter visitor.**

The breeding range of the Firecrest covers much of central and southern Europe, the species being absent from Fennoscandia in the north and Russia in the east. The southerly populations are thought to be resident while those to the north and east migrate to the south and west. There has been a steady northerly expansion with breeding noted for the first time in The Netherlands in 1928 and in Denmark in 1961, although it remains rare there. Apart from one doubtful record in 1927, breeding was first proved in the British Isles in 1962, in the New Forest. In the following years singing males were heard in a number of counties and up to 23 were found in a single wood in Buckinghamshire. By the late 1980s, the numbers breeding in southern central England had increased and the range had expanded to the west (the Forest of Dean in particular), the coast of Suffolk and isolated areas in Wales and south-west England (New Atlas). The Winter Atlas showed a concentration in the coastal areas of south-west England from Hampshire around to Somerset. The wintering population is thought to consist of Continental birds and would account for the passage records in autumn.

Stevenson cited two examples of the 'Fire-crested Wren' – the first caught in the rigging of a ship five miles off the coast of Norfolk in early October 1836 and the second taken from a flock of Goldcrests at Yarmouth in 1843. William Fisher, a Yarmouth naturalist of the mid-19th century, had given a man a commission to obtain all the Goldcrests he could (with a view to obtaining a Firecrest) and when about 30 had been brought to him, the Firecrest above appeared amongst the victims! Another was also shot on the Breydon wall on 21st October 1863. Riviere stated that up until 1913, five others had reached the county only for all to end on the taxidermists' benches – all between late October and April. Between 1836 and 1966, a further 50 were recorded (Seago 1967) and it has been noted annually since 1958. In line with increases throughout its breeding range, the number of migrants reaching Norfolk in autumn and spring has risen, particularly since the early 1970s.

At about the same time birds were first recorded in mid-summer. In 1973 a pair was found in Wells Woods on 23rd June and was still present a month later, although there was no evidence of breeding. Successful breeding has been proved in the county on four occasions – in 1984 a pair was observed carrying food and one juvenile was seen near Norwich, in 1990 a pair with young were seen at Wolferton with the nest situated in a larch, in 1994 pairs were seen with five young at Wells and with four young at Sandringham.

There has also been a series of records of birds singing and holding territory. Up to four singing males were present at Sheringham Park between 1980 and 1985, but the only evidence to indicate a breeding attempt was a male Firecrest accompanying a female Goldcrest which was carrying nest material to the top of a larch on 31st May 1982. In the 1990s there have been a number of records from the Lynford/Mundford area especially from Lynford Arboretum. Up to four singing males have been found in a single year and six separate sites have held birds. In 1995, a male Firecrest was seen in the company of a female Goldcrest and four recently fledged young. The youngsters had no trace of the supercilium that young Firecrests have when they leave the nest. Whether these were hybrids or whether the Firecrest was helping to feed a brood of Goldcrests will not be known. Instances of hybridisation have been noted in other counties.

On 13th May 1997, at Lynford, a male Firecrest was watched singing from a fir tree. After four or five phrases of typical Firecrest song, it produced a series of Goldcrest song phrases before reverting to Firecrest song. Whether this mimicry was to defend its territory from both species or whether it was to maximise its chances of attracting a mate is open to debate. Certainly no female Firecrest was seen in the area at this time or on subsequent dates. On 1st June, a young bird was seen to beg food from a male Firecrest but since the head pattern of the young bird was not seen clearly the possibility of hybridisation could not be excluded. Other localities to hold Firecrests during the summer of 1997 were Lynford Stag and Sandringham.

A variety of woodland has been used by singing males in Norfolk – larch at Sheringham, Corsican pine, fir and oak in the Brecks, as well as the atypical range that is present in Lynford Arboretum. It is highly likely that due to the amount of suitable habitat throughout the county, a number of singing birds go undetected each summer. The New Atlas stated that female and young birds are difficult to find even when the males have been located. Hence, Norfolk might already host a small breeding population each year.

The first spring migrants are seen in mid-March with passage continuing to the end of May. The peak occurs in late March and early April, the majority being recorded at coastal sites with the most favoured localities being Holme and Wells. The highest day-counts have been at least eight at Wells/Holkham on 28th May 1994 and seven at Caister on 23rd April 1994. Peak years for the number of spring migrants have been 1983, 1994 and 1995 with 44, 72 and 47, respectively, compared with an average of twelve each spring during the 1970s. The earliest autumn migrants have been at Yarmouth on 9th August 1993 and at Holme on 27th August 1982. Passage usually extends from mid-September to the end of November with the largest numbers being noted in late September and early October. Firecrests have been much more numerous in autumn in recent years with annual totals of 30, 42, 37, 110 and 51 between 1993 and 1997, compared with an average of ten each autumn in the 1970s The unprecedented number of autumn migrants in 1996 was due to an influx between 17th and 24th September involving at least 94 birds at 29 sites, with maximum counts of ten in Yarmouth Cemeteries and seven at Sea Palling on 21st September.

Formerly the Firecrest was not thought of as a winter bird in Norfolk but increasing numbers have been recorded at this season. The species has been reported each winter since 1991, involving at least 35 birds, some of which have remained throughout the winter and have still been present the following spring. A wide variety of localities across the county have hosted Firecrests in winter with the Brecks being particularly favoured. Even in well-watched areas their presence may only be detected as a result of birds having been caught during ringing operations, and so it is not unreasonable to suppose that some go undetected. Birds were present at Lynford Arboretum from winter 1994–95, throughout the summer of 1995 and into the following winter, the first evidence of birds having been resident in Norfolk. If present trends continue, and in the absence of severe winters, increasing numbers can be expected to become resident in the county and a small breeding population may become established.

Over 100 Firecrests have been ringed in Norfolk and one has been recovered – ringed at Holme on 13th October 1975, it was found at Wick, Caithness on 11th February 1976, providing one of the most surprising recoveries from Norfolk ringing.

*Peter Dolton*

## Spotted Flycatcher *BY MY GARDEN, CHEDGRAVE. 11·7·1999.* *Muscicapa striata*

**A common summer visitor and fairly common passage migrant.**

Spotted Flycatchers breed widely throughout the Western Palearctic from the Mediterranean northwards and winter in sub-Saharan Africa, the majority south of the Equator. They are one of the last migrants to arrive in spring and, apart from the Northern Isles, breed throughout Britain and Ireland.

In Stevenson's day they were known locally as the 'wall bird', due to their habit of nesting on the branch of a wall fruit tree. Nowadays, breeding Spotted Flycatchers can be found along woodland margins (especially near freshwater), in copses, parkland, large gardens and churchyards. In Norfolk, they were one of the few summer migrants to have been recorded in all of the 10km squares in the two BTO Breeding Atlases, as well as the Norfolk Atlas, when they were also found in almost 50% of the tetrads covered. The species has been in a long-term decline since the early 1960s, with the British breeding population dropping by about 75% by the late 1980s, the biggest fall occurring between 1983 and 1984, which coincided with a failure of the Sahel rains (Marchant *et al.* 1990). Spotted Flycatchers pass through the Sahel region on both spring and autumn passage, and this combined with the tendency in recent years to experience cooler, wetter early summers is thought to be responsible for this decline. Sadly, the Spotted Flycatcher has certainly become less numerous in Norfolk during the 1990s. Although 19 breeding pairs were located at Holkham Park in 1996, this had fallen to ten in 1997. This was also the year in which the species did not breed at East Tuddenham for the first time in 23 years and for even longer at Holme. However, results from the 1994–97 BBS are inconclusive with the species being recorded in 10–24% of the 1km squares visited in Norfolk, but with no obvious trend apparent.

The first birds of the spring are usually recorded in late April or early May, although it is often late May before the species is widespread. Spring passage is unremarkable and continues on the coast until late May or even early June, with unusually late migrants in June 1998 at Holme on 13th and Weybourne on 17th. The highest counts have been 40 at Holme on 26th May 1985 and 14 at Scolt Head on 25th May 1989, while a total of 13 moving west at Sheringham on 30th May 1996 was unusual. The earliest recorded dates for the county have been 16th April 1983 at Dereham and 21st April 1984 at Holme (there are very few British records before mid-April).

Autumn passage commences in mid-August with stragglers passing as late as mid-October. Maximum counts have been 150 at Winterton in the 'fall' on 4th September 1965, and 100 at Winterton on 15th August 1976 and at Holkham Meals on 17th August 1986. About 50 were present on Blakeney Point during the 'fall' on 4th–5th September 1958 and 45 at Holme on 18th September 1995. During 14th–15th September 1993, counts of 25 were made at both Holme and Wells. Comparatively few are normally recorded at coastal sites in autumn and 15–20 at South Lopham Fen on 26th August 1996 and ten at Stanford Training Area on 6th September 1997 are perhaps an indication that the main passage is away from the coast. Occasional birds are seen after mid-October and there are two November records, both near Norwich –on 4th November 1972 at Old Catton and on 3rd–10th November 1957 at Thorpe.

About 1,000 Spotted Flycatchers have been ringed in Norfolk, resulting in six foreign recoveries. In common with the Blackcap, the Spotted Flycatcher shows a migratory divide at 12°E; birds from western Europe, including the British Isles, move south-west to Iberia, then south to West Africa and beyond. Three ringed pulli have been recovered in autumn in Iberia, two in Spain and one in Portugal, and a first-year bird ringed at Banningham on 1st September 1992 was found dead at Agoncillo, Logroño, Spain on 30th September. Another ringed at Stow Bedon on 4th September 1969 was found dead at Menton, Alpes

Maritimes, France on 22nd June 1971, but it may well have died several weeks earlier while on passage. The most southerly recovery from Norfolk was one ringed at Sheringham on 17th September 1976 and found at Rabat, Morocco in the following May. Movements within the British Isles have included one ringed in Sussex in September 1977 and found dead in Norfolk the following May, and a nestling ringed at Shimpling in 1994 recovered in Northumberland the following June. Finally, four Spotted Flycatchers ringed on autumn passage at Sheringham in 1975 were retrapped at the same site the next autumn, two of them within two days of the original trapping date. As there was no evidence to indicate that they were local breeders and they were not retrapped on any other dates, it suggests that they were following a similar route for their autumn migration in each year (Taylor 1984b).

*Moss Taylor*

# Red-breasted Flycatcher                    *Ficedula parva*

**A rare spring migrant and very scarce autumn migrant.**

The Red-breasted Flycatcher breeds from southern Sweden south to northern Greece, extending across eastern Europe and Siberia to the Pacific. It winters in the Indian subcontinent and south-east Asia (Vinicombe & Cottridge 1996). It arrives in Britain in autumn as a result of reversed migration.

The first Norfolk record (and only the eighth for Britain) was of a first-winter female shot by Mr F. M. Ogilvie at Cley on 13th September 1890 (Stevenson). It remains on display in the Ogilvie collection at Ipswich Museum. The sand and plants in the case are authentic from the site. By the time that Riviere published his county avifauna, the total had risen to 17, all of which referred to birds that had been collected, and these constituted half of the English records. The majority had occurred in September, in addition to others which had been seen but not obtained. However, the third county record involved one shot at Rollesby Broad on 10th December 1896 which is on display at the City of Birmingham Museum (Allard 1990). It remains the only December record for Norfolk.

Since then the county total has risen to over 245. The species has been recorded annually since 1951 with an average of seven per year. Only eleven have been recorded in spring, representing 4% of the county total, a figure which matches the national average. The spring records are as follows:

1952: A male at Burnham Norton on 9th May
1964: Holme on 24th May
1968: Holme on 1st–2nd June, trapped on first date
1972: Brancaster on 7th May
1979: Blakeney Point on 4th June
1980: An immature male singing in pines at Holme on 27th May
1984: Holkham on 22nd–28th May
       Horsey on 23rd–24th May and possibly the same bird on 28th May
1985: Blakeney Point on 19th–24th May
1991: A male in song at Waxham on 18th May
1994: Blakeney Point on 21st May

In autumn, occasional birds are recorded in the last week of August, with the majority appearing in September and October. Although their arrival usually coincides with east or north-east winds, since 1980 there has been a small but definite peak in the number of records during the third week of September. The earliest records have been on 21st August 1971 at Blakeney Point and on 22nd August at Blakeney in 1968 and on Blakeney Point in 1984. Red-breasted Flycatchers are usually recorded singly, but there were up to three at Blakeney Point on 4th–10th October 1966 and on 14th September 1975, and three at Holkham Meals on 3rd–7th October 1992. The highest counts, however, were in 1989 with five at Wells East Hills on 10th–11th September (when also two at Holkham Meals) and five at Blakeney Point on 12th September. The maximum annual autumn totals have been 26 in 1984, 19 in 1989 and 18 in both 1968 and 1972. There have been only two records this century after the end of October – at Blakeney Point on 12th November 1983 and at Sandringham on 23rd November 1986.

Five Red-breasted Flycatchers have been found inland, including the one at Sandringham. The other records were at West Acre on 29th August 1963, Kelling Heath on 18th September 1975, Salthouse Heath on 18th October 1984 and one trapped at Morley St Botolph, near Wymondham on 26th October 1985. An exhausted bird was found on a gas production platform 72km north-east of Yarmouth on 2nd October 1979. A total of 22 Red-breasted Flycatchers has been ringed in Norfolk.

*Moss Taylor*

## Collared Flycatcher                                    *Ficedula albicollis*

**A very rare vagrant; two records.**

The Collared Flycatcher breeds in mainly deciduous forest from eastern France and Italy eastwards through central Europe to western Russia. It winters in tropical Africa. It is a very rare vagrant to the British Isles; most have appeared in May or early June.

Collared Flycatcher
(Richard Richardson)

A male present at Holme Reserve on 4th–6th May 1969 constituted the first county record. It was trapped by Peter Clarke on the first day and was much appreciated by many watchers during its three-day stay. Another male was seen briefly at Cley, initially on the East Bank on 5th May 1995 (Gantlett 1995b).

A first-summer male flycatcher present at the western end of Holkham pines 12th–13th May 1985 and showing some characteristics of Collared Flycatcher was considered to have been a possible Pied x Collared Flycatcher hybrid (Bloomfield 1993).

*Peter Allard*

## Pied Flycatcher                                         *Ficedula hypoleuca*

**A scarce spring migrant and fairly common autumn migrant; has bred on two occasions.**

The Pied Flycatcher breeds from north-west Africa across Europe to central Siberia. It winters in West Africa, south of the Sahara. In Britain, it breeds especially in the western sessile oakwoods, in northern England, and sparingly in Scotland. Sporadic breeding in eastern England was fairly frequent during the 19th century, particularly following large spring influxes of Scandinavian Pied Flycatchers, but has been rare this century (68–72 BTO Atlas).

Stevenson described it as a frequent spring visitor, especially in the Horsey area, and gave details of a major influx in May 1849, when 19 were collected within a 30-mile radius of Norwich. He was unable to cite a single autumn record between 1849 and 1866. In September 1895 the first autumn migration on any large scale was witnessed at Cley, after which autumn records outnumbered those in spring (Riviere). A late spring influx on 1st June 1898 at Yarmouth North Denes was noted by Patterson (Allard 1990). Of several records of possible breeding during the 19th century, the one most favoured by Riviere related to a pair which nested under the eaves of a shed at Somerton in 1878, from which a clutch of seven eggs was taken, but subsequently destroyed.

Since 1950, an average of about 15 Pied Flycatchers have been recorded in spring, with peaks of 86 in 1970 and up to four at 25 localities in 1978. The first spring migrants are rarely recorded before mid-April, the earliest normally being seen in late April and early May. Extreme dates have been 10th April 1993 and 14th April 1996, both at Holme. Spring passage continues through May with the odd straggler being found in early June. Maximum spring counts have been 20 at Blakeney Point on 3rd May 1956, 16 at Holkham on 11th May 1993, and ten at Horsey on 10th May 1960 and at Holkham Meals on 17th May 1988.

In 1978, following a late spring predominated by easterly winds, unusual numbers of Pied Flycatchers were recorded throughout the county and the species bred successfully at Felbrigg, the first proven breeding record for Norfolk. The choice of a hole in a Scot's pine as the nest-site, the late laying date (after 9th June) and the spring weather conditions all suggest that the pair was of Scandinavian stock (Taylor & Taylor 1979). The second breeding record for the county was at Holme in 1996, where a female laid a clutch of four infertile eggs in a nest box. Although she was present at the site from 28th May to 22nd June, a male was only seen from 14th to 18th June, and the nest was deserted. The nest and eggs are now in the collection at the Castle Museum, Norwich.

There have been over a dozen other mid-summer records, some of which have involved males in song for several days, such as one at Cranworth from 22nd May to 5th June 1975. The Cromer to Holt Ridge, which includes the Felbrigg estate, was favoured again in the early 1980s, with a male in song on several dates in late May 1981 at Sheringham Park and in June, the same or another Pied Flycatcher was in song and visiting a nest box in nearby Hundred Acre Wood. In 1982 a male was again in song in the same area, and in May 1985 and 1986 a male was in song for over a week in an Aylmerton garden, during which time it frequently entered a nest box (Taylor 1987a). During the 1990s singing males have made extended stays at Swanton Novers, Blickling and in Breckland.

Pied Flycatchers
(Bryan Bland)

The first birds of the autumn often appear in early August and passage continues until mid-October, numbers depending largely on the presence of east or north-east winds. There are two July records of coastal migrants, on 21st July 1955 at Blakeney Point and on 21st July 1988 at Horsey. Pied Flycatchers are one of the most characteristic species involved in 'falls' of Scandinavian drift migrants, indeed for many observers they epitomise late August and September. The early autumn of 1965 will long be remembered for the unprecedented number of Scandinavian migrants which made landfall on the east coast of England during classic 'fall' conditions, when Suffolk and the east coast of Norfolk were particularly affected. On 3rd–4th September, 500 Pied Flycatchers were at Winterton and there were many hundreds, perhaps thousands, in the neighbourhood of Yarmouth (Allard 1990). Numbers in other autumns have been overshadowed by these impressive totals. Apart from 100 at Horsey on 21st August 1954, all other day-counts of 100 or more have been made at Holkham Meals, with 200 on 4th September 1958, and 100 on 3rd September 1961, 1st September 1962 and 17th August 1986. Maximum counts at other sites have been 85 at Holme on 3rd September 1958 and 75 at Blakeney Point on 15th August 1977. A few birds are generally found inland in most years but the vast majority remain along the coastal strip. Only a few have been recorded in late October and there have been four November records – on 1st November at Holme (1973) and Wells town (1993), on 10th November 1983 at Waxham and the latest on 17th November 1957 at Horsey.

In 1985, there were two unusual-plumaged Pied Flycatchers both at Holkham Meals. The first, a first-summer male on 12th–13th May, was considered by the BBRC to have been a possible Pied x Collared Flycatcher hybrid (Bloomfield 1993) and the second a leucistic bird on 29th September 1985.

Over 700 Pied Flycatchers have been ringed in Norfolk, five of which have been recovered abroad – Norway, Spain (2), Portugal and Morocco, while two have been controlled from the Frisian Islands and one from Helgoland, all off Germany. Most, if not all, the Pied Flycatchers ringed in Norfolk in autumn originate from Scandinavia or further east. This is demonstrated by one ringed at Winterton on 4th September 1974 and found at Sando, Norway on 23rd May 1976, while one ringed at Westerland, Frisian Islands on 21st September 1965 was controlled at Holme five days later (the year of the great 'fall' described above) and another ringed on Helgoland on 19th August 1986 was controlled at Lessingham twelvedays later. Two autumn-ringed birds from Blakeney Point and Holme were both recovered later the same autumn in Navarra, Spain, and another from Holme was found the following autumn at Vila Franca, Portugal, both areas known to be used by Pied Flycatchers for pre-migratory fattening prior to their crossing of the Sahara. Spring migrants in Norfolk clearly originate from both Continental and British stock, as shown by one ringed at Mellum, Frisian Islands on 22nd August 1967 killed by a car at Morston on 15th May 1970 and an adult male ringed at Sheringham on 12th May 1981 controlled in a nest box at Cockermouth, Cumbria on 10th June 1985. The only African recovery is an autumn-ringed bird from Hunstanton recovered at Ajdir, Morocco two years later in spring.

*Moss Taylor*

| **Bearded Tit** | *TITCHWELL RSPB. (22+) 8·10·1986.*<br>*BY HARDLEY FLOODS. (2) 29·12·1999.* | ***Panurus biarmicus*** |

**A scarce resident and partial migrant with periodic eruptive movements.**

The Bearded Tit breeds across the middle latitudes of the Western Palearctic being concentrated in small and often isolated fragments of reed marsh. In Britain Bearded Tits bred over much of eastern England south to Kent and west to Hampshire in the first half of the 19th century, but by the end of the century, due to severe winters, reclamation of marshland, collecting for both eggs and skins, and by trapping for sale as cage birds, Norfolk became the sole stronghold. A notable expansion was first recorded in the autumn of 1959 (Axell 1966) followed by the arrival of Continental birds from the mid-1960s into eastern and southern England. The population in the British Isles in 1988–91 was thought to be about 400 pairs (New Atlas).

Lubbock (1845) remarked that he 'requested a fen man to shoot some Bearded Tits for preservation . . . I furnished him with some of the very smallest dust shot . . . he watched some Reed Pheasants just before dark when they make a ball of themselves . . . He brought me six killed at one shot.' Stevenson described the 'wholesale slaughter' the birds were subjected to by collectors. Five dozen eggs were obtained by a single dealer at Hickling. A Yarmouth dealer, George Smith, received 113 eggs during a fortnight in 1876. Not surprisingly by 1889 only two pairs were nesting at Hickling and Heigham Sounds. At the end of the 19th century the Broadland population was thought to be 33 pairs. Due to protection the numbers steadily increased. By 1909, 30 pairs were breeding in the Hickling/Horsey area and Emma Turner (1924) was aware of 17 nests. At Hoveton and Sutton Bearded Tits had become almost abundant.

Riviere found that estimating the number nesting in Broadland was 'a matter of considerable difficulty . . . the chief stronghold is within the area comprising Hickling Broad, Whiteslea, Heigham Sounds and Horsey Mere where Jim Vincent reported between 15 and 30 pairs according to the severity or mildness of the preceding winter'. A very few pairs were known to breed in the Waveney Valley and also in the Yare Valley, at Rockland and Surlingham Broads. Cley Marshes were occupied in 1914 and Wiveton Marshes in 1917. Ornithological recording reached a low ebb in the 1930s. Fortunately, Jim Vincent's diaries have survived and in 1932 following mild winters, the breeding stock totalled 35–40 pairs in the Hickling/Horsey reedbeds.

The birds are at times affected by severe winters. Those of 1916–17, 1939–40 and 1946–47 were particularly disastrous while others which were as cold, or even colder, had relatively little influence on numbers. Thus after 1962–63, the worst winter of the 20th century, the British population fell by little more than a half, whereas it had been almost extinguished by the less severe one of 1946–47, when for an unbroken six weeks blizzards buried the Broadland reedbeds in several feet of half-frozen snow. The determining factor is the amount of snow. Heavy snowfalls completely cover the reeds and seal off the food supply (68–72 BTO Atlas).

Within a dozen or so years of the 1946–47 winter more Bearded Tits were breeding in Britain than had been recorded for more than a century. The reason was a series of milder winters allowing the breeding population in East Anglia to flourish. Bearded Tits are prolific breeders and during the warm dry summer of 1955 the Thurne reedbeds contained impressive numbers. At Horsey, Anthony Buxton (*in litt.*) reported '150 flying young . . . each pair had hatched three broods . . . in one nest the second brood consisted of nine arranged in two layers . . . all flew. Volatile flights were frequent and on one occasion birds were flying so high that I could no longer see them – until all returned over the Mere before descending into the very reeds from which they had started.' By September 1959 the Broads' reed marshes again held large numbers of adults and young; a single flock of 90 at Horsey was without precedent. Such crowding again resulted in eruptive behaviour. Groups were flying almost vertically upwards from the reeds. At first these exploratory flights ended in a rapid return and headlong dive into the reeds. One calm morning adventurous groups rose high heading for the coast. The majority, undecided as to whether to advance or retire, returned in a rush to the familiar reeds but a few pioneers carried on until lost to sight.

Large-scale eruptive behaviour continued until the mid-1980s. The birds moved overland in all directions, some travelled many hundreds of kilometres, others much less. As a result, Bearded Tits were discovered in autumn and winter in many counties where they were previously unrecorded and as far from East Anglia as Anglesey, Lancashire and Northumberland. Some travelled out to sea to the Scilly Isles. Ringing confirmed they were capable of true migration, returning to breeding sites after wintering elsewhere. Ringing has also shown that common wintering sites may be used by birds breeding in different colonies. Bearded Tits show a propensity for travelling in pairs. Yet not so many years ago this species was still thought to be sedentary and incapable of this kind of behaviour.

In The Netherlands, Bearded Tit populations had been greatly affected by the creation and then part destruction of vast new reedbeds, as large areas of the Ijsselmeer (the former Zuider Zee) had been reclaimed and by stages drained to create new agricultural land. The Oost Flevoland polder, separated during 1950–56, had been sown with reed seed from the air. By 1962 it contained reedbeds extending over 100km$^2$. Despite the great frost of 1963 the Bearded Tit colonies increased rapidly having a highly successful season in 1965. During August and September that year Dutch ringers were surprised to catch 2,050 Bearded Tits. Only 10% of the ringed birds were being retrapped in the same areas and it was considered that the autumn population had reached an unprecedented total of 20,000 individuals.

From the beginning of October 1965 flocks of Bearded Tits appeared all along the Dutch coast. Others were reported in France as far as Bordeaux. A few found their way to the Channel Isles and also to Ireland. Seven Bearded Tits ringed at Oost Flevoland that autumn were controlled in England and Wales – the first real proof that immigration into Britain was possible. Doubtless it was mainly Dutch arrivals which heralded a period of range expansion in Britain. During the years of abundance the *Norfolk Bird Reports* contained a wealth of observations. October became the peak month for movements into and through the county; the size and frequency of the parties being greatest in the late 1960s and early 1970s.

In the Fens, the first arrivals reached King's Lynn Beet Factory settling ponds on 24th October 1965 followed by 30 there on 21st January 1968 (including birds ringed at Walberswick and Minsmere in Suffolk), 90 (60 were caught and ringed including one Dutch and several British marked birds) on 24th December 1972 and 60 during the 1981–82 winter. Up to three pairs bred at this beet factory in 1983–1990. Additional Fenland records involving up to eight birds, came from Wisbech Sewage Farm, Welney Washes and Wissington Beet Factory.

Edging the Wash, Snettisham attracted 41 moving south along the shore on 22nd October 1967 with further peaks there of 35 on 11th October 1986 and 43 on 2nd November 1986. At Dersingham Decoy the first record was of 15 (including one ringed at Holme two years earlier on 22nd October 1966) and there were regular occurrences from 13th October 1967 until the end of November with two ringing controls from Suffolk. Along the north coast two pairs appeared on the saltings at Holme on 14th December 1964; seven were flying high over Wells on 12th October 1966 and at the town boating lake 15 moved west on 18th October 1968 with 13 there circling ever higher before departing in the same direction on 7th October 1972. During October 1971 five passed through a Sheringham garden moving west on 2nd with one at The Hood on Blakeney Point among Long-tailed Tits on 6th and two in gorse at Morston on 28th. At Brancaster 48 were noted on 3rd October 1972 and 30 more three days later all moving in a south-westerly direction; 50 were trapped and ringed at Salthouse on 22nd September 1973. A pair briefly visited sea buckthorn at Hunstanton Golf Course on 16th October 1981, five passed Blakeney Point on 22nd October 1983 where two were in *Suaeda* on 27th September 1986 and a procession of 90 travelled west at Holme on 27th September 1985.

In east Norfolk, Breydon attracted a pair on the saltings on 1st October 1955, four were found in a minute reedbed almost in Yarmouth Railway Station yard on 5th October 1964 increasing to eight on the 11th with twelve visiting the eastern saltings on 23rd October 1971. During the invasion years Cantley Beet Factory contained large reedbeds which regularly held Bearded Tits. Among those wintering in January 1965 were birds ringed at Walberswick, Suffolk as juveniles the previous August. During December 1971 over 100 were there with a similar total (including 57 caught and ringed) in autumn 1972. Nearby, the Surlingham/Rockland reedbeds also became a winter stronghold with 100 during December 1964. Not to be outdone Strumpshaw attracted an all-time late autumn peak of 300 in 1977; of this total, 200 remained the following February when a large-scale exodus commenced at the onset of cold weather leaving only two breeding pairs. There was a further influx of 50 at Strumpshaw during January–February 1982 with over 100 in November–December that year. Other records of over 20 birds came from the River Yare between Eaton and Earlham including the University Broad between 1967 and 1984. Four lingered at Colney/Bawburgh Gravel Pits from 13th October to 17th November 1985.

In the Waveney Valley many Bearded Tits headed up-river during early October 1961 and 60 were present between St Olaves and Haddiscoe on 14th January 1979. Redgrave and Lopham Fens attracted a peak of 35 on 12th October 1987. Inland records, mostly during mid-winter, have come from five Breckland meres between 1963 and 1993, the largest group was eight at Stanford Water on 26th–28th December 1965.

Before the exciting events of 1965 there was little evidence of Continental Bearded Tits arriving in East Anglia. Riviere was unable to accept an entry in *British Association Report No 9* of a flock at Yarmouth on 13th November 1887 which appeared at a great height from the east. Perhaps more convincing, was a report by Horace Alexander of a group of ten shooting down out of the sky into a Cley reedbed on 16th October 1948. Two years later on a day in November 1950 Richard Richardson watched two Bearded Tits coming in low from the direction of the sea at Cley before disappearing into the first patch of reeds. The same observer saw two appearing over the dunes at Blakeney Point on 5th October 1961. It now appears likely that some Bearded Tits have always travelled long distances from breeding sites. In the days when there were few ornithologists and no ringers in the reedbeds, most of these birds would have gone unnoticed and the few that were recorded would have been regarded as vagrants. The huge numbers in the Flevoland polders were a transient event and the autumn irruptions have become a thing of the past.

Cley Marsh was colonised again in 1951 with nesting becoming annual from 1956. Nesting began at Salthouse in 1961 followed by Titchwell in 1966 and Overy Staithe in 1975. Many of the small-scale breeding colonies (often established as a result of autumn influxes) have since been abandoned. None nests nowadays at Barton, Cantley Beet Factory, Cockshoot, Holme, King's Lynn Beet Factory, Ranworth, Snettisham or Woodbastwick. However, Blakeney Freshes, Brancaster and Burnham Norton remain occupied.

The breeding population in Norfolk attained a peak of 240 pairs in 1980 when the upper Thurne stronghold contained 167 pairs. A co-ordinated survey in 1992 resulted in a total of 94–115 pairs at ten sites. Bearded Tits, especially in Broadland, have steadily declined. For example, the once large colony at Hickling Broad and Heigham Sounds, which contained 108 pairs in 1980, had reduced to 60 pairs in 1985, 33 pairs in 1994 and 25 pairs in 1998.

A winter survey along the north Norfolk coast between Holme and Salthouse during January 1998 revealed a total of 176 birds. The largest numbers were found at Titchwell (40), Cley (55) and Salthouse (30).

Bearded Tits are insectivorous in the summer, but change to seed eating from the late autumn to early spring. Seeds taken in the winter are usually those of the common reed, but especially in autumn, wandering flocks may be found in beds of common nettle or greater willowherb. The birds often follow reed-cutters closely to seek out overwintering insects from the cut stems.

Emma Turner found Bearded Tits to be early breeders, with the earliest nest containing a single egg on 31st March 1923; the latest held a brood of five just ready to fly on 22nd September 1907. Jim Vincent once found a nest with four eggs on 1st April 1936 and the Hickling reed-cutters discovered another containing two eggs on 24th March 1941. A pair there in 1944 nested in the reed fence of a shooting butt; Reed Warblers became close neighbours successfully breeding in the same fence.

The only albino recorded was one seen by Jim Vincent at Hickling on 19th September 1911.

Over 300 Bearded Tits have been ringed in Norfolk, one of which has been recovered abroad. It was ringed at Cantley Beet Factory on 31st December 1973 and was controlled near Antwerp, Belgium on 13th August 1974. The only foreign-ringed Bearded Tit to have been found in the county was controlled at King's Lynn in December 1972, it had been ringed at Kroonspolder, Vlieland in The Netherlands on 1st September. There have been many controls of Bearded Tits involving movements between the Norfolk reedbeds and those at Walberswick and Minsmere in Suffolk, and Goole in Humberside, and smaller numbers to or from Hertfordshire, Essex, Cambridgeshire and Leicestershire. A particularly interesting multiple recovery concerned one ringed at Murston, Kent in June 1972, which was controlled at Salthouse in October and was back breeding at Murston the following May. While another ringed at Murston in June 1972, which was controlled with the bird above at Salthouse in October, was controlled again at King's Lynn the following March.

*Michael Seago & Stewart Linsell*

## Long-tailed Tit   MY GARDEN - CHEDGRAVE. 15·8·1999.   *Aegithalos caudatus*

**A common resident and scarce passage migrant, mainly in autumn.**

The Long-tailed Tit breeds in the middle latitudes of the Western Palearctic, being found throughout Europe, except in Iceland, northern Fennoscandia and most of the Mediterranean islands. It is present in most parts of the British Isles, apart from city centres, the Fens, upland areas and the Northern Isles (68–72 BTO Atlas).

In Norfolk, it is found in most woodlands, particularly in clearings and along the edges, in overgrown hedgerows, in scrub especially where gorse is present such as on golf courses and commons, on heathland with scattered trees and in large gardens. It was present in 46% of the tetrads for the Norfolk Atlas, being noticeably absent in the Fens and the open country in Broadland (Kelly 1986). The number of 1km squares covered in Norfolk for the BBS, in which Long-tailed Tits were recorded, fell from 37–38% in 1994–95 to 23–26% in 1996–97. Family parties remain in flocks during the winter, when they wander more widely and are frequent visitors to gardens, even those in the larger towns. Because of their small size and almost total dependence on an insectivorous diet, Long-tailed Tits are very susceptible to severe winter weather. Up to 80% of the population may perish at such times (New Atlas). However, many flocks visiting gardens in winter have learnt to feed on fat and, following a request for information in the local press in 1994, parties of up to 16 were reported feeding on peanuts in over 100 gardens throughout the county and so the habit must be fairly widespread. Winter flocks of 50–60 birds have been not uncommon in the past, although there has been a suggestion since the mid-1990s that flock sizes have decreased recently. However, a flock containing 65 Long-tailed Tits was present at Sennowe Park in November 1997.

As long ago as the end of the 19th century the arrival on the Norfolk coast of presumed immigrants was being recorded. On 1st October 1899 'hundreds' were present in Yarmouth town gardens (Patterson 1905) and Pashley's garden at Cley was 'full of them' on 20th October 1899 (Riviere). Since the late 1950s, flocks of Long-tailed Tits have been recorded flying in off the sea on a number of occasions, mostly in October, but some as late as the end of November. The largest coastal gatherings have been 50 at Blakeney on 18th October 1968 and 30 at Holme on 15th October 1994, while a party of 20 with two Blue Tits arrived at Winterton on 8th October 1967. At Blakeney in 1969 a flock of 50 Long-tailed Tits on 14th–16th October had increased to 100 on 18th–19th October and 150 by the end of the month, presumably as a result of newly-arrived immigrants. The species was unusually plentiful in autumn 1971 around the north and east Norfolk coasts, with a maximum of 200 moving through Happisburgh on 31st October. In most autumns flocks of Long-tailed Tits are noted moving west along the north Norfolk coast, mainly in October.

The central European race *A. c. europaeus*, which is presumably involved in some of these autumn arrivals, is indistinguishable from the British race *A. c. rosaceus*, which is sedentary. However, the nominate northern race *A. c. caudatus* has an all-white head and is a rare visitor to the British Isles. Birds showing the characteristics of this race have been identified in Norfolk on seven occasions – some, at least, out of a party of ten at Cley on 2nd October 1961, at least two at Blakeney on 21st–22nd October and 9th–10th November 1961, 11–13 at Blakeney on 8th October 1966, three at Winterton on 20th April 1975, two at Fritton on 24th March 1978 and one at Hopton on 10th November 1980.

Over 10,000 Long-tailed Tits have been ringed in Norfolk and most of those which have been recovered were ringed between late September and early November. For a species which is generally considered to be sedentary, some surprisingly distant recoveries have resulted. Some of the most interesting have involved small flocks ringed and controlled together at a later date. Six ringed at Tottington on 8th October 1983 were controlled at Happisburgh on 20th October, while seven ringed at Landguard Point, Suffolk on 23rd October 1983 were also controlled at Happisburgh one week later. The speed of movement around the north Norfolk coast was shown by six ringed at Trimingham on 11th October 1975, controlled the next day at Sheringham, a distance of 13km, while seven ringed at Sheringham on 5th November 1995 were controlled 19km to the west at Wells on 8th November. Other recoveries, involving from one to three birds, have related to movements between Norfolk and Essex, Lincolnshire, Cambridgeshire and Hertfordshire. The longest, however, concerned two birds ringed together at Winterton on 7th October 1973 and controlled together at Brownsea Island in Poole Harbour, Dorset on 22nd October.

Proof that at least some of the coastal movement has involved Continental birds was obtained when one ringed at Happisburgh on 22nd October 1983 was recovered at De Panne, West Vlaanderen, Belgium on 8th September 1984. This remains the only foreign recovery of a British-ringed Long-tailed Tit.

*Moss Taylor*

## **Marsh Tit** MY GARDEN - CHEDGRAVE. 10-3-2000.          *Parus palustris*

**A fairly common resident.**

In the Western Palearctic, the Marsh Tit breeds in the lowlands of the middle and upper latitudes, showing a strong preference for deciduous woodland, especially that dominated by beech and oak. It is present throughout much of England and Wales, but is absent from the Fens, much of northern England, and Scotland and Ireland (New Atlas). Although in Europe it shows a preference for damp areas, in Britain it tends to favour drier woodland, in contrast to the Willow Tit.

It was only realised that the Willow Tit was a British resident in the early 20th century and so historical information on the distribution and status of the Marsh Tit in Norfolk is unreliable. In 1930, Riviere stated that the Marsh Tit was 'resident and in number equalling, or perhaps slightly less than, the Coal Tit'. The next county avifauna described it as 'A resident in deciduous woodland, but rather local' (Seago 1967). Nationally, there was no evidence of a change in status to 1960, but BTO Common Bird Census data showed that an otherwise unsuspected long-term decline in the population began in the late 1960s (Marchant *et al.* 1990). In Norfolk, the number of 10km squares in which the species was recorded for the 1968–72 BTO Atlas was 59, falling to 49 during the years of the Norfolk Atlas (1980–85). During the 1994–97 BBS it has been found in 9–12% of the 1km squares covered in Norfolk.

Marsh Tits continue to be reported from all parts of the county, mixed deciduous woodland being favoured, where oaks provide a plentiful supply of caterpillars for feeding nestlings and beechmast is available during the winter months. Pairs are also found in alder carrs, orchards, parks and large gardens, but pure coniferous woodland is avoided. Pairs tend to be fairly widely spread as they require a territory of 4–5ha, comparatively large for the size of the bird (European Atlas). Two of the highest concentrations appear to be at Holkham Park, where 15 pairs were present in 1996, and Bacton Wood with at least 30 pairs in 1997. The Norfolk Atlas found the species' strongholds to be in the hinterland of Norwich, in Breckland, the well-timbered areas to the north-east of King's Lynn, along the Cromer to Holt Ridge and along the upper Bure (Kelly 1986).

In winter, Marsh Tits remain paired and stay within their breeding territory. Unpaired birds join roving tit flocks, as do pairs but they only remain with the flock as long as it is within their territory (Winter Atlas). Like Coal Tits, they hoard food and will visit garden bird tables.

Ringing has demonstrated that Marsh Tits are very sedentary, with less than 1% of recoveries being made more than 50km away from the site of ringing. In Norfolk, 1,100 have been ringed since 1983 with the only recovery greater than 10km being a juvenile ringed at Garboldisham on 5th July 1996 and controlled at Thetford on 8th December, a distance of 13km.        *Moss Taylor*

## **Willow Tit** WATTON. 27-11-1988.          *Parus montanus*

**A fairly common but localised and declining resident.**

As a breeding bird, the Willow Tit is widely distributed across the temperate middle and upper middle latitudes of the Western Palearctic, extending into Asia. It is found in both the northern forests and the damp, mixed woodlands in the lowlands. It is fairly widespread in England and Wales but has a patchy distribution in northern and western England, and in southern Scotland, and is absent from Ireland (New Atlas).

As a result of the similarity between Marsh and Willow Tits it was not realised that the latter existed as a separate species in Britain until 1897. The first Norfolk record, however, was one killed at Loddon in January 1893 which was identified retrospectively; the second was also from the south of the county, having been obtained near Beccles on 9th August 1912 (Riviere). Breeding was first proved in Norfolk at Kelling in 1934. Between 1949 and 1962, Willow Tits were recorded at 58 well-scattered localities throughout the county, being most widespread in Broadland and Breckland (Seago 1967). During the 1990s, it has been reported from up to about 80 localities in a single year, although it was found in 226 tetrads

(16%) during the fieldwork for the Norfolk Atlas. This suggests that, at least during 1980–85, it was more widespread than the annual records would imply. However, during the four years 1994–97, it was recorded in a maximum of only 9% of the 1km squares covered for the BBS in Norfolk and it was not found in a single square in the last year, mirroring the decline mentioned below.

Compared with the Marsh Tit, it favours damper woodland habitats, where decaying tree stumps, soft enough to be excavated by the birds as nest cavities, are found. Such conditions are present in Broadland birch and alder carrs, riverside woods and scrub, and the wooded surrounds of overgrown, flooded gravel pits. In Breckland, at Thetford Warren, it inhabits the deciduous trees planted around the margins of coniferous plantations (Kelly 1986). As it will nest in smaller wooded areas than the Marsh Tit, it is also found in farmland spinneys and scrub, as well as in the larger deciduous woods in the county. It is largely absent from the treeless Fens. Willow and Marsh Tits occasionally hybridise and an apparently mixed pair bred at Sheringham Park in 1992 (M. Taylor pers. obs.).

During the winter, pairs tend to remain in their breeding territories along with a few juveniles and less readily join the roving mixed-tit flocks (European Atlas). They make little use of nuts as a source of food (Winter Atlas) and consequently they are infrequent visitors to garden bird tables. Like Marsh Tits, they are food hoarders, but generally of invertebrate items.

Nationally, the population of Willow Tits increased during the mid-1960s and mid-1970s, peaking in 1975, but a decline subsequently occurred (Marchant *et al*. 1990). In Norfolk a noticeable decline since the 1980s has become apparent at Holkham Meals, where the species was once fairly common, reducing to only two to three pairs in 1987–90 and none in 1992. This compares strikingly with the Marsh Tit which has shown a marked increase since the late 1970s (Bloomfield 1993). In Sheringham, the annual ringing totals in the 10km square TG14, during the years 1973–78 were 46 Willow Tits and 22 Marsh Tits, while for the six years 1983–88 they were 17 Willow and 15 Marsh Tits. As the ringing localities were similar during the two periods, it would appear that there had been a real decline in the number of Willow Tits (Taylor 1990). Certainly since the mid-1990s, many observers have commented on the increasing difficulty in locating the species. An increase in numbers of Great Spotted Woodpeckers and grey squirrels may be at least partly responsible for a decline in Willow Tits. The young are readily accessible in their nests contained in soft or rotten wood.

The British race of the Willow Tit *P. m. kleinschmidti* is highly sedentary and although there was no evidence that Willow Tits were involved in the tit irruptions from the Continent in 1957 and 1959, two birds showing the characteristics of the northern race *P. m. borealis* have been recorded in Norfolk. One was at Sandringham on 23rd November 1980 and another at East Ruston on 21st November 1996; while a palish individual was present in Yarmouth cemeteries on 26th October 1960, a site at which the species has been recorded on only one other occasion (Allard 1990).

Since 1983, over 800 Willow Tits have been ringed in Norfolk, with the number being ringed annually in the county equalling or outnumbering Marsh Tits from 1983 to 1991. Since then, the proportion of Willow Tits has fallen steadily, being only one-fifth of the Marsh Tit total in 1997. The longest movements have been two which moved 6km between the sites of ringing and recovery, again confirming the sedentary nature of the species. *Moss Taylor*

## Coal Tit    MY GARDEN - CHEDGRAVE. 4·8·1999.    *Parus ater*

**A common resident and rare autumn passage migrant.**

The Coal Tit breeds widely in the upper and middle latitudes of the Western Palearctic, from the boreal zone in the north to the Mediterranean zone in the south. Eastwards its range extends into Asia, as far as the Pacific. It is widespread throughout Britain and Ireland being absent only from the outer Scottish Isles, although it is thinly distributed in the treeless Fens (68–72 BTO Atlas).

Coal Tits are closely associated with coniferous forests, being one of the commonest and most characteristic species. However, even in the sessile oakwoods of northern and western Britain and Ireland, and in the birch woods of northern Scotland, they outnumber both Blue and Great Tits (Yapp 1962). In Norfolk, one of their strongholds is the extensive forestry plantations in Breckland, but they are found throughout the county wherever conifers are present. Pines, firs, larches, yews, cypresses and various exotic evergreens are all attractive to Coal Tits and so the species is found in parks, gardens and cemeteries, as well as in mixed and broad-leaved woodland. Unlike other species of tits, they usually nest in holes in the ground or in exposed roots of trees. Although the species was recorded in all of the 10km squares in the Norfolk Atlas, it was found in only 36% of the tetrads and few were noted in the Fens or Broadland; the distribution map showed a very similar range to that for the Goldcrest. During the 1994–97 BBS it was recorded in 27–31% of the 1km squares visited in Norfolk. In winter, Coal Tits are less closely associated with conifers and are often found in mixed parties of tits. They are also frequent visitors to garden bird tables. Their habit of storing food enables them to survive during periods of severe weather, despite their small body size (Winter Atlas).

The nominate race *P. a. ater*, which breeds on the Continent, is an irregular visitor to the county. The first records were of birds obtained at Northrepps on 15th January 1866 and at Lakenham the following spring (Riviere). Both specimens remain in the collection at the Castle Museum, Norwich. Records of presumed Continental birds in recent years have included three which arrived on the beach at Cley on 19th September 1954 and one in from the sea at Cley on 28th August 1958. The only Coal Tits reported in Norfolk, in association with the large influx of Blue Tits from the Continent in autumn 1957 were one to two on Blakeney Point on 21st September. During a smaller irruption of tits in 1959 up to four Coal Tits showing the characteristics of the Continental race *ater* were at Cley from 11th September to 22nd October. Other presumed migrants have been recorded at Winterton, Scratby, Caister and Yarmouth. In 1996 from mid-September onwards, Norfolk, along with the rest of the British east and south coasts, received a large influx of Continental Coal Tits, many of which were seen to be moving westwards along the north Norfolk coast. The highest counts included 22 at Holme on 18th–19th September, 13 at Wells and twelve at Snettisham on 20th September and 15 at Wells on 20th October, while at Hunstanton cliffs a total of 42 flew south during October, peaking at 13 on 10th October. Although many of these were probably Continental birds, some at Holme were of the British race *P. a. britannicus* which occurs every autumn on coastal passage. The only suggestion of a spring movement was a count of twelve at Holme on 27th March 1994.

British Coal Tits are largely sedentary and despite about 3,000 having been ringed in Norfolk, only a few have been recovered at any distance from the ringing site. One ringed at Titchwell on 13th October 1975 was killed by a cat at Gaywood, King's Lynn on 18th June 1976, while one ringed at Kettlestone on 6th October 1996 was controlled at Garboldisham on 29th December. Movements of British Coal Tits over 100km are very unusual, but one ringed at Snape, Suffolk on 1st February 1984 and recovered at Snettisham on 3rd April 1986 had flown 104km and was one of four long-distance recoveries reported that year, while another ringed at Potters Bar, Hertfordshire on 26th October 1985 was found dead at Thetford in August 1990, a distance of 103km. *Moss Taylor*

## **Blue Tit** MY GARDEN - CHEDGRAVE. 8·7·1999. *Parus caeruleus*

**An abundant resident and scarce passage migrant.**

The breeding range of the Blue Tit covers the lowlands of the middle latitudes of the Western Palearctic, extending from North Africa to central Fennoscandia, where, during the 20th century, there has been a dramatic spread northwards reaching beyond the Arctic Circle. It is found throughout the British Isles, except for the most mountainous areas of Scotland and the Northern Isles (New Atlas). The population in temperate Europe has remained generally stable for many years, although large fluctuations are characteristic. Declines follow harsh winter weather and cold rainy summers, to be followed by a rapid recovery as conditions become more favourable.

In Norfolk, the Blue Tit has always been the most widespread and most numerous tit. It was recorded in 93% of the tetrads for the Norfolk Atlas, being absent only from parts of the treeless Fens and the Halvergate Levels. During 1994–96 it was found in 83–84% of the 1km squares covered for the BBS in Norfolk, increasing to 98% in 1997. It is most abundant in the mature stands of oak and beech, found in the larger areas of woodlands around the county, although it can be found wherever mature trees provide suitable nest holes, such as hedgerows, parks, orchards and gardens. Blue Tits are readily attracted to nest boxes and breeding densities in suburban gardens may approach those in woodland, but reproductive rates are relatively low (Cowie & Hinsley 1987).

After the breeding season, Blue Tits begin to forage more widely, not infrequently even being found in reedbeds. During the autumn they gather into mixed feeding flocks with Great Tits, Long-tailed Tits, Treecreepers, *Phylloscopus* and *Sylvia* warblers, to be joined later by Nuthatches and Marsh Tits (Winter Atlas). The largest groups of feeding Blue Tits to have been reported were 100 at East Winch Common on 5th September 1993 and 100 at How Hill on 1st October 1993. Beech woods are particularly favoured during the winter months, the Blue Tit's agility enabling it to take beechmast still on the tree, while Great Tits are forced to feed on the ground. As winter progresses and the natural foods become depleted, Blue Tits become more dependent on peanuts, sunflower seeds and other artificial foods provided in gardens.

Birds of the nominate Continental race *P. c. caeruleus* are rare visitors to Norfolk. The first was recorded by Riviere at Cley in October 1921 and Blue Tits seen on the Cockle light-vessel on 14th March 1883, and Lynn Well light-vessel on 20th September 1925 and 1st October 1926 were all presumably of this race. In mid-September 1957 an unprecedented irruption of tits took place into Britain as a result of a high late-summer population in mainland Europe, with record numbers of Continental Blue Tits being seen in Norfolk (Cramp *et al.* 1960). Large influxes and westerly movements were noted at Blakeney Point, Cley and Cromer on 20th–22nd September, with marked increases in numbers in Norwich at the same time. Further influxes were recorded on the north coast in October and early November. At Scolt Head up to 30 were present on 9th October and over 60 were in *Suaeda* bushes between Morston and Stiffkey on 20th November. The most impressive passage, however, was from the Wash area on 13th October, with counts of coasting birds of 40 per hour at Holme, 600 in one and a half hours at Hunstanton and 300 per hour at Snettisham. Offshore, Blue Tits were reported from several herring-drifters and lightships, up to 40km off the Norfolk coast. During the following winter, the incidence of Blue Tits opening milk-bottle tops and entering houses to tear paper increased dramatically.

Since then, apparent immigrants have only been reported on two occasions –two were seen to fly in from the sea at Winterton, with 20 Long-tailed Tits, on 8th October 1967 and one flew in from the sea at Gorleston on 30th October 1983. However, Blue Tits clearly on passage have been recorded – mostly in October – at Snettisham, Hunstanton, Holme, Holkham, Blakeney Point and Sheringham, although these are more likely to have involved wandering British birds. The maximum daily counts have been 45 at Holme, 43 at Snettisham and 30 on Blakeney Point. The only spring movements to have been reported were both at Sheringham – eleven flying west on 18th March 1994 and five west on 12th March 1997.

The Blue Tit is the most commonly ringed bird in the British Isles and in Norfolk about 35,000 have been ringed since 1983. British Blue Tits are also one of the most sedentary and less than 1% of those recovered have moved more than 100km. Recoveries appear to show a pattern of movement around the east and north Norfolk coasts in autumn (including two ringed in Suffolk), with two birds continuing west into Northamptonshire and Birmingham from west Norfolk. Perhaps those Blue Tits seen coasting in autumn are just such birds. There is a suggestion of a return movement south in spring. Four of the most distant recoveries have involved birds ringed as nestlings – three from Norfolk to Northamptonshire, Essex and Lincolnshire respectively and one to Norfolk from Suffolk. The oldest recovery was a juvenile ringed at Sheringham on 2nd September 1980 and found dead at Corton, Suffolk on 8th June 1986.

*Moss Taylor*

| **Great Tit** | MY GARDEN - CHEDGRAVE. 8-7-1999.<br>DITTO - YOUNG LEFT NESTBOX. 25-5-2000. | ***Parus major*** |

**An abundant resident, and passage migrant in varying numbers.**

In the Western Palearctic, the Great Tit breeds from the subarctic to the Mediterranean zones, extending from Ireland in the west to eastern Russia and into Asia in the east. It occurs in every European country, where it is one of the most abundant birds. It is resident over much of its southern and central range, but an irregular irruptive migrant from the northern areas. It breeds extensively throughout Britain and Ireland, except for the highest parts of the Scottish Highlands and the Northern Isles (68–72 BTO Atlas).

In Norfolk it occurs throughout the county, in any area where deciduous trees are found – woodlands, scrub, farmland hedgerows, parks and gardens. It is also present, but in smaller numbers, in coniferous woodland such as that in the Brecks. In the Norfolk Atlas it is shown in 90% of the tetrads, being absent only from some coastal areas, parts of Broadland and in the Fens. During the 1994–97 BBS it was found in 71–88% of the 1km squares covered in Norfolk, with no apparent trend over the years. After the breeding season post-fledging dispersal occurs. As Great Tits are heavily dependent on beechmast during the winter months, the extent of winter wandering is directly related to the size of the crop. In good beechmast years, the birds tend to remain in the woodland for much of the winter, whereas in poor years, Great Tits wander more widely and visit gardens in larger numbers to seek alternative sources of food (Winter Atlas).

Great Tits of the nominate race *P. m. major*, which occur on the Continent, are irregular visitors to the British Isles. The first recorded large-scale irruption affecting Norfolk took place in the late autumn of 1910, during which flocks were seen to arrive from the sea at Yarmouth and several birds were caught which proved to be of the Continental race (Ticehurst 1932). However, during the irruption of tits in 1957 there were only two records of apparent immigrants, on both occasions at Blakeney Point. Confirmation that Continental birds do arrive in Norfolk was provided when one ringed at Westenschouven, The Netherlands on 21st October 1971 was controlled at Salthouse eight days later, and a nestling ringed in Overijssel on 26th June 1995 was controlled near Stoke Ferry on 23rd June 1996, a date suggesting that it was breeding in the county.

Since the mid-1980s both ringers and observers around the Norfolk coast have been aware of a noticeable spring passage in certain years between mid-March and early April. First noticed in 1984 and 1985, previous numbers were eclipsed by counts in 1994 which included 161 west at Holme on 18th March and 153 west also at Holme on 27th March.

Although over 20,000 Great Tits have been ringed in the county, apart from the first Dutch-ringed bird mentioned above, no recoveries were considered of sufficient interest to be included in the *Norfolk Bird Report* until 1978. The subsequent pattern of recoveries has suggested a movement from areas to the south of Norfolk (London, Essex and Suffolk), around the coast and then south-west from the Wash. Amongst the more distant movements have been birds ringed in Staffordshire and found nesting the following summer at Hillington, another ringed in Buckinghamshire in December controlled on passage the following spring at Sheringham, one ringed on spring passage at Sheringham controlled six weeks later on a nest box in Nottinghamshire and one ringed at Gillingham controlled at Tring, Hertfordshire, in the garden of Beech Grove, the former headquarters of the BTO, from where the ring had been first issued!

*Moss Taylor*

# Red-breasted Nuthatch                    *Sitta canadensis*

**A very rare vagrant; one record.**

The Red-breasted Nuthatch is a Nearctic species breeding in the evergreen forests of Canada, and the western and north-eastern areas of the USA. It is primarily resident although, depending upon the conifer seed crop, birds breeding in the north of the range are sometimes highly migratory, wintering as far south as the southern USA. The sole British and Norfolk record was the second for the Western Palearctic, following the first in Iceland in May 1970.

The finding of a small nuthatch by Mr and Mrs R. Aley, showing a black crown and white supercilium, feeding on a grassy path at the west end of Holkham Meals on the evening of 13th October 1989, led to one of the main ornithological events of the year. It was identified as a male Red-breasted Nuthatch the following morning by observers who initially heard it calling. The news soon spread and on 15th October an estimated 2,000 birders came to view this New World vagrant. For the remainder of the year, and up to 6th May 1990, it ranged widely with the wintering tit flocks between Meals House and the western end of the woods. Highly mobile, it continued to delight or frustrate a procession of birders, and on at least two occasions it appeared at the Wells end of the woods near the drinking pool. However, towards the end of its stay it became more obliging and was often found visiting the Royal beach chalet at Burrow Gap where it drank from the guttering (Anon 1990).

*Peter Allard*

## Nuthatch (Wood Nuthatch)    MERTON PARK (LORD W'S)    *Sitta europaea*
WATTON. 23·3·1976.

**A fairly common resident.**

The Nuthatch, a characteristic bird of lowland woodlands, breeds across the middle continental latitudes of the Palearctic. It occupies most of the suitable habitat in Europe, except for northern Scandinavia and Russia, Finland, Scotland, Ireland and the Mediterranean islands. It disappeared from the northern parts of its range in England during the 19th century, but in recent years has spread north, especially in Cumbria. Nevertheless, it still has a patchy distribution with many suitable sites unoccupied.

It has always been recorded in Norfolk as a reasonably common resident of mature deciduous and mixed woodland throughout the county. Stevenson also stated that he had found them frequenting most of the large gardens in the close vicinity of Norwich, such as at Bracondale, Thorpe and Earlham. He also recorded a complete albino killed at Lyng in 1846. During fieldwork for the Norfolk Atlas, it was found in 27% of the tetrads, although it went unrecorded in wide tracts of the county. It was most widespread in Breckland, in a well-wooded band of country extending north-north-west from the Brecks towards Hunstanton, around Norwich and along the Cromer to Holt Ridge. The parkland at Holkham, Raynham, Sennowe and Lexham also held good numbers (Kelly 1986). Large gardens with mature trees can also support breeding Nuthatches and they readily visit garden bird tables. Pure coniferous stands are generally avoided. During fieldwork for the 1994–97 BBS it was found in 2–9% of the 1km squares surveyed in Norfolk.

Although nationally the population appears to be stable, some observers in Norfolk have noted a decline in recent years. The species is seen far less frequently in the Hethersett area and a reduction of 50% in the number of breeding pairs at Holkham Park between 1985 and 1995 was attributed to the removal of a large number of old trees. However, 30 pairs were located at Holkham in 1996, compared with only 18 pairs the previous year, increasing to 36 pairs in 1997 and so perhaps the trend has been reversed. At East Tuddenham, where Nuthatches are now rarely seen, the decline has been blamed on ever-increasing numbers of grey squirrels which are eating hazel nuts before they have ripened. In 1995, the species was noted to be absent from Great Ryburgh and Boyle Wood, where it formerly bred.

Nuthatches are very sedentary, living in pairs and tending to remain within their territory throughout the year. However, in late spring and autumn 1996 many more than usual were recorded at coastal sites, with records of singles from 28th May to 8th June at Snettisham, Holme, Holkham Meals and Sheringham, and one or two during the autumn at Holme, Titchwell and Burnham Overy, with five at Holkham Meals on 15th September.

Only about 180 Nuthatches have been ringed in Norfolk since 1983, but one of them has produced a most surprising recovery – ringed at Reedham on 26th September 1987 and retrapped there on 20th February 1988, it was subsequently recovered at Colchester, Essex on 14th April 1990, a distance of 87 km. This compares with the next most distant recovery of 52km, from over 30,000 Nuthatches that have been ringed in Britain.

*Moss Taylor*

# Wallcreeper                                  *Tichodroma muraria*

**A very rare vagrant; one record in 1792.**

The Wallcreeper is an unmistakable species inhabiting the mountainous regions of southern Europe from the Pyrenees and Alps discontinuously east through Turkey and the Balkans to China. Although dispersive in winter, it is prone to occasional altitudinal movements.

The first British record was of one shot at Stratton Strawless on 30th October 1792. A reproduction of an excellent water colour drawing of two of the primary wing feathers painted at the time (leaving no doubt as to its identification) together with interesting correspondence extracts, between Robert Marsham and Gilbert White, appear in Stevenson. The initial letter reports that 'my man has just now shot me a bird which was flying about my house; I am confident I have never seen its likeness before. But on application to Mr Willughby I conclude it is a Wallcreeper or Spidercatcher'.

*Peter Allard*

*MY GARDEN-CHEDGRAVE.*

# Treecreeper (Eurasian Treecreeper)   *21·8·2000.*   **Certhia familiaris**

**A common resident and rare autumn migrant.**

The Treecreeper, a strictly arboreal species, is distributed across the Palearctic and breeds in most European countries, although it is largely replaced by the Short-toed Treecreeper *C. brachydactyla* in the Iberian Peninsula and Italy. On the Continent, it is usually found in upland coniferous forests, whereas in the British Isles it is a widespread resident of all types of woodland, but especially deciduous, and is only absent from the treeless highlands, open moorland and the Fens (68–72 BTO Atlas).

In Norfolk it is found wherever there are mature broad-leaved trees, especially oaks, such as deciduous or mixed woodland, parks, farmland hedgerows, churchyards or large gardens. It also occurs in coniferous woodland, as in the Brecks, but at a lower density. One of the highest concentrations reported in recent years has been at Holkham Park, where 30 singing males were located in both 1995 and 1997, and many more were probably present. The Norfolk Atlas recorded the species in 34% of the tetrads, and between 1994 and 1997 the number of 1km squares in Norfolk in which it was found during fieldwork for the BBS varied from 6% to 20%, but with no clear trend over the four years. Even during the breeding season, occasional birds turn up in unusual habitats, such as one on the Berney Marshes on 14th June 1995.

Communal roosting in excavated cavities in the soft, fibrous bark of giant wellingtonias was first discovered in Norfolk in 1926. In the 1960s, up to nine Treecreepers roosted each winter in such sites at Keswick Park (Seago 1967). An interesting observation made at Wroxham Broad in 1996 involved a pair which spent some time mobbing a Jay, before the Jay turned, caught and ate one of them! Stevenson recorded an albino nestling, alongside a normally-plumaged sibling in 1854.

The British race of the Treecreeper *C. f. britannica* is sedentary, but the nominate northern race *C. f. familiaris* is a partial migrant and eruptive in the north of the range, although normally remaining within Fennoscandia. Two birds in Norfolk have shown the characteristics of the northern race – at Weybourne on 4th November 1978 and at Holme on 2nd November 1987. Other birds, which may have been migrants, have included one at Holme on 10th October 1954, one found dead on Cley Marsh on 26th October 1954, one on Blakeney Point on 28th–29th September 1985 and a 'tight flock' of about 15 at Holkham Meals, also on 28th September 1985. While a total of nine has been found in the Yarmouth Cemeteries between late September and early November, including two on 1st November 1973 (Allard 1990).

Over 1,200 have been ringed in Norfolk since 1983 but the only recovery involved a movement of a few kilometres from Titchwell to Hunstanton. *Moss Taylor*

## Penduline Tit (Eurasian Penduline Tit)  *Remiz pendulinus*

**A very rare vagrant; six records involving nine individuals.**

The Penduline Tit is an irruptive and dispersive species breeding in Europe discontinuously from Spain, southern France, The Netherlands and Germany eastwards to Turkey. In recent years the population has been expanding, especially in the Low Countries and into Denmark. It is a rare, but increasing vagrant to Britain.

The first to be recorded in Norfolk was a calling male discovered by Dave Hewitt at Hickling Broad close to Rush Hills on 4th April 1987. It remained in the area until at least 10th April, but throughout its stay was highly elusive despite being present close to the main footpath. A vocal bird, it was occasionally heard delivering a subdued song (Gantlett 1988). This was the twelfth record for Britain since the first in 1966.

The second record was one which made an all too brief visit to an area close to Cley Mill on 13th October 1990. The following year an adult male frequented Titchwell reedbeds on 9th–10th May 1991, with another male at the same locality from 23rd to 28th April 1993. Remarkably a party of four Penduline Tits (a male and three immatures or females) was seen at Heigham Sounds on 20th December 1997. Despite an extensive search the following day, they were not seen again. Titchwell's reedbeds were again favoured when a male appeared on 1st January 1998, being seen again on 6th, 21st and then intermittently from 25th January until 4th April. During its stay it also made occasional visits to Holme Marsh, over 4km to the west.

Worthy of note, although not claimed for Norfolk, is an offshore record concerning an exhausted juvenile picked up on a gas production platform 130km north of Cromer on 23rd September 1994. It subsequently died in care. *Peter Allard*

## Golden Oriole (Eurasian Golden Oriole)  *Oriolus oriolus*

**A very scarce summer visitor and spring passage migrant; rare in autumn.**

The Golden Oriole breeds throughout the Western Palearctic as far as latitude 60°N, thereby just extending into southern Fennoscandia. Wintering areas are in sub-Saharan Africa. Evidence points to a more westerly route being taken in spring than in autumn. In Britain, the Golden Oriole breeds regularly only in the Fenland basin and occurs as a spring migrant, especially on the English south and east coasts, with on average 50 records per year.

Stevenson gave 15 certain records in Norfolk prior to 1861, of these two were in April, ten in May, one in July and two in August. Two instances of breeding are given but neither could be said to be above suspicion. A Mr Scales of Beechamwell had eggs of Golden Oriole in his collection which were alleged to have come from Norfolk, but doubt was cast on this and they were thought to have been imported from The Netherlands. A record of breeding in the garden of the rectory at Ormesby, where the nest and eggs were seen by the Revd Lucas, was not considered proven as the record had only hearsay evidence to back it up. There is a further record in either 1850 or 1852 from near Norwich when Edward Booth saw the nest and obtained an egg. This was documented in 1852 and was also mentioned in the 1876 edition of *Catalogue of cases of Birds in Dykes Road Museum, Brighton*. Two other records could quite possibly refer to breeding birds – a pair shot at Diss in 1829 and another pair shot at Lakenham on 18th May 1852. Riviere added a further seven examples all killed in the county, together with two or three birds 'whose lives had been spared'. Between 1930 and 1970 there were records of ones and twos covering 28 years, the majority in the second half of May. The extensive woodland at Horsey Hall was a favoured haunt, especially following the 1938 sea flood when it became an oasis within an extensive desert.

In 1967 Golden Orioles were found to be breeding in Suffolk. The area was a large poplar wood which extended to the county boundary. This site held a maximum of 14 pairs in 1971. It will be a matter of conjecture as to how many, if any, other nearby areas were occupied with Golden Orioles at this time and whether any of these would have been in Norfolk. The likely areas were given little attention by birdwatchers prior to this time. The poplars had been planted for commercial reasons and were destined to become matchsticks and pallets. As the trees have a short lifespan of some 40 years it meant that the large area of habitat was felled in the late 1960s. These would have been degraded and suffered from storm damage even if they had remained. It is thought that at this point, the Golden Orioles moved into surrounding areas and hence into Norfolk, where a male or a pair was present each summer at the same locality from 1967 (although there was an unpublished record of one pair breeding in Norfolk in 1966), breeding successfully in 1971 when three young were produced. A pair bred at the same site in 1972 but then two years followed with no conclusive proof of breeding. Since then numbers have gradually built up and from the mid-1980s birds have been known to breed annually. The original breeding site in Suffolk has since been acquired by the RSPB and largely developed into a mosaic of reedbeds and shallow pools, together with a new planting of 40ha of poplars.

Golden Orioles are very reliant on poplars and every nest found in Norfolk has been in one. The Golden Oriole Group which monitors the population throughout Fenland have recorded the following number of pairs in Norfolk. It should be understood that proving breeding can be very difficult. The nests are high in the canopy and are not easily visible from the ground.

**Table 43. Total number of confirmed breeding pairs of Golden Orioles and number of other potential breeding sites at which the species was recorded in Norfolk 1985–98.**

| Year | Confirmed breeding pairs | Other sites where birds recorded |
|------|--------------------------|----------------------------------|
| 1985 | 5  |    |
| 1986 | 7  |    |
| 1987 | 12 | 4  |
| 1988 | 8  | 4  |
| 1989 | 9  | 5  |
| 1990 | 5  | 10 |
| 1991 | 9  | 4  |
| 1992 | 9  | 5  |
| 1993 | 9  | 5  |
| 1994 | 6  | 10 |
| 1995 | 5  | 11 |
| 1996 | 4  | 9  |
| 1997 | 5  | 8  |
| 1998 | 6  | 6  |

There has been one instance of a pair nesting away from the Fens, at a site in central Norfolk in 1994, but no birds were present in subsequent years.

The breeding birds return in the first few days of May. The males are thought to precede the females although pairs have been settled on a territory by 4th May. On arrival the males are vocal, especially if there are other birds close by in adjacent woods and shelter belts, as they seek to set up and maintain a territory. Settled pairs that are isolated from others can quickly become very silent and easily overlooked. Birds continue to arrive throughout May. Adverse northerly winds such as in 1998 can put back their arrival. In 1996 there was obviously an influx of newly arrived birds in the first few days of June. This coincided with unprecedented numbers of painted lady butterflies and silver Y moths.

Poor weather during incubation and while feeding the nestlings can affect breeding success. A combination of high winds and heavy rainfall is thought to have caused a high failure rate each year from 1994 to 1996. If there is cold weather as well, the food required might be in short supply, in addition to the problems associated with a tenuously-attached nest high in the poplar canopy. Having fledged, the young are still fed by parents and there is dispersal away from the breeding areas. There have been very few records from the breeding sites after 10th August.

Away from the breeding areas, migrants have been seen each spring since 1967. Numbers have varied from single records in 1975 and 1976 to twelve in 1987, with an average of five per year. The earliest records have been at Strumpshaw Fen on 11th April 1994 and at Blickling on 13th April 1969; only four others have been recorded in April. Spring passage continues until late June with a clear peak in the second half of May. Spring birds have been recorded at many sites along the coast, on occasions in song. Favoured localities have been Holme with 17 records, Titchwell 14, Horsey 12 and Winterton 11. Other favoured inland sites have been Kelling, Salthouse Heath and Strumpshaw Fen. The peak at the end of May is later than that for the country as a whole. On average 50–60 are recorded each spring in the British Isles, with most on the Isles of Scilly and in the south coast counties (Dymond *et al.* 1989). These birds are considered to be overshooting birds from south-west Europe, whereas those breeding in East Anglia are thought to be an adjunct to the Dutch population. In autumn, there have been a number of records from Welney which relate to dispersal of the breeding population. There are only four records from August onwards, away from the breeding areas, with by far the latest on Scolt Head on 9th October 1959.

Since 1988 nestlings ringed in Norfolk have produced three recoveries. One ringed on 17th June 1988 was found dead 11km to the south-east on 28th July 1989. The other two relate to birds ringed on the same day, 22nd June 1993, though from separate nests. One died after hitting a window at Burstall, near Ipswich, Suffolk on 10th August 1993 and the other was controlled at Dunwich, Suffolk on 30th August 1993. The direction of movement would suggest that our birds cross the Channel and migrate with the Dutch population. A bird that was ringed at Gibraltar Point in its first year in 1986 was subsequently observed at a nest in Norfolk in 1995, the ring number being read as the bird brought in food. If others live as long as this bird then the species would be able to maintain its level of population and not suffer too much in the long term from a poor breeding season. *Peter Dolton*

# Isabelline Shrike *Lanius isabellinus*

**A very rare vagrant; seven records.**

The Isabelline Shrike breeds from Iran eastwards through Afghanistan and Kazakhstan to Mongolia and winters in south and south-west Asia and north-east Africa. There are three distinct races. It is a rare, but nearly annual vagrant to Britain since the first in September 1950.

The first Isabelline Shrike for Norfolk was a first-winter bird found by M. J. Carter at Walcott on 10th September 1961. It was trapped, ringed and photographed and remained in the area until 14th. Another first-winter bird occurred at Overy Dunes, frequenting bushes and bramble scrub, on 12th–13th October 1975 during the exceptional late autumn arrival of Siberian vagrants. It showed characteristics of the race *L. i. phoenicuroides* which breeds in central Asia, the Kirghiz Steppes and Iran. An obliging first-winter individual showing characteristics of the nominate race *L. i. isabellinus,* which breeds in Chinese Turkestan, Tian Shan and Lap Nor, frequented hedgerows near the coast road at Wells on 1st–5th November 1987. What was almost certainly the same bird was at Wembury in Devon on 8th–14th November. Another first-winter bird was seen briefly in scrub at Horsey Gap on 26th October 1988.

A singing male at Snettisham on 1st–2nd May 1995 was only the third British spring record (Lawton 1995). A male at Texel, in The Netherlands on 4th May could have been the same bird reorienting. Another first-winter Isabelline Shrike showing characteristics of the race *isabellinus* was found in scrub at Horsey Gap on 11th–13th October 1996. A similar bird showing characteristics of the same race was at Holme on 14th October, the day after departure of the Horsey Gap individual. This bird arrived in an exhausted state and was clearly very hungry – within a few hours it had caught and eaten a Long-tailed Tit, whereas the one at Horsey had fed on lizards and beetles. It was also very skulking initially. It was considered to be a different bird to that at Horsey Gap and it lingered at Holme until 21st October (Lawton 1997).

*Peter Allard*

## Red-backed Shrike                                         *Lanius collurio*

**A scarce passage migrant; formerly a scarce summer visitor which last bred in 1988.**

The Red-backed Shrike breeds in the middle latitudes of the Western Palearctic, the range extending from Russia westwards through Finland and southern Scandinavia (where it favours forest gaps) then southwards to northern Spain and the Mediterranean. It winters in eastern tropical and South Africa, north to Kenya, tending to feed on other passerine migrants on passage rather than building-up fat reserves prior to migration. Many countries in north-west Europe have reported major population declines.

A long-term reduction in Britain began accelerating from the mid-1900s although 300 breeding pairs were located in 1952. This total had reduced to 80 or 90 pairs by 1971, more than three-quarters of them restricted to the Brecks and coastal heaths of East Anglia (Bibby 1973). The Red-backed Shrike is now extinct as a breeding species here. The reasons for this depressing situation are not fully understood. The decline has been linked to climatic change resulting in a reduction in the availability of large flying insects – the bird's main prey item. A period of warm dry summers during the 1930s and 1940s ought to have been beneficial. Other factors including scrub clearance and the use of pesticides may have been significant, yet apparently suitable habitat remains. However, the activities of egg-collectors are thought to have hastened the final disappearance. Equally serious was the caging of young shrikes by unscrupulous aviculturists; a number of broods disappeared in Breckland during the 1970s and invariably the pair involved failed to rear young for that season. The autumn migratory movement is south-easterly across Europe developing a southerly trend as Greece is approached; the activities of Mediterranean bird-trappers must have taken a further toll.

Stevenson described the Red-backed Shrike as 'a constant summer visitant though not in large numbers and regularly breeds in the county'. On occasions it was known to attack the call-birds of the local bird-catchers. Distribution was largely unchanged at the time of Riviere who remarked on small numbers also appearing as coastal passage migrants. Examples had been taken on light-vessels off the coast between August and October. Red-backed Shrikes were typically found breeding on dry heaths and brecks containing scattered blackthorn and hawthorn (providing hunting lookout posts) together with tangles of wild rose and bramble. Also favoured were neglected hedgerows, scrubby railway cuttings, golf courses, young conifer plantations, abandoned chalk pits and gardens. In Breckland following detailed recording since 1974, more nests were found in hawthorns than any other tree.

Little detail is available before the Second World War regarding nesting although at Hickling, Jim Vincent writing in 1921 remarked that the species 'has become rather rare of later years due to the cutting down of high rough hedges'. Even so he recorded four nests in 1922 and three or four pairs nested annually on the estate until at least 1943. At that time there were complaints concerning Italian prisoners of war at Hickling setting horsehair nooses to catch shrikes.

Post-war the increasing popularity of birdwatching resulted in increased observations. In 1948 although an impressive 14 pairs of Red-backed Shrikes were located on Salthouse and Kelling Heaths together with four or five pairs at Muckleburgh Hill, other localities were soon to become lost. The last known nest at Bradwell was in 1950, at Caister Golf Course in 1951, at Belton Common in 1962 and at Gorleston in 1967. During the 1960s the county total varied between 15 and 27 pairs. Broadland was abandoned in 1964.

Between 6 and 18 pairs nested annually in the 1970s, but the appearance of unmated birds, usually males, was becoming a frequent event. On the outskirts of Norwich regular sites until 1969 included

Eaton and Old Catton; also up to four pairs on Mousehold Heath where a nest was photographed by Reggie Gaze in 1963. At the last named site the birds always established a 'larder' on coils of barbed wire edging the Army barracks. The east coast stronghold between Horsey and Winterton, where six pairs had nested in 1967, collapsed in 1978.

By 1980 nesting was restricted to five pairs in the Brecks and a single pair at Weybourne. In addition a solitary male held territory at Cley for two weeks. The final breeding successes in north Norfolk were at Weybourne in 1981 and at Holme in 1983. Breckland became the last retreat with three pairs taking up residence in 1984 followed by two pairs in 1985 and three pairs again in 1986. The very last pair guarded by the Forestry Commission, RSPB and volunteers, bred successfully at the Santon Downham picnic site in the same bushes in both 1987 and 1988. A solitary male returned in 1989 lingering almost a month, but failed to find a mate despite the brief appearance of two females several kilometres away. A solitary male appeared at Santon Downham on 16th May 1990 staying until 30th June and an additional male and a female put in a one-day visit on 23rd May. Thorough searches the following spring failed to locate a single bird. Detailed recording by Ron Hoblyn from 1974 onwards indicated that a total of 178 young had reached the flying stage in the Norfolk Brecks (Hoblyn 1991).

Almost all the passage migrants appearing in Norfolk have been at localities on or near the coast. Those inland were usually at former breeding sites and were probably unmated wanderers. Most spring birds occurred between the last week of May and the second week of June with stragglers until the month's end. The earliest was a male at Weybourne on 30th March 1957 followed by a female at Stiffkey three days later. A high total of twelve spring migrants appeared from 9th May to 4th June 1978 and a similar number from 8th May to 2nd June 1985, while at least 18 were noted between 2nd May and 14th June 1998.

The autumn passage has extended from late August until the third week of October. Most have been seen on a single date, but singles remained at Holme on 2nd–18th September 1974, at Strumpshaw from 20th August to 4th September 1981 and at Holme from 27th August to 16th September 1983. In more recent years all have doubtless belonged to the Fennoscandian breeding population displaced by north-east winds. A total of 14 featured during the great 'fall' of early September 1965, followed by 25 or more in 1976 and 60 during a series of 'falls' in 1977 when there were six at Holkham Meals, six at Waxham and twelve at Winterton on 21st August and still nine there on 27th. In 1979 the autumn total exceeded 20 with 23 in 1984. The latest occurrences have included one at Holme on 16th November 1986 and probably the same bird from 23rd November to 1st December at Hunstanton. During the decade 1988–1997 there were totals of 105 and 147 migrants in spring and autumn respectively.

There have been two distant recoveries of Red-backed Shrikes affecting Norfolk – a juvenile ringed at Middleton on 24th July 1961 was controlled at Benacre, Suffolk on 1st September, and another juvenile ringed at Landguard Point, Suffolk on 11th August 1986 was controlled in Breckland on 25th July 1989.

*Michael Seago*

# Lesser Grey Shrike                                                   *Lanius minor*

**A rare vagrant.**

The Lesser Grey Shrike breeds in temperate, Mediterranean and steppe climates in the middle continental latitudes of the Western Palearctic, from north-west Iberia, France and Germany, eastwards into Asia. It winters in southern Africa. In Britain it is a rare, less than annual and probably declining spring and autumn vagrant; only Shetland has recorded more than Norfolk.

The first county example was obtained at Yarmouth in spring 1869 and another taken in a greenhouse there on 28th May 1875 is currently on view at the Castle Museum, Norwich (Seago 1967). Two further specimens were obtained before the first documented sight record in 1956. This heralded a period of relative abundance with a further twelve recorded by 1982, including the longest-staying British example – at Ringstead from 22nd July to 3rd September 1979 (Evans 1994). Since then three more have been recorded – at Potter Heigham on 1st–8th September 1991, at Sheringham on 16th–17th September 1994 and at Burnham Overy Dunes on 5th–18th September 1996, taking the county total to 19.

A decline in the western European breeding population doubtless explains the dwindling number of British records at the current time. Climatic changes are considered a likely cause, Lesser Grey Shrikes being vulnerable to cooler and wetter summers.

The pattern of occurrence in Norfolk is biased slightly towards spring (mainly mid-May), although in recent years, autumn records, mainly in September, have predominated. This shifting pattern reflects changes in the breeding population with spring overshoots becoming rarer.

*John R. Williamson*

## Great Grey Shrike                                    *Lanius excubitor*

**A very scarce passage migrant and winter visitor.**

The distribution of the Great Grey Shrike extends across four continents. With such a wide range it is not surprising that there should be considerable variation in plumage and a number of races are recognised. The largest shrike in the Western Palearctic, its range extends from the Atlantic eastwards towards northern Asia from high to middle latitudes. The northern populations vacate breeding areas in winter. In Britain, as in much of western Europe, it is in decline.

Stevenson regarded the Great Grey Shrike as 'both a spring and autumn visitant'. It was not uncommon for one to be netted by the bird-catchers when pouncing upon an unfortunate decoy. Arthur Patterson kept one which had come to grief in the mesh of a clap-net at Yarmouth. Riviere's description of the species as 'an uncertain and irregular passage migrant and winter visitor' holds good today. Numbers appearing in Norfolk have always fluctuated doubtless as a result of variations in breeding success. Unusual numbers appeared in the county in the winter of 1880–81 and at least 14 were received by the local taxidermists and dealers.

The Great Grey Shrike is attracted to heaths, commons, tall hedgerows and scattered thorns in an open setting especially in the vicinity of the coast. The first autumn arrivals reach Norfolk during the second half of September; the earliest being one at Holme on 11th September 1989. Exhausted birds have appeared on coastal fishing vessels and on light-vessels. The Haisboro' light-vessel recorded single birds in both 1959 and 1962 and at the Inner Dowsing a Great Grey Shrike took three Redstarts and a Chiffchaff on 6th October 1968. As a rule shrikes are solitary, but on 23rd October 1955 five appeared among the marrams and *Suaeda* bushes between Blakeney Point and Cley. Each had mapped out its hunting ground and was reducing the numbers of immigrant Robins and Goldcrests with which it had so recently travelled. There was an impressive influx during the first days of October 1966 when a total of ten arrived between Morston and Salthouse. At Horsey and Winterton four were on show on 3rd November 1974. More unusual was a group of three inland at Stanford Water on 21st November 1953.

Great Grey Shrikes featured prominently between the mid-1960s and the early 1990s. A peak of 64 localities was attained during 1974. This abundance was doubtless a result of forestry changes in Scandinavia producing extensive clearfell areas. Salthouse Heath became a classic site for Great Greys, one or more usually maintaining territory there from late October until the following April. At times what must have been the same bird would return for several years in succession often perching on precisely the same branches each winter. At Salthouse one bird was recorded capturing a variety of birds including Meadow Pipit, Pied Wagtail, Redwing, Chaffinch, Brambling and Linnet. Another wintering in the vicinity of the Thurne Broads caused concern when it seized a Bearded Tit. Prey items can be as large as a stoat and the bird is quite capable of catching Swallows in flight. A flock of Siskins at Santon Warren provided one shrike with an abundance of prey. Following an aerial pursuit a Great Grey Shrike will not hesitate to enter dense thorn bushes to flush hiding birds.

Springtime departure has been most noticeable from March to mid-April, although in earlier years birds were not uncommon up to the last week in May. In 1965 one lingered at Snettisham from 16th May until 3rd June. Adverse weather between 6th and 17th April 1971 resulted in an exceptional number of Great Grey Shrikes along the north Norfolk coast; at least 14 were in evidence awaiting more favourable conditions before crossing the North Sea. Singles were present at Weybourne from 19th May to 13th June 1972 and at Kelling Quags on 7th–8th June 1983. The latter bird may well have been the same as at Winterton from 13th June to 16th July 1983.

Despite the decline of wintering Great Grey Shrikes in recent years, with not a single overwintering bird reported in 1997, a major autumn influx occurred from 3rd October 1998 with at least 20 reported during the first half of October.

*John R. Williamson*

# Woodchat Shrike

*Lanius senator*

A rare vagrant, mainly in spring.

Woodchat Shrike
(Gary Wright)

Four races of Woodchat Shrike breed across the Western Palearctic in the middle and lower middle latitudes, mainly in the Mediterranean climatic zone. The winter range is in sub-Saharan Africa north of the Equator and in small numbers in southern Arabia. The western races *L. s. senator* and *L. s. rutilana* are the forms which occur in the British Isles, where it is an annual vagrant.

For many years the first county record was considered to have been one obtained at Yarmouth on 29th April 1859 which remains on display in the Castle Museum, Norwich. However, boundary changes added one shot by a farmer at Bradwell in April 1829 which therefore became the first for Norfolk (Ticehurst 1932). Riviere added two further records – at Yarmouth on 16th May 1885 and Framingham Earl on 2nd June 1901.

A further 41 years were to pass before the next occurrence – at Beeston Common on 16th May 1942. The county total currently stands at 47 – all single birds and almost half the total appearing in May. Earliest dates have been singles at Winterton on 20th–22nd April 1997 and at Holme on 24th–26th April 1964. Eight have appeared in June, including a long-stayer at Weybourne and Lower Kelling from 22nd June to 19th July 1993, five in July, two in both August and September and three in October. The latest sightings have been at Holme on 4th October 1965, Overstrand on 6th–7th October 1997 and Cley on 14th October 1966. Records have been annual since 1992. The highest annual totals have been four in both 1960 and 1997. Sixteen of Norfolk's Woodchat Shrikes have been found between Blakeney Point and Sheringham, including coastal heath localities, with others at several sites along the Norfolk coast from Holme to Winterton. In Breckland there have been sightings at Stanford and Great Cressingham.

A dramatic decline has taken place in the north and west of the breeding range in recent years, probably due to a combination of climatic change, afforestation, intensified farming and drought conditions in winter quarters. Despite this, spring and early summer records in Norfolk have increased. The tendency to a more prolonged stay is in keeping with a species extending its breeding range and may perhaps indicate a more southerly origin of recent birds.

*John R. Williamson*

# Jay (Eurasian Jay)

CHEDGRAVE –
MY GARDEN - 20-6-2000.

*Garrulus glandarius*

**A common resident; occasional irruptive passage migrant and winter visitor.**

Jays are virtually ubiquitous in mainland Europe, being absent only from the extreme north. They breed in predominantly lowland woodland, both broad-leaved and coniferous, but especially favouring oak, beech and hornbeam. They are the most arboreal of all the members of the crow family, although after the breeding season Jays disperse to more open areas. The populations in the west and south of the range are sedentary, whereas those to the north and east are eruptive migrants. In Britain, the population declined during the 19th century as a result of persecution by landowners and gamekeepers, but increased during both World Wars. The recovery was also aided by the afforestation with conifers by the Forestry Commission. The species is now absent from very few areas of England and Wales, most noticeably the Fens and uplands of the Pennines, and it has a scattered distribution in Scotland and Ireland.

The Jay always appears to have been a common and widespread resident in Norfolk (Stevenson and Riviere). It was recorded in 50% of the tetrads for the Norfolk Atlas and was the most widespread of the resident crows, being found wherever there were areas of fairly dense cover, such as woodland, scrub and forestry plantations. Unlike many other woodland birds it is not generally attracted to forest edges, glades or clearings (Yapp 1962). During fieldwork for the 1994–97 BBS it was recorded in 25–35% of the 1km squares visited in Norfolk.

The British race of the Jay *G. g. rufitergum* is generally sedentary, but eruptive; diurnal migrations of the northern and central European race *G. g. glandarius*, which tends to breed in coniferous forests, occur from time to time. The Jay's habit of burying items of food, especially acorns, indicates a particularly strong and ancient association with oaks, and these Continental eruptions are related to annual fluctuations in the acorn crop. A poor crop or crop failure invariably causes a mass movement. Over the years, there have been occasional records in Norfolk of small numbers of Jays apparently migrating, such as 1975 when 14 were counted at Titchwell on 11th October and four were seen to arrive in off the sea at Winterton on the following day.

In 1983, however, the largest recorded influx of Continental Jays occurred between late September and early November, many thousands of birds being involved. The invasion took place along a broad front, from Humberside to the south coast. The vast majority were recorded from south-west England, where a flock of 1,000 was observed in fields near Land's End, while 3,000 flew west past Plymouth in parties of up to 300. In Norfolk unprecedented numbers were recorded from late September. The peak month was October, when large numbers were recorded flying over inland, as well as coastal, sites. Some of the more notable counts were two parties of 50 which flew north at Reedham on 10th, 50 flying north at Moulton St Mary on 12th, 134 west at Cley (which probably included 94 heading west in ten minutes at Weybourne) on 13th, 173 west (including 86 in one hour) at Titchwell on 14th and 138 at Snettisham on 19th. On the east Norfolk coast, where birds flew north, south or west on striking land, 87 flew south at Winterton and 115 came in off the sea in parties of 20–30 birds at Yarmouth on 17th, while 100 were at Stokesby on 19th. Autumn totals included 198 south at Wolferton and nearly 300 west at both Titchwell and Holme. There were very few records from the Fens, and as most flew south from Hunstanton it suggested that the birds followed the coastline of the Wash and moved into Lincolnshire. The winter of 1983–84 was also unusual in that, as a result of the failure of the British acorn crop, resident British Jays were also on the move searching for food and possibly swelling the numbers recorded (Warren 1984). The following spring, a return passage was noted between March and July, peaking in May–June. In May, the birds were flying mainly eastwards along the north coast and southwards on the east coast, with a maximum of 47 in several small groups in four hours at Horsey on 23rd May.

Perhaps surprisingly, influxes of Continental Jays, albeit on a much smaller scale, were also recorded in Norfolk in the autumns of 1993, 1994 and 1996. In 1993, maximum counts included 20 in off the sea at Holme on 23rd September, up to 90 passing west between Sheringham and Overy Dunes on the following day, 43 west at Holme on 1st October, 45 west at Sheringham on 4th October and 27 flying inland in two hours at Winterton on 9th October. Between 30th September and 2nd October, four Jays ringed in the Weybourne area showed the characteristics of the nominate Continental race *glandarius*. One of the four was retrapped at the site of ringing on 1st January 1994, providing the first evidence of overwintering by a Continental Jay (Young-Powell 1994). The following spring, a 'return' passage was noted between late April and the end of May, with maximum counts of 19 west at Beeston on 29th April, 30 at Horsey Gap on 30th April, 16 west at Holme on 22nd May and 22 at Horsey on 28th May. During the autumn of 1994, Continental migrants were noted at most coastal sites in October and records included 14 in off the sea at Cromer on 10th and a similar number in off the sea at Holme on 12th. Once again, in 1996, there was an almost total failure of the acorn crop, both in Britain and across Europe, resulting in another classic influx of migrants between 16th September and late October. Highest October counts included 131 through Holme on 9th, 40 at Old Hunstanton Park on 10th, 38 west at Sheringham on 11th, 41 south at Snettisham on 13th, 45 west at Holme on 24th and a monthly total of 203 south at Hunstanton cliffs, including 43 on 14th. Again a marked 'return' passage was noted between mid-April and late May 1997. Migrating Jays were recorded at many coastal sites around the county with peak numbers in early May. On 1st May 25 flew west and four east at Sheringham, and at Cromer eight flew in from the sea and 41 moved west. Counts on 3rd May included 35 west and five east at Sheringham while 26 flew out to sea at Waxham. The only other notable movements were 19 at Sea Palling on 5th May and 18 north at Eccles on 18th May.

Over 450 Jays have been ringed in Norfolk but only one has been recovered more than a few kilometres from the site of ringing – a nestling ringed at Mundford on 10th June 1955 was recovered at Fulbourn, Cambridgeshire on 21st March 1956. Another ringed at Gibraltar Point, Lincolnshire on 21st April 1984 and recovered at Hanworth in January 1985 may have been one involved in the irruption in autumn 1983, as recoveries of over 50km in the British Isles are unusual. However, one ringed at Queen Mary Reservoir, Surrey in March 1989 and recovered at King's Lynn one year later, did not occur during a major Jay influx.

*Moss Taylor*

## Magpie (Black-billed Magpie)    *Pica pica*

*CHEDGRAVE COMMON.*
*27-9-1999.*

**A common resident and rare passage migrant.**

The Magpie has a continuous breeding range throughout Europe and Asia, from the upper to the lower middle latitudes of the Western Palearctic. It is a sedentary species with limited dispersal, mainly in the north of its range. It is found throughout England, Wales and Ireland, but is quite localised in Scotland, where it is absent from the uplands and islands (New Atlas). Prior to the 19th century, Magpies were far more widespread in Scotland, but due to persecution by gamekeepers, as elsewhere in Britain, a marked decline occurred and Magpies probably reached their lowest numbers nationally at the start of the 20th century. Largely as a result of the lapse in keepering during the First World War, numbers began to increase, although they remained scarce in eastern and southern England until the 1930s. The Second World War had a similar effect, and thereafter Magpies began to expand into more open countryside and suburban areas (68–72 BTO Atlas). This increase in numbers has continued to such an extent that, as a result of its great adaptability, urban densities have increased spectacularly in Britain, Ireland and parts of central and eastern Europe, and the species is now a familiar bird, even in town gardens.

In Norfolk, Stevenson described the Magpie as 'extremely scarce' in the 19th century. Its stronghold was in the north-east of the county and it was particularly scarce in the west and around Norwich. By the time of the First World War, it had become 'almost extinct' as a breeding species, but as in other parts of Britain began to recover in the 1920s and a keeper in south-west Norfolk shot 28 in 1924 (Riviere). Between 1940 and the early 1950s it became abundant (Seago 1977) and a party of 35 was recorded at Ovington in 1953, at a time when they were continuing to increase in many localities. However, numbers once more declined and 30 flying north-east at Hautbois on 27th February 1967 was considered to be 'an unusual number nowadays'. Since the 1970s the species has once again become more numerous. By 1992, a feeding flock of 50 was noted at Saddlebow on 14th March and further evidence of the species' dramatic increase in west Norfolk was shown by the total of 1,400 trapped in the Stanford Training Area and on three Breckland estates in 1993. The Magpie is renowned for its response to the use of a caged 'call-bird'. In east Norfolk, Berney Arms was colonised in 1987 and the remote Halvergate Marshes in 1996, the year in which it first bred in Yarmouth Cemeteries.

Magpies nest in areas of rough scrub, tall hedgerows, clumps of trees and along woodland edges. Where persecution is low, the species prefers to breed near towns, villages and farms (European Atlas). During fieldwork for the Norfolk Atlas (1980–85), Magpies were recorded in 623 tetrads (43%), being scarce or absent only in dense Breckland plantations, in much of the Broads and Fens, and from the 'well manicured' farmland of west-central and north-west Norfolk. The species was found in every 10km square in Norfolk for the New Atlas (1988–91) and indications are that it has continued to spread. During the 1994–97 BBS it was recorded in 60–64% of the 1km squares visited in Norfolk. Although Magpies are known to take the eggs of gamebirds and songbirds, it has never been proved to have had a detrimental effect on the overall breeding success of other bird species. Indeed, research has found that the Magpie's diet consists mainly of invertebrates in the summer and plant material in the winter, with only a minority of individuals taking any birds or eggs (Tatner 1983).

Adult Magpies remain in their territory throughout the year, rarely moving more than 0.5km, even to roost. Immatures up to two years old, spend most of their time in loose flocks of up to 25 birds (Winter

Atlas). It is these birds which form the large roosts, which have been noted in Norfolk since the early 1950s, with the birds dispersing to their home ranges the following morning. The first sizeable roost to be reported contained 80 birds in sallows and alders at Surlingham. Roosts are formed from October onwards, breaking up in late March or April. The largest and best-recorded roost is at Roydon Common. Known since 1982, when a maximum of 37 Magpies were present in February, it is still in use over 15 years later. Between 1989 and 1993, at least 100 birds were counted each winter, with a maximum of 150 in December 1992 and 140 in November 1993; over 100 were again present in December 1997 and a record count of 173 was made on 8th February 1998. Other large roosts have included up to 150 birds at Buxton Heath in 1987–88, 75–100 at Lopham Fen in 1994 and up to 73 at Ringstead Common in 1993–96.

As long ago as Stevenson's time there was a suggestion that Magpies might occasionally arrive in Norfolk with other winter visitors, presumably from the Continent. Many were present, along with Jays, during the severe weather of the 1846–47 winter and unusual numbers were again encountered in early 1857. Riviere also mentioned occasional small parties in the immediate vicinity of the coast and an apparent arrival of immigrants at Weybourne and Sheringham on 10th October 1882. During the 1950s, there were a few records of small parties of Magpies apparently migrating, such as 31 west at Overstrand on 17th March 1957 and 10 west at Happisburgh on 1st November 1959. Between 1954 and 1968 the crews of light-vessels off the Norfolk coast maintained bird diaries. On just two occasions were Magpies recorded – ten west at the Haisboro' on 1st November 1959 and 20 passing the Smith's Knoll 40km off Yarmouth on 18th October 1966. Bloomfield (1993) stated that 'During September and October small numbers of migrants are often noted flying west at coastal sites [in the Holkham area]' and gives as an example 18 west at Overy on 20th September 1987. In 1996, there was a highly unusual and unprecedented series of records of birds on obvious migration in both spring and autumn. In spring, ten flew out to sea and one flew high south-east at Winterton on 27th March, seven flew east at Sheringham on 3rd April and two flew high out to sea at Holme on 9th April. And in autumn, four flew south at Hunstanton cliffs on 7th October and one flew in off the sea at Scolt on 11th October. Again in 1997 one flew west at a height over Scolt Head on April 13th, and southerly movements involving 10–11 birds on each occasion were noted at Hunstanton on three dates between 6th and 19th October. Although the species is mostly sedentary in Scandinavia, incipient migratory movements have been observed from the south-western tip of Sweden, at Falsterbo, in some autumns, coinciding with the end of a spell of fine weather and sometimes associated with movements of Jays and Nutcrackers (BWP). However, there have been no ringing recoveries involving movements of Magpies to or from Britain.

Over 150 Magpies have been ringed in Norfolk, of which one has been recovered outside the county – a nestling ringed at Snettisham in 1991 was found at Fulston, Lincolnshire in May 1994. There have only been two other movements of over 10km – a nestling from Salthouse to Warham, and one ringed at Burnham Market in August 1991 recovered at Narford in October.

*Moss Taylor*

# Nutcracker (Spotted Nutcracker)     *Nucifraga caryocatactes*

**A rare vagrant; an unprecedented influx of at least 104 birds in autumn 1968.**

The Nutcracker inhabits the coniferous forests of southern Fennoscandia and central Europe eastwards across central Asia to Kamchatka. There are two distinct races in Europe, both of which are highly dependent on the cone crop, especially that of the arolla pine. If this crop fails, as occurred in 1968, it becomes an irruptive species, especially the slender-billed race *N. c. macrorhynchos* which breeds from north-east Russia eastwards across Siberia. The thick-billed race *N. c. caryocatactes* breeds from southern Fennoscandia south through Europe to northern Italy and the Balkans and is generally sedentary.

The first Norfolk record of a Nutcracker was one shot at Rollesby on 30th October 1844, a year of marked immigration of this species into western Europe. This specimen was formerly in the collection of G. H. Gurney at Keswick Hall. Further examples were obtained off Yarmouth on 7th October 1853, near Wisbech on 8th October or November 1859, at Gorleston on 8th October 1864 and Hunworth on 8th November 1888. The last bird was formerly in the Connop collection at Rollesby Hall. The one observed, but not shot, near Thetford early in May 1899 and mentioned by Riviere remains doubtful. In 1911 two were killed, a female near Hempstead on 6th October and another female at Sparham on 9th October; the latter is preserved at the Castle Museum, Norwich. Riviere mentioned that with the possible exception of the 1853 record, all the specimens obtained appeared to be of the slender-billed race. Another was seen at Letheringsett on 6th October 1930.

The year 1968 will long be remembered for the invasion of Nutcrackers when an unprecedented influx occurred in the autumn. Their arrival was heralded by large numbers in the Baltic, particularly in Sweden where 4,400 were counted flying north-north-west at Holmon Island on 11th August, although the peak of the invasion was at the end of August. A further 20 reached as far west as Belgium in the first three weeks of August. This irruption affected many countries in northern Europe from Russia, Estonia and other Baltic States through Finland, Sweden, Norway, Poland, Germany, Denmark, The Netherlands (where 100 corpses were passed to one taxidermist), Belgium and northern France to the Channel Islands. Although it seems likely that most were of the slender-billed race *macrorhynchos*, substantial numbers of the thick-billed race *caryocatactes* were recorded moving west in Finland. Of the few Norfolk specimens critically examined, all were *macrorhynchos* (Allard 1969 and Hollyer 1970).

The invasion of 1968 involved at least 315 birds in the British Isles with Norfolk recording 104 (the highest county total, followed by Suffolk with 94 and Kent 34). Each arrival phase coincided with a spell of north-easterly or light variable winds. Many birds were tired on arrival and allowed close approach. One was unfortunately shot at Baconsthorpe on 13th September and of four found dead, one is preserved in the Castle Museum, Norwich. One was caught and ringed at Holme Bird Observatory. The first phase of arrivals in 1968 occurred on 6th–17th August and involved 23 birds. The first were noted at Ditchingham and Trunch on 6th and were followed by several sightings at Wells/Holkham on 8th–10th and at Holme and Thornham on 11th. The arrival continued throughout the county with birds noted at 16 localities, including three together on Gorleston cliffs on 15th. The second and main arrival phase totalled at least 54 birds at 35 localities and took place from 21st August to 19th September. Three were at Holkham Meals on 27th with no less than six at Caister on 14th September. The final arrival phase was from 27th September to 26th October involving 27 birds at 21 localities, mostly singles, but including four together at Hickling on 28th–29th October. The final sighting during the influx was a tame, rather bedraggled bird in Holkham Meals on 11th January 1969 (Allard 1969).

This remarkable influx was triggered by a shortage of food in the forests of west Siberia – a combination of pine crop failure and a lack of hazel nuts. Their diet in Norfolk was wide and varied, and included pine cone seeds, ants, large beetles and assorted fruit, especially apples. They were attracted to a variety of habitats, including churchyards, golf courses, coastal pine belts, large lawns and even roadside verges. Most birds only made a brief stay and to many this was a death-wandering. Although few corpses were found, one suspects that very few returned to their native forests.

Since then, a further three Nutcrackers have been reported, but as expected none lingered. One was photographed at Cringleford on 28th October 1971, one was at Gunton on 6th October 1978 and another at Itteringham on 23rd September 1979.                                                              *Peter Allard*

## Jackdaw (Eurasian Jackdaw)        MY GARDEN - CHEDGRAVE 27-11-1999.        *Corvus monedula*

**A very common resident, and fairly common winter visitor and passage migrant.**

The Jackdaw breeds throughout the Western and Eastern Palearctic from subarctic regions of Fennoscandia and Russia, south to the Mediterranean, North Africa and the Himalayas. Plumage contrasts between the nape, collar and darker body are variable within breeding populations and between sexes, but on these criteria four subspecies are also recognised, including the nominate *C. m. monedula* of Scandinavian origin. The western European race *C. m. spermologus* breeds throughout lowland Britain and Ireland avoiding only moorland and montane habitats.

In Norfolk the status and distribution appears to have changed since the 19th century. Stevenson commented that 'The large number of churches in Norwich afford ample accommodation in their various steeples for these noisy denizens', and the same would have applied to the many other churches throughout the county. He also mentioned pairs nesting in the Hunstanton cliffs. The Norfolk Atlas, however, demonstrated that the species then had a very scattered range, with certain areas having concentrations of Jackdaws separated by tracts of country with few if any; during the fieldwork it was found in only 36% of the tetrads. But there may well have been some recovery in numbers since then as during the 1994–97

BBS it was recorded in 60–67% of the 1km squares surveyed in Norfolk.

Jackdaws favour wooded areas on the edge of farmland. Expansive areas of open farmland, fen and saltmarsh are less frequently visited, except by transient winter flocks. The species is also uncommon on clearfell areas or about the interior of Breckland's conifer plantations. However, it is numerous in the surrounding countryside, towns, villages and leafy suburbs. The species is semi-colonial such that its breeding distribution tends to reflect the availability of suitable cavity nest sites, such as holes in trees and old buildings, including disused drainage mills on the marshes. Its habit of commandeering chimney pots for nesting often makes the species a conspicuous and boisterous neighbour. Larger breeding concentrations in recent years have included 50–100 pairs at Felbrigg, 29 pairs at East Wretham and 20 pairs in Blakeney Village. While large stands of mature deciduous woodland and adjoining parkland, such as at Holkham, will continue to support good populations, even if they are less conspicuous than elsewhere.

In winter, Jackdaws typically form mixed flocks with Rooks and Carrion Crows. They forage far and wide, mainly over grazing paddocks, pig farms and tilled land. When returning to traditional woodland roosts in the evening, these flocks can be an impressive site, sometimes passing in complete silence, at other times accompanied by tumbling aerobatics and much noise. Winter gatherings in recent years have included 3,000 roosting at Buckenham in January 1991, 850 near Roydon Common, 750 at Taverham, 700 at Pentney Gravel Pits, 600 at Lynford, Sculthorpe/Barsham and Northrepps, 500 at Thetford Nunnery Lakes and Holkham Park, 450 at Attlebridge, 400 at Welney and Houghton, and 340 at Merton. While a mixed roost of 30,000 Rooks and Jackdaws at Buckenham in 1995 was a remarkable record.

Breeding adult Jackdaws are extremely sedentary in Britain, and visit their breeding sites regularly throughout the year. By contrast, northern European populations are highly migratory, moving south and west in winter to milder climates including Britain and Ireland. In Norfolk, variable numbers have been recorded on passage in autumn, between mid-September and early November. Between 4th and 7th November 1956, many were seen arriving with Rooks at Cley and 180 flew east at Holme on 18th October 1993, where 59 were seen to arrive in off the sea on 17th September 1994. At Hunstanton cliffs 82 flew south on 2nd November 1994 and the autumn total of 251 in 1997 included 66 on 18th October. Similar numbers have occasionally been recorded in spring, between late February and the end of April, although counts of migrants flying out to sea at Winterton in 1976, of 105 on 28th March and 73 on 4th April were unusual. An exceptional spring passage was recorded in 1995 with several coastal localities reporting record numbers. Maximum site-counts were 30 west at Holme on 23rd March, at Mundesley 215 east on 24th March, 278 east on 2nd April and 101 east on 3rd April, and at Winterton 180 south and 80 north on 2nd April and 285 south on 3rd April.

Vagrancy is known mainly from birds showing characteristics of the eastern race *C. m. soemeringii* which are scarce but regular in most years, and probably overlooked. Records come not just from well-watched coastal areas, such as Cley, where from one to two were reported throughout 1996, but also from inland. For example in the same year one or two birds showing the characteristics of this race were noted at Easton, Attlebridge, Bawburgh, Colney, Keswick, Lenwade and Thetford.

Four ringed Jackdaws have shown movements between Norfolk and the Continent – one ringed at Humulu, Denmark on 11th June 1950 was recovered at Kilverstone the following April, one ringed at Bloemendaal, The Netherlands in July 1975 was found at Burgh Castle in March 1977 and a nestling ringed at Zandvoort, The Netherlands in 1995 was recovered near Hilborough on 24th April 1996. The only foreign recovery of a Norfolk-ringed Jackdaw concerned one ringed at Salhouse on 27th December 1966 which was recovered ten years later at Skaraborg, Sweden on 1st May 1976; it remains the only Swedish recovery of a British-ringed Jackdaw.

*Ian G. Henderson*

## Rook   MY GARDEN - CHEDGRAVE. 24-12-1999. ("GONZO")   *Corvus frugilegus*

**A very common resident and scarce passage migrant.**

The noisy, gregarious Rook breeds only in the boreal and temperate middle latitudes of the Western Palearctic south to central France and eastwards to the north of the Alps. It is found very sparingly in Switzerland and Austria. In eastern Europe it is widespread but is highly localised in southern Fennoscandia. The range extends eastward into western Iran and further north across Russia to the Altai Mountains. Within Europe many Rooks are partial migrants heading west and south especially in colder winters. At this season numbers are far higher than in summer in western Europe. In the British Isles, Rooks are almost entirely resident in lowland areas and occupy arable, grassland, wood pastures and parkland, and even in towns and villages where adjacent countryside is readily accessible.

Stevenson remarked that there are 'probably few counties in England where rookeries are more generally distributed than in Norfolk, this finely timbered district affording every attraction from the nobleman's mansion with its park and pleasure grounds to the snug manor house with its lofty elms or dark avenue of limes'. In the vicinity of Norwich he described rookeries 'at Costessey, Earlham, Keswick, Bowthorpe, Shotesham, Caistor, Crown Point, Bixley and Spixworth' – all within a few miles of the city with 'smaller communities within the walls including a colony of 20 nests in Surrey Street. A few pairs nested in St. Faith's Lane, Pottergate, Chapelfield and Bethel Street.'

Riviere described the Rook as 'very common at all seasons . . . Rookeries are numerous and well distributed throughout the county whilst vast numbers of immigrant birds arrive upon the coast in autumn. This immigration usually begins early in October, is at its height towards the end of this month and is continued throughout the first fortnight of November.' Flocks arrived, together with Jackdaws and Hooded Crows, from the east at intervals all day especially if the stream had been delayed by gales. On the days of greatest movement, Rooks could be heard arriving after dark. Fine days saw arrivals travelling high; but in strong winds it became wavetop flight. Before automation, when light-vessels off the Norfolk coast were manned, the crews did not welcome the sudden arrival of migrants, often including hundreds of Rooks and also Jackdaws, when mist or fog rapidly descended. The vessels soon became covered in droppings. Highly unusual was a mid-afternoon arrival of a large number of Rooks on a Royal Navy battleship heading south off the Norfolk coast during November 1922 or 1923. 'After circling very high many settled on the stays and aerials of the warship to such an extent that at times all the wires were covered in a line of birds.' All remained aboard until early the next morning when fog sirens resulted in a rapid mass departure. Photographs of this event appear in *British Birds* (Woodward 1954). A return movement was a regular feature between late February and mid-April. However, on occasions despite fine conditions on the coast during light easterly winds, dense fog banks offshore always resulted in a rapid return to the starting point. In addition Riviere described a spring arrival similar, but on a far smaller scale to that of autumn,

As a largely agricultural county Norfolk supports a large breeding population of Rooks. Highly colonial, the birds form colonies in stands of tall deciduous and coniferous trees. However, the extensive conifer plantations in the Brecks are avoided. Exceptionally, nests are in hawthorn scrub as at Bunwell and up to twelve pairs have nested on pylons edging the Norwich southern bypass at Keswick.

There is a limited tradition of rookery surveys in Norfolk. In 1961 the Yarmouth and Gorleston total was 85 nests declining to 47 a decade later and to just ten in 1995. In 1971 visits to eleven rookeries within 5km of Norwich Cathedral resulted in a total of 426 nests; all but one of these rookeries have since been abandoned. A near-complete national survey in 1975 suggested a substantial fall in the county Rook population between 1946 and 1975. During the latter year 347 rookeries held 7,184 nests. Following a pilot survey in 1994 a full-scale census during 1995–96 produced a total of the order of 17,600 nests contained in 340 rookeries The largest complexes were at Reedham/Wickhampton overlooking Halvergate Marshes with 522 nests, Magpie Plantation, Docking with 500 and Larling with 444 (Landells & Seago 1997a, 1997b). The decline in Rook numbers up to the 1960s or 1970s had been blamed on changes in farming including the trend to winter cereals and perhaps pesticide use. These changes have continued to be an integral part of modern agriculture since 1975 and yet a remarkable increase has taken place in the size of rookeries. The impression is that Rooks are well-tolerated in the county although there are cases where mainly young birds are shot. The increased numbers may be influenced by the rapid spread of outdoor pig farms, a ban on stubble burning and a series of mild winters.

Rooks forage in fields and marshes often in company with Jackdaws and Starlings. Breydon muds are patrolled by birds nesting in Yarmouth. Refuse tips and picnic sites are an attraction. Others search roadside verges where tousled black bundles indicate overconfidence. During the period Scroby Sands held colonies of breeding terns, Rooks regularly headed towards the sandbank from Caister, presumably to scavenge. Most rookeries are abandoned after the young have flown, colonies from a wide area joining forces and nightly occupying a common roost. As in Riviere's day, the sable armies trail across the sky in loose formation. Each flight line contains regularly used assembly points. Reaching the favoured wood the birds often spiral to great heights before tumbling downward in rapid oblique flight with wings half-closed performing the 'crows' wedding'. Each tree becomes black with birds. A deafening chorus reminds one of a steam-age railway station and the noise continues until an hour or so after sunset. Calling, in fact, continues at a low level all night. Among the most impressive winter roosts have been those at Buckenham, Didlington, Docking, Gimingham, Seamere (Hingham), Shipdham, Taverham, Tidall Wood (Ditchingham) and Worthing (Bressingham).

A springtime passage westward along the north Norfolk coast is on a very small scale nowadays. In 1997 the maximum day-count was 35 passing Sheringham on 1st May. Autumn movements are but a shadow of their former scale. In 1997 for example, just over 200 headed west at Hunstanton between 29th September and 15th November with a day-peak of 34 on 14th October. Rooks have steadily declined in eastern Europe, including the Baltic States, and in central European Russia there has been a tendency for progressively shorter migration flights.

Over 100 Rooks have been ringed in Norfolk but none has been recovered outside the county. For-eign-ringed birds have come from The Netherlands (3), Germany and Lithuania, the last bird ringed as a nestling in May 1931 and found at Thornham in October. Another ringed at Spurn, Humberside on 8th November 1961 was recovered near Swaffham one month later, while one ringed at Whipsnade Park, Bedfordshire in October 1936 was found at Wells in February 1945.

*Michael Seago*

## Carrion Crow          *Corvus corone*

HARDLEY FLOODS. 23·3·1999.

Carrion Crow          *C. c. corone*

A very common resident and scarce passage migrant.

## Hooded Crow          *C. c. cornix*

THURTON. 3·4·2000.

A very scarce passage migrant and winter visitor, formerly fairly common.

The Carrion Crow *Corvus corone* is one of the most widespread of all Palearctic birds and is abundant throughout its range. The race *C. c. corone* occurs in two separate populations, one in south-west Europe and the other in the Eastern Palearctic, separated by the race *C. c. cornix* which occupies northern, central and eastern Europe, and most of the Mediterranean region. The border between the two races, however, wanders erratically across Europe and hybridisation occurs in the narrow contact zone. Both races are resident over most of the range, although parts of the northern populations migrate south and west in autumn. Since the mid-1970s, their ranges have expanded in almost half the European countries, due to the Crow's ability to adapt to artificial changes in the environment, particularly habitat fragmentation.

Taking the two races together, the Crow is the second most widespread species in Britain and Ireland, after the Skylark (68–72 BTO Atlas). The Carrion Crow breeds in England, Wales, and southern and eastern Scotland, while the Hooded Crow occupies Ireland, and the north and west of Scotland. During the 19th century it was the most hated and persecuted bird by gamekeepers and landowners, being system-atically poisoned, shot and trapped, while the eggs and young were also destroyed (Historical Atlas). As with other members of the crow family, numbers recovered as a result of minimal persecution during the two World Wars.

In Norfolk, as a result of the widespread control of Carrion Crows, Stevenson, writing of its status in the mid-19th century, stated that 'a few pairs are still met with in different portions of the county'. Even in the early 20th century, Riviere still classified it as 'very scarce', the species' stronghold being in Breckland. Writing about Cley, Pashley (1925) said 'I have never yet seen this bird in the flesh, nor known it to have been ever seen or taken in the neighbourhood', clearly demonstrating how rare it was at this time. Nowa-days, the Carrion Crow is a very common and widespread species, having been recorded in every 10km square and in 40% of the tetrads covered for the Norfolk Atlas. During the 1994–97 BBS it was noted in 78–86% of the 1km squares visited in Norfolk. It occurs in most habitats, being most abundant in open areas with scattered trees and in woodland, although it avoids really dense forests. Both Broadland and Breckland provide these requirements and are two of the county's strongholds.

Carrion Crows nest solitarily and breeding pairs tend to remain in their territories during the winter.

Non-breeders, however, form foraging groups in the winter and often roost communally. The best-known roost of Carrion Crows is at Roydon Common, where 200–300 have gathered between November and February since at least 1971. The highest counts were in the mid-1980s, with 400 in February 1985 and November 1986, but an amazing 700 on 11th January 1986. More recently, 352 were counted flying into the roost in January 1994 and 335 were counted on 25th January 1998. Other sites to have hosted large Carrion Crow roosts include Surlingham with 100 in 1989, Docking 135 in 1994 and 310 in December 1997, Grimston Warren 135 and Welney 80, both in 1994.

Evidence for the immigration of Carrion Crows from Denmark and The Netherlands in autumn is inconclusive (Winter Atlas), but a small passage has been noted over many years at several sites around the Norfolk coast from Holme in the west to Yarmouth in the south. Spring passage is recorded between early March and mid-May with unusually heavy movements recorded in 1995, with 60 north at Winterton on 1st April, 24 east at Mundesley the following day, and 28 west and 10 east at Weybourne on 21st April. Good numbers were again recorded in 1996, with 30 south at Horsey on 15th April, a loose flock of 30 on Cromer Golf Course on 22nd April and 35 west at Holme on 27th April. For the third spring in succession, larger numbers than usual were noted in 1997 which included 60 west at Cromer on 28th April, 108 west at Scolt Head and 30 west at Sheringham on 1st May, and 33 west at Scolt Head and 37 west at Sheringham on 10th May. A smaller passage is also noted annually between mid-September and early November.

The status of the Hooded Crow has changed dramatically since the early 1960s. Sir Thomas Browne recorded it as a winter visitor during the 17th century. In Stevenson's day it was considered a separate species from the Carrion Crow and its alternative names were the 'Royston, Danish or Grey-backed Crow', while in east Norfolk it was known as the 'Kentish Crow'. It remained a winter visitor to Norfolk in 'large numbers' from October to April, frequenting the Broads, riverside marshes and the coast. Some indication of the numbers involved is shown by a report of 200–300 flying high to the west at Blakeney in parties of up to ten, one day in autumn 1847, while on 28th March 1848, a Mr Dowell 'witnessed the return of many of these birds to their breeding places, a long string of scattered Hooded Crows, flying high with much noise, towards the N.E., wind blowing from S. and S.S.W.' (Stevenson). Patterson (1904) described hundreds, many of them apparently paired, gathering on the Breydon 'flats' in late March, in preparation for their 'northern flight'.

Large numbers were still visiting the county in the 1920s and 1930s, when many hundreds wintered in the Holkham area, roosting in the pines at Holkham Meals and on the Wells East Hills. At Scolt Head each autumn 'countless hordes moved from east to west and others came in from the sea. Sometimes they flew so low that their wings made flickering shadows on the windows [of the Watcher's Hut] and almost brushed the heads of anyone standing on the sandhills. Slowly, silently and relentlessly they went on their way' (Turner 1928). Jim Vincent's diaries recorded 'hundreds of Hooded Crows feeding on dead fish round the edges of Hickling Broad' following extensive sea flooding on 13th February 1938; many birds remained until mid-April. During the 1950s, Hooded Crows continued to be fairly common winter visitors. As Carrion Crows became more widespread inland, pressure from territory-holding pairs caused the migrant Hoodies to become concentrated in the coastal areas and very few were found inland in Norfolk. This is well-illustrated nationally in the Winter Atlas, with Hooded Crows in eastern England virtually being confined to the coastal strip. The last recorded count of over 100 birds was made at Wells, when 173 were present on 9th November 1955. The maximum count the following year was 66 at Stiffkey in November, falling to 37 at Wells by 1959. Thereafter, Hooded Crows became scarce in north Norfolk and the main concentrations were in the east of the county. Caister held up to 80 in 1960 and 69 the following year, while for a number of years the Winterton/Horsey area became the favoured locality with maximum counts of 40 roosting in a single dead tree on 7th April 1974, 45 on 26th October 1975 and 79 on 3rd April 1976 (all of which would have included passage migrants). At about this time, similar numbers began to be recorded in west Norfolk with 35 at Snettisham and Sandringham Common in late 1975, up to 72 roosting at Dersingham Common in 1976 and up to 20 roosting with the Carrion Crows at Roydon Common.

A further marked decline was noted in 1978, although 25 were found roosting with Carrion Crows at Barton Fen in February. By the mid-1980s very few wintered in Norfolk and the last one to do so in the Yarmouth area was present from 14th November 1985 to 31st March 1986. Despite this decline one has continued to winter in the Horsey area in recent years. As the number of overwintering Hoodies decreased, so did those recorded on spring and autumn passage around the coast. Whereas 100 passed through Snettisham in October 1972 and a total of 44 flew west at Sheringham on 16th April 1977, only the occasional bird is now noted at a few sites each spring and autumn. For the first time since 1953, the *Norfolk Bird Report 1996* listed all records of Hooded Crows within the county; these amounted to only three to four in winter, eight in spring and four in autumn, while the total number of records in 1997 was about 25, over half of which were noted on spring passage between 7th March and 10th May. In addition two were seen on an oil rig 95km east of Yarmouth on 20th October.

Since the 1960s the number of Hooded Crows overwintering in the Low Countries and northern France has also declined markedly, apparently reflecting a shift in the wintering areas (more of the population in Fennoscandia and eastern Europe is remaining resident throughout the year), rather than a decline in breeding numbers (European Atlas). Although there have been no ringing recoveries, the Hooded Crows on the east coast of England are believed to originate from Scandinavia and Denmark. One shot at Yarmouth on 8th November 1908 carried a note around its neck, stating in Danish that it had been marked on a ship off the coast of Denmark on 23rd October.

Hooded Crows have bred successfully in Norfolk on a few occasions. The first recorded instance being near King's Lynn in 1816 and subsequently breeding was suspected in the county in 1867, 1920 and 1922. In 1967 a pair reared young at Sheringham and in 1982, a pair, one of which had a damaged wing, bred at Waxham rearing one young. In recent years there have also been three instances of mixed pairs with Carrion Crows breeding successfully – at Winterton in 1968 and 1998, and at Sheringham in 1976. Hooded Crows have been seen in summer on a number of other occasions and Hooded x Carrion Crow hybrids are occasionally recorded. Since 1989 at Burgh Castle and to a lesser extent at Belton, two to three hybrids (up to 80% Hooded Crow and which could easily be mistaken as purely of that race) have been present and have bred annually with Carrion Crows. Six hybrids feeding on Burgh Castle Marshes on 14th January 1998 included two which were 80% Hooded Crows.

*Moss Taylor*

# Raven (Common Raven)               *Corvus corax*

**A rare vagrant; formerly bred, on the last occasion in 1859.**

The Raven is a widely-distributed Holarctic species, breeding throughout much of the Western Palearctic, being absent only from large parts of England, France, Hungary and northern Italy. As a result of persecution by farmers and gamekeepers, a steady decline occurred in Britain and the rest of Europe from the mid-19th century. Since the early 1950s the range of the Raven has expanded to once again cover much of northern and central Europe. This natural recolonisation has occurred as a result of reduced persecution, as well as active conservation measures, including reintroduction schemes in Germany, Belgium and The Netherlands, where 50 breeding pairs and 31 territorial pairs had become established by 1992.

During the 17th century Ravens were widespread throughout the British Isles, being found scavenging alongside Red Kites in the streets of London, although in Norfolk, Sir Thomas Browne wrote '[Ravens occur] in great plenty near Norwich, and on this account there are so few kites seen hereabouts'. Even as recently as the beginning of the 19th century they probably bred in every county in Britain (Historical Atlas), including Norfolk, where as late as 1829, Ravens were found in woods in every part of the county. Nesting sites included the ruined steeple at South Walsham and at Earlham next Norwich. By 1846 the species was still breeding in Norfolk, but in small and decreasing numbers and the range soon contracted to the western and northern counties, as they became victims of keepering and farming practices. A specimen obtained at Hargham in April 1854 is still on display at the Ancient House Museum in Thetford. The last Norfolk nest, containing five well-grown young, was taken at Beachamwell in 1859 (Stevenson). By 1866, the Raven was described as only an occasional winter visitor to Norfolk and the last three dated records in the 19th century were at Sheringham in October 1875, two at Overstrand on 20th November 1876 and one at Northrepps in April 1877.

The species was not seen again in the county until 1931, and between then and 1953 a total of eight was recorded in the Blakeney, Cley and Sheringham areas. Since then the species has remained a rarity in Norfolk and some records have undoubtedly referred to escapes:

1972: Two flew west at Weybourne on 5th November

1974: Warham on 11th May

1981: One overwintered in the South Creake area and was shot in mistake for a Carrion Crow in 1982

1985: A very tame individual, considered to be an escape at Lady Anne's Drive, Holkham on 31st March

1986: Sparham and Lyng on 1st June. The date suggested an escape, but a check of possible sources proved negative
One flew in off the sea at Wells on 15th November

1993: One in the Somerton/Winterton/Horsey/Hickling/Waxham area from 20th November to at least 27th February 1994. During its stay, it was also recorded at Breydon, Scratby, Caister, Stalham and Martham

1994: Sparham on 25th May and probably the same bird at Breydon on 4th June; as in 1986, the dates suggested a suspect origin and its comparative tameness was remarked upon when seen at Breydon
Strumpshaw on 19th October

1996: Holkham/Burnham Overy area on 12th–13th May

1997: One flew north at Winterton and was subsequently seen at Horsey on 22nd March
Another flew in from the sea at Horsey, heading directly inland, on 18th April

The records in the 1990s may well be related to the successful reintroduction scheme in The Netherlands, especially as other Ravens were seen in Suffolk and Bedfordshire towards the end of 1993, and one was seen on a North Sea oil platform earlier in the autumn (Rooney 1994a).

*Moss Taylor*

## Starling (Common Starling) *Sturnus vulgaris*

MY GARDEN - CHEDGRAVE · 8·7·1999.

**An abundant resident, winter visitor and passage migrant.**

The Starling is mainly a lowland species, occurring throughout the Palearctic between 40° and 70°N. It breeds in most of Europe, with the exception of Iberia where it is largely replaced by the Spotless Starling *S. unicolor*. It is one of the most adaptable and successful of birds, having been introduced into parts of North America, Africa and Australia. It is virtually ubiquitous in the British Isles, being absent only from remote moorland and mountainous areas (New Atlas). In winter, the resident British population is augmented by large numbers of immigrants from the Continent.

A decline in the numbers of Starlings and a contraction of their range in Britain during the 18th century, possibly due to climatic changes, was followed by a steady increase from about 1830 to the 1950s. Since then, the population throughout Europe has once again fallen, especially since the 1970s, affecting both the number of resident Starlings in Britain and the overwintering population from the Continent. A large proportion of our wintering birds come from Finland, where dairy farms have largely disappeared, resulting in the loss of grazing pastures, the main foraging habitat of the Starling. This in turn has resulted in a falling reproductive output and a marked reduction in the Finnish Starling population (European Atlas). Britain's resident Starlings have also suffered as a direct result of the reduction in the acreage of fallow and grassland and the increase in autumn-sown arable crops (Feare 1994).

In Norfolk the Starling remains a widespread, if less numerous breeding species. During fieldwork for the Norfolk Atlas it was recorded in 95% of the tetrads and was the fifth most widespread species. Subsequently it has been found in 76–82% of the 1km squares covered in Norfolk during the 1994–97 BBS. It has two main breeding requirements – a hole or crevice in which to nest and nearby grassland for foraging (New Atlas) and therefore during the breeding season it is largely absent from open arable land, marshland and extensive conifer plantations.

Following fledging, large flocks of Starlings begin to gather in mid-summer and a westerly passage is often noted in north Norfolk from early June, but whether these are British or Continental birds is unclear. Normally day-counts do not exceed a couple of thousand birds and 10,000 flying west at Paston on 26th June 1983 was most unusual. It is at this time of year that roosts begin to form in reedbeds and several thousand Starlings may gather by early July at such localities as Cley, Holme and at various sites in Broadland.

The main autumn immigration of Continental Starlings takes place in October and early November, when flock after flock can be seen arriving along the coast of Norfolk. When light-vessels off the coast were manned, Starlings regularly descended in their thousands at night in foggy and rainy conditions. The largest estimates were of 10,000 at the Outer Dowsing on both 23rd and 24th October 1957. The most complete observations were made by a team of observers, organised by Jeffrey Boswall and including Bert Axell, on the Smith's Knoll light-vessel 40km from Yarmouth from mid-September until mid-November 1953. During the eight weeks a total of 24,000 birds of 65 species was recorded (Peakall 1956). Unfortunately, their arrival nowadays can hardly be described as 'tidal waves', as they were up to the late 1970s. Some of the highest counts were 150,000 west at Sheringham on 27th October 1978, with 200,000–250,000 west at Scolt Head and 100,000 flying into the Wash in just three hours the following day. However, daily observations at Hunstanton during the mid- to late 1990s have demonstrated impressive numbers still arriving in late autumn. A total count of 514,000 flew south between 23rd September and 13th November 1995, including over 100,000 on both 23rd and 30th October, while the autumn of 1996 produced 339,000 south and at Scolt Head 120,000 flew west on 11th October. The autumn total at Hunstanton in 1997 was 409,000 flying south peaking at 87,000 on 16th October.

The arrival of these vast numbers of Continental birds means that the autumn reedbed roosts have held some very impressive totals. Turner (1924) described the Hickling roost as containing 'millions' of birds, with lines of Starlings arriving at the roost, stretching for over two miles from Potter Heigham Church to Hickling Mill. Riviere commented: 'With the first frosts, however, or the advent of rough weather, and usually no later than the first week of December, the reed-beds are vacated for the winter roosts, for which plantations of larch or spruce are usually chosen, the same covert being used annually for many years in succession.' One of the best-known such winter roosts was at Egmere near Holkham, which was occupied from November 1951 until 1958. The roost-site consisted of a 2.4ha larch plantation in a depression, to which birds would travel from up to 50km away. Three main flight lines were used with birds arriving from the south, south-east and north-east. The absence of birds arriving from the west suggested that an alternative roost existed in that direction. The number of birds roosting in a single tree varied from 250 to 850, in the favoured south-east corner of the roost which was lower and therefore more sheltered. By counting the number of trees which were occupied, an amazing 3,500,000 Starlings were estimated to be using the roost in early January 1955 (Bagnall-Oakeley 1956). The guano gathered on the ground under the trees to a depth of more than 30cm and the roost was eventually deserted when the trees died from the weight of birds and accumulated droppings on the lower branches.

Sir Thomas Browne (1835–1836) included records of vast communal roosts as early as the mid-17th century, while Stevenson gave details of a roosting flock which covered thirty acres of a wood near Fakenham on 4th September 1864. Another vast Starling roost was at North Creake in late autumn 1958. Swelled by huge numbers of immigrants, said to have involved probably the heaviest recorded arrival of Continental Starlings, the roost contained many hundreds of thousands of birds (no count was attempted). Roost-sites are often changed for no apparent reason during the course of a winter, as demonstrated by that at North Creake which was evacuated overnight on 22nd December 1957, most of the birds subsequently using shrubberies around Heydon Hall, 27km away (Bagnall-Oakeley 1959). Other localities which used to host large Starling roosts included Welney, Dersingham, Ketteringham, Lower Gresham, Stratton Strawless, Crostwick and Marham, where an estimated 2,000,000 were present on 1st March 1984. These vast Starling roosts appear to be a thing of the past and the largest in recent times have included 10,000 at Thompson Water in November–December 1994, up to 20,000 at Horsey in autumn 1995 and 30,000 at Strumpshaw in November 1996, while in October 1997 roost counts included 35,000 at Titchwell, 12,000 at Martham North Broad and 10,000 at Rockland/Wheatfen.

Winter roosts generally break up in mid-March, at which time an exodus of Continental Starlings is often noted along the north Norfolk coast. Ted Ellis once described a remarkable hold-up of Starlings between 3rd and 5th April 1937. The preceding days had been warm until cold coastal fog descended. At Sheringham exhausted birds tumbled down chimneys and 50 were counted in a shop window in the High Street. Many were washed ashore at Eccles and elsewhere. In Norwich thousands poured into trees surrounding the Castle waking people a quarter mile away, while hundreds of boughs, some as much as six inches in diameter, littered the Castle mound. Branches were also snapped off in Chapelfield, Unthank and

Newmarket Roads. In Yarmouth many birds entered houses, others littered the roads and yet others fluttered round street lamps. The birds were packed like swarms of bees in the trees in St Nicholas' churchyard making a noise like escaping steam. Numbers involved in spring, however, are normally far smaller than this. The spring passage in 1996 was far more pronounced than usual, particularly at Sheringham where easterly movements in March included 2,400 on 21st and 8,000 on 30th, with 3,600 on April 1st and 3,400 on 3rd, on which date 1,000 per hour were flying south at Winterton.

Both albino and leucistic Starlings are occasionally recorded, as well as birds with excessively long, decurved bills. Over 15,000 Starlings have been ringed in Norfolk producing in excess of 1,000 recoveries of which almost 250 have been abroad. Most of the Starlings have been ringed between November and March, when the population in Norfolk consists of both local birds and winter visitors from mainland Europe. The majority of the foreign breeding season recoveries have been from The Netherlands (16), Germany (22), Fennoscandia (20), the Baltic States (9) and Russia (13), while two-thirds of the 86 foreign-ringed birds found in Norfolk have come from either The Netherlands or the Baltic States. The only foreign recovery of a Starling ringed in Norfolk outside the winter period concerned a juvenile ringed on 2nd August 1967, and therefore probably a locally-bred bird, which was recovered in southern Norway on 17th April 1969. Unusually large numbers of Starlings appeared in Norfolk in January 1976 as a result of severe weather across the whole of Europe. Birds were clearly being displaced much further west than usual and amongst the many recoveries of Starlings ringed at this time were several unusually far to the east in Russia, including one at 54°E in Komi, Russia, a locality which is 1,000km to the east of Moscow and almost in the foothills of the Ural Mountains. Another ringed during the same period was found in northern Italy the next winter, an area to which central European Starlings normally migrate in autumn, thus providing further evidence of the westward displacement in early 1976. By coincidence two Starlings ringed at the same Lithuanian locality on 21st July 1985 were both recovered in west Norfolk during the winter of 1985–86. An unusual southerly movement in spring involved a Starling ringed on Fair Isle on 27th March 1963 which was found at Blakeney Point two weeks later.

*Moss Taylor*

# Rose-coloured Starling (Rosy Starling)       *Sturnus roseus*

**A rare vagrant, mainly in mid-summer.**

The Rose-coloured Starling breeds in the lower middle latitudes of the eastern part of the Western Palearctic, extending from the Balkans and the Black Sea eastwards into Asia. It winters mainly in the Indian subcontinent. The species' remarkably nomadic and irruptive lifestyle is related to the intermittent presence of swarms of locusts which cross the Mediterranean from North Africa. As a direct result of this, it is recorded in large numbers well to the west of its normal range and in such years, a few adults and first-year birds reach the British Isles from May to August. A second wave – of juveniles in September and October – is due to reversed migration (Vinicombe & Cottridge 1996).

The species has been recorded in Norfolk on 32 occasions, following the first, shot at Rougham in June 1747 (Riviere). During the 19th century 15 more were recorded, of which six were found at Yarmouth. Between 1871 and 1937 only a single Rose-coloured Starling was noted in Norfolk – one obtained at Toftrees in April 1907. Despite the increase in observer coverage in recent years, the species has remained a rarity in the county and there have been only 15 records since 1937, including the only two records of juveniles:

> 1937: An adult male near Kelling and at Cley/Salthouse on 7th July
> 1945: Cley on 11th June
> 1971: Snettisham on 2nd June
>       An adult at Wells on 1st–23rd November
> 1975: An adult at Winterton on 31st July
> 1979: A first-summer at Salthouse and Cley on 19th–27th May
> 1982: An adult at Hunstanton on 22nd May
>       An adult at Little Walsingham on 17th–24th June
> 1983: An adult at Holme on 3rd June

Hickling on 12th June

A juvenile at Blakeney Point on the early date of 22nd August

1987: An adult at Stalham on 14th–25th June

1994: Winterton on 7th June and presumed the same at Sea Palling on 9th June

1997: A juvenile at Blakeney on 20th–27th October

An adult at Beeston Regis from 15th November to 14th February 1998 and what was possibly the same bird at Diss from 20th March to 4th April 1998

Since 1937, more records have occurred in June than in any other month, whereas during the 19th century, August was the favoured month. Very few places can claim more than one record and the coastal bias during recent years probably reflects the distribution of observers.

*Moss Taylor*

## House Sparrow    MY GARDEN-CHEDGRAVE. 8-7-1999.    *Passer domesticus*

**An abundant, but declining, resident.**

The range of the House Sparrow encompasses almost the whole of Europe, even extending above the Arctic Circle, the species being absent only from Iceland and replaced by the hybrid Italian Sparrow in Italy. As a result of introductions worldwide it is now probably the most widespread passerine species.

In England the population increased substantially during the 18th century, alongside that of the human population, as it did in Scotland during the 19th century. However, there has been a recent decline in numbers, particularly in western Europe. Although much of the evidence is anecdotal, observations are so widespread in Britain, The Netherlands and western Germany that there is little doubt that a significant decrease has occurred since the 1970s (European Atlas). Changes in agricultural practices, in particular the autumn sowing of cereals and the increased use of pesticides and herbicides are believed to be partly responsible. The BTO Garden Bird Feeding Survey demonstrated a 15–20% decrease in the numbers of House Sparrows visiting suburban gardens between 1978 and 1988. This may have been associated with the use of garden insecticides and an increase in the suburban population of domestic cats and Tawny Owls.

In Norfolk the House Sparrow has always been abundant, being closely associated with man throughout the year. This situation is confirmed in *Norfolk at Work* by Neil Storey (1997) featuring old-time photographs including a sparrow-catcher at Swanton Abbot in 1925. The nets are festooned with dozens of birds. The majority nest in holes in buildings and other man-made structures, although occasional domed nests are found in hedgerows and bushes. In the Norfolk Atlas it was recorded in 95% of the tetrads and was the eighth most widespread species. However, it was found to be totally absent from coastal squares with habitats limited to saltings, shingle, cliffs and cliff-top pasture, from open farmland, forest and much of the Stanford Battle Area, where a lack of food and frequent military disturbance prevented House Sparrows from colonising the derelict buildings (Kelly 1986). Unfortunately, over the years, very little information has been received by the County Bird Recorders concerning House Sparrows. Nevertheless, there does appear to have been a genuine decline in numbers, in both urban and rural localities. In 1993, an RSPB set-aside survey revealed that House Sparrows were only present on one in ten farms, scattered across Norfolk and colony extinctions were noted at Aylmerton and East Tuddenham in 1996. However, data obtained from a variety of habitats for the BBS in Norfolk showed that it was present in 60–61% of the 1km squares covered during the four years 1994–97. The largest flocks reported in recent years have been 125 at Welney in May 1993, 100 at Baconsthorpe in July–August 1996 and 150 daily at Pasta Foods factory, Yarmouth in September–December 1997.

Throughout most of its European range, the House Sparrow is described as almost completely sedentary. Riviere, however, stated that 'arrivals of House-Sparrows undoubtedly take place from abroad in autumn, when they have been killed upon several occasions at lightships off the Norfolk coast'. Young birds are also known to disperse in the autumn, when a southerly movement is recorded along the east coast of Britain (Winter Atlas). In 1956, flocks of House Sparrows were noted flying west in mid- to late October and again in early December, in company with Chaffinches and Bramblings. Since 1972, small numbers have been recorded in most years flying west at Sheringham in both spring and autumn with a maximum count of 120 west on 10th October 1976. Recent observations at Hunstanton cliffs have also demonstrated a small southerly passage at this site in autumn, where in 1996, a total of 165 flew south in October and 41 in November.

Partial albino and leucistic House Sparrows are not infrequently seen and single House x Tree Sparrow hybrids have been ringed at Cley and Sheringham. Over 3,000 House Sparrows have been ringed in the county but their largely sedentary nature is shown by the fact that not one recovery has warranted inclusion in the ringing section of the *Norfolk Bird Report*. However, one ringed at Gibraltar Point, Lincolnshire on 2nd November 1964 was found in Norwich on 11th February 1967.

*Moss Taylor*

WELNEY W.T. 21-2-1982.

## Tree Sparrow (Eurasian Tree Sparrow)                    *Passer montanus*

**A scarce resident and passage migrant, which has shown a marked decline in recent years.**

The Tree Sparrow is resident over much of its range. It breeds across the middle latitudes of Europe, although there is a preference for the temperate areas over the warmer Mediterranean climes. Thus, it is found over much of Europe but only in the south of Fennoscandia where its range is expanding. The northern populations undergo eruptive movements in autumn.

Tree Sparrows were widespread across England and Wales at the end of the 19th century except for the far south-west of England and west Wales. The range had expanded in the latter part of the century due, it was thought, to immigrants from the Continent. The 20th century saw a period of stability up until the 1930s when a decline set in, causing the range to contract and the bird to become absent from parts of Scotland and Wales. There was then a transient increase especially in the early 1960s with some areas holding breeding pairs for the first time in 30 years. However, since the start of the 1980s there has been a widespread decline across all of its range.

Stevenson wrote that it was a localised resident which was not plentiful anywhere and was confined to certain areas. He qualified this by suggesting that the extreme wariness of the bird made its true status uncertain. It would disperse in winter in search of food and would be netted in stack-yards. Autumn would bring immigrants from the Continent and flocks were noted in winter at West Harling but never in summer. More evidence of its migratory nature comes from a Mr Blyth who reported a flock coming on board a vessel as it passed off the coast of Norfolk on 8th October 1833 which totalled over 100 as the vessel entered the Thames Estuary. Riviere described its distribution as local and that it was noted in small, scattered colonies with passage records from the coast and lightships in autumn and then again in March and April.

During fieldwork for the Norfolk Atlas it was recorded in 527 tetrads (36%) which covered every 10km square, but its distribution was patchy and its unobtrusive nature may have meant that some small, isolated colonies may have been overlooked. The main concentrations were east and south-east of King's Lynn, north of Thetford, the environs of Norwich especially to the immediate west, and around Sheringham.

In recent times the massive decline has been such that in 1992 only one breeding colony was reported, that of four pairs at Welney. However, others doubtless were present but simply not recorded. In 1993, breeding was noted at twelve localities and then 15 in 1994, by which time it had almost totally disappeared from east Norfolk. A total of 31 pairs was recorded during the 1997 breeding season at eleven localities, mainly in the west and north of the county. The percentage of tetrads covered in Norfolk for the BBS during the four years 1994–97, in which Tree Sparrows were found, was 12%, 22%, 13% and 9% respectively; the latter three years suggesting a continuing decline. It is to be hoped that set-aside schemes will produce feeding areas to counter the loss of stack-yards, the effect of early ploughing of stubble fields in autumn and the planting of winter cereals. However, one colony along Cowles Drove had decreased from nine pairs in 1993 to two in 1997 and was deserted in 1998 although set-aside was nearby in the latter years.

The largest flock in the county was recorded in 1958 when 1,500 were in the Eye Field at Cley for the first three months of the year. In recent years, the only three-figure flocks have been gatherings of 100 at Shingham on 6th February 1990, at South Pickenham in December 1993, at Rowley Corner, Great Cressingham in January 1995 and at Choseley in February 1995, 160 at Great Cressingham in January 1996 and 110 at West Beckham also in January 1996. Three of the localities mentioned above are within 5km of each other. This would seem to be a classic case of a relatively common species not attracting attention until its numbers had declined. The flocks mentioned above would have been commonplace when the population was at its highest in the early 1960s. In east Norfolk parties of up to about 100 wintered on the Halvergate Marshes until about 1970. Nowadays smaller flocks of up to 50 are noted annually in the county. The favoured areas being in the north-west, especially Choseley and Ringstead, and from around the Pickenhams and the Cressinghams in the west of the county.

Passage birds were recorded along the north and east coasts from March to late May and again from August to October. In earlier years, some of the highest counts were made at Sheringham – 400 west on 26th April 1977 and 350 west and 58 east on 10th October 1976 were the maximum spring and autumn day-counts. In recent years, however, very few counts have exceeded ten. The maxima have been twelve west at Holme on 5th October 1993, eight at Waxham on 27th October 1995 and 16 at Hunstanton cliffs on 16th October 1996.

In 1996, a male Tree Sparrow was seen copulating with a female House Sparrow at Wramplingham over the winter and spring. There was also a single male House Sparrow present at the Tree Sparrow site in Cowles Drove throughout the summer of 1995. Single House x Tree Sparrow hybrids have been ringed at Cley and Sheringham.

About 1,000 Tree Sparrows have been ringed in Norfolk, but very few have been recovered. One ringed at Cley on 15th December 1957 became the first-ever foreign recovery of a British-ringed Tree Sparrow when it was found near Rheine, Westphalia, Germany on 19th November the following year, since when there have been only four further foreign recoveries from British ringing. Two ringed in Essex and one in Cambridgeshire have been found in Norfolk.

*Peter Dolton*

## Rock Sparrow *Petronia petronia*

**A very rare vagrant; one record.**

The Rock Sparrow breeds throughout much of southern Europe, North Africa, the Middle East and central Asia. Although primarily sedentary throughout its range, it is known to undertake dispersive movements and regular short-distance migrations.

One found and identified at Cley on the morning of 14th June 1981 by Steve Gantlett and Richard Millington was subsequently seen by three more observers. It was watched for half an hour, in the company of a male Linnet, feeding along the ruts in the tufted gravel strip between the beach and Cley Eye field, before flying off westwards towards Blakeney Point at 08:30 hrs. Despite an intensive search, it was never seen again (Gantlett 1985). It constitutes the only British record.

*Peter Allard*

## Chaffinch  MY GARDEN, CHEDGRAVE. 8·7·1999. *Fringilla coelebs*

**An abundant resident, and very common passage migrant and winter visitor.**

The Chaffinch, one of the most familiar and widespread of European birds, occurs throughout the entire Western Palearctic in the temperate wooded areas, from the Mediterranean up to the tundra edge. The species winters entirely within the Western Palearctic, with nearly all of the birds from the north-east of the range migrating in autumn, to winter in the south-west alongside the resident local population. It is one of the most numerous and abundant species in Britain and Ireland, being absent from only a few upland areas of Scotland (New Atlas).

The species was described by Riviere as being extremely abundant throughout the year. He also commented that large numbers arrived in autumn and that a two-way migration occurred in spring, with immigrants and emigrants arriving and leaving the Norfolk coast simultaneously.

Nowadays, the Chaffinch is one of Norfolk's most abundant and widespread breeding birds being found wherever trees or bushes are present, such as woodland, hedgerows, scrub, parkland and gardens. It was present in over 90% of the tetrads surveyed for the Norfolk Atlas, being absent only from the treeless areas of Halvergate Marshes, some coastal regions and parts of the Fens (Kelly 1986). Nationally, Chaffinches are one of the few seed-eating passerine species not to be undergoing a population decline (Marchant *et al.* 1990), indeed it is likely that the population is increasing. Although it is not possible to detect this in

Norfolk, from the current information available it is likely that the national trend is being mirrored in the county. During the 1994–97 BBS it was recorded in 93–98% of the 1km squares surveyed in the county.

The months of March and April are the main spring migration period for the Chaffinch. At suitable localities on the coast Chaffinches gather into flocks prior to their departure to the breeding areas in Fennoscandia and the Continent. At Sheringham, for instance, flocks of up to 200 birds were noted in late March and early April 1979, before they left overnight when weather conditions were suitable. Visible migration is less frequently observed in spring than autumn, but easterly movements of up to 350 birds daily were recorded at Sheringham, in mid-April during the 1970s and more recently a total of 560 flew east at Paston on 27th March 1994.

Compared with the spring, the migration of Chaffinches along the north Norfolk coast is much more noticeable in autumn. Passage occurs between mid-September and mid-November, with peak numbers during the second half of October. At Sheringham, where records of visible migration have been kept for over 20 years, unprecedented numbers were noted in 1978 with 6,000 west on 27th October, 30,000 west on 28th October (a day on which 50,000 passed both Scolt Head and Hunstanton) and 3,000 west on 29th October. Up to 1997, the maximum day-counts at Sheringham in the 1990s had not exceeded 500 west, except for 1996 with 1,000 west on 11th October and 800 west and 100 in from the north on 23rd October. Intensive recording at Hunstanton cliffs since 1994 has demonstrated that very impressive numbers still pass south here each autumn. For instance, between 23rd September and 13th November 1995 the total was 25,220, peaking at 4,680 on 22nd October and 4,420 the following day. In 1996, the autumn total was 45,288 with maximum daily counts of 6,759 on 11th October and 12,882 on 23rd October. However, all these totals were surpassed in autumn 1997 with record counts on 16th October which included 50,599 south at Hunstanton cliffs, 10,000+ west at Holme and 24,000 west or in from the sea at Sheringham. On the following day 24,790 flew south at Hunstanton, where the autumn total between late September and mid-November was an amazing 89,830.

Despite these large numbers on autumn passage, surprisingly few sizeable flocks have been reported in recent winters. However, during 1993, flocks of up to 250 were present at scattered localities throughout the county, with 1,200 at Thetford in January, 800 at Feltwell in January–February and 350 at Ringstead in November, while during the first three months of 1996, flocks of 300 were present at Thetford and Holkham Park, 400 at West Harling and 500 at Roudham Heath. The large winter flocks can be highly mobile and are usually associated with other finches and buntings, particularly Bramblings. The species undertakes some cold-weather movements, when birds may go to Ireland (Winter Atlas), but this will generally involve only the immigrant part of the population, the resident breeding population generally being very sedentary.

About 20,000 Chaffinches have been ringed in Norfolk, but surprisingly only 15 have been recovered abroad. All of these foreign recoveries have involved birds ringed between October and April, most of which were recovered in spring or autumn. They have involved movements to Belgium (4), Germany (3), Denmark (2), Norway (4) and Sweden (2). Three were reported during the breeding season – two in the southern half of Norway and one in Denmark. In addition, 13 foreign-ringed Chaffinches have been found in Norfolk, including eleven from The Netherlands (although no Norfolk-ringed Chaffinches have been recovered there) and one from Belgium. The only bird ringed during the summer was a juvenile from southern Norway recovered at Watton the following March. The Belgian-ringed bird produced a movement in an unexpected direction in spring – it was ringed at Den Haan on 30th April 1982 and was controlled at Sheringham ten days later. The only other notable recovery was one ringed at Boughton in March 1971 and controlled at Lisburn, County Antrim in January 1973.

*Stephen J. Browne*

## Brambling     BLAKENEY POINT (1) 9-10-1986.          *Fringilla montifringilla*

**Common winter visitor and very common passage migrant, mostly in the autumn.**

The Brambling is very much the northern counterpart of the Chaffinch, breeding continuously across the northern parts of the Palearctic from Norway to the Pacific, and favouring birch woods where it can be abundant. Almost all Bramblings vacate breeding areas in the winter and migrate to warmer latitudes as far as North Africa, central China and Japan. Numbers vary greatly between years, depending largely upon the availability of beechmast which is the favoured food of the species. Since the supply of beechmast is irregular, flocks of Bramblings are seldom faithful to particular sites between different winters. Hard weather can also cause movements of birds, if their food supply is covered by snow (Clement *et al.* 1993). A handful of pairs nest in northern Britain most years, but large-scale colonisation does not seem to be imminent.

Riviere reported that the species was a regular passage migrant and winter visitor, with most arriving in October and November, and some remaining as late as April. This latter comment perhaps indicates that birds are now occurring later into the spring, as April records are now not at all unusual and large flocks can occur.

Bramblings
(Bryan Bland)

More recent observations have shown that autumn migrants start to appear on the coast from mid-September in most years, although the main passage is during October and early November. The scale of passage varies greatly between years, with peak day-counts of over 100 not unusual. More concentrated observations at Hunstanton cliffs in recent years have revealed much larger daily peaks, with maxima of 3,950 on 22nd October and 4,550 on 30th October 1995, out of a total of 13,130 during the period 23rd September to 13th November. The following year, the total for October and November at Hunstanton cliffs was much lower at 3,585, with a daily maximum of 977 on 11th October. Such counts may reveal interesting differences between years, although the numbers themselves may be much too low since it is thought that Bramblings migrate largely at night. They were well known as autumn visitors to the crews of light-vessels off the Norfolk coast. Nowadays exhausted migrants seek refuge on the rig platforms. Most soon continue their journey; others fall victim to Long-eared Owls – their fellow travellers.

The species occurs widely throughout the county during the winter, but is never found anywhere near so ubiquitously as the Chaffinch, with flocks localised and determined largely by the availability of beechmast; although other food-sources are also used (linseed stubbles have been noted as increasingly important in recent winters). As with Greenfinches, Bramblings are increasingly attracted to gardens containing peanut and sunflower seed feeders. At Thorpe St Andrew, Michael Seago recorded daily visits during the 1997–98 winter between mid-December and 25th April. The overall wintering numbers for Britain are thought to vary from as low as about 50,000 in poor years to two million when at their most plentiful. However, these numbers are small when compared with the flocks wintering in central Europe; a roosting flock estimated at 72 million birds was recorded in Switzerland in 1951! Stevenson recorded an extraordinary southward migration, lasting over several days, which was witnessed by S. Bligh at Framingham in the severe weather of January 1865. Impressive numbers descended in the Norwich area during the first days of 1975. Over 1,200 were feeding in the beech woods at County Hall. Here they remained during January and early February, together with 600 at the nearby Colman Works, with 300 at Colney and at Arminghall, 400 at Twenty Acre in Brooke Wood, 10km to the south-east of the city. Between 6,500 and 7,000 Bramblings were estimated entering the wood on 26th January arriving on a narrow flight path from the north over a period of just over an hour. But one can only speculate as to how many were arriving from other compass points!

Numbers recorded wintering in Norfolk have also shown great variation, with few flocks reaching double figures in some winters. Over 8,000 occupied a mustard field at Mintlyn during October 1966 and

1,500 were attracted to seed kale at Sharrington in December 1972, while 2,000 at Caister on 15th February 1976 remained in the area for a week. In December 1996, birds were so scarce that only four records, each in single figures, were noted. On the other hand, four-figure flocks recorded during the last few years have included 2,250 on 2nd February 1992 on uncut linseed at Wereham, 2,500 at Thetford in early 1993, 1,000 at Feltwell in late 1993, 1,500 at Binham and 1,000 at Holt in January 1994, 1,200 at Mundford in February 1994 and 1,200 at Quarles/North Creake in January 1998.

Wintering birds can still be present in good numbers into early April, such as 600 at Weeting on 8th April 1991. But most tend to have slipped away by the middle of April. Coastal passage in the spring is very much less noticeable than in the autumn. The last of the spring are usually only a handful in May, although interestingly, birds have been noted as late as June on at least four occasions since the mid-1980s – singles at Pentney on 5th June 1986, Holme on 10th June 1987, Kelling on 9th June 1989 and Happisburgh on 5th June 1993. In addition an exceptionally late one appeared at Bexwell near Downham Market on 28th July 1973. There is no suggestion of the species ever having bred within the county except for a mention by Riviere of a female seen gathering birch-bark at North Wootton on 30th April 1923; the bird was not seen subsequently and no nest was found.

Over 3,500 Bramblings have been ringed in Norfolk which have resulted in an interesting series of recoveries, many of which were ringed at Mintlyn in the early 1970s. A total of 35 foreign recoveries has been reported from Belgium (8), The Netherlands (3), France (5), Denmark, Germany (6) and Italy (2) of birds on passage or in different wintering areas in subsequent years, and from Norway (5), Sweden (2), Finland (2) and Russia, countries in which the species commonly breeds. The first two recoveries in Norway in 1967 were the first British-ringed Bramblings to have been recovered in that country, while one ringed at Boughton in February 1967 and found at Ukhta, Komi, USSR on 17th May 1970 remains the only British-ringed Brambling to have been recovered in Russia. Movements to southern Europe are unusual although there has been a total of eleven British-ringed Bramblings to Italy. The longest interval between ringing and recovery involved a first-winter bird ringed at Mintlyn in December 1971 and recovered in Finland seven years later, one year short of the longevity record for a British-ringed Brambling. Eleven foreign-ringed Bramblings have been found in the county – from The Netherlands (2), Norway (6), Denmark (2) and Sweden. Many movements have been reported within the southern half of England, as well as one to Yorkshire. The longest have concerned one ringed at Burnham Market which was recovered three years later in Londonderry, Northern Ireland, and another ringed near Plymouth, Devon in February 1986, found at Welney in April 1987.

*Andy Musgrove*

## Serin (European Serin) WELLS. 24·6·1986. *Serinus serinus*

**A very scarce vagrant.**

The Serin is a familiar bird of Continental and particularly Mediterranean Europe but breeds only sporadically in Fennoscandia. It has become an annual visitor to Britain since the 1960s and has bred irregularly in southern England.

It was first recorded in Norfolk on 13th June 1885 in the Apollo Gardens at Yarmouth, the bird being shot the next day. Between then and 1922 a further six birds appeared, all of them in Yarmouth and all singles except for two on 1st April 1897. The next records were not until the 1960s when singles were seen at Holme on 23rd August 1965 and 15th April 1968, followed by a male in song at the Wells end of Holkham Meals on 13th May 1971. Between 1975 and 1998 the species was recorded annually, except for 1988 and 1989, with from one to four each year. The county total stands at 58 records.

The majority have been in spring, often following periods of a generally southerly airstream, suitable for northward-bound migrants to overshoot their destination. The peak period for arrivals has been between mid-April and late May, with the earliest on 2nd–3rd April 1995 at Bawburgh, on 8th April 1996 at Blakeney Point and on 9th April 1976 at Holme. Many of the males have been in full song and a number have also held territory over the summer months, most notably one in the Holkham/Wells area between 1984 and 1987. This male, with a unique Wren-like song, frequented Wells Woods from 4th to 18th July 1984 and again from 18th April to 22nd May 1985, before moving to Wells town, where it remained near the Field Study Centre and adjoining gardens from 20th June to 11th August. Both localities were again

SAW HiM ON 24ᵗʰ JUNE 1986. (AT FIELD-STUDY CENTRE)

visited between 1st May and 17th August 1986, and from 8th April to 11th August 1987 (Evans 1998).

Most of the spring and summer records have been along the coast between Hunstanton and Cromer, although there have been a few records inland and along the east Norfolk coast. These have included singing males at Sandringham from 5th June to 7th July 1993, at Potter Heigham from 25th June to 19th August 1995, at Gaywood Park, King's Lynn from 31st May to 13th July 1996 and one ringed at Pensthorpe on 15th May 1997. A pair at Holme on 25th April 1986 and two at Winterton on 18th April 1998 were the only multiple sightings apart from the two at Yarmouth on 1st April 1897. Of the 25 records between 1965 and 1986, eleven were at Holme, although there has not been one there since then. A total of eleven has also been recorded in the Wells/Holkham area.

Only six Serins have been recorded in autumn, the earliest at Sheringham on 18th August and the latest two both at Holkham on 19th October 1985 and 2nd November 1982. Surprisingly, six have been reported in winter – singles at Yarmouth on 31st January 1887 and 28th January 1911, a male ringed at Garboldisham on 5th February 1993 which was found dead five days later, a first-winter male at Cromer from 26th December 1995 to 26th February 1996, a different bird at Repps on 12th January 1996 and a first-winter male at Martham from 18th November 1997 to 19th March 1998. Two Serins have been ringed in the county.

*Steve Votier*

## [Citril Finch                                     *Serinus citrinella*

The claimed sole British record of Citril Finch – an adult female taken alive on Yarmouth North Denes by John Quinton on 29th January 1904 – was investigated between 1989 and 1992 (Allard 1995a). The bird was kept alive for two days by Edward Saunders the Yarmouth taxidermist before being sent to John Henry Gurney in Norwich for identification. Following Gurney's examination, Howard Saunders admitted the bird to the British List. Thomas Gunn, famed Norwich taxidermist, prepared the bird as a mounted specimen and it soon passed into the collection of Sir Vauncey Harpur Crewe in Derbyshire. The specimen remained with him until his death and was auctioned in 1925 or 1926 and presented to the Booth Museum, Brighton, where it still remains.

The bird was photographed in 1989 and doubts were raised as to its correct identification. With assistance from others, particularly Lee Evans, it was eventually identified as a male Cape or Yellow-crowned Canary.

Following re-identification, the record of Citril Finch at Yarmouth is no longer acceptable and in 1994 the BOURC deleted it from the British List.]

*Peter Allard*

MY GARDEN - CHEDGRAVE.

## Greenfinch (European Greenfinch)  8·7·1999.          *Carduelis chloris*

**A common resident and passage migrant, mainly in autumn.**

The Greenfinch is very much a Western Palearctic bird, occurring commonly throughout Europe, North Africa and the Middle East but only penetrating a little way into central Asia. Many populations are largely sedentary but those in the northernmost part of the range migrate south to avoid the winter (Clement *et al.* 1993). In the British Isles it is one of the most abundant and widespread of the cardueline finches, being absent only from high, mainly treeless areas in central Wales, north-west Scotland and Shetland (New Atlas).

The 'Green Linnet', as it used to be known, was considered a common bird by both Stevenson and Riviere who recognised that, although the species was largely resident, migratory individuals occurred on the coast in autumn. The Norfolk Atlas revealed, as would be expected, that Greenfinches occurred throughout almost the whole county, with records from 86% of tetrads. Their densest populations are in large gardens and shrubberies, where they can be locally more common than Chaffinches, although overall they were recorded in 100 fewer tetrads, breeding less commonly in Norfolk in areas of open farmland, heathland or dense conifer plantations. During the 1994–97 BBS the species was found in 55–68% of the 1km squares covered in Norfolk. The Greenfinch is one of the most numerous birds in Norfolk and its attractive plumage, vocal nature and liking for garden bird feeders ensure that it is familiar to many people.

Although the species is one of scrub, woodland edge and large gardens during the breeding season, at other times of year it occurs more widely in open areas such as arable farmland and open coast. During the winter, Greenfinches often flock together with other species such as Linnets and Yellowhammers. They are greatly dependent upon weed-seeds as food, although they will take a few insects in the summer, and local numbers depend greatly upon a supply of seeds. One of the largest feeding flocks reported in Norfolk was of 2,000 on fields at Winterton on 23rd February 1975, with 1,500 still present on 9th March. More recently 700 were at Burgh Castle in February 1984, 600 at Thetford in January 1993 and 600 at Magdalen in January–February 1992 and December 1993. As the amount of natural food declines through the winter, so Greenfinches increasingly take advantage of peanuts and sunflower seeds put out in garden feeders and it is likely that this new source of food has gone some way to counteract the reduction in natural foods which has been a well-documented side effect of the modernisation of agriculture. An indication of the number of Greenfinches taking advantage of this artificial food source is shown by a total of 915 ringed in a Sheringham garden between November 1986 and April 1987, of which 281 were caught in January alone.

In recent years, more detailed studies at coastal migration sites have revealed some impressive movements of Greenfinches, particularly in October. At Hunstanton cliffs, 200 flew south in 90 minutes on 10th October 1994 and between 23rd September and 13th November 1995 a total of 1,360 Greenfinches flew south, with maximum day-counts of 175 on 21st October and 220 two days later; while in October and November 1996 the total was almost 4,600 of which 1,189 flew south on 11th October. Elsewhere the maximum count at Holme has been 190 east on 18th October 1994, the same date on which 90 flew east at Sheringham, where the highest counts have been 400 west on 22nd October 1992 and 200 west on 14th October 1993. The origin of these migrants is uncertain. Greenfinches were rarely recorded at the light-vessels, although several Greenfinches, some of which were exhausted and in the sea, were at the Newarp and Smith's Knoll on 23rd October 1958, while in recent years several Norwegian-ringed Greenfinches have been controlled in the county in winter.

Mid-winter movements are rarely recorded, but 250 flew west at Sheringham on 14th January 1979. A light spring passage is recorded along the coast in late March and early April with maximum counts of 55 west on 2nd April 1995 and 75 west the following day, both at Holme. An albino was at Witchingham on 1st December 1955.

In recent years, the Greenfinch has been the most commonly ringed passerine in Norfolk, with over 50,000 having been ringed, the vast majority since 1980. This was partly due to the Greenfinch being the subject of a special study by Norfolk ringers during the mid-1980s, as well as the species' increasing dependence on artificial feeding sites during the winter months. Over 1,000 Norfolk-ringed Greenfinches have been recovered, 19 abroad (the first as recently as 1980) and nearly 50 others outside the county. In addition over 200 ringed outside Norfolk have been found in the county, as well as 13 with foreign rings, the majority as a result of having been controlled by other ringers. Recoveries within the British Isles have suggested a southerly movement in spring and early summer with a return movement northwards by the end of the year, and an easterly movement as winter proceeds.

A Greenfinch ringed at Sheringham in January 1984 and recovered in eastern Norway almost exactly a year later was only the fourth recovery of a British-ringed Greenfinch in that country. Since then an increasing number of recoveries have been reported between the east coast counties of England and Norway. From Norfolk alone 13 Greenfinches have been recovered in southern Norway, all between October and April; of these, nine were reported in April. In addition ten Norwegian-ringed Greenfinches have been found in the county, eight of which had been ringed in October–November; again all were from the southern part of Norway. One ringed in Rogaland on 30th October 1997 was controlled at Ormesby one week later, one of several controlled later the same autumn; while one ringed at Sheringham on 8th April 1995 was controlled in Vest-agder three weeks later, indicating a return movement in spring. However, no Norfolk-ringed Greenfinches have been found in Norway during the summer months.

Other international movements affecting Norfolk have involved recoveries in France, The Netherlands, Germany and Denmark (the only two from British ringing), while three Belgian-ringed Greenfinches have been found in the county. The most interesting multiple recovery concerned one ringed at Garboldisham on 16th April 1991, controlled in Dorset in November 1992 and again at Abberton Reservoir, Essex in November 1993.

*Andy Musgrove*

MY GARDEN- CHEDGRAVE.

## Goldfinch (European Goldfinch)  29-11-1999. (2)  *Carduelis carduelis*

### A common resident and passage migrant.

The Goldfinch breeds in a band across the Palearctic from southern Fennoscandia in the north to North Africa in the south. It is found mainly in lowlands throughout the cultivated landscapes of Europe and being a prolific seed-eater, it favours conditions where dry weather enables food plants to flourish and dry as seed is set, hence its particular abundance in Mediterranean countries. There has been a marked expansion of its range since the 1960s, with a northward spread into Scotland and Fennoscandia, as well as extending southwards. Birds breeding in north-west Europe move south and west of the range to winter in Iberia in large numbers. It is widespread in Britain and Ireland, being absent only from the open mountains and moorland, especially in north-west Scotland, and the Northern and Western Isles (New Atlas).

Stevenson described the Goldfinch, which was also known as 'King Harry' or 'King Harry Redcap' in Norfolk and Suffolk, as 'by no means uncommon throughout the year'. However, Patterson (1905) found that, as a result of the bird-catchers, its numbers had so decreased that it had become almost a rarity in the Yarmouth area. By 1930 Riviere believed that it had increased in numbers during the early decades of the 20th century and was once more fairly common throughout the county and he had personally recorded up to 100 feeding on alders in Broadland. During fieldwork for the Norfolk Atlas it was recorded in 86% of the tetrads and during the 1994–97 BBS it was found in 63–75% of the 1km squares covered in Norfolk. It therefore remains a widespread breeding bird throughout the county, wherever there are bushes or tall trees in which to nest and open ground with weeds on which it can feed on the seeds. It particularly favours farmland, parkland, orchards and gardens.

Coastal passage is well marked in spring although numbers vary annually. Peak numbers occur between mid-April and mid-May, the largest movements often being on days characterised by warm southerly and south-westerly winds. Regular observations at Sheringham and Holme have produced some of the most notable counts with the vast majority of birds passing west along the north Norfolk coast. In 1976, westerly passage was recorded at Sheringham from 1st May to 13th June, in parties of up to 30 birds, with peak counts of 600 on 1st May and 520 on 11th May. During the same period 490 Goldfinches were ringed in a small coastal wood (Dead Man's Wood) at Sheringham, an unprecedented number for a single site in Britain in spring. At the same time, even larger numbers were being recorded at Happisburgh, where maximum counts were 750 north on 30th April and 2,000 south on 10th May. The following year an even more impressive count was made at Sheringham with 1,700 west on 26th April, while at Happisburgh 750 flew north on 6th May and 1,200 on 13th May. Other notable counts at Sheringham have been 550 west on 14th May 1978 and 600 west on 1st May 1993; although the number recorded on visible migration in 1995 was smaller, up to 280 were present in Dead Man's Wood in late April and early May. Similarly impressive counts were made at Holme in 1996 with 550 west on 22nd April and 850 on 27th April.

Autumn passage is on a far smaller scale from mid-September to mid-November, although a series of daily counts from Hunstanton cliffs produced a total of 1,360 birds moving south between 23rd September and 13th November 1995, with a peak of 220 on 23rd October, compared with a daily maximum of only 43 south in October 1996. Riviere was not aware of a single record from a light-vessel off the Norfolk coast and there has only been one reported subsequently at the Haisboro' on 11th November 1959. Post-breeding gatherings in late summer and autumn are commonplace, particularly in areas containing thistles or teasels. Some notable autumn flocks have included 250 at Blakeney on 13th September 1955, 200 on the Breydon saltings in September–October 1975, 1,000 at Crostwick Old Hall on 21st September 1981, 250 at West Runton on 19th September 1992, 250 at Snettisham in September–October 1993 and 250 at Lynn Point in August 1994.

Wintering flocks are a regular sight in Norfolk, although usually in relatively small numbers. A remarkably large winter roost in evergreen oaks and hollies at Thorpe St Andrew reached a peak of 500 in mid-January 1973; 250 were still present a month later. More recently counts have included 350 at Wereham in January–February 1992 and at least 300 at Grimston in January 1995.

About 3,000 Goldfinches have been ringed in Norfolk. Ringing data collected in spring 1976 at Dead Man's Wood, Sheringham showed that significantly more females were caught. Assuming that the majority of these Goldfinches were of British stock, which had wintered in Iberia and were returning to their British breeding areas, it confirms observations made elsewhere that males are more likely to overwinter in Britain

(Newton 1972, Taylor 1976). Goldfinches ringed in Norfolk in spring have been recovered in France in February, Belgium in April, Spain in October and December, and Portugal in December, while one ringed at Sheringham on 23rd April 1983 was controlled at Oostkapelle, The Netherlands on both 11th September 1983 and 16th September 1984 suggesting fidelity to a Dutch site while on passage to its Iberian wintering area. Four autumn-ringed birds have been found in Belgium and two each in France and Spain, including one ringed at Dersingham on 22nd September 1967 which was recovered at Lambier, Spain five weeks later. Three ringed as nestlings in Norfolk have been recovered in Belgium, France and Spain, while eight foreign-ringed Goldfinches have been found in the county – from Belgium (4) Spain (2), France and The Netherlands.

*Steve Votier*

## Siskin (Eurasian Siskin) *Carduelis spinus*

MY GARDEN- CHEDGRAVE.
6-3-2000. (♂♀)

**A scarce, but increasing breeding resident, and common winter visitor and passage migrant.**

The Siskin breeds in the coniferous forests of the boreal and temperate zones from Britain and Ireland in the west to Sakhalin in the Far East. The main areas are from the Alps north-east across eastern Europe and into Fennoscandia. Spruce is most commonly occupied but pine and fir are also utilised. There has been an expansion into western Europe giving a fragmented distribution due to increased conifer planting. Marked annual fluctuations are noted at the southern edge of the range. The northern populations are migratory with birds moving south and west in autumn but those breeding in the south are resident.

In the 19th century the Siskin was a very localised breeder in Britain and records from the south of England might have related to escapes from captivity. In Britain, the trends in breeding numbers followed the extent of coniferous afforestation. During the First World War this was reduced and the restocked plantations did not attain the stage of maturity when seeds are produced until the 1930s. As a consequence, the numbers built up from a low point. By the 1950s, singing birds were noted in a number of southern counties. The Siskin is widely distributed in Wales, Scotland and northern England. The breeding population is thought to have multiplied tenfold between the two BTO Atlas studies with large increases in south Wales, southern Scotland and northern England, and smaller ones in south-west and southern England, but the increase was less marked in East Anglia.

The Siskin is now known as a wintering bird in gardens in towns and villages across the country, feeding at bird tables. This behaviour was first noted in 1963 in Surrey and from there the habit spread reaching Suffolk and Cambridgeshire in the winter of 1970–71 (Spencer & Gush 1973). The species now winters across much of Britain with largest numbers around centres of human population, showing the dependence on artificial feeding.

In Stevenson's time, Siskins were noted regularly at the end of autumn and again on their return northwards at the end of January. The numbers varied considerably from year to year and were not thought to be weather-dependent. There was one record of a female, which appeared to be nesting, taken by a Norwich bird-catcher in the month of May. Riviere stated that the Siskin was a regular winter visitor but in fluctuating numbers, with first arrivals usually in the second half of September. The Pagets (1834) considered it to be not uncommon and Patterson (1905) called it 'an uncertain autumnal visitor sometimes in great numbers'. In 1901 a Yarmouth bird-catcher took 140 in one morning, which were sold as cage birds at one shilling for each male and two pennies for a female. The return movement was very early in the year with only one record known after the end of February, that being a flock in beech trees at Hunworth in late April 1925.

There had been an increase in numbers coinciding with the expansion of Thetford Forest and boosted by irruptions which occurred in 1959, 1960 and 1961. Flocks of up to 350 at Kelling and Winterton indicated arrival from the Continent, while inland, large numbers recorded at Fowlmere, Stanford and Didlington showed that Siskins had a preference for food sources near to water.

Throughout the 1960s birds were being seen more frequently in summer and breeding was proved at Ringland when three fledged young were seen on 9th August 1961. In 1963 there were records from St Helen's Well and Two Mile Bottom in Thetford Forest, and in 1964 a pair was seen carrying nest material at Santon Downham. Breeding was proved at St Helen's Well in 1967 and possibly it also occurred there in 1969 and 1970. Pairs were seen in the Brecks each year with males singing in the early summer as well as in other areas of the county – a female was gathering nest material at West Newton in 1973, a moulting female was trapped at South Runcton in August 1976 and breeding was proved at Wells in 1979.

The Norfolk Atlas estimated that no more than ten pairs bred in any one year though some pairs could have been overlooked in the extensive conifer plantations. The main centre was at Thetford Forest between Mundford and Hilborough. The only places away from the Brecks where breeding was confirmed were at Sheringham in the north and at St Olaves in the south-east of the county. A number of records, especially of singing males, referred to birds on passage.

In 1982, large numbers were present from early spring especially in Swaffham Forest where one particular Forestry Commission fire tank was used as a drinking pool by many birds. Concentrated netting caught a total of 266 birds between 26th March and mid-May. By using retrap data, the overall number of Siskins using the site was estimated to be about 1,200. During April, females were caught with early signs of brood patches indicating breeding nearby and in May a recently-fledged juvenile was caught. It was thought that there could have been twelve pairs present and 40 young reared (Hale 1983a).

At present, small numbers breed annually in Thetford Forest and one or two pairs are present most years at Wells/Holkham. Elsewhere Wolferton, Holt, Weybourne, Sheringham and Northrepps have hosted breeding pairs. Breeding was first proved at Weybourne in 1996 when a pair brought three recently-fledged young to feed on peanuts in a garden in the village. The following year, the same garden-feeders hosted six to eight pairs of adults throughout the summer, during which time at least 40 young were estimated to have been taken there by their parents – up to 15 young being present at any one time. However, in 1998 only two broods appeared in the garden (J. Wallis pers. obs.). There is clearly potential for the Siskin to become more numerous as a breeding bird in the county.

Autumn passage is noted from early September through to the middle of November. Early birds were noted at Cley on 3rd September 1965 and at several places on 5th September 1995, while in 1997, 20 flew east at Paston on 30th August and six were noted at Eccles on 30th. Numbers have increased up to the present day but there are considerable variations from year to year. In 1976, there was only a single record in autumn – six at Holkham on 28th October. Otherwise flocks of as many as 50 were thought to be exceptional in the 1970s. The highest day-counts recorded prior to the 1990s were 80 moving south at Hunstanton on 28th October 1978.

In more recent years far larger numbers have been recorded. In 1993 there were two main waves of arrivals. On 16th September, 800 were counted on passage at Sheringham, 100 at Wells East Hills, a further 100 at Holkham and 400 at Holme. Some duplication may have occurred in these counts since most birds were coasting westwards but the total would have been well in excess of 1,000. These numbers were exceeded the following month when at Sheringham 2,600 flew west on 15th October and another 1,000 the next day. Three-figure counts were noted around the coast from Waxham to Hunstanton with several hundred moving per hour at Holkham and Hunstanton. The peak movement was at Paston on 30th October with 660 per hour. In November, the direction of the movement was reversed with most birds moving east and the highest numbers were on the east coast, for instance 300 at Waxham on 5th and 100 at Horsey on 7th. By contrast, numbers were much lower in 1994 with few flocks over 30. A total of 1,200 south at Snettisham on 22nd October 1995 was an exceptional number in a year when few counts were into double figures. The highest counts in 1996 were 450 in off the sea at Holme on 19th September, 210 on 21st and 200 at Holkham on 22nd, while the peak count in 1997 was 400 north at Waxam on 25th October.

Numbers present in mid-winter have increased markedly. In the 1950s and 1960s flocks of over 100 were recorded only in the irruption years of 1959, 1960, 1961 and 1963. Most of these were in the Brecks with the largest flocks at Fowlmere, Stanford Water and Didlington where up to 300 were present. No other counts exceeded 80 up until 1980. In that year there were 200 at Langford on 24th February and 200 at Bodney in February 1981. These might have involved birds that had wintered to the south and west of Norfolk and were on return passage, as in most years the numbers in the Brecks peaked in February or March. Large flocks in Breckland with smaller numbers widespread across the rest of the county was the pattern of distribution until the start of the 1990s. Since then other areas have held three-figure flocks in the middle of winter and these have included Broadland localities such as Ranworth, Reedham and Surlingham, as well as Beeston Regis, Letheringsett and Blickling in the north of the county, and Lynford in the west. Two of the highest counts in recent years have been 380 at Swangey Gravel Pit in November 1997 and 400 at Narborough in December 1997.

In Norfolk, Siskins were first noted feeding on peanuts at bird tables in the latter months of 1971, when this was noted at five widely-separated sites in the county – Cromer, Framingham Earl, Horsey, Northwold and Thorpe St Andrew. It is believed that this feeding method is learnt and passed on by example and so the communal nature of the Siskins' behaviour would enable this to spread rapidly across the county and country. In 1994 Michael Seago made an appeal in the *Eastern Daily Press* for records of Siskins feeding in gardens and at bird tables. This brought no fewer than 156 responses. Perhaps, in retrospect, it would have been more enlightening to find out whether there were any gardens which had not hosted any Siskins! It seemed that all gardens with suitable large trees, a supply of peanuts and a water feature had visits from the species. Most are seen in gardens in February and March as the natural food supply of birch and alder is exhausted. Most of these birds will continue to use gardens through to mid-April with some staying until early May before departure. Birds tend to linger longer in those that are near to breeding and potential breeding areas.

An indication of the numbers present and using a garden can be gauged from ringing records. The number of birds using a particular garden feeder will be far higher than the maximum seen at any one time. A ringer operating in his garden in Garboldisham caught 717 different individuals during 1994 and 604 the following year. Likewise at Sheringham, 576 were caught in a single garden between March and April 1994.

Spring passage is noted along the coast from early March to mid-April with smaller numbers in early May. Numbers are lower than in autumn with maximum counts not exceeding 50 in most years. However, 1995 was exceptional with 100 north at Winterton on 4th March and a westward movement at Holme which peaked at 450 on 22nd March and 1,500 on 25th March. The only other three-figure spring passage counts have been 206 west at Holme on 13th March 1993 with 187 and 130 on the following two days.

Prior to 1994 the annual ringing total of Siskins in Norfolk had never exceeded 250. However, as a result of an unprecedented influx of Siskins into many Norfolk gardens in the first quarter of 1994, more than 3,000 were ringed between January and April. Since then, this late winter influx into gardens has become an almost annual event and by the end of 1998 over 14,000 Siskins had been ringed in the county. By gathering information from ringers operating in different parts of Norfolk during the opening months of 1994, some interesting facts emerged (Taylor 1995, Taylor & Moores 1995). The two features which seemed to be most attractive to Siskins were first mature trees in which they could loaf, preen and sing, and second a small pond. Unlike other studies, the sex ratios were almost equal, and 75% of the birds were in their first-winter. The males and older birds tended to desert the gardens earlier in the spring, presumably in order to return first to their breeding areas to establish territories. A clear peak in the numbers being trapped occurred during the first week of April, after which there was a fairly rapid departure with none ringed after 22nd April. During the four months there was much interchange of ringed birds between sites but not one was controlled outside Norfolk during this period, despite the fact that 32 Siskins ringed in other counties were controlled in Norfolk. These included birds ringed during the same 1993–94 winter period from London and the Home Counties to the south, Gloucestershire and Avon in the west, Staffordshire and Derbyshire in the Midlands, and Cleveland and Tyne and Wear in the north-east. One had even been ringed in Tayside, Scotland. There had also been one Dutch and two Belgian-ringed controls during this time. All these movements suggested that the Siskins were part of the previous autumn's influx and were gathering in Norfolk prior to their return to the Continent by way of the shortest sea-crossing between the British Isles and the Low Countries. Further evidence to support this came with the recovery of three of the Norfolk-ringed Siskins later in the spring in Belgium, Norway and Germany, while three more ringed in early 1994 were recovered in later years in France, Lithuania and Russia.

Since the winter of 1993–94 ever more recoveries of Norfolk-ringed Siskins have been reported and the total currently stands at almost 400 of which over 70 have been in Scotland and 45 abroad. Over half the foreign recoveries have come from Belgium (12) and The Netherlands (10), with six from southern Norway, four each from Denmark and Germany, three from Sweden and the Baltic States, and one from Finland, France and the Balearic Islands. Many of the 16 foreign-ringed recoveries in Norfolk were of birds ringed in the autumn and recovered in March; they had been ringed in Belgium (6), The Netherlands (4), Norway (3), Poland (2), Sweden and Finland. The results of ringing have clearly demonstrated that Siskins which winter in East Anglia or pass through the area in spring are from breeding populations both in Scotland and mainland Europe. The Scottish connection is particularly well demonstrated by one ringed in Grampian on 20th April 1995, controlled at Garboldisham on 23rd February 1996 and found dead in Glasgow on 23rd May 1996.
*Peter Dolton*

# Linnet (Common Linnet) | TITCHWELL. 8-9-1985. *Carduelis cannabina*

**A very common resident and partial migrant, and common passage migrant.**

The Linnet is widely distributed as a breeding bird throughout the Western Palearctic, except in Iceland, northern Fennoscandia and northern Russia. It breeds throughout the British Isles, except in the central and western Highlands of Scotland, the Hebrides and Shetland. Numbers declined dramatically between 1970 and 1990 in much of Europe, but in particular in Britain, Ireland, The Netherlands and Finland, due largely to the use of agricultural herbicides.

During the 19th century, a widespread decline in the number of Linnets was attributed to the activities of bird-catchers, who sold them as cagebirds. Legislation in Britain, however, had the desired effect and by the 1930s, the Linnet was once more a very common breeding bird in Norfolk (Riviere). At that time though, it was described as a breeding summer visitor, being very rare between December and mid-February.

Despite the national decline in numbers, it has remained widespread throughout the county during the summer months. It was recorded in 83% of the tetrads for the Norfolk Atlas. Areas from which it was absent included the centre of Norwich, parts of the Halvergate Levels and the mature coniferous plantations of Breckland (Kelly 1986). During the 1994–97 BBS it was found in 62–76% of the 1km squares covered in Norfolk, the higher counts being in the later years. Linnets often breed in small loose colonies of four to six pairs, favouring patches of gorse on commons, heathland and golf courses, in hedgerows, young forestry plantations, along woodland edges, in parks and gardens, in bushes along railway embankments and on the coast in *Suaeda* and sea buckthorn. At least 25 breeding pairs were present at Scolt Head in 1997.

In winter, as at other times of the year, Linnets feed almost exclusively on weed seeds taken from the ground. The changes in agricultural practice, such as the use of herbicides and autumn-sown crops have thus reduced the available food sources for the species during the winter months. It therefore seems paradoxical that Linnets are nowadays fairly common, if localised, in winter in Norfolk, whereas Riviere described them as very rare. They may be difficult to locate at this time of year as the entire population from an area may congregate into one or more flocks (Winter Atlas). The largest winter flocks in recent years have been on set-aside on the cliff-top fields at Weybourne, where 800 were present in November 1994, and a similar number on the cliff-top fields at West Runton in November 1996, up to 500 at Flitcham and Winfarthing, and 300 at Choseley and Harpley Common. Smaller numbers also winter annually on the saltings around the coast, although no recent counts have approached the flock of 500 at Thornham in November 1953. However, almost 2,000 were counted during a low-tide survey of all intertidal habitat between Holme and Weybourne in November 1997. The only notable mid-winter movements involved 500 west on 14th January 1979 and 170 east on 31st January 1996 both at Sheringham, which were related to periods of hard weather.

In autumn, Riviere described a large arrival as taking place annually, with birds moving from east to west along the north Norfolk coast, while in the 19th century 'thousands' appeared each October on Yarmouth North Denes (Patterson 1905). Nowadays, autumn passage, which takes place in September and October, involves far fewer birds, although the build-up of coastal feeding flocks includes those on passage, such as 500 at Holkham beach on 29th September 1990. A total of 800 west at Sheringham on 27th October 1978 was exceptional, although recent counts on the east coast of the Wash have demonstrated that an annual southerly movement is occurring. Recent autumn totals past Hunstanton cliffs have included 700 in 1995 and 1,200 in 1996, but only 347 in 1997, while 1,500 flew south at Snettisham in one hour on 22nd October 1995. Despite Linnets being diurnal migrants, very few have been recorded flying in off the sea.

The reverse is true in spring, with a marked annual passage of Linnets, whereas Riviere described them as being far less numerous than in autumn. The reason for this change is unclear. Spring passage lasts from mid-March to mid-May, peaking in April. As in autumn, passage birds will temporarily join feeding flocks, resulting in some very impressive counts, such as 750 at Gore Point in mid-April 1992, 1,000 at Horsey on 12th April 1993 and 500 at Snettisham in April 1994. Visible migration generally involves birds flying north in east Norfolk and west along the north Norfolk coast. The highest counts were in the 1970s and early 1980s – at Sheringham 3,000 west on 16th and 2,500 west on 26th April 1977 and 1,500 west on 28th April 1978, at Paston 1,000–1,400 west on five dates between 10th April and 3rd May 1981, at Happisburgh 2,000 north on 30th April 1976 and 1st May 1977, and at Winterton 5,000 north on 25th

April 1976. Maximum counts in recent years have included 1,300 west at Holme on 5th April 1995, 790 west at Sheringham on 10th April 1993, 830 east on 24th April 1994 and 700 per hour west on 1st May 1995 both at Paston.

Over 2,000 Linnets have been ringed in Norfolk, resulting in 20 foreign recoveries. Except for two, all those recovered abroad were ringed in Norfolk between May and September, with the majority recovered in October and November. Four were found in Belgium, including one which was seen caged in an Antwerp market and later released in The Netherlands, seven in the Landes region of south-west France and four in Spain. The exception was one ringed at Salthouse on 29th November 1953 and recovered at Vicenza, Italy on 10th November 1954. This remains only one of two British-ringed Linnets to be recovered in Italy, out of over 700 foreign recoveries for the species. It clearly was an exceptional movement. Seven foreign-ringed Linnets, all ringed between November and May, have been found in Norfolk, three from Belgium and two each from France and Spain. The most notable recovery within the British Isles concerned one ringed at a roost at Gillingham on 28th October 1978 which was controlled at North Ronaldsey, Orkney on 18th April 1979.

*Moss Taylor*

**Twite** BREYDON WATER. 1-12-1992.                    *Carduelis flavirostris*

**A fairly common but localised winter visitor and scarce passage migrant; has declined in recent years.**

The breeding distribution of the Twite is very unusual, in that there are two totally separate populations 2,500km apart – one in north-west Europe, the other extending from the Caucasus to central and eastern Asia. The European population, which breeds on moorland and rocky short-sward grassland, is found predominantly in western Norway and the British Isles. It is the only passerine, except for the endemic Scottish Crossbill, to breed or winter in Britain in internationally important numbers. Range contractions in north-west Scotland and north-west England have occurred as a result of habitat fragmentation, reclamation and overgrazing, but this has been partly offset by an increase in the population in south-east Scotland and an apparently new population in Wales. The Irish population remains in severe decline. During winter many Twite move to coastal sites (Winter Atlas).

Surprisingly, Stevenson stated 'The Twite is, I believe, only an occasional visitant to Norfolk, on its migratory course, passing southwards in autumn, and again re-appearing for a brief space in the spring', although he did mention small flocks near the pilot's house at Blakeney in the autumn and winter of 1852–53. Whereas Patterson (1905) described occasional rushes of Twite, in what was known locally as 'a Twite year', when ' [they become] quite a nuisance to the bird-catchers, whose nets they persist in entering', for example, in November 1881 he stated that 'thousands were passing'. Riviere described the species as an irregular passage migrant and winter visitor and included a flock of 300 at Hunstanton on 7th November 1912.

Twite wintering on the saltmarshes of Norfolk and the rest of East Anglia come largely from birds breeding in northern England (the Scottish and Irish populations are generally sedentary) and the Norfolk saltmarshes have represented an important wintering site for this population. Some birds, however, arrive from across the North Sea (particularly in harsh weather conditions), swelling the wintering population. Numbers appeared to reach a peak in the 1970s and 1980s, although as many as 400 were at Thornham on 8th December 1959. The majority of birds were present from the Wash eastwards to Blakeney Point, with certain areas favoured each winter. Titchwell regularly held a minimum of 200 Twite and often 400–500, with a peak of 1,000 in January 1974. Flocks in the Scolt Head area totalled 500–1,000 in most winters from 1980 to 1989, Wells peaked at 600 in 1981 and up to 500 wintered at Blakeney Point from 1978 to 1983. The most recent report of a large Twite flock concerned up to 600 on Holkham beach in November–December 1991.

Numbers have been far lower in subsequent winters and a survey organised by the Norfolk Bird Club on 23rd January 1994, which included all the county's saltmarshes, found only six flocks containing a total of 298 Twite – 50 at Holme, 40 at Brancaster Staithe, 140 at Holkham Gap, 41 at Blakeney Point and 27 at Breydon in two flocks. Observers also covered the Lincolnshire part of the Wash on the same date and no Twite were found (Brown 1994). This compared with a census in February 1986 during which a total of 17,000 Twite was counted around the entire Wash, although this had fallen to 4,000–6,000 the following winter, when many of the population may have crossed the North Sea to winter in the Low Countries, alongside the Norwegian population. In east Norfolk the fall in numbers has been equally dramatic. Whereas an average of 70–100 Twite wintered regularly in the Breydon area, peaking at 150 in January 1973, the last regular wintering flock was recorded in 1994, since when the species has become an uncertain visitor in small numbers, but mainly in October.

Colour-ringing studies have shown that birds move regularly between different sites during the same winter period, making assessments of actual numbers difficult. However, since the survey in January 1994, numbers in Norfolk do appear to have recovered a little, with 500 between Holme and Hunstanton in November 1994, and 430 between Holme and Morston in January 1995. Maximum counts in February 1996 were 170 at Brancaster Harbour and 220 at Holkham, while a low-tide count of all suitable habitat in November 1997 resulted in a total of 490 Twite being located between Holme and Blakeney Harbour, including maximum counts of 159 at Scolt Head and 105 in Blakeney Harbour.

Twite breeding in the Pennines move out in a south-easterly direction from late August, reaching the east coast in peak numbers between September and November (Winter Atlas). That at least some of those wintering in Norfolk come from the Pennines was demonstrated by three colour-ringed nestlings from two separate nests in the Halifax area of Yorkshire which were subsequently seen at Holkham (see below). The first birds of the autumn are generally seen in Norfolk in early October, occasionally in September. The earliest were singles at Snettisham on 18th August 1986 and at Blakeney on 4th September 1975. Others have been recorded in the last week of September, including 25 at Scolt Head on 25th September 1994. The Twite is the only passerine which is regularly recorded migrating eastwards along the north Norfolk coast in autumn, such as 60 east on 23rd October 1989 and 47 east on 14th October 1990, both at Sheringham. However, the highest day-counts of birds on passage both involved Twite flying west – 140 at Sheringham on 31st October 1976 and 105 at Holme on 6th November 1994.

Twite begin to leave the county in March with very few remaining by the end of April, although 400–500 were still present at Wells on 21st April 1975. The latest spring records have been at Breydon on 2nd May 1986, two at Sheringham on 2nd May 1997, two at Cley on 6th May 1979, one at Paston on 6th May 1987 and two at Holme on 14th May 1985. There have been three mid-summer records – at Horsey Warren on 25th June 1967, a male with Redpolls and Goldfinches at Keswick Mill on 17th–18th June 1975 and two at Blakeney Point on 7th June 1986.

Despite the reduction in the number of Twite wintering in the county, small parties continue to be recorded inland on an almost annual basis. The largest inland flock remains up to 50 which were present at Wisbech Sewage Farm from 18th March to 22nd April 1962; during the same period up to 13 were at Welney until mid-March. Elsewhere in the Fens 13 were at Hilgay on 27th March 1978, up to nine at Ten Mile Bank in 1984 and 1986, 20 at Black Horse Drove on 8th April 1986 and twelve at Southery Fen on 11th October 1989. In the Broads, Hickling was a favoured locality between 1975 and 1986, with maximum counts of 35 on 3rd October 1975 and about 30 in February and October 1979, February 1982 and October 1984. Other Broadland sites holding parties of Twite have included 33 along the River Bure at Mautby on 4th January 1992 and twelve along the River Waveney at Fritton on 21st January 1996.

About 50 Twite have been ringed in Norfolk since 1980 but there have been no recoveries outside the county. However, three nestlings colour-ringed at two different sites in West Yorkshire on 8th June 1995, were seen at Holkham the following winter.

*Steve Votier*

LODDON BOATYARD. (3) 31-12-1999.

| **Redpoll (Common Redpoll)** | HOLKHAM. NNR. 7-10-1986. | *Carduelis flammea* |

**A fairly common resident, winter visitor and passage migrant.**

The Redpoll has a circumpolar distribution, broadly covering the subarctic and coniferous boreal zones to the tundra edge. During the 1800s Lesser Redpolls *C. f. cabaret* were confined to northern parts of Britain, Ireland and the Alps. Numbers increased in lowland Britain at the turn of the 20th century, rapidly contracted and then expanded again during the 1950s at which time the central European population also increased. Birds spilled into The Netherlands, Germany and Denmark reaching southern Sweden and Belgium in the 1970s, where they are currently on the increase.

In Britain and Ireland the Lesser Redpoll is a bird of pioneer woodland, especially birch, and is also common in the establishment and pre-thicket stages of coniferous plantations, where birch often develops (New Atlas). During the period of the 68–72 BTO Atlas it was found to be fairly widespread throughout the British Isles, except for an area of scarcity in central southern England. Numbers peaked during the mid-1970s and the species was believed to be as common as it had been for at least 100 years. However, since then the British and Irish population has been on the decline, caused by the combination of succession of birch woodlands (which had developed rapidly after wartime clearances) and the removal of hedgerows and other disruptive practices associated with intensive agriculture (New Atlas).

Stevenson failed to comment on the abundance of the Redpoll as a breeding species in Norfolk, but did say that it was a regular winter visitor and was very numerous in some years. Riviere described it as being 'by no means uncommon', particularly in Broadland. There followed an apparent decline with most records during the 1950s coming from the Brecks and north Norfolk. By the mid-1960s it was considered to be as common as the Linnet in certain areas. During fieldwork for the Norfolk Atlas it was found in 31% of the tetrads and Kelly described it as 'widespread where its preferred breeding habitats are extensive, but scarce elsewhere'. The favoured regions were alder carrs, and birch, thorn and willow thickets in Broadland, birch heathland and young forestry plantations, with particularly high concentrations on the heaths and marginal land along the Cromer to Holt Ridge. It was also found in a band extending north-north-west from Breckland to the hinterland of Hunstanton (Kelly 1986). At its peak it was also nesting on farmland and in gardens. Since then there has been a steady decline throughout the county and during the 1994–97 BBS it was recorded in only 4–7% of the 1km squares surveyed in Norfolk. During the breeding seasons of 1995 and 1996, Lesser Redpolls were reported from 35–40 well-scattered sites in the county, but from only 27 localities in 1997.

Although Riviere was able to find little evidence of 'true' migration involving Redpolls, passage birds are regularly recorded on the coast in autumn and spring. Autumn passage is recorded between mid-September and mid-November, but numbers involved are very small with counts rarely reaching double figures. Some of the higher counts, for instance in late autumn 1995, of 50 south at Hunstanton on 4th November and 34 north at Yarmouth on 5th November may well have involved birds of the nominate race *C. f. flammea*, the Mealy Redpoll, which became widespread in November and December. The most spectacular autumn influx, however, was recorded on 28th October 1963 when at least 500 were estimated to have arrived between the Marrams and Cley Beach Road. The *Norfolk Bird Report 1963* continued:

> Considerable numbers remained in the area until Nov. 10th appearing paler, sandier and smarter looking than native lesser redpolls though differing little in size. The impression was of miniature editions of the Greenland race *rostrata* and this was further enhanced by the clear-cut blackish striping on flanks and rich, sandy buff throat and fore-breast [Richard Richardson].

These were presumably also birds of the nominate race (see below).

Wintering flocks have often involved large numbers of Redpolls, the sizes of these flocks suggesting that some birds of the race *cabaret* do arrive from the Continent to winter in the county. The larger counts, generally of birds feeding in birch or alder trees, have been of 100 at Binham in December 1988, 100 at Thetford in January 1993, 70 at Catfield Fen in October 1993, 90 at Pentney Gravel Pit in November 1994, 120 at Woodbastwick in December 1994, 110 at Swaffham Forest in March 1997 and 100 at Kelling Heath on 3rd April 1997. As in autumn, only small numbers of Lesser Redpolls are seen on visible migration in spring. However, large numbers have been noted feeding on passage at coastal sites such as Dead Man's Wood, Sheringham. In 1976, for instance there was a steady passage through this site from mid-March to early May during which time 322 were ringed, as well as 51 Mealy Redpolls (Taylor 1976). At Holme in 1995 the monthly totals for the number of Redpolls seen flying west were 38 in March, 83 in April and 27 in May.

The possibility that some of the birds recorded on passage could include Mealy Redpolls is likely, making an understanding of the status of passage birds difficult. However, considering the regularity with which Lesser Redpolls are observed grounded at coastal sites, it does seem likely that some Continental birds are involved. The unusually large westerly movement of 105 Redpolls at Holme on 20th April 1993, which followed a winter when Mealy Redpolls were relatively scarce, provides further circumstantial evidence.

The nominate race *flammea*, the Mealy Redpoll, breeds in lowland conifers, and alpine birch and willow in Fennoscandia and northern Russia. Long-term trends are poorly known but the population of Mealy Redpolls fluctuates considerably from year to year depending on the availability of seed. In Swedish Lapland the population can increase tenfold, to be followed by a dramatic decrease as seed crops crash (EBCC). These fluctuations govern the numbers occurring in Britain, bumper years seeing tens of thousands arrive, compared with years when they are a comparative rarity. Numbers may also be affected by weather conditions – periods of unusually low temperatures in Fennoscandia and prevailing easterly winds force the birds to move south and westwards into Britain.

Birds can arrive anytime during the late autumn or through the winter period, particularly during influx years when weather conditions become suitable. On average only between one and 20 are reported annually from a wide range of coastal and inland sites. The earliest dates on which Mealy Redpolls have been recorded in Norfolk have been 22nd September 1977 at Morston, 27th September 1986 at Holkham, 30th September 1978 at Winterton and three at Sandringham on 30th September 1990. During influx years, when large flocks occur, the difficulties of specific identification make accurate counts of each redpoll species and race virtually impossible. In the winters of 1972–73, 1975–76, 1984–85, 1990–91 and 1995–96 major influxes occurred with numbers of Mealy Redpolls far exceeding more typical years. In 1984 the first reports were on 7th November when small numbers were recorded at a wide range of sites; numbers built up during the winter months to produce peak counts of 100 at Holkham Meals and 50 at Mousehold Heath during early 1985. An early report of three Mealy Redpolls at Sandringham on 30th September 1990 was the forerunner of another considerable influx from 18th October with widely scattered records from coastal sites. By the end of the year a flock at Holkham Meals had increased to 40. Further influxes during the winter led to substantial flocks building up during the start of 1991, the largest groups being 130 at Holkham/Wells in January–February, up to 60 at Mousehold Heath in March, 25 at Strumpshaw on March 2nd and up to 20 at Weybourne in February–March.

An even larger influx took place in autumn 1995 as Mealy Redpolls were forced out of Fennoscandia and eastern Europe by plummeting temperatures and snow. The first were reported at Snettisham on 24th October, followed by parties of up to 40 at a range of coastal and inland sites. Numbers increased during November and December with up to 60 at six sites and maximum counts of 50–100 at Heigham Sound in November and 90 at Holt Lowes in December. Freezing conditions with a biting easterly wind brought increased numbers at the start of 1996, with many reports of flocks between 50 and 120, in addition to 200 at both Cockshoot and Ranworth Broads in January; 240 at Sharp Street Fen, 230 at Woodbastwick and 200 at Wroxham in February; 250 at Wroxham Broad in March increasing to at least 500 in April. These huge numbers represent a major influx but considerable interest in the redpoll complex (and particularly in Arctic Redpolls) has perhaps biased the number of records during these influx years, with some observers spending all their time looking for redpolls during the winter months.

The number of passage birds during the spring correlates closely with occurrences during the previous autumn and winter periods. Generally only small numbers are seen but many may be lost by joining existing flocks or by passing through areas receiving less attention at the onset of spring. The most noticeable spring passage was in 1996, with birds recorded moving along the coast in good numbers from early March to early May, commencing with 45 west at Sheringham on 10th March. Assessing the relative proportions of redpoll species and races is almost impossible in flight but the majority of birds passing Sheringham were strikingly pale and were most likely to have been Mealy or even Arctic Redpolls. The latest spring Mealy Redpolls have been six at Holme on 9th May 1976 and four at Caister on 12th May 1985.

Several thousand Redpolls have been ringed in the county, the majority in the 1960s and 1970s. An analysis of the recoveries of Norfolk-ringed Lesser Redpolls (Hale 1983b) provided an insight into their movements. Recoveries of birds ringed in the summer showed that they dispersed just after completion of the post-breeding moult, moving generally southwards or westwards within Britain, but also with considerable numbers wintering in The Netherlands, northern France, Germany and particularly Belgium (from where 32 out of the 41 foreign recoveries have been reported). While a female Lesser Redpoll ringed as a juvenile in Norfolk was controlled two years later as a breeding bird in Belgium – clearly some of the emigration was not only seasonal but represented range expansion. Redpolls found in Norfolk and ringed elsewhere in England have all come from eastern England or the Home Counties. Amongst the foreign-ringed birds from Belgium, The Netherlands and France that have been found in Norfolk were two Dutch-ringed Redpolls recovered later the same spring – one controlled at Holme on 31st May 1973 had been ringed four weeks earlier and the other controlled at Sheringham on 20th April 1977 ringed five weeks earlier. Clearly at that time there was a spring movement of birds that had wintered on the Continent returning through the Low Countries. The longest movement within the British Isles involved one ringed at Earlham on 1st January 1991 which was recovered 759km away at Old Shoremore, Scotland only 15km south of Cape Wrath.

*Steve Votier*

## Arctic Redpoll                                       *Carduelis hornemanni*

**A rare winter visitor and passage migrant.**

The Arctic Redpoll is a circumpolar breeder in subarctic and high Arctic areas being found further north than any other passerine apart from the Snow Bunting. The nominate form Hornemann's Redpoll *C. h. hornemanni* breeds in north Greenland and adjacent parts of Canada, whilst Coues' Redpoll *C. h. exilipes* breeds across northern Eurasia, Alaska and the remainder of Canada. In the Western Palearctic, Arctic Redpolls winter mainly in Fennoscandia, northern Europe and Russia. Periodically small numbers move much further south and west, usually in association with large irruptions of Mealy Redpolls, in response to shortages of birch and spruce cone seeds. Both forms occur as vagrants to the British Isles and while *exilipes* is recorded with some regularity, *hornemanni* is a much more irregular vagrant mainly to the Northern Isles – but similarities between the two races means that nominate birds may go under-recorded. There have been 150–160 accepted records of Arctic Redpoll in Norfolk, although the figure of 228 given by Bloomfield (1997b), is probably a more accurate reflection of numbers.

The first Norfolk record was of a female taken from a group of Mealy Redpolls on the North Denes at Yarmouth on 26th October 1910. This was followed by a male obtained at Marsham on 4th January 1926, both occurring in years 'remarkable for a large immigration of Mealy Redpolls' (Riviere). The third Norfolk record was one seen by Commander C. E. Hamond at Stiffkey Greens on 3rd–4th November 1945 (Hamond 1946). In describing this bird and another in Northumberland in the same month, the editors of *British Birds* introduced for the first time the name Arctic Redpoll. A further 21 years were to pass before the next one in the county, at Wells from 28th September to 10th October 1966, again with a large flock of Mealy Redpolls. Since then the species has become almost annual, except for the period 1977–83. The earliest arrivals have been on 27th September 1972 at Holme, on 28th September 1966 at Wells and on 29th September 1966 at Holme. The latest records in spring have been four at Wells on 7th April 1991 and one showing the characteristics of the race *hornemanni* at Brancaster on 17th–18th April 1994.

The first influx of Arctic Redpolls, involving nine birds, occurred from September to December 1972 – which included the first multiple occurrences and the first three to be ringed in the county all at Wiveton. A single bird in October 1975 was associated with large numbers of Mealy Redpolls, whilst the following spring three records suggested a return passage. Despite a major arrival of Mealy and Arctic Redpolls along the British east coast and the Northern Isles during autumn 1984, only one was accepted in Norfolk – at Titchwell on 12th November. The remainder of the winter saw attention turn to the large numbers of redpolls present in the county, and up to four Arctic Redpolls were found with the Mealy Redpolls at Holkham between 19th January and 14th April 1985.

A further major influx occurred in 1990–91, with the first birds arriving in late October at coastal sites, as biting easterly winds and murky conditions drove Scandinavian migrants to ground. Mixed species flocks began to build in December with multiple observations occurring by the end of the year. A harsh winter saw flocks continue to build, further supplemented by returning birds. Maximum counts included up to 20 Arctic Redpolls on 10th–20th March 1991 at Mousehold Heath, Norwich, at least twelve and possibly as many as 15 at Holkham Meals from December 1990 to 17th February 1991 and up to nine at Filby/Rollesby Broads on 7th–17th March 1991. The autumn of 1995 saw another remarkable influx of redpolls from November onwards, of an even greater magnitude than five years earlier. Large numbers of redpolls arrived in November with the first accepted Arctic being recorded on Blakeney Point on 18th November. This was followed by a scattering of records through November and December from mainly coastal sites, with the first birds inland at North Wootton on 20th December. The first multiple occurrences were noted at the end of December and numbers continued to increase as bitterly cold east and north-east winds drove birds out from Scandinavia. Notable counts included at least four at Cromer from 20th December 1995 to the end of February 1996, four at Syderstone Common on 26th December 1995, up to eight at Langham from 11th January to 22nd March 1996, eight at Sheringham on 3rd February 1996, up to eight at Wroxham Broad from 7th February to 2nd April 1996 and nine at Stonepit Heath, Kelling on 23rd February 1996.

The true numbers of Arctic Redpolls involved in the 1995–96 influx will always be open to debate. It is a difficult species to identify and the highly mobile nature of feeding flocks can make for exasperating identification problems. The overall numbers during arrival years may also be biased – the time that birders spend in suitable redpoll habitat is probably disproportionately high during influx years. There is also clearly variance in between-year observations – the massive increase in the numbers of observers during the 1990s and the increase in knowledge makes Arctic Redpolls appear much more abundant, which seems unlikely.

There have been two records of Arctic Redpolls suspected of belonging to the race *hornemanni* – at Wells from 28th September to 10th October 1966, which was filmed by Dick Bagnall-Oakeley, and a male at Brancaster on 17th–18th April 1994. A total of five Arctic Redpolls has been ringed in the county.

*Steve Votier*

# Two-barred Crossbill                                    *Loxia leucoptera*

**A very rare vagrant.**

The Two-barred Crossbill of the race *L. l. bifasciata* inhabits boreal larch and cedar forests from Finland east across northern Russia into Siberia and northern China. In North America the nominate race *L. l. leucoptera* ranges from Alaska through Canada to the northern states. Like the Crossbill it wanders widely during years of poor cone crops. The species is a rare vagrant to the British Isles. Its appearance is hardly annual although during irruption years one or two are occasionally encountered amidst flocks of Crossbills.

The inclusion of this species on the Norfolk list has a chequered history. Stevenson included it on the strength of two records, both of which were subsequently discarded. The first, claimed to have been obtained at Thetford on 10th May 1846 was shown to have come from Bury St Edmund's, Suffolk. The second, which was said to have been caught alive in the rigging of a ship which came into Yarmouth in October 1870, proved to be of the American race *leucoptera* and was therefore subsequently rejected. The bird lived in Stevenson's aviary until December 1874 and the specimen is still in the Castle Museum, Norwich. When Riviere wrote his avifauna, the species was still not on the county list, despite one having been obtained at Burgh Castle. At that time, the locality was still included within Suffolk!

The county total currently stands at nine:

> 1889: A male shot at Burgh Castle on 1st September
> 1966: A male at Holkham Meals from 21st September to 25th November
> 1969: An immature at Blakeney Point on 15th September
> 1975: A male at Sandringham on 16th February
> 1980: A female at Santon Warren on 7th June
> 1990: A male at Sandringham Warren from 29th September to 14th October
>          A female at Lynford Arboretum from 24th November to 1st June 1991
> 1997: A male ringed at Thetford Forest on 21st August
> 1998: A female at Sandringham on 23rd–24th May (subject to acceptance by the BBRC)

The specimen shot at Burgh Castle passed into the vast Connop collection at Rollesby Hall and is currently at Birmingham City Museum. A second bird was also seen at the time it was shot (Allard 1990) but has not been included in the county total, due to insufficient details. The birds in 1966 and 1990 both occurred during large Crossbill irruptions, as a result all three species of crossbill were present at Holkham Meals and Lynford Arboretum simultaneously.

*Andrew Bloomfield*

# Crossbill (Common Crossbill)   *Loxia curvirostra*

A scarce resident, occurring in larger numbers during irruption years.

Crossbills
(Nik Borrow)

The Common Crossbill has a patchy breeding distribution from eastern Spain, south-east France, Italy, throughout Fennoscandia and from Poland eastwards into the vast taiga forests of northern Russia reaching northern India and China. Other populations are present in north-west Africa, the Balearic Islands, Corsica, Sardinia, Cyprus and Turkey. It is also found in North America ranging across northern Canada and south from Alaska through the western provinces and states to Texas.

Throughout its range the Common Crossbill breeds early in the year and its presence depends solely on the abundance of food (larch, spruce and pine cones are favoured) followed by dispersion, initially over short distances, to coincide with the formation of new *Picea* cones. Irruptions to areas mainly to the south and west, are triggered when high population levels coincide with poor cone crops (Newton 1972).

In the British Isles, Crossbills are found mainly in the coniferous forests of Scotland, northern England, Wales, the Peak District, the New Forest, Breckland, Forest of Dean and southern Devon. Numbers fluctuate with good and poor irruption years, although suitable habitat is becoming even more widespread as upland coniferous plantations are fast maturing (New Atlas). Irruptive invasions of Britain have been documented as far back as 1251 and 1593, and in the 17th century Sir Thomas Browne wrote of a bird 'of fine colours and prittie note, differing from other birds with the upper and lower bill crossing and of a very tame nature'. Browne regarded it as a summer rather than a winter visitor to Norfolk.

Miss Anna Gurney recorded a nest at Sheringham in 1829, a record not mentioned by Stevenson who stated that he knew of no instances of breeding in the county although he thought that the Brecks might be suitable. He wrote that this might be due to the breeding season being in the middle of winter. A pair shot at Blickling in July 1855 and three pairs shot at Yarmouth in May 1856 could have been breeding birds. Despite good numbers occurring in 1853–54 (five pairs were shot at Bowthorpe alone) and 1861, it was not until 1889 that nesting was again noted. In that year many pairs were said to have bred in Breckland with one man taking six clutches of eggs, while other pairs bred in south-west Norfolk. Following the irruption in 1909 (said at the time to have been the greatest ever) the Crossbill became a familiar bird in Breckland with many nests being found in shelter-belts of Scots pines during the early months of 1910.

According to Riviere Crossbills then nested annually until 1923. Another large irruption was noted in 1925 followed by a further increase in the breeding stock during 1926. This demonstrates the cyclic pattern of numbers present with the population being replenished by immigrants during invasions. This is followed by a gradual decline in the succeeding years until the next invasion augments the local population which is thought not to be self-sustaining. Between the two World Wars a succession of highly skilled egg collectors patrolled the roads edged with shelter belts around Thetford periodically pausing to point out Crossbills' nests at the ends of projecting branches and excitedly instructing more agile companions to examine them. Eggs may be found and occasionally young have left nests in Breckland before mid-January. At times eggs must have been laid by mid-December. End-of-year nesting might include young Crossbills breeding in the same year in which they were hatched. Even in the most severe winters broods of young have been found in February. Collectors have described some hen Crossbills sitting so tightly that it became impossible to lift them off the nest. One sitting bird even stayed put under a blanket of snow. In the 1930s, the conifer plantations around Thetford were maturing and expanding to produce a much greater area of suitable pine forest. The Norfolk Atlas recorded Crossbills away from Thetford Forest around Dersingham, Sandringham and Wolferton, at Holkham Meals and along the Cromer to Holt Ridge. In east Norfolk, breeding has been noted occasionally at Fritton, Herringfleet and Ormesby (where there were two pairs in 1967).

Since the invasions of 1898 (when up to 32 were taken in the first week of August to a Yarmouth taxidermist) and 1909, there have been notable invasions in 1925, 1927, 1953, 1962, 1963, 1966, 1977, 1985, 1990, 1991 and 1997. During an irruption year the first birds generally begin to appear in May and June with movements continuing until the autumn. Coniferous woodlands are an obvious magnet but roaming flocks of tired migrants can be encountered in the strangest of places. New arrivals have occasionally been noted feeding on thistles, yellow-horned poppies, Alexander seeds, grubs extracted from galls on poplars and spilt grain, and have been seen drinking in house gutters as well as the more usual pools and puddles.

Large flocks encountered through the years have included 100 at High Kelling in May 1959, 70 at Holkham in August 1966 and 100 at Santon Warren in April 1981. The large invasion of 1990 took place from mid-June onwards with new birds arriving until the end of the year and records came from 78 separate localities. Flocks in excess of 40 were noted at Bacton, Craymere Beck, Felbrigg, Holkham, Holme, Holt Lowes, Lynford (130), Sandringham (220 in September), Santon Downham (200 in October), Swanton Novers, Thetford Warren and Wolferton. The year 1991 was equally noteworthy with numbers remaining high and records from over 70 sites including large flocks in May at Thetford (300), Lynford (100) and Holkham Meals (85). Surprisingly no breeding records were received. In 1992 however, pairs bred at Holkham Meals, they were widespread in the Brecks with 25 singing males in the Lynford and Mundford area and birds were present at Holme and Sheringham. By 1996, the breeding population was at a very low ebb with only eight or nine singing males located.

The summer of 1997 produced another influx with records from many localities from 24th June onwards, with 60 at Strumpshaw, 70 at Thorpe and 30 at Docking on that date and 100 at Swanton Novers on 3rd July. Flocks in diminishing numbers were recorded into the spring of 1998. The marked tailing off in records from Thetford Forest in April possibly indicated a return of birds to the Continent. However, birds remained widespread during May including over 160 at Sandringham, 120 in Sheringham Park and over 100 at Lynford.

About 60 Crossbills had been ringed in the county prior to 1997 of which 43 were caught in 1990. However, by specifically targeting the species in 1997, nearly 130 were ringed in that year, the majority in Breckland. Whereas previously there had been only one recovery – a bird ringed at Swaffham Heath in June 1982 controlled at Fowlmere on 12th August 1983, two more controls have resulted from the 1997 ringing; one only 10km from the site of ringing, but the other at West Blean Woods, Kent the following May.

*Andrew Bloomfield & Peter Dolton*

# Parrot Crossbill                                          *Loxia pytyopsittacus*

**A rare vagrant, with exceptional numbers during the irruption of 1990; bred in 1984 and 1985.**

The Parrot Crossbill, like the Common Crossbill, is normally a resident species subject to irruptive movements depending upon food availability. Due, however, to its smaller population size this seems to happen less frequently. It is a vagrant to the British Isles that breeds in mature pine forests in Norway, Sweden, Finland and Russia. During years with poor crops of pine cones, irruptions occur and Parrot Crossbills are noted further south and west than normal. Notable influxes to the British Isles have occurred in both 1982–83 and 1990–91. Norfolk fared well and even managed to attract Britain's first breeding birds in 1984 and 1985.

The first Norfolk record dates back to 1851 when a male was shot at Riddlesworth. On 22nd March 1888 two females were shot from a group of seven at Earlham and have been preserved at the Castle Museum, Norwich. Another specimen was obtained, a male, at Langham in September 1907. There were no further records until the Crossbill influx of 1966 when a male was at the Wells end of Holkham Meals on 10th–12th November. During a mini invasion of Parrot Crossbills into Britain in the autumn of 1982, a male again at the Wells end of Holkham Meals on 16th–17th October was the only accepted record, despite several other claimed sightings of the species in Norfolk. The following year, however, up to seven were found, again in the same general area of Holkham Meals, where they remained from 26th October to 20th November. A pair stayed to the year's end. As no other new arrivals had been noted in Britain in the autumn of 1983, it was thought that the group had probably lingered on from the 1982 influx, elsewhere in the British Isles.

In 1984, up to six Parrot Crossbills still remained around the beach car park at Wells where it soon became clear that a pair was beginning to indulge in breeding behaviour. In addition to the usual nesting materials such as twigs, moss, grass and feathers the female also lined the nest with a considerable amount of hair kindly trimmed off his beard by Bryan Bland, the well-known Norfolk birder! (Davidson 1985). The nest was situated high up in the canopy of a Corsican pine right beside the busy footpath and car park at Wells. From Britain's first two broods only one of four youngsters survived. In 1985, a pair once again returned to breed at Wells, the first nest as before in a Corsican pine adjacent to a busy footpath and the second also in close proximity to drinking water from puddles in the car park. Two broods were raised, from which four and two young fledged, respectively (Land & Lewis 1986). In June, the family minus one juvenile had moved to the western end of Holkham Meals. On 17th–18th July, a male and four juveniles were found at Cley and these were presumably the Wells birds. By August, a pair was again back at Wells where they stayed, along with two juveniles until October. Six Parrot Crossbills were found at Wolferton on 19th January 1986, where they remained until 26th January, on which date three reappeared in the Wells car park, building up to an impressive flock of twelve by early March. Despite a pair still being present on 4th May there were no further sightings and it seemed that Britain's first pioneer breeding colonists had finally deserted the area.

Following the large influx of Crossbills in 1990, Britain again experienced another arrival of Parrot Crossbills in the late autumn. The first birds of the influx were seen in the Upper Sheringham/Weybourne area on 13th October, where the species was seen intermittently until 8th December, peaking at nine on 24th October and 14 on 10th November. Other localities in the county shared in this irruption, with records from Babingley, Holme (4), Holkham, Lynford, Sprowston (3) and Stiffkey. Despite breeding occurring in the Suffolk Breckland there was no repeat of the 1984 and 1985 events in Norfolk.

*Andrew Bloomfield*

# Common Rosefinch                                     *Carpodacus erythrinus*

A very scarce vagrant.

Breeding across a large area from Fennoscandia and central Europe through Russia to the Pacific, the Common Rosefinch is a widespread species. It is a late migrant, arriving towards the end of May and beginning to leave in late July, thus spending most of the year in its Asian wintering areas or on migration. Once regarded as a rarity in the British Isles, numbers have increased steadily since the 1980s and now that sporadic breeding takes place, this bird is forecast to become a future colonist.

The first Norfolk and fourth British record was of a female netted on 3rd September 1892 on the North Denes, Yarmouth by a bird-catcher named Jessop. Remarkably it was kept alive in captivity by the Yarmouth taxidermist Walter Lowne until June 1896. A further 77 years were to pass before the next one, a juvenile, was found in the county, by Dave Holman and Norman Williams, at Blakeney Point on 19th August 1973, which remained until the following day. The next year a first-summer male sang from dense scrub at Walsey Hills, Cley on 26th May. A further four were recorded between 1975 and 1986, and the species has become annual since 1989. Since then an average of five have been reported each year with eight in 1991 and 1995, and nine in 1992.

Spring arrivals have peaked between the last week of May and mid-June with the earliest on 22nd May 1995 at Sheringham, and on 24th May 1991 and 25th May 1992, both at Holme. In 1995 a series of records from Winterton gave the first hint of possible breeding. After a single on 11th June, a minimum of two singing first-summer males and a female were present on 12th June, with a pair remaining until 5th July, during which time they were observed collecting nesting material. This has been the only occasion that Common Rosefinches have remained in the county for more than three to four days, the majority being seen on one day only.

Of the 57 Norfolk records, under a third have occurred in autumn of which most have been between late August and the third week of September. The earliest in autumn was on 19th August 1973 at Blakeney Point and the latest on 13th October 1993 at Overy Dunes and on 20th–24th October 1991 at Holme. The majority of records refer to single birds but two have been present at Holme, Warham Green and Blakeney Point, with three at Cromer on 9th June 1991, in addition to those mentioned earlier at Winterton. Apart from a red male ringed at Sheringham on 22nd May 1995, all records have referred to first-summer males (several of which have been singing), females or autumn immatures. Most of the birds have been recorded in north Norfolk, with twelve at Holme, 9 in the Blakeney/Cley/Salthouse area, eleven between Weybourne and Sheringham and 7 at West Runton/Cromer. A singing first-summer male at Hempstead on 23rd June 1995 is the only inland record. Seven have been ringed in the county, all since 1973.

*Steve Votier*

*MY GARDEN. CHEDGRAVE. ♀ 23-11-1999. ♂ 2-7-2000.*

## Bullfinch (Common Bullfinch)    *Pyrrhula pyrrhula*

**A common resident, which has declined, and scarce passage migrant.**

The Bullfinch breeds across most of the temperate Western Palearctic, extending eastwards as far as Japan. It is present throughout much of the British Isles, being absent only from the Outer Hebrides, the Northern Isles and the Isle of Man (New Atlas). Throughout much of its European range its abundance has remained unchanged. In the British Isles, however, a marked decline occurred in the 1980s, following an increase in numbers and an extension of its range, especially from the mid-1950s. The initial increase in abundance was attributed to the coincidental decline of its main predator, the Sparrowhawk (Newton 1993), since when the fortune of each species has been reversed.

Writing about the Bullfinch in 1866, Stevenson said 'So much has been written upon the destruction of buds in our gardens and orchards, by this species in particular . . .' From this it is apparent that the enmity between fruit growers and the Bullfinch has been going on for well over 100 years. However, the marked increase in numbers in Norfolk up to the mid-1960s was obviously causing major problems in commercial orchards. At that time, 500 Bullfinches were being trapped annually at a fruit farm at Great Hautbois and almost double that number at Westwick.

Despite the bright colour of the male, Bullfinches, which are often seen in pairs, tend to be inconspicuous and rather secretive. During the breeding season they are found in areas with dense cover, such as overgrown hedgerows, blackthorn thickets, churchyards and gardens, as well as along woodland edges and in young forestry plantations. During fieldwork for the Norfolk Atlas the species was recorded in 60% of the tetrads, being mainly absent from the Fens, open farmland and areas of grazing marshes. Since then the species has continued to decline, although the proportion of 1km squares covered in Norfolk in which it was found during the 1994–97 BBS has remained constant at 20–24%.

Bullfinches flock in winter and at their peak some very impressive numbers were recorded – 100 at Weybourne in December 1962 and 50 on Kelling Heath in 1963, while a 'remarkable number' were feeding in a carrot field at Blakeney on 29th January 1963, and 49 were picked up dead there the following day, presumably as a result of poisoning. In the early 1980s, large flocks were still being reported, such as 49, including only five females, at Ringstead on 8th January 1981. Since then many observers have commented on a reduction in the number of Bullfinches seen together and parties of 10–15 have been the exception rather than the rule, however, up to 30 were present at Ringstead in November–December 1996, 25 at Kettlestone Common on 26th September 1997 and 23 at Holkham Meals on 7th February 1998.

Bullfinches of the British race *P. p. pileata*, are usually sedentary, whereas the nominate race *P. p. pyrrhula*, breeding in northern Europe, is a partial migrant. Small numbers of Bullfinches, of indeterminate race, are recorded most autumns moving along the north Norfolk coast, such as twelve west at Sheringham on 4th November 1978, 8 west at Holkham and 6 west at Holme on 20th October 1990, and on the Wash 20 south at Snettisham on 22nd October 1995. At Holkham, birds have been seen to arrive from the sea and have also been found at Wells East Hills (Bloomfield 1993).

The first definite Norfolk record of the northern race *pyrrhula* was one shot by Arthur Smith on Yarmouth Denes on 22nd January 1893, the specimen is in the collection at the Castle Museum, Norwich. During the same year, Bullfinches were recorded on the Newarp light-vessel in March and the Outer Dowsing light-vessel in May. After 66 years, on 11th November 1959, Norfolk's second northern race

Bullfinch, a male, was seen at Blakeney and the third was ringed at Holme on 2nd November 1968. Perhaps as a result of increasing observer awareness and skill, northern Bullfinches were recorded in the county each year from 1994 to 1996. In 1994, when many *pyrrhula* race birds were trapped in Shetland, Yorkshire and a few in Suffolk, one to three were seen in October at six coastal localities between Holme and Winterton, 29 flew south at Hunstanton on 2nd November, two were at Beeston Regis Heath on 27th November and 13–15 were seen by many observers at Lynford Arboretum in December. The following year, at least four remained at Lynford Arboretum in the early months and one was seen at Overstrand on 30th December, where more were noted in January. During the autumn of 1996, singles were present at Holme and Sheringham, and four at Titchwell.

Over 3,500 Bullfinches have been ringed in Norfolk. Recoveries within the county have involved movements from South Runcton to Burnham Overy and from Sheringham to Fakenham, while another ringed at Sheringham on 5th November 1976 was recovered at Leiston, Suffolk the following March. One ringed in October 1961 at Sandwich Bay, Kent was recovered at Flitcham the following April; one ringed at Little Hallingbury, Essex in December 1971 was found at Forncett End in May 1972 and one ringed at Gibraltar Point, Lincolnshire in December 1970 was controlled on the other side of the Wash at Holme, two years later.
*Moss Taylor*

## Hawfinch        *Coccothraustes coccothraustes*

**A scarce resident and rare passage migrant.**

Patchily distributed across the Palearctic, the Hawfinch is found in a wide range of habitats that provide a supply of large seeds, from Britain eastwards to Japan. It is found across the whole of Europe, except for Ireland, northern Fennoscandia and parts of Spain and Italy. It has a very localised distribution in Britain with a concentration in south-east England (New Atlas). Since the 1960s there has been an increase over much of its range but by contrast the British population has shown a marked reduction. A comparison of the number of 10km squares in which the species was recorded between the two BTO Breeding Atlases showed a reduction of 30%. The decline was related to the destruction and fragmentation of deciduous woodland and the removal of old orchards (New Atlas).

Early writers considered the Hawfinch a rare bird in Norfolk, only appearing as an irregular migrant. Stevenson described a young bird, shot at Kimberley in 1856 (and which he acquired for his collection), as the first locally-bred example he had seen. However, by 1890 it was stated that it 'now nests regularly in various localities . . . and numbers seem to be on the increase'. During the 19th century large numbers appeared occasionally as winter visitors. The Pagets (1834) recorded 'a large flight' at Yarmouth in January 1823. The largest recorded influx took place during the severe winter of 1859–60 beginning in early December, survivors lingering until the first week of April 1860. Observations included a large flock arriving in an exhausted state in gardens at Yarmouth, while 40 specimens were received by one Norwich taxidermist (almost half had been obtained at East Carlton and Ketteringham). Further arrivals took place in 1872–73 when 60 were shot in and around Diss among yew trees and gardens stocked with bullaces. A further ten met their end at East Carlton. During November 1876, a total of 30 was taken in a single garden at Diss where the attraction was again yew berries. Many were reported in the county during November and December 1878 and in January 1881, when a Norwich bird-stuffer received 20 in a fortnight. The last recorded immigration was in 1889–90 when between 90 and 100 were handled by the three principal Norwich taxidermists. Hawfinches found garden peas irresistible and often met an untimely end at the hands of head gardeners in Victorian Norfolk. At Toftrees near Fakenham one exasperated gardener shot 15 during June 1896. The specimens found a ready sale in the local taxidermist's shop. Pashley (1925) also made reference to the Hawfinches destructive effect on peas and added that 'They are very often seen in a plum orchard at Blakeney in late summer and autumn'.

Nowadays, occurrences in Norfolk are widely spaced, with small numbers being recorded from many different localities. Where suitable woodland occurs (mixed broad-leaved, particularly hornbeam and cherry) Hawfinches may form small colonies, but most of Norfolk's birds breed in isolated pockets. The highly elusive nature of this enigmatic finch clouds its true status, but breeding has been confirmed at sites all across the county, with an even larger number of possible breeding attempts. During fieldwork for the Norfolk Atlas it was found in only 26 tetrads, the majority in Breckland. It was recorded in 21 of the 10km squares in Norfolk during fieldwork for the 68–72 BTO Atlas, in 16 for the Norfolk Atlas (1980–85) and in only twelve for the New Atlas (1988–91). Whilst being widely scattered, a number of traditional sites with relatively high concentrations of birds, provide a further indication of the trend in the county population. Large numbers were recorded at East Wretham in 1973, when 45 were seen during February. For the next twelve years large gatherings were reported from this site (peak totals being 183 in January 1975 and 151 in February 1980) roosting in hornbeams and birches, with regular breeding attempts. By 1986 only a handful of birds were using the site with the only significant count since then being 32 in March 1988. Holkham Park is also associated with Hawfinches where birds regularly winter and also small numbers breed. During the 1980s numbers varied considerably but counts of 25 in March 1984, 18 in February 1985 and 25 in March 1988 compare with peak counts during the 1990s of only ten in 1990, 1991 and 1996. During 1997 the only locality at which double-figure counts were recorded was Barnham Cross Common, peaking at 35 in February, 20 in March and up to 14 during the other winter months; while the only breeding season records were from Lynford Arboretum and Hilborough, where a pair bred success-fully. All these observations suggest that Norfolk Hawfinches are moving in the same downward direction as the rest of the British population. Other sites where Hawfinches have been regularly recorded in recent years have included Lynford Arboretum, Mundford and Thetford in the Brecks, Felbrigg and High Kelling in north Norfolk, and Costessey in central Norfolk, while 30–40 were at Melton Constable Park on 24th August 1990.

Small numbers of Continental Hawfinches undoubtedly pass through the county, but their true status is confused by the possible small-scale movement of breeding stock. Occasional records of young birds at coastal sites during the late summer seem to suggest some post-breeding dispersal, but such reports remain scarce. There have been a number of records of coastal migrants during the late autumn and early spring which fit into the pattern of Scandinavian immigrants seen annually in small numbers on the Northern Isles of Scotland. Most interesting were a series of records in autumn 1993 with one at Yarmouth on 30th October, two at Wells on 2nd November and one at Waxham on 4th November – all coinciding with an easterly airstream and other passerines arriving from the Continent, and in spring 1995 with singles at Holme on 22nd April, at Blakeney on 23rd April and at Yarmouth Cemeteries on 29th April. As with the birds breeding and wintering in Norfolk the picture is not well understood.

*Steve Votier*

# Black-and-white Warbler        *Mniotilta varia*

A very rare vagrant; two records.

Black-and-white Warbler
(Gary Wright)

A strikingly conspicuous North American wood warbler, the Black-and-white Warbler breeds in the east-ern USA and Canada and winters from south-eastern USA to northern South America. It is a very rare autumn vagrant to Britain with only one spring record.

A Black-and-white Warbler was seen in a mixed flock of tits and finches at How Hill, Ludham by M. R. McDonnell on 3rd December 1985. It was an addition to the county list and one of the highlights of the year. It remained in the area of Pigeon Wood until at least 15th December and was extremely agile and often elusive, only giving brief views. Over 2,000 people went to see it during its 13-day stay. It was photographed on 12th December as it fed out in the open for over an hour (McDonnell 1986).

Remarkably, given Norfolk's geographical position, a second bird was found in Whitlingham Lane, Trowse, Norwich, on 9th November 1996, remaining until 15th. This bird, aged as a first-winter male, kept close company with a roving flock of Long-tailed Tits and was as unexpected as the first one at How Hill.

*Peter Allard*

## Lark Sparrow                                 *Chondestes grammacus*

**A very rare vagrant; one record.**

The Lark Sparrow is a Nearctic seed-eater which breeds from central southern Canada across most of the USA, except for the eastern States, south to Mexico, and winters in the southern parts of its range. Small numbers also winter on the Yucatan peninsula suggesting that birds cross the Gulf of Mexico on migration. It is a very rare vagrant to the British Isles, with only one previous record – a bird in Suffolk in June–July 1981.

A Lark Sparrow in immaculate plumage, found at Waxham on 15th May 1991 by Barry Jarvis, remained until 17th May. A confiding individual, although occasionally elusive, it fed mainly in one area around the farmyard close to Waxham Great Barn (Anon 1992b).

*Peter Allard*

## White-throated Sparrow                       *Zonotrichia albicollis*

**A very rare vagrant; one record.**

The White-throated Sparrow breeds abundantly in North America from central and north-west Canada to Newfoundland, and in the extreme north-east USA. It winters in the eastern and south-western States of the USA south to Mexico. The species is a rare vagrant to the British Isles with about half the records in Scotland.

A first-winter male found by Harold Jenner remained at Herringfleet between 16th November 1968 and 1st January 1969 when it was found dead. The cause of death was pneumonia. This was the eighth occurrence for the British Isles. Originally a Suffolk record, but following boundary changes in 1974 which resulted in this portion of the parish of Herringfleet being included in Norfolk, it became an addition to the Norfolk list.

*Peter Allard*

## Lapland Bunting (Lapland Longspur)          *Calcarius lapponicus*

**A scarce winter visitor and passage migrant, mainly in autumn; three mid-summer records.**

The Lapland Bunting has a circumpolar distribution in the Arctic/alpine zones, breeding in areas of willow scrub and moss tundra largely above 60°N. The majority of the European population winters in the Ukraine and southern Russia, while some Greenland birds migrate south-eastwards to Europe. In the British Isles the small numbers of wintering birds are largely confined to the east coast from southern Scotland to Kent.

Stevenson knew of only two records, both taken alive. The first was caught at Postwick during severe weather on 26th January 1855. It survived in the aviary of John Henry Gurney until May 1856, assuming full summer plumage in both springs. It remains on display in the Castle Museum, Norwich. The second was netted at Crostwick in about March 1862 and was shown to the Zoological Society. The third example was also caught alive, and noticed in a cage with Skylarks on the market at Yarmouth on 24th December 1868. It survived for three years and proved to be a good songster (Allard 1990). This was one of only five records during the 30 years from 1862. In October and November 1892 the first of a series of major influxes began when over 50 examples were shot or netted at Yarmouth. Riviere reported that subsequently it became a regular winter visitor with particularly large numbers arriving in 1893, 1897, 1904, 1905 and 1922. During the following 40 years or so, there were further influxes in 1950, 1953, 1956,

1958, 1964 and 1965, with the largest party being 100 at Morston on 31st December 1956; with 50–100 in the same area in December 1958 and February 1959 (Seago 1967). Since then large numbers have occurred in a number of other years, including 1977, 1980, 1982, 1987, 1993 and 1995.

At least 150 birds were present along the north Norfolk coast in October 1977 and other recent peak numbers have included 130 at Halvergate Marshes on 27th January 1980, 100–120 at Burnham Norton in February 1982 and 125 on 22nd January 1987, and 53 in the Breydon area on 17th November 1987. In 1993 a total of 105 was spread over eleven sites with a similar figure of 100 at 21 sites in September 1995. In addition to the peak years, the Lapland Bunting has appeared annually along the north and east coasts of the county both on passage and as a winter visitor. Since 1953 records have come from nearly three dozen coastal localities stretching from Terrington in the west to Gorleston in the east.

Regular wintering on the Breydon/Halvergate Marshes began in 1960 with numbers increasing to a peak of 50 on 9th February 1964. Smaller parties wintered on these marshes throughout the 1970s with large numbers present again in 1980, with 85 on 20th January increasing to an exceptional 130 on 27th. Since then, although wintering annually until 1995–96, the only notable numbers have been up to 53 in November–December 1987 and 38 in December 1993. The rough marshes used regularly from the 1960s to the early 1980s have been ploughed and the short well-grazed ones appear to be unsuitable for Lapland Buntings. During the 1980s another favourite wintering site was the marshes at Burnham Norton where, in addition to the peak numbers mentioned above, counts have varied annually with 30–40 in December 1980, only twelve in March 1983, 80 in March 1985, 40 in November 1988 and a maximum of 20 during the 1992–93 winter.

In addition to their favoured coastal localities there have been a number of inland records. These have included twelve which flew over Holkham Lake on 22nd January 1956 and others, usually singles, at Welney, Cantley Beet Factory and Buckenham on a number of occasions. The species has also been recorded inland at Brundall, Burnham Market, Choseley, Colney Gravel Pits, Filby Broad, Fritton, Hassingham, Hickling, How Hill, King's Lynn Beet Factory, Martham Broad, Melton Constable, Pentney Gravel Pits, Potter Heigham, Rockland Broad, Strumpshaw, Thorpe and Wisbech Sewage Farm.

Lapland Bunting
(*Norman Arlott*)

The first birds have usually been noted by mid-September with the earliest dates being 30th August 1975 at Blakeney, 6th September at Cley (1957) and Holme (1995), 7th September at Cley (1956 and 1967) and 8th September at Winterton and Breydon (both 1968), Cley (1988) and Blakeney Point (1993). The main passage is from mid-September to the first half of November with the majority of sightings coming from the well-watched localities such as Holme, Cley, Weybourne, Sheringham and Winterton. For example, at Sheringham 16 were present on 17th September 1993 increasing to 32 by 30th with 13 still in the area on 5th November, while nine flew west on 6th December. In 1995 a similar pattern was recorded with birds passing from 10th September and with monthly maxima of 18 on 24th October and 16 on 9th November. In autumn 1977 at Winterton a total of 46 flew south from 14th September, including 14 on 29th October. Two years later at the same location 20 moved south on 29th and twelve on 30th September 1979, while in September 1993 a total of 30 birds was present.

Frequently some linger well into the spring by which time many of the males have assumed summer plumage. There have been a number of April records including a bird in song at Cley on 24th–26th April 1992. In May, Lapland Buntings have been seen at Weybourne (1963, 1981), Horsey (1973, 1982), West Runton (1977), Hunstanton Golf Course (1978), Titchwell (1980), Sheringham (1982, 1993), Cley/Salthouse (1982) and Blakeney Point (1988, 1989, 1990). The latest dates in the month have been 26th–27th May 1993 at Sheringham, 27th–29th May 1977 at West Runton and 29th May 1981 at Weybourne. A very late female was at Salthouse on 21st June 1981 and a first-summer male arrived from the west at Weybourne on the most unusual date of 4th July 1991, during a stiff easterly breeze. These last two records complete the calendar, with Lapland Buntings having been recorded in the county during every month of the year.

*Don Dorling*

## Snow Bunting

*Plectrophenax nivalis*

CLEY. (3) 7·10·1986.
BLAKENEY PoiNT (9 or 10) 9·10·1986.

**A fairly common winter visitor and passage migrant.** TITCHWELL. 26·11·1988.

The Snow Bunting, which is the most northerly breeding passerine, has a circumpolar breeding range in the Arctic/alpine zone. The southern limit of the European population extends to Iceland and southern Norway with small numbers breeding in most years on the Cairngorms in Scotland. The majority of birds move south for the winter, those in Europe usually to the coast of the North Sea coasts. It was originally thought that the British wintering birds were of the race *P. n. nivalis* coming from the Greenland and Scandinavian populations and that the Icelandic race *P. n. insulae* was largely sedentary. However, it is now known that two-thirds of the wintering birds in both Scotland and The Netherlands are *insulae*, a pattern followed in Norfolk.

In Stevenson's day the Snow Bunting was a regular winter visitor, numbers depending on the severity of the weather. Then, as now, the winter flocks were mainly distributed along the coast feeding on the seeds of various dune, shingle and saltmarsh plants. Their stay was generally between October and March but Stevenson included early arrivals at Waxham and Blakeney on 27th September in 1848 and 1854 respectively. The earliest date known to Patterson and Riviere was a bird at Belton on 11th September 1897. Since then even earlier arrivals of Snow Buntings have occurred – on 1st September at Winterton (1968), on 5th September at Holme, Blakeney and Cley (1971) and on 7th September at Yarmouth (1953), Blakeney and Cley (1968) and Holme (1968 and 1996). These early arrivals are usually only followed by small numbers until late October and early November when the main influx occurs, at which time small parties are noted flying in from the north-east or flying west along the north Norfolk coast.

Frequently in the past these winter visitors gathered in considerable flocks. Patterson (1905) mentioned that at times hundreds were netted and sent to the London markets. Some of the largest flocks reported in more recent times have been 650 on the Berney Marshes on 10th February 1963, 500 at Stiffkey on 14th December 1965, 500 at Cley in November 1967, 350 at Breydon in November 1961 and 350 at Blakeney Point on 9th December 1979. In the 1980s there were 300 at Titchwell in November and December 1984, 410 at Holkham on 29th November 1986 and 350 at Paston on 16th November 1988. Maximum numbers have continued to decline and it has been unusual for a party to exceed 100 during the 1990s; exceptions being 150 at Titchwell in 1993, 250 at Holme in January 1997 and 276 at Cley/Salthouse in November 1997. A survey of the intertidal habitat between Holme and Weybourne in November 1997 produced a total of about 600 which had decreased to 50 a month later.

The majority of Snow Buntings leave Norfolk at the end of March or in early April. A few linger with records during May, for example, at Hunstanton on 5th May 1979, Horsey on 13th May 1990, Winterton on 16th May 1976 and Breydon on 25th May 1983. Summer records are exceptional but have included a male in breeding plumage at Blakeney Point from 17th July to 21st August 1970, a female there in June 1986 and a female on the Eye Field, Cley on 5th–7th June 1989.

Although the majority of birds winter along the coast there are many inland records. The one on a grave-stone in Yarmouth Cemeteries on 10th November 1962 and the 95 seen at Halvergate Marshes were not far from their coastal haunts, but others have ventured or been blown much further away from the sea. For example, they have been recorded in the Broads at Hickling and in Breckland at Frog Hill on 6th December 1964 after a north-west gale, Barnham Cross Common where one to five were present from 7th January to 4th March 1973, and at Bexwell and Weeting. In the west of the county they have occurred at Welney, Wisbech Sewage Farm, Ten Mile Bank, Downham Market, West Acre, West Walton and Roydon Common. More centrally they have been seen at Coston, Cranwich, Watton and Elsing. In the east Snow Buntings have been reported at Buckenham in the Yare Valley on at least five occasions, also at Burgh Castle, Strumpshaw, Hassingham and nearer to Norwich at Old Catton where a single bird appeared on 9th March 1973 and another at Whitlingham Lane, Trowse on 13th November 1996.

Since 1991 considerable numbers of Snow Buntings have been ringed in Norfolk producing some very interesting results. The two races wintering in Britain have both been recognised; the darker birds from Iceland, *insulae*, and the paler Scandinavian *nivalis*. Initially the ratio between the races was 50:50 but it has subsequently followed the Scottish and Dutch pattern with 80–85% of the birds being Icelandic. Of these over 80% are females, mainly first-winter, with only three adult males being caught in three years (Atkinson 1993). In 1995 the majority of the wintering party at Salthouse were birds of the Icelandic race *insulae* and these had left by 23rd February leaving behind 15 birds of the race *nivalis* of Greenland or Scandinavian origin.

There is evidence of site loyalty with one bird ringed at Titchwell in February 1989 returning to Hunstanton exactly two years later, although one ringed at Hunstanton in January 1991 was found in The Netherlands in January 1993, and another ringed at Hunstanton in January 1993 was seen in The Netherlands in November. Moves in the reverse direction are demonstrated with birds ringed in Belgium and The Netherlands in December 1996 being seen at Holkham and Salthouse in January and February 1997, respectively. The longest movements have involved one ringed at Salthouse in December 1995 seen in Bremerhaven, Germany in January 1998 and another ringed at Hunstanton in January 1997 controlled at Akureyri, Iceland in February 1998. A number of reports of colour-ringed birds have involved Snow Buntings passing through the Grampian Highlands a few weeks before or after being seen in Norfolk in January. One particularly interesting multiple recovery concerned a bird ringed at Heacham in January 1996 which was seen on passage in Glen Coe, Highland Region on 7th May 1996 and on Harris, Western Isles two days later. Another ringed at Salthouse in January 1998 was controlled on Fair Isle on 25th March 1998. Mid-winter movements to Cleveland occurred in 1994, while one recorded at Salthouse in November 1993 was found at Foulness, Essex in January 1994. The rapid speed at which Snow Buntings move around is illustrated by one colour-ringed at Salthouse on 14th February 1997 and seen near Mablethorpe, Lincolnshire the next day.

*Don Dorling*

# Pine Bunting                                        *Emberiza leucocephalos*

**A very rare vagrant; one record.**

The breeding range of the Pine Bunting extends from the eastern parts of Russia eastwards across central Asia and Siberia, with the species wintering mainly in Pakistan, north-west India and northern China. It is a rare spring and autumn vagrant to the British Isles.

A male, probably first-winter, associating with Yellowhammers was found by Ricky Fairhead and Robert Wilton at Hopton on 28th October 1995. This bird was initially located just across the border into Suffolk, but became an addition to the county list when it finally flew across the road (and boundary) in the afternoon, to the delight of the gathered crowd (Fairhead & Wilton 1997).

*Peter Allard*

**Yellowhammer**   CHEDGRAVE MANOR. 9-1-2000. (♂)   *Emberiza citrinella*
                   SALTHOUSE HEATH. 23-6-1986.

**A common, but declining, resident and scarce passage migrant.**

The breeding range of the Yellowhammer extends across the upper and middle latitudes of the Western Palearctic, being absent only from Iceland, most of the Iberian peninsula and the Mediterranean islands. In the east of its range, in the Urals, it hybridises with the Pine Bunting. Apart from Britain, where it is sedentary, it is a partial short-distance migrant in most of its range. It breeds in open country throughout much of the British Isles, although it is absent or sparsely distributed on the higher ground in northern England, Wales, the uplands and islands of Scotland, and large areas of western Ireland (New Atlas).

It is a common resident in Norfolk, having been found in 89% of the tetrads for the Norfolk Atlas, being absent only from the Halvergate Marshes, the Fens and the more central parts of the City of Norwich. The fieldwork for the Norfolk Atlas was completed in 1985, since when a decline in the species has continued. This has been attributed to the change from spring to autumn-sown cereal, and the loss of stack-yards and hedgerows. Despite this, it can still be found in many types of open country within the county, such as heaths, commons, farmland and roadside hedges, young conifer plantations and along railway embankments. Counts of breeding pairs in recent years have included 22 at East Wretham Heath in 1995, and 15 at Flitcham and 25–30 in the Choseley/Titchwell/Thornham area in 1996. A dramatic decline has been noted in east Norfolk – a survey in 1960 of the immediate villages surrounding Yarmouth revealed at least 160 pairs, by 1996 only 19–20 pairs could be located. Also the area between Winterton and Hemsby held twelve pairs in 1995, but only six in 1996 and five in 1998. However, during the 1994–97 BBS, Yellowhammers have been found in 86–92% of the 1km squares covered in Norfolk, a remarkably constant figure.

In winter, Yellowhammers gather into feeding flocks mainly on stubbles and saltmarshes, although large flocks have become far less widespread in recent years, as fields of winter stubble have become less common. For example, very few were found on farmland in north-west Norfolk in the early months of 1996 despite extensive searching and none now winter on the Breydon and Halvergate Marshes. Nevertheless, some very impressive winter flocks have been located in recent years – 400 at North Walsham and 250 at West Bilney in 1991, 250 at Syderstone Common in 1992, 200 at Elsing in 1995, and 200 at Paston, 354 at Ringstead and 500 at Hindringham in 1996.

A small spring passage of Yellowhammers is generally recorded between mid-March and mid-April, involving a few birds only, the maximum day-count being 23 west at Sheringham on 26th March 1981. Autumn passage extends from early October to mid-November, again with only small numbers of birds being recorded. The highest counts have been 17 west at Weybourne on 22nd November 1988 and 20 west at Sheringham on 2nd October 1995. Observers at Hunstanton cliffs in October and November 1996, recorded a total of 59 flying south. Both Stevenson and Riviere mentioned occasional birds found at light stations in Norfolk and some of the migrants recorded nowadays may refer to birds from the Continent.

A leucistic Yellowhammer was recorded at Salthouse on 1st October 1989 and greyish individuals but with a faint yellowish wash were ringed at Sheringham in autumn 1977 and 1988.

Over 2,600 Yellowhammers have been ringed in Norfolk but only two have been recovered outside the county. One ringed at Salthouse on 10th October 1971 was recovered at North Somercoates, Lincolnshire on 28th January 1973. The other ringed at Waxham on 21st September 1974 was found in Zuid-Holland, The Netherlands on 3rd January 1976. Only two other British-ringed Yellowhammers have been recovered abroad, both in France. Another ringed at Boyton, Suffolk on 9th February 1969 was controlled at Blakeney Point on 4th May 1969.

*Moss Taylor*

## Cirl Bunting                                                 *Emberiza cirlus*

**A rare vagrant.**

The Cirl Bunting, a mainly resident species, breeds across Europe from Portugal in the west to Turkey in the east, extending as far north as France and in the south to the Mediterranean. Birds breeding in England are at the northern edge of their range where a marked contraction has taken place during the 20th century, probably due to climatic and agricultural changes. The current small British breeding population is mainly restricted to Devon. However, with careful management and conservation it has increased from 118 pairs in 1989 to 453 in 1998.

Stevenson gave two Norfolk records – one shot at an undisclosed locality in 1849 and a pair killed in 1855, one of which later came into the possession of the Earl of Leicester. This male is still in the Holkham collection and labelled 'shot Holkham' (Bloomfield 1993). Southwell recorded a further five specimens – two females netted by Edward Booth at Hickling in the autumn of 1875, two males killed near Breydon South Wall on 29th January 1888 (now at the City of Birmingham Museum) and another male shot at Holkham in January 1888 which is also in the Holkham collection. Riviere recorded that two were killed at Cley on 16th September 1904, and these were also noted by Pashley (1925), who stated that he had received 'six or seven', but gave no other details.

Since then the following have been recorded:

> 1936: Two at Hickling on 13th April
> 1953: A female at Salthouse on 29th October
>         A male at Wolferton on 14th December 1953
> 1954: Morston on 5th October
> 1968: A male in song at Neatishead from early May for some weeks
> 1969: A male with Yellowhammers on Halvergate Marshes on 23rd February

*Peter Allard*

# Ortolan Bunting

*Emberiza hortulana*

**A very scarce passage migrant.**

The Ortolan Bunting breeds in Fennoscandia and much of Continental Europe, although the distribution in the central part of its range is sparse and patchy. Since the 1950s there has been a steady decline in many parts of its range, particularly in north-western Europe. In France it is now confined to the southern half of the country, while it has not bred in The Netherlands since 1993. This contraction of its range appears to be associated with adverse changes in agricultural practices and hunting pressure in the south-west. It winters in sub-Saharan Africa, north of the Equator.

The first fully authenticated Norfolk record was of a bird netted at Yarmouth in April 1866 and kept alive for two days. Six more were caught on Yarmouth Denes on 5th May 1871 and the first autumn records were at Blakeney on 12th September 1884 and 5th September 1889. Riviere also knew of a further 20 September records, including six at Cley in September 1909. One shot at Cley on 13th November 1899 remains the latest date for the county.

Since 1950 there have been 45 records in spring and 168 in autumn, but with a marked decline in autumn numbers during the last three decades as shown in Table 44.

**Table 44. The number of Ortolan Buntings recorded in spring and autumn in Norfolk during the last five decades.**

|        | Spring | Autumn |
|--------|--------|--------|
| 1950s  | 7      | 59     |
| 1960s  | 4      | 53     |
| 1970s  | 8      | 24     |
| 1980s  | 18     | 11     |
| 1990s  | 8      | 21     |

With one exception, the frequency of spring records has not changed during the last five decades, with no more than two Ortolan Buntings being recorded annually. The exception was the period 1983–85, when a total of 13 was found in May. In each of these years, this month was characterised by cold, wet weather often associated with north-easterly winds and these conditions no doubt accounted for the four to five Ortolan Buntings each spring. The arrival date of two-thirds of the 42 spring records has fallen within the first 15 days of May. The earliest have been at Cley on 21st April 1984 and Salthouse Heath on 22nd April 1957, and the latest in spring at Cley on 30th May 1994. Spring birds are far more widespread than in autumn, although including Salthouse Heath all have been at coastal sites. In north Norfolk, Holme has claimed the most spring records with six, while several sites between Weybourne and Paston have hosted the species. In east Norfolk, the species has been found at five localities, with four sightings in the Horsey area.

Despite the marked increase in observer coverage in recent years, the decreased abundance in autumn, compared with the 1950s and 1960s, is clearly a reflection of the species decline in western Europe. Cley and Blakeney Point have always been the best places in the county to find Ortolan Buntings. In 1955, out of an autumn total of 14, no less than 13 were seen on Blakeney Point, including five on 8th September. In 1956 a total of 16 was found between Blakeney Point and Salthouse, including up to eight daily from 30th August to 4th September and up to five on 8th–14th September. The only others in the county were four between Morston and Stiffkey on 21st September. An autumn total of twelve in 1958, included six between Blakeney Point and Cley on 2nd–6th September. At this time, the species was clearly a regular autumn migrant in small numbers. The only other year in which good numbers of Ortolan Buntings were recorded in Norfolk was 1968, with an autumn total of 20. Once again, Blakeney Point had the majority with peaks of three to four on 24th August and six on 14th September, but there were also four at Holkham Meals on 1st September. Since then, no more than two have been seen together in the county.

Since 1950, despite the change in the numbers of Ortolan Buntings, the timing of their autumn passage through the county has remained the same, with the majority of birds appearing between the last week of August and the end of September. The two earliest have been on Blakeney Point on 13th August 1977 and 14th August 1976. There have been four October records: two singles on 4th, one at Blakeney

Point on 16th October 1985 and one at Holme on 25th October 1981. The latest date since 1900 was one at Weybourne on 7th November 1970. Three Ortolan Buntings have been ringed in Norfolk: singles at Cley, Waxham and Happisburgh.

*Moss Taylor*

## Yellow-browed Bunting     *Emberiza chrysophrys*

**A very rare vagrant; one record.**

The Yellow-browed Bunting is restricted as a breeding species to a relatively small area in central Siberia east of Lake Baikal and winters in south-east China. it is a very rare autumn vagrant to the British Isles with only four records.

An immature or female was found at Holkham Meals by Mike Parker, Dave Holman and John Kemp on 19th October 1975, the highlight of a vintage month for Siberian vagrants (Kemp 1990). It is almost certainly the most easterly-distributed passerine to have occurred in the British Isles. It was an addition to the British List and arrived during the same period as a Black-throated Thrush, Isabelline Shrike and Olive-backed Pipit – each new to the county list and all appearing in the Holkham Meals area.

*Peter Allard*

## Rustic Bunting     *Emberiza rustica*

**A rare spring and autumn vagrant.**

The Rustic Bunting breeds across the entire European and Asian boreal zone, from eastern Norway east-wards to the Pacific. It winters mainly in eastern China, Korea and Japan (Vinicombe & Cottridge 1996). Its breeding range has been expanding since 1895, in recent years especially in Fennoscandia. This no doubt has accounted for the increase in the number of British records during the 1990s, which included 44 in 1993 and 22 in 1996, both years in which three were found in Norfolk.

The species was added to the Norfolk list in 1958, when a female was found on Blakeney Point by Peter Wolstenholme on 10th September; it was subsequently trapped and ringed. Since then the county total has risen to 14. With the exception of one at Horsey, all have occurred along the north coast between Holkham and Sheringham.

    1958: A female at Blakeney Point on 10th–13th September was trapped
    1972: A first-winter male at Wells on 17th–22nd October
    1975: Cley on 18th October
           A male at Cley on 19th–22nd October
    1985: A male at Salthouse on 16th May
    1987: A male at Cley on 23rd May
    1993: Horsey Gap on 15th–18th September
           Sheringham on 16th–17th September.
           Holkham Meals on 18th September
    1994: Salthouse on 22nd–23rd May
    1996: A first-winter female at Sheringham from 27th March to 1st April was trapped
           One, possibly a male, at Weybourne on 9th April
           A male in song at Kelling Water Meadows and later at Cley on 19th May
    1998: A female or first-winter at Stiffkey Fen on 4th October

Of the six spring records, four occurred in the period 16th–23rd May and were probably Scandinavian-bound birds brought across in easterly winds. The March and April birds were more likely to have been ones that had overwintered in the Western Palearctic and were returning north. The eight autumn records fall into two distinct periods: 10th–18th September (four) and 5th–22nd October (four); their arrival in the British Isles is almost certainly due to reversed migration.

*Moss Taylor*

# Little Bunting

*Emberiza pusilla*

**A rare autumn vagrant; three spring records.**

The Little Bunting breeds in the boreal and arctic zones from eastern Fennoscandia across northern Siberia to the Pacific, and winters in eastern Asia. During the 1930s, it spread westwards into Fennoscandia, especially Finland, and partly as a result of this it has become far more common as an autumn visitor to Britain in recent years.

The first Norfolk record was of a female shot at Cley on 19th October 1908 (Riviere). It remained an extreme rarity in the county until the early 1980s, with only a single record in each decade from the 1930s until the 1970s, when there was one in both 1976 and 1977. Since then the county total has risen to 31 and it has failed to appear in only five of the years since 1981. The best year was 1994 when four were found at scattered coastal localities between Overy Dunes and Winterton. The first 14 Norfolk records were all on the coast from Holkham east to Sheringham.

There have been just three spring records – at Cromer on 27th April 1991, a male in song at Holme on 25th–30th April 1995 and one in a garden at East Wretham on 20th–21st April 1997, the only inland record for the county. Presumably these are birds moving north having overwintered in France or Iberia. The earliest autumn record was at Blakeney Point on 5th September 1945 with the majority of birds arriving between mid-September and mid-October. There have been four November records – two on 1st–2nd, one on 6th November 1983 at Blakeney Point and the latest on 11th November 1984 at Holkham Meals. Most birds have occurred in north Norfolk, the first for the east of the county being at Yarmouth Cemeteries on 9th–10th September 1989. Three have been ringed in Norfolk, one at Sheringham in 1982 and two at Weybourne in 1998.

*Moss Taylor*

# Yellow-breasted Bunting

*Emberiza aureola*

**A very rare vagrant; four records.**

The Yellow-breasted Bunting's breeding range extends from Finland eastwards through Russia, Siberia and into Japan. It winters in India and south-east Asia. The species is a rare, but almost annual vagrant to the British Isles. The majority of the records have been in Shetland in autumn.

The first British record of this bunting, an immature female, was obtained by E. C. Arnold at Cley on 21st September 1905. It is still in the collection at the Castle Museum, Norwich. A second bird, also an immature female, was shot at Wells Marshes on 5th September 1907. This was the second British record and is in the Holkham Hall collection. Another specimen can also be seen in the Holkham collection, although no date or location is indicated; it is highly likely to be of local origin. The next was obtained at Cley on 4th September 1913, an immature bird, also shot by E. C. Arnold. More recently, a female or immature was at Holme on 19th–20th September 1992 (Hibberd 1992).

*Peter Allard*

# Reed Bunting

HARDLEY FLOODS. ♂. 29·5·2000.

*Emberiza schoeniclus*

**A common resident and fairly common passage migrant.**

The Reed Bunting breeds throughout the middle, upper and lower latitudes of the Western Palearctic. In Britain and Ireland it is a very widely distributed bird of wetlands, arable farmland and young forestry plantations, although it is generally absent from the higher upland areas, especially in Scotland (New Atlas).

Stevenson commented that the Reed (or Black-headed Bunting) was a striking looking resident bird breeding in the wetlands of Norfolk, especially the Broads. He noted that in winter it was more widely spread across farmland, especially around stack-yards and farm buildings.

The breeding range of this species in Norfolk is still largely related to wetland areas in similar localities to the Sedge Warbler. It has also been noted in young conifer plantations, along dry ditches and rape fields (Kelly 1986). The male's rather monotonous short song can be commonly heard in reedbeds, along reedy dykes, rivers and around gravel pits. Reed Buntings were recorded in 33% of the tetrads covered for the

Norfolk Atlas, with confirmed breeding in one third of these. Results from the 1994–97 BBS showed that 22–32% of the 1km squares visited in Norfolk held Reed Buntings. The periphery of the county, especially the west, north and east (the Broads) hold the most important concentrations for this species. In north Norfolk 106 pairs were present at Brancaster Harbour and 57 at Scolt Head, all in *Suaeda*, in 1997, while Blakeney Point has attracted 20 pairs and others breed along the north coast saltings. A large summer concentration is known in the Fens at Welney where 50 pairs have been plotted and elsewhere inland at least 15 pairs were present at the Stanford Training Area in 1997. It is also occasionally heard in spring singing in agricultural land some distance from any substantial areas of water.

Although changes in Reed Bunting populations in Norfolk are largely unknown, it is likely that numbers of breeding birds have declined in line with other parts of the British Isles (a 60% decline from 1969 to 1994, as shown by the BTO Common Birds Census). Long-term declines are probably due to the draining of wetlands and grazing marshes (so numbers and distribution will almost certainly have declined since Stevenson's time) and the intensification of agriculture. Cold winters result in short-term declines.

**Reed Bunting**
*(Norman Arlott)*

Reed Buntings tend to winter in small flocks in wetlands and on farmland. Stubble fields were greatly favoured. However, the switch from spring-sown to autumn-sown cereals has almost removed stubble from the landscape. The country-wide distribution appears similar to that during the breeding season. Flock sizes are usually less than 50 birds, although 170 were present at Thetford in January 1993 and 100 at Ringstead on 27th January 1998. A decrease since 1989 is very apparent in the Halvergate and Breydon Marshes – where formerly large flocks were seen in winter, only ones and twos are now present. Winter flocks feed on the seeds of grasses and other herbaceous plants, at or near the ground. It is the feeding habitat which makes the birds so susceptible to severe winters, especially when snow covers feeding areas for long periods. Nowadays, belts of saltmarsh *Suaeda* have proved to be a very important habitat for this species. A survey of all intertidal habitat between Holme and Weybourne in November–December 1997 found a total of 473, including 115 at Scolt Head and at 108 Blakeney Point. Reed Buntings have long been known to visit gardens at this season; numbers appearing at feeding stations are on the increase. At Martham, for example, millet sprays attached to the branches of a weeping willow have attracted up to ten birds at a time.

In autumn, from September to early November, there is usually a light passage of birds along the coast. Nowadays numbers rarely exceed 50 in a day at any locality, whereas 120 were present at Winterton on 2nd October 1969. The autumn total at Hunstanton cliffs in 1997 was 87 south, peaking at 31 on 18th October; while a 'fall' occurred on the north coast in late September-early October 1998 with peak counts on Scolt Head of 80 on 28th September and 120 on 5th October. Some of these birds will have come from northern Europe and while some stay in this country others continue further south in Europe. In contrast, spring passage appears to be virtually non-existent. British Reed Buntings are largely sedentary. Ringing results show about 40% of females and 80% of males move no further than 5km between summer and winter (Winter Atlas).

Over 2,500 Reed Buntings have been ringed in Norfolk, but none has been recovered outside the British Isles. However, one ringed on the Channel Island of Jersey on 7th January 1976 was controlled at Titchwell almost exactly a year later. Birds ringed in Norfolk in autumn or winter have been recovered in Suffolk, Essex and Buckinghamshire, while a male ringed at Winterton on 9th September 1973 was controlled at Budleigh Salterton, Devon on 17th November and then at Lisburn, County Antrim on 5th January 1976, a most extraordinary multiple recovery. Other notable movements have included one ringed at Greater Manchester on 30th March 1974 recovered at Bradwell in January 1980, and another ringed at Farlington Marsh, Hampshire on 27th October 1982 was controlled at Cantley exactly one year later.

*Nick Carter*

## Black-headed Bunting | *Emberiza melanocephala*

**A very rare vagrant; one record.**

The Black-headed Bunting breeds from eastern Italy eastwards to Iran and winters in northern and central India. It is an almost annual vagrant to the British Isles, appearing primarily in late spring. Small numbers are kept in captivity but most records, especially of immature birds, are considered to be genuine wild vagrants.

A first-summer male found by G. J. White frequented coastal fields between Salthouse and Cley from 30th April to 3rd May 1979. A highly mobile and vocal first-winter bunting present at Blakeney Point on 10th–11th September 1989 was either this species or a Red-headed Bunting.

*Peter Allard*

## Corn Bunting | *Miliaria calandra*

**A scarce, and declining, resident and very scarce passage migrant.**

The Corn Bunting is a widespread species, occurring from the Canary Islands in the west to central Asia in the east but does not reach further north than Denmark. In the British Isles the Corn Bunting's range formerly included most of Scotland, Wales and Ireland but range contraction during the 20th century has left a fragmented distribution centred in southern and central England (New Atlas).

The Corn Bunting is a breeding bird of open farmland and one would expect it to be common in the prairie cereal farmland of Norfolk. However, range contraction at the national level has been mirrored by fragmentation of the range in Norfolk. Formerly Corn Buntings were generally distributed, though not particularly common in Norfolk (Stevenson) but during the early 1900s they started to disappear from many eastern districts and by the 1960s were virtually confined to the coast and Fens (Seago 1977). Jim Vincent's Hickling diaries recorded a flock of 200 on 21st January 1923 'the largest number I have seen for a long time'. In 1971 there were 30 singing males along the coast between Holme and Mundesley. By the time of the Norfolk Atlas only 8% of tetrads were occupied, these being just inland of the north-west coast and patchily in south-west Norfolk and in the Fens (Kelly 1986). Four pairs at Caister in the 1970s had disappeared by 1990 (Allard 1990). During the 1994 and 1995 BBS, Corn Buntings were recorded in 10–12% of the 1km squares visited in Norfolk, but none was located in 1996 and it was found in only 7% of the squares in 1997. In 1996 there were 15 pairs in the coastal hotspot around Choseley/Titchwell/Thornham, with another 30 singing males in the Fens and around the coast. The highest breeding concentrations in 1997 were 20 pairs at Feltwell/Brandon Creek and seven at East Ruston/Happisburgh.

In the early years of the *Norfolk Bird Report* Corn Buntings were rarely reported, probably owing to their 'common' status rather than any sparcity of records. Later issues contained only details concerning winter flocks. Corn Buntings in Britain are sedentary or partially migratory, forming flocks from the end of the breeding season until the following April (BWP). Most reports of winter flocks involved 50–65 birds with only a few of 100 or more, such as 250 at Lynn Point in February 1984, 340 at Denver Sluice in February 1991 but absent the next day and 172 at Choseley in February 1994. At Ringstead up to 75 were present in February 1996 and 1997, 60 at Lynn Point and Welney in 1996, and 90 at Feltwell in 1997. However, a flock of 309 feeding on stubbles at Welney on 13th January 1997 may indicate a reversal of the downward trend. There are few records of birds on passage owing to the sedentary nature of British Corn Buntings and less than 50 have been ringed in the county in recent years.

*Simon Gillings*

# CATEGORY D SPECIES AND A SELECTED LIST OF CATEGORY E SPECIES

*by*

## Peter Allard

Until 1993 the annual *Norfolk Bird Report* did not publish records of species which were considered to have escaped from captivity or which had been intentionally released into the wild. However, there had been exceptions to this practice which included certain Category D species and others such as Demoiselle Crane and Northern Bobwhite. Since 1993, an attempt has been made to address the increasing number of escapees in the county and the *Norfolk Bird Report* now annually carries a section on selected introductions, hybrids, escapes and feral species occurring in Norfolk.

## CATEGORY D

These are species for which there is reasonable doubt that they have ever occurred in a natural state in the British Isles (this excludes the Republic of Ireland). The number of species in Category D has been reduced by the BOU following a revision of the categories in 1997. Records of the following Category D species relate to Norfolk; in addition, Dark-eyed Junco and Indigo Bunting are included here as the Norfolk records of these two species have been placed in Category D.

## White Pelican (Great White Pelican)        *Pelecanus onocrotalus*

The White Pelican is one of the rarest breeding species in the Western Palearctic, being confined to the wetlands of Romania, Greece, Albania and Turkey. In autumn birds move south to Egypt and East Africa where they spend the winter. Although widely kept in captivity, it is a long-distance migrant and genuine vagrancy could occur.

Riviere referred to the discovery of a Pelican's humerus in the peat of Feltwell Fen, suggesting the possibility that this bird may at one time have been an inhabitant of East Anglia. He also mentioned that Sir Thomas Browne (1835–36) stated that he had in his collection 'an onocrotalus or pelican shott upon Horsey Fenne 1663, May 22 . . . a fowle wh' none could remember upon this coast. About the same time I heard one of the King's pellicans [*sic*] was lost at St. James', perhaps this might bee the same.'

The first dated record during the 20th century involved a White Pelican which was seen to fly in off the sea and settle on Breydon mudflats on 21st July 1906 during a spell of very warm weather. It departed eastwards the following day. A White Pelican in Kent from late July to October the same year was possibly the same individual. Another was seen on Breydon on 24th September 1915. This bird on being disturbed rose to a great height and flew away to the north-east. One also appeared on Breydon in the summer of 1935. An adult visited Scroby Sands off Yarmouth on 9th–10th July 1964 and arrived at Breydon on 15th where it remained until 31st January 1965. It was later found dead on the River Thet at East Harling on 20th February 1965. This bird was initially quite approachable and was photographed by the writer. A party of three, all adults, arrived on Breydon in a very tired state on 31st August 1971 and remained there until 2nd September. Finally, an adult was present on Lound Waterworks on 13th July 1989 and stayed to at least 23rd, occasionally visiting the adjacent Fritton Lake.

## Greater Flamingo        *Phoenicopterus ruber*

The Greater Flamingo is usually regarded as an escape in this country, but vagrancy is possible. There are two distinct populations, those in the western Mediterranean area are mainly resident, wintering in the Camargue and North Africa, while birds breeding from the eastern Caspian population migrate southwards to Iraq, Kuwait and coastal Arabia.

Early Norfolk records of flamingos from 1902 onwards (the first was shot in the Wash on 22nd November that year) were poorly documented and failed to eliminate other species of flamingo. Riviere recorded seven such examples, but all were considered to have escaped from collections. Escaped flamingos, are still a feature at the present time.

TITCHWELL - 23·6·1986 AND 24·5·1987.

However, there are two records of Greater Flamingo which could relate to wild individuals. The first, an immature, probably a first-winter bird, appeared at Breydon on 5th–6th October 1990. This bird was not ringed and later moved through Suffolk into Kent. The Camargue population had exceptional breeding success in 1990.

A second wanderer also of unknown origin and previously present in Kent from October 1994 visited Breydon on 15th–25th May 1995 and again on 22nd–29th April 1996. It was at Titchwell and Thornham Harbour next day, remaining until 4th May. In 1997, it again visited Breydon (from Kent) on 28th July, was at Hickling the next day and Titchwell from 30th July to 7th August, revisiting Breydon on 8th August. Again in 1998, in exceptionally mild conditions, it appeared at Breydon after leaving its south coast haunts on 14th–18th February and visited Hickling from 21st February to 1st March. Another at Breydon on 4th August 1998, which was still present into 1999, was traced to having escaped from Belfast Zoo, reaching Norfolk via Cheshire.

More remarkable, Taylor (1987a) included 12 Greater Flamingos circling offshore at Weybourne on 14th July 1980. Later in the afternoon 12 flew west at Sheringham, while local fishermen reported seeing a party of 34, about 6km offshore. Unfortunately, details were never submitted to the BBRC. In addition, an adult at Weybourne on 2nd January 1993 was later found dead at Sheringham.

## Falcated Duck                                                      *Anas falcata*

The Falcated Duck breeds in the southern half of Siberia, west to the Angara basin, south to Mongolia, China and Japan and north to Sakhalin and the Kuril Islands. It winters over much of eastern Asia, extending as far west as India and Nepal. This species is common in captivity and the possibility of escapes is always present. Although unlikely, a natural occurrence cannot be ruled out and the species is included in Category D. There are four records which could relate to one wandering individual.

An adult drake Falcated Duck was identified by John Kemp at Welney in company with Wigeon on 9th–10th December 1986 and was seen again on 27th December. What was presumably the same bird reappeared at Welney on 20th August 1987 and remained until 8th October. Another, or the same drake, joined Wigeon at Cley on 7th–15th May 1988 and appeared again at Cley the following spring and remained with Wigeon on 11th–28th May 1989.

## Baikal Teal                                                        *Anas formosa*

The Baikal Teal is a widespread species, formerly extremely abundant and found across eastern Siberia, breeding from the Angara River east to Kamchatka and also the Arctic coastline in the north, to the shores of Lake Baikal in the south. Extensive shooting on wintering grounds in Japan has drastically reduced the population. A relatively common species in captivity and despite being a long-distance migrant, the chances of natural vagrancy are considered very slim. The species is placed in Category D with ten British records.

A drake Baikal Teal of unknown origin, full-winged and in perfect condition, was shot by Mr G. Cain at Wells on 21st December 1929. The specimen is at the Castle Museum, Norwich.

## Saker (Saker Falcon)                                               *Falco cherrug*

The Saker is a large falcon breeding in south-eastern Europe and throughout most of central and southern Asia to Mongolia and central China. In winter, the majority move into north-east Africa.

Sakers, together with Lanners *F. biarmicus*, are extremely popular with falconers and many dealers interbreed them producing a large number of variable hybrids. Although genuine vagrancy is possible, it is believed that almost all records in the British Isles have related to escapes from captivity.

The first published record of a Saker in Norfolk was one seen over the sea at Sheringham on 23rd October 1990 heading west and later coasting in at Weybourne. Others have been recorded at Holkham on 17th October 1995 and again at Sheringham on 23rd September 1996. The remaining published records have referred to individuals wearing jesses and bells, while several, including one at Burnham Overy Dunes on 7th August 1993, have displayed features of both Saker and Lanner.

## Dark-eyed Junco                                                    *Junco hyemalis*

The Dark-eyed Junco is a Nearctic species breeding abundantly in coniferous forests across the whole of northern North America, from Alaska and Canada to Newfoundland and wintering in the south of its range. Formerly named the Slate-coloured Junco, it is a rare vagrant to the British Isles, mainly in spring.

One was caught exhausted on an oil supply vessel alongside the Shell Bravo gas platform 49/26T in the Lemon Bank gas field 55km east-north-east of Happisburgh on 24th May 1980. It was transported by helicopter and identified at the Castle Museum, Norwich, on 28th May. Watched by over 50 birders, it was released at Holme Reserve on 31st May where it remained until at least 6th June.

## Chestnut Bunting                                          *Emberiza rutila*

The Chestnut Bunting breeds in southern, central and south-eastern Siberia and migrates south-west to winter in Burma, southern China and south-east Asia. It is a long-distance migrant and despite being relatively uncommon in captivity in Britain, all previous British records have been admitted to Category D.

A male Chestnut Bunting was found at Salthouse on 30th May 1998 by Duncan Macdonald. It was only the sixth to be found in the British Isles. It frequented a garden in the village and remained until 1st June giving admirers and photographers excellent views during its stay. Its origin will never be known for certain, but its arrival coincided with other eastern migrants following north-easterly winds (Macdonald & Wessels 1998).

## Red-headed Bunting                                    *Emberiza bruniceps*

The Red-headed Bunting breeds in central Asia and Kazakhstan in a wide area between the Caspian Sea and the Altai Mountains. It winters in Pakistan and northern India. Large numbers were imported into the British Isles and other European countries in the late 1950s and 1960s, but since then, numbers in captivity have decreased. Its status is difficult to assess, but most, if not all, county records probably relate to escapes. All 12 records, however, fall in the spring passage period from 2nd May to 27th June.

The first was an adult male at Cley on 5th June 1960 identified by Billy Bishop, S. Jones and P. New. Since then a total of 12 has been recorded in the county:

> 1960: An adult male at Cley on 5th June
> 1961: An adult male at Cley on 2nd–3rd May, was ringed by Cley Bird Observatory
> An adult male at Salthouse on 13th–14th May
> An adult male on Breydon Wall on 13th and 20th May
> 1963: A male at Scolt Head on 22nd May
> A female at Ormesby St Michael on 27th June. It was found dead next day and is now at the Castle Museum, Norwich
> 1964: An adult male on Corton light-vessel, 10km off Hopton, on 17th June
> 1965: A male at Cley from 14th May to 7th June
> 1966: A male at Blakeney on 6th June
> 1977: A male at Sheringham Golf Course on 16th May
> 1982: A male at Holme on 18th-22nd May, presumably the same at Thornham Point, Titchwell on 27th–29th May
> 1986: A male at Thornham Point, Titchwell on 1st–11th June

## Indigo Bunting                                          *Passerina cyanea*

The Indigo Bunting is a Nearctic species breeding chiefly in eastern and central USA and wintering from Mexico to Panama and the Caribbean. Relatively small numbers are kept in captivity in Britain. The species was recently admitted to Category A of the British List on the basis of a bird on Ramsey Island, Wales in October 1996. The remaining few records are held in Category D.

An adult male Indigo Bunting was found by Mick Saunt at Holkham Meals on 21st October 1988. It remained in The Dell until 30th October. The bird attracted much interest and discussion relating to its abnormal moult, age and origin. Its arrival coincided with that of three other Nearctic passerines – a Cliff Swallow *Hirundo pyrrhonota* in Cleveland, Northern Waterthrush *Seiurus noveboracensis* in Lincolnshire and Northern Mockingbird *Mimus polyglottos* in The Netherlands (Williamson 1990). Despite the circumstantial evidence the record was placed in Category D in 1992, where it remains.

# CATEGORY E

These are species that have been recorded as introductions, transportees or escapees from captivity, and whose breeding populations (if any) are thought not to be self-sustaining. Many Category E species have been recorded in the wild in Norfolk and the list will obviously continue to increase as wildlife and waterfowl parks, and the keeping of exotic species by individuals, become more popular. The more interesting species have been included in detail. Some, such as the Purple Gallinule and Black Woodpecker are of historic interest, while Spotted Eagle and South Polar Skua have been included because of possible Norfolk connections (although the latter is not included in any BOU Category). Others such as Black Swan and Wood Duck need to be monitored carefully for possible future category changes. Also included in this section are two species, Hooded Merganser and Northern Mockingbird, which although included in the British List under Category A, are not believed to have been recorded in Norfolk in an apparently natural state.

## Pink-backed Pelican                                    *Pelecanus rufescens*

The Pink-backed Pelican is a subtropical and tropical African species with a breeding range extending from Senegal and Ethiopia to Natal and Botswana, and is an unlikely vagrant to Britain.

The first to be recorded in Norfolk was a subadult bird flying west at Holkham and Burnham Norton on 25th February 1989. It had been seen earlier at Radipole in Dorset and on 26th February it arrived at Skegness in Lincolnshire, where it eventually died.

Another flew west at Sheringham, Weybourne and Stiffkey on 18th September 1995 before heading south at Snettisham. On the following day it was found on the River Ouse at Ten Mile Bank where it remained a further day.

## Black Swan                                              *Cygnus atratus*

The Black Swan is a resident of Australia, Tasmania and New Zealand. A very small population of feral or escaped Black Swans has recently become established in Broadland, centred on Salhouse Broad, the River Bure at Wroxham and to a lesser extent the Trinity Broads. Initially poorly documented, it appears that the first Black Swans were noted in Broadland prior to 1980.

Remarkably, in this early period, one was seen flying east over the sea past Mundesley on 22nd November 1982. One wintered with Mute and Bewick's Swans at Horsey in 1984 and the first in a now regular series of Breydon sightings occurred in June 1987. A pair bred on a small pond at Walcott in 1989 by which time at least one pair was regularly breeding, although not always successfully, at Salhouse Broad, and up to three wintered on the Burnham Norton and Holkham Marshes, one of which spent time with Mute Swans on Wells Quay. By 1993 birds were also being seen at Earsham. At this time all reports of Black Swans in Norfolk were being published. There were at least three breeding pairs in the Salhouse/ Wroxham area in 1994 with an additional pair raising five young at Waxham. Individuals have been wandering away from Broadland with regular sightings at Welney. In 1995 they were recorded at an additional seven sites, increasing to 11 by 1997.

The population in Norfolk in 1998 is unknown, but is believed to be between 20–40 birds and appears to be slowly increasing. It is uncertain whether all records are submitted for publication.

## Ross's Goose    HARDLEY FLOODS. 27·11·2000. (BLUE PHASE)          *Anser rossii*

The Ross's Goose is a close relative of the Snow Goose with a restricted breeding range in Arctic Canada and on the shores of Hudson Bay and the Beaufort Sea. The population has increased substantially in the last 20 years and its wintering areas, once exclusively restricted to California, now include Texas and Louisiana with small numbers seen regularly on the eastern seaboard of North America. Despite being widely kept in captivity and having been recorded in a feral state in the British Isles, it is a potential wild vagrant to this country.

An adult Ross's Goose was present with Greylag Geese in the Yare Valley at Rockland St Mary and Claxton on 8th–19th February 1991 during a spell of arctic weather. Several observers considered that the Greylag Geese, which associated with the Ross's Goose, were possibly wild individuals and not from the local feral population. It is interesting to note that an adult Ross's Goose, perhaps the same individual, frequented fields with Icelandic Greylag Geese in Findhorn Bay, Grampian on 15th–19th March 1991 moving to Lossiemouth, Grampian from 23rd March to 16th April (Proctor 1991). The Ross's Goose was later reported on northward migration at Kinlochbervie, Sutherland on 16th May. More recently, one was at Snettisham throughout 1996. None of the sightings was accepted by the BBRC as having involved a genuinely wild bird.

## Wood Duck                                                          *Aix sponsa*

A former Category D species, the Wood Duck is now placed in Category E of the BOU's British List. It is a North American species which breeds in two separate populations and is commonly kept in wildfowl collections in Europe. However, genuine vagrants have been suspected of having occurred in western Europe, but assessment of records is extremely difficult. Although it was first introduced into England in the 1870s, it has not been as successful in colonising the British Isles as its close relative, the Mandarin.

The true status of Wood Duck in Norfolk is unknown, but certainly all records are regarded as having involved birds which have escaped from collections. Prior to 1995, sightings of this duck generally went unrecorded with few being published. Breeding was confirmed in the 10km square TF63 (the Dersingham/ Snettisham area) during fieldwork for the 1968–72 BTO Atlas, while the Norfolk Atlas revealed possible breeding on the River Wensum at Bylaugh. Additional sightings have also been reported at Postwick and Strumpshaw in the Yare Valley, at Salhouse Broad and on Holkham Park Lake on 15th June 1984. Since 1995 it has been recorded at Bramerton Wood End, Lound Waterworks, Ormesby Broad, Potter Heigham, Salhouse Broad, Sparham Pools, Strumpshaw and Surlingham.

## Hooded Merganser                                        *Lophodytes cucullatus*

The Hooded Merganser is a Nearctic species breeding from south-east Alaska south to Oregon and Florida and wintering in the southern USA and Mexico. A popular species in wildfowl collections it is placed in Category A on the strength of a 1830–31 Welsh record and a 1957 Irish record. All other records are considered to be either of unknown or captive origin.

An adult drake Hooded Merganser was alleged to have been obtained at Yarmouth in 1829 and a second male said to have been killed in the county in the winter of 1837–38. Riviere stated that there were sufficient reasons for doubting the authenticity of the former specimen whilst there would appear to be little or no evidence that the latter was really obtained in Norfolk. There are two recent records, a female of unknown origin was at Titchwell on 2nd June 1990 moving to Holme on 3rd and remaining until 15th June. A second female, not carrying a ring and wary, was at Holme on 25th–28th January 1997, reappearing at Titchwell on 21st–22nd February. It was back at Holme on 9th–11th March and returned to Titchwell on 10th April. It had possibly been present in the area since 2nd January.

## Spotted Eagle                                                 *Aquila clanga*

The Spotted Eagle is an uncommon eagle breeding from north-east Europe eastwards across Siberia. Small numbers winter in Turkey, northern Israel, Egypt and Ethiopia and very occasionally west to southern France, The Netherlands and Spain. It is an extremely rare vagrant to the British Isles, the last authentic record being in 1915. Two records relate to Norfolk, one an offshore specimen, albeit at a considerable distance, and the second claimed in 1934.

On 17th October 1907 an exhausted immature Spotted Eagle captured on a boat 140 miles off Norfolk was sent to the Zoological Gardens in London. The second occurrence related to an immature reported at Hickling on 8th March 1934 by Jim Vincent, whose description of the bird in his diaries is unfortunately rather brief. The bird's size is recorded as larger than an Osprey with all dark brown plumage except for some light golden marks on the shoulders. Wings noted as broad with openings between the primaries, and the tail was short. The head and neck were drawn into the body. He noted there was no upward sweep of the primaries. On 15th March Vincent visited South Kensington Natural History Museum and, after seeing skins, his diaries recorded that he was convinced the bird was an immature Spotted Eagle. On 18th March what was possibly the same bird was seen at Waxham; Vincent was familiar with the White-tailed Eagle.

# Northern Bobwhite
## *Colinus virginianus*

A central and eastern Nearctic quail, the Northern Bobwhite was formerly called the Bob-white Quail. A number were released at Rackheath and elsewhere in Norfolk in 1961. The following year, birds were recorded at Holkham, Taverham, Hainford, West Somerton and near Wymondham.

It was interesting to note that they frequently perched in trees and other vantage points calling, rather than on the ground. This introduced population soon died out and no further records have been received.

# Chukar
## *Alectoris chukar*

The natural range of the Chukar extends from the east Balkans and Turkey through to Asia. It has declined in recent years over most of its south-eastern European breeding range. In 1970 over 2,000 Chukars and Chukar x Red-legged Partridge hybrids were released on the South Downs. In the following year, hybrids were again released there, and in two other localities. By 1972, releases were much more widespread, ranging from Hampshire to Angus in Scotland (New Atlas).

Exactly when the first Chukars and hybrids were released in Norfolk is unknown, nor are there any data to indicate how widespread the practice became. However, it is known that during the early 1980s about 800,000 hand-reared Red-legged Partridges were released annually in the British Isles, most being various admixtures and hybrids of Red-legged Partridge and Chukar (Winter Atlas). Presumably, therefore, such birds were present in many parts of Norfolk. Fortunately for the Red-legged Partridge, the introduction of these hybrids was not a success, as in the field they were only able to produce one seventh as many young as pure Red-legged Partridge pairs. The licence under which the release of hybrids was allowed was withdrawn in December 1992, since when it has been illegal to release them.

In Norfolk, few records of Chukar were submitted, in part probably due to the fact that few observers ever looked carefully at Red-legged Partridges. The problem was compounded, however, by many of the progeny of these hybrid pairs reverting to type and on visual evidence alone it was not possible to determine whether the birds were of pure stock. The last reported sightings of Chukars in Norfolk were of a pair at Bacton, one at Heydon Park and up to 18 in the Salthouse/Wiveton area in 1994, and a pair of hybrids at West Runton on 8th March 1995.

# Purple Gallinule (Purple Swamphen)
## *Porphyrio porphyrio*

The Purple Gallinule is a mainly sedentary species with four races recognised within the Western Palearctic – one in the western Mediterranean, one in the Nile Delta and two in the Middle East and Caspian region; these races are sometimes considered to represent three separate species. Although quite scarce in captivity in Britain, small numbers of Purple Gallinules are known to be kept. All British records are believed to relate to birds of captive origin. Large numbers of these birds were formerly imported into the country especially in the latter half of the 19th century. In 1897, 60 were released at Woburn Abbey, Bedfordshire, a year in which a number were shot in Norfolk.

The following Norfolk records of Purple Gallinules have been traced:

1876: One killed at Tatterford on 10th October
1877: One shot at Hickling Broad on 7th September
      Barton Broad on 1st November
1879: One shot at Barton Broad on 23rd August
1885: One shot at Horning on 16th October
1892: One shot at Stoke Ferry in November
1897: One shot at Martham Broad on 23rd June
      Another bird shot on 3rd July
      One shot at Barton Broad on 31st July with other birds seen on 3rd August and 11th September
1898: Heigham Sounds on 4th June
      One shot at Barton Broad on 14th July
1899: Sutton Broad on 21st October
1900: One shot at Barton Broad (exact date lost), bird set-up by J. Cole of Norwich and sold at auction in 1996

1902:  One shot at Hickling Broad on 11th October
1903:  Stalham on 1st July
1908:  Horsey on 3rd June
       Barton Broad on 7th August
1913:  Barton Broad on 13th October
1937:  A first-winter at Horsey from 8th to 2nd October

The number of birds which found their way to Barton Broad is remarkable. In addition, birds resembling the Indian race *P. p. poliocephalus* were shot at Stoke Ferry in November 1892 (presumably different to the other bird shot at the same locality on the same date) and another seen at Cley from 20th July to 19th September 1978.

# Demoiselle Crane                                         *Anthropoides virgo*

The Demoiselle Crane is a highly migratory species breeding from Turkey eastwards across central Asia to China wintering mainly in North Africa. Very small numbers are kept in captivity and all records in this country are believed to have involved escaped birds.

The Demoiselle Crane has occurred in Norfolk on a number of occasions, although not always reported. The earliest were of two showing signs of captivity which were shot at Brancaster on 31st July 1899 and were suspected of having escaped from Woburn Park, Bedfordshire. One on Wiveton Marsh on 17th June 1924 had earlier been seen to fly in off the sea. It was very wild, full-winged and in perfect condition. Another was at Holme on 9th September 1961. A remarkable party of six was observed at Horsey on 23rd April 1967 in fields close to the coast road; these birds were never traced as having escaped.

A Demoiselle Crane which frequented Breydon and Halvergate Marshes from May 1977 was finally captured on the helideck of a North Sea gas platform in late August. Another at Wells caravan site on 23rd–24th October 1991 was traced as having escaped from the Pensthorpe collection.

# South Polar Skua                                        *Catharacta maccormicki*

The South Polar Skua breeds in Antarctica, north along the Antarctic Peninsula to the South Orkney and South Shetland Islands. Its winter range is poorly understood, but it performs a trans-equatorial migration in the Pacific and perhaps on a smaller scale in the Atlantic. The whole population is estimated at 5,000–8,000 pairs making it an extremely rare bird in global terms.

There are at present no accepted British records although a number of birds have been claimed since 1982. The first record of South Polar Skua in the North Atlantic, and indeed in the northern hemisphere, was one purchased by J. H. Gurney junior at Leadenhall Market, London in October 1869. Norfolk (and Yarmouth in particular) was accepted as the likely origin of this skua which was at the time identified as a dark phase Great Skua. The specimen still bears Gurney's original label reading 'Great Skua, Leadenhall October 1869, J. Gatcombe, Yarmouth'. The most probable source of the bird was the crew of a lightship or sailing smack serviced from Yarmouth at that time. They were known to pass their spare time shooting seabirds for additional income from game-dealers and taxidermists. The specimen remained labelled as a Great Skua in the Castle Museum, Norwich for many years until examined by Dr W. R. P. Bourne and Dr D. S. Lee in 1993 and re-identified as a moderately dark South Polar Skua. This is an intriguing account, but the record cannot be claimed for Norfolk, as the original source of the bird was likely to be 'somewhere in the North Sea'.

Robert McCormick, who shot the type-specimen in the Antarctic Sea on 12th January 1841 and had the bird named after him, was born at Yarmouth in 1800.

# Laughing Dove (Palm Dove)                               *Streptopelia senegalensis*

The Laughing Dove is an abundant species resident across large parts of Africa, the Middle East, western Asia and the Indian subcontinent. It has recently expanded its range into Turkey and the Balkans.

In Britain, it is widely kept in captivity, but vagrancy is not impossible. There are several British records, the first of which was in Norfolk – an adult at West Walton Fen from 14th May to 26th July 1974.

# Black Woodpecker                                    *Dryocopus martius*

The Black Woodpecker is a resident of the coniferous and mixed woodlands throughout much of Europe except for southern Iberia and the Mediterranean basin. It first bred in Belgium in 1908 and The Netherlands in 1913. Since the early 1950s it has spread into the lowland areas of north-west Europe linked with the maturing of deciduous woodlands and the rapid spread of Norway spruce. It now breeds close to the Channel coast in France. There are no definite records of it having occurred in the British Isles as a natural vagrant.

Two Black Woodpeckers were said to have been obtained by Francis Drake at Billingford, near Scole in 1835, but the record was rejected both by Stevenson and Riviere. Richard Fitter, who in 1959 analysed all the claimed sightings in the British Isles, also rejected the Billingford record (Fitter 1959).

# Northern Mockingbird                              *Mimus polyglottos*

The Northern Mockingbird is an abundant Nearctic species which is mostly sedentary, but birds from northern regions and north-eastern USA appear to be partially migratory. Although a Category A species, there are doubts concerning the origin of the single Norfolk occurrence.

One in worn plumage frequented Blakeney Point on 20th–28th August 1971. It was filmed by Ted Eales and Dick Bagnall-Oakeley. Although identification was proved, it was considered to be a possible escape from captivity.

**The following is a selected list of additional Category E species known to have occurred in Norfolk in recent years:**

| | |
|---|---|
| Chilean Flamingo | *Phoenicopterus chilensis* |
| Marabou Stork | *Leptoptilos crumeniferus* |
| Sacred Ibis | *Threskiornis aethiopicus* |
| African Spoonbill | *Platalea alba* |
| White-faced Whistling Duck | *Dendrocygna viduata* |
| Lake Duck | *Oxyura vittata* |
| Swan Goose | *Anser cygnoides* |
| Bar-headed Goose | *Anser indicus* |
| Emperor Goose | *Anser canagicus* |
| Hawaiian Goose | *Branta sandvicensis* |
| Paradise Shelduck | *Tadorna variegata* |
| Australian Shelduck | *Tadorna tadornoides* |
| Muscovy Duck | *Cairina moschata* |
| Ringed Teal | *Callonetta leucophrys* |
| Maned Duck | *Chenonetta jubata* |
| Chiloe Wigeon | *Anas sibilatrix* |
| Speckled Teal | *Anas flavirostris* |
| Cape Teal | *Anas capensis* |
| Chestnut Teal | *Anas castanea* |
| White-cheeked Pintail | *Anas bahamensis* |
| Silver Teal | *Anas versicolor* |
| Hottentot Teal | *Anas hottentota* |
| Cinnamon Teal | *Anas cyanoptera* |
| Rosy-billed Pochard | *Netta peposaca* |
| Barrow's Goldeneye | *Bucephala islandica* |
| Harris's Hawk | *Parabuteo unicinctus* |

| | |
|---|---|
| Red-tailed Hawk | *Buteo jamaicensis* |
| Tawny Eagle | *Aquila rapax* |
| Lanner | *Falco biarmicus* |
| Silver Pheasant | *Lophura nycthemera* |
| Reeve's Pheasant | *Syrmaticus reevsii* |
| Indian Peafowl | *Pavo cristatus* |
| Black Crowned Crane | *Balearica pavonina* |
| Peruvian Thick-knee | *Burhinus superciliaris* |
| Diamond Dove | *Geopelia cuneata* |
| Sulphur-crested Cockatoo | *Cacatua galerita* |
| Cockatiel | *Nymphicus hollandicus* |
| Eastern Rosella | *Platycercus eximius* |
| Budgerigar | *Melopsittacus undulatus* |
| Grey Parrot | *Psittacus erithacus* |
| Peach-faced Lovebird | *Agapornis roseicollis* |
| Alexandrine Parakeet | *Psittacula eupatria* |
| Grey-headed Parakeet | *Psittacula finschii* |
| Plum-headed Parakeet | *Psittacula cyanocephala* |
| Red-breasted Parakeet | *Psittacula alexandri* |
| Red-spectacled Amazon | *Amazona pretrei* |
| Eurasian Eagle Owl | *Bubo bubo* |
| Red-vented Bulbul | *Pycnonotus cafer* |
| Comoros Black Bulbul | *Hypsipetes parvirostris* |
| Oriental Magpie Robin | *Copsychus saularis* |
| Red-billed Leiothrix | *Leiothrix lutea* |
| Yellow-bellied Sunbird | *Nectarinia venusta* |
| Red-billed Blue Magpie | *Urocissa erythrorhyncha* |
| Purple Glossy Starling | *Lamprotornis purpureus* |
| Blue-eared Glossy Starling | *Lamprotornis chalybaeus* |
| Common Hill Myna | *Gracula religiosa* |
| Yellow-fronted Canary | *Serinus mozambicus* |
| Long-tailed Rosefinch | *Uragus sibiricus* |
| Pallas's Rosefinch | *Carpodacus roseus* |
| Crimson-rumped Waxbill | *Estrilda rhodopyga* |
| Red-eared Waxbill | *Estrilda troglodytes* |
| Red Avadavat | *Amandava amandava* |
| Zebra Finch | *Poephila guttata* |
| Black-headed Munia | *Lonchura malacca* |
| White-headed Munia | *Lonchura maja* |
| Red-billed Weaver | *Spermophaga ruficapilla* |
| Village Weaver | *Ploceus cucullatus* |
| Red-billed Quelea | *Quelea quelea* |
| Northern Red Bishop | *Euplectes franciscanus* |
| Sudan Golden Sparrow | *Auripasser luteus* |
| Yellow-headed Blackbird | *Xanthocephalus xanthocephalus* |

# APPENDIX 1:

## SSSIS IN THE NORFOLK
## PART OF BRECKLAND IN 1998

| Name | Ha | Habitat/Interest |
|---|---|---|
| Barnhamcross Common* | 68.90 | Grass heath |
| Bridgham & Brettenham Heaths* | 441.75 | Heathland & grass heath |
| Cranberry Rough* | 81.85 | Basin mire & carr woodand |
| Cranwich Camp | 13.04 | Grass heath & species |
| Didlington Park Lakes* | 25.67 | Lakes, wildfowl & fen species |
| East Harling Common | 15.03 | Pingos, fen & species |
| East Wretham Heath* | 140.91 | Meres & grass heath |
| Elm Road, Thetford | 5.02 | Grass heath |
| Field Barn Heaths, Hilborough | 18.64 | Grass heath |
| Foulden Common* | 138.64 | Pingos, fen & species |
| Gooderstone Warren | 23.89 | Grass heath |
| Great Cressingham Fen | 14.21 | Fen & grassland |
| Grime's Graves* | 66.41 | Heathland & grass heath |
| Hooks Well Meadows, Gt. Cressingham | 15.34 | Fen & flood plain grassland |
| Middle Harling Fen | 12.70 | Fen & grassland |
| Narborough Railway Embankment | 7.78 | Grassland & species |
| Old Bodney Camp | 32.26 | Grass & lichen heath |
| Stanford Training Area* | 4,655.18 | Heathland, grass heath, fen, carr, meres, pingos & species |
| The Brinks, Northwold | 16.30 | Grassland |
| Thetford Golf Course & Marsh* | 122.48 | Heathland, grass heath & fen |
| Thompson Water, Carr & Common* | 155.33 | Grassland, pingos, woodland & species |
| Weeting Heath** | 141.06 | Grass heath, species |
| Wretham Park Meres* | 29.28 | Meres & wildfowl |
| Total: | 6,241.67ha | |

**Note:** A further 32 SSSIs, together covering an area of 2,363ha, are located in the Suffolk part of Breckland.

**Key**

* Listed as an SSSI in the 1981 Schedule. Two further sites were included on this, but were deleted in the latest revision on the grounds that they are no longer of sufficient interest to justify retention as SSSIs.
** A National Nature Reserve as well as an SSSI.

The 'species' mentioned in the third column include rare plants and invertebrates, as well as birds such as Stone Curlews and Woodlarks.

**Sources**

Rothera, S. (1998). *Breckland Natural Area Profile*. English Nature, Norwich.
Hectarage figures from English Nature HQ, Peterborough.

# APPENDIX 2:

## NATURE RESERVES IN NORFOLK (see Note 1)

| Name | Grid Ref | Ha (*Note 2*) | Body responsible | Tenure | Year established | National Status |
|---|---|---|---|---|---|---|
| Alderfen Broad | TG 354194 | 21 | NWT | Owned | 1930 | SSSI |
| Ashwellthorpe Lwr. Wood | TM 140980 | 37 | NWT | Owned | 1992 | – |
| Barnhamcross Common | TL 865813 | 67 | Norfolk CC | NRA | 1986 | LNR & SSSI |
| Barton Broad | TG 362215 | 164 (144) | NWT | Owned | 1945 | Part of Ant Marshes NNR (S 35) |
| Berney Marshes | TG 466055 | 365 (256) | RSPB | Owned | 1985 | SSSI |
| Blakeney Point | TG 015458 | 1097 (581) | NT | Owned | 1912 | NNR (S 35) |
| Booton Common | TG 112229 | 9 | NWT | NRA | 1980 | SSSI |
| Bowthorpe Marsh | TG 178082 | 6 | Norwich CC | Owned | 1989 | LNR |
| Brancaster Manor | TG 800450 | 626 | NT | Owned | 1967 | Part of N. Norfolk Coast SSSI |
| Brettenham Heath | TL 930860 | 234 | EN | Leased | 1982 | NNR |
| Breydon Water | TG 488070 | 453 | Norfolk CC & GYBC | Owned & Leased | 1968 | LNR & SSSI (*see Note 3*) |
| Buckenham & Cantley Marshes | TG 355054 & TG 370040 | 351 | RSPB | Owned | 1993 | Part of Mid-Yare NNR (S 35) |
| Bure Marshes | TG 335169 | 412 | EN | NRA | 1958 | NNR |
| Burgh Common | TG 448131 | 4 | NWT | Leased | 1984 | Part of SSSI |
| Calthorpe Broad | TG 412258 | 44 | EN | Owned | | NNR |
| Catfield Fen | TG 370213 | 24 | BBS | Owned | 1992 | Part of Ant Marshes NNR |
| Cley Marshes | TG 055445 | 180 (165) | NWT | Owned | 1926 | Part of N. Norfolk Coast SSSI |
| Cockshoot Broad | TG 346162 | (*see Note 4*) | NWT | Owned | 1949 | Part of Bure Marshes NNR |
| Danby Wood | TG 219058 | 3.5 | Norwich CC | Owned | 1989 | LNR |
| Dersingham Bog | TF 675289 | 159 | EN | NRA | 1989 | SSSI |
| Dunston Common | TG 227026 | 4 | S. Norfolk DC | Owned | 1996 | – |
| Earlham Park Woods | TG 188078 | 8 | Norwich CC | Owned | 1989 | LNR |
| East Winch Common | TF 700158 | 32 | NWT | Owned | 1973 | SSSI |
| East Wretham Heath | TL 910882 | 141 | NWT | Owned | 1940 | SSSI |
| Eaton Common | TG 204055 | 6 | Norwich CC | S of R | 1994 | LNR |
| Ebb & Flow Marshes | TG 350163 | 43 | NWT | Owned | 1996 | Part of Bure Broads & Marshes SSSI |
| Felmingham Cutting | TG 248287 | 1 | Norfolk CC | Owned | 1989 | LNR |
| Foxley Wood | TG 054225 | 124 | NWT | Owned | 1988 | SSSI |
| Gt. Eastern Pingo Trail | TM 938960 | 10 | Norfolk CC | Owned | 1991 | LNR & Part SSSI |
| Heigham Holmes | TG 445205 | 186 | NT | Owned | 1986 | Part of Upper Thurne Broads & Marshes SSSI |
| Hethel Old Thorn | TG 171005 | 0.025 | NWT | Owned | 1962 | – |
| Hickling Broad | TG 420215 | 559 (464) | NWT | Owned & Leased | 1945 | NNR |
| Hindringham Meadow | TF 965377 | 7 | Norfolk CC | Owned | 1992 | LNR |
| Hockham Fen | TL 934936 | 8 | NWT | Owned | 1962 | Part of SSSI |
| Hoe Rough | TF 978168 | 14 | NWT | Owned | 1989 | – |
| Holkham | TF 880450 & TF 940455 | 3851 (3955) | EN | NRA & Leased | 1967 | NNR |
| Holme Bird Observatory | TF 717450 | 2 | NOA | Owned | 1962 | Part of N. Norfolk Coast SSSI |
| Holme Dunes | TF 715449 | 255 (162) | NWT | Owned & Leased | 1965 | Part of N. Norfolk Coast SSSI |
| Holt Lowes | TG 087376 | 12 | NWT | NRA | 1980 | Part of SSSI |
| Honeypot Wood | TF 933143 | 9 | NWT | Owned | 1987 | SSSI |

| | | | | | | |
|---|---|---|---|---|---|---|
| Horsey Mere | TG 450220 | 202 | NT | Owned | 1948 | Part of Upper Thurne Broads & Marshes SSSI |
| Horsey Warren | TG 465240 | 57 | NT | Owned | 1948 | Part of SSSI |
| How Hill Fens | TG 365195 | 148 | Broads Authy. | Owned | 1983 | SSSI |
| Knapton Cutting | TG 299329 | 0.9 | Norfolk CC | Owned | 1990 | LNR |
| Lion Wood | TG 250088 | 9 | Norwich CC | Owned | 1989 | LNR |
| Litcham Common | TF 885172 | 28 | Norfolk CC | NRA | 1984 | LNR |
| Lolly Moor | TF 992104 | 3 | NWT | NRA | 1978 | – |
| Marston Marshes | TG 215055 | 26 | Norwich CC | Owned | 1984 | LNR |
| Martham Broad & Starch Grass | TG 458203 | 60 (10) | NWT | Owned & Leased | 1928 | NNR (S 35) |
| Morston Marshes | TF 015445 | 225 | NT | Owned | 1973 | Part of N. Norfolk Coast SSSI |
| Mousehold Heath | TG 245103 | 92 | Norwich CC | Owned | 1994 | LNR |
| Narborough Railway Line | TF 754112 | 8 | NWT | Owned | 1985 | SSSI |
| New Buckenham Com. | TM 093907 | 40 | NWT | Owned | 1984 | SSSI |
| Ranworth Broad | TG 355154 | (see Note 4) | NWT | Owned | 1949 | Part of Bure Marshes NNR |
| Redgrave & Lopham Fen | TM 050797 | 125 | SWT | Owned & Leased | 1966 | NNR (S 35) (see Note 5) |
| Redwell Marsh | – | 14 | NOA | Owned | 1974 | Part of N. Norfolk Coast SSSI |
| Ringstead Downs | TF 691400 | 11 | NWT | NRA | 1972 | SSSI |
| Roydon Common | TM 690224 | 181 (57) | NWT | Owned | 1963 | NNR (S 35) |
| Roydon Fen | TM 100798 | 20 | S. Norfolk DC | S of R | 1995 | – |
| Salthouse Marshes | TG 070444 | 83 | NWT | Owned & Leased | 1971 | Part of N. Norfolk Coast SSSI |
| Scarning Fen | TF 982122 | 4 | NWT | Owned | 1961 | Part of SSSI |
| Scolt Head Island | TF 813464 | 738 | EN | Leased | 1924 | Part of N. Norfolk Coast SSSI |
| Smallburgh Fen | TF 326245 | 8 | NWT | Leased | 1972 | SSSI |
| Southrepps Common | TG 262350 | 12 | Norfolk CC | Owned | 1990 | LNR |
| South Walsham Fen | TG 350128 | 1.5 | Norfolk CC | Owned | 1989 | LNR |
| Snettisham | TF 650330 | 1315 (43) | RSPB | Owned & Leased | 1972 | Part of SSSI |
| Sparham Pools | TG 075179 | 12 | NWT | NRA | 1974 | – |
| Stiffkey Marshes | TF 972442 | 197 | NT | Owned | 1976 | Part of N. Norfolk Coast SSSI |
| Strumpshaw Fen | TG 340068 | 197 (127) | RSPB | Owned & Leased | 1974 | Part of Mid-Yare NNR |
| Surlingham & Rockland marshes, fens & broads | TG 307071 & TG 335050 | 254 (108) | RSPB | Owned & Leased | 1980 | Part of SSSI & part of Mid-Yare NNR |
| Swanton Novers Woods | TG 014313 | 85 (60) | EN | NRA | 1974 | NNR |
| Syderstone Common | TF 830318 | 44 | NWT | Owned | 1978 | SSSI |
| Ted Ellis Reserve (= Wheatfen) | TG 330056 | 57 | TET | Owned & Leased | 1987 | Part of Yare Broads & Marshes SSSI |
| Thompson Common | TL 935965 | 133 | NWT | Owned | 1981 | SSSI |
| Thursford Wood | TF 978332 | 10 | NWT | Owned | 1957 | – |
| Titchwell Marsh | TF 755442 | 379 (166) | RSPB | Owned & Leased | 1973 | Part of N. Norfolk Coast SSSI |
| Toll's Meadow, Wymondham | TG 112012 | 1.5 | Norfolk CC | NRA | 1997 | LNR |
| Upton Fen | TG 382137 | 55 | NWT | Owned | 1979 | SSSI |
| Walsey Hills | TG 061441 | 1 | NOA | Owned | 1973 | – |
| Wayland Wood | TL 924996 | 32 | NWT | Owned | 1976 | SSSI |
| Weeting Heath | TL 757884 | 137 | NWT | Owned | 1942 | NNR |
| Welney Wildfowl Refuge | TL 545950 | 290 (40) | WWT | Owned | 1967 | Part of SSSI |
| Wensum Valley | TG 214099 | 7 | Norwich CC | Owned | 1994 | LNR |
| Whitlingham Marsh | TG 284076 | 17 | S. Norfolk DC | NRA | 1996 | LNR |
| Winterton Dunes | TG 490210 | 109 | EN | NRA | 1956 | NNR |
| Wiveton Down | TG 033422 | 7 | Norfolk CC | Owned | 1991 | LNR & SSSI |

## Notes

1. Various sites have been omitted from this Table owing to difficulties of access to them, or because of their small size or susceptibility to damage by trampling. It should be remembered that in addition to the reserves listed, there are literally hundreds of County Wildlife Sites; these are safeguarded by their private owners. Other sites are protected by local authorities, and by the Woodland Trust.

2. These hectarages represent the present size of the sites concerned. The figures in brackets indicate the hectarage, when known, of the reserve when it was first established.

3. In 1988, responsibility for the management of 375ha of this LNR was assumed by the RSPB under a management agreement negotiated with the Norfolk CC The remainder of the site, which is owned by the Great Yarmouth Bird Club, is managed jointly by the Yarmouth & District Wildfowlers' Association and the Yarmouth Naturalists' Society.

4. Cockshoot and Ranworth Broads, together with the fens adjoining them, have a combined hectarage of 130. This figure is included in the total given for the Bure Marshes NNR, of which these sites form a part.

5. Part of this reserve is in Suffolk

**Note. Access to some of the above sites is restricted in the interests of breeding birds, and for other reasons. The organisation responsible for the management of the site should always be contacted beforehand if there is any uncertainty about the arrangements for visiting.**

## Abbreviations

| | |
|---|---|
| **BBS** | British Butterfly Society |
| **EN** | English Nature |
| **GYBC** | Great Yarmouth Bird Club |
| **LNR** | Local Nature Reserve established under S 21 of the National Parks & Access to the Countryside Act, 1949 |
| **NNR** | National Nature Reserve managed by English Nature |
| **NOA** | Norfolk Ornithologists' Association |
| **NRA** | Nature Reserve Agreement |
| **NT** | National Trust |
| **NWT** | Norfolk Wildlife Trust (formerly the Norfolk Naturalists Trust) |
| **RSPB** | Royal Society for the Protection of Birds |
| **S of R** | Scheme of Regulation |
| **SSSI** | Site of Special Scientific Interest scheduled under S 28 of the Wildlife & Countryside Act, 1981 |
| **S 35** | National Nature Reserve designated in accordance with S 35c of the Wildlife & Countryside Act, 1981 |
| **TET** | Ted Ellis Trust |
| **WWT** | Wildfowl and Wetland Trust (formerly the Wildfowl Trust) |

# BIBLIOGRAPHY

Adams, S. 1995. Curlew Sandpipers on the Wash. *Wash Wader Ringing Group Report 1993–94*: 30–34.

Addison, C. 1931. *Report of the National Park Committee.* Cmnd. 3851. HMSO, London.

Alexander, H. G. 1949. Bearded Tits at Cley and in Sussex. *Brit. Birds* 42: 289–292.

Allard, P. R. 1968. White Storks in Norfolk. *Norfolk Bird Report 1967*: 162–163.

Allard, P. R. 1969. Invasion of Nutcrackers. *Norfolk Bird Report 1968*: 292–294.

Allard, P. R. 1970. Arctic and Sahara vagrants – Cream-coloured Courser. *Norfolk Bird Report 1969*: 12–13.

Allard, P. R. 1971. Black Redstart breeding studies. *Norfolk Bird Report 1970*: 188–190.

Allard, P. R. 1972. Bewick's Swans in South-east Norfolk. *Norfolk Bird Report 1971*: 340.

Allard, P. R. 1973. Successful scavengers. *Norfolk Bird Report 1972*: 29.

Allard, P. R. 1982. Greater Sandplover at Breydon Water. *Norfolk Bird Report 1981*: 89.

Allard, P. R. 1983. An exceptional Brent Goose movement. *Norfolk Bird Report 1982*: 208–209.

Allard, P. R. 1984a. Yarmouth District Mediterranean Gulls. *Norfolk Bird Report 1983*: 349–351.

Allard, P. R. 1984b. Little Auk fly-past. *Norfolk Bird Report 1983*: 354.

Allard, P. R. 1987. Breydon Water tern platforms. *Norfolk Bird Report 1986*: 408–409.

Allard, P. R. 1988. Breydon Water: a century of protection. Norfolk Bird Report for 1987. *Transactions of the Norfolk and Norwich Naturalists' Society*, 28 (2), 87–88.

Allard, P. R. 1990. *The Birds of Great Yarmouth.* Norfolk and Norwich Naturalists' Society.

Allard, P. R. 1992. Caspian Terns in East Norfolk. *Norfolk Bird Report 1991*: 26–32.

Allard, P. R. 1994. The Red–flanked Bluetail in Yarmouth Cemeteries. *Norfolk Bird Club Bulletin* 13: 8–10.

Allard, P. R. 1995a. Setting the record straight: the Yarmouth Citril Finch. *Norfolk Bird Report 1994*: 366–367.

Allard, P. R. 1995b. Red-flanked Bluetail – A first for Norfolk. *Norfolk Bird Report 1994*: 368.

Allard, P. R. 1996. Misidentification of Bewick's and Whooper Swans in Norfolk. *Norfolk Bird Club Bulletin* 20: 6–7.

Allard, P. R. 1997. The Bufflehead – a Norfolk bird or not? *Norfolk Bird Club Bulletin* 22: 8–9.

Allard, P. R. 1998. Memories of Short-eared Owls on Halvergate Marshes. *Norfolk Bird Club Bulletin* 30: 8–10.

Allard, P. R. 1999. Mediterranean Gulls at Great Yarmouth. *Norfolk Bird Club Bulletin* 33: 3–4.

Allard, P. R. & Ramsay, H. 1970. Arctic and Sahara vagrants – Cream-coloured Courser and Sabine's Gull. *Norfolk Bird Report 1969*: 12–14.

Allison, H. & Morley, J. P. 1989. *Blakeney Point and Scolt Head Island.* National Trust, Blickling.

Allport, G., O'Brien, M. & Cadbury, C. J. 1986. Survey of Redshank and other breeding birds on saltmarshes in Britain in 1985. *NCC CSD Report 649.*

Anon. 1986a. Curlew Sandpiper influx. *Norfolk Bird Report 1985*: 249.

Anon. 1986b. Greater Sandplover, vagrant from Southern Russia. *Norfolk Bird Report 1985*: 250.

Anon. 1986c. Little Whimbrel: A bird new to England in Norfolk. *Norfolk Bird Report 1985*: 251.

Anon. 1986d. Nesting Parrot Crossbills at Wells. *Norfolk Bird Report 1985*: 256–259.

Anon. 1986e. Little Gulls in Norfolk. *Norfolk Bird Report 1985*: 260–261.

Anon. 1989. Great Yarmouth Little Tern colony. *Norfolk Bird Report 1988*: 259.

Anon. 1990. Red-breasted Nuthatch in Norfolk – A new British bird. *Norfolk Bird Report 1989*: 412–413.

Anon. 1992a. A transatlantic trio new to Norfolk: Ring-billed, Franklin's and Laughing Gulls. *Norfolk Bird Report 1991*: 258–260.

Anon. 1992b. Lark Sparrow – new to Norfolk. *Norfolk Bird Report 1991*: 261.

Anon. 1993: Nesting Mediterranean Gulls: New to Norfolk. *Norfolk Bird Report 1992*: 433–434.

Anon. 1997. A trio of eastern vagrants new to Norfolk: Blyth's Reed Warbler, Blyth's Pipit and 'Two Barred' Greenish Warbler. *Norfolk Bird Report 1996*: 244–247.

Atkinson, P. W. 1993. A few results of Snow Bunting ringing in Norfolk. *Norfolk Bird Club Bulletin* 3: 7–8.

Atkinson, P. W. 1996. The origins, moult and movements of Bar-tailed Godwits on the Wash, England. *Bird Study* 43: 60–72.

Axell, H. E. 1966. Eruptions of Bearded Tits during 1959–65. *Brit. Birds* 69: 473–489.

Babbs, S., Cook, A. S. & Durdin, C. 1997. Broads E.S.A. Wintering Waterfowl Survey 1996/1997. *Norfolk Bird Club Bulletin* 24: 6–7.

Babington, C. 1884–86. *Catalogue of the Birds of Suffolk.* Van Voorst, London.

Bagnall-Oakeley, R. P. 1956. The Egmere Starling roost. *Norfolk Bird Report 1955*: 17–23.

Bagnall-Oakeley, R. P. 1959. North Norfolk Starling roosts *Norfolk Bird Report 1958*: 22–24.

Bagnall-Oakeley, R. P. 1969. Short-eared Owl roost near Docking *Proceedings of the Heacham and West Norfolk Natural History Society* 3 (1): 1.

Bagnall-Oakeley, R. P. 1972. Great Spotted Woodpeckers excavating holes in autumn. *Brit. Birds* 65: 399.

Baillie, S. R. 1990. Integrated population monitoring of breeding birds in Britain and Ireland. *Ibis* 132: 151–166.

Bainbridge, I. P. & Minton, C. D. T. 1978. The migration and mortality of the Curlew in the British Isles. *Bird Study* 25: 39–50.

Baker, R. 1985. Norfolk duck decoys. *Transactions of the Norfolk and Norwich Naturalists' Society* 27: 1–8.

Bannerman, D. A. & Lodge G. E. 1963. *The Birds of the British Isles Vol XI.* Oliver & Boyd, Edinburgh.

Beekman, J. H. 1985. Population size and breeding success of Bewick's Swans wintering in Europe in 1983/84. *Wildfowl* 36: 5–12.

Bell, D. G. 1965. Studies of less familiar birds 133. Long-tailed Skua. *Brit. Birds* 58: 139–145.

Berry, R. 1968. Dersingham Decoy. *Norfolk Bird Report 1967*: 176–178.

Berry, R. 1969. Dersingham Decoy. *Norfolk Bird Report 1968*: 305–306.

Berry, R. 1971. Wader studies on the Wash. *Norfolk Bird Report 1970*: 176–179.

Berry, R. 1979. Nightjar habitats and breeding in East Anglia. *Brit. Birds* 72: 207–218.

Berthold, P. & Terrill, S. B. 1988. Migratory behaviour and population growth of Blackcaps wintering in Britain and Ireland: some hypotheses. *Ringing and Migration* 9: 153–159.

Berthold, P., Mohr, G. & Querner, U. 1990. Sterung und potentielle Evolutions-geschwindigkeit des obligaten Teilzieherverhaltens: Ergebnisse eines Zweiweg-Selektionsexperiments mit der Monchsgrasmucke Sylvia atricapilla. *J. Orn.* 131: 33–45.

Bibby, C. J. 1973. The Red-backed Shrike: a vanishing British species. *Bird Study* 20: 103–110.

Bibby, C. J. 1981. Wintering Bitterns in Britain. *Brit. Birds* 74: 1–10.

Bibby, C. J. 1982. Polygyny and the breeding ecology of the Cetti's Warbler *Cettia cetti. Ibis* 124: 288–301.

Bibby, C. J. 1983. Studies of west Palearctic Birds 186. Bearded Tit. *Brit. Birds* 76: 549–563.

Bishop, W. F. 1957. Spotted Sandpiper in Norfolk. *Brit. Birds* 50: 490–491.

Bishop, W. F. 1983. *Cley Marsh and its Birds.* Boydell, Woodbridge.

Blaker, G. B. 1933. The Barn Owl in England. *Bird Notes and News* 15: 169–172, 207–211.

Bloomfield, A. 1993. *Birds of The Holkham Area.* Published privately by the author.

Bloomfield, A. 1994. Aberrant Redwing at Holkham Park. *Norfolk Bird Club Bulletin* 10: 15–16.

Bloomfield, A. 1997a. Vagrant warblers at Holkham Meals. *Norfolk Bird Club Bulletin* 22: 46.

Bloomfield, A. 1997b. Arctic Redpolls in Norfolk. *Norfolk Bird Club Bulletin* 23: 6–10.

Bloomfield, A. 1997c. Norfolk Surf Scoters. *Norfolk Bird Club Bulletin* 24: 17.

Bloomfield, A. 1998. Pale-bellied Brent Geese in Norfolk. *Norfolk Bird Club Bulletin* 30: 6–8.

Bloomfield, A. & McCullum, J. 1999. The Stock Dove and its status in North Norfolk. *Norfolk Bird Club Bulletin* 33: 5–6.

Bloomfield, A. & Seago, M. J. 1999. 1998 Grey Heron survey. *Norfolk Bird Club Bulletin* 33: 9–11.

Bottomley, J. B., Bottomley, S. & Bagnall-Oakeley. 1967. Wilson's Phalaropes in England in autumn 1967. *Brit. Birds* 60: 516–517.

Bowden, C. G. R. 1990. Woodlarks in Breckland. *Norfolk Bird Report 1989*: 433–435.

Bowden, C. G. R. & Hoblyn, R. A. 1987. Woodlarks in Breckland. *Norfolk Bird Report 1986*: 418–419.

Bowden, C. G. R. & Hoblyn, R. A. 1990. The importance of restocked conifer plantations for Woodlarks in Britain: implications and consequences. *RSPB Conservation Review* 4.

Bowman, N. 1994. Presumed Ring-necked x Tufted Duck hybrid at Wroxham Broad. *Norfolk Bird Club Bulletin* 9: 4–5.

Boyd, W. 1988. Black-winged Stilts breeding at Holme. *Norfolk Bird Report 1987*: 89–96.

Branson, N. J. B. A. 1985. *Wash Wader Ringing Group Report 1983–84.*

Branson, N. J. B. A. & Minton, C. D. T. 1976. Moult, measurements and migration of the Grey Plover. *Bird Study* 23: 257–266.

Brenchley, A. 1986. The breeding distribution of the Rook (*Corvus frugilegus* L.) in Great Britain since the 1920s. *J. Zool. Lond. (A)* 210: 261–278.

Brindley, E., Norris, K., Cook, A., Babbs, S., Forster Brown, C., Massey, P., Thompson, R. & Yaxley, R. 1998. The abundance and conservation status of Redshank *Tringa totanus* nesting on saltmarshes in Great Britain. *RSPB Research Report.*

Broads Authority 1996. *Restoration of the Norfolk Broads.* Scientific Reports on EU LIFE Project No. 92–93/UK/031. BARS 14a – The Control of Nutrient Release from Sediment. BARS 14b – Biomanipulation as a Restoration Tool. BARS 14c – Factors Affecting Water Plant Recovery. BARS 14d – Mechanisms Controlling the Stability of Restored Broads. Broads Authority, Norwich.

Brouwer, G. A. 1964. *Status of the Spoonbill in Europe.* Rijksmusuem van Natuurlijke Historic, Leiden, 1964.

Brown, A. 1994. Twite – what Twite? The results of the NBC mid-winter Twite count. *Norfolk Bird Club Bulletin* 9: 12–13.

Brown, J. 1981. Communal roosting by Hen Harriers. *Norfolk Bird Report 1980*: 266–267.

Brown, J. 1993. Brancaster Harbour Turnstones. *Norfolk Bird Report 1992*: 431–432.

Brown, J., Lawton, N. & Rooney, M. E. S. 1997. Calandra Lark on Scolt Head – a new bird for Norfolk. *Norfolk Bird Club Bulletin* 24: 4–5.

Brown, J., Lawton, N. & Rooney, M. E. S. 1998. Calandra Lark – new to Norfolk. *Norfolk Bird Report 1997*: 554–555.

Browne, S., Rehfisch, M. & Balmer, D. 1997. The life and hard times of the Golden Pheasant. *BTO News* 210: 13.

Browne, T. 1835–36. *Natural History of the County of Norfolk*. Wilkins' edn, 4 vols. London.

Bruhn, J. F.W. 1966. Ringing Sand Martins: a preliminary report. *Norfolk Bird Report 1965*: 300–302.

Bruhn, J. F. W. 1972. Sand Martins. *Norfolk Bird Report 1971*: 325.

Bruhn, J. F. W. 1976. Black-headed Gull recoveries. *Norfolk Bird Report 1975*: 28–29.

Bryant, D. M. 1981. Moulting Shelducks in the Wash. *Norfolk Bird Report 1980*: 264–265.

Bubb, P. 1987. The Little Tern colony at Yarmouth. *Norfolk Bird Report 1986*: 414–416.

Buckingham, D. L. 1998. Variations and occurrence of *intermedius* Lesser Black-backed Gulls in southern England. *Brit. Birds* 91: 60–62.

Buckley, J. 1974. Short-eared Owls and their prey. *Norfolk Bird Report 1973*: 86–88.

Buckley, J. & Goldsmith, J. G. 1972. Barn Owls and their prey in east Norfolk. *Norfolk Bird Report 1971*: 320–324.

Buckley, J. & Goldsmith, J. G. 1975. The prey of the Barn Owl (*Tyto alba alba*) in east Norfolk. *Mammal Review* 5: 13–16.

Bull, A. L. 1985. Ringed Plover Survey. *Norfolk Bird Report 1984*: 102.

Bull, A. L. & Taylor, M. 1984. Mute Swan Census 1983. *Norfolk Bird Report 1983*: 340–341.

Buxton, A. 1943. Report of the Norfolk Nature Reserves Investigation Committee. Typescript. Copy in the author's possession.

Cadbury, C. J., Green, R. E. & Allport, G. 1987. Redshanks and other breeding waders of British saltmarshes. *RSPB Conservation Review* 1: 37–40.

Campbell, L., Cayford, J. & Pearson, D. 1996. Bearded Tits in Britain and Ireland. *Brit. Birds* 89: 335–346.

Camphuysen, C. J. 1989. Beached bird survey in the Netherlands, 1915–1988. *Techn. Rapport Vogelbescherming* 1, Amsterdam.

Cannon, A. 1998. *The Garden BirdWatch Handbook*. BTO, Thetford.

Carter, I. 1998. Wing-tagged Red Kites in Norfolk. *Norfolk Bird Club Bulletin* 28: 7–10.

Cawthorne, R. A. 1982. Hard facts about cold weather. *BTO News* 119: 1–2.

Chestney, R. 1993. *Island of Birds*. Quiller, London.

Clark, J. & Clark, N. 1992. Wash wader casualties following severe weather. *Norfolk Bird Report 1991*: 263–264.

Clark, J. A., Adams, S. Y., Peach, W. J. & Simons, J. R. 1996. Report on Bird Ringing in Britain and Ireland for 1994. *Ringing & Migration* 17: 36–79.

Clark, J. A., Baillie, S. R., Clark, N. A. & Langston, R. H. W. 1993. Estuary wader capacity following severe weather mortality. *BTO Research Report* 103.

Clark, J. M. & Eyre, J. A. (eds.) 1993. *Birds of Hampshire*. Hampshire Ornithological Society.

Clark, N. A. 1982. The effects of the severe weather in December 1981 and January 1982 on waders in Britain. *WSG Bulletin* 34: 5–7.

Clark, N. A. 1993. The Wash Oystercatchers. *Norfolk Bird Report 1992*: 434–435.

Clark, N. A. 1995. Oystercatchers starvation on the Wash: A case of poor food supplies. *Wash Wader Ringing Group Report 1993–94*.

Clark, N. A. & Davidson, N. C. 1986. WSG project on the effects of severe weather on waders: sixth progress report. *WSG Bulletin* 46: 7–8.

Clarke, M. R. 1979. Ivory Gull, wanderer from the High Arctic. *Norfolk Bird Report 1978*: 6–7.

Clarke, R. 1986. Hen Harrier winter roost survey. *Norfolk Bird Report 1985*: 262–264.

Clarke, R. 1987. Hen Harrier winter roost survey. *Norfolk Bird Report 1986*: 410–412.

Clarke, R. 1995. *The Marsh Harrier*. Hamlyn, London.

Clarke, R. 1996. *Montagu's Harrier*. Arlequin Press, London.

Clarke, R. and Hewson, G. 1993. Diets of Hen Harriers and Merlins roosting at Roydon Common. *Norfolk Bird Report 1992*: 439–443.

Clarke, W. G. 1894. A Breckland Ramble. *Naturalists' Journal*, 3, 90–107

Clarke, W. G. 1903. The meres of Wretham Heath. *Transactions of the Norfolk and Norwich Naturalists' Society* 7 (4), 499–511.

Clarke, W. G. 1937. *In Breckland Wilds*. 2nd edn, Heffer, Cambridge.

Clement, P. 1997. Selected introductions, hybrids, escapes and ferals seen in Norfolk during 1995. *Norfolk Bird Club Bulletin* 24: 8–12.

Clement, P., Harris, A. & Davis, J. 1993. *Finches and Sparrows: An Identification Guide*. Christopher Helm, London.

Colston, P. R. 1995. Pallid Swift – a first for Norfolk. *Norfolk Bird Report 1994*: 367.

Conder, P. 1962. The return of the Black-tailed Godwit, in *The Return of the Osprey*: 203–215. Collins, London.

Cooper, R. H. W. 1987. Migration strategies of shorebirds during the non-breeding season with particular reference to the Sanderling (*Calidris alba*). Unpublished PhD Thesis, University of Durham.

Cornwallis, R. K. 1961. Four Invasions of Waxwings during 1956–60. *Brit. Birds* 54: 1–30.

Cornwallis, R. K. & Townsend, A. D. 1968. Waxwings in Britain and Europe during 1965–66. *Brit. Birds* 61: 91–118.

Cottier, E. J. & Lea D. 1969. Black-tailed Godwits, Ruffs and Black Terns breeding on the Ouse Washes. *British Birds* 62: 259–270.

Cowan, T., Macey, I. & Nicholson, A. 1994. Siberian Thrush, Burnham Overy Dunes 18th September 1994. *Norfolk Bird Club Bulletin* 13: 5–6.

Coward, T. A. 1923, The birds of Blakeney Point: a visit in the breeding season. *Transactions of the Norfolk and Norwich Naturalists' Society*, 11 (4), 344–359.

Cowie, R. J. & Hinsley, S. A. 1987. Breeding success of Blue Tits and Great Tits in suburban gardens. *Ardea* 75: 81–90.

Cozens-Hardy, A. W. & Oliver, F. W. 1914. The National Trust – Report of the Blakeney Point Committee of Management for 1913. *Transactions of the Norfolk and Norwich Naturalists' Society*, 9 (5), 702–711.

Cozens-Hardy, A. W. & Oliver, F. W. 1915. Report of the Blakeney Point Committee of Management for 1914. *Transactions of the Norfolk and Norwich Naturalists' Society*, 10 (1), 51–59.

Cozens-Hardy, A. W. & Oliver, F. W. 1918. Report of the Blakeney Point Committee of Management for 1915 and 1916. *Transactions of the Norfolk and Norwich Naturalists' Society*, 10 (3), 237–241.

Cramp, S. (ed.) 1977–94. *The Handbook of the Birds of Europe, The Middle East and North Africa: The Birds of the Western Palearctic*. Vol. 1–9. Oxford University Press, Oxford.

Cramp, S., Pettet, A. & Sharrock, J. T. R. 1960. The irruption of tits in autumn 1957. *Brit. Birds* 53: 49–77, 99–117, 176–192.

Cranswick, P. A. *Wildfowl & Wader Counts/ The Wetland Bird Survey 1983/84–1995/96*. BTO/WWT/RSPB/JNCC.

Cranswick, P. A., Waters, R. J., Musgrove, A. J. & Pollit, M. S. 1997. *The Wetland Bird Survey 1995–96: Wilfowl and Wader Counts*. BTO/WWT/RSPB/JNCC, Slimbridge.

Cross, E. 1994. The farmer and the Pink-feet can be friends? *Norfolk Bird Report 1993*: 115–118.

Daukes, A. H. 1952. Exceptional migratory rush at Cley. *Wild Bird Protection in Norfolk 1951*.

Daukes, A. H. 1954. Semi-palmated Sandpiper in Norfolk. *Brit. Birds* 47: 131–132.

Davidson, C. 1985. Parrot Crossbills: a new breeding species. *Norfolk Bird Report 1984*: 98–102.

Davidson, N. C. & Clark, N. A. 1985. The effects of the severe weather in January and February 1985 on waders in Britain. *WSG Bulletin* 44: 10–16.

Day, J. 1981. Status of Bitterns in Europe since 1976. *Brit. Birds* 74: 10–16.

Day, J. & Wilson, J. 1978 Breeding Bitterns in Britain. *Brit. Birds* 71: 285–300.

del Hoyo, J., Elliott, A. & Sargatal, J. (eds.) 1996. *Handbook of the Birds of the World Vol 3. Hoatzin to Auks*. Lynx Edicions, Barcelona.

Delany, S. 1993. Introduced and escaped geese in Britain in summer 1991. *Brit. Birds* 86: 591–599.

Dennis, R. 1991a. *Ospreys*. Colin Baxter, Grantown-on-Spey.

Dennis, R. 1991b. *Peregrine Falcons*. Colin Baxter, Grantown-on-Spey.

Dorling, D. A. 1988. Great Bustards. *Norfolk Bird Report 1987*: 97–98.

Dormer, G. 1977. Black Throated Thrush – vagrant from the Taiga Forest. *Norfolk Bird Report 1976*: 99–100.

Dowell, S. D. 1991. Grey Partridges in Norfolk. *Norfolk Bird Report 1990*: 103–105.

Dresser, H. E. 1897. Notes on Pallas' Willow Warbler and some other rare European warblers. *Transactions of the Norfolk and Norwich Naturalists' Society*, 6 (3), 280–290.

Duffey, E. A. G. 1976. Breckland, in *Nature in Norfolk. A Heritage in Trust*. 62–77. Jarrold, Norwich.

Dunmore, G. E. 1983. Vagrants from the east. *Norfolk Bird Report 1982*: 204–207.

Durdin, C. J. 1984. The great auk wreck. *Norfolk Bird Report 1983*: 360–364.

Durdin, C. J. 1993. Yarmouth's Little Terns. *Norfolk Bird Report 1992*: 430–431.

Durdin, C. J. 1994. The auk wreck of February 1994. *Norfolk Bird Club Bulletin* 9: 6–8.

Durdin, C. J. 1998. January Blackbird nest at Norwich City Hall. *Norfolk Bird Club Bulletin* 29: 4–7.

Dymond, J. N., Fraser, P. A. & Gantlett, S. J. M. 1989. *Rare Birds in Britain and Ireland*. T. & A. D. Poyser, Calton.

Easy, G. M. S. 1979. Late autumn land bird immigration in north-west Norfolk. *Norfolk Bird Report 1978*: 8–10.

Ebbinge, B. S. 1988. A multifactional explanation of the variation in breeding performance of Brent Geese. *Ibis* 131: 196–204.

Ellwood, J. & Ruxton, J. 1970. *Goose Conservation. The New Wildfowler in the 1970s* (eds. N. M. Sedgwick, P. Whittaker & J. G. Harrison). Barrie and Jenkins, London.

English Nature. 1994. *3rd. Report: 1 April–31 March, 1994*. Peterborough.

Evans, A. D. 1988. Individual differences in bill morphology and foraging behaviour of wintering Curlews. Unpublished PhD Thesis, University of Edinburgh.

Evans, L. G. R. 1994. *Rare Birds in Britain 1800–1990*. LGRE Publications, Amersham.

Evans, L. G. R. 1996. Lady Amherst's and Golden Pheasants in Britain. *Birding World* 9: 108–111.

Evans, L. G. R. 1998. *Rare and Scarce Migrant Birds of Norfolk* LGRE Publications, Amersham.

Eve, V. 1993. White-fronted Goose influx. *Norfolk Bird Club Bulletin* 3: 4–6.

Fairhead, R. & Wilton, R. 1997. Pine Bunting – A first for Norfolk. *Norfolk Bird Report 1995:* 593.

Feare, C. J. 1994. Changes in numbers of Common Starlings and farming practice in Lincolnshire. *Brit. Birds* 87: 200–204.

Fielding-Harmer, R. 1890. *A List of All The Birds Shot on Breydon Water up to 1890.*

Fisher, P. 1998. The Birds of the Wash, 1971–1996. *Norfolk Bird Report 1997:* 565–588.

Fiszer, M. 1997. A Pallid Swift at Mundesley. *Norfolk Bird Club Bulletin* 26: 9–10.

Fitter, R. S. R. 1959. The status of the Great Black Woodpecker in the British Isles. *Bull. BOC* 79: 79–87, 102–113.

Flower, W. U. 1969. Over 60 Wrens roosting together in one nest box. *Brit. Birds* 62: 157–158.

Forsman, D. & Millington, R. 1996. The Stiffkey Harrier. *Norfolk Bird Club Bulletin* 18: 9–10.

Fournier, O. & Spitz, F. 1969. *Oiseaux* 39: 242–251.

Fowler, E. 1976. Some Norfolk naturalists: a historical survey. *Nature in Norfolk. A Heritage in Trust.* 9–17. Jarrold, Norwich.

Fowler, S. & Buisson, R. 1995. Towards an RSPB water resources policy. *RSPB Conservation Review* 9: 53–59.

Fraser, P. 1997. How many rarities are we missing? *Brit. Birds* 90: 94–101.

Frost, C. 1987. A History of British Taxidermy. (Limited Edition)

Furness, R. W. 1987. *The Skuas.* T. & A. D. Poyser, Calton.

Gantlett, S. J. M. 1985. Rock Sparrow: A bird new to Britain in Norfolk. *Norfolk Bird Report 1984:* 105–106.

Gantlett, S. J. M. 1986. Boy George lives. *Cley Bird Club Newsletter* 1: 7.

Gantlett, S. J. M. 1987. Lesser Crested Tern: new to Norfolk. *Norfolk Bird Report 1986:* 412–413.

Gantlett, S. J. M. 1988. Penduline Tit: new to Norfolk. *Norfolk Bird Report 1987:* 100–101.

Gantlett, S. J. M. 1993. The Pacific Swift at Cley. *Norfolk Bird Club Bulletin* 5: 8–10.

Gantlett, S. J. M. 1994. Pacific Swift at Cley – new to Norfolk. *Norfolk Bird Report 1993:* 133–134.

Gantlett, S. J. M. 1995a. *The Birds of Cley. (5th edn).* Published privately.

Gantlett, S. J. M. 1995b. The Collared Flycatcher at Cley. *Norfolk Bird Club Bulletin* 16: 7–9.

Gantlett, S. J. M., Holman, D. & Millington, R. 1994. The Oriental Pratincole in Norfolk. *Norfolk Bird Report 1993:* 131.

Gantlett, S. J. M. & Millington, R. 1992. The Pacific Golden Plover at Cley, Norfolk. *Birding World* 4: 438–439.

Gensbol, B. 1984. *Collins Guide to the Birds of Prey of Britain and Europe, North Africa and the Middle East.* Collins, London.

George, M. 1992. *The Land Use, Ecology and Conservation of Broadland.* Packard, Chichester.

Gibbons, D. W., Reid, J. B. & Chapman, R. A. 1993. *The New Atlas of Breeding Birds in Britain and Ireland 1988–1991.* T. & A. D. Poyser, London.

Gilbert, R. 1996. Predation on Blakeney Point's tern colonies *Norfolk Bird Club Bulletin* 18: 14–16.

Gill, J. A. 1991. Pink-footed Geese in Norfolk 1990–1991. *Norfolk Bird Report 1990:* 110–111.

Gill, J. A. 1996. Habitat choice in Pink-footed Geese: quantifying the constraints determining winter site use. *Journal of Applied Ecology* 33: 884–892.

Gill, J. A. & McNeill, D. P. 1996. The distribution of Icelandic Black-tailed Godwits Colour-ringed on the Wash. *Norfolk Bird Club Bulletin* 18: 12–13.

Gillings, S. & Wotton, S. 1996. The Woodlark: then and now. *BTO News* 207: 10–11.

Glue, D. E. 1977a. Feeding ecology of the Short-eared Owl in Britain and Ireland. *Bird Study* 24: 70–78.

Glue, D. E. 1977b. Breeding biology of Long-eared Owls. *Brit. Birds* 70: 318–331.

Glue, D. E. & Bowman, F. 1998. Nesting Woodlarks and Stonechats thrive as flycatchers and tits take a tumble. *BTO News* 219: 8–9.

Golley, M. 1993a. Identification of *argentatus* Herring Gull. *Birding World* 6: 32–38.

Golley, M. 1993b. Red-necked Stint at Cley: a first for Norfolk. *Norfolk Bird Report 1992:* 437–438

Golley, M. 1993c. Desert Warbler at Blakeney Point. *Norfolk Bird Club Bulletin* 5: 7–8.

Golley, M. 1993d. Paddyfield Warbler: a first for Norfolk. *Norfolk Bird Club Bulletin* 7: 12–13.

Golley, M. 1994. Desert Warbler: a first for Norfolk. *Norfolk Bird Report 1993:* 132.

Golley, M. & Millington, R. 1997. Blyth's Reed Warbler at Warham: a first for Norfolk. *Norfolk Bird Club Bulletin* 22: 25–27.

Golley, M., Millington, R., Wright, T. & Kemp, J. 1997. A trio of eastern vagrants new to Norfolk. *Norfolk Bird Report 1996:* 244–247.

Gooders, J. & Boyer, T. 1986. *Ducks of Britain and the Northern Hemisphere.* Dragon's World, Limpsfield and London.

Gould, J. 1832–1837. *The Birds of Europe.* Published privately, London.

Green, R. 1989. Conservation of Stone Curlews. *Norfolk Bird Report 1988:* 254–258.

Gurney, J. H. 1881–1912. Ornithological notes from Norfolk (32 Parts). *Zoologist 1881–1912.*

Gurney, J. H. 1888. Pallas's Sandgrouse *Zoologist 1888:* 442–456.

Gurney, J. H. 1921. Ornithological notes for Norfolk for 1920. *Brit Birds* 14: 242.

Gurney, J. H. Sr. & Fisher, W. R. 1846. An account of the birds found in Norfolk, including notices of some of the rarer species which have occurred in the adjoining counties. *Zoologist 1846.*

Gurney, J. H. Sr. & Fisher, W. R. 1849. Ornithological and other observations in Norfolk, December 1846 to October 1848 (16 parts). *Zoologist 1847–1849*.

Gurney, J. H. & Turner, E. L. 1915. Notes on a Long-eared Owl nesting on the ground in Norfolk. *Brit. Birds* 9: 58–67.

Gurney, R. 1920. Breeding Stations of the Black-headed Gull in the British Isles. *Transactions of the Norfolk and Norwich Naturalists' Society* 10: 416–447.

Hagemeijer, E. J. M. & Blair, M. J. (eds.) 1997. *The EBCC Atlas of European Birds: Their Distribution and Abundance*. T. & A. D. Poyser, London.

Haggett, G. 1994. Woodlands and forestry in Breckland, in Lambley, P. W. (ed.) *Ecological Change in Breckland*. 35–38. English Nature, Norwich.

Hale, A. J. 1983a. An irruption of Siskins. *Norfolk Bird Report 1982*: 207.

Hale, A. J. 1983b. Lesser Redpoll migration in Norfolk. *Norfolk Bird Report 1982*: 216–217.

Hamond, C. E. 1946. Arctic Redpolls in Northumberland and Norfolk. *Brit. Birds* 39: 50–151.

Hampshire, J. & Lockwood, P. R. 1992. Harrier and Merlin observations in a Broadland winter roost 1990–1991. *Norfolk Bird Report 1991*: 255–257.

Hardy, A. R. 1992. Habitat use by farmland Tawny Owls *Strix aluco* in *'The Ecology and Conservation of European Owls'* (eds. C. A. Galbraith, I. R. Taylor & S. Percival): 55–63 Peterborough JNCC (UK Nature Conservation No. 5).

Harold, R. 1994. Holkham Grazing Marshes NNR. *Norfolk Bird Report 1993*: 123–130.

Harrison, R. H. 1973. Halvergate without wildfowl. *Norfolk Bird Report 1972*: 45–46.

Harrop, H. 1991. The status of Red-crested Pochard. *Birding World* 4: 171–175.

Hatton, D. & Varney, P. 1989. Red-breasted Nuthatch in Norfolk – a new British Bird. *Birding World* 2: 354–356.

Hayman, P. 1999. Stone Curlews in Norfolk Breckland in 1998. *Norfolk Bird Club Bulletin* 32: 2–3.

Hazell, J. A. 1987. White-billed Diver: a bird new to Norfolk. *Norfolk Bird Report 1986*: 419–420.

Heath, P. 1994. Another Lanceolated Warbler in Norfolk. *Norfolk Bird Club Bulletin* 13: 6–8.

Hedley-Bell, T. 1948. Solitary Sandpiper in Norfolk. *Brit. Birds* 41: 354–355.

Hibberd, G. F. 1992. The Holme Yellow-breasted Bunting. *Norfolk Bird Club Bulletin* 1: 8–9.

Hibberd, G. F. 1993a. Ruppell's Warbler – New to Norfolk. *Norfolk Bird Report 1992*: 436–437.

Hibberd, G. F. 1993b. Survey of breeding waders on grazing meadows along the north Norfolk coast. *Norfolk Bird Club Bulletin* 4: 8–12.

Hibberd, G. F. 1995. The Rough-legged Buzzard influx of 1994–95. *Norfolk Bird Club Bulletin* 17: 13–14.

Hibberd, G. F. & Lawton, N. M. 1996. Hunstanton Cliffs – The Falsterbo of Norfolk. *Norfolk Bird Club Bulletin* 19: 4–11.

Higham, W. E. 1949. *Birds in Camera*. Collins, Edinburgh and London.

Hirons, G. J. M. 1982. The effects of fluctuating rodent numbers on breeding success in the Tawny Owl *Strix aluco*. *Mammal Review* 12 (4): 155–157.

Hobbs, R. 1985. The Bawburgh Dipper. *Norfolk Bird Report 1984*: 97.

Hoblyn, R. 1991. Red-backed Shrike in Breckland 1974–1990. *Norfolk Bird Report 1990*: 88–90.

Hollom, P. A. D. 1960. *The Popular Handbook of Rarer British Birds*. H. F. & G. Witherby, London.

Holloway, S. 1996. *The Historical Atlas of Breeding Birds in Britain and Ireland 1875–1900*. T. & A. D. Poyser, London.

Hollyer, J. N. 1970. The invasion of Nutcrackers in autumn 1968. *Brit. Birds* 63: 353–373.

Holman, D. & Nicholson, D. 1993. Oriental Pratincole at Gimmingham. *Norfolk Bird Club Bulletin* 5: 5–7.

Holve, H. 1996. *Broads Natural Area Profile & Detailed Reserve Evaluation*. (Two vols. edited by C. Doarks & J. Madgwick) English Nature & Broads Authority, Norwich.

Hosking, E. 1955. Scops Owl in Norfolk *Brit. Birds* 48: 90.

Hudson, R. 1965. The spread of the Collared Dove in Britain & Ireland. *Brit. Birds* 58: 105–139.

Hudson, R. 1974. Allen's Gallinule in Britain and the Palearctic. *Brit. Birds* 67: 405–412.

Hughes, B. & Sellers, R. 1998. Inventory of Cormorant roosts and inland breeding sites in Britain. *Norfolk Bird Club Bulletin* 28: 10–13.

Hunt, J. 1815–22. *British Ornithology*.

Hunt, J. 1829. *A General History of the County of Norfolk*. Stacey, Norwich.

Image, R. A. 1987. Montagu's and Marsh Harriers in Norfolk 1982–1986. *Norfolk Bird Report 1991*: 405–408.

Image, R. A. 1992. Montagu's and Marsh Harriers in west Norfolk 1987–1991. *Norfolk Bird Report 1991*: 270–272.

Image, R. A. 1994a. Montagu's Harriers in Norfolk 1994. *Norfolk Bird Club Bulletin* 11: 4.

Image, R. A. 1994b. Autumn roosting Marsh Harriers in west Norfolk 1983–1993. *Norfolk Bird Report 1993*: 119–121.

Ireland, P. L. 1990. A Knot catch to remember. *Norfolk Bird Report 1989*: 437–438.

James, P. (ed.). 1996. *Birds of Sussex*. Sussex Ornithological Society.

Jarvis, B. W. 1988. Red-rumped Swallows in Norfolk. *Norfolk Bird Report 1987*: 98–99.

Johnson, I. G. 1970. The Water Pipit as a winter visitor to the British Isles. *Bird Study* 17: 297–319.

Johnson, P. N. 1990. Barn Owls in North Norfolk. *Norfolk Bird Report 1989*: 430–431.

Johnson, P. N. 1991. Barn Owls in North Norfolk. *Norfolk Bird Report 1990*: 91–95.

Jones, R. 1983. Wickhampton Heronry. *Norfolk Bird Report 1982*: 203–204.

Jones, R. 1984. Grey Herons in Norfolk: an exploratory survey. *Norfolk Bird Report 1983*: 364–365.

Jones, R. 1991. Grey Herons in Norfolk. *Norfolk Bird Report 1990*: 114–115.

Jonsson, L. 1998. Baltic Lesser Black-backed Gull *Larus fuscus fuscus* – moult, ageing and identification. *Birding World* 11: 295–317.

Joyce, B. 1998. Securing the future – £3 million project for Norfolk wildlife. *Tern*, No. 58, 8–9.

Joyner, S. C. 1984. Booted Warbler – an addition to the County List. *Norfolk Bird Report 1983*: 366–367.

Kelly, G. 1986. *The Norfolk Bird Atlas*. Norfolk and Norwich Naturalists' Society, Norwich.

Kelsey, M. G. 1989. A comparison of the song and territorial behaviour of a long-distance migrant, the Marsh Warbler *Acrocephalus palustris*, in summer and winter. *Ibis* 131: 403–414.

Kemp, J. B. 1981. Breeding Long-eared Owls in west Norfolk. *Norfolk Bird Report 1980*: 262–265.

Kemp, J. B. 1982. West Norfolk Long-eared Owl survey. *Norfolk Bird Report 1981*: 90–91.

Kemp, J. B. 1984. A note on Barnacle Geese. *Norfolk Bird Report 1983*: 380.

Kemp, J. B. 1990. Yellow-browed Bunting: First for Britain. *Norfolk Bird Report 1989*: 436.

Kemp, J. B. 1991. Status and habits of Whooper Swans in Norfolk. *Norfolk Bird Report 1990*: 99–100.

Kemp, J. B. 1992. Winter diet of Long-eared Owls. *Norfolk Bird Report 1991*: 281–286.

Kemp, J. B. 1993–1998. *Welney Bird Reports 1992–1997*.

Kemp, J. B. 1995. Breeding Lapwing and Redshank at Welney Washes. *Norfolk Bird Report 1994*: 361–364.

Kemp, J. B. 1996. Visible migration of Whooper and Bewick's Swans in Norfolk. *Norfolk Bird Club Bulletin* 18: 10–12.

Kemp, J. B. 1997a. Norfolk's first Two-barred Greenish Warbler *Norfolk Bird Club Bulletin* 22: 29–31.

Kemp, J. B. 1997b. Britain's First Canvasback at Welney WWT. *Norfolk Bird Club Bulletin* 23: 4–6.

Kemp, J. B. 1998. Canvasback – A first for Norfolk. *Norfolk Bird Report 1997*: 553–554.

Kew, A. J. 1995. *Wash Wader Ringing Group Report 1993–94*.

Kew, A. J. 1997. *Wash Wader Ringing Group Report 1995–96*.

Kightley, C. 1987. Blue–winged Teal: A first for Cley. *Cley Bird Club Newsletter* 7: 1–2.

King, J. 1997. Lesser White–fronted Geese: problems and solutions. *Birding World* 10: 2.

Kirby, J. S., Kirby, K. K. & Woolfall, S. J. 1989. Curlew Sandpipers in Britain and Ireland in autumn 1988. *Brit. Birds* 82: 399–409.

Knox, A. 1988. Taxonomy of the Rock/Water Pipit superspecies *Anthus petrosus, spinoletta* and *rubescens*. *Brit. Birds* 81: 206–211.

Lack, P. 1986. *The Atlas of Wintering Birds in Britain and Ireland*. T. & A. D. Poyser, Calton.

Lack, P. 1992. *Birds on Lowland Farms*. HMSO, London.

Lambert, J. M. 1953. The past, present and future of the Norfolk Broads. *Transactions of the Norfolk and Norwich Naturalists' Society* 17: 223–258.

Lambley, P. W. (ed.) 1994. *Ecological Change in Breckland*. Unpublished Report. English Nature, Norwich.

Lambley, P. W. 1997. *The North Norfolk Natural Area Profile*. English Nature, Norwich.

Land, R. & Lewis, P. 1986. Nesting Parrot Crossbills at Wells. *Norfolk Bird Report 1985*: 256–259.

Landells, W. & Seago, M. J. 1997a. The County Rookery Survey. *Norfolk Bird Report 1995*: 608–611.

Landells, W. & Seago, M. J. 1997b. The current breeding status and recent history of the Rook in Norfolk. *Norfolk Bird Report 1996*: 248–255.

Langslow, D. 1997. Foreword. In *North Norfolk Natural Area Profile*. English Nature, Norwich.

Langston, R. 1988. The Wash – Mecca for Waders. *Norfolk Bird Report 1987*: 105–111.

Latham, J. 1785. *A General History of Birds*. Winchester.

Lawton, N. 1995. Isabelline Shrike at Snettisham Coastal Park 2nd May 1995. *Norfolk Bird Club Bulletin* 16: 5–6.

Lawton, N. 1997. Isabelline Shrikes in Norfolk, October 1996. *Norfolk Bird Club Bulletin* 24: 17–18.

Lawton, N. 1999. Shorelarks in Norfolk – past and present. *Norfolk Bird Club Bulletin* 32: 4–8.

Lever, C. 1987. *Naturalised Birds of the World*. Longman, London.

Ley, R. L. 1943. Notes from Yarmouth. *Wild Bird Protection in Norfolk 1942*: 9–10.

Liley, D. In prep. PhD Thesis, UEA, Norwich.

Lines, J. 1987. White-winged Lark: a bird new to Norfolk. *Norfolk Bird Report 1986*: 416–417.

Linsell, S. 1990. *Hickling Broad and its Wildlife*. Dalton, Lavenham.

Long, S. H. 1921. Wild bird protection in Norfolk. *Transactions of the Norfolk and Norwich Naturalists' Society,* 11 (2), 194–199.

Long, S. H. 1926. Wild bird protection in Norfolk in 1926. *Transactions of the Norfolk and Norwich Naturalists' Society* 12 (2), 188–203.

Long, S. H. 1929. Wild bird protection in Norfolk in 1929. *Transactions of the Norfolk and Norwich Naturalists' Society* 12 (5), 677–694.

Long, S. H. 1932. Wild bird protection in Norfolk in 1931. *Transactions of the Norfolk and Norwich Naturalists' Society* 13 (2), 145–158.

Long, S. H. 1934. Wild bird protection in Norfolk in 1933. *Transactions of the Norfolk and Norwich Naturalists' Society* 13 (4), 371–388.

Long, S. H. 1936. Wild bird protection in Norfolk in 1935. *Transactions of the Norfolk and Norwich Naturalists' Society* 14 (1), 86–105.

Lubbock, R. 1845. *Observations on the Fauna of Norfolk, and more particularly on the district of the Broads.* Charles Muskett, Norwich.

Lubbock, R. 1879. *Observations on the fauna of Norfolk.* New edition edited by T. Southwell.

McCallum, J. 1997a. Norfolk's second Paddyfield Warbler. *Norfolk Bird Club Bulletin* 22: 23–24.

McCallum, J. 1997b. Rock Pipits in Norfolk. *Norfolk Bird Club Bulletin* 25: 16–17.

McCallum, J. 1998a. Holkham Lake's Cormorants. *Norfolk Bird Club Bulletin* 27: 6–10.

McCallum, J. 1998b. Holkham Lake's Cormorants. *Norfolk Bird Club Bulletin* 28: 15–16.

McCallum, J. 1998c. Timothy (Martin) Lubbock 1955–1998. *Norfolk Bird Club Bulletin* 29: 16.

McCallum, J. 1998d. Observations of four north Norfolk birds. *Norfolk Bird Club Bulletin* 29: 10–13.

Macdonald, D. & Wessels, P. 1998. The Chestnut Bunting in Norfolk. *Birding World* 11: 217–219.

McDonnell, M. R. 1986. Black and White Warbler: a bird new to Norfolk. *Norfolk Bird Report 1985*: 252–253.

McElwee, S. 1997. The Soft-plumaged Petrel in Norfolk. *Norfolk Bird Club Bulletin* 25: 8–11.

McElwee, S. 1998. Fea's/Zino's Petrel in Norfolk. *Norfolk Bird Report 1997*: 557.

McMullen, R. 1997. Huge loss of hedges charted in parish *Eastern Daily Press* of 28th June 1997, Eastern Counties Newspapers, Norwich.

McNeill, D. & Reed, J. 1993. Nesting Mediterranean Gulls: new to Norfolk. *Norfolk Bird Report 1992*: 433–434.

McNeill, D. 1993a. Sandwich Terns on Blakeney Point. *Norfolk Bird Club Bulletin* 2: 9–13.

McNeill, D. 1993b. Tern research on Blakeney Point. *Norfolk Bird Club Bulletin* 5: 14–16.

McNeill, D. 1994. Protecting the Norfolk Plover – a first-hand account. *Norfolk Bird Club Bulletin* 11: 10–12.

Madge, S. & Burn, H. 1988. *Wildfowl. An Identification Guide to the Ducks, Geese and Swans of the orld.* Christopher Helm, London.

Madgwick, J. 1996. *Restoration of the Norfolk Broads.* Final Report on EU LIFE Project No. 92–93/UK/031. BARS 14. Broads Authority, Norwich.

Marchant, J. H., Hudson, R., Carter, S. P. & Whittington, P. A. 1990. *Population Trends in British Breeding Birds.* BTO, Tring.

Marchant, J. H. & Wilson, A. 1996. Common Birds Census: 1994–95 index report *BTO News 204*: 9–13.

Margary, I. D. 1926. *Quarterly Journal of the Royal Meteorological Society* 52: 217.

Mead, C. J. 1974. *Bird Ringing.* BTO, Tring.

Mead, C. J. & Harrison, J. D. 1979. Sand Martin movements within Britain and Ireland. *Bird Study* 26: 73–86.

Meiklejohn, M. & Richardson, R. A. 1953. Red-rumped Swallow in Norfolk. *Brit. Birds* 46: 263–264.

Meltofte, H. 1985. Populations and breeding schedules of waders, *Charadrii*, in high arctic Greenland. *Meddr. Gronland, Biosci.* 16: 1–43.

Middleton, J. 1996. Wing lengths and weights of Wheatears *Oenanthe oenanthe* caught on the north west coast of Norfolk. *The North West Norfolk Ringing Group Annual Report 1996*: 38–48.

Millington, R. G. 1992. The Red-necked Stint in Norfolk – the second British record. *Birding World* 5: 295–298.

Millington, R. G. 1997a. The Canvasback in Norfolk – a new British bird. *Birding World* 10: 16–18.

Millington, R. G. 1997b. Norfolk's first breeding White Wagtails. *Norfolk Bird Club Bulletin* 26: 10–11.

Millington, R. G. 1998a. White Wagtails breeding at Cley – a Norfolk first. *Norfolk Bird Report 1997*: 555–556.

Millington, R. G. 1998b. The Cley Cormorants. *Cley Bird Club Newsletter* 49: 17–19.

Millington, R. G. 1998c. *Locustella* warblers in autumn 1998. *Birding World* 11: 387–389.

Ministry of Town & Country Planning. 1947a. *Conservation of Nature in England & Wales.* Report of the Wild Life Conservation Special Committee. Chairman: Dr J. S. Huxley. Cmnd. 7122. HMSO, London.

Ministry of Town & Country Planning 1947b. *Report of the National Parks Committee (England & Wales).* Chairman: Sir Arthur Hobhouse. Cmnd. 7121. HMSO, London.

Minton, C. D. T. 1956. White-rumped Sandpiper in Lincolnshire and Norfolk. *Brit. Birds* 49: 150–151.

Minton, C. D. T. 1970. Wader studies on the Wash. *Norfolk Bird Report 1969*: 15–18.

Mitchell, C. 1997. Ringed Pink-footed Geese in Norfolk. *Norfolk Bird Report 1995*: 616–620.

More, A. G. 1865. On the distribution of birds in Great Britain during the nesting season. *Ibis* 1: 119–142.

Morris, P. A. 1988. The work of Walter Lowne, taxidermist of Great Yarmouth. *Transactions of the Norfolk and Norwich Naturalists' Society* 28: 33–44.

Moyes, J. A. W. 1984. Wisbech Sewage Farm – the end. *Norfolk Bird Report 1983*: 355–359.

Moyes, J. A. W. 1986. Wisbech Sewage Farm – the final chapter. *Norfolk Bird Report 1985*: 255.

Murfitt, R. C. & Weaver, D. J. 1983. Breeding waders of wet meadows in Norfolk. *Norfolk Bird Report 1982*: 196–202.

Myers, E. T. 1985. Ross's Gull, vagrant from the High Arctic. *Norfolk Bird Report 1984*:6–97.

Myers, E. T. 1987. Red-rumped Swallow at Cley. *Cley Bird Club Newsletter* 6: 3.

Myers, E. T. & Jarvis, B. W. 1988. Red-rumped Swallows in Norfolk. *Norfolk Bird Report 1987*: 98–99.

Nature Conservancy Council 1989. *Guidelines for the Selection of Biological SSSIs: Rationale, Operational Approach and Criteria.* Nature Conservancy Council, Peterborough.

Naylor, K. A. 1996. *Rare Birds of Norfolk*. Published privately.

Newton, I. 1972. *Finches*. New Naturalist 55, Collins, London.

Newton, I. 1993. Studies of West Palearctic birds 192. Bullfinch. *Brit. Birds* 86: 638–648.

Nisbet, I. C. T. 1955. Bewick's Swans in the fenlands; the past and present status. *Brit. Birds* 48: 533–537.

Nisbett, I. C. T. 1956. Records of Wood Sandpipers in Britain in the autumn of 1952. *Brit. Birds* 49: 49–62.

Norgate, F. 1858–1902. Refers to a two-volume diary of Frank Norgate covering that period held in Norfolk Record Office, NRO Reference MC 175–12 & MC 175–13.

Norris, C. A. 1945. Summary of a report on the distribution and status of the Corncrake. *Brit. Birds* 38: 143–148.

O'Brien, M. & Buckingham, D. 1989. A survey of breeding waders on grassland within the Broads Environmentally Sensitive Area in 1988. *RSPB Research Department Report*.

O'Brien, M. & Smith, K. W. 1992. Changes in status of waders breeding on wet grasslands in England and Wales between 1982 and 1988. *Bird Study* 39: 165–176.

O'Sullivan, J. M. 1976. Bearded Tits in Britain and Ireland 1966–74. *Brit. Birds* 74: 473–489.

Ogilvie, M. A. 1975. *Ducks of Britain and Europe*. T. & A. D. Poyser, Berkhamsted.

Ogilvie, M. A. & the Rare Breeding Birds Panel. 1995. Rare breeding birds in the United Kingdom in 1992. *Brit. Birds* 88: 67–93.

Ogilvie, M. A. & the Rare Breeding Birds Panel. 1996. Rare breeding birds in the United Kingdom in 1994. *Brit. Birds* 89: 387–417.

Oliver, F. W. 1914. Report of the Blakeney Point Laboratory for the year 1913. *Transactions of the Norfolk and Norwich Naturalists' Society* 9 (5), 711–722.

Oliver, F. W. 1915. Report of the Blakeney Point Laboratory for the year 1914. *Transactions of the Norfolk and Norwich Naturalists' Society* 10 (1), 59–74.

Oliver, F. W. 1918. Report of the Blakeney Point Laboratory for the years 1915 and 1916. *Transactions of the Norfolk and Norwich Naturalists' Society* 10 (3), 241–255.

Oliver, F. W. 1923. Report of the Blakeney Point Laboratory for the years 1920–1923. *Transactions of the Norfolk and Norwich Naturalists' Society* 11 (4), 396–422.

Oliver, F. W. 1926. Report of the Blakeney Point Research Station: 1924–1926. *Transactions of the Norfolk and Norwich Naturalists' Society* 12 (2), 207–228.

Oliver, F. W. 1927. Nature Reserves. *Transactions of the Norfolk and Norwich Naturalists' Society* 12 (3), 317–322.

Oliver, F. W. & Salisbury, E. J. 1913. The topography and vegetation of the National Trust reserve known as Blakeney Point. *Transactions of the Norfolk and Norwich Naturalists' Society* 9 (4), 485–542.

Orchel, J. 1992. *Forest Merlins in Scotland*. The Hawk and Owl Trust.

Owen, M. 1977. *Wildfowl of Europe*. Macmillan, London.

Owen, M., Atkinson-Willes, G. L. & Salmon, D. G. 1986. *Wildfowl in Great Britain*. 2nd edn, Cambridge University Press, Cambridge.

Paget, C. J. & Paget, J. 1834. *Sketch of the Natural History of Great Yarmouth and its Neighbourhood*. Yarmouth.

Parslow, J. 1973. *Breeding Birds of Britain and Ireland: A Historical Survey*. T. & A. D. Poyser, Berkhamstead.

Parslow-Otsu, M. 1991. Bean Geese in the Yare Valley, Norfolk. *Brit. Birds* 84: 161–170.

Parslow-Otsu, M. 1992. Norfolk's Bean Geese. *Norfolk Bird Report 1991*: 273–276.

Pashby, B. S. & Cudworth, J. 1969. The Fulmar 'wreck' of 1962. *Brit. Birds* 62: 97–109.

Pashley, H. N. 1925. *Notes on the Birds of Cley, Norfolk*. H. F. & G. Witherby, London.

Patterson, A. H. 1904. *Notes of an East Coast Naturalist*. Methuen, London.

Patterson, A. H. 1905. *Nature In Eastern Norfolk*. Methuen, London.

Patterson, A. H. 1907. *Wildlife on a Norfolk Estuary*. Methuen, London.

Payn, W. H. 1962. *The Birds of Suffolk*. Barrie and Rockliff, London.

Peach, W. J., Thompson, P. S. & Coulson, J. C. 1994. Annual and long–term variations in the survival rates of British Lapwings *Vanellus vanellus*. *Journal of Applied Ecology* 63: 60–70.

Peakall, D. B. 1956. Migration at the Smith's Knoll light–vessel, Autumn 1953. *Brit. Birds* 49: 373–388.

Percival, S. M. 1990. Recent trends in Barn Owl and Tawny Owl populations in Britain. *BTO Research Report No. 57*. BTO, Tring.

Percy, Lord W. 1951. *Three Studies of Bird Life*. Country Life, London.

Petch, C. P, & Swann, E. L. 1968. *Flora of Norfolk*. Jarrold, Norwich.

Potts, G. R. 1986. *The Partridge*. Collins, London.

Powers, F. D. 1885. Ornithological notes at Cley and Blakeney: Sept. 3–19, 1884. *Transactions of the Norfolk and Norwich Naturalists' Society*, 4 (1), 36–43.

Prater, A. J. & Davies, M. 1978. Wintering Sanderlings in Britain. *Bird Study* 25: 33–38.

Prater, A. J. 1981. *Estuary Birds of Britain and Ireland*. Poyser, Calton.

Prater, A. J. 1995. Avian Grazers and their Impact on Reedswamps in the Thurne Broads, Norfolk. Unpublished Ph. D. Thesis, University of East Anglia, Norwich.

Pratley, P. 1982. The first River Warbler in mainland Britain. *Norfolk Bird Report 1981:* 89–90.

Pratley, P. 1984. River Warbler in Norfolk. *Brit. Birds* 77: 213–214.

Proctor, B. 1991. The Ross's Goose in Grampian. *Birding World* 4: 137–140.

Prokosch, P. 1988. Das Schleswig-Holsteinische Wattenmeer als Frujahrs-Aufenhaltsgebiet arktische Watvogel-Populationen am Bespiel von Kiebeitzregen-pfeifer (*Pluvialis squatarola* L. 1759), Knutt (*Calidris canutus* L 1758) und Pfuhlschnepfe (*Limosa lapponica* L. 1758). *Corax* 12: 274–442.

Rackham, O. 1986a. *The History of the Countryside*. Dent, London.

Rackham, O. 1986b. The ancient woods of Norfolk. *Transactions of the Norfolk and Norwich Naturalists' Society* 27: 161–177.

Ramsay, H. R. 1970. Arctic and Sahara vagrants – Sabine's Gull *Norfolk Bird Report 1969*: 13–14.

Ramsay, H. R. 1973. Wash wader spectacular. *Norfolk Bird Report 1972*: 28–29.

Ramsay, H. R. 1978. Avocets at Cley 1977. *Norfolk Bird Report 1977*: 231–232.

Ratcliffe, D. A. 1977. *A Nature Conservation Review*. 2 vols. Cambridge University Press, Cambridge.

Redpath, S. M. 1994. Censusing Tawny Owls *Strix aluco* by the use of imitation calls. *Bird Study* 41: 192–198.

Reed, T. 1985. Estimates of British breeding wader populations. *WSG Bulletin* 45: 11–12.

Rehfisch, M. & Clark, N. 1994. Wader roosting refuges: how far apart should they be? *Wash Wader Ringing Group Report 1993/94*: 40–43.

Richardson, R. A. 1956. Bigamy in Swallow. *Brit. Birds* 49: 503.

Richardson, R. A. 1970. The Godwits of Cley. *Norfolk Bird Report 1969*: 5–11.

Richardson, R. A. 1971. The Godwits of Cley *Norfolk Bird Report 1970*: 180–186.

Richardson, R. A. & Bishop, W. F. 1969. The Godwits of Cley. *Norfolk Bird Report 1968:* 284–291.

Richardson, R. A., Seago, M. J. & Church, A. 1957. Collard Doves in Norfolk: A new bird to the British List. *Brit. Birds* 58: 239–246.

Richardson, R. A., Spence, B. R., Alexander, H. G. & Williamson, K. 1962. Radde's Bush Warbler in Norfolk. *Brit. Birds* 55: 166–168.

Ridlington, R. 1993. Brent Goose research: A Norfolk perspective. *Norfolk Bird Club Bulletin* 3: 13–14.

Riley, D., Shepherd, K. & Votier, S. 1993. Lanceolated Warbler new to Norfolk. *Norfolk Bird Club Bulletin* 7: 14–15.

Riviere, B. B. 1921. The autumn movements of gulls on the Norfolk coast. *Transactions of the Norfolk and Norwich Naturalists' Society* 11: 104–127.

Riviere, B. B. 1928. Ornithological Report from Norfolk for 1927. *Brit. Birds* 21: 245.

Riviere, B. B. 1930. *A History of the Birds of Norfolk*. H. F. & G. Witherby, London.

Riviere, B. B. 1932. Ornithological Report for Norfolk for 1931. *Brit. Birds* 25: 351–352.

Riviere, B. B. 1946. Eastern Turtle-dove in Norfolk. *Brit. Birds* 39: 184.

Roberts, E. L. 1956. Exceptionally late Shore Larks in Norfolk. *Brit. Birds* 49: 502.

Robertson, A. W. P. 1954. *Bird Pageant*. Batchworth Press, London.

Robson, B. 1994. Reedbed management and Bitterns at Titchwell RSPB Reserve. *Norfolk Bird Club Bulletin* 12: 14–19.

Rogers, M. J. 1981. Isabelline Wheatear in Norfolk. *Brit. Birds* 74: 181–182.

Rogers, M. J. 1982. Ruddy Shelducks in Britain in 1965–79. *Brit. Birds* 75: 446–455.

Rogers, M. J. and the Rarities Committee with comments by D. J. Britton. 1982. Report on rare birds in Great Britain in 1981. *Brit. Birds* 75: 482–533.

Rooney, M. E. S. 1993. Breeding gulls and terns in Norfolk. *Norfolk Bird Club Bulletin* 7: 8–11.

Rooney, M. E. S. 1994a. Ravens in Norfolk. *Norfolk Bird Club Bulletin* 9: 9–10.

Rooney, M. E. S. 1994b. An exceptional spring movement of Stonechats. *Norfolk Bird Club Bulletin* 10: 12–15.

Rooney, M. E. S. 1994c. The origins of Barnacle Geese wintering in Norfolk. *Norfolk Bird Club Bulletin* 11: 4–5.

Rooney, M. E. S. 1994d. Breeding gulls and terns in Norfolk 1994. *Norfolk Bird Club Bulletin* 12: 10–12.

Rooney, M. E. S. & Eve, V. 1993. Breeding Ringed Plovers and Oystercatchers along the Norfolk coast 1993. *Norfolk Bird Club Bulletin* 6: 15–18.

Rose, P. M. & Scott, D. A. 1997 *Waterfowl Population Estimates* (2nd edn).

Rothera, S. 1998. *Breckland Natural Area Profile*. English Nature, Norwich.

Round, P. D. 1980. Survey of the Yare Basin. *Norfolk Bird Report 1979*: 98–102.

Rowan, W. 1918. Annotated list of the birds of Blakeney Point, Norfolk. *Transactions of the Norfolk and Norwich Naturalists' Society* 10 (3), 256–279.

Schmitt, S. 1994. Study of Fulmars at Hunstanton Cliffs. *The North West Norfolk Ringing Group Annual Report 1994*: 35–37.

Schneidau, L. 1998. *Norfolk County Wildlife Sites: Handbook*. Norfolk Wildlife Trust, Norwich.

Schober, H. 1937. *Das Breckland*. English trans. of Thesis: University of Breslau. English Nature, Norwich.

Scott, P. 1935. *Morning Flight*. Country Life, London.

Scott, P. 1955. Ring–necked Duck in Gloucestershire: a new British bird. *Brit. Birds* 48: 377–378.

Seago, M. J. 1953. Large gatherings of Turtle Doves. *Brit. Birds* 46: 113.

Seago, M. J. 1967. *Birds of Norfolk*. Jarrold, Norwich.

Seago, M. J. 1974. Great Crested Grebe survey. *Norfolk Bird Report 1973*: 89–91.

Seago, M. J. 1977. *Birds of Norfolk*. (2nd edn) Jarrold, Norwich.

Seago, M. J. 1990. Pink-footed Geese movements and distribution. *Norfolk Bird Report 1989*: 414–420.

Seago, M. J. 1991. White-fronted Geese in Norfolk. *Norfolk Bird Report 1990*: 101–103.

Seago, M. J. 1993. An unacceptable Norfolk record of Baird's Sandpiper. *Brit. Birds* 86: 22.

Seago, M. J. 1997a. European Bee-eaters in Norfolk. *Norfolk Bird Club Bulletin* 25: 11–12.

Seago, M. J. 1997b. The Waxwing invasion. *Norfolk Bird Report 1996*: 241–244.

Seago, M. J. 1998. A brief history of the Red Kite in Norfolk. *Norfolk Bird Club Bulletin* 28: 6–7.

Seago, M. J. 1999. 1998 Great Crested Grebe survey. *Norfolk Bird Club Bulletin* 33: 12–13.

Sharrock, J. T. R. 1974. *Scarce Migrant Birds in Britain and Ireland*. T. & A. D. Poyser, Berkhamsted.

Sharrock, J. T. R. 1976. *The Atlas of Breeding Birds in Britain and Ireland*. T. & A. D. Poyser, Berkhamsted.

Sharrock, J. T. R. & Fraser, P. 1997. How many rarities are we missing? *Brit. Birds* 90: 297.

Shawyer, C. R. 1987. *The Barn Owl in the British Isles: Its Past, Present and Future*. The Hawk and Owl Trust.

Sheail, J. 1976. *Nature in Trust*. Blackie, Glasgow.

Shepherd, K. 1978–80. *Dead Man's Reports 1978–80*.

Shepherd, K. 1987–91. *Dead Man's Reports 1987–91*.

Shepherd, K. 1992–94. *Sheringham Bird Observatory Reports 1987–91*.

Shepherd, K. 1993. An enormous Spring movement of Redwings. *Norfolk Bird Club Bulletin* 4: 14–16.

Shepherd, K. & Votier, S. 1994a. Paddyfield Warbler – a first record for Norfolk. *Norfolk Bird Report 1993*: 134.

Shepherd, K. & Votier, S. 1994b. Lanceolated Warbler – New for Norfolk. *Norfolk Bird Report 1993*: 135–136.

Sheppard, R. & Whitear, W. 1826. A catalogue of the Norfolk and Suffolk birds, with remarks. *Transactions of the Linnean Society* 15: 1–62.

Shewell, E. L. 1959. The waterfowl of Barberspand. *Ostrich Supplement* 3: 160–179.

Sills, N. 1983. The first ten years at Titchwell Marsh, in Norfolk Bird and Mammal Report 1982. *Transactions of the Norfolk and Norwich Naturalists' Society* 26 (4), 190–195.

Sills, N. 1984. Marsh Harriers at Titchwell Marsh Reserve (1980–1983) Part 1. *Norfolk Bird Report 1983*: 342–348.

Sills, N. 1985. Marsh Harriers at Titchwell Marsh Reserve (1980–1983) Part 2. *Norfolk Bird Report 1984*: 84–95.

Simms, E. 1992. *British Larks, Pipits & Wagtails*. New Naturalist 78, HarperCollins, London.

Sitters, H. P. 1986. Woodlarks in Britain 1968–83. *Brit. Birds* 79: 105–116.

Skeen, R. 1997. Observations of Titchwell's Black-winged Stilt. *Norfolk Bird Club Bulletin* 26: 11–13.

Skeen, R. 1998. Titchwell's Transatlantic duo. *Norfolk Bird Club Bulletin* 31: 16–17.

Sladen Wing, J. 1936. Sooty Tern in Norfolk. *Brit. Birds* 29: 187.

Slater, C. 1987. Fulmar population changes. *Norfolk Bird Report 1986*: 421–423.

Smith, G. 1980. Pallas's Grasshopper Warbler in Norfolk. *Brit. Birds* 73: 417–418.

Smith, K. W. 1983. The status and distribution of waders breeding on wet lowland grasslands in England and Wales. *Bird Study* 30: 177–192.

Society for the Promotion of Nature Reserves 1945. *National Nature Reserves and Conservation Areas in England and Wales*. Memorandum No. 6 of the Conference on Nature Preservation in post–war Reconstruction. S.P.N.R. c/o British Museum (Natural History), London.

Southwell, T. 1879. Norfolk decoys. *Transactions of the Norfolk and Norwich Naturalists' Society* 2: 538–555.

Southwell, T. 1901. On the breeding of the Crane in East Anglia. *Transactions of the Norfolk and Norwich Naturalists' Society* 7: 160–170.

Sowerby, J. 1804–1806. *The British Miscellany: or, coloured figures of new, rare, or little known animal subjects; many not before ascertained to be inhabitants of the British Isles*. (2 vols), Sowerby, London.

Spencer, R. 1975. Changes in the distribution of recoveries of ringed Blackbirds. *Bird Study* 22: 177–190.

Spencer, R. & Gush, G. H. 1973. Siskins feeding in gardens. *Brit. Birds* 66: 91–99.

Spencer, R. & Hudson, R. 1976. Report on bird-ringing for 1974. Special Supplement to *Bird Study* 23.

Stanley, P. I. & Minton, C. D. T. 1972. The unprecedented westward migration of Curlew Sandpipers in autumn 1969. *Brit. Birds* 65: 365–380.

Stanley, P. I., Brough, T., Fletcher, M. R., Horton, N. & Rochard, J. B. A. 1981. The origins of Herring Gulls wintering inland in south-east England. *Bird Study* 28: 123–132.

Steers, J. A. (ed.) 1960. *Scolt Head Island*. Heffer, Cambridge.

Stevenson, H. 1866–90. *The Birds of Norfolk*. Vol. 1–3. John Van Voorst and Gurney & Jackson, London.

Stevenson, H. 1875. Note on Baillon's Crake. *Transactions of The Norfolk and Norwich Naturalists' Society* 2: 64.

Stevenson, H. 1883. On the occurrence of the Dusky Petrel or Shearwater (*Puffinus obscurus*) in Norfolk in 1858 – its first known appearance in England. *Transactions of the Norfolk and Norwich Naturalists' Society* 3: 467–473.

Stoddart, A. M. 1990a. Yellow-browed Warblers in Norfolk. *Norfolk Bird Report 1989*: 420–423.

Stoddart, A. M. 1990b. Yellow-browed Warbler showing characters of the race *humei*. *Norfolk Bird Report 1989*: 424.

Stoddart, A. M. 1990c. Pacific Golden Plover : new to Norfolk. *Norfolk Bird Report 1989*: 429.

Stoddart, A. M. 1995a. *Tristis* Chiffchaffs in Norfolk. *Norfolk Bird Club Bulletin* 16: 9–11.

Stoddart, A. M. 1995b. Siberian Chiffchaffs in Norfolk. *Norfolk Bird Report 1994*: 364–365.

Stoddart, A. M. & Eldridge, M. I. 1992. Snowy Owl in Norfolk. *Norfolk Bird Report 1991*: 267.

Stone, B. H., Sears, J., Cranswick, P. A., Gregory, R. D., Gibbons, D. W., Rehfisch, M. M., Aebischer, N. J. & Reid, J. B. 1997. Population estimates of birds in Britain and in the United Kingdom. *Brit. Birds* 90: 1–22.

Storey, N. 1997. *Norfolk at Work*.

Sutherland, W. J. & Allport, G. A. 1991. The distribution and ecology of naturalised Egyptian Geese *Alopochen aegyptiacus* in Britain. *Bird Study* 38: 128–134.

Svensson, L. 1992. *Identification Guide to European Passerines*. 4th edn. Published privately, Stockholm.

Syroechkovski, E. E., Zockler, C. & Lappo, E. 1998. Status of Brent Goose in northwest Yakutia, East Siberia. *Brit. Birds* 91: 565–572.

Tate, P. 1977. *East Anglia and its birds*. H. F. & G. Witherby, London.

Tatner, P. 1983. The diet of urban Magpies *Pica pica*. *Ibis* 125: 90–107.

Taylor, M. 1972. Congenital bill deformity in nestling Swallow. *Brit. Birds* 65: 355–356.

Taylor, M. 1976. Cardueline finches in North Norfolk, Spring 1976. *Sheringham Ringing Report 1976*: 10–14.

Taylor, M. 1979a. *Dead Man's Wood Annual Report*.

Taylor, M. 1979b. Mute Swan census. *Norfolk Bird Report 1978*: 7.

Taylor, M. 1981. Blackcap migration in Norfolk. *Norfolk Bird Report 1980*: 261–262.

Taylor, M. 1982. Fieldfare and Redwing migration as shown by Norfolk ringing recoveries. *Norfolk Bird Report 1981*: 84–85.

Taylor, M. 1984a. The BTO in Norfolk. *Norfolk Bird Report 1983*: 339.

Taylor, M. 1984b. The patterns of migration and partial migration at a north Norfolk bird-ringing site. *Ringing & Migration* 5: 65–78.

Taylor, M. 1985. Origins and movements of Norfolk Fulmars. *Norfolk Bird Report 1984*: 103–104.

Taylor, M. 1987a. *The Birds of Sheringham*. Poppyland, North Walsham.

Taylor, M. 1987b. Mandarins in Norfolk. *Norfolk Bird Report 1986*: 417–418.

Taylor, M. 1987c. A quarter of a century at Cley. *Cley Bird Club Newsletter* 4: 5–6.

Taylor, M. 1988. Lapwing Breeding Survey. *Norfolk Bird Report 1987*: 103–104.

Taylor, M. 1990. Willow and Marsh Tit. *Brit. Birds* 83: 511.

Taylor, M. 1993. 1992–93 National Bearded Tit Survey. *Norfolk Bird Club Bulletin* 5: 10–12.

Taylor, M. 1995. Siskin Bonanza. *Ringers' Bulletin* 9: 1.

Taylor, M. 1997a. The Little Auk 'Wreck'. *Norfolk Bird Report 1995*: 600–601.

Taylor, M. 1997b. The origins of Rock Pipits in Norfolk. *Norfolk Bird Report 1995*: 606–607.

Taylor, M. 1998. The Birds of Felbrigg Park. *Norfolk Bird Report 1997*: 559–564.

Taylor, M. & Moores, S. 1995. Siskin ringing in Norfolk. *Norfolk Bird Report 1994*: 370–373.

Taylor, N. & Taylor, M. 1979. Pied Flycatcher – a new breeding species for Norfolk. *Norfolk Bird Report 1978*: 4–5.

Thomas, M. & Atkins, J. 1998. The Yarmouth Little Tern Colony during 1997. *Norfolk Bird Report 1997*: 558.

Thrower, W. 1980. A wild goose storm disaster. *Norfolk Bird Report 1979*: 102–104.

Ticehurst, C. B. 1932. *A History of the Birds of Suffolk*. Gurney and Jackson, London.

Tolhurst, S. 1997. *An Investigation into the Use of Domestic Herbivores for Fen Grazing Management*. Report produced for the Broads Authority, English Nature and the Norfolk Wildlife Trust, Norwich.

Toms, M. P. 1996. *Barn Owl Survey Report on the A143 Broome Bypass proposal*. Unpublished report for AERC, Cheshire.

Toms, M. P. 1997. Project Barn Owl: Evaluation of an annual monitoring programme. *BTO Research Report No. 177*.

Toms, M. P. & Clark, J. A. 1998. Bird ringing in Britain and Ireland in 1996. *Ringing & Migration* 19: 95–168.

Tucker, G. M. & Heath, M. F. 1994. *Birds in Europe: Their Conservation Status*. (BirdLife Conservation Series no 3.) BirdLife International, Cambridge.

Turner, E. L. 1924. *Broadland Birds*. Country Life, London.

Turner, E. L. 1926. Surf-Scoters in Norfolk. *Brit. Birds* 19: 234–235.

Turner, E. L. 1928. *Birdwatching on Scolt Head*. Country Life, London.

Tyler, G. 1992. Will the Bittern survive? *Norfolk Bird Report 1991*: 268–270.

Tyler, G. 1994. Management of reedbeds for Bitterns and opportunities for reedbed creation. *RSPB Conservation Review* 8: 57–62.

Tyrvainen, H. 1975. The winter irruption of the Fieldfare *Turdus pilaris* and the supply of rowan-berries. *Or. Fenn.* 52: 23–31.

Varney, P. 1988. Slender-billed Gull: new to Norfolk. *Norfolk Bird Report 1987*: 101–102.

Varney, P. 1990. Red-breasted Nuthatch in Norfolk – a new British Bird. *Norfolk Bird Report 1989*: 412–413.

Vickery, J. & Sutherland, W. J. 1996. Changing perceptions of the Dark-bellied Brent Goose. *British Wildlife* 7: 341–347.

Vincent, J. (1913–1942) References in various texts include items from Jim Vincent's personal diaries and extracts from the Hickling Game Books (Courtesy of Norfolk Wildlife Trust) both researched by Michael Seago.

Vinicombe, K. E. & Chandler, R. J. 1982. Movements of Ruddy Ducks during the hard winter of 1978/79. *Brit. Birds* 75: 1–11.

Vinicombe, K. E. & Cottridge, D. 1996. *Rare Birds in Britain & Ireland. A Photographic Record.* Harper-Collins, London.

Vinicombe, K. E. & Hopkin, P. J. 1993. The Great Black-headed Gull in Britain. *Brit. Birds* 86: 201–205.

Vinicombe, K. E., Marchant, J. & Knox, A. 1993. Review of the status and categorisation of feral birds on the British List. *Brit. Birds* 86: 611.

Votier, S. & Shepherd, K. 1994. A large albino shearwater off Sheringham, Norfolk. *Norfolk Bird Club Bulletin* 11: 6–7.

Walker, R. J. & Gregory, J. 1987. Little Whimbrel in Norfolk. *Brit. Birds* 80: 494–497.

Wallace, D. I. M. 1968. September movements at Bacton Gap. *Norfolk Bird Report 1967*: 163–164 & 188.

Wallace, D. I. M. 1971. American Marsh Hawk in Norfolk. *Brit. Birds* 64: 537–542.

Warren, A. 1984. The Jay invasion. *Norfolk Bird Report 1983*: 351–353.

Waterson, M. 1995. *The National Trust: The First Hundred Years.* National Trust, BBC books.

Watson, K. M. 1921. The Tern colony on Blakeney Point. *Transactions of the Norfolk and Norwich Naturalists' Society* 11 (2), 168–179.

Weaver, D. 1997. Breeding waders in the Broads ESA. *Norfolk Bird Report 1995*: 594–600.

Weaver, D. & Durdin, C. 1996. RSPB Broadland Breeding Wader Survey 1995. *Norfolk Bird Club Bulletin* 21: 28–30.

Wells, C. 1981. The Titchwell Gull-billed Tern. *Norfolk Bird Report 1980*: 267–268.

White, D. J. B. 1981. *An Annotated Checklist of the Birds of Blakeney Point, Norfolk.* National Trust, Blickling.

Wilkinson, P. J. 1979. Siberian Thrush in Norfolk. *Brit. Birds* 72: 122–123.

Williamson, J. R. 1990. Indigo Bunting: an addition to the County List. *Norfolk Bird Report 1989*: 431–432.

Williamson, J. R. 1991. White-tailed Eagles in Norfolk. *Norfolk Bird Report 1990*: 84–87.

Williamson, J. R. 1997a. Buzzards in Norfolk. *Norfolk Bird Report 1995*: 602–606.

Williamson, J. R. 1997b. The Waxwing invasion – a county perspective. *Norfolk Bird Club Bulletin* 21: 8–11.

Williamson, J. R. 1997c. Spring *flava* wagtails in Norfolk. *Norfolk Bird Club Bulletins* 25: 14–17 and 26: 2–3.

Williamson, J. R. & Chamberlain, A. 1996. Albino shearwaters in the North Sea – the continuing saga. *Norfolk Bird Club Bulletin* 19: 3–4.

Williamson, T. 1993. *The Origins of Norfolk.* Manchester University Press, Manchester.

Willughby, F. & Ray, J. 1676–1678 *Ornithologia.* London.

Winstanley, D., Spencer, R. & Williamson, K. 1974. Where have all the Whitethroats gone? *Bird Study* 21: 1–14.

Witherby, H. F., Jourdain, F. C. R., Ticehurst, N. F. & Tucker, B. W. 1938–41. *The Handbook of British Birds.* Vols. 1–5. Witherby, London.

Woodward, H. 1954. Large numbers of Rooks perching on the rigging of a ship. *Brit. Birds* 47: 27.

Wotton, S. 1996. *The Status of Cetti's Warbler in Norfolk in 1996.* Published privately.

Wotton, S. 1999. Woodlarks in Norfolk in 1997. *Norfolk Bird Club Bulletin* 32: 11–14.

Wright, T. 1997a. Blyth's Pipit – A new bird for Norfolk. *Norfolk Bird Club Bulletin* 22: 27–29.

Wright, T. 1997b. *Sheringham Bird Observatory Report 1997.*

Wyllie, I., Dale, L. & Newton, I. 1996. Unequal sex-ratio, mortality causes and pollutant residues in Long-eared Owls in Britain. *Brit. Birds* 89: 429–436.

Wynde, R. & Hume, R. 1997. Cormorants, Black Plague or Black Beauty? *RSPB Birds Winter 1997.*

Wynne, G. 1997. Hen Harriers and Red Grouse. *RSPB Birds 1997*: 25–59.

Yapp, W. B. 1962. *Birds and Woods.* Oxford University Press, London.

Yarrell, W. 1837–1843. *A History of British Birds.* Van Voorst, London.

Yaxley, R. 1995. Birds on set-aside in Norfolk. *Norfolk Bird Report 1994*: 356–360.

Young-Powell, M. 1994. Migration of Jays in Norfolk. *Norfolk Bird Club Bulletin* 8: 14.

Young-Powell, M. 1995–96. *Sheringham Bird Observatory Reports 1995–96.*

**Note** The annual *Norfolk Bird Reports 1953–1997* mentioned in the text and in the above list, form annual parts and use the page number sequence of the *Transactions of the Norfolk and Norwich Naturalists' Society.*

# INDEX

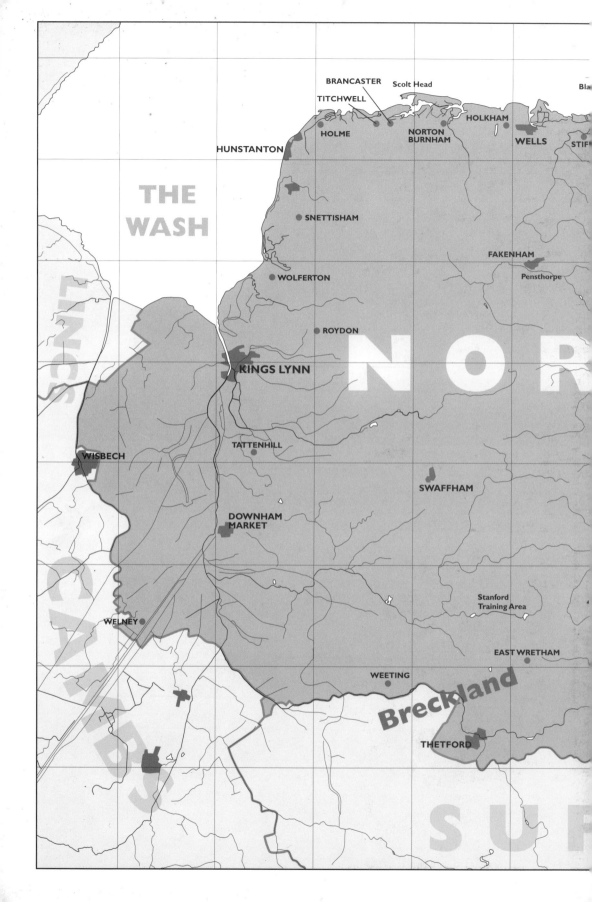